PEARSON CUSTOM LIBRARY

PEARSON

Cover Art: Courtesy of Photodisc, Photodisc/Getty Images, Age Fotostock America, Inc., and Photo Researchers, and Getty Images. "Atom. Elementary Particle. 3D Background of Nuclear Physics." courtesy of Aleksandr Bedrin/Fotolia. "3D rendered silver glossy core molecules structure High resolution" courtesy of Iaroslav Neliubov/Shutterstock.

Pearson Learning Solutions, 501 Boylston Street, Suite 900, Boston, MA 02116
A Pearson Education Company
www.pearsoned.com

Printed in the United States of America.

9 17

ISBN 10: 1-269-76870-0
ISBN 13: 978-1-269-76870-2

Table of Contents

Periodic Table of the Elements

1A 1	2A 2	3B 3	4B 4	5B 5	6B 6	7B 7	8B 8	8B 9	8B 10	1B 11	2B 12	3A 13	4A 14	5A 15	6A 16	7A 17	8A 18
1 H 1.0079																	2 He 4.0026
3 Li 6.941	4 Be 9.0122											5 B 10.811	6 C 12.011	7 N 14.0067	8 O 15.9994	9 F 18.9984	10 Ne 20.1797
11 Na 22.9898	12 Mg 24.3050											13 Al 26.9815	14 Si 28.0855	15 P 30.9738	16 S 32.066	17 Cl 35.4527	18 Ar 39.948
19 K 39.0983	20 Ca 40.078	21 Sc 44.9559	22 Ti 47.88	23 V 50.9415	24 Cr 51.9961	25 Mn 54.9380	26 Fe 55.847	27 Co 58.9332	28 Ni 58.69	29 Cu 63.546	30 Zn 65.39	31 Ga 69.723	32 Ge 72.61	33 As 74.9216	34 Se 78.96	35 Br 79.904	36 Kr 83.80
37 Rb 85.4678	38 Sr 87.62	39 Y 88.9059	40 Zr 91.224	41 Nb 92.9064	42 Mo 95.94	43 Tc (98)	44 Ru 101.07	45 Rh 102.9055	46 Pd 106.42	47 Ag 107.8682	48 Cd 112.411	49 In 114.82	50 Sn 118.710	51 Sb 121.75	52 Te 127.60	53 I 126.9045	54 Xe 131.39
55 Cs 132.9054	56 Ba 137.327	57 La 138.9055	72 Hf 178.49	73 Ta 180.9479	74 W 183.85	75 Re 186.207	76 Os 190.2	77 Ir 192.22	78 Pt 195.08	79 Au 196.9665	80 Hg 200.59	81 Tl 204.3833	82 Pb 207.2	83 Bi 208.9804	84 Po (209)	85 At (210)	86 Rn (222)
87 Fr (223)	88 Ra (226)	89 Ac (227)	104 Rf (261)	105 Db (262)	106 Sg (263)	107 Bh (262)	108 Hs (265)	109 Mt (266)									

58 Ce 140.115	59 Pr 140.9076	60 Nd 144.24	61 Pm (145)	62 Sm 150.36	63 Eu 151.965	64 Gd 157.25	65 Tb 158.9253	66 Dy 162.50	67 Ho 164.9303	68 Er 167.26	69 Tm 168.9342	70 Yb 173.04	71 Lu 174.967
90 Th 232.0381	91 Pa 231.0359	92 U 238.0289	93 Np (237)	94 Pu (244)	95 Am (243)	96 Cm (247)	97 Bk (247)	98 Cf (251)	99 Es (252)	100 Fm (257)	101 Md (258)	102 No (259)	103 Lr (260)

Chemistry and Measurements

LOOKING AHEAD

Visit **www.masteringchemistry.com** for self-study materials and instructor-assigned homework.

Flirt - SuperStock

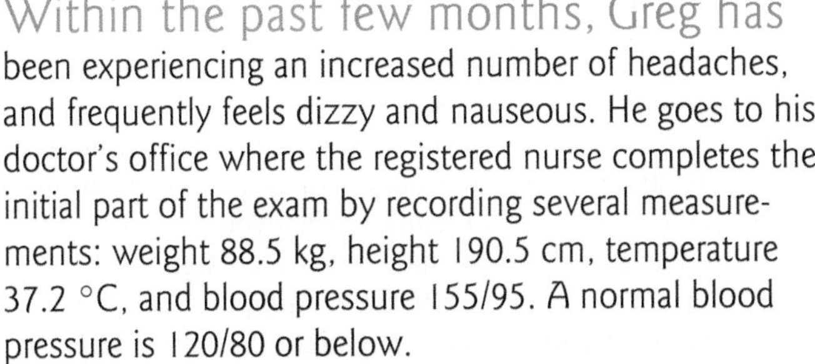

Within the past few months, Greg has been experiencing an increased number of headaches, and frequently feels dizzy and nauseous. He goes to his doctor's office where the registered nurse completes the initial part of the exam by recording several measurements: weight 88.5 kg, height 190.5 cm, temperature 37.2 °C, and blood pressure 155/95. A normal blood pressure is 120/80 or below.

When Greg sees his doctor, he is diagnosed as having high blood pressure (hypertension). The doctor prescribes 40 mg of Inderal (propranolol), which is used to treat hypertension and to be taken twice daily. The registered nurse fills the prescription at the pharmacy, which consists of 20-mg tablets. The nurse completes a calculation and determines that Greg needs to take 2 tablets each time.

Two weeks later, Greg visits his doctor again, who determines that his blood pressure is still elevated at 152/90. The doctor increases the dosage of Inderal to 60 mg, twice daily. The registered nurse informs Greg that he needs to increase his dosage to 3 tablets, twice daily.

Career: Registered Nurse

In addition to assisting physicians, registered nurses work to promote patient health, and prevent and treat disease. They provide patient care and help patients cope with illness. They take measurements such as a patient's weight, height, temperature, and blood pressure; make conversions; and calculate drug dosages. Registered nurses also maintain detailed medical records of patient symptoms, prescribed medications, and any reactions.

From Chapter 1 of *General, Organic, and Biological Chemistry: Structures of Life*, Fourth Edition. Karen C. Timberlake.

Chemistry and measurement are important parts of our everyday lives. Levels of toxic materials in the air, soil, and water are discussed in news reports. We read about radon in our homes, holes in the ozone layer, trans fats, and global climate change. We also read about nonpolluting fuels, solar energy, new techniques of DNA analysis, and new discoveries in medicine. Understanding chemistry and measurement helps us make informed choices about our world.

Think about your day; you probably made some measurements. Perhaps you checked your weight by stepping on a scale. If you did not feel well, you may have taken your temperature. If you made some rice for dinner, you added two cups of water to one cup of rice. If you stopped at the gas station, you watched the gas pump measure the number of gallons of gasoline you put in the car.

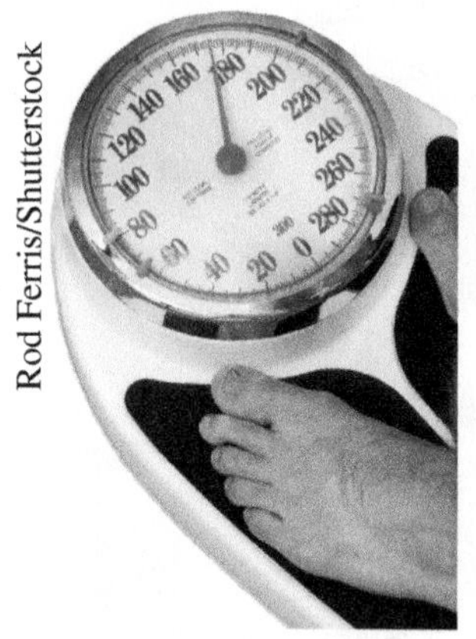

Rod Ferris/Shutterstock

Your weight on a bathroom scale is a measurement.

Measurement is an essential part of health careers such as nursing, dental hygiene, respiratory therapy, nutrition, and veterinary technology. The temperature, height, and weight of a patient are measured in degrees Celsius, meters, and kilograms, respectively. Samples of blood and urine are collected and sent to a laboratory where glucose, pH, urea, and protein levels are measured by the clinical technicians.

By learning about measurement, you will develop skills for solving problems and working with numbers in chemistry. If you intend to go into a health career, an understanding and assessment of measurements will be an important part of your evaluation of a patient's health.

LEARNING GOAL

Define the term chemistry *and identify substances as chemicals.*

1 Chemistry and Chemicals

Chemistry is the study of the composition, structure, properties, and reactions of matter. *Matter* is another word for all the substances that make up our world. Perhaps you imagine that chemistry is done only in a laboratory by a chemist wearing a lab coat and protective lab glasses. Actually, chemistry happens all around you every day and has an impact on everything you use and do. You are doing chemistry when you cook food, add chlorine to a swimming pool, or drop an antacid tablet into water. Plants grow because chemical reactions convert carbon dioxide, water, and energy to carbohydrates. Chemical reactions take place when you digest food and break it down into substances that you need for energy and health.

Pearson Education

Antacid tablets undergo a chemical reaction when dropped into water.

Branches of Chemistry

The field of chemistry is divided into several branches. Those of most interest to us are general, organic, and biological chemistry. General chemistry is the study of the composition, properties, and reactions of matter. Organic chemistry is the study of substances that contain the element carbon. Biological chemistry is the study of the chemical reactions that take place in biological systems.

Today, chemistry is often combined with other sciences such as geology and physics to form cross-disciplines such as geochemistry and physical chemistry. Geochemistry is the study of the chemical composition of ores, soils, and minerals of the surface of the Earth and other planets. Physical chemistry is the study of the physical nature of chemical systems, including energy changes.

U.S. Geological Survey

A geochemist collects newly erupted lava samples from Kilauea Volcano, Hawaii.

AndreasReh/iStockphoto

Biochemists analyze laboratory samples.

Chemistry Link to History

EARLY CHEMISTS: THE ALCHEMISTS

For many centuries, chemists have studied changes in various substances. From the time of the ancient Greeks to about the sixteenth century, alchemists described a substance in terms of four components of nature: earth, air, fire, and water. By the eighth century, alchemists searched for an unknown substance called a philosopher's stone that they thought would turn metals into gold, as well as prolong youth and postpone death. Although these efforts failed, the alchemists did provide information on the processes and chemical reactions involved in the extraction of metals from ores. The alchemists also designed some of the first laboratory equipment and developed early laboratory procedures.

The alchemist Paracelsus (1493–1541) thought that alchemy should be about preparing new medicines, not about producing gold. Using observation and experimentation, he proposed that a healthy body was regulated by a series of chemical processes that could be unbalanced by certain chemical compounds and rebalanced by using minerals and medicines. For example, he determined that inhaled dust, not underground spirits, caused lung disease in miners. He also thought that goiter was a problem caused by contaminated water, and he treated syphilis with compounds of mercury. His opinion of medicines was that the right dose makes the difference between a poison and a cure. Today, this idea is part of the risk analysis of medicines. Paracelsus changed alchemy in ways that helped to establish modern medicine and chemistry.

Jan van der Straet/SuperStock

Alchemists in the Middle Ages developed laboratory procedures.

The Print Collector/Alamy

Swiss alchemist and physician Paracelsus (1493–1541) believed that chemicals and minerals could be used as medicines.

Chemicals

A **chemical** is a substance that always has the same composition and properties wherever it is found. All the things you see around you are composed of one or more chemicals. Chemical processes take place in chemistry laboratories, manufacturing plants, and pharmaceutical labs, as well as every day in nature and in our bodies. Often the terms *chemical* and *substance* are used interchangeably to describe a specific type of material.

Every day, you use products containing substances that were prepared by chemists. Soaps and shampoos contain chemicals that remove oils on your skin and scalp. When you brush your teeth, the substances in toothpaste clean your teeth, prevent plaque formation, and stop tooth decay. Some of the chemicals used to make toothpaste are listed in Table 1.

Pearson Education/Eric Schrader

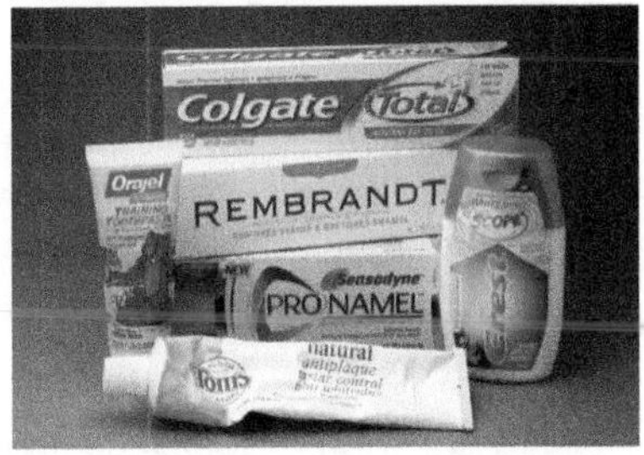

Toothpaste is a combination of many chemicals.

TABLE 1 Chemicals Commonly Used in Toothpaste

Chemical	Function
Calcium carbonate	Used as an abrasive to remove plaque
Sorbitol	Prevents loss of water and hardening of toothpaste
Sodium lauryl sulfate	Used to loosen plaque
Titanium dioxide	Makes toothpaste white and opaque
Triclosan	Inhibits bacteria that cause plaque and gum disease
Sodium fluorophosphate	Prevents formation of cavities by strengthening tooth enamel with fluoride
Methyl salicylate	Gives toothpaste a pleasant wintergreen flavor

In cosmetics and lotions, chemicals are used to moisturize, prevent deterioration of the product, fight bacteria, and thicken the product. Your clothes may be made of natural materials such as cotton, or synthetic substances such as nylon or polyester. Perhaps you wear a ring or watch made of gold, silver, or platinum. Your breakfast cereal is probably fortified with iron, calcium, and phosphorus, while the milk you drink is enriched with vitamins A and D. Antioxidants are chemicals added to your cereal to prevent it from spoiling. Chemicals you may encounter in the kitchen are shown in Figure 1.

Photos.com

FIGURE 1 Many of the items found in a kitchen are chemicals or products of chemical reactions.

Q What are some other chemicals found in a kitchen?

CONCEPT CHECK 1 **Chemicals**

Why is the copper in copper wire an example of a chemical?

ANSWER

Copper has the same composition and properties wherever it is found. Thus, copper is a chemical.

QUESTIONS AND PROBLEMS

1 Chemistry and Chemicals

In every chapter, odd-numbered exercises in the *Questions and Problems* are paired with even-numbered exercises. The answers for the magenta, odd-numbered *Questions and Problems* are given at the end of this chapter. The complete solutions to the odd-numbered *Questions and Problems* are in the *Student Solutions Manual.*

LEARNING GOAL: *Define the term* chemistry *and identify substances as chemicals.*

1 Obtain a bottle of multivitamins, and read the list of ingredients. What are four chemicals from the list?

2 Obtain a box of breakfast cereal, and read the list of ingredients. What are four chemicals from the list?

3 A “chemical-free” shampoo includes the ingredients: water, cocomide, glycerin, and citric acid. Is the shampoo truly “chemical-free”?

4 A “chemical-free” sunscreen includes the ingredients: titanium dioxide, vitamin E, and vitamin C. Is the sunscreen truly “chemical-free”?

2 A Study Plan for Learning Chemistry

LEARNING GOAL

Develop a study plan for learning chemistry.

Here you are taking chemistry, perhaps for the first time. Whatever your reasons are for choosing to study chemistry, you can look forward to learning many new and exciting ideas.

Features in This Text Help You Study Chemistry

This text has been designed with study features to complement your individual learning style. On the inside of the front cover is a periodic table of the elements. On the inside of the back cover are tables that summarize useful information needed throughout your study of chemistry. Each chapter begins with *Looking Ahead*, which outlines the topics in the chapter. A *Learning Goal* at the beginning of each section previews the concepts you are to learn. At the end of the text, there is a comprehensive *Glossary and Index*, which lists and defines key terms used in the text.

Before you begin reading, obtain an overview of a chapter by reviewing the topics in *Looking Ahead*. As you prepare to read a section of the chapter, look at the section title and turn it into a question. For example, for Section 1 "Chemistry and Chemicals," you could ask "What is chemistry?" or "What are chemicals?" When you are ready to read through that section, review the *Learning Goal*, which tells you what to expect in that section. As you read, try to answer your question. Throughout the chapter, you will find *Concept Checks* that will help you understand key ideas. When you come to a *Sample Problem*, take the time to work it through and compare your solution to the one provided. Then try the associated *Study Check*. Many *Sample Problems* are accompanied by a *Guide to Problem Solving* (*GPS*), which gives the steps needed to work the problem. At the end of each section, you will find a set of *Questions and Problems* that allows you to apply problem solving immediately to the new concepts.

Throughout each chapter, boxes titled *Chemistry Link to Health*, *Chemistry Link to the Environment*, *Chemistry Link to Industry*, and *Chemistry Link to History* help you connect the chemical concepts you are learning to real-life situations. Many of the figures and diagrams use macro-to-micro illustrations to depict the atomic level of organization of ordinary objects. These visual models illustrate the concepts described in the text and allow you to "see" the world in a microscopic way.

At the end of each chapter, you will find several study aids that complete the chapter. *Concept Maps* show the connections between important concepts, and *Chapter Reviews* provide a summary. The *Key Terms*, which are in boldface type in the text, are listed with their definitions. *Understanding the Concepts*, a set of questions that use art and structures, helps you visualize concepts. *Additional Questions and Problems* and *Challenge Problems* provide additional problems to test your understanding of the topics in the chapter. The problems are paired, which means that each of the odd-numbered problems is similar to the following even-numbered problem. The answers to all the *Study Checks*, as well as the answers to the odd-numbered *Questions and Problems*, are provided at the end of each chapter. If the answers provided match your answers, you most likely understand the topic; if not, you need to study the section again.

After some chapters, problem sets called *Combining Ideas* test your ability to solve problems that combine material from more than one chapter.

Using Active Learning to Learn Chemistry

A student who is an active learner continually interacts with the chemical ideas while reading the text, working problems, and attending lecture. Let's see how this is done.

As you read and practice problem solving, you remain actively involved in studying, which enhances the learning process. In this way, you learn small bits of information at a time and establish the necessary foundation for understanding the next section. You should also note any questions you have about the reading to discuss

Design Pics Inc./Alamy

Students discuss a chemistry problem with their professor during office hours.

TABLE 2 Steps in Active Learning

1. Read each *Learning Goal* for an overview of the material.
2. Form a question from the title of the section you are going to read.
3. Read the section, looking for answers to your question.
4. Self-test by working *Concept Checks*, *Sample Problems*, and *Study Checks*.
5. Complete the *Questions and Problems* that follow that section, and check the answers for the magenta odd-numbered problems.
6. Work the exercises in the *Study Guide* and go to *www.masteringchemistry.com* for self-study materials and instructor-assigned homework (optional).
7. Proceed to the next section, and repeat the above steps.

with your professor and laboratory instructor. Table 2 summarizes these steps for active learning. The time you spend in lecture is also useful as a learning time. By keeping track of the class schedule and reading the assigned material before lecture, you become aware of the new terms and concepts you need to learn. Some questions that occur during your reading may be answered during the lecture. If not, you can ask for further clarification from your professor.

track5/iStockphoto

Studying in a group can be beneficial to learning.

Many students find that studying with a group can be beneficial to learning. In a group, students motivate each other to study, fill in gaps, and correct misunderstandings by learning together. Studying alone does not allow the process of peer correction. In a group, you can cover the ideas more thoroughly as you discuss the reading and practice problem solving with other students. You may find it is easier to retain new material and new ideas if you study in short sessions throughout the week rather than all at once. Waiting to study until the night before an exam does not give you time to understand concepts and practice problem solving.

Thinking About Your Study Plan

As you embark on your journey into the world of chemistry, think about your approach to studying and learning chemistry. You might consider some of the ideas in the following list. Check those ideas that will help you learn chemistry successfully. Commit to them now. *Your* success depends on *you*.

My study of chemistry will include the following:

________ reading the chapter before a lecture
________ going to lecture
________ reviewing the *Learning Goals*
________ keeping a problem notebook
________ reading the text as an active learner
________ self-testing by working *Questions and Problems* following each section and checking answers at the end of the chapter
________ being an active learner during lecture
________ organizing a study group
________ seeing the professor during office hours
________ completing exercises in the *Study Guide*
________ working through the tutorials at *www.masteringchemistry.com*
________ attending review sessions
________ organizing my own review sessions
________ studying as often as I can

CONCEPT CHECK 2 **A Study Plan for Learning Chemistry**

Which of the following activities would you include in your study plan for learning chemistry successfully?

a. skipping lecture
b. forming a study group
c. keeping a problem notebook
d. waiting to study the night before the exam
e. becoming an active learner

ANSWER

Your success in chemistry can be improved by:
b. forming a study group
c. keeping a problem notebook
e. becoming an active learner

QUESTIONS AND PROBLEMS

2 A Study Plan for Learning Chemistry

LEARNING GOAL: *Develop a study plan for learning chemistry.*

5 What are four things you can do to help yourself to succeed in chemistry?

6 What are four things that would make it difficult for you to succeed in chemistry?

7 A student in your class asks you for advice on learning chemistry. Which of the following might you suggest?
a. Form a study group.
b. Skip lecture.
c. Visit the professor during office hours.
d. Wait until the night before an exam to study.
e. Become an active learner.
f. Work the *Learning Exercises* in the *Study Guide.*

8 A student in your class asks you for advice on learning chemistry. Which of the following might you suggest?
a. Do the assigned problems.
b. Don't read the book; it's never on the test.
c. Attend review sessions.
d. Read the assignment before a lecture.
e. Keep a problem notebook.
f. Do the tutorials at *www.masteringchemistry.com.*

3 Units of Measurement

LEARNING GOAL

Write the names and abbreviations for metric or SI units used in measurements of length, volume, mass, temperature, and time.

Scientists and health professionals throughout the world use the **metric system** of measurement. The **International System of Units (SI)**, or Système International, is the official system of measurement throughout the world except for the United States. In chemistry, we use metric and SI units for length, volume, mass, temperature, and time (see Table 3).

TABLE 3 Units of Measurement

Measurement	Metric	SI
Length	meter (m)	meter (m)
Volume	liter (L)	cubic meter (m^3)
Mass	gram (g)	kilogram (kg)
Temperature	degree Celsius (°C)	kelvin (K)
Time	second (s)	second (s)

Suppose today, you walk 2.1 km to campus carrying a backpack that has a mass of 12 kg, when the temperature is 22 °C. Perhaps you have a mass of 58.2 kg and a height of 165 cm. You may be more familiar with these measurements stated in the U.S. system of measurement: Then you walk 3 mi carrying a backpack that weighs 26 lb. The temperature would be 72 °F. You have a weight of 128 lb and a height of 65 in.

There are many measurements in everyday life.

UNITS LISTED ON LABELS

Read the labels on a variety of products such as sugar, salt, soft drinks, vitamins, and dental floss.

QUESTIONS

1. What metric or SI units of measurement are listed on the labels?
2. What type of measurement does each indicate?
3. Write the metric or SI amounts in terms of a number plus a unit.

Length

The metric and SI unit of length is the **meter (m)**. A meter is 39.4 inches (in.), which makes it slightly longer than a yard (yd). The **centimeter (cm)**, a smaller unit of length, is commonly used in chemistry and is about as wide as your little finger. For comparison, there are 2.54 cm in 1 in. (see Figure 2). Some useful relationships between different units for length follow:

$$1 \text{ m} = 100 \text{ cm}$$
$$1 \text{ m} = 39.4 \text{ in.}$$
$$1 \text{ m} = 1.09 \text{ yd}$$
$$2.54 \text{ cm} = 1 \text{ in.}$$

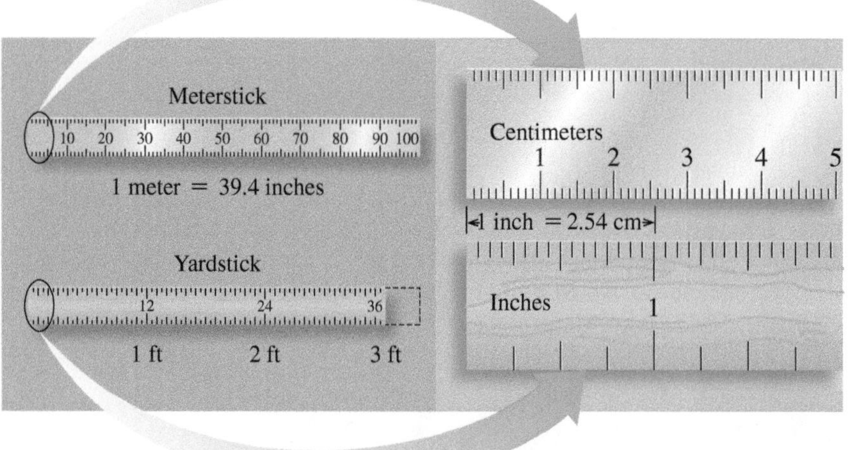

FIGURE 2 Length in the metric and SI systems is based on the meter, which is slightly longer than a yard.

Q How many centimeters are in a length of one inch?

Volume

Volume is the amount of space a substance occupies. A **liter (L)** is slightly larger than a quart (qt), ($1 \text{ L} = 1.06 \text{ qt}$). In a laboratory or a hospital, chemists work with metric units of volume that are smaller and more convenient, such as the **milliliter (mL)**. There are 1000 mL in 1 L (see Figure 3). The SI unit of volume is the cubic meter (m^3), a unit that is

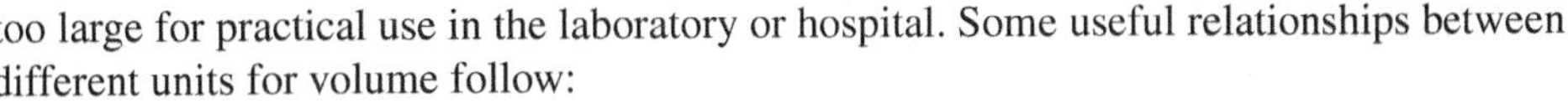

Pearson Education

FIGURE 3 Volume is the space occupied by a substance. In the metric system, volume is based on the liter, which is slightly larger than a quart.

Q How many milliliters are in 1 quart?

National Institute of Standards and Technology

The standard kilogram for the United States is stored at the National Institute of Standards and Technology (NIST).

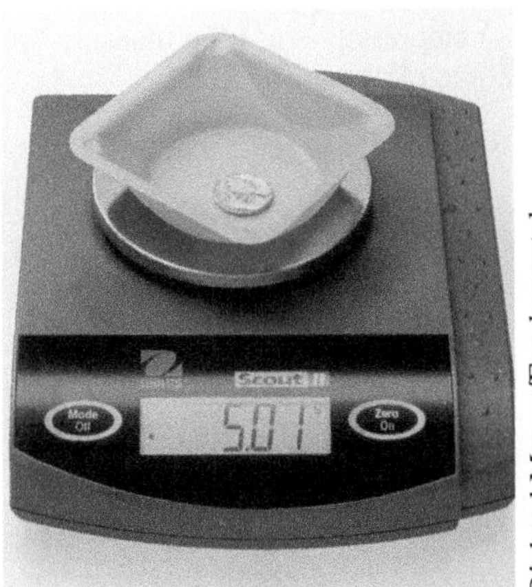

Richard Megna/Fundamental Photographs

FIGURE 4 On an electronic balance, a nickel has a mass of 5.01 g in the digital readout.

Q What is the mass of 10 nickels?

too large for practical use in the laboratory or hospital. Some useful relationships between different units for volume follow:

$$1\ \text{L} = 1000\ \text{mL}$$
$$1\ \text{L} = 1.06\ \text{qt}$$
$$946\ \text{mL} = 1\ \text{qt}$$
$$1000\ \text{L} = 1\ \text{m}^3$$

Mass

The **mass** of an object is a measure of the quantity of material it contains. The SI unit of mass, the **kilogram (kg)**, is used for large masses such as body weight. In the metric system, the unit for mass is the **gram (g)**, which is used for small masses. There are 1000 g in one kilogram. It takes 2.20 lb to make 1 kg, and 454 g are equal to one pound. Some useful relationships between different units for mass follow:

$$1\ \text{kg} = 1000\ \text{g}$$
$$1\ \text{kg} = 2.20\ \text{lb}$$
$$454\ \text{g} = 1\ \text{lb}$$

You may be more familiar with the term *weight* than with mass. Weight is a measure of the gravitational pull on an object. On Earth, an astronaut with a mass of 75.0 kg has a weight of 165 lb. On the Moon, where the gravitational pull is one-sixth that of Earth, the astronaut has a weight of 27.5 lb. However, the mass of the astronaut, 75.0 kg, is the same as on Earth. Scientists measure mass rather than weight because mass does not depend on gravity.

In a chemistry laboratory, an electronic balance is used to measure the mass of a substance in grams (see Figure 4).

Pearson Education

FIGURE 5 A thermometer is used to determine temperature.

Q What kinds of temperature readings have you made today?

Temperature

Temperature tells us how hot something is, how cold it is outside, or helps us determine if we have a fever (see Figure 5). In the metric system, temperature is measured using degrees Celsius. On the **Celsius (°C) temperature scale**, water freezes at 0 °C and boils at 100 °C, while on the Fahrenheit (°F) scale, water freezes at 32 °F and boils at 212 °F. In the SI system, temperature is measured using the **Kelvin (K) temperature scale**, on which the lowest temperature is 0 K. A unit on the Kelvin scale is called a kelvin and is not written with a degree sign.

A stopwatch is used to measure the time of a race.

Time

The SI and metric basic unit of time is the **second (s)**. However, we also measure time in units of years (y), days, hours (h), or minutes (min). The standard device now used to determine a second is an atomic clock. Some useful relationships between different units for time follow:

$$1 \text{ day} = 24 \text{ h}$$
$$1 \text{ h} = 60 \text{ min}$$
$$1 \text{ min} = 60 \text{ s}$$

SAMPLE PROBLEM 1 **Units of Measurement**

State the type of measurement indicated by the unit in each of the following:

a. 25 g **b.** 0.85 L **c.** 36 m **d.** 17 °C

SOLUTION

a. A gram (g) is a unit of mass.
b. A liter (L) is a unit of volume.
c. A meter (m) is a unit of length.
d. A degree Celsius (°C) is a unit of temperature.

STUDY CHECK 1

What type of measurement is indicated by the unit in 45 s?

QUESTIONS AND PROBLEMS

3 Units of Measurement

LEARNING GOAL: *Write the names and abbreviations for metric or SI units used in measurements of length, volume, mass, temperature, and time.*

9 State the type of measurement in each of the following statements:
a. I filled my gas tank with 12 L of gasoline.
b. My friend is 170 cm tall.
c. We are 385 000 km away from the Moon.
d. The horse won the race by 1.2 s.

10 State the type of measurement in each of the following statements:
a. I rode my bicycle 15 km today.
b. My dog weighs 12 kg.
c. It is hot today. It is 30 °C.
d. I used 2 L of water to fill my fish tank.

11 State the name of the unit and the type of measurement indicated for each of the following quantities:
a. 4.8 m **b.** 325 g **c.** 1.5 L **d.** 480 s **e.** 28 °C

12 State the name of the unit and the type of measurement indicated for each of the following quantities:
a. 0.8 mL **b.** 3.6 cm **c.** 14 kg **d.** 35 h **e.** 373 K

LEARNING GOAL

Write a number in scientific notation.

4 Scientific Notation

In chemistry, we use numbers that are very large or very small. We might measure something as tiny as the width of a human hair, which is about 0.000 008 m. Or perhaps we want to count the number of hairs in the average human scalp, which is about 100 000 hairs (see Figure 6). In this text, we add spaces between sets of three digits when it helps to make the places easier to count. However, we will see that it is more convenient to write small and large numbers in scientific notation.

Item	Value	Scientific Notation
Width of a human hair	0.000 008 m	8×10^{-6} m
Hairs on a human scalp	100 000 hairs	1×10^{5} hairs

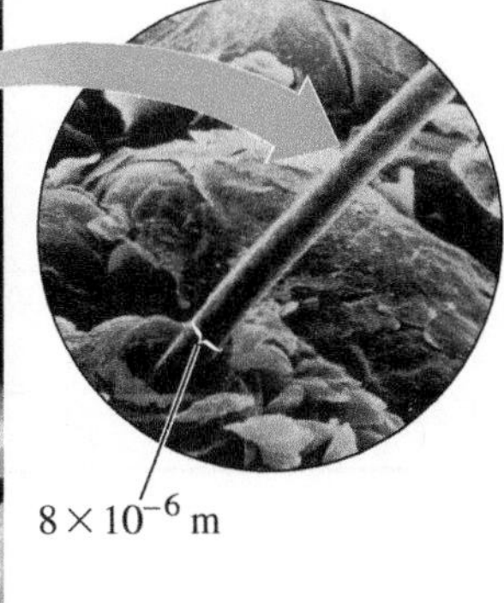

Jason Stitt/Shutterstock

Anatomy/University "la Sapienza" Rome/Science Photo Library

FIGURE 6 Humans have an average of 1×10^5 hairs on their scalps. Each hair is about 8×10^{-6} m wide.

Q Why are large and small numbers written in scientific notation?

Writing a Number in Scientific Notation

TUTORIAL
Scientific Notation

A number written in **scientific notation** has three parts: a coefficient, a power of 10, and a unit of measurement. For example, 2400 m is written in scientific notation as 2.4×10^3 m. The coefficient is 2.4, and 10^3 shows that the power of 10 is 3 and the unit of measurement is meter (m). The coefficient is obtained by moving the decimal point to the left to give a coefficient that is at least 1 but less than 10. Because we moved the decimal point three places, the power of 10 is 3, written as 10^3. When a number greater than 1 is converted to scientific notation, the power of 10 is positive. *A number greater than 1 written in scientific notation has a positive power of 10.*

$$2400.\ \text{m} = 2.4 \times 1000 = \underset{\text{Coefficient}}{2.4} \times \underset{\text{Power of 10}}{10^3}\ \underset{\text{Unit}}{\text{m}}$$

← 3 places

When a number less than 1 is written in scientific notation, the power of 10 is a negative number. *A number less than 1 written in scientific notation has a negative power of 10.* For example, the number 0.000 86 is written in scientific notation by moving the decimal point four places to give a coefficient of 8.6. Because the decimal point was moved four places to the right, the power of 10 is a negative 4, written as 10^{-4}.

$$0.00086\ \text{g} = \frac{8.6}{10\,000} = \frac{8.6}{10 \times 10 \times 10 \times 10} = \underset{\text{Coefficient}}{8.6} \times \underset{\text{Power of 10}}{10^{-4}}\ \underset{\text{Unit}}{\text{g}}$$

4 places →

Table 4 gives some examples of numbers written as positive and negative powers of 10. The powers of 10 are a way to keep track of the decimal point in the decimal number. Table 5 gives several examples of writing measurements in scientific notation.

Science Photo Library/Alamy

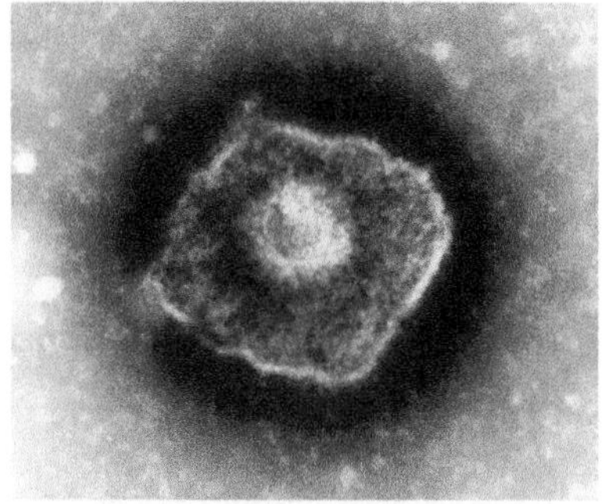

A chickenpox virus has a diameter of 3×10^{-7} m.

TABLE 4 Some Powers of 10

Number	Multiples of 10	Scientific Notation	Powers of Ten
10 000	$10 \times 10 \times 10 \times 10$	1×10^4	Some positive powers of 10
1 000	$10 \times 10 \times 10$	1×10^3	
100	10×10	1×10^2	
10	10	1×10^1	
1	0	1×10^0	
0.1	$\frac{1}{10}$	1×10^{-1}	Some negative powers of 10
0.01	$\frac{1}{10} \times \frac{1}{10} = \frac{1}{100}$	1×10^{-2}	
0.001	$\frac{1}{10} \times \frac{1}{10} \times \frac{1}{10} = \frac{1}{1000}$	1×10^{-3}	
0.0001	$\frac{1}{10} \times \frac{1}{10} \times \frac{1}{10} \times \frac{1}{10} = \frac{1}{10\,000}$	1×10^{-4}	

TABLE 5 Some Measurements Written in Scientific Notation

Measured Quantity	Measurement	Scientific Notation
Volume of gasoline used in the United States each year	550 000 000 000 L	5.5×10^{11} L
Diameter of Earth	12 800 000 m	1.28×10^7 m
Time for light to travel from the Sun to Earth	500 s	5×10^2 s
Mass of a typical human	68 kg	6.8×10^1 kg
Mass of a hummingbird	0.002 kg	2×10^{-3} kg
Diameter of a chickenpox (*varicella zoster*) virus	0.000 000 3 m	3×10^{-7} m
Mass of a bacterium (mycoplasma)	0.000 000 000 000 000 000 1 kg	1×10^{-19} kg

TUTORIAL
Using Scientific Notation

Scientific Notation and Calculators

You can enter a number in scientific notation on many calculators using the EE or EXP key. After you enter the coefficient, press the EXP (or EE) key and enter only the power of 10, because the EXP function key already includes the $\times$ 10 value. To enter a negative power of 10, press the plus/minus (+/−) key or the minus (−) key, depending on your calculator. As you work through these problems, read the instruction manual for your particular calculator to determine the proper sequence for using the keys.

Number to Enter	Method	Display Reads
4×10^6	4 EXP (EE) 6	4 06 or 4^{06} or 4 E06
2.5×10^{-4}	2.5 EXP (EE) +/− 4	2.5−04 or 2.5^{-04} or 2.5 E−04

When a calculator display appears in scientific notation, it is shown as a number between 1 and 10, followed by a space and the power of 10. To express this display in scientific notation, write the coefficient value, write $\times$ 10, and use the power of 10 as an exponent.

Calculator Display	Expressed in Scientific Notation
7.52 04 or 7.52^{04} or 7.52 E04	7.52×10^4
5.8−02 or 5.8^{-02} or 5.8 E−02	5.8×10^{-2}

On many scientific calculators, a number is converted into scientific notation using the appropriate keys. For example, the number 0.000 52 can be entered, followed by pressing the 2nd or 3rd function key and the SCI key. The scientific notation appears in the calculator display as a coefficient and the power of 10.

0.000 52 [2nd or 3rd function key] [SCI] = 5.2−04 or 5.2^{-04} or 5.2 E−04 = 5.2×10^{-4}

Key Key

Converting Scientific Notation to a Standard Number

When a number in scientific notation has a positive power of 10, the standard number is written by moving the decimal point to the right for the same number of places as the power of 10. Placeholder zeros are used to give additional decimal places.

$$8.2 \times 10^2 = 8.2 \times 100 = 820$$

When a number written in scientific notation has a negative power of 10, the standard number is written by moving the decimal point to the left for the same number of places. Placeholder zeros are added in front of the coefficient as needed.

$$4.3 \times 10^{-3} = 4.3 \times \frac{1}{1000} = 0.0043$$

SAMPLE PROBLEM 2 Scientific Notation

Write each of the following in scientific notation:

a. 45 000 m **b.** 0.0092 g **c.** 143 mL

SOLUTION

a. To write a coefficient greater than 1 but less than 10, move the decimal point four places to the left to give 4.5×10^4 m.

b. To write a coefficient greater than 1 but less than 10, move the decimal point three places to the right to give 9.2×10^{-3} g.

c. To write a coefficient greater than 1 but less than 10, move the decimal point two places to the left to give 1.43×10^2 mL.

STUDY CHECK 2

Write the following measurements in scientific notation:

a. 425 000 m **b.** 0.000 000 8 g

QUESTIONS AND PROBLEMS

4 Scientific Notation

LEARNING GOAL: *Write a number in scientific notation.*

13 Write each of the following measurements in scientific notation:
a. 55 000 m **b.** 480 g **c.** 0.000 005 cm
d. 0.000 14 s **e.** 0.007 85 L **f.** 670 000 kg

14 Write each of the following measurements in scientific notation:
a. 180 000 000 g **b.** 0.000 06 m
c. 750 °C **d.** 0.15 mL
e. 0.024 s **f.** 1500 cm

15 Which number in each of the following pairs is larger?
a. 7.2×10^3 cm or 8.2×10^2 cm
b. 4.5×10^{-4} kg or 3.2×10^{-2} kg
c. 1×10^4 L or 1×10^{-4} L
d. 0.000 52 m or 6.8×10^{-2} m

16 Which number in each of the following pairs is smaller?
a. 4.9×10^{-3} s or 5.5×10^{-9} s
b. 1250 kg or 3.4×10^2 kg
c. 0.000 000 4 m or 5×10^{-8} m
d. 2.50×10^2 g or 4×10^{-2} g

17 Write each of the following as standard numbers:
a. 1.2×10^4 s
b. 8.25×10^{-2} kg
c. 4×10^6 g
d. 5×10^{-3} m

18 Write each of the following as standard numbers:
a. 3.6×10^{-5} L
b. 8.75×10^4 cm
c. 3×10^{-2} mL
d. 2.12×10^5 kg

LEARNING GOAL

Identify a number as measured or exact; determine the number of significant figures in a measured number.

5 Measured Numbers and Significant Figures

When you make a measurement, you use some type of measuring device. For example, you may use a meterstick to measure your height, a scale to check your weight, or a thermometer to take your temperature.

Measured Numbers

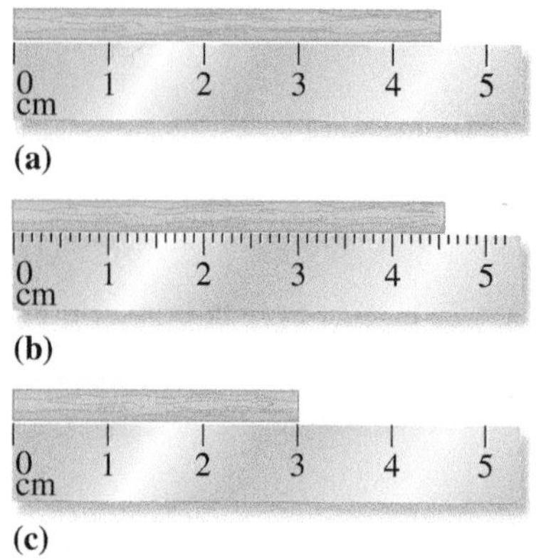

FIGURE 7 The lengths of the rectangular objects are measured as **(a)** 4.5 cm and **(b)** 4.55 cm.

Q What is the length of the object in (c)?

Measured numbers are the numbers you obtain when you measure a quantity using a measuring tool. Suppose you are going to measure the lengths of the objects in Figure 7. You would select a metric ruler that may have lines marked in 1 cm divisions, or perhaps in divisions of 0.1 cm. To report the length of each object, you observe the numerical values of the marked lines at the end of the object. Then, you *estimate* the final number by visually dividing the space between the marked lines. This estimated number is the final digit that is reported for any measured number.

For example, in Figure 7a, the end of the object is between the marks of 4 cm and 5 cm. Thus, you know that its length is more than 4 cm but less than 5 cm. Now you could estimate that the end is halfway between 4 cm and 5 cm and report its length as 4.5 cm. However, another student might report the length of this object as 4.4 cm because people do not estimate the same way. Therefore, there is always some uncertainty about the estimated number in every measurement.

The metric ruler shown in Figure 7b is marked at every 0.1 cm. With this ruler, you can now estimate the value of the hundredths place (0.01 cm). Now you could know that the end of the object is between 4.5 and 4.6 cm. Perhaps you report the length of the object as 4.55 cm, while another student may report its length as 4.56 cm. Both results are acceptable.

In Figure 7c, the end of the object appears to line up with the 3-cm mark. Because the divisions are marked in units of 1 cm, the estimated digit in the tenths place (0.1 cm) is 0. The reported measurement for length is reported as 3.0 cm, not 3. This means that the uncertainty of the measurement (the last digit) is in the tenths place (0.1 cm).

Significant Figures

SELF-STUDY ACTIVITY
Significant Figures

TUTORIAL
Counting Significant Figures

In a measured number, the **significant figures (SFs)** *are all the digits including the estimated digit.* Nonzero numbers are always counted as significant figures. However, a zero may or may not be significant, depending on its position in a number. Table 6 gives the rules and examples of counting significant figures.

TABLE 6 Significant Figures in Measured Numbers

Rule	Measured Number	Number of Significant Figures
1. A number is a *significant figure* if it is		
a. not a zero	4.5 g	2
	122.35 m	5
b. one or more zeros between nonzero digits	205 m	3
	5.008 kg	4
c. one or more zeros at the end of a decimal number	50. L	2
	25.0 °C	3
	16.00 g	4
d. in the coefficient of a number written in scientific notation	4.8×10^5 m	2
	5.70×10^{-3} g	3
2. A zero is *not significant* if it is		
a. at the beginning of a decimal number	0.0004 s	1
	0.075 m	2
b. used as a placeholder in a large number without a decimal point	850 000 m	2
	1 250 000 g	3

Scientific Notation and Significant Zeros

When one or more zeros in a large number are significant, they are shown more clearly by writing the number in scientific notation. For example, if the first zero in the measurement 500 m is significant, it is written as 5.0×10^2 m. In this text, we will place a decimal point after a significant zero at the end of a number. For example, a measurement written as 500. g indicates that *both zeros* are significant figures. To show this clearly, we can write it as 5.00×10^2 g. We will assume that zeros at the end of large numbers without a decimal point are not significant. Therefore, we write 400 000 g as 4×10^5 g, which has only one significant figure.

CONCEPT CHECK 3 **Significant Zeros**

Identify the significant and nonsignificant zeros in each of the following measured numbers:

a. 0.000 250 m **b.** 70.040 g **c.** 1 020 000 L

ANSWER

a. The zeros preceding the first nonzero digit of 2 are not significant. The zero in the last decimal place following the 5 is significant.
b. The zeros between nonzero digits or at the end of decimal numbers are significant. All zeros in 70.040 g are significant.
c. The zeros between nonzero digits are significant. The zero between 1 and 2 is significant, but the four zeros following the 2 are not significant.

Exact Numbers

Exact numbers *are those numbers obtained by counting items or using a definition that compares two units in the same measuring system.* Suppose a friend asks you to tell her the number of coats in your closet or the number of classes you are taking in school. Your answer would be given by counting the items. It was not necessary for you to use any type of measuring tool. Suppose someone asks you to state the number of seconds in one minute. Without using any measuring device, you would give the definition: 60 seconds in one minute. *Exact numbers are not measured, do not have a limited number of significant figures, and do not affect the number of significant figures in a calculated answer.* For more examples of exact numbers, see Table 7.

Kameleon007/iStockphoto

The number of baseballs is counted, which means 2 is an exact number.

TABLE 7 **Examples of Some Exact Numbers**

Items	Defined Equalities	
Counted Numbers	**U.S. System**	**Metric System**
8 doughnuts	1 ft = 12 in.	1 L = 1000 mL
2 baseballs	1 qt = 4 cups	1 m = 100 cm
5 capsules	1 lb = 16 oz	1 kg = 1000 g

CONCEPT CHECK 4 **Measured Numbers and Significant Figures**

Identify each of the following numbers as measured or exact, and give the number of significant figures in each measured number:

a. 42.2 g **b.** 3 eggs **c.** 5.0×10^{-3} cm **d.** 450 000 km **e.** 1 ft = 12 in.

ANSWER

a. The mass of 42.2 g is a measured number because it is obtained with a measuring tool. There are three SFs in 42.2 g because non-zero digits are always significant.
b. The value of 3 eggs is an exact number because it is obtained by counting rather than using a measuring tool.

c. The length of 5.0×10^{-3} cm is a measured number because it is obtained with a measuring tool. There are two SFs in 5.0×10^{-3} cm because all the numbers in the coefficient of a number written in scientific notation are significant.
d. The distance of 450 000 km is a measured number because it is obtained with a measuring tool. There are only two SFs in 450 000 km because the zeros at the end of a large number without a decimal point are not significant.
e. The lengths of 1 ft and 12 in. contain exact numbers because the relationship 1 ft = 12 in. is a definition in the U.S. system of measurement. The relationship of number of inches in one foot was obtained by definition; no measuring tool was used.

QUESTIONS AND PROBLEMS

5 Measured Numbers and Significant Figures

LEARNING GOAL: *Identify a number as measured or exact; determine the number of significant figures in a measured number.*

19 Identify the number in each of the following as measured or exact and give the reason for your choice:
a. A person weighs 67.5 kg.
b. A patient is given 2 tablets of medication.
c. In the metric system, 1 m is equal to 1000 mm.
d. The distance from Denver, Colorado, to Houston, Texas, is 1720 km.

20 Identify the number in each of the following as measured or exact and give the reason for your choice:
a. There are 31 students in the laboratory.
b. The oldest known flower lived 1.2×10^8 y ago.
c. The largest gem ever found, an aquamarine, has a mass of 104 kg.
d. A laboratory test shows a blood cholesterol level of 184 mg/100 mL.

21 Identify the measured number(s), if any, in each of the following pairs of numbers:
a. 3 hamburgers and 6 oz of meat
b. 1 table and 4 chairs
c. 0.75 lb of grapes and 350 g of butter
d. 60 s = 1 min

22 Identify the measured number(s), if any, in each of the following pairs of numbers:
a. 5 pizzas and 50.0 g of cheese
b. 6 nickels and 16 g of nickel
c. 3 onions and 3 lb of onions
d. 5 miles and 5 cars

23 Indicate the significant zeros, if any, in each of the following measurements:
a. 0.00380 m **b.** 5.04 cm **c.** 800. L
d. 3.0×10^{-3} kg **e.** 85 000 g

24 Indicate the significant zeros, if any, in each of the following measurements:
a. 20.5 °C **b.** 5.00 m **c.** 0.000 070 L
d. 120 000 y **e.** 6.003×10^2 g

25 How many significant figures are in each of the following measurements?
a. 11.005 g **b.** 0.000 32 m **c.** 36 000 000 m
d. 1.80×10^4 g **e.** 0.8250 L **f.** 30.0 °C

26 How many significant figures are in each of the following measurements?
a. 20.60 L **b.** 1036.48 g **c.** 4.00 m
d. 18.4 °C **e.** 60 800 000 g **f.** 5.0×10^{-3} L

27 Identify the number in each of the following pairs that contains more significant figures:
a. 11.0 m and 11.00 m
b. 405 K and 405.0 K
c. 0.0120 s and 12 000 s
d. 250.0 L and 2.5×10^{-2} L

28 Identify the number in each of the following pairs that contains fewer significant figures:
a. 28.33 g and 2.8×10^{-3} g
b. 0.0250 m and 0.2005 m
c. 150 000 s and 1.50×10^4 s
d. 3.8×10^{-2} L and 3.80×10^5 L

LEARNING GOAL

Give the correct number of significant figures in a final answer by adding or removing digits in a calculator result.

TUTORIAL
Significant Figures in Calculations

6 Significant Figures in Calculations

In the sciences, we measure many things: the length of a bacterium, the volume of a gas sample, the temperature of a reaction mixture, or the mass of iron in a sample. The numbers obtained from these types of measurements are often used in calculations. The number of significant figures in the measured numbers limits the number of significant figures that can be given in the calculated answer.

Using a calculator will usually help you do calculations faster. However, calculators cannot think for you. It is up to you to enter the numbers properly, press the correct function keys, and give an answer with the correct number of significant figures.

Rounding Off

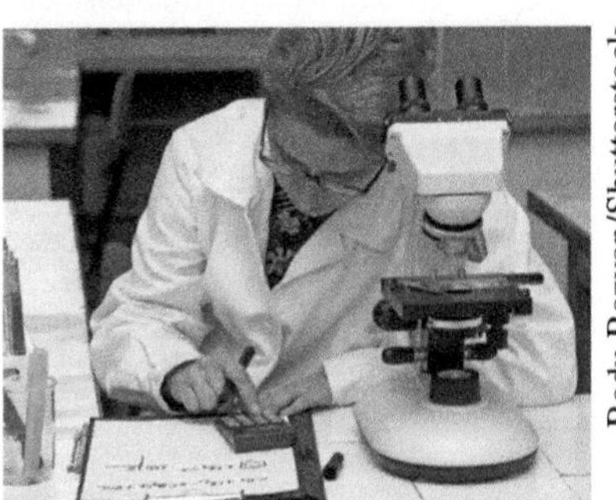

A technician uses a calculator in the laboratory.

Suppose you decide to buy carpeting for a room that measures 5.52 m by 3.58 m. Each measurement of length has three significant figures because the measuring tape limits your estimated place to 0.01 m. To determine how much carpeting you need, you would calculate the area of the room by multiplying 5.52 times 3.58. If you used a calculator, the display shows the numbers 19.7616. However, the display has too many numbers, which is the result of the multiplication process. Because each of the original measurements has three significant figures, the display numbers of 19.7616 must be *rounded off* to three significant figures, 19.8. Therefore, you can order carpeting that will cover an area of 19.8 m^2 (square meters).

Each time you use a calculator, it is important to look at the original measurements and determine the number of significant figures that can be used for the answer. You can use the following rules to round off the numbers in a calculator display:

Rules for Rounding Off

1. If the first digit to be dropped is *4 or less*, then it and all following digits are simply dropped from the number.
2. If the first digit to be dropped is *5 or greater*, then the last retained digit of the number is increased by 1.

Number to Round Off	Three Significant Figures	Two Significant Figures
8.4234	8.42 (drop 34)	8.4 (drop 234)
14.780	14.8 (drop 80, increase the last retained digit by 1)	15 (drop 780, increase the last retained digit by 1)
3262	3260* (drop 2, add 0) 3.26×10^3	3300* (drop 62, increase the last retained digit by 1, add 00) 3.3×10^3

*The value of a large number is retained by using placeholder zeros to replace dropped digits.

CONCEPT CHECK 5 **Rounding Off**

Identify the digits to drop, whether the last retained digit increases by 1 or not, and give the correctly rounded-off value of 2.8456 m to each of the following:

a. three significant figures
b. two significant figures

ANSWER

a. To round off 2.8456 m to three significant figures, drop the last two digits, 56. Because the first digit dropped is 5, the last retained digit is increased by 1 to give 2.85 m.
b. To round off 2.8456 m to two significant figures, drop the final three digits, 456. Because the first digit dropped is 4, the last retained digit does not change to give 2.8 m.

SAMPLE PROBLEM 3 **Rounding Off**

Round off each of the following calculator displays to three significant figures:

a. 35.7823 m
b. 0.002 625 L
c. 3.8268×10^3 g
d. 1.2836 kg

SOLUTION

a. 35.8 m
b. 0.002 63 L
c. 3.83×10^3 g
d. 1.28 kg

STUDY CHECK 3

Round off each of the numbers in Sample Problem 3 to two significant figures.

Emin Kuliyev/Shutterstock

A calculator is helpful in working problems and doing calculations faster.

Multiplication and Division

In multiplication or division, the final answer is written so it has the same number of significant figures as the measurement with the fewest significant figures (SFs). Some examples of rounding off numbers from multiplication and division follow:

Example 1

Multiply the following measured numbers: 24.65×0.67

24.65	⊠	0.67	⊜	16.5155	⟶	17
Four SFs		Two SFs		Calculator display		Final answer, rounded off to two SFs

The answer in the calculator display has more digits than the measured numbers allow. The measurement 0.67 has the fewer number of significant figures, two. Therefore, the numbers in the calculator display are rounded off to give two significant figures in the answer.

Example 2

Solve the following using measured numbers:

$$\frac{2.85 \times 67.4}{4.39}$$

A problem with multiple steps is worked on a calculator by multiplying the numbers in the numerator, and then dividing by the numbers in the denominator. We might press the keys in the following order, but be sure to use the correct operation process for your calculation:

2.85	⊠	67.4	⊞ ÷	4.39	⊜	43.75626424	⟶	43.8
Three SFs		Three SFs		Three SFs		Calculator display		Final answer, rounded off to three SFs

All of the original measurements in this problem have three significant figures. Therefore, the calculator result is rounded off to give an answer with three significant figures, 43.8.

Adding Significant Zeros

Sometimes, a calculator display consists of a small whole number. Then we add one or more significant zeros to the calculator display to obtain the correct number of significant figures. For example, suppose the calculator display is 4, but you used measurements that have three significant numbers. Then two significant zeros are added to give 4.00 as the correct answer.

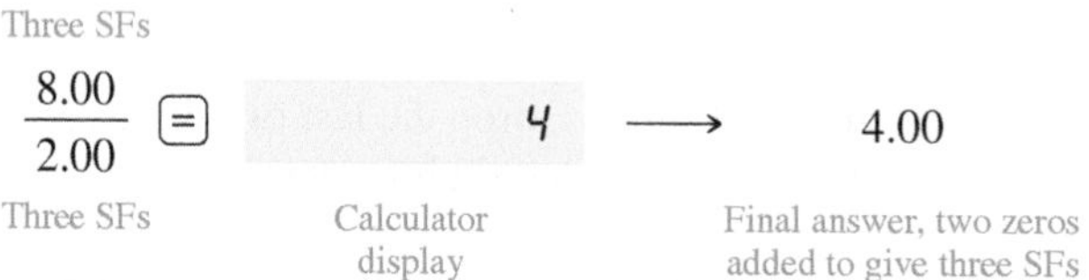

CONCEPT CHECK 6 Significant Figures in Multiplication and Division

Perform the following calculations of measured numbers. Give each answer with the correct number of significant figures.

a. $\dfrac{2.075}{(8.42)(0.0045)}$ b. $\dfrac{2.0 \times 6.00}{4.00}$

ANSWER

a.

2.075	÷	8.42	÷	0.0045	=	54.76378992	⟶	55
Four SFs		Three SFs		Two SFs		Calculator display		Final answer, rounded off to two SFs

b.

2.0	×	6.00	÷	4.00	=	3.	⟶	3.0
Two SFs		Three SFs		Three SFs		Calculator display		Final answer, one significant zero added to give two SFs

Addition and Subtraction

In addition or subtraction, the final answer is written so that it has the same number of decimal places as the measurement having the fewest decimal places. Some examples of addition and subtraction follow:

Example 3

Add:

	2.045	Three decimal places
+	34.1	One decimal place
	36.145	Calculator display
	36.1	Answer, rounded off to one decimal place

When numbers are added or subtracted to give answers ending in zero, the zero does not appear after the decimal point in the calculator display. For example, if you do the subtraction 14.5 g − 2.5 g on your calculator, the display shows 12. The correct answer, 12.0 g, is obtained by placing a significant zero after the decimal point.

Example 4

Subtract:

	14.5 g	One decimal place
−	2.5 g	One decimal place
	12.	Calculator display
	12.0 g	Answer, one zero added to give one decimal place

SAMPLE PROBLEM 4 Addition and Subtraction

Perform each of the following calculations and give the answers with the correct number of decimal places:

a. 27.8 cm + 0.235 cm **b.** 153.247 g − 14.82 g

SOLUTION

a. 28.0 cm **b.** 138.43 g

STUDY CHECK 4

Perform each of the following calculations and give the answers with the correct number of decimal places:

a. 82.45 mg + 1.245 mg + 0.000 56 mg **b.** 4.259 L − 3.8 L

QUESTIONS AND PROBLEMS

6 Significant Figures in Calculations

LEARNING GOAL: *Give the correct number of significant figures in a final answer by adding or removing digits in a calculator result.*

29 Round off each of the following measurements to three significant figures:
a. 1.854 kg **b.** 184.2038 L **c.** 0.004 738 265 cm
d. 8807 m **e.** 1.832×10^5 s

30 Round off each of the measurements in Problem 29 to two significant figures.

31 Perform each of the following calculations and give answers with the correct number of significant figures:
a. 45.7×0.034 **b.** $0.002\,78 \times 5$
c. $\frac{34.56}{1.25}$ **d.** $\frac{(0.2465)(25)}{1.78}$

32 Perform each of the following calculations and give answers with the correct number of significant figures:
a. 400×185 **b.** $\frac{2.40}{(4)(125)}$
c. $0.825 \times 3.6 \times 5.1$ **d.** $\frac{3.5 \times 0.261}{8.24 \times 20.0}$

33 Perform each of the following calculations, and give answers with the correct number of decimal places:
a. 45.48 cm + 8.057 cm
b. 23.45 g + 104.1 g + 0.025 g
c. 145.675 mL − 24.2 mL **d.** 1.08 L − 0.585 L

34 Perform each of the following calculations, and give answers with the correct number of decimal places:
a. 5.08 g + 25.1 g
b. 85.66 cm + 104.10 cm + 0.025 cm
c. 24.568 mL − 14.25 mL **d.** 0.2654 L − 0.2585 L

LEARNING GOAL

Use the numerical values of prefixes to write a metric equality.

SELF-STUDY ACTIVITY
Metric System

TUTORIAL
SI Prefixes and Units

7 Prefixes and Equalities

In the metric and SI systems of units, a **prefix** attached to any unit increases or decreases its size by some factor of 10. For example, the prefixes *milli* and *micro* are used to make the smaller units milligram (mg) and microgram (μg). Table 8 lists some of the metric prefixes, their symbols, and their decimal values.

TABLE 8 Metric and SI Prefixes

Prefix	Symbol	Numerical Value	Scientific Notation	Equality
Prefixes That Increase the Size of the Unit				
peta	P	1 000 000 000 000 000	10^{15}	1 Pg = 10^{15} g 1 g = 10^{-15} Pg
tera	T	1 000 000 000 000	10^{12}	1 Tg = 10^{12} g 1 g = 10^{-12} Tg
giga	G	1 000 000 000	10^{9}	1 Gm = 10^{9} m 1 m = 10^{-9} Gm
mega	M	1 000 000	10^{6}	1 Mg = 10^{6} g 1 g = 10^{-6} Mg
kilo	k	1 000	10^{3}	1 km = 10^{3} m 1 m = 10^{-3} km
Prefixes That Decrease the Size of the Unit				
deci	d	0.1	10^{-1}	1 dL = 10^{-1} L 1 L = 10 dL
centi	c	0.01	10^{-2}	1 cm = 10^{-2} m 1 m = 100 cm
milli	m	0.001	10^{-3}	1 ms = 10^{-3} s 1 s = 10^{3} ms
micro	μ	0.000 001	10^{-6}	1 μg = 10^{-6} g 1 g = 10^{6} μg
nano	n	0.000 000 001	10^{-9}	1 nm = 10^{-9} m 1 m = 10^{9} nm
pico	p	0.000 000 000 001	10^{-12}	1 ps = 10^{-12} s 1 s = 10^{12} ps
femto	f	0.000 000 000 000 001	10^{-15}	1 fs = 10^{-15} s 1 s = 10^{15} fs

The prefix *centi* is like cents in a dollar. One cent would be a "centidollar" or 0.01 of a dollar. That also means that one dollar is the same as 100 cents. The prefix *deci* is like the value of a dime in a dollar. One dime would be a "decidollar" or 0.1 of a dollar. That also means that one dollar is the same as 10 dimes.

The relationship of a prefix to a unit can be expressed by replacing the prefix with its numerical value. For example, when the prefix *kilo* in kilometer is replaced with its value of 1000, we find that a kilometer is equal to 1000 meters. Some relationships using the prefix *kilo* follow:

1 **kilo**meter (1 km) = **1000** meters (1000 m = 10^3 m)
1 **kilo**liter (1 kL) = **1000** liters (1000 L = 10^3 L)
1 **kilo**gram (1 kg) = **1000** grams (1000 g = 10^3 g)

The U.S. Food and Drug Administration (FDA) has determined the daily values (DVs) of nutrients for adults and children age 4 or older. Some examples of the daily values that have prefixes are listed in Table 9.

TABLE 9 Daily Values for Selected Nutrients

Nutrient	Amount Recommended
Vitamin B_{12}	6 μg
Vitamin C	60 mg
Calcium	1000 mg
Copper	2 mg
Iodine	150 μg
Iron	18 mg
Magnesium	400 mg
Niacin	20 mg
Potassium	3500 mg
Sodium	2400 mg
Zinc	15 mg

CONCEPT CHECK 7 **Prefixes**

Fill in each of the blanks with the correct prefix:

a. 1000 g = 1 ____ g **b.** 0.01 m = 1 ____ m **c.** 1×10^6 L = 1 ____ L

ANSWER

a. The prefix for 1000 is *kilo*; 1000 g = 1 kg
b. The prefix for 0.01 is *centi*; 0.01 m = 1 cm
c. The prefix for 1×10^6 is *mega*; 1×10^6 L = 1 ML

SAMPLE PROBLEM 5 **Prefixes**

The storage capacity for a hard disk drive (HDD) is specified using prefixes: megabyte (MB), gigabyte (GB), or terabyte (TB). Indicate the storage capacity in bytes of each of the following hard disk drives. Suggest a reason for describing a HDD storage capacity in gigabytes or terabytes.

a. 5 MB **b.** 2 GB

SOLUTION

a. The prefix *mega* (M) in MB is equal to 1 000 000 or 1×10^6. Thus, 5 MB is equal to 5 000 000 (5×10^6) bytes.
b. The prefix *giga* (G) in GB is equal to 1 000 000 000 or 1×10^9. Thus, 2 GB is equal to 2 000 000 000 (2×10^9) bytes.

Expressing HDD capacity in gigabytes or terabytes gives a more reasonable number to work with than a number with many zeros or a large power of 10.

STUDY CHECK 5

A hard drive has a storage capacity of 1.5 TB. How many bytes are stored?

Alias Studiot Oy/Shutterstock

A 1 terabyte hard disk drive stores 10^{12} bytes of information.

Monkey Business Images/Shutterstock

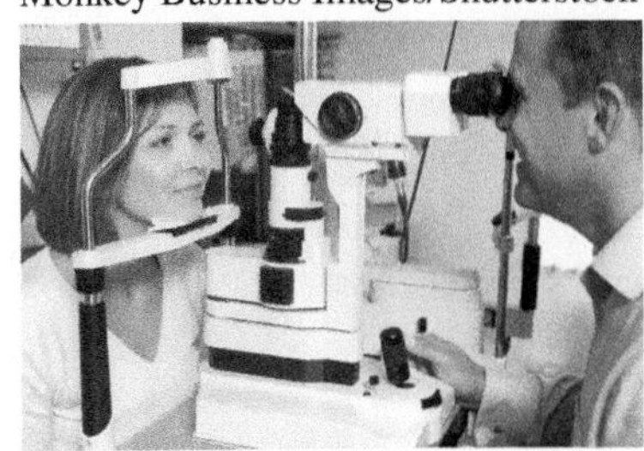

Using a retinal camera, an ophthalmologist photographs the retina of an eye.

Measuring Length

An ophthalmologist may measure the diameter of the retina of an eye in centimeters (cm), whereas a surgeon may need to know the length of a nerve in millimeters (mm). When the prefix *centi* is used with the unit meter, it becomes *centimeter*, a length that is one-hundredth of a meter (0.01 m). When the prefix *milli* is used with the unit meter, it becomes *millimeter*, a length that is one-thousandth of a meter (0.001 m). There are 100 cm and 1000 mm in a meter (see Figure 8).

Pearson Education

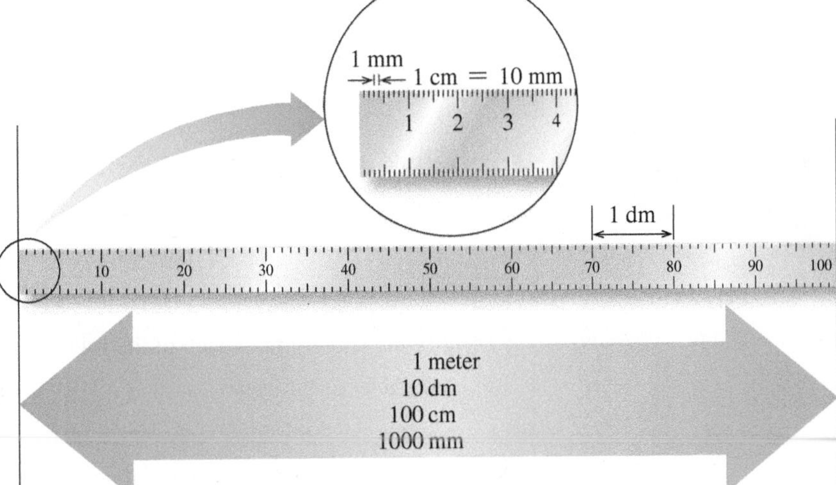

FIGURE 8 The metric length of 1 meter is the same length as 10 dm, 100 cm, and 1000 mm.
Q How many millimeters (mm) are in 1 centimeter (cm)?

First Quantity			Second Quantity	
1	m	=	100	cm
↑	↑		↑	↑
Number +	unit		Number +	unit

This example of an equality shows the relationship between meters and centimeters.

TABLE 10 Some Typical Laboratory Test Values

Substance in Blood	Typical Range
Albumin	3.5–5.0 g/dL
Ammonia	20–150 μg/dL
Calcium	8.5–10.5 mg/dL
Cholesterol	105–250 mg/dL
Iron (male)	80–160 μg/dL
Protein (total)	6.0–8.0 g/dL

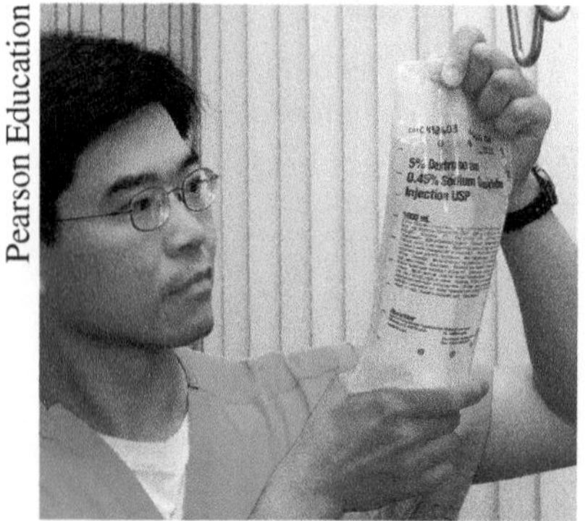
Pearson Education

FIGURE 9 A plastic intravenous fluid bag contains 1000 mL.

Q How many liters of solution are in the intravenous fluid bag?

Pidjoe/iStockphoto

A laboratory technician transfers a small volume using a micropipette.

An **equality** shows the relationship between two units that measure the same quantity. For example, we know that 1 m is the same length as 100 cm. Then the equality for this relationship is written as 1 m = 100 cm. Each quantity in this equality describes the same length but in a different unit. Every time we write an equality, we show each quantity as both a number and a unit.

Other examples of equalities between different metric units of length follow:

$$1 \text{ m} = 100 \text{ cm} = 1 \times 10^2 \text{ cm}$$
$$1 \text{ m} = 1000 \text{ mm} = 1 \times 10^3 \text{ mm}$$
$$1 \text{ cm} = 10 \text{ mm} = 1 \times 10^1 \text{ mm}$$

Measuring Volume

Volumes of 1 L or smaller are common in the health sciences. When a liter is divided into 10 equal portions, each portion is a deciliter (dL). There are 10 dL in 1 L. Laboratory results for blood work are often reported in mass per deciliter. Table 10 lists typical laboratory test values for some substances in the blood.

When a liter is divided into a thousand equal parts, each smaller part is a milliliter (mL). In a 1-L container of physiological saline, there are 1000 mL of solution (see Figure 9). Other examples of equalities between different metric units of volume follow:

$$1\text{L} = 10 \text{ dL} = 1 \times 10^1 \text{ dL}$$
$$1 \text{ L} = 1000 \text{ mL} = 1 \times 10^3 \text{ mL}$$
$$1 \text{ dL} = 100 \text{ mL} = 1 \times 10^2 \text{ mL}$$

The **cubic centimeter** (abbreviated as **cm^3** or **cc**) is the volume of a cube with dimensions of 1 cm on each side. A cubic centimeter has the same volume as a milliliter, and the units are often used interchangeably.

$$1 \text{ cm}^3 = 1 \text{ cc} = 1 \text{ mL}$$

When you see *1 cm*, you are reading about length; when you see *1 cc* or *1 cm*^{3} or *1 mL*, you are reading about volume. A comparison of units of volume is illustrated in Figure 10.

Measuring Mass

When you go to a doctor for a physical examination, your mass is recorded in kilograms, whereas the results of your laboratory tests are reported in grams, milligrams (mg), or micrograms (μg). A kilogram is equal to 1000 g. As an equality, this is written as 1 kg = 1000 g. One gram represents the same mass as 1000 mg. Some examples of equalities between different metric units of mass follow:

$$1 \text{ kg} = 1000 \text{ g} = 1 \times 10^3 \text{ g}$$
$$1 \text{ g} = 1000 \text{ mg} = 1 \times 10^3 \text{ mg}$$
$$1 \text{ mg} = 1000 \, \mu\text{g} = 1 \times 10^3 \, \mu\text{g}$$

CONCEPT CHECK 8 **Metric Prefixes**

Identify the larger unit in each of the following:

a. centimeter or kilometer **b.** mg or μg

ANSWER

a. A kilometer (1000 m) is larger than a centimeter (0.01 m).
b. A mg (0.001 g) is larger than a μg (0.000 001 g)

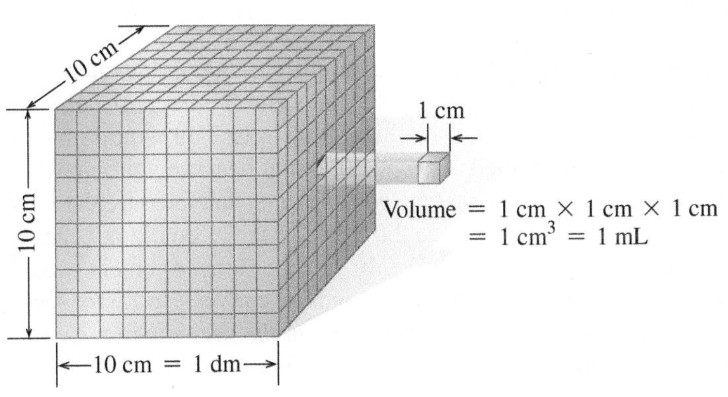

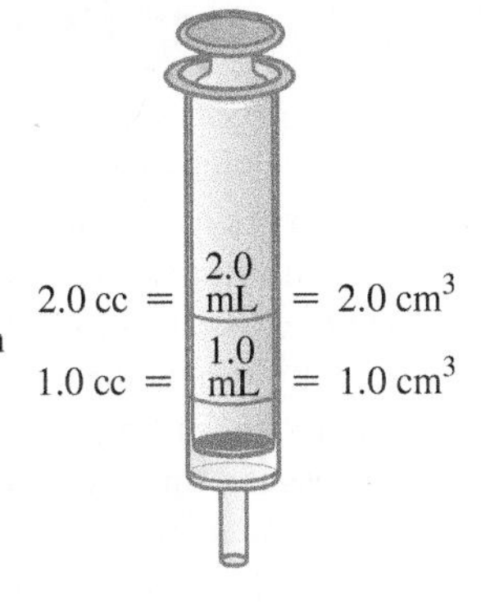

Volume = 10 cm × 10 cm × 10 cm
= 1000 cm^3
= 1000 mL
= 1 L

FIGURE 10 A cube measuring 10 cm on each side has a volume of 1000 cm^3, or 1 L; a cube measuring 1 cm on each side has a volume of 1 cm^3 (cc), or 1 mL.

Q What is the relationship between a milliliter (mL) and a cubic centimeter (cm^3)?

SAMPLE PROBLEM 6 Writing Metric Relationships

Complete the following list of metric equalities:

a. 1 L = _____ dL **b.** 1 km = _____ m **c.** 1 cm^3 = _____ mL

SOLUTION

a. 10 dL **b.** 1000 m **c.** 1 mL

STUDY CHECK 6

Complete the following metric equalities:

a. 1 kg = _____ g **b.** 1 mL = _____ L

QUESTIONS AND PROBLEMS

7 Prefixes and Equalities

LEARNING GOAL: *Use the numerical values of prefixes to write a metric equality.*

35 The speedometer is marked in both km/h and mi/h. What is the meaning of each abbreviation?

Pearson Education

36 In a French car, the odometer reads 2250. What units would this be? What units would it be if this were an odometer in a car made for the United States?

37 Write the abbreviation for each of the following units:
a. milligram **b.** deciliter **c.** kilometer
d. picogram **e.** microliter **f.** nanosecond

38 Write the complete name for each of the following units:
a. cm **b.** ks **c.** dL **d.** Gm **e.** μg **f.** ps

39 Write the numerical values for each of the following prefixes:
a. centi **b.** kilo **c.** milli **d.** tera **e.** mega **f.** pico

40 Write the complete name (prefix + unit) for each of the following numerical values:
a. 0.1 g **b.** 1×10^{-6} g **c.** 1000 g **d.** 0.01 g
e. 0.001 g **f.** 1×10^{12} g

41 Complete the following metric relationships:
a. 1 m = _____ cm **b.** 1 m = _____ nm
c. 1 mm = _____ m **d.** 1 L = _____ mL

42 Complete the following metric relationships:
a. 1 Mg = _____ g **b.** 1 mL = _____ μL
c. 1 g = _____ kg **d.** 1 g = _____ mg

43 For each of the following pairs, which is the larger unit?
a. milligram or kilogram **b.** milliliter or microliter
c. m or km **d.** kL or dL **e.** nanometer or picometer

44 For each of the following pairs, which is the smaller unit?
a. mg or g **b.** centimeter or millimeter
c. mm or μm **d.** mL or dL **e.** mg or Mg

LEARNING GOAL

Write a conversion factor for two units that describe the same quantity.

8 Writing Conversion Factors

Many problems in chemistry and the health sciences require a change of units. You make changes in units every day. For example, suppose you spent 2.0 hours (h) on your homework, and someone asked you how many minutes that was. You would answer 120 minutes (min). You must have multiplied 2.0 h × 60 min/h, because you knew that one hour is equal to 60 minutes. The relationship between two units that measure the same quantity is called an **equality**. When you expressed 2.0 h as 120 min, you did not change the amount of time you spent studying. You changed only the unit of measurement used to express the time. *Any equality can be written as fractions called* **conversion factors** *with one of the quantities in the numerator, and the other quantity in the denominator.* Be sure to include the units when you write the conversion factors. Two conversion factors are always possible from any equality.

Two Conversion Factors for the Equality 60 min = 1 h

$$\frac{\text{Numerator}}{\text{Denominator}} \quad \begin{matrix}\longrightarrow \\ \longrightarrow\end{matrix} \quad \frac{60\text{ min}}{1\text{ h}} \quad \text{and} \quad \frac{1\text{ h}}{60\text{ min}}$$

These conversion factors are read as "60 minutes per 1 hour," and "1 hour per 60 minutes." The term *per* means "divide." This relationship may also be written as 60 min/h. Some common relationships are given in Table 11. It is important that the equality you select to form a conversion factor is an actual relationship between the two units.

TABLE 11 Some Common Equalities

Quantity	Metric (SI)	U.S.	Metric–U.S.
Length	1 km = 1000 m 1 m = 1000 mm 1 cm = 10 mm	1 ft = 12 in. 1 yd = 3 ft 1 mi = 5280 ft	2.54 cm = 1 in. (exact) 1 m = 39.4 in. 1 km = 0.621 mi
Volume	1 L = 1000 mL 1 dL = 100 mL 1 mL = 1 cm^3	1 qt = 4 cups 1 qt = 2 pt 1 gal = 4 qt	946 mL = 1 qt 1 L = 1.06 qt
Mass	1 kg = 1000 g 1 g = 1000 mg	1 lb = 16 oz	1 kg = 2.20 lb 454 g = 1 lb
Time	1 h = 60 min 1 min = 60 s	1 h = 60 min 1 min = 60 s	

Exact and Measured Numbers in Equalities

The numbers in any equality between metric units or between U.S. system units are obtained by definition. Because numbers in a definition are exact, they are not used to determine significant figures. For example, the equality of 1 g = 1000 mg is defined, which means that both of the numbers 1 and 1000 are exact. *However, equalities between metric and U.S. units are obtained by measurement.* For example, the equality of 1 lb = 454 g is obtained by measuring the grams in exactly 1 lb. In this equality, the measured quantity 454 has three significant figures, whereas the 1 is exact. An exception is the relationship of 1 in. = 2.54 cm where 2.54 has been defined as exact.

Metric Conversion Factors

We can write conversion factors for the metric relationships we have studied. For example, from the equality for meters and centimeters, we can write the following factors:

Metric Equality	Conversion Factors
1 m = 100 cm	$\frac{100\text{ cm}}{1\text{ m}}$ and $\frac{1\text{ m}}{100\text{ cm}}$

Both of these conversion factors represent the same equality; one is just the inverse of the other. *The usefulness of conversion factors is enhanced by the fact that we can turn a conversion factor over and use its inverse.* The numbers 100 and 1 in this equality between metric units and its conversion factors are *exact* numbers.

CONCEPT CHECK 9 **Conversion Factors**

Identify the correct conversion factors for the equality for gigagrams and grams.

a. $\frac{1\ \text{Gg}}{1 \times 10^{9}\ \text{g}}$ **b.** $\frac{1 \times 10^{-9}\ \text{g}}{1\ \text{Gg}}$ **c.** $\frac{1 \times 10^{9}\ \text{Gg}}{1\ \text{g}}$ **d.** $\frac{1 \times 10^{9}\ \text{g}}{1\ \text{Gg}}$

ANSWER

Using the prefix table, we can write the equality for gigagrams and grams as $1\ \text{Gg} = 1 \times 10^{9}\ \text{g}$. Answers **a** and **d** are correctly written conversion factors that represent this equality.

Pearson Education/Eric Schrader

In the United States, the contents of many packaged foods are listed in both U.S. and metric units.

Metric–U.S. System Conversion Factors

Suppose you need to convert from pounds, a unit in the U.S. system, to kilograms in the metric (or SI) system. A relationship you could use is:

$$1\ \text{kg} = 2.20\ \text{lb}$$

The corresponding conversion factors would be:

$$\frac{2.20\ \text{lb}}{1\ \text{kg}} \quad \text{and} \quad \frac{1\ \text{kg}}{2.20\ \text{lb}}$$

In this metric–U.S. equality, the number in 2.20 lb is obtained from the measurement of exactly 1 kg.

CONCEPT CHECK 10 **Writing Conversion Factors from Equalities**

Write an equality and its conversion factors, and state whether the numbers are exact or measured for each of the following:

a. millimeters and meters
b. quarts and milliliters

ANSWER

Equality	Conversion Factors	Exact or Measured Quantities
a. 1 m = 1000 mm	$\frac{1000\ \text{mm}}{1\ \text{m}}$ and $\frac{1\ \text{m}}{1000\ \text{mm}}$	In the definition of a metric equality, both 1 and 1000 are exact quantities.
b. 1 qt = 946 mL	$\frac{946\ \text{mL}}{1\ \text{qt}}$ and $\frac{1\ \text{qt}}{946\ \text{mL}}$	In a U.S–metric equality, the 1 is exact and the 946 is measured (three significant figures).

SI AND METRIC EQUALITIES ON PRODUCT LABELS

Read the labels on some food products. List the amount of product given in different units. Write a relationship for two of the amounts for the same product and container. Look for measurements of grams and pounds or quarts and milliliters.

QUESTIONS

1. Use the stated measurement to derive a metric–U.S. conversion factor.
2. How do your results compare to the conversion factors we have described in this text?

Equalities and Conversion Factors Stated Within a Problem

An equality may also be stated within a problem that applies only to that problem. For example, the cost of 1 kilogram of oranges or the speed of a car in kilometers per hour would be specific relationships for that problem only. However, it is still possible to identify these relationships within a problem and to write corresponding conversion factors.

Pearson Education/Eric Schrader

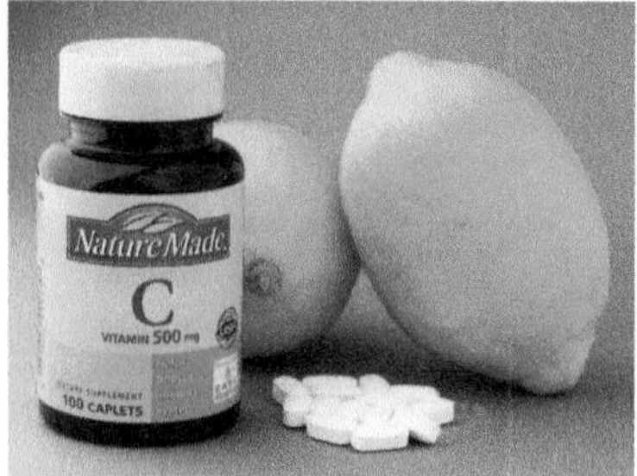

Vitamin C, an antioxidant needed by the body, is found in fruits such as lemons.

From each of the following statements, we can write an equality, and its conversion factors, and identify each number as exact or give its significant figures:

1. The motorcycle was traveling at a speed of 85 km/h.

Equality	Conversion Factors	Significant Figures or Exact
85 km = 1 h	$\frac{85\text{ km}}{1\text{ h}}$ and $\frac{1\text{ h}}{85\text{ km}}$	The 85 in 85 km is measured: It has two significant figures. The 1 in 1 h is exact.

2. One tablet contains 500 mg of vitamin C.

Equality	Conversion Factors	Significant Figures or Exact
1 tablet = 500 mg of vitamin C	$\frac{500\text{ mg vitamin C}}{1\text{ tablet}}$ and $\frac{1\text{ tablet}}{500\text{ mg vitamin C}}$	The 500 in 500 mg is measured: It has one significant figure. The 1 in 1 tablet is exact.

TUTORIAL
Using Percentage as a Conversion Factor

Conversion Factors from Percent, ppm, and ppb

When a *percent* (%) is given in a problem, it gives the parts of a specific substance in 100 parts of the total. *To write a percentage as a conversion factor, we choose a unit and express the numerical relationship of the parts of this unit to 100 parts of the whole.* For example, a person might have 18% body fat by mass. The percent quantity can be written as 18 mass units of body fat in every 100 mass units of body mass. Different mass units such as grams, kilograms (kg), or pounds (lb) can be used, but both units in the factor must be the same.

Pearson Education

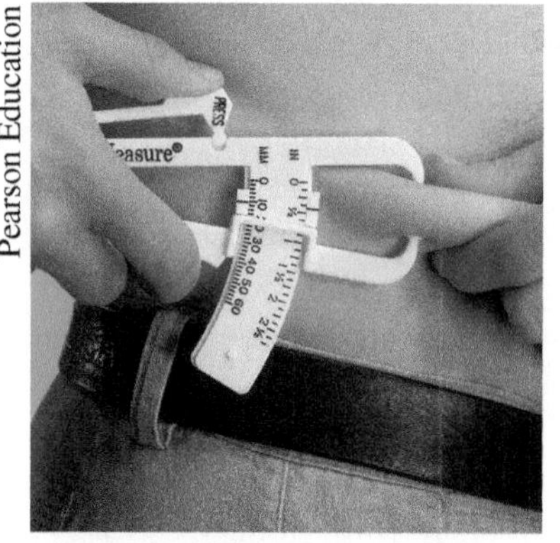

The thickness of the skin fold at the waist is used to determine the percent body fat.

CONCEPT CHECK 11 **Equalities and Conversion Factors Stated in a Problem**

A person has 18% body fat by mass. What equality and conversion factors can be written for this statement using the unit of kilogram? State the equality, write the conversion factors, and identify each number as exact or give its significant figures.

ANSWER

Equality	Conversion Factors	Significant Figures or Exact
18 kg of body fat = 100 kg of body mass	$\frac{100\text{ kg body mass}}{18\text{ kg body fat}}$ and $\frac{18\text{ kg body fat}}{100\text{ kg body mass}}$	The 18 in 18 kg is measured: It has two significant figures. The 100 in 100 kg is exact.

When scientists want to indicate very small ratios, they use numerical relationships called *parts per million* (ppm) or *parts per billion* (ppb). The ratio of parts per million is the same as the milligrams of a substance per kilogram (mg/kg). The ratio of parts per billion equals the micrograms of a substance per kilogram (μg/kg).

Ratio	Units
parts per million (ppm)	milligrams per kilogram (mg/kg)
parts per billion (ppb)	micrograms per kilogram (μg/kg)

For example, the maximum amount of lead that is allowed by the Food and Drug Administration (FDA) in glazed pottery bowls is 2 ppm.

Equality	Conversion Factors	Significant Figures or Exact
2 mg of lead = 1 kg of glaze	$\frac{2\text{ mg lead}}{1\text{ kg glaze}}$ and $\frac{1\text{ kg glaze}}{2\text{ mg lead}}$	The 2 in 2 mg is measured: It has one significant figure. The 1 in 1 kg is exact.

SAMPLE PROBLEM 7 Conversion Factors Stated in a Problem

Write the equality and its corresponding conversion factors, and identify each number as exact or give its significant figures for each of the following statements:

a. There are 325 mg of aspirin in 1 tablet.
b. One kilogram of bananas costs $1.25 at the grocery store.
c. The EPA has set the maximum level for mercury in tuna at 0.5 ppm.

SOLUTION

a. There are 325 mg of aspirin in 1 tablet.

Equality	Conversion Factors	Significant Figures or Exact
325 mg of aspirin = 1 tablet	$\frac{325\text{ mg aspirin}}{1\text{ tablet}}$ and $\frac{1\text{ tablet}}{325\text{ mg aspirin}}$	The 325 in 325 mg is measured: It has three significant figures. The 1 in 1 tablet is exact.

b. One kilogram of bananas costs $1.25 at the grocery store.

Equality	Conversion Factors	Significant Figures or Exact
1 kg of bananas = $1.25	$\frac{\$1.25}{1\text{ kg bananas}}$ and $\frac{1\text{ kg bananas}}{\$1.25}$	The 1.25 in $1.25 is measured: It has three significant figures. The 1 in 1 kg is exact.

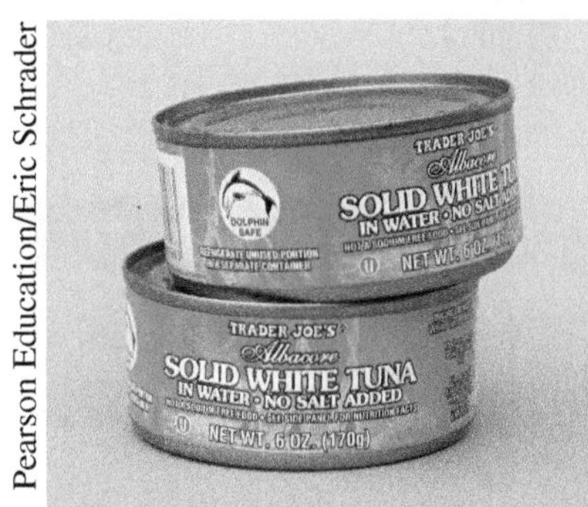

Pearson Education/Eric Schrader

The maximum amount of mercury allowed by the EPA in tuna is 0.5 ppm.

c. The EPA has set the maximum level for mercury in tuna at 0.5 ppm.

Equality	Conversion Factors	Significant Figures or Exact
0.5 mg of mercury = 1 kg of tuna	$\frac{0.5\text{ mg mercury}}{1\text{ kg tuna}}$ and $\frac{1\text{ kg tuna}}{0.5\text{ mg mercury}}$	The 0.5 in 0.5 mg is measured: It has one significant figure. The 1 in 1 kg is exact.

STUDY CHECK 7

Write the equality and its corresponding conversion factors, and identify each number as exact or give its significant figures for each of the following statements:

a. A cyclist in the Tour de France bicycle race reaches a top speed of 62.2 km/h.
b. The permissible level of arsenic in water is 10 ppb.

Chemistry Link to Health

TOXICOLOGY AND RISK-BENEFIT ASSESSMENT

Each day we make choices about what we do or what we eat, often without thinking about the risks associated with these choices. We are aware of the risks of cancer from smoking, and we know there is a greater risk of having an accident if we cross a street where there is no light or crosswalk.

A basic concept of toxicology is the statement of Paracelsus that the right dose is the difference between a poison and a cure. To evaluate the level of danger from various substances, natural or synthetic, a risk assessment is made by exposing laboratory animals to the substances and monitoring the health effects. Often, doses much greater than humans might encounter are given to the test animals.

Many hazardous chemicals or substances have been identified by these tests. One measure of toxicity is the LD_{50} or lethal dose, which is the concentration of the substance that causes death in 50% of the test animals. A dose is typically measured in ppm (mg/kg) of body mass or ppb (μg/kg).

Other evaluations also need to be made, but it is easy to compare LD_{50} values. Parathion, a pesticide, with an LD_{50} of 3 ppm would be highly toxic. That means that half the test animals given 3 mg of parathion per kg of body mass would be expected to die. Salt (sodium chloride) with an LD_{50} of 3750 ppm has a much lower toxicity. You would need to ingest a huge amount of salt before any toxic effect would be observed. Although the risk to animals based on dose can be evaluated in the laboratory, it is more difficult to determine the impact in the environment because there is also a difference between continued exposure and a single, large dose of the substance.

Table 12 lists some LD_{50} values and compares pesticides and common substances in our everyday lives, in order of increasing toxicity.

Carlos Alvarez/iStockphoto

The LD_{50} of caffeine is 192 ppm.

TABLE 12 Some LD_{50} Values for Pesticides and Common Materials Tested in Rats

Substance	LD_{50} (ppm)
Table sugar	29 700
Boric acid	5140
Baking soda	4220
Table salt	3750
Ethanol	2080
Aspirin	1100
Caffeine	192
DDT	113
Dichlorvos (pesticide strips)	56
Sodium cyanide	6
Parathion	3

QUESTIONS AND PROBLEMS

8 Writing Conversion Factors

LEARNING GOAL: *Write a conversion factor for two units that describe the same quantity.*

45 Write the equality and conversion factors for each of the following pairs of units:
a. centimeters and meters **b.** milligrams and grams
c. liters and milliliters **d.** deciliters and milliliters

46 Write the equality and conversion factors for each of the following pairs of units:
a. centimeters and inches **b.** pounds and kilograms
c. pounds and grams **d.** quarts and liters

47 Write the equality and conversion factors, and identify the numbers as exact or give the number of significant figures for each of the following statements:
a. One yard is 3 ft. **b.** One kilogram is 2.20 lb.
c. One minute is 60 s. **d.** A car goes 27 miles on 1 gal of gas.
e. Sterling silver is 93% by mass silver.

48 Write the equality and conversion factors, and identify the numbers as exact or give the number of significant figures for each of the following statements:
a. One liter is 1.06 qt.
b. At the store, oranges are $1.29 per lb.
c. There are 7 days in 1 week.
d. One deciliter contains 100 mL.
e. An 18-carat gold ring contains 75% gold by mass.

49 Write the equality and conversion factors, and identify the numbers as exact or give the number of significant figures for each of the following statements:
a. A bee flies at an average speed of 3.5 m per second.
b. The daily requirement for potassium is 3500 mg.
c. An automobile traveled 46.0 km on 1 gal of gasoline.
d. The label on a bottle reads 50. mg of Atenolol per tablet.
e. The pesticide level in plums was 29 ppb.
f. A low-dose aspirin tablet contains 81 mg of aspirin.

50 Write the equality and conversion factors, and identify the numbers as exact or give the number of significant figures for each of the following statements:
a. The label on a bottle reads 10 mg of furosemide per mL.
b. The daily requirement for iodine is 150 μg.
c. The nitrate level in well water was 32 ppm.
d. Gold jewelry contains 58% by mass gold.
e. The price of a gallon of gasoline is $3.19.
f. One capsule of fish oil contains 360 mg of omega-3 fatty acids.

9 Problem Solving

LEARNING GOAL

Use conversion factors to change from one unit to another.

The process of problem solving in chemistry often requires the conversion of an initial quantity given in one unit to the same quantity but in different units. By multiplying the given unit by one or more conversion factors, it can be converted to the needed unit as shown in Sample Problem 8.

TUTORIAL
Unit Conversions

TUTORIAL
Metric Conversions

TUTORIAL
Introduction to Unit Analysis Method

SAMPLE PROBLEM 8 **Problem Solving Using Conversion Factors**

In radiological imaging such as PET or CT scans, dosages of pharmaceuticals are based on body mass. If a person weighs 164 lb, what is that body mass in kilograms?

SOLUTION

Step 1 **State the given and needed quantities.**

Analyze the Problem

Given	Need
164 lb	kilograms

Step 2 **Write a plan to convert the given unit to the needed unit.** In our problem analysis, we see that the given unit is in the U.S. system of measurement and the needed unit is in the metric system. Therefore, we use the conversion factor that relates the U.S. unit lb to the metric unit kg.

pounds → U.S.–Metric factor → kilograms

Step 3 **State the equalities and conversion factors.**

1 kg = 2.20 lb

$$\frac{2.20\text{ lb}}{1\text{ kg}} \quad \text{and} \quad \frac{1\text{ kg}}{2.20\text{ lb}}$$

Step 4 **Set up the problem to cancel units and calculate the answer.** Write the given, 164 lb, and the conversion factor with the unit lb in the denominator (bottom number), which cancels the unit lb of the given unit.

Unit for answer goes here

$$164\,\cancel{\text{lb}} \times \frac{1\text{ kg}}{2.20\,\cancel{\text{lb}}} = 74.5\text{ kg}$$

Given — Conversion factor — Answer

Look at how the units cancel. The unit lb cancels out and the needed unit kg is the one that remains. This is a helpful way to check that a problem is set up properly.

$$\cancel{\text{lb}} \times \frac{\text{kg}}{\cancel{\text{lb}}} = \text{kg} \quad \text{Unit needed for answer}$$

The calculator display gives a numerical answer, which is rounded off to give a final answer with the proper number of significant figures (SFs).

$$164 \;\boxed{\times}\; \frac{1}{2.20} \;\boxed{=}\; 164 \;\boxed{\div}\; 2.20 \;\boxed{=}\; 74.54545455 \longrightarrow 74.5$$

164: Three SFs; 2.20: Three SFs; 74.54545455: Calculator display; 74.5: Three SFs (rounded off)

When the value of 74.5 is combined with the unit, kg, the final answer of 74.5 kg is obtained. With few exceptions, answers to numerical problems contain a number and a unit.

STUDY CHECK 8

If 1890 mL of orange juice is prepared from orange juice concentrate, how many liters of orange juice is that?

Guide to Problem Solving Using Conversion Factors

1. State the given and needed quantities.
2. Write a plan to convert the given unit to the needed unit.
3. State the equalities and conversion factors.
4. Set up the problem to cancel units and calculate the answer.

Using Two or More Conversion Factors

In problem solving, two or more conversion factors are often needed to complete the change of units. In setting up these problems, one factor follows the other. Each factor is arranged to cancel the preceding unit until the needed unit is obtained. Once the problem is set up to cancel units properly, the calculations can be done without writing intermediate results. The process is worth practicing until you understand unit cancellation, the steps on the calculator, and rounding off to give a final answer. In this text, the final answer will be based on obtaining a final calculator display and rounding off (or adding zeros) to give the correct number of significant figures.

CONCEPT CHECK 12 **Cancellation of Units**

Cancel the units in the following set up and give the unit needed in the answer.

$$3.5\ \text{L} \times \frac{1000\ \text{mL}}{1\ \text{L}} \times \frac{0.48\ \text{g}}{1\ \text{mL}} \times \frac{1000\ \text{mg}}{1\ \text{g}} =$$

ANSWER

All units in both the numerator and denominator cancel except for mg in the numerator, which is the unit needed for the answer.

$$3.5\ \cancel{\text{L}} \times \frac{1000\ \cancel{\text{mL}}}{1\ \cancel{\text{L}}} \times \frac{0.48\ \cancel{\text{g}}}{1\ \cancel{\text{mL}}} \times \frac{1000\ \text{mg}}{1\ \cancel{\text{g}}} = \text{needed unit is mg}$$

MC™

TUTORIAL
Determining the Correct Dosage

Clinical Calculations Using Conversion Factors

Conversion factors are also useful for calculating medications. For example, if an antibiotic is available in 5-mg tablets, the dosage can be written as a conversion factor: 5 mg/1 tablet. When you do a clinical problem, you often start with a doctor's order that contains the quantity you need to give to the patient, and use the dosage as a conversion factor as shown in Sample Problem 9.

SAMPLE PROBLEM 9 **Problem Solving Using Two Conversion Factors**

Synthroid is a synthetic thyroid hormone that is used as a replacement or supplemental therapy for diminished thyroid function. A dosage of 0.200 mg is prescribed. One tablet contains 50 μg of Synthroid. How many tablets are required to provide the prescribed dosage?

SOLUTION

Step 1 **State the given and needed quantities.**

Analyze the Problem

Given	Need
0.200 mg of Synthroid	tablets for dosage
1 tablet = 50 μg of Synthroid	

Step 2 **Write a plan to convert the given unit to the needed unit.**

milligrams → Metric factor → micrograms → Clinical factor → number of tablets

Step 3 **State the equalities and conversion factors.**

1 mg = 1000 μg

$$\frac{1\ \text{mg}}{1000\ \mu\text{g}} \text{ and } \frac{1000\ \mu\text{g}}{1\ \text{mg}}$$

1 tablet = 50 μg of Synthroid

$$\frac{1\ \text{tablet}}{50\ \mu\text{g Synthroid}} \text{ and } \frac{50\ \mu\text{g Synthroid}}{1\ \text{tablet}}$$

Step 4 **Set up the problem to cancel units and calculate the answer.**

$$\underset{\text{Three SFs}}{0.200\ \cancel{\text{mg}}} \times \frac{1000\ \cancel{\mu\text{g Synthroid}}}{1\ \cancel{\text{mg}}}\ (\text{Exact}) \times \frac{1\ \text{tablet}}{50\ \cancel{\mu\text{g Synthroid}}}\ (\text{Exact / One SF}) = 4\ \text{tablets (Exact (counting number))}$$

Using a sequence of two or more conversion factors is an efficient way to set up and solve problems, especially if you are using a calculator. Once you have the problem set up, the calculations can be done without writing out the intermediate values. This process is worth practicing until you understand unit cancellation and the mathematical calculations.

STUDY CHECK 9

One medium bran muffin contains 4.2 g of fiber. How many ounces (oz) of fiber are obtained by eating three medium bran muffins?

SAMPLE PROBLEM 10 Using a Percent as a Conversion Factor

TUTORIAL
Using Percentage as a Conversion Factor

A person who exercises regularly has 16% body fat. If this person weighs 155 lb, what is the mass, in kilograms, of body fat?

SOLUTION

Step 1 **State the given and needed quantities.**

Analyze the Problem

Given	Need
155 lb of body weight	kilograms of body fat
100 lb of body weight = 16 lb of body fat	

Step 2 **Write a plan to convert the given unit to the needed unit.**

pounds of body weight → U.S.–Metric factor → kilograms of body mass → Percent factor → kilograms of body fat

Step 3 **State the equalities and conversion factors.**

1 kg of body mass = 2.20 lb of body weight

$$\frac{2.20\ \text{lb body weight}}{1\ \text{kg body mass}} \text{ and } \frac{1\ \text{kg body mass}}{2.20\ \text{lb body weight}}$$

16 kg of body fat = 100 kg of body mass

$$\frac{16\ \text{kg body fat}}{100\ \text{kg body mass}} \text{ and } \frac{100\ \text{kg body mass}}{16\ \text{kg body fat}}$$

Step 4 **Set up the problem to cancel units and calculate the answer.**

$$\underset{\text{Three SFs}}{155\ \cancel{\text{lb body weight}}} \times \frac{1\ \cancel{\text{kg body mass}}}{2.20\ \cancel{\text{lb body weight}}}\ (\text{Exact / Three SFs}) \times \frac{16\ \text{kg body fat}}{100\ \cancel{\text{kg body mass}}}\ (\text{Two SFs / Exact})$$

$$= 11\ \text{kg of body fat}$$

STUDY CHECK 10

Uncooked lean ground beef can contain up to 22% fat by mass. How many grams of fat are in 0.25 lb of the ground beef?

QUESTIONS AND PROBLEMS

9 Problem Solving

LEARNING GOAL: *Use conversion factors to change from one unit to another.*

51 Use metric conversion factors to solve the following problems:

a. The height of a student is 175 cm. How tall is the student in meters?
b. A cooler has a volume of 5500 mL. What is the capacity of the cooler in liters?
c. A hummingbird has a mass of 0.0055 kg. What is the mass of the hummingbird in grams?

52 Use metric conversion factors to solve the following problems:

a. The daily requirement of phosphorus is 800 mg. How many grams of phosphorus are needed?
b. A glass of orange juice contains 0.85 dL of juice. How many milliliters of orange juice are in the glass?
c. A package of chocolate instant pudding contains 2840 mg of sodium. How many grams of sodium are in the pudding?

53 Solve each of the following problems using one or more conversion factors:

a. A container holds 0.750 qt of liquid. How many milliliters of lemonade will it hold?
b. In England, a person is weighed in stones. If one stone has a weight of 14.0 lb, what is the mass, in kilograms, of a person who weighs 11.8 stones?
c. The femur, or thighbone, is the longest bone in the body. In a 6-ft-tall person, the femur is 19.5 in. long. What is the length of that femur in millimeters?
d. How many inches thick is an arterial wall that measures 0.50 μm?

54 Solve each of the following problems using one or more conversion factors:

a. You need 4.0 oz of a steroid ointment. If there are 16 oz in 1 lb, how many grams of ointment does the pharmacist need to prepare?
b. During surgery, a person receives 5.0 pt of plasma. How many milliliters of plasma were given?
c. Solar flares containing hot gases can rise to 120 000 miles above the surface of the Sun. What is that distance in kilometers?
d. A filled gas tank contains 18.5 gallons of unleaded fuel. If a car uses 46.0 L, how many gallons of fuel remain in the tank?

55 The singles portion of a tennis court is 27.0 ft wide and 78.0 ft long.

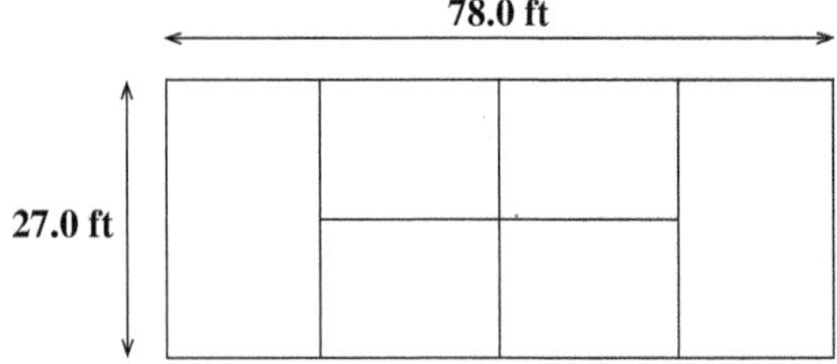

a. What is the length of the court in meters?
b. What is the area of the court in square meters (m^2)?
c. If a serve is measured at 185 km/h, how many seconds does it take for the tennis ball to travel the length of the court?

56 A football field is 300. feet long between goal lines.

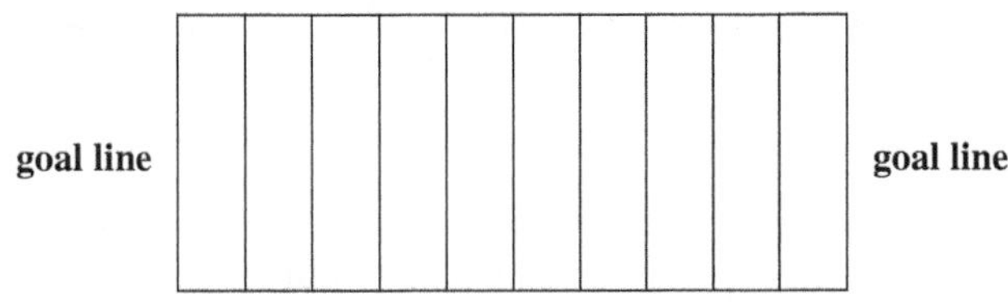

a. What distance, in meters, does a player run if he catches the ball on his own goal line and scores a touchdown?
b. If a player catches the football and runs 45 yards, how many meters did he gain?
c. If a player runs at a speed of 36 km/h, how many seconds does it take to run from the 50-yard line to the 20-yard line?

57 Use conversion factors to solve the following clinical problems:

a. You need 250 L of distilled water for a dialysis patient. How many gallons of water is that?
b. A patient needs 0.024 g of a sulfa drug. There are 8-mg tablets in stock. How many tablets should be given?
c. The daily dose of ampicillin for the treatment of an ear infection is 115 mg/kg of body weight. What is the daily dose, in mg, for a 34-lb child?

58 Use conversion factors to solve the following clinical problems:

a. A physician has ordered 1.0 g of tetracycline to be given every 6 h to a patient. If your stock on hand is 500-mg tablets, how many will you need for 1 day's treatment?
b. An intramuscular medication is given at 5.00 mg/kg of body weight. If you give 425 mg of medication to a patient, what is the patient's weight in pounds?
c. A physician orders 325 mg of atropine, intramuscularly. If atropine were available as 0.50 g/mL of solution, how many milliliters would you need to give?

59 **a.** Oxygen makes up 46.7% by mass of Earth's crust. How many grams of oxygen are present if a sample of Earth's crust has a mass of 325 g?
b. Magnesium makes up 2.1% by mass of Earth's crust. How many grams of magnesium are present if a sample of Earth's crust has a mass of 1.25 g?
c. A plant fertilizer contains 15% by mass nitrogen (N). In a container of soluble plant food, there are 10.0 oz of fertilizer. How many grams of nitrogen are in the container?
d. In a candy factory, nutty chocolate bars contain 22.0% by mass pecans. If 5.0 kg of pecans were used for candy last Tuesday, how many pounds of nutty chocolate bars were made?

Radius Images - Alamy

Agricultural fertilizers applied to a field provide nitrogen for plant growth.

60 **a.** Water is 11.2% by mass hydrogen. How many kilograms of water would contain 5.0 g of hydrogen?
b. Water is 88.8% by mass oxygen. How many grams of water would contain 2.25 kg of oxygen?
c. Blueberry high-fiber muffins contain 51% dietary fiber. If a package with a net weight of 12 oz contains 6 muffins, how many grams of fiber are in each muffin?
d. A jar of crunchy peanut butter contains 1.43 kg of peanut butter. If you use 8.0% of the peanut butter for a sandwich, how many ounces of peanut butter did you take out of the container?

10 Density

LEARNING GOAL

Calculate the density or specific gravity of a substance; use the density or specific gravity to calculate the mass or volume of a substance.

The mass and volume of any object can be measured. If we compare the mass of the object to its volume, we obtain a relationship called **density**.

$$\text{Density} = \frac{\text{mass of substance}}{\text{volume of substance}}$$

Every substance has a unique density, which distinguishes it from other substances. For example, lead has a density of 11.3 g/mL, whereas cork has a density of 0.26 g/mL. From these densities, we can predict if these substances will sink or float in water. If a substance, such as cork, is less dense than water, it will float. However, a lead object sinks in water because its density is greater than that of water (see Figure 11). A lead object would float on liquid mercury, because lead is less dense than the liquid.

TUTORIAL
Density and Specific Gravity

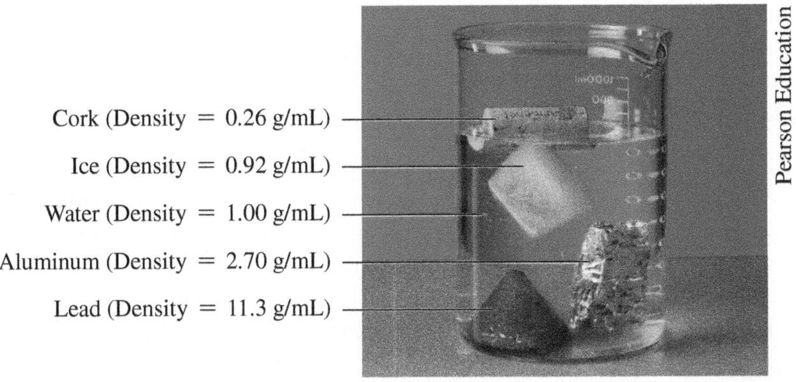

Pearson Education

FIGURE 11 Objects that sink in water are more dense than water; objects that float are less dense.

Q Why does an ice cube float and a piece of aluminum sink?

Density is used in chemistry and medicine in many ways. For example, density can be used to identify an unknown substance. If we calculate a density of a pure metal as 10.5 g/mL, then we might identify it as silver, but not lead or aluminum.

Metals such as gold and lead tend to have higher densities, whereas gases have very low densities. In the metric system, the densities of solids and liquids are usually expressed as grams per cubic centimeter (g/cm^3) or grams per milliliter (g/mL). The densities of gases are usually stated as grams per liter (g/L). Table 13 gives the densities of some common substances.

TABLE 13 Densities of Some Common Substances

Solids (at 25 °C)	Density (g/mL)	Liquids (at 25 °C)	Density (g/mL)	Gases (at 0 °C, 1 atm)	Density (g/L)
Cork	0.26	Gasoline	0.74	Hydrogen	0.090
Wood (maple)	0.75	Ethanol	0.79	Helium	0.179
Ice (at 0 °C)	0.92	Olive oil	0.92	Methane	0.714
Sugar	1.59	Water (at 4 °C)	1.00	Neon	0.902
Bone	1.80	Urine	1.003–1.030	Nitrogen	1.25
Salt (NaCl)	2.16	Plasma (blood)	1.03	Air (dry)	1.29
Aluminum	2.70	Milk	1.04	Oxygen	1.43
Cement	3.00	Mercury	13.6	Carbon dioxide	1.96
Diamond	3.52				
Iron	7.86				
Silver	10.5				
Lead	11.3				
Gold	19.3				

CONCEPT CHECK 13 Density

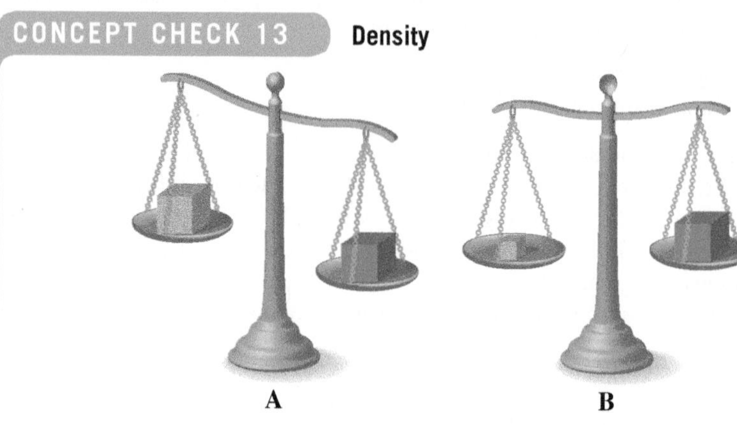

a. In diagram **A**, the gray cube has a density of 4.5 g/cm^3. Is the density of the green cube the same, lower than, or higher than the gray cube?

b. In diagram **B**, the gray cube has a density of 4.5 g/cm^3. Is the density of the green cube the same, lower than, or higher than the gray cube?

ANSWER

a. The green cube has the same volume as the gray cube. However, the green cube has a larger mass on the scale, which means that its mass/volume ratio is larger. Thus, the density of the green cube is higher than the density of the gray cube.

b. The green cube has the same mass as the gray cube. However, the green cube has a greater volume, which means that its mass/volume ratio is smaller. Thus, the density of the green cube is lower than the density of the gray cube.

Guide to Calculating Density

1 State the given and needed quantities.

2 Write the density expression.

3 Express mass in grams and volume in milliliters (mL) or cm^3.

4 Substitute mass and volume into the density expression and calculate the density.

SAMPLE PROBLEM 11 Calculating Density

High-density lipoprotein (HDL) contains large amounts of proteins and small amounts of cholesterol. If a 0.258-g sample of HDL has a volume of 0.215 cm^3, what is the density, in g/cm^3, of the HDL sample?

SOLUTION

Step 1 **State the given and needed quantities.**

Analyze the Problem

Given	Need
0.258 g of HDL	density (g/cm^3) of HDL
0.215 cm^3 of HDL	

Step 2 **Write the density expression.**

$$\text{Density} = \frac{\text{mass of substance}}{\text{volume of substance}}$$

Step 3 **Express mass in grams and volume in cm³.**

Mass of HDL sample = 0.258 g

Volume of HDL sample = $0.215\ \text{cm}^3$

Step 4 **Substitute mass and volume into the density expression and calculate the density.**

$$\text{Density} = \frac{\overset{\text{Three SFs}}{0.258\ \text{g}}}{\underset{\text{Three SFs}}{0.215\ \text{cm}^3}} = \frac{1.20\ \text{g}}{1\ \text{cm}^3} = \underset{\text{Three SFs}}{1.20\ \text{g/cm}^3}$$

STUDY CHECK 11

Low-density lipoprotein (LDL) contains small amounts of proteins and large amounts of cholesterol. If a 0.380-g sample of LDL has a volume of $0.362\ \text{cm}^3$, what is the density of the LDL sample, in g/cm^3?

Density of Solids

The density of a solid is calculated from its mass and volume. When a solid is completely submerged, it displaces a volume of water that is equal to the volume of the solid. In Figure 12, the water level rises from 35.5 mL to 45.0 mL. This means that 9.5 mL of water is displaced and that the volume of the object is 9.5 mL. The density of the zinc is calculated as follows:

$$\text{Density} = \frac{\overset{\text{Four SFs}}{68.60\ \text{g zinc}}}{\underset{\text{Two SFs}}{9.5\ \text{mL}}} = \underset{\text{Two SFs}}{7.2\ \text{g/mL}}$$

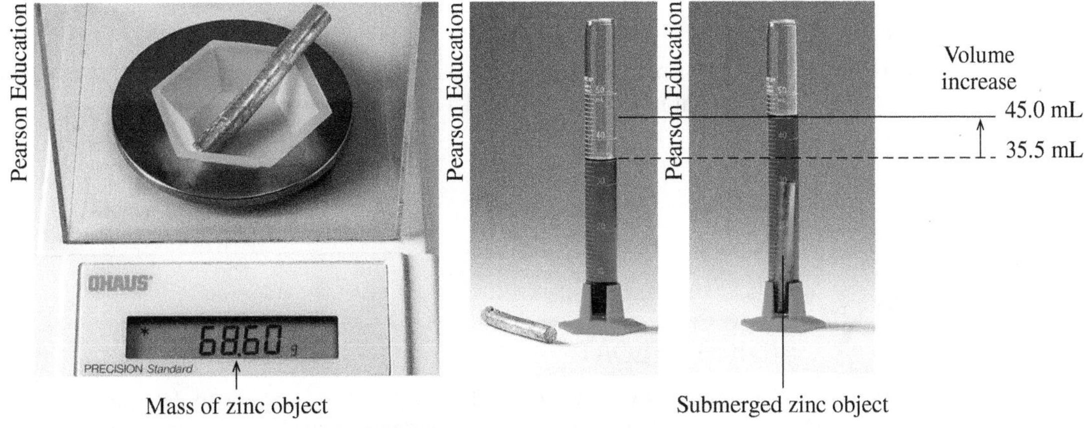

FIGURE 12 The density of a solid can be determined by volume displacement because a submerged object displaces a volume of water equal to its own volume.

Q How is the volume of the zinc object determined?

DJMattaar/iStockphoto

Lead weights in a belt counteract the buoyancy of a scuba diver.

SAMPLE PROBLEM 12 Using Volume Displacement to Calculate Density

A lead weight used in the belt of a scuba diver has a mass of 226 g. When the lead weight is placed in a graduated cylinder containing 200.0 mL of water, the water level rises to 220.0 mL. What is the density of the lead weight (g/mL)?

SOLUTION

Step 1 **State the given and needed quantities.**

Analyze the Problem

Given	Need
226 g of lead	density (g/mL) of lead
water level + lead = 220.0 mL	
water level (initial) = 200.0 mL	

Step 2 **Write the density expression.**

$$\text{Density} = \frac{\text{mass of substance}}{\text{volume of substance}}$$

Step 3 **Express mass in grams and volume in milliliters (mL).**

Mass of lead weight = 226 g

The volume of the lead weight is equal to the volume of water displaced, which is calculated as follows:

Water level after object submerged	=	220.0 mL
Water level before object submerged	=	−200.0 mL
Water displaced (volume of lead weight)	=	20.0 mL

Step 4 **Substitute mass and volume into the density expression and calculate the density.** The density is calculated by dividing the mass (g) by the volume (mL). Be sure to use the volume of water displaced and *not* the original volume of water.

$$\text{Density} = \frac{\overset{\text{Three SFs}}{226\text{ g}}}{\underset{\text{Three SFs}}{20.0\text{ mL}}} = \frac{11.3\text{ g}}{1\text{ mL}} = \underset{\text{Three SFs}}{11.3\text{ g/mL}}$$

STUDY CHECK 12

A total of 0.500 lb of glass marbles is added to 425 mL of water. The water level rises to a volume of 528 mL. What is the density (g/mL) of the glass marbles?

Explore Your World

SINK OR FLOAT

1. Fill a large container or bucket with water. Place a can of diet and a can of nondiet soft drink in the water. What happens? Using information on the label, how might you account for your observations?
2. Design an experiment to determine the substance that is the most dense in each of the following:
   - **a.** water and vegetable oil
   - **b.** water and ice
   - **c.** rubbing alcohol and ice
   - **d.** vegetable oil, water, and ice

Chemistry Link to Health

BONE DENSITY

The density of our bones determines their health and strength. Our bones are constantly gaining and losing minerals such as calcium, magnesium, and phosphate. In childhood, bones form at a faster rate than they break down. As we age, the breakdown of bone occurs more rapidly than new bone forms. As the loss of bone minerals increases, bones begin to thin, causing a decrease in mass and density. Thinner bones lack strength, which increases the risk of fracture. Hormonal changes, disease, and certain medications can also contribute to the thinning of bone. Eventually, a condition of severe thinning of bone known as *osteoporosis* may occur. *Scanning electron micrographs* (SEMs) show (a) normal bone and (b) bone in osteoporosis caused by the loss of bone minerals.

Bone density is often determined by passing low-dose X-rays through the narrow part at the top of the femur (hip) and the spine (c). These locations are where fractures are more likely to occur, especially as we age. Bones with high density will block more of the X-rays compared to bones that are less dense. The results of a bone density test are compared to a healthy young adult, as well as to other people of the same age.

Recommendations to improve bone strength include supplements of calcium and vitamin D. Weight-bearing exercise such as walking and lifting weights can also improve muscle strength, which in turn, increases bone strength.

P. La Motta, Dept. Anatomy, University La Sapienza, Rome/Photo Researchers, Inc.

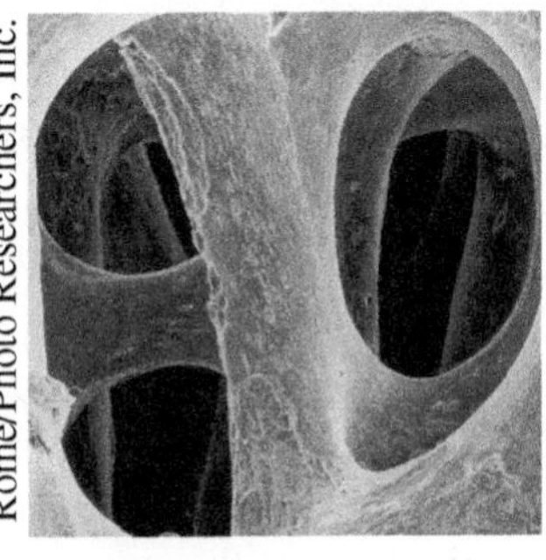

(a) Normal bone

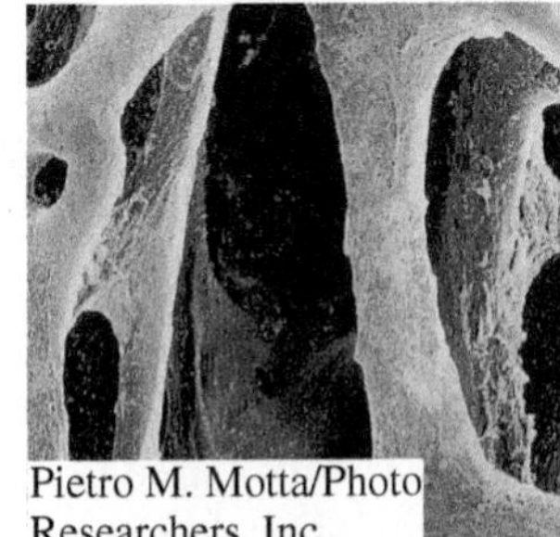

Pietro M. Motta/Photo Researchers, Inc.

(b) Bone with osteoporosis

VOISIN/PHANIE/Photo Researchers, Inc.

(c) Viewing a low-dose X-ray of the spine

Problem Solving Using Density

Density can be used as a conversion factor. For example, if the volume and the density of a sample are known, the mass in grams of the sample can be calculated as shown in Sample Problem 13.

Pearson Education

SAMPLE PROBLEM 13 Problem Solving Using Density

If the density of milk is 1.04 g/mL, how many grams of milk are in 0.50 qt of milk?

SOLUTION

Step 1 State the given and needed quantities.

Analyze the Problem

Given	Need
0.50 qt of milk	grams of milk
density of milk = 1.04 g/mL	
(1 mL of milk = 1.04 g)	

Step 2 Write a plan to calculate the needed quantity.

quarts → U.S.–Metric factor → liters → Metric factor → milliliters → Density factor → grams

Step 3 Write equalities and their conversion factors, including density.

$$1\text{ L} = 1.06\text{ qt} \qquad \frac{1\text{ L}}{1.06\text{ qt}} \text{ and } \frac{1.06\text{ qt}}{1\text{ L}}$$

$$1\text{ L} = 1000\text{ mL} \qquad \frac{1\text{ L}}{1000\text{ mL}} \text{ and } \frac{1000\text{ mL}}{1\text{ L}}$$

$$1\text{ mL} = 1.04\text{ g} \qquad \frac{1\text{ mL}}{1.04\text{ g}} \text{ and } \frac{1.04\text{ g}}{1\text{ mL}}$$

Guide to Using Density

1. State the given and needed quantities.
2. Write a plan to calculate the needed quantity.
3. Write equalities and their conversion factors, including density.
4. Set up the problem to calculate the needed quantity.

Step 4 **Set up the problem to calculate the needed quantity.**

$$\underset{\text{Two SFs}}{0.50\ \cancel{qt}} \times \underset{\text{Three SFs}}{\overset{\text{Exact}}{\frac{1\ \cancel{L}}{1.06\ \cancel{qt}}}} \times \underset{\text{Exact}}{\overset{\text{Exact}}{\frac{1000\ \cancel{mL}}{1\ \cancel{L}}}} \times \underset{\text{Exact}}{\overset{\text{Three SFs}}{\frac{1.04\ g}{1\ \cancel{mL}}}} = \underset{\text{Two SFs}}{490\ g\ (4.9 \times 10^2\ g)}$$

STUDY CHECK 13

The density of maple syrup is 1.33 g/mL. A bottle of maple syrup contains 740 mL of syrup. What is the mass of the syrup?

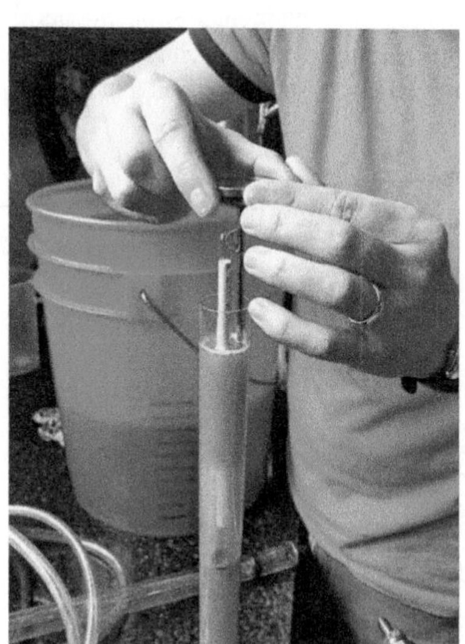

Michael R. Wright

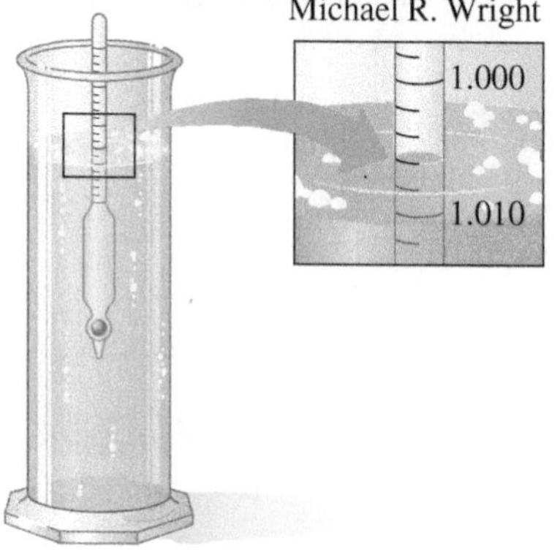

FIGURE 13 When the specific gravity of beer measures 1.010 or less with a hydrometer, the fermentation process is complete.

Q If the hydrometer reading is 1.006, what is the density, in g/mL, of the liquid?

Specific Gravity

Specific gravity (sp gr) *is a relationship between the density of a substance and the density of water.* Specific gravity is calculated by dividing the density of a sample by the density of water, which is 1.00 g/mL at 4 °C. A substance with a specific gravity of 1.00 has the same density as water. A substance with a specific gravity of 3.00 is three times as dense as water, whereas a substance with a specific gravity of 0.50 is just one-half as dense as water.

$$\text{Specific gravity} = \frac{\text{density of sample}}{\text{density of water}}$$

Specific gravity is one of the few unitless values you will use in chemistry. An instrument called a *hydrometer* is often used to measure the specific gravity of fluids such as battery fluid or a sample of urine. In Figure 13, a hydrometer is used to measure the specific gravity of a fluid. In the calculations for specific gravity, the units of density must match. Then all units cancel to leave only a number as the answer.

SAMPLE PROBLEM 14 **Problem Solving with Specific Gravity**

John took 2.0 teaspoons (tsp) of cough syrup. If the syrup has a specific gravity (sp gr) of 1.20, and there are 5.0 mL in 1 tsp, what was the mass, in grams, of the cough syrup?

SOLUTION

Step 1 **State the given and needed quantities.**

Analyze the Problem

Given	Need
2.0 tsp of cough syrup	grams of cough syrup
sp gr 1.20	
1 tsp = 5.0 mL	

Step 2 **Write a plan to calculate the needed quantity.**

teaspoons → U.S.–Metric factor → milliliters → Density factor → grams

Step 3 **Write equalities and their conversion factors, including density.** For problem solving, it is convenient to convert the specific gravity value (1.20) to density.

Density = (sp gr) × 1.00 g/mL = 1.20 g/mL

1 tsp = 5.0 mL

$$\frac{1\ \text{tsp}}{5.0\ \text{mL}} \text{ and } \frac{5.0\ \text{mL}}{1\ \text{tsp}}$$

1 mL = 1.20 g

$$\frac{1\ \text{mL}}{1.20\ \text{g}} \text{ and } \frac{1.20\ \text{g}}{1\ \text{mL}}$$

Step 4 Set up the problem to calculate the needed quantity.

Two SFs Three SFs

$$2.0\,\cancel{\text{tsp}} \times \frac{5.0\,\cancel{\text{mL}}}{1\,\cancel{\text{tsp}}} \times \frac{1.20\text{ g}}{1\,\cancel{\text{mL}}} = 12\text{ g of cough syrup}$$

Two SFs Exact Exact Two SFs

STUDY CHECK 14

An ebony carving has a mass of 275 g. If ebony has a specific gravity of 1.12, what is the volume, in milliliters, of the carving?

QUESTIONS AND PROBLEMS

10 Density

LEARNING GOAL: *Calculate the density or specific gravity of a substance; use the density or specific gravity to calculate the mass or volume of a substance.*

61 In an old trunk, you find a piece of metal that you think may be aluminum, silver, or lead. After laboratory testing, you find it has a mass of 217 g and a volume of 19.2 cm^3. Using Table 13, what is the metal you found?

62 Suppose you have two 100-mL graduated cylinders. In each cylinder, there is 40.0 mL of water. You also have two cubes: One is lead, and the other is aluminum. Each cube measures 2.0 cm on each side. After you carefully lower each cube into the water of its own cylinder, what will the new water level be in each of the cylinders?

63 What is the density (g/mL) for each of the following samples?

a. A 20.0-mL sample of a salt solution that has a mass of 24.0 g.

b. A cube of butter weighs 0.250 lb and has a volume of 130. mL.

c. A gem has a mass of 45.0 g. When the gem is placed in a graduated cylinder containing 20.0 mL of water, the water level rises to 34.5 mL.

d. A liquid is added to an empty container with a mass of 115.25 g. When 0.100 pt of liquid is added, the total mass of the container and liquid is 182.48 g.

115.25 g **182.48 g**

64 What is the density (g/mL) for each of the following samples?

a. The fluid in a car battery, if it has a volume of 125 mL and a mass of 155 g.

b. A plastic material weighs 2.68 lb and has a volume of 3.5 L.

Dallas Events, Inc./ Shutterstock

Titanium is used to make heads of drivers.

c. A 5.00-mL urine sample from a patient suffering from symptoms resembling those of diabetes mellitus. The mass of the urine sample is 5.025 g.

d. A lightweight head on the driver of a golf club is made of titanium. If the volume of a sample of titanium is 114 cm^3 and the mass is 514.1 g, what is the density of titanium?

65 Use the density values in Table 13 to solve each of the following problems:

a. How many liters of ethanol contain 1.5 kg of ethanol?

b. How many grams of mercury are present in a barometer that holds 6.5 mL of mercury?

c. A sculptor has prepared a mold for casting a bronze figure. The figure has a volume of 225 mL. If bronze has a density of 7.8 g/mL, how many ounces of bronze are needed in the preparation of the bronze figure?

d. How many kilograms of gasoline fill a 12.0-gallon gas tank? (1 gallon = 4 qt)

66 Use the density values in Table 13 to solve each of the following problems:

a. A graduated cylinder contains 18.0 mL of water. What is the new water level, in milliliters, after 35.6 g of silver metal is submerged in the water?

b. A fish tank holds 35 gallons of water. How many pounds of water are in the fish tank?

c. The mass of an empty container is 88.25 g. The mass of the container and a liquid with a density of 0.758 g/mL is 150.50 g. What is the volume, in milliliters, of the liquid in the container?

d. A cannon ball made of iron has a volume of 115 cm^3. What is the mass, in kilograms, of the cannon ball?

67 Solve each of the following specific gravity problems:

a. A urine sample has a density of 1.030 g/mL. What is the specific gravity of the sample?

b. A liquid has a volume of 40.0 mL and a mass of 45.0 g. What is the specific gravity of the liquid?

c. The specific gravity of a vegetable oil is 0.85. What is its density?

68 Solve each of the following specific gravity problems:

a. A glucose solution has a density of 1.02 g/mL. What is its specific gravity?

b. A bottle containing 325 g of cleaning solution is used for carpets. If the cleaning solution has a specific gravity of 0.850, what volume, in milliliters, of solution was used?

c. Butter has a specific gravity of 0.86. What is the mass, in grams, of 2.15 L of butter?

CONCEPT MAP

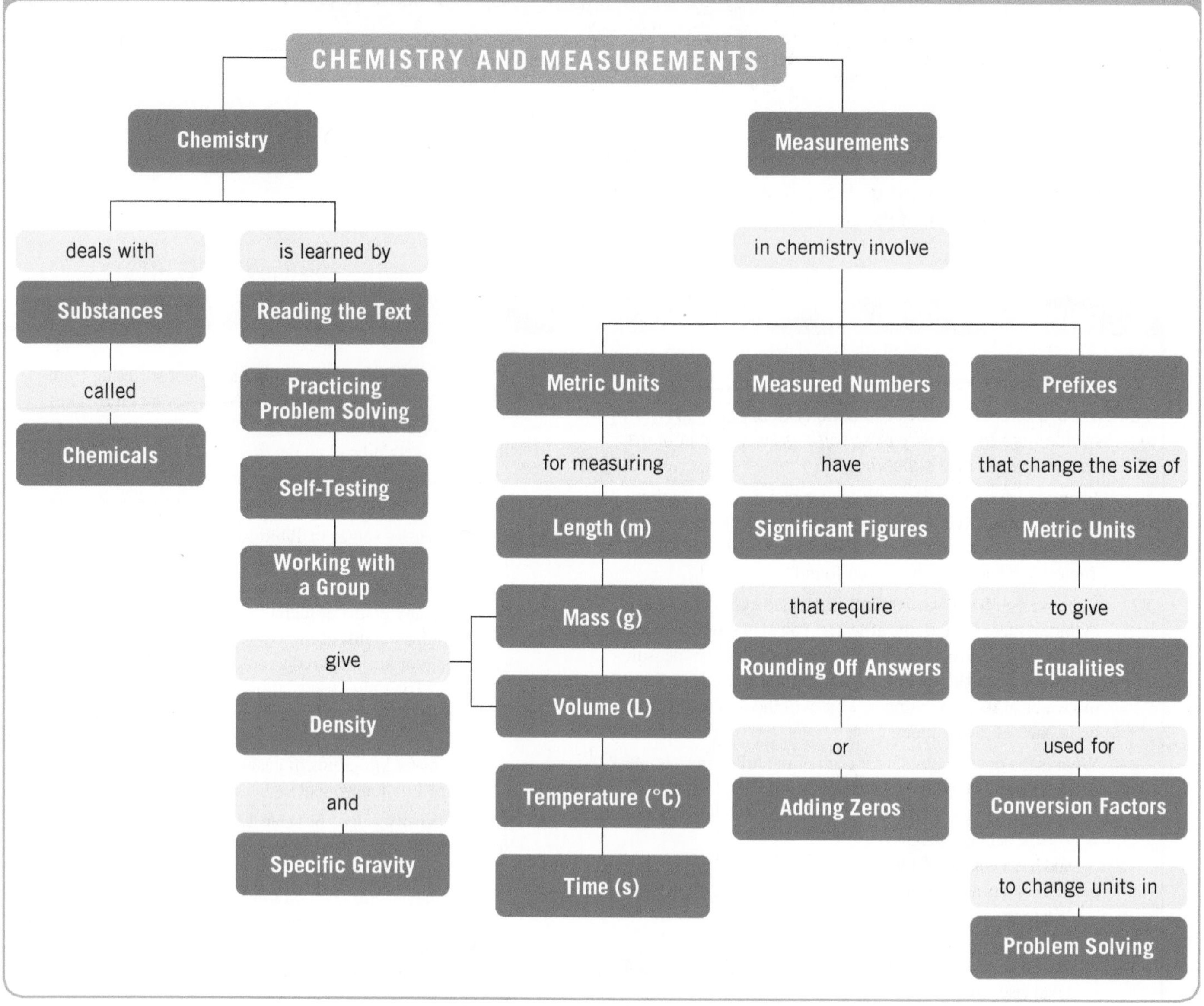

- **CHEMISTRY AND MEASUREMENTS**
  - **Chemistry**
    - deals with **Substances** called **Chemicals**
    - is learned by **Reading the Text**, **Practicing Problem Solving**, **Self-Testing**, **Working with a Group**
  - **Measurements** in chemistry involve
    - **Metric Units** for measuring **Length (m)**, **Mass (g)**, **Volume (L)**, **Temperature (°C)**, **Time (s)**
      - Mass (g) and Volume (L) give **Density** and **Specific Gravity**
    - **Measured Numbers** have **Significant Figures** that require **Rounding Off Answers** or **Adding Zeros**
    - **Prefixes** that change the size of **Metric Units** to give **Equalities** used for **Conversion Factors** to change units in **Problem Solving**

CHAPTER REVIEW

1 Chemistry and Chemicals

LEARNING GOAL: *Define the term* chemistry *and identify substances as chemicals.*

- Chemistry is the study of the composition, structure, properties, and reactions of matter.
- A chemical is any substance that always has the same composition and properties wherever it is found.

Pearson Education

2 A Study Plan for Learning Chemistry

track5/iStockphoto

LEARNING GOAL: *Develop a study plan for learning chemistry.*

- A study plan for learning chemistry utilizes the features in this text and develops an active learning approach to the study of chemistry.
- By using the *Learning Goals* in the chapter and working the *Concept Checks*, *Sample Problems*, *Study Checks*, and the *Questions and Problems* that follow each section, you can successfully learn chemistry.

3 Units of Measurement

LEARNING GOAL: *Write the names and abbreviations for metric or SI units used in measurements of length, volume, mass, temperature, and time.*

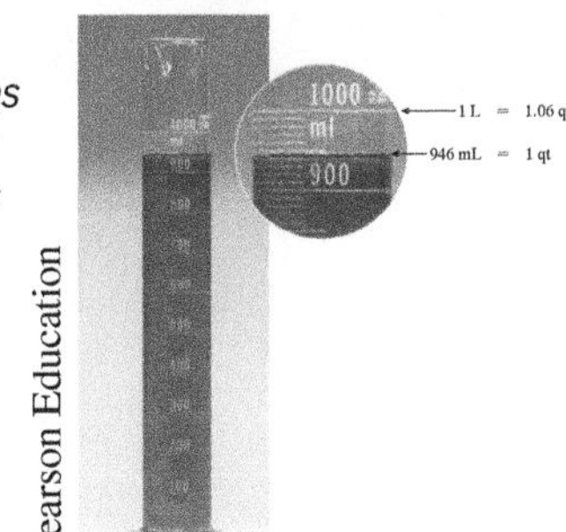

Pearson Education

- In science, physical quantities are described in units of the metric system or International System (SI).
- Some important units are meter (m) for length, liter (L) for volume, gram (g) and kilogram (kg) for mass, and degree Celsius (°C) and Kelvin (K) for temperature.

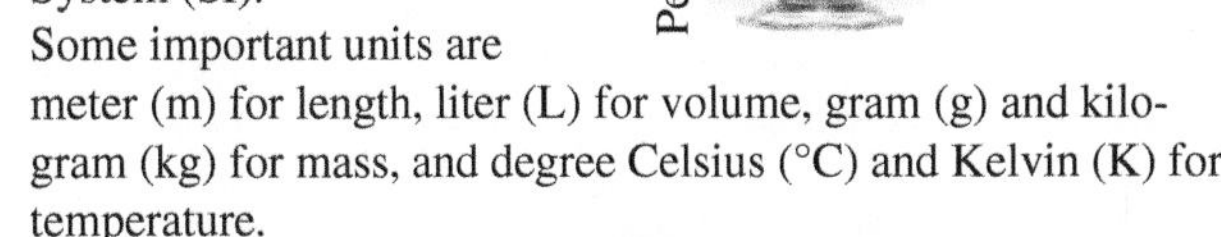

4 Scientific Notation

LEARNING GOAL: *Write a number in scientific notation.*

Jason Stitt/Shutterstock

- Large and small numbers can be written using scientific notation in which the decimal point is moved to give a coefficient of at least 1 but less than 10, and the number of spaces moved is shown as a power of 10.
- A large number will have a positive power of 10, while a small number will have a negative power of 10.

5 Measured Numbers and Significant Figures

LEARNING GOAL: *Identify a number as measured or exact; determine the number of significant figures in a measured number.*

0 cm 1 2 3 4 5
(a)
0 cm 1 2 3 4 5
(b)
0 cm 1 2 3 4 5
(c)

- A measured number is any number obtained by using a measuring device.
- An exact number is obtained by counting items or from a definition; no measuring device is needed.
- Significant figures are the numbers reported in a measurement including the estimated digit. Zeros in front of a decimal number or at the end of a nondecimal number are not significant.

6 Significant Figures in Calculations

LEARNING GOAL: *Give the correct number of significant figures in a final answer by adding or removing digits in a calculator result.*

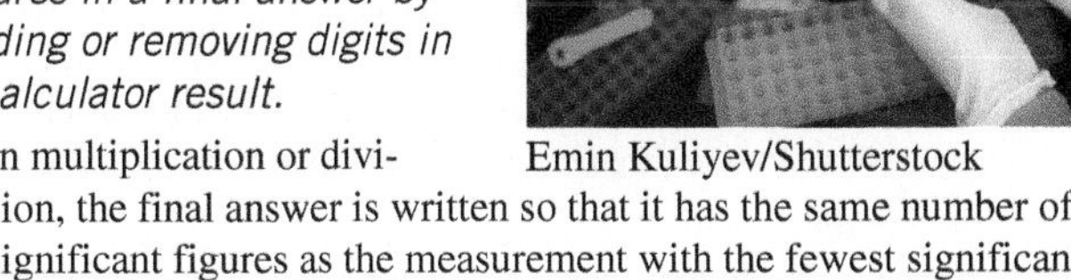
Emin Kuliyev/Shutterstock

- In multiplication or division, the final answer is written so that it has the same number of significant figures as the measurement with the fewest significant figures.
- In addition and subtraction, the final answer is written so that it has the same number of decimal places as the measurement with the fewest decimal places.

7 Prefixes and Equalities

LEARNING GOAL: *Use the numerical values of prefixes to write a metric equality.*

- A prefix placed in front of a metric or SI unit changes the size of the unit by factors of 10.
- Prefixes such as *centi*, *milli*, and *micro* provide smaller units; prefixes such as *kilo*, *mega*, and *tera* provide larger units.
- An equality shows the relationship between two units that measure the same quantity of length, volume, mass, or time.
- Examples of equalities are 1 m = 100 cm, 1 qt = 946 mL, 1 kg = 1000 g, and 1 min = 60 s.

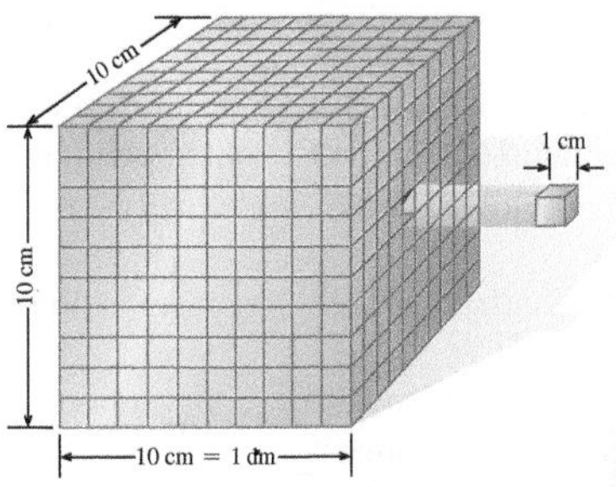

8 Writing Conversion Factors

LEARNING GOAL: *Write a conversion factor for two units that describe the same quantity.*

Pearson Education/Eric Schrader

- Conversion factors are used to express an equality in the form of a fraction.
- Two conversion factors can be written for any relationship in the metric or U.S. system.
- A percentage is written as a conversion factor by expressing matching units in the relationship as the parts to 100 parts of the whole.
- Extremely small percentage values are written as parts per million (ppm) or parts per billion (ppb).

9 Problem Solving

LEARNING GOAL: *Use conversion factors to change from one unit to another.*

- Conversion factors are useful when changing a quantity expressed in one unit to a quantity expressed in another unit.
- In the process, a given unit is multiplied by one or more conversion factors that cancel units until the needed unit for the answer is obtained.

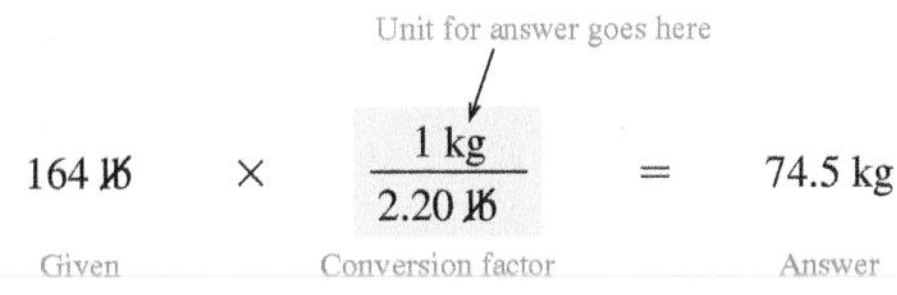

10 Density

LEARNING GOAL: *Calculate the density or specific gravity of a substance; use the density or specific gravity to calculate the mass or volume of a substance.*

- The density of a substance is a ratio of its mass to its volume, usually g/mL or g/cm^3.
- The units of density can be used to write conversion factors that convert between the mass and volume of a substance.
- Specific gravity (sp gr) compares the density of a substance to the density of water, 1.00 g/mL.

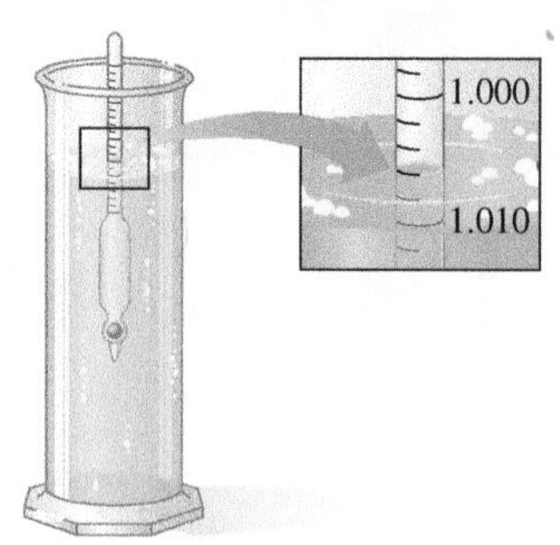

KEY TERMS

Celsius (°C) temperature scale A temperature scale on which water has a freezing point of 0 °C and a boiling point of 100 °C.

centimeter (cm) A unit of length in the metric system; there are 2.54 cm in 1 in.

chemical A substance that has the same composition and properties wherever it is found.

chemistry The science that studies the composition, structure, properties, and reactions of matter.

conversion factor A ratio in which the numerator and denominator are quantities from an equality or given relationship. For example, the conversion factors for the relationship 1 kg = 2.20 lb are written:

$$\frac{2.20 \text{ lb}}{1 \text{ kg}} \quad \text{and} \quad \frac{1 \text{ kg}}{2.20 \text{ lb}}$$

cubic centimeter (cm^3 or cc) The volume of a cube that has 1-cm sides; 1 cm^3 is equal to 1 mL.

density The relationship of the mass of an object to its volume expressed as grams per cubic centimeter (g/cm^3), grams per milliliter (g/mL), or grams per liter (g/L).

equality A relationship between two units that measure the same quantity.

exact number A number obtained by counting or by definition.

gram (g) The metric unit used in measurements of mass.

International System of Units (SI) A system of units that modifies the metric system.

Kelvin (K) temperature scale A temperature scale on which the lowest possible temperature is 0 K.

kilogram (kg) A metric mass of 1000 g and equal to 2.20 lb. The kilogram is the SI standard unit of mass.

liter (L) The metric unit for volume that is slightly larger than a quart.

mass A measure of the quantity of material in an object.

measured number A number obtained when a quantity is determined by using a measuring device.

meter (m) The metric unit for length that is slightly longer than a yard. The meter is the SI standard unit of length.

metric system A system of measurement used by scientists and in most countries of the world.

milliliter (mL) A metric unit of volume equal to one-thousandth of a liter (0.001 L).

prefix The part of the name of a metric unit that precedes the base unit and specifies the size of the measurement. All prefixes are related on a decimal scale.

scientific notation A form of writing large and small numbers using a coefficient that is at least 1 but less than 10, followed by a power of 10.

second (s) The standard unit of time in the SI and metric system.

significant figures (SFs) The numbers recorded in a measurement.

specific gravity (sp gr) A relationship between the density of a substance and the density of water:

$$\text{sp gr} = \frac{\text{density of sample}}{\text{density of water}}$$

temperature An indicator of the hotness or coldness of an object.

volume The amount of space occupied by a substance.

UNDERSTANDING THE CONCEPTS

The chapter sections to review are shown in parentheses at the end of each question.

69 Which of the following will help you develop a successful study plan? (2)

a. Skip lecture and just read the text.
b. Work the *Sample Problems* as you go through a chapter.
c. Go to your professor's office hours.
d. Read through the chapter, but work the problems later.

70 Which of the following will help you develop a successful study plan? (2)

a. Study all night before the exam.
b. Form a study group and discuss the problems together.
c. Work problems in a notebook for easy reference.
d. Copy the answers to homework from a friend.

71 A balance measures mass to 0.001 g. If you determine the mass of an object that weighs about 30 g, would you record the mass as 30 g, 32 g, 32.1 g, or 32.075 g? Explain your choice by writing two to three complete sentences that describe your thinking. (5)

72 When three students use the same meterstick to measure the length of a paper clip, they obtain results of 5.8 cm, 5.75 cm, and 5.76 cm. If the meterstick has millimeter markings, what are some reasons for the different values? (5)

73 In the following pairs, which measurement has more significant figures? (4, 5)
a. 2.0500 m and 0.0205 m
b. 600.0 K and 60 K
c. 0.000 705 s and 75 000 s
d. 2550 L and 2.550×10^{-2} L

74 In the following pairs, which measurement has fewer significant figures? (4, 5)
a. 2.80×10^{-3} g and 0.0028 g
b. 8.005 m and 0.00805 m
c. 163 000 s and 1.630×10^{2} s
d. 0.03080 cm and 308 cm

75 Indicate if each of the following is an exact number or a measured number: (5)

a. number of legs
b. height of the table
c. number of chairs at the table
d. area of tabletop

76 Measure the length of each of the objects in diagrams (**a**), (**b**), and (**c**) using the metric rule in the figure. Indicate the number of significant figures for each and the estimated digit for each. (5)

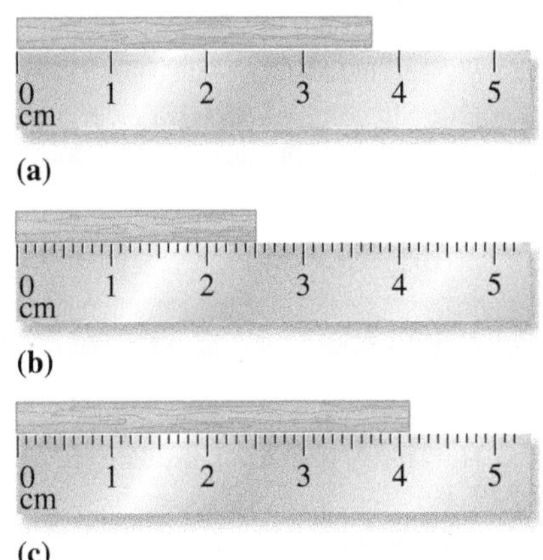

77 Measure the length and width of the rectangle, including the estimated digit, using a metric rule. (5)

a. What is the length and width of this rectangle measured in centimeters?
b. What is the length and width of this rectangle measured in millimeters?
c. How many significant figures are in the length measurement?
d. How many significant figures are in the width measurement?
e. What is the area of the rectangle in cm^2?
f. How many significant figures are in the calculated answer for area?

78 Each of the following represents a container of water and a cube. Some cubes float while others sink. Match diagrams **1**, **2**, **3**, or **4** with one of the following descriptions and explain your choices: (10)

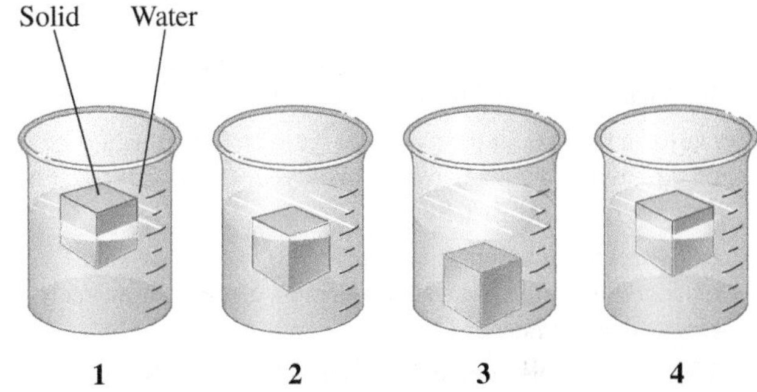

a. The cube has a greater density than water.
b. The cube has a density that is 0.60–0.80 g/mL.
c. The cube has a density that is 1/2 the density of water.
d. The cube has the same density as water.

79 What is the density of the solid object that is weighed and submerged in water? (10)

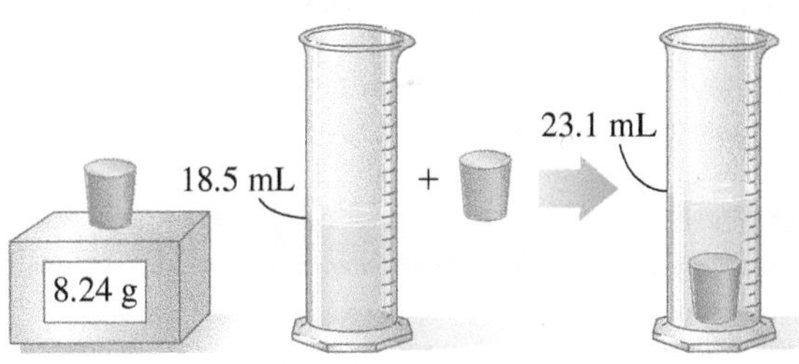

80 Consider the following solids. The solids **A**, **B**, and **C** represent aluminum, gold, and silver. If each has a mass of 10.0 g, what is the identity of each solid? (10)

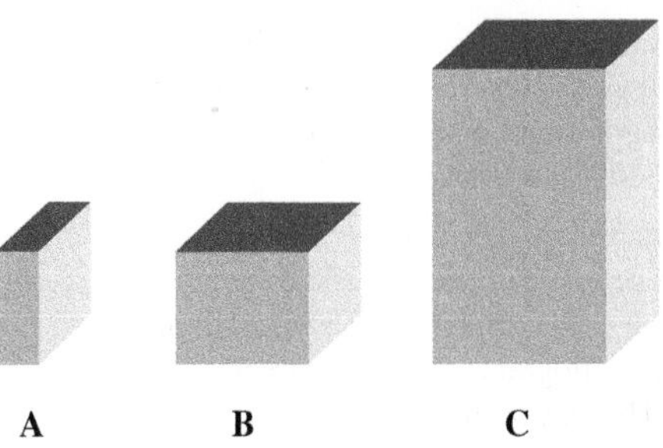

Density of aluminum = 2.70 g/mL
Density of gold = 19.3 g/mL
Density of silver = 10.5 g/mL

ADDITIONAL QUESTIONS AND PROBLEMS

For instructor-assigned homework, go to www.masteringchemistry.com.

81 Round off or add zeros to the following calculated answers to give a final answer with three significant figures: (4, 5)
a. 0.000 012 58 L **b.** 3.528×10^2 kg
c. 125 111 m **d.** 58.703 g

82 Round off or add zeros to the following calculated answers to give a final answer with two significant figures: (4, 5)
a. 0.004 mL **b.** 34 677 g
c. 4.393 cm **d.** 1.74×10^3 ms

83 What is the total mass, in grams, of a dessert containing 137.25 g of vanilla ice cream, 84 g of fudge sauce, and 43.7 g of nuts? (6)

84 A fish company delivers 22 kg of salmon, 5.5 kg of crab, and 3.48 kg of oysters to your seafood restaurant. (3, 6)
a. What is the total mass, in kilograms, of the seafood?
b. What is the total number of pounds?

85 During a workout at the gym, you set the treadmill at a pace of 55.0 m/min. How many minutes will you walk if you cover a distance of 7500 ft? (3, 9)

86 Bill's recipe for onion soup calls for 4.0 lb of thinly sliced onions. If an onion has an average mass of 115 g, how many onions does Bill need? (3, 9)

87 The following nutrition information is listed on a box of crackers: (9)

Serving size 0.50 oz (6 crackers)

Fat 4 g per serving

Sodium 140 mg per serving

a. If the box has a net weight (contents only) of 8.0 oz, about how many crackers are in the box?
b. If you ate 10 crackers, how many ounces of fat did you consume?
c. How many grams of sodium are used to prepare 50 boxes of crackers in part **a**?

88 The price of 1 lb of potatoes is \$1.75. If all the potatoes sold today at the store bring in \$1420, how many kilograms of potatoes did grocery shoppers buy? (9)

89 In Mexico, avocados are 48 pesos per kilogram. What is the cost, in cents, of an avocado that weighs 0.45 lb if the exchange rate is 13.0 pesos to the dollar? (9)

90 An aquarium store unit requires 75 000 mL of water. How many gallons (1 gal = 4 qt) of water are needed? (9)

91 **a.** Some athletes have as little as 3.0% body fat. If such a person has a body mass of 65 kg, how many pounds of body fat does that person have? (9)
b. In a process called *liposuction*, a doctor removes fat deposits from a person's body. If body fat has a density of 0.94 g/mL and 3.0 liters of fat are removed, how many pounds of fat were removed from the patient? (9)

92 Celeste's diet restricts her intake of protein to 24 g per day. If she eats an 8.0-oz burger that is 15.0% protein, has she exceeded her protein limit for the day? How many ounces of a burger would be allowed for Celeste? (3, 7, 9)

93 The water level in a graduated cylinder initially at 215 mL rises to 285 mL after a piece of lead is submerged. What is the mass, in grams, of the lead (see Table 13)? (9, 10)

94 A graduated cylinder contains 155 mL of water. A 15.0-g piece of iron and a 20.0-g piece of lead are added. What is the new water level, in milliliters, in the cylinder (see Table 13)? (9, 10)

95 Sterling silver is 92.5% silver by mass, with a density of 10.3 g/cm^3. If a cube of sterling silver has a volume of 27.0 cm^3, how many ounces of pure silver are present? (9, 10)

96 A typical adult body contains 55% water. If a person has a mass of 65 kg, how many pounds of water does she have in her body? (9)

CHALLENGE QUESTIONS

The following groups of questions and problems are related to the topics in this chapter. However, they do not all follow the chapter order, and they require you to combine concepts and skills from several sections. These problems will help you increase your critical thinking skills and prepare for your next exam.

97 A sunscreen preparation contains 2.50% by mass benzyl salicylate. If a tube contains 4.0 oz of sunscreen, how many kilograms of benzyl salicylate are needed to manufacture 325 tubes of sunscreen? (9)

98 A mouthwash is 21.6% by mass alcohol. If one bottle contains 0.358 pt of mouthwash with a density of 0.876 g/mL, how many kilograms of alcohol are in 180 bottles of the mouthwash? (9, 10)

Cristian Ciureanu/Alamy

A mouthwash may contain ethyl alcohol.

99 A car travels at 55 mi/h and travels 11 kilometers on one liter of gasoline. How many gallons of gasoline are needed for a 3.0-h trip? (9, 10)

100 If a recycling center collects 1254 aluminum cans and there are 22 aluminum cans in 1 lb, what volume, in liters, of aluminum was collected (see Table 13)? (9, 10)

101 For a 180-lb person, calculate the quantities of each of the following that must be ingested to provide the LD_{50} for caffeine given in Table 12: (8, 9)
a. cups of coffee if one cup is 12 fl oz and there are 100. mg of caffeine per 6.0 fl oz of drip-brewed coffee
b. cans of cola if one can contains 50. mg of caffeine
c. tablets of No-Doz if one tablet contains 100. mg of caffeine

102 The label on a 1-pt bottle of mineral water lists the following components. If the density is the same as pure water and you drink three bottles of water in one day, how many milligrams of each component will you obtain? (8, 9, 10)
a. calcium 28 ppm **b.** fluoride 0.08 ppm
c. magnesium 12 ppm **d.** potassium 3.2 ppm
e. sodium 15 ppm

103 In the manufacturing of computer chips, cylinders of silicon are cut into thin wafers that are 3.00 inches in diameter and have a mass of 1.50 g of silicon. How thick (mm) is each wafer if silicon has a density of 2.33 g/cm^3? (8, 9, 10) (The volume of a cylinder is $V = \pi r^2 h$.)

104 A circular pool with a diameter of 27 ft is filled to a depth of 50. in. Assume the pool is a cylinder ($V = \pi r^2 h$). (8, 9, 10)

a. What is the volume of water in the pool in cubic meters?

b. The density of water is 1.00 g/cm^3. What is the mass, in kilograms, of the water in the pool?

105 A package of aluminum foil is 66.7 yd long, 12 in. wide, and 0.000 30 in. thick. If aluminum has a density of 2.70 g/cm^3, what is the mass, in grams, of the foil? (8, 9, 10)

106 An 18-karat gold necklace is 75% gold by mass, 16% silver, and 9.0% copper. (8, 9, 10)

a. What is the mass, in grams, of the necklace if it contains 0.24 oz of silver?

b. How many grams of copper are in the necklace?

c. If 18-karat gold has a density of 15.5 g/cm^3, what is the volume in cubic centimeters?

107 What is a cholesterol level of 1.85 g/L in units of mg/dL? (7, 8, 9, 10)

108 An object has a mass of 3.15 oz. When it is submerged in a graduated cylinder initially containing 325.2 mL of water, the water level rises to 442.5 mL. What is the density (g/mL) of the object? (8, 9, 10)

ANSWERS

Answers to Study Checks

1 time

2 a. 4.25×10^5 m **b.** 8×10^{-7} g

3 a. 36 m **b.** 0.0026 L **c.** 3.8×10^3 g **d.** 1.3 kg

4 a. 83.70 mg **b.** 0.5 L

5 1.5×10^{12} bytes

6 a. 1000 g (1×10^3 g) **b.** 0.001 L (1×10^{-3} L)

7 a. 62.2 km = 1 h; $\frac{62.2 \text{ km}}{1 \text{ h}}$ and $\frac{1 \text{ h}}{62.2 \text{ km}}$

The 1 h is exact; the 62.2 has three SFs.

b. 1 μg of arsenic = 1 kg of water; $\frac{1\ \mu\text{g arsenic}}{1 \text{ kg water}}$ and $\frac{1 \text{ kg water}}{1\ \mu\text{g arsenic}}$

The 1 in 1 kg of water is exact; the 1 in 1 μg has one SF.

8 1.89 L

9 0.44 oz

10 25 g of fat

11 1.05 g/cm^3

12 2.20 g/mL

13 980 g of syrup

14 246 mL

Answers to Selected Questions and Problems

1 Many chemicals are listed on a vitamin bottle such as vitamin A, vitamin B_3, vitamin B_{12}, folic acid, etc.

3 No. All of the ingredients listed are chemicals.

5 Among the things you can do to help yourself succeed in chemistry are: form a study group, review the *Learning Goals*, attend class regularly, go to office hours, work the problems in the text, and become an active learner.

7 **a, c, e, f**

9 a. volume **b.** length **c.** length **d.** time

11 a. meter; length **b.** gram; mass **c.** liter; volume **d.** second; time **e.** degree Celsius; temperature

13 a. 5.5×10^4 m **b.** 4.8×10^2 g **c.** 5×10^{-6} cm **d.** 1.4×10^{-4} s **e.** 7.85×10^{-3} L **f.** 6.7×10^5 kg

15 a. 7.2×10^3 cm **b.** 3.2×10^{-2} kg **c.** 1×10^4 L **d.** 6.8×10^{-2} m

17 a. 12 000 s **b.** 0.0825 kg **c.** 4 000 000 g **d.** 0.005 m

19 a. Measured; measurement of mass requires a measuring device.

b. Exact; tablets are counted.

c. Exact; both numbers in a metric definition are exact.

d. Measured; distance is measured with a measuring device.

21 a. 6 oz of meat **b.** none **c.** 0.75 lb; 350 g **d.** none (definitions are exact)

23 a. The zero following the 8 is significant.

b. The zero between nonzero digits is significant.

c. Both zeros in a number with a decimal point are significant.

d. The zero in the coefficient is significant.

e. None; zeros in a large number with no decimal point are not significant.

25 a. five SFs **b.** two SFs **c.** two SFs **d.** three SFs **e.** four SFs **f.** three SFs

27 a. 11.00 m **b.** 405.0 K **c.** 0.0120 s **d.** 250.0 L

29 a. 1.85 kg **b.** 184 L **c.** 0.004 74 cm **d.** 8810 m **e.** 1.83×10^5 s

31 a. 1.6 **b.** 0.01 **c.** 27.6 **d.** 3.5

33 a. 53.54 cm **b.** 127.6 g **c.** 121.5 mL **d.** 0.50 L

35 km/h is kilometers per hour; mi/h is miles per hour.

37 a. mg **b.** dL **c.** km **d.** pg **e.** μL **f.** ns

39 a. 0.01 **b.** 1000 **c.** 0.001 (1×10^{-3}) **d.** 1×10^{12} **e.** 1 000 000 (1×10^6) **f.** 1×10^{-12}

41 a. 100 cm **b.** 1×10^9 nm **c.** 0.001 m **d.** 1000 mL

kilogram **b.** milliliter **c.** km
kL **e.** nanometer

45 a. 1 m = 100 cm; $\frac{100\text{ cm}}{1\text{ m}}$ and $\frac{1\text{ m}}{100\text{ cm}}$
b. 1 g = 1000 mg; $\frac{1000\text{ mg}}{1\text{ g}}$ and $\frac{1\text{ g}}{1000\text{ mg}}$
c. 1 L = 1000 mL; $\frac{1000\text{ mL}}{1\text{ L}}$ and $\frac{1\text{ L}}{1000\text{ mL}}$
d. 1 dL = 100 mL; $\frac{100\text{ mL}}{1\text{ dL}}$ and $\frac{1\text{ dL}}{100\text{ mL}}$

47 a. 1 yd = 3 ft; $\frac{3\text{ ft}}{1\text{ yd}}$ and $\frac{1\text{ yd}}{3\text{ ft}}$
The numbers 1 and 3 are both exact.
b. 1 kg = 2.20 lb; $\frac{2.20\text{ lb}}{1\text{ kg}}$ and $\frac{1\text{ kg}}{2.20\text{ lb}}$
The number 1 is exact; the number 2.20 has three SFs.
c. 1 min = 60 sec; $\frac{60\text{ sec}}{1\text{ min}}$ and $\frac{1\text{ min}}{60\text{ sec}}$
The numbers 1 and 60 are both exact.
d. 1 gal = 27 mi; $\frac{1\text{ gal}}{27\text{ mi}}$ and $\frac{27\text{ mi}}{1\text{ gal}}$
The number 1 is exact; the number 27 has two SFs.
e. 93 g of silver = 100 g of sterling;
$\frac{93\text{ g silver}}{100\text{ g sterling}}$ and $\frac{100\text{ g sterling}}{93\text{ g silver}}$
The number 100 is exact; the number 93 has two SFs.

49 a. 3.5 m = 1 s; $\frac{3.5\text{ m}}{1\text{ s}}$ and $\frac{1\text{ s}}{3.5\text{ m}}$
The number 1 is exact; the number 3.5 has two SFs.
b. 3500 mg of potassium = 1 day;
$\frac{3500\text{ mg potassium}}{1\text{ day}}$ and $\frac{1\text{ day}}{3500\text{ mg potassium}}$
The number 1 is exact; the number 3500 has two SFs.
c. 46.0 km = 1 gal; $\frac{46.0\text{ km}}{1\text{ gal}}$ and $\frac{1\text{ gal}}{46.0\text{ km}}$
The number 1 is exact; the number 46.0 has three SFs.
d. 50. mg of Atenolol = 1 tablet;
$\frac{50.\text{ mg Atenolol}}{1\text{ tablet}}$ and $\frac{1\text{ tablet}}{50.\text{ mg Atenolol}}$
The number 1 is exact; the number 50. has two SFs.
e. 29 μg of pesticide = 1 kg of plums;
$\frac{29\ \mu\text{g pesticide}}{1\text{ kg plums}}$ and $\frac{1\text{ kg plums}}{29\ \mu\text{g pesticide}}$
The number 1 is exact; the number 29 has two SFs.
f. 81 mg of aspirin = 1 tablet;
$\frac{81\text{ mg aspirin}}{1\text{ tablet}}$ and $\frac{1\text{ tablet}}{81\text{ mg aspirin}}$
The number 1 is exact; the number 81 has two SFs.

51 a. 1.75 m **b.** 5.5 L **c.** 5.5 g

53 a. 710. mL **b.** 75.1 kg **c.** 495 mm
d. 2.0×10^{-5} in.

55 a. 23.8 m **b.** 196 m^2 **c.** 0.463 s

57 a. 66 gal **b.** 3 tablets
c. 1800 mg (1.8×10^3 mg)

59 a. 152 g of oxygen **b.** 0.026 g of magnesium
c. 43 g of N **d.** 50. lb of chocolate bars

61 lead; 11.3 g/mL

63 a. 1.20 g/mL **b.** 0.877 g/mL
c. 3.10 g/mL **d.** 1.42 g/mL

65 a. 1.9 L **b.** 88 g
c. 62 oz **d.** 34 kg

67 a. 1.03 **b.** 1.13
c. 0.85 g/mL

69 b and **c**

71 You should record the mass as 32.075 g. Because your balance will weigh to the nearest 0.001 g, the mass values should be reported to 0.001 g.

73 a. 2.0500 m **b.** 600.0 K
c. 0.000 705 s **d.** 2.550×10^{-2} L

75 a. exact **b.** measured
c. exact **d.** measured

77 a. length = 6.96 cm; width = 4.75 cm
b. length = 69.6 mm; width = 47.5 mm
c. three SFs
d. three SFs
e. 33.1 cm^2
f. three SFs

79 1.8 g/mL

81 a. 0.000 0126 L **b.** 3.53×10^2 kg
c. 125 000 m **d.** 58.7 g

83 265 g

85 42 min

87 a. 96 crackers
b. 0.2 oz of fat
c. 110 g of sodium

89 76 cents

91 a. 4.3 lb of body fat **b.** 6.2 lb

93 790 g

95 9.07 oz of pure silver

97 0.92 kg

99 6.4 gal

101 a. 79 cups **b.** 310 cans
c. 160 tablets

103 0.141 mm

105 3.8×10^2 g of aluminum foil

107 185 mg/dL

Energy and Matter

LOOKING AHEAD

1 Energy
2 Temperature
3 Classification of Matter
4 States and Properties of Matter
5 Specific Heat
6 Energy and Nutrition

Visit **www.masteringchemistry.com** for self-study materials and instructor-assigned homework.

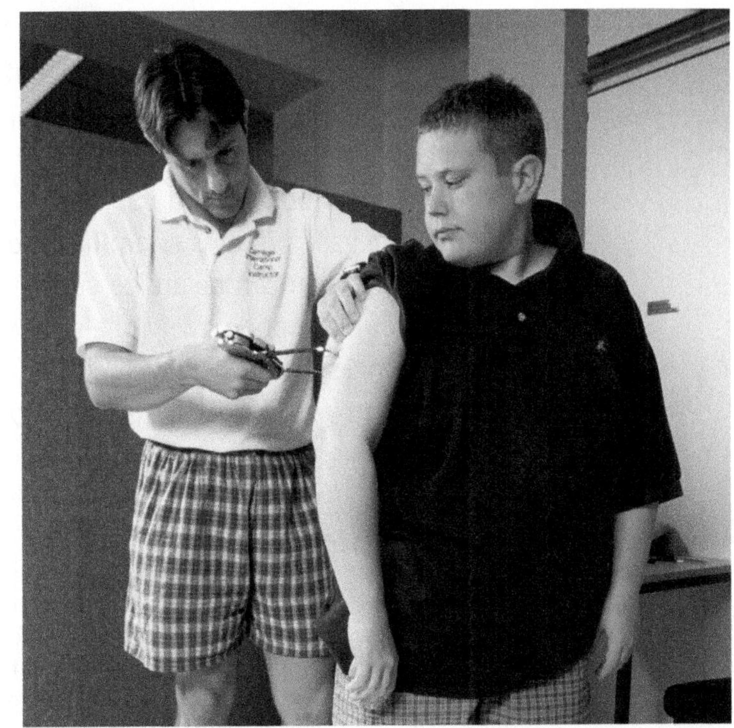

Network Photographer/Alamy

Charles is 13 years old and overweight for his age. His doctor is worried that Charles is at risk for type 2 diabetes and advises his mother to make an appointment with a dietician. Daniel, a dietician, explains to them that choosing the appropriate foods is important to living a healthy lifestyle, losing weight, and preventing or managing diabetes.

Daniel also explains that food contains potential or stored energy, and different foods contain different amounts of potential energy. For instance, carbohydrates contain 4 kcal/g while fats contain 9 kcal/g. He then explains that diets high in fat require more exercise to burn the fats, as they contain more potential energy. Daniel encourages Charles and his mother to include whole grains, fruits, and vegetables in their diet instead of foods high in fat or sugar. They also discuss food labels and that smaller serving sizes of healthy foods are necessary in order to lose weight. Before leaving, Charles and his mother are given a menu for the following two weeks, and a diary to keep track of what, and how much, they actually consume.

Career: Dietician

Dieticians specialize in helping individuals learn about good nutrition and the need for a balanced diet. This requires them to understand biochemical processes, the importance of vitamins, and food labels, as well as the differences between carbohydrates, fats, and proteins in terms of their energy content and how they are metabolized. Dieticians work in a variety of environments including hospitals, nursing homes, school cafeterias, and public health clinics. In these environments, they create personalized diets for individuals diagnosed with a specific disease, or create meal plans for those in a nursing home.

From Chapter 2 of *General, Organic, and Biological Chemistry: Structures of Life*, Fourth Edition. Karen C. Timberlake.

Almost everything we do involves energy. We use energy when we walk, play tennis, study, and breathe. We use energy when we warm water, cook food, turn on lights, use a washing machine, and drive our cars. Of course, that energy has to come from something. In our bodies, the food we eat provides us with energy. Energy from fossil fuels or the Sun is used to heat a home or water for a pool.

Every day, we see a variety of materials with many different shapes and forms. To a scientist, all of this material is *matter*. Matter is everywhere around us: the orange juice we had for breakfast, the water we put in the coffee maker, the plastic bag we put our sandwich in, our toothbrush and toothpaste, the oxygen we inhale, and the carbon dioxide we exhale are all forms of matter.

When we look around us, we see that matter takes the physical state of a solid, a liquid, or a gas. Water is a familiar substance that we observe in all three states. In the solid state, water can be an ice cube or a snowflake. It is a liquid when it comes out of a faucet or fills a pool. We will also see that a substance can change state. For example, water changes state when ice melts, liquid evaporates from a pond, or water boils to form a gas. When water vapor in the atmosphere condenses, clouds are formed.

LEARNING GOAL

Identify energy as potential or kinetic; convert between units of energy.

1 Energy

When you are running, walking, dancing, or thinking, you are using energy to do **work**, which is any activity that requires energy. In fact, **energy** is defined as the ability to do work. Suppose you are climbing a steep hill and you become too tired to go on. At that moment, you do not have sufficient energy to do any more work. Perhaps you sit down and have lunch. In a while, you will have obtained energy from the food, and you will be able to do more work and complete the climb (see Figure 1).

Potential and Kinetic Energy

All energy can be classified as potential energy or kinetic energy. **Kinetic energy** is the energy of motion. Any object that is moving has kinetic energy. **Potential energy** is determined by the position of an object or by the chemical composition of a substance. A boulder resting on top of a mountain has potential energy because of its location. If the boulder rolls down the mountain, the potential energy becomes kinetic energy. Water stored in a reservoir has potential energy. When the water goes over the dam and falls to the stream below, its potential energy becomes kinetic energy. Foods and fossil fuels have potential energy stored in the bonds of their molecules. When you digest food or burn gasoline in your car, potential energy is converted to kinetic energy to do work.

Jennifer Photography Imaging/ iStockphoto

FIGURE 1 Water at the top of dam stores potential energy.

Q What happens to the potential energy of the water at the top of the dam when the water goes over the dam and falls to the stream below?

CONCEPT CHECK 1 **Potential and Kinetic Energy**

Identify each of the following as an example of potential or kinetic energy:

a. gasoline **b.** skating **c.** a candy bar

ANSWER

a. Gasoline is burned to provide energy and heat; it contains potential energy in the bonds of its molecules.
b. A skater uses energy to move; skating is kinetic energy (energy of motion).
c. A candy bar has potential energy. When digested, it provides energy for the body to do work.

Heat and Energy

TUTORIAL
Heat

TUTORIAL
Energy Conversions

Heat, also known as *thermal energy*, is associated with the motion of particles. A frozen pizza feels cold because heat flows from your hand to the pizza. The faster the particles move, the greater the heat or thermal energy of the substance. In the frozen pizza, the particles are moving very slowly. As heat is added and the pizza becomes warmer, the motions of the particles in the pizza increase. Eventually, the particles have enough energy to make the pizza hot and ready to eat.

Units of Energy

The SI unit of energy and work is the **joule (J)** (pronounced like "jewel"). The joule is a small amount of energy, so scientists often use the kilojoule (kJ), 1000 joules. To heat water for one cup of tea, you need about 75 000 J or 75 kJ of heat. Table 1 shows a comparison of energy in joules for several energy sources.

You may be more familiar with the unit **calorie (cal)**, from the Latin *calor*, meaning "heat." The calorie was originally defined as the amount of energy (heat) needed to raise the temperature of 1 g of water by 1 °C. Now one calorie is defined as *exactly* 4.184 J. This equality can also be written as two conversion factors:

$$1 \text{ cal} = 4.184 \text{ J (exact)}$$

$$\frac{4.184 \text{ J}}{1 \text{ cal}} \quad \text{and} \quad \frac{1 \text{ cal}}{4.184 \text{ J}}$$

One *kilocalorie* (kcal) is equal to 1000 calories, and one *kilojoule* (kJ) is equal to 1000 joules.

$$1 \text{ kcal} = 1000 \text{ cal}$$
$$1 \text{ kJ} = 1000 \text{ J}$$

TABLE 1 A Comparison of Energy for Various Resources

Energy in Joules	
10^{27}	
	Energy radiated by the Sun per second (10^{26})
10^{24}	
	World reserves of fossil fuel (10^{23})
10^{21}	
	Energy consumption for one year in the U.S. (10^{20})
10^{18}	
	Solar energy reaching the Earth per second (10^{17})
10^{15}	
10^{12}	
	Energy use per person in one year in the U.S. (10^{11})
10^{9}	
	Energy from one gallon of gasoline (10^{8})
10^{6}	Energy from one serving of pasta, or a doughnut, or needed to bicycle one hour (10^{6})
10^{3}	
	Energy used to sleep one hour (10^{5})
10^{0}	

SAMPLE PROBLEM 1 **Energy Units**

When 1.0 g of diesel fuel burns in a diesel car engine, 48 000 J are released. What is this energy in calories?

SOLUTION

Step 1 State the given and needed quantities.

Analyze the Problem

Given	Need
48 000 J	calories

Wendell and Carolyn/iStockphoto

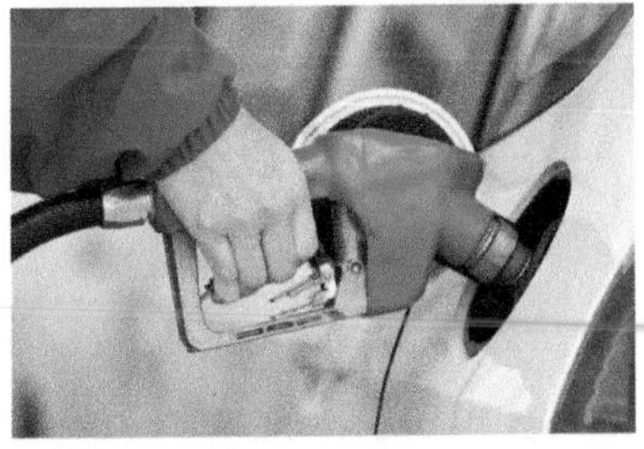

Diesel fuel reacts in a car engine to produce energy.

Step 2 **Write a plan to convert the given unit to the needed unit.**

joules → Energy factor → calories

Step 3 **State the equalities and conversion factors.**

$$1 \text{ cal} = 4.184 \text{ J}$$

$$\frac{4.184 \text{ J}}{1 \text{ cal}} \quad \text{and} \quad \frac{1 \text{ cal}}{4.184 \text{ J}}$$

Step 4 **Set up the problem to calculate the needed quantity.**

$$\underset{\text{Two SFs}}{48\,000 \cancel{\text{J}}} \times \underset{\text{Exact}}{\overset{\text{Exact}}{\frac{1 \text{ cal}}{4.184 \cancel{\text{J}}}}} = \underset{\text{Two SFs}}{11\,000 \text{ cal } (1.1 \times 10^4 \text{ cal})}$$

STUDY CHECK 1

The burning of 1.0 g of coal produces 8.4 kcal. How many kilojoules are produced?

QUESTIONS AND PROBLEMS

1 Energy

LEARNING GOAL: *Identify energy as potential or kinetic; convert between units of energy.*

1 Indicate whether each of the following statements describes potential or kinetic energy:
a. water at the top of a waterfall
b. kicking a ball
c. the energy in a lump of coal
d. a skier at the top of a hill

2 Indicate whether each of the following statements describes potential or kinetic energy:
a. the energy in your food
b. a tightly wound spring
c. an earthquake
d. a car speeding down the freeway

3 State whether each of the following involves an increase or decrease in potential energy:
a. A roller coaster climbs up a ramp in a roller-coaster ride.
b. A skier at the top of the jump begins to ski down the course.
c. Water at the top of a waterfall drops to the pool below.

4 State whether each of the following involves an increase or decrease in potential energy:
a. A gondola goes to the top of a mountain.
b. Water is pumped up to a high water tower.
c. Gasoline is added to a gas tank.

5 The energy needed to keep a 75-watt lightbulb burning for 1.0 h is 270 kJ. Calculate the energy required to keep the lightbulb burning for 3.0 h in each of the following energy units:
a. joules **b.** kilocalories

6 A person uses 750 kcal on a long hike. Calculate the energy used for the hike in each of the following energy units:
a. joules **b.** kilojoules

LEARNING GOAL

Given a temperature, calculate a corresponding value on another temperature scale.

TUTORIAL
Temperature Conversions

2 Temperature

Temperatures in science are measured and reported in *Celsius* (°C) units. On the Celsius scale, the reference points are the freezing point of water, defined as 0 °C, and the boiling point of water, 100 °C. In the United States, everyday temperatures are commonly reported in *Fahrenheit* (°F) units. On the Fahrenheit scale, pure water freezes at exactly 32 °F and boils at exactly 212 °F. A typical room temperature of 22 °C would be the same as 72 °F. Normal human body temperature is 37.0 °C, which is the same temperature as 98.6 °F.

On the Celsius and Fahrenheit temperature scales, the temperature difference between freezing and boiling is divided into smaller units called *degrees*. On the Celsius scale, there are 100 degrees Celsius between the freezing and boiling points of water. On the Fahrenheit scale, there are 180 degrees Fahrenheit between the freezing and boiling points of water. That makes a degree Celsius almost twice the size of a degree Fahrenheit: 1 °C = 1.8 °F (see Figure 2).

$$180 \text{ degrees Fahrenheit} = 100 \text{ degrees Celsius}$$

$$\frac{180 \text{ degrees Fahrenheit}}{100 \text{ degrees Celsius}} = \frac{1.8\ ^\circ\text{F}}{1\ ^\circ\text{C}}$$

We can write a temperature equation that relates a Fahrenheit temperature and its corresponding Celsius temperature.

$$T_F = \underset{\substack{\text{Changes} \\ ^\circ\text{C to } ^\circ\text{F}}}{1.8(T_C)} + \underset{\substack{\text{Adjusts} \\ \text{freezing point}}}{32}$$

In this equation, the Celsius temperature is multiplied by 1.8 to change °C to °F; then 32 is added to adjust the freezing point from 0 °C to 32 °F. Both values, 1.8 and 32, are exact numbers.

To convert from Fahrenheit to Celsius, the temperature equation is rearranged to obtain T_C.

$$T_C = \frac{T_F - 32}{1.8}$$

Scientists have learned that the coldest temperature possible is −273 °C (more precisely, −273.15 °C). On the *Kelvin* scale, this temperature, called *absolute zero*, has the value of 0 K. Temperature units on the Kelvin scale are called kelvins (K); no degree symbol is used. Because there are no lower temperatures, the Kelvin scale has no negative temperature values. Between the freezing point of water, 273 K, and the boiling point, 373 K, there are 100 kelvins, which makes a kelvin equal in size to a Celsius unit.

$$1 \text{ K} = 1\ ^\circ\text{C}$$

We can write an equation that relates a Celsius temperature to its corresponding Kelvin temperature by adding 273. Table 2 gives a comparison of some temperatures on the three scales.

$$T_K = T_C + 273$$

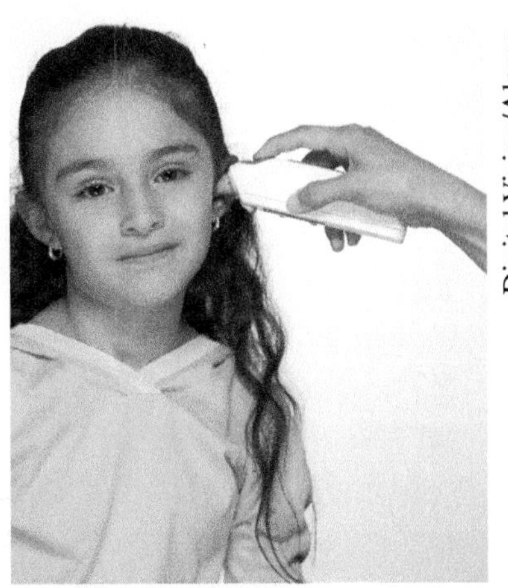

A digital ear thermometer is used to measure body temperature.

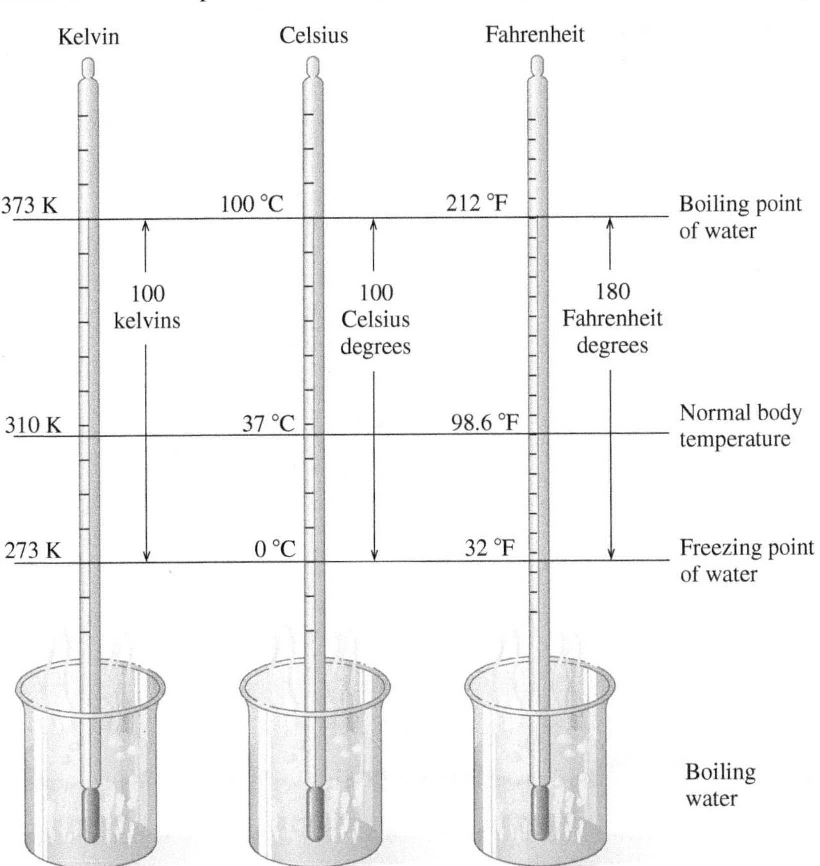

FIGURE 2 A comparison of the Fahrenheit, Celsius, and Kelvin temperature scales between the freezing and boiling points of water.

Q What are the values for the freezing point of water on the Fahrenheit, Celsius, and Kelvin temperature scales?

TABLE 2 A Comparison of Temperatures

Example	Fahrenheit (°F)	Celsius (°C)	Kelvin (K)
Sun	9937	5503	5776
A hot oven	450	232	505
A desert	120	49	322
A high fever	104	40	313
Room temperature	70	21	294
Water freezes	32	0	273
An Alaskan winter	−66	−54	219
Helium boils	−452	−269	4
Absolute zero	−459	−273	0

Chemistry Link to Health

VARIATION IN BODY TEMPERATURE

Normal human body temperature is considered to be 37.0 °C, although it varies throughout the day and from person to person. Oral temperatures of 36.1 °C are common in the morning and climb to a high of 37.2 °C between 6 P.M. and 10 P.M. Temperatures above 37.2 °C for a person at rest are usually an indication of disease. Individuals who are involved in prolonged exercise may also experience elevated temperatures. Body temperatures of marathon runners can range from 39 °C to 41 °C because heat production during exercise exceeds the body's ability to release heat.

Changes of more than 3.5 °C from the normal body temperature begin to interfere with bodily functions. Body temperatures above 41 °C, *hyperthermia*, can lead to convulsions, particularly in children, which may cause permanent brain damage. Heatstroke occurs above 41.1 °C. Sweat production stops, and the skin becomes hot and dry. The pulse rate is elevated, and respiration becomes weak and rapid. The person can become lethargic and lapse into a coma. Damage to internal organs is a major concern, and treatment, which must be immediate, may include immersing the person in an ice-water bath.

At the low temperature extreme of *hypothermia*, body temperature can drop as low as 28.5 °C. The person may appear cold and pale and have an irregular heartbeat. Unconsciousness can occur if the body temperature drops below 26.7 °C. Respiration becomes slow and shallow, and oxygenation of the tissues decreases. Treatment involves providing oxygen and increasing blood volume with glucose and saline fluids. Injecting warm fluids (37.0 °C) into the peritoneal cavity may restore the internal temperature.

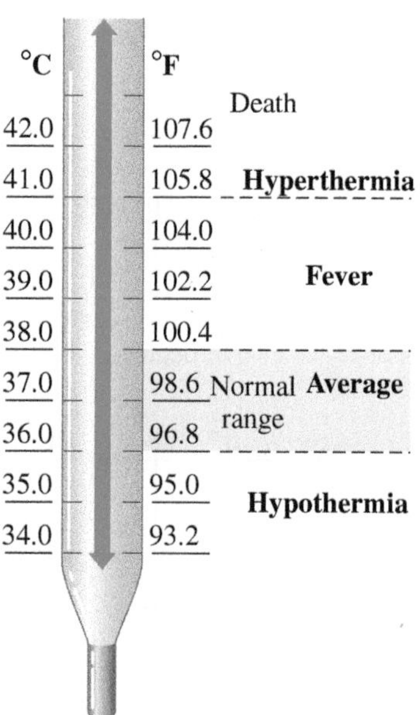

SAMPLE PROBLEM 2 **Converting from Celsius to Fahrenheit Temperature**

During the winter, the thermostat in a room is set at 21 °C. To what temperature, in Fahrenheit degrees, should you set the thermostat?

SOLUTION

Step 1 **State the given and needed quantities.**

Analyze the Problem

Given	Need
21 °C	T in degrees Fahrenheit

Step 2 **Write a temperature equation.**

$$T_F = 1.8(T_C) + 32$$

Step 3 **Substitute in the known values and calculate the new temperature.** In the equation, *the values of 1.8 and 32 are exact numbers*, which do not affect the number of SFs.

$$T_F = 1.8(21) + 32 \quad \text{1.8 is exact; 32 is exact}$$

$$= 70.\ °F \quad \text{Answer to the ones place}$$

STUDY CHECK 2

In the process of making ice cream, rock salt is added to crushed ice to chill the ice cream mixture. If the temperature drops to −11 °C, what is the temperature in degrees Fahrenheit?

Guide to Calculating Temperature

1. State the given and needed quantities.
2. Write a temperature equation.
3. Substitute in the known values and calculate the new temperature.

SAMPLE PROBLEM 3 Converting from Fahrenheit to Celsius Temperature

In a type of cancer treatment called *thermotherapy*, temperatures as high as 113 °F are used to destroy cancer cells. What is that temperature in degrees Celsius?

SOLUTION

Step 1 **State the given and needed quantities.**

Analyze the Problem

Given	Need
113 °F	*T* in degrees Celsius

Step 2 **Write a temperature equation.**

$$T_C = \frac{T_F - 32}{1.8}$$

Step 3 **Substitute in the known values and calculate the new temperature.**

$$T_C = \frac{(113 - 32)}{1.8} \quad \text{32 is exact; 1.8 is exact}$$

$$= \frac{81}{1.8} = 45\ °C \quad \text{Answer to the ones place}$$

STUDY CHECK 3

A child has a temperature of 103.6 °F. What is this temperature on a Celsius thermometer?

SAMPLE PROBLEM 4 Converting from Celsius to Kelvin Temperature

A dermatologist may use cryogenic liquid nitrogen at −196 °C to remove skin lesions and some skin cancers. What is the temperature, in kelvins, of the liquid nitrogen?

SOLUTION

Step 1 **State the given and needed quantities.**

Analyze the Problem

Given	Need
−196 °C	*T* in kelvins

Step 2 **Write a temperature equation.** To calculate the Kelvin temperature, we use the equation that relates Celsius and Kelvin temperatures.

$$T_K = T_C + 273$$

Step 3 **Substitute in the known values and calculate the new temperature.**

$$T_K = -196 + 273$$
$$= 77\ K$$

STUDY CHECK 4

On the planet Mercury, the average night temperature is 13 K, and the average day temperature is 683 K. What are these temperatures in degrees Celsius?

Chemistry Link to the Environment

CARBON DIOXIDE AND GLOBAL WARMING

Earth's climate is a product of interactions between sunlight, the atmosphere, and the oceans. The Sun provides us with energy in the form of solar radiation. Some of this radiation is reflected back into space. The rest is absorbed by the clouds, atmospheric gases including carbon dioxide, and Earth's surface. For millions of years, concentrations of carbon dioxide have fluctuated. However, in the past 100 years, the amount of carbon dioxide (CO_2) gas in our atmosphere has increased significantly. From the years 1000 to 1800, the atmospheric carbon dioxide averaged 280 ppm. But since the beginning of the Industrial Revolution in 1800, the level of atmospheric carbon dioxide has risen from about 280 ppm to about 390 ppm, a 40% increase.

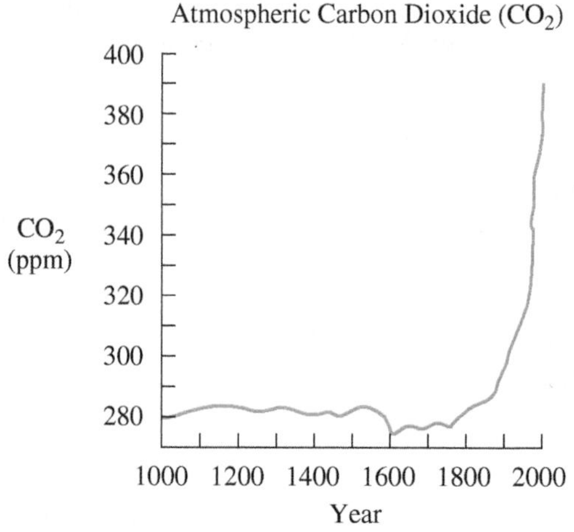

As the atmospheric CO_2 level increases, more solar radiation is trapped by atmospheric gases, which raises the temperature at Earth's surface. Some scientists have estimated that if the carbon dioxide level doubles from its level before the Industrial Revolution, the average global temperature could increase by 2.0 °C to 4.4 °C. Although this seems to be a small temperature change, it could have dramatic impact worldwide. Even now, glaciers and snow cover in much of the world have diminished. Ice sheets in Antarctica and Greenland are melting rapidly and breaking apart. Although no one knows for sure how rapidly the ice in the polar regions is melting, this accelerating change will contribute to a rise in sea level. In the twentieth century, the sea level rose 15 to 23 cm, and some scientists predict the sea level will rise 1 m in this century. Such an increase will have a major impact on coastal areas.

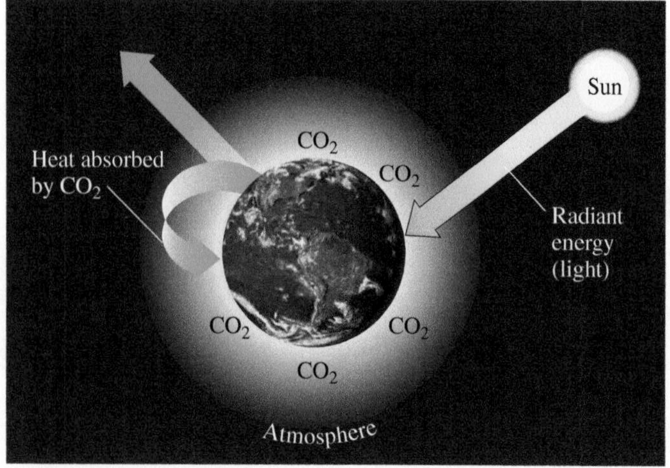

NASA

Heat from the Sun is trapped by the CO_2 layer in the atmosphere.

Until recently, the carbon dioxide level was maintained as algae in the oceans and trees in the forests utilized the carbon dioxide. However, the ability of these and other forms of plant life to absorb carbon dioxide is not keeping up with the increase in carbon dioxide levels. Most scientists agree that the primary source of the increase of carbon dioxide is the burning of fossil fuels such as gasoline, coal, and natural gas. The cutting and burning of trees in the rain forests (deforestation) also reduces the amount of carbon dioxide removed from the atmosphere.

Worldwide efforts are being made to reduce the carbon dioxide produced by burning fossil fuels that heat our homes, run our cars, and provide energy for industries. Scientists are exploring ways to provide alternative energy sources and to reduce the effects of deforestation. Meanwhile, we can reduce energy use in our homes by using appliances that are more energy efficient, such as replacing incandescent light bulbs with fluorescent lights. Such an effort worldwide will reduce the possible impact of global warming, and at the same time, save our fuel resources.

QUESTIONS AND PROBLEMS

2 Temperature

LEARNING GOAL: Given a temperature, calculate a corresponding value on another temperature scale.

7 Your friend who is visiting from Canada just took her temperature. When it reads 99.8, she becomes concerned that she is quite ill. How would you explain this temperature to your friend?

8 You have a friend who is using a recipe for flan from a Mexican cookbook. You notice that he set your oven temperature at 175 °F. What would you advise him to do?

9 Solve the following temperature conversions:
a. 37.0 °C = _____°F **b.** 65.3 °F = _____°C
c. −27 °C = _____K **d.** 224 K = _____°C
e. 114 °F = _____ °C

10 Solve the following temperature conversions:
a. 25 °C = _____°F **b.** 155 °C = _____°F
c. −25 °F = _____°C **d.** 62 °C = _____ K
e. 545 K = _____ °C

11 **a.** A patient with hyperthermia has a temperature of 106 °F. What does this read on a Celsius thermometer?
b. Because high fevers can cause convulsions in children, a doctor wants to be called if a child's temperature goes over 40.0 °C. Should the doctor be called if a child has a temperature of 103 °F?

12 **a.** Hot compresses are prepared with water heated to 145 °F. What is the temperature of the hot water in degrees Celsius?
b. During extreme hypothermia, a boy's temperature dropped to 20.6 °C. What was his temperature on the Fahrenheit scale?

3 Classification of Matter

LEARNING GOAL

Classify examples of matter as pure substances or mixtures.

Matter is anything that has mass and occupies space. Matter makes up all the things we use, such as water, wood, plates, plastic bags, clothes, and shoes. The different types of matter are classified by their composition.

TUTORIAL
Classification of Matter

Pure Substances

There are two kinds of pure substances: elements and compounds. A **pure substance** is matter that has a fixed or constant composition. An **element**, the simplest type of a pure substance, is composed of only one kind of material such as silver, iron, or aluminum. Every element is composed of *atoms*, which are extremely tiny particles that make up each type of matter. Silver is composed of silver atoms, iron of iron atoms, and aluminum of aluminum atoms. A full list of the elements is found on the inside front cover of this text.

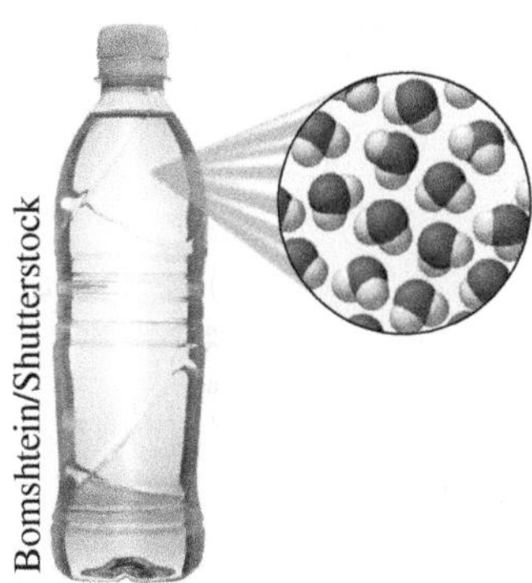

Bomshtein/Shutterstock

A molecule of water consists of two atoms of hydrogen (white) for one atom of oxygen (red) and has a formula of H_2O.

anthonysp/iStockphoto

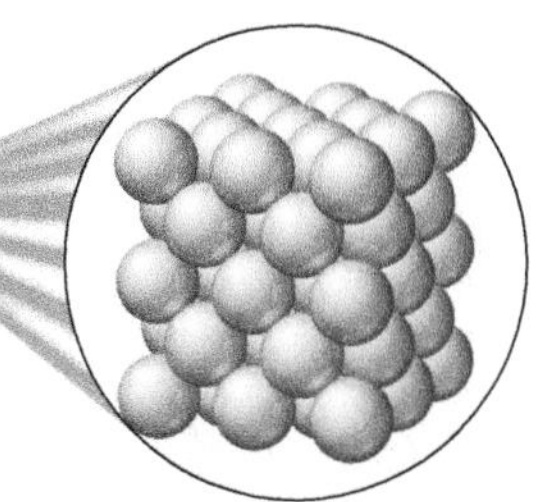

An aluminum can consists of many atoms of aluminum.

A **compound** is also a pure substance, but it consists of two or more elements chemically combined in the same proportion. In many compounds, the atoms of the elements are held together by attractions called *bonds*, which form small groups of atoms called molecules. For example, a molecule of the compound water, H_2O, has two hydrogen atoms for every one oxygen atom, and is represented by the formula H_2O. This means that water found anywhere always has the same composition of H_2O. Another compound that consists of a combination of hydrogen and oxygen is called hydrogen peroxide. However, it has two hydrogen atoms for every two oxygen atoms, and is represented by the formula H_2O_2. Thus, water (H_2O) and hydrogen peroxide (H_2O_2) are different compounds, which means they have different properties.

Pure substances that are compounds can be broken down by chemical processes into their elements. They cannot be broken down through physical methods such as boiling or sifting. For example, the compound in ordinary table salt, NaCl, is chemically broken down into the elements sodium and chlorine as seen in Figure 3. Elements cannot be broken down further.

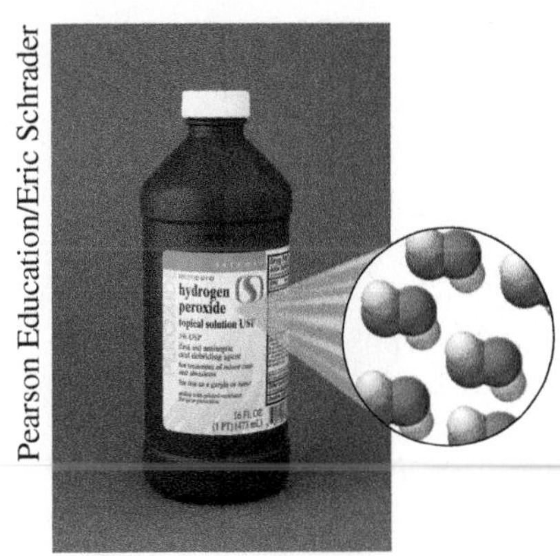

Pearson Education/Eric Schrader

A molecule of hydrogen peroxide consists of two atoms of hydrogen (white) for two atoms of oxygen (red) and has a formula of H_2O_2.

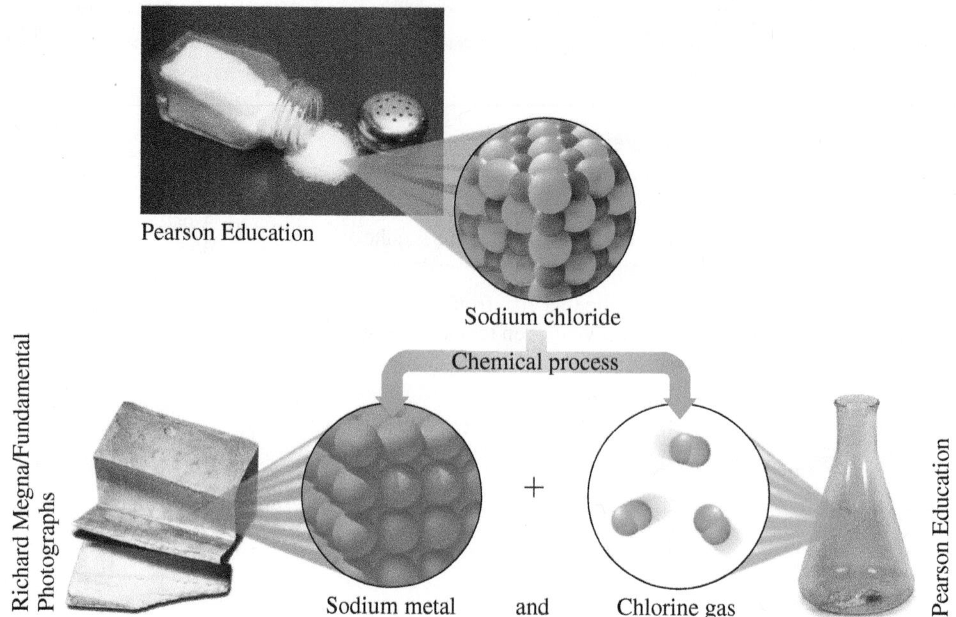

FIGURE 3 A chemical process called decomposition breaks down NaCl to produce the elements sodium and chlorine.

Q How do elements and compounds differ?

TUTORIAL
Classifying Matter

Mixtures

In a **mixture**, two or more substances are physically mixed, but not chemically combined. Much of the matter in our everyday lives consists of mixtures (see Figure 4). The air we breathe is a mixture of mostly oxygen and nitrogen gases. The steel in buildings and railroad tracks is a mixture of iron, nickel, carbon, and chromium. The brass in doorknobs and fixtures is a mixture of zinc and copper. There are different types of brass, which contain between 20% zinc to 50% zinc. Different types of brass have different properties, depending on the ratio of copper to zinc. Tea, coffee, and ocean water are mixtures, too. Unlike compounds, the composition of a mixture is not consistent, but can vary. For example, two sugar–water mixtures may look the same, but the one with the higher ratio of sugar to water would taste sweeter.

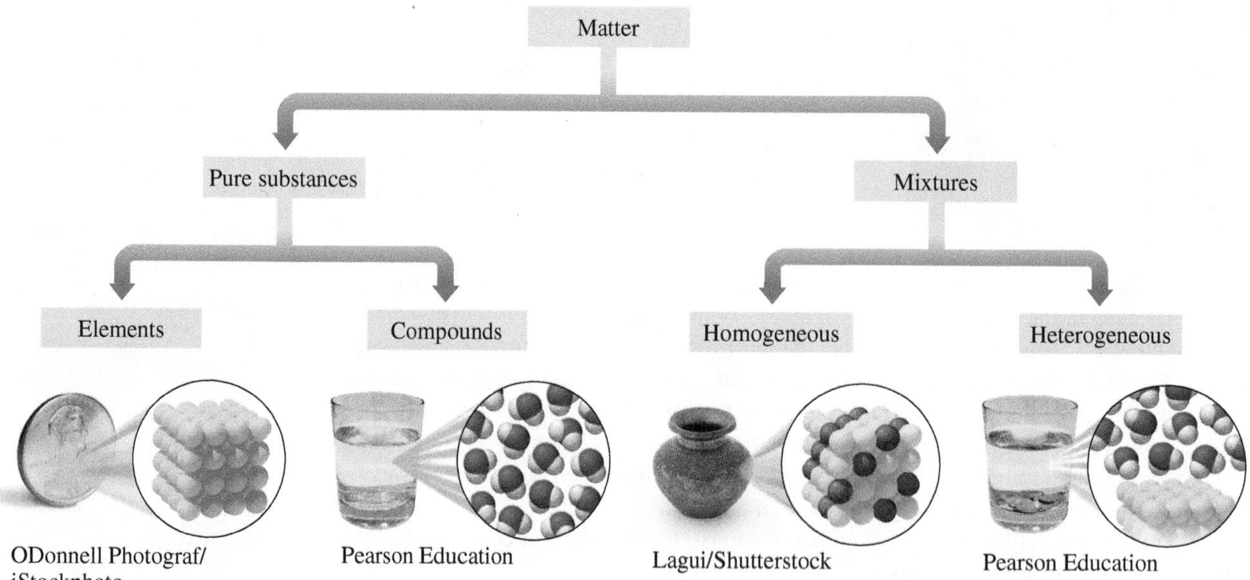

FIGURE 4 Matter is organized by its components: elements, compounds, and mixtures. **(a)** The element copper consists of copper atoms. **(b)** The compound water consists of H_2O molecules. **(c)** Brass is a homogeneous mixture of copper and zinc atoms. **(d)** Copper metal in water is a heterogeneous mixture of copper atoms and H_2O molecules.

Q Why are copper and water pure substances, but brass is a mixture?

Physical processes can be used to separate mixtures because there are no chemical interactions between the components. For example, different coins such as nickels, dimes, and quarters can be separated by size; iron particles mixed with sand can be picked up with a magnet; and water is separated from cooked spaghetti by using a strainer (see Figure 5).

Dorling Kindersley

Physical method of separation

Dorling Kindersley

FIGURE 5 A mixture of spaghetti and water is separated using a strainer, a physical method of separation.

Q Why can physical methods be used to separate mixtures but not compounds?

CONCEPT CHECK 2 **Pure Substances and Mixtures**

Classify each of the following as a pure substance or a mixture:

a. sugar in a sugar bowl
b. a collection of nickels and dimes
c. coffee with milk and sugar

ANSWER

a. Sugar is a compound, which is a pure substance.
b. The nickels and dimes are physically mixed, but not chemically combined, which makes the collection a mixture.
c. The coffee, milk, and sugar are physically mixed, but not chemically combined, which makes it a mixture.

Types of Mixtures

Mixtures are classified as homogeneous or heterogeneous. In a *homogeneous mixture*, also called a *solution*, the composition is uniform throughout the sample. Familiar examples of homogeneous mixtures are air, which contains oxygen and nitrogen gases; and salt water, a solution of salt and water.

In a *heterogeneous mixture*, the components do not have a uniform composition. For example, a mixture of oil and water is heterogeneous because the oil floats on the surface of the water. Other examples of heterogeneous mixtures include the raisins in a cookie and the pulp in orange juice.

In the chemistry laboratory, mixtures are separated by various methods. Solids are separated from liquids by *filtration*, which involves pouring a mixture through a filter paper set in a funnel. In *chromatography*, different components of a liquid mixture separate as they move at different rates up the surface of a piece of chromatography paper.

Richard Megna/ Fundamental Photographs

A mixture of a liquid and a solid is separated by filtration.

SAMPLE PROBLEM 5 **Classifying Mixtures**

Classify each of the following as a pure substance (element or compound) or as a mixture (homogeneous or heterogeneous):

a. copper wire
b. a chocolate chip cookie
c. Nitrox, a breathing mixture of oxygen and nitrogen for scuba

SOLUTION

a. Copper is an element, which is a pure substance.
b. A chocolate chip cookie does not have a uniform composition, which makes it a heterogeneous mixture.
c. The gases oxygen and nitrogen have a uniform composition in Nitrox, which makes it a homogeneous mixture.

STUDY CHECK 5

A salad dressing is prepared with oil, vinegar, and chunks of blue cheese. Is this a homogeneous or heterogeneous mixture?

Pearson Education

Oil and water form a heterogeneous mixture.

Pearson Education/ Eric Schrader

Different substances are separated as they travel at different rates up the surface of chromatography paper.

Chemistry Link to Health

BREATHING MIXTURES FOR SCUBA

The air we breathe is composed mostly of the gases oxygen (21%) and nitrogen (79%). The homogeneous breathing mixtures used by scuba divers differ from the air we breathe, depending on the depth of the dive. For example, a breathing mixture known as Nitrox contains more oxygen gas (up to 32%) and less nitrogen gas (68%) than air. A breathing mixture with less nitrogen gas decreases the risk of *nitrogen narcosis*, which causes mental confusion and is associated with breathing regular air while diving. With deep dives, there is more chance of nitrogen narcosis. Another breathing mixture, Heliox, contains oxygen and helium, which is typically used for diving to more than 200 feet. By replacing nitrogen with helium, nitrogen narcosis does not occur. However, at dive depths over 300 ft, helium is associated with severe shaking and body temperature drop.

A breathing mixture used for dives over 400 ft is Trimix, which contains oxygen, helium, and some nitrogen. The addition of nitrogen lessens the problem of shaking that comes with breathing high levels of helium. Both Heliox and Trimix are used by only professional, military, or other highly trained divers.

Nicolas DUPONT/Fotolia

A Nitrox mixture is used to fill scuba tanks.

QUESTIONS AND PROBLEMS

3 Classification of Matter

LEARNING GOAL: *Classify examples of matter as pure substances or mixtures.*

13 Classify each of the following as an element, compound, or mixture:
- **a.** baking soda ($NaHCO_3$)
- **b.** a blueberry muffin
- **c.** ice (H_2O)
- **d.** zinc (Zn)
- **e.** Trimix (oxygen, nitrogen, and helium) in a scuba tank

14 Classify each of the following as an element, compound, or mixture:
- **a.** a soft drink
- **b.** propane (C_3H_8)
- **c.** a cheese sandwich
- **d.** an iron (Fe) nail
- **e.** salt substitute (KCl)

15 Classify each of the following mixtures as homogeneous or heterogeneous:
- **a.** vegetable soup
- **b.** seawater
- **c.** tea
- **d.** tea with ice and lemon slices
- **e.** fruit salad

16 Classify each of the following mixtures as homogeneous or heterogeneous:
- **a.** nonfat milk
- **b.** chocolate-chip ice cream
- **c.** gasoline
- **d.** peanut butter sandwich
- **e.** cranberry juice

LEARNING GOAL

Identify the states and the physical and chemical properties of matter.

TUTORIAL
Properties and Changes of Matter

4 States and Properties of Matter

On Earth, matter exists in one of three physical states called the *states of matter*: solids, liquids, and gases. A **solid**, such as a pebble or a baseball, has a definite shape and volume. You can probably recognize several solids within your reach right now such as books, pencils, or a computer mouse. In a solid, strong attractive forces hold the particles, such as atoms or molecules, close together. The particles in a solid are arranged in such a rigid pattern, their only movement is to vibrate slowly in their fixed positions. For many solids, their rigid structures produce crystals.

A **liquid** has a definite volume, but not a definite shape. In a liquid, the particles move slowly in random directions but are sufficiently attracted to each other to maintain a definite volume, although not a rigid structure. Thus, when oil, water, or vinegar is poured from one container to another, the liquid maintains its own volume but takes the shape of the new container.

A **gas** does not have a definite shape or volume. In a gas, the particles are far apart, have little attraction to each other, and move at extremely high speeds, taking the shape and volume of their container. The helium gas in a balloon fills the entire volume of the balloon. Table 3 compares the three states of matter.

Siede Preis/Photodisc/Getty Images

Amethyst, a solid, is a purple form of quartz (SiO_2).

Raphel Auvray/SuperStock

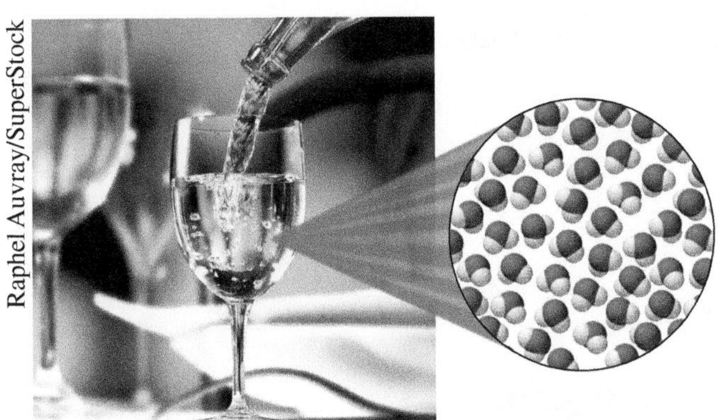

Water as a liquid takes the shape of its container.

Lisay/iStockphoto

A gas takes the shape and volume of its container.

TABLE 3 A Comparison of Solids, Liquids, and Gases

Characteristic	Solid	Liquid	Gas
Shape	Has a definite shape	Takes the shape of the container	Takes the shape of the container
Volume	Has a definite volume	Has a definite volume	Fills the volume of the container
Arrangement of Particles	Fixed, very close	Random, close	Random, far apart
Interaction Between Particles	Very strong	Strong	Essentially none
Movement of Particles	Very slow	Moderate	Very fast
Examples	Ice, salt, iron	Water, oil, vinegar	Water vapor, helium, air

CONCEPT CHECK 3 **States of Matter**

Identify the state(s) of matter described by the substance in each of the following:

a. no change in volume when placed in a different container
b. has an especially low density
c. shape depends on the container
d. has a definite shape and volume

ANSWER

a. Both a solid and a liquid have their own volume that does not depend on the volume of their container.
b. In a gas, the particles are far apart, which gives a small mass per volume, or a low density.
c. Both a liquid and a gas take the shape of their containers.
d. A solid has a rigid arrangement of particles that gives it a definite shape and volume.

Elena Elisseeva/Shutterstock

Copper, used in cookware, is a good conductor of heat.

TABLE 4 Some Physical Properties of Copper

Characteristic	Physical Property
Color	Orange-red
Odor	Odorless
Melting point	1083 °C
Boiling point	2567 °C
State at 25 °C	Solid
Luster	Shiny
Conduction of electricity	Excellent
Conduction of heat	Excellent

Physical Properties and Physical Changes

One way to describe matter is to observe its physical properties. If you were asked to describe yourself, you might list your characteristics such as the color of your eyes and skin, or the length, color, and texture of your hair.

Physical properties are those characteristics that can be observed or measured without affecting the identity of a substance. Typical physical properties include the shape, state, color, melting point, and boiling point of a substance. For example, you might observe that a penny has the physical properties of a round shape, an orange-red color, a solid state, and a shiny luster. Table 4 gives examples of physical properties of copper found in pennies, electrical wiring, and copper pans.

Water is a substance that is commonly found in all three states: solid, liquid, and gas. When matter undergoes a **physical change**, its state or its appearance changes, but its composition remains the same. The solid form of water—snow or ice—has a different appearance than its liquid or gaseous form, but all three states are water (see Figure 6).

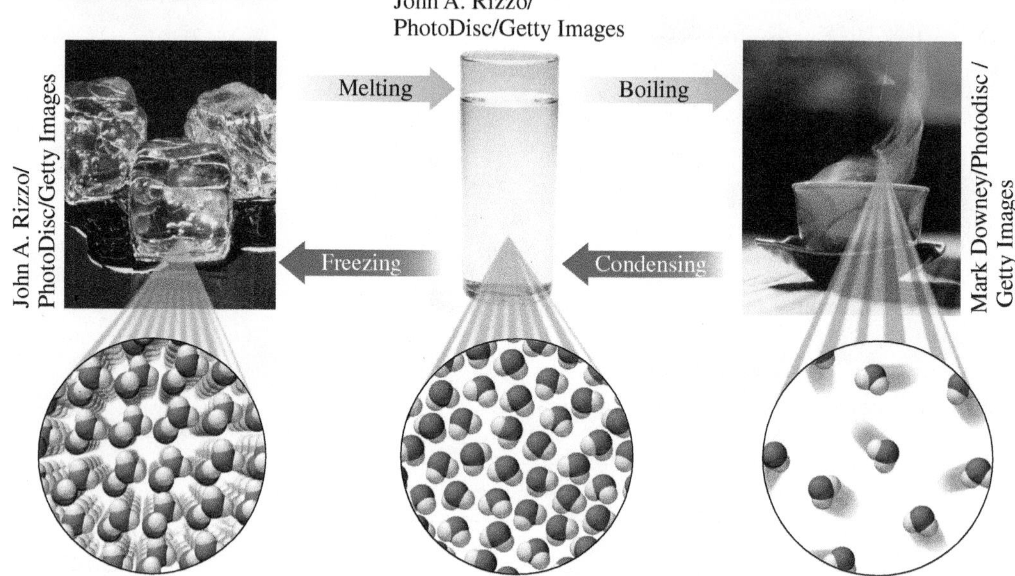

FIGURE 6 Water changes state from a solid to a liquid and from a liquid to a gas as heat is added.
Q Is heat added or released when liquid water freezes?

Melting and Freezing

Matter undergoes a **change of state** when it is converted from one state to another state (see Figure 6). As heat is added to a solid, the particles in the rigid structure move faster. At a temperature called the **melting point (mp)**, the solid is converted to a liquid. During **melting**, energy is absorbed to overcome the attractive forces that hold the particles together in the solid; the rigid solid structure changes to a random association of particles in the liquid. During a change of state, the temperature of a substance remains constant.

If the temperature of a liquid is lowered, the reverse process takes place. Heat is removed from the liquid, which causes its particles to move slower. Eventually, the attractive forces are sufficient to form a solid. The substance is in the process of **freezing**, changing from a liquid to a solid. The temperature at which a liquid changes to a solid is its **freezing point (fp)**, which is the same temperature as the melting point.

Every substance has its own freezing (melting) point: Solid water (ice) melts at 0 °C when heat is added, and freezes at 0 °C when heat is removed. Gold melts at 1064 °C and freezes at 1064 °C. Nitrogen melts at −210 °C and freezes at −210 °C.

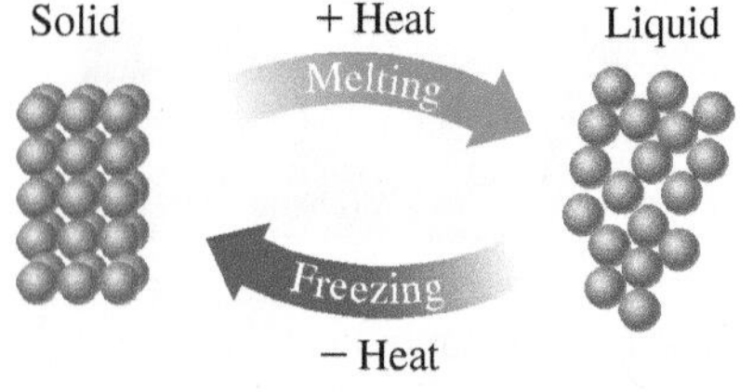

Melting and freezing are reversible processes.

Evaporation, Boiling, and Condensation

Water in a mud puddle disappears, unwrapped food dries out, and clothes hung on a clothesline dry. **Evaporation** occurs when water molecules at the surface acquire sufficient kinetic energy to escape from the liquid and form a gas. As the warmer water molecules leave the liquid, heat is removed, which cools the remaining liquid water. At higher temperatures, more water molecules evaporate. At the **boiling point (bp)**, all the molecules within a liquid gain enough energy to overcome the attractive forces between them and become a gas. We can observe the **boiling** of a liquid such as water as gas bubbles form throughout the liquid, rise to the surface, and escape.

When heat is removed from a gas, a reverse process takes place. In **condensation**, water vapor is converted back to liquid as the water molecules lose energy and slow down. Condensation occurs at the same temperature as boiling but differs because heat is removed. You may have noticed that condensation occurs when you take a hot shower and the water vapor forms droplets on your mirror.

Liquid + Heat Gas
Vaporization
Condensation
− Heat

Vaporization and condensation are reversible processes.

Temperature Curves

A *heating curve* can be drawn to illustrate the changes of temperature and changes of state as heat is added to a substance. A diagonal line indicates a warming of a solid as heat is added. When the temperature of the solid reaches the melting point, it begins to change to liquid. This melting process, which occurs at constant temperature, is drawn as a horizontal line.

As heat is added to the liquid, its temperature begins to rise, which is shown as a diagonal line. At the boiling point, the liquid obtains enough energy to change to a gas, which is drawn as a horizontal line. At the boiling point, the temperature is constant. Once all the liquid becomes a gas, another diagonal line shows the temperature increase as heat is added to the gas.

In a *cooling curve*, the temperature of a substance decreases as heat is removed. If we begin with a gas sample of water vapor (steam) at 140 °C, a diagonal line shows the decrease in temperature to the boiling (condensation) point. Then a change from gas to liquid takes place, which is shown as a horizontal line. The temperature at condensation remains constant until all of the water vapor has changed into liquid water. Another diagonal line then shows the decrease in temperature as liquid water cools until it reaches the freezing point. At the freezing point of water (0 °C), a horizontal line indicates that water is freezing. Once all of the water is frozen, a diagonal line is drawn below the freezing point as more heat is removed from the solid water (ice).

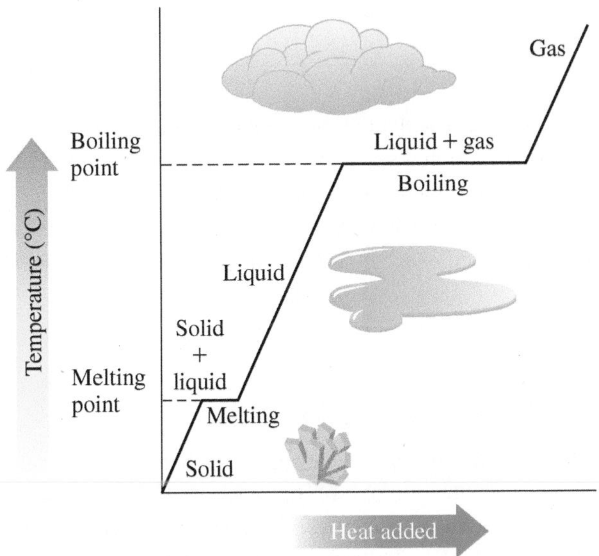

A heating curve illustrates the change in temperature and changes in state as heat is added.

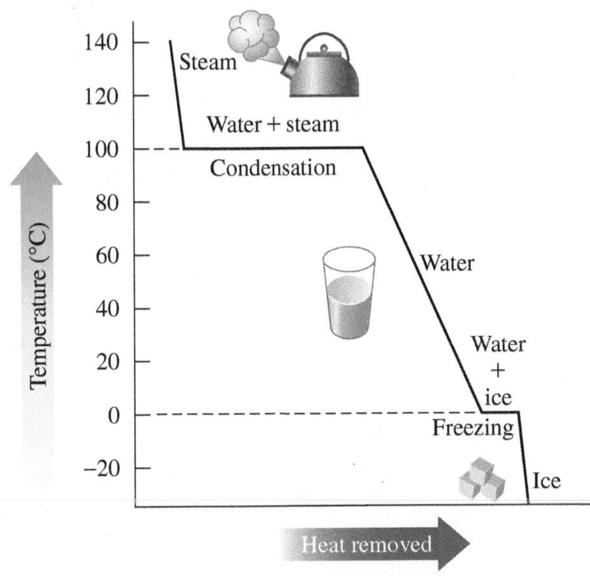

A cooling curve for water illustrates the change in temperature and changes in state as heat is removed.

Sublimation and Deposition

In a process called **sublimation**, the particles on the surface of a solid change directly to a gas with no temperature change and without going through the liquid state. In the reverse process called **deposition**, gas particles change directly to a solid.

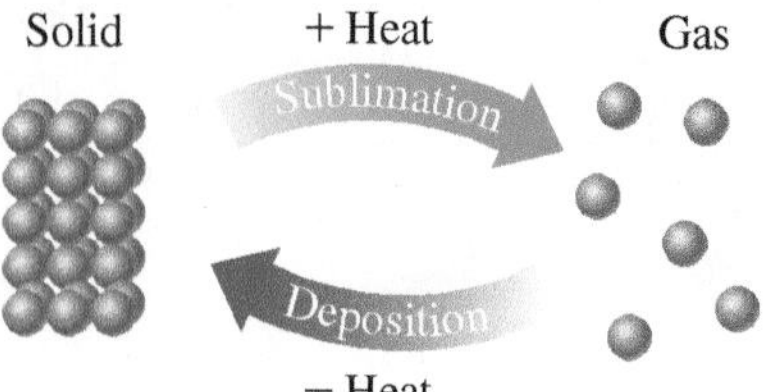

Sublimation and deposition are reversible processes.

Dry ice sublimes at −78 °C.

Water vapor will change to a solid on contact with a cold surface, such as these frozen peas.

Pearson Education

Freeze-dried foods have a long shelf life because they contain no water.

For example, dry ice, which is solid carbon dioxide (CO_2), undergoes sublimation at −78 °C. It is called "dry" because it does not form a liquid as it warms. In extremely cold areas, snow does not melt, but sublimes directly to water vapor. In a frost-free refrigerator, the water in the ice on the walls of the freezer and in frozen foods sublimes when warm air is circulated through the compartment during the defrost cycle. When frozen foods are left in the freezer for a long time, so much water sublimes that foods, especially meat, become dry and shrunken, a condition called *freezer burn*. Deposition occurs in a freezer when water vapor forms ice crystals on the surface of freezer bags and frozen food.

Freeze-dried foods prepared by sublimation are convenient for long-term storage and for camping and hiking. A food that has been frozen is placed in a vacuum chamber where it dries as the ice sublimes. The dried food retains all of its nutritional value and needs only water to be edible. A food that is freeze-dried does not need refrigeration because bacteria cannot grow without moisture.

The physical appearance of a substance can change in other ways, too. Suppose that you dissolve some salt in water. The appearance of the salt changes, but you could re-form the salt crystals by heating the mixture and evaporating the water. Thus, in a physical change, there are no new substances produced. Table 5 gives more examples of physical changes.

Salt crystals form as water evaporates from seawater.

TABLE 5 Examples of Some Physical Changes

Type of Physical Change	Example
Change of State	Boiling water
	Freezing of liquid water to solid water (ice)
Change of Appearance	Dissolving sugar in water
Change of Shape	Hammering a gold ingot into shiny gold leaf
	Drawing copper into thin copper wire
Change of Size	Cutting paper into tiny pieces for confetti
	Grinding pepper into smaller particles

Westend61 GmbH/Alamy

In a physical change, a gold ingot is hammered to form gold leaf.

Chemical Properties and Chemical Changes

Chemical properties are those that describe the ability of a substance to change into a new substance. When a **chemical change** takes place, the original substance is converted into a new substance, which has different physical and chemical properties. For example, the rusting or corrosion of a metal such as iron is a chemical property. In the rain, an iron (Fe) nail reacts with oxygen (O_2) to form rust (Fe_2O_3). A chemical change has taken place: Rust is a new substance with new physical and chemical properties. Table 6 gives examples of chemical changes.

TABLE 6 Examples of Some Chemical Changes

Type of Chemical Change	Changes in Properties
Tarnishing of Silver	Shiny, silver metal reacts in air to give a black, grainy coating.
Burning Wood	A piece of pine burns with a bright flame, producing heat, ashes, carbon dioxide, and water vapor.
Caramelizing Sugar	At high temperatures, white, granular sugar changes to a smooth, caramel-colored substance.
Formation of Rust	Iron, which is gray and shiny, combines with oxygen to form orange-red rust.

Pearson Education

In a chemical change, the iron on the surface of nails reacts with oxygen to form rust.

Table 7 summarizes physical and chemical properties, and physical and chemical changes.

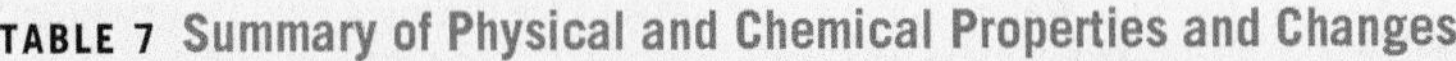

TABLE 7 Summary of Physical and Chemical Properties and Changes

	Physical	Chemical
Property	A characteristic of a substance such as color, shape, odor, luster, size, melting point, and density.	A characteristic that indicates the ability of a substance to form another substance: Paper can burn, iron can rust, and silver can tarnish.
Change	A change in a physical property that retains the identity of the substance: A change of state, a change in size, or a change in shape and appearance.	A change in which the original substance is converted to one or more new substances: Paper burns, iron rusts, and silver tarnishes.

Rafa Irusta/Shutterstock

Flan has a topping of caramelized sugar.

CONCEPT CHECK 4 Physical and Chemical Properties

Classify each of the following as a physical or chemical property:

a. Gasoline is a liquid at room temperature.
b. Gasoline burns in air.
c. Gasoline has a pungent odor.

ANSWER

a. A liquid is a state of matter, which makes it a physical property.
b. When gasoline burns, it changes to different substances with new properties, which is a chemical property.
c. The odor of gasoline is a physical property.

SAMPLE PROBLEM 6 Physical and Chemical Changes

Classify each of the following as a physical or chemical change:

a. An ice cube melts to form liquid water.
b. An enzyme breaks down the lactose in milk.
c. Peppercorns are ground into flakes.

SOLUTION

a. A physical change occurs when the ice cube changes state from solid to liquid.
b. A chemical change occurs when an enzyme breaks down lactose into simpler substances.
c. A physical change occurs when the size of an object changes.

STUDY CHECK 6

Which of the following are chemical changes?

a. Gas bubbles form when baking powder is mixed with vinegar.
b. A log is chopped for firewood.
c. A log is burned in a fireplace.

QUESTIONS AND PROBLEMS

4 States and Properties of Matter

LEARNING GOAL: *Identify the states and the physical and chemical properties of matter.*

17 Indicate whether each of the following describes a gas, a liquid, or a solid:
- **a.** This substance has no definite volume or shape.
- **b.** The particles in a substance do not interact with each other.
- **c.** The particles in a substance are held in a rigid structure.

18 Indicate whether each of the following describes a gas, a liquid, or a solid:
- **a.** The substance has a definite volume but takes the shape of the container.
- **b.** The particles in this substance are very far apart.
- **c.** This substance occupies the entire volume of the container.

19 Describe each of the following as a physical or chemical property:
- **a.** Chromium is a steel-gray solid.
- **b.** Hydrogen reacts readily with oxygen.
- **c.** Nitrogen freezes at −210 °C.
- **d.** Milk will sour when left in a warm room.

20 Describe each of the following as a physical or chemical property:
- **a.** Neon is a colorless gas at room temperature.
- **b.** Apple slices turn brown when exposed to air.
- **c.** Phosphorus will ignite when exposed to air.
- **d.** At room temperature, mercury is a liquid.

21 What type of change, physical or chemical, takes place in each of the following?
- **a.** Water vapor condenses to form rain.
- **b.** Cesium metal reacts explosively with water.
- **c.** Gold melts at 1064 °C.
- **d.** A puzzle is cut into 1000 pieces.
- **e.** Cheese is grated on top of pasta.

22 What type of change, physical or chemical, takes place in each of the following?
- **a.** Gold is hammered into thin sheets.
- **b.** A silver pin tarnishes in the air.
- **c.** A tree is cut into boards at a sawmill.
- **d.** Food is digested.
- **e.** A chocolate bar melts.

23 Describe each property of the element fluorine as physical or chemical.
- **a.** is highly reactive
- **b.** is a gas at room temperature
- **c.** has a pale, yellow color
- **d.** will explode in the presence of hydrogen
- **e.** has a melting point of −220 °C

24 Describe each property of the element zirconium as physical or chemical.
- **a.** melts at 1852 °C
- **b.** is resistant to corrosion
- **c.** has a grayish-white color
- **d.** ignites spontaneously in air when finely divided
- **e.** is a shiny metal

25 Identify each of the following changes of state as melting, freezing, sublimation, or deposition:
- **a.** The solid structure of a substance breaks down as liquid forms.
- **b.** Coffee is freeze-dried.
- **c.** Water on the street turns to ice during a cold wintry night.
- **d.** Ice crystals form on a package of frozen corn.

26 Identify each of the following changes of state as melting, freezing, sublimation, or deposition:
- **a.** Dry ice in an ice-cream cart disappears.
- **b.** Snow on the ground turns to liquid water.
- **c.** Heat is removed from 125 g of liquid water at 0 °C.
- **d.** Frost forms on a cold morning.

27 Identify each of the following changes of state as evaporation, boiling, or condensation:
- **a.** The water vapor in the clouds changes to rain.
- **b.** Wet clothes dry on a clothesline.
- **c.** Lava flows into the ocean and steam forms.
- **d.** After a hot shower, your bathroom mirror is covered with water.

28 Identify each of the following changes of state as evaporation, boiling, or condensation:
- **a.** At 100 °C, the water in a pan changes to steam.
- **b.** On a cool morning, the windows in your car fog up.
- **c.** A shallow pond dries up in the summer.
- **d.** A teakettle whistles when the water is ready for tea.

29 Draw a heating curve for a sample of ice that is heated from −20 °C to 140 °C. Indicate the segment of the graph that corresponds to each of the following:
a. solid **b.** melting **c.** liquid
d. boiling **e.** gas

30 Draw a cooling curve for a sample of steam that cools from 110 °C to −10 °C. Indicate the segment of the graph that corresponds to each of the following:
a. solid **b.** freezing **c.** liquid
d. condensing **e.** gas

LEARNING GOAL

Use specific heat to calculate the quantity of heat lost or gained during a temperature change.

TUTORIAL
Specific Heat Calculations

5 Specific Heat

Every substance can absorb or lose heat. When you bake a potato, you place it in a hot oven. If you are cooking pasta, you add the pasta to boiling water. You already know that adding heat to water increases its temperature until it boils. Every substance has its own characteristic ability to absorb heat. Certain substances absorb more heat than others to reach a certain temperature.

The energy requirements for different substances are described in terms of a physical property called *specific heat.* The **specific heat (*SH*)** for a substance is defined as the number of joules (or calories) needed to change the temperature of exactly 1 g of a substance by exactly 1 °C. To calculate the specific heat of a substance, we measure the heat in joules (or calories), the mass in grams, and the ΔT, which is the change in temperature, in degrees Celsius. The symbol delta in ΔT means "change in."

$$\text{Specific heat } (SH) = \frac{\text{heat}}{\text{mass} \times \Delta T} = \frac{\text{J (or cal)}}{1\text{ g} \times 1\text{ °C}}$$

Now we can write the specific heat for water using our definition in Section 1 for the joule and calorie, which is 1.00 cal = 4.184 J.

$$\text{Specific heat } (SH) \text{ of } H_2O(l) = \frac{4.184\text{ J}}{\text{g °C}} = \frac{1.00\text{ cal}}{\text{g °C}}$$

If we look at Table 8, we see that 1 g of water requires 4.184 J (or 1.00 cal) to increase its temperature by 1 °C. Water has a large specific heat that is about five times the specific heat of aluminum. Aluminum has a specific heat that is about twice that of copper. Therefore, the absorption of 4.184 J (or 1.00 cal) by 1 g of water will raise its temperature by 1 °C. However, adding the same amount of heat (4.184 J or 1.00 cal) will also raise the temperature of 1 g of aluminum by about 5 °C and 1 g of copper by about 10 °C. The low specific heats of aluminum and copper mean they transfer heat efficiently, which makes them useful in cookware.

The high specific heat of water has a major impact on the temperatures in a coastal city compared to an inland city. A large mass of water near a coastal city can absorb or release five times the energy absorbed or released by the same mass of rock near an inland city. This means that in the summer, a body of water absorbs large quantities of heat, which cools a coastal city, and then in the winter that same body of water releases large quantities of heat, which provides warmer temperatures. A similar effect happens with our bodies, which contain 70% by mass water. Water in the body absorbs or releases large quantities of heat in order to maintain an almost constant body temperature.

TABLE 8 Specific Heats of Some Substances

Substance	(J/g °C)	(cal/g °C)
Elements		
Aluminum, $Al(s)$	0.897	0.214
Copper, $Cu(s)$	0.385	0.0920
Gold, $Au(s)$	0.129	0.0308
Iron, $Fe(s)$	0.452	0.108
Silver, $Ag(s)$	0.235	0.0562
Titanium, $Ti(s)$	0.523	0.125
Compounds		
Ammonia, $NH_3(g)$	2.04	0.488
Ethanol, $C_2H_5OH(l)$	2.46	0.588
Sodium chloride, $NaCl(s)$	0.864	0.207
Water, $H_2O(l)$	4.184	1.00

CONCEPT CHECK 5 Comparing Specific Heats

Water has a specific heat that is about six times larger than that of sandstone. How would the temperature change during the day and night if you live in a house next to a large lake compared to a house built in the desert on sandstone?

ANSWER

In the day, the water in the lake will absorb six times the quantity of energy that sandstone will, which will keep the temperature in a house on a large lake more comfortable and cooler than a house in the desert. In the night, the water in the lake will release energy that warms the surrounding air so that the temperature will not drop as much as in the desert.

SAMPLE PROBLEM 7 Calculating Specific Heat

What is the specific heat, in cal/g °C, of lead if 13.6 cal will raise the temperature of 35.6 g of lead by 12.5 °C?

SOLUTION

Step 1 State the given and needed quantities.

Analyze the Problem

Given	Need
13.6 cal absorbed	specific heat of lead (cal/g °C)
35.6 g of lead	
ΔT = 12.5 °C	

Guide to Calculating Specific Heat

1 State the given and needed quantities.

2 Write the relationship for specific heat.

3 Set up the problem to calculate the specific heat.

Step 2 **Write the relationship for specific heat.** In the relationship for specific heat (*SH*), the quantity of heat is divided by the mass and by the temperature change (ΔT).

$$\text{Specific heat } (SH) = \frac{\text{heat}}{\text{mass } \Delta T}$$

Step 3 **Set up the problem to calculate the specific heat.** Substitute the quantity of heat, in calories, the mass, in grams, and the temperature change (ΔT), in degrees Celsius, into the relationship for specific heat.

$$\text{Specific heat } (SH) = \frac{13.6 \text{ cal}}{35.6 \text{ g } 12.5 \text{ °C}} = 0.0306 \frac{\text{cal}}{\text{g °C}}$$

STUDY CHECK 7

What is the specific heat of sodium metal (J/g °C) if 123 J are needed to raise the temperature of 4.00 g of sodium by 25.0 °C?

TUTORIAL
Specific Heat Calculations

Calculations Using Specific Heat

When we know the specific heat relationship for a substance, we can rearrange it to obtain a useful expression called the *heat equation*.

$$\text{Specific heat } (SH) = \frac{\text{heat}}{\text{mass} \times \Delta T}$$

$$\text{Heat} = \text{mass} \times \Delta T \times \text{specific heat } (SH) \quad \text{Heat equation}$$

Using the heat equation, we can calculate the quantity of heat lost or gained by a substance by substituting in the known quantities for the mass, the change in temperature, and its specific heat.

$$\text{Heat} = \text{mass} \times \text{temperature change} \times \text{specific heat}$$

$$\text{Heat} = \text{mass} \times \Delta T \times SH$$

$$\text{cal} = \cancel{\text{g}} \times \cancel{\text{°C}} \times \frac{\text{cal}}{\cancel{\text{g}}\,\cancel{\text{°C}}}$$

$$\text{J} = \cancel{\text{g}} \times \cancel{\text{°C}} \times \frac{\text{J}}{\cancel{\text{g}}\,\cancel{\text{°C}}}$$

Guide to Calculations Using Specific Heat

1. State the given and needed quantities.
2. Calculate the temperature change (ΔT).
3. Write the heat equation.
4. Substitute in the given values and solve, making sure units cancel.

SAMPLE PROBLEM 8 **Calculating Heat with an Increase in Temperature**

How many joules are absorbed by 45.2 g of aluminum (Al) if its temperature rises from 12.5 °C to 76.8 °C (see Table 8)?

SOLUTION

Step 1 **State the given and needed quantities.**

Analyze the Problem

Given	Need
45.2 g of aluminum	joules absorbed by aluminum
SH for aluminum = 0.897 J/g °C	
$T_{initial}$ = 12.5 °C	
T_{final} = 76.8 °C	

Step 2 **Calculate the temperature change (ΔT).** The temperature change ΔT is the difference between the final and initial temperatures.

$$\Delta T = T_{final} - T_{initial} = 76.8\ °C - 12.5\ °C = 64.3\ °C$$

Step 3 **Write the heat equation.**

$$\text{Heat} = \text{mass} \times \Delta T \times SH$$

Step 4 **Substitute in the given values and solve, making sure units cancel.**

$$\text{Heat} = 45.2\ \cancel{g} \times 64.3\ \cancel{°C} \times \frac{0.897\ J}{\cancel{g}\,\cancel{°C}} = 2610\ J\ (2.61 \times 10^3\ J)$$

STUDY CHECK 8

Some cooking pans have a layer of copper on the bottom. How many kilojoules are needed to raise the temperature of 125 g of copper from 22 °C to 325 °C (see Table 8)?

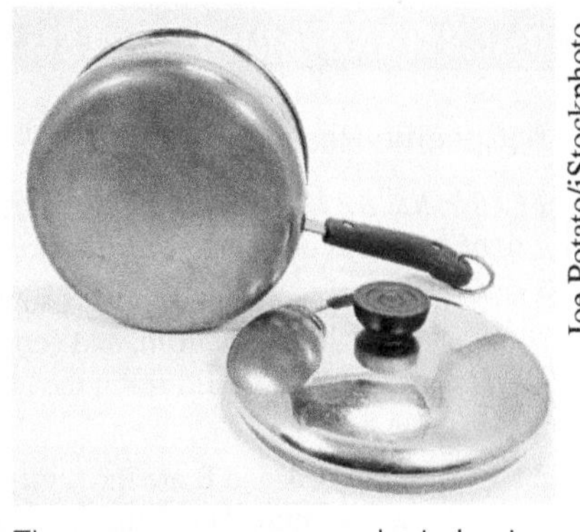

Joe Potato/iStockphoto

The copper on a pan conducts heat rapidly to the food in the pan.

Chemistry Link to Health

STEAM BURNS

Hot water at 100 °C will cause burns and damage to the skin. If 25 g of hot water at 100 °C falls on a person's skin, the temperature of the water will drop to body temperature, 37 °C. The heat released can cause severe burns. This amount of heat can be calculated from the temperature change, 100 °C − 37 °C = 63 °C.

$$25\ \cancel{g} \times 63\ \cancel{°C} \times \frac{4.184\ J}{\cancel{g}\,\cancel{°C}} = 6600\ J$$

However, getting steam on the skin is even more dangerous. The condensation of the same quantity of steam to liquid at 100 °C releases much more heat—almost ten times as much. This amount of heat can be calculated using the heat of vaporization, which is 2260 J/g for water.

$$25\ \cancel{g} \times \frac{2260\ J}{1\ \cancel{g}} = 57\ 000\ J$$

When we combine the quantity of heat released from the condensation and cooling of the water from 100 °C to 37 °C, we see that most of the heat is from the condensation of steam. This large amount of heat released on the skin is what causes damage from steam burns.

Condensation (100 ¡C)	= 57 000 J
Cooling (100 ¡C to 37 ¡C)	= 6 600 J
Heat released	= 64 000 J (rounded off)

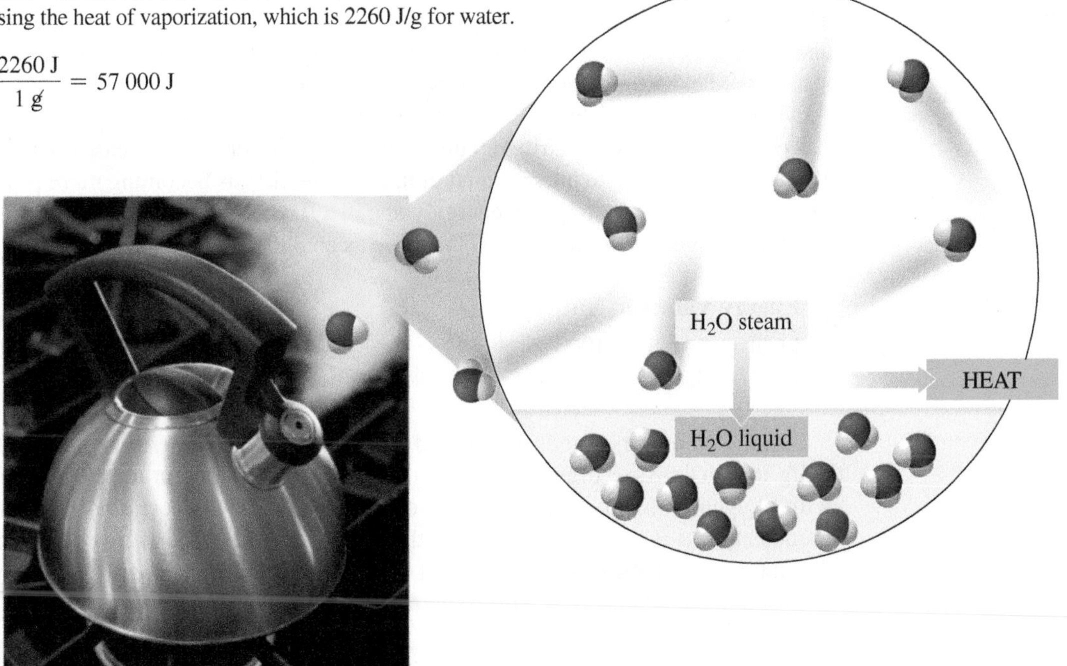

Comstock Complete

When steam condenses, a large quantity of heat is released.

QUESTIONS AND PROBLEMS

5 Specific Heat

LEARNING GOAL: *Use specific heat to calculate the quantity of heat lost or gained during a temperature change.*

31 If the same amount of heat is supplied to samples of 10.0 g each of aluminum, iron, and copper, all at 15 °C, which sample would reach the highest temperature (see Table 8)?

32 Substances A and B are the same mass and at the same initial temperature. When the same amount of heat is added to each, the final temperature of A is 55 °C higher than the temperature of B. What does this tell you about the specific heats of A and B?

33 Calculate the specific heat (J/g °C) for each of the following:
a. a 13.5-g sample of zinc heated from 24.2 °C to 83.6 °C that absorbs 312 J of heat
b. a 48.2-g sample of a metal that absorbs 345 J when its temperature increases from 35.0 °C to 57.9 °C

34 Calculate the specific heat (J/g °C) for each of the following:
a. an 18.5-g sample of tin that absorbs 183 J when its temperature increases from 35.0 °C to 78.6 °C
b. a 22.5-g sample of a metal that absorbs 645 J when its temperature increases from 36.2 °C to 92.0 °C

35 What is the amount of energy involved in each of the following?
a. calories to heat 25 g of water from 15 °C to 25 °C
b. joules to heat 15 g of water from 22 °C to 75 °C
c. kilocalories to heat 150 g of water in a kettle from 15 °C to 77 °C

36 What is the amount of energy involved in each of the following?
a. calories given off when 85 g of water cools from 45 °C to 25 °C
b. joules given off when 25 g of water cools from 86 °C to 61 °C
c. kilocalories absorbed when 5.0 kg of water warms from 22 °C to 28 °C

37 Calculate the energy, in joules and calories, for each of the following (see Table 8):
a. required to heat 25.0 g of water from 12.5 °C to 25.7 °C
b. required to heat 38.0 g of copper from 122 °C to 246 °C
c. lost when 15.0 g of ethanol cools from 60.5 °C to −42.0 °C
d. lost when 112 g of iron cools from 118 °C to 55 °C

38 Calculate the energy in joules and calories, for each of the following (see Table 8):
a. required to heat 5.25 g of water from 5.5 °C to 64.8 °C
b. lost when 75.0 g of water cools from 86.4 °C to 2.1 °C
c. required to heat 10.0 g of silver from 112 °C to 275 °C
d. lost when 18.0 g of gold cools from 224 °C to 118 °C

LEARNING GOAL

Use the energy values to calculate the kilojoules (kJ) or kilocalories (kcal) in a food.

TUTORIAL
Nutritional Energy

CASE STUDY
Calories from Hidden Sugar

6 Energy and Nutrition

The food we eat provides energy to do work in the body, which includes the growth and repair of cells. Carbohydrates are the primary fuel for the body, but if carbohydrate reserves are exhausted, fats and then proteins can be used for energy.

For many years in the field of nutrition, the energy from food was measured in Calories or kilocalories. The nutritional unit **Calorie, Cal** (with an uppercase C), is the same as 1000 cal, or 1 kcal. The international unit, kilojoule (kJ), is becoming more prevalent. For example, a baked potato has an energy value of 110 Calories, which is 110 kcal or 460 kJ. A typical diet of 2100 Cal (kcal) is the same as an 8800 kJ diet.

Energy Values in Nutrition

1 Cal = 1 kcal = 1000 cal
1 Cal = 4.184 kJ = 4184 J

In the laboratory, foods are burned in a calorimeter to determine their energy value (kJ/g or kcal/g) (see Figure 7). A sample of food is placed in a steel container filled with oxygen with a measured amount of water that fills the surrounding chamber. The food sample is ignited, releasing heat that increases the temperature of the water. From the mass of the food and water as well as the temperature increase, the energy value of the food is calculated. We will assume that the energy absorbed by the calorimeter is negligible.

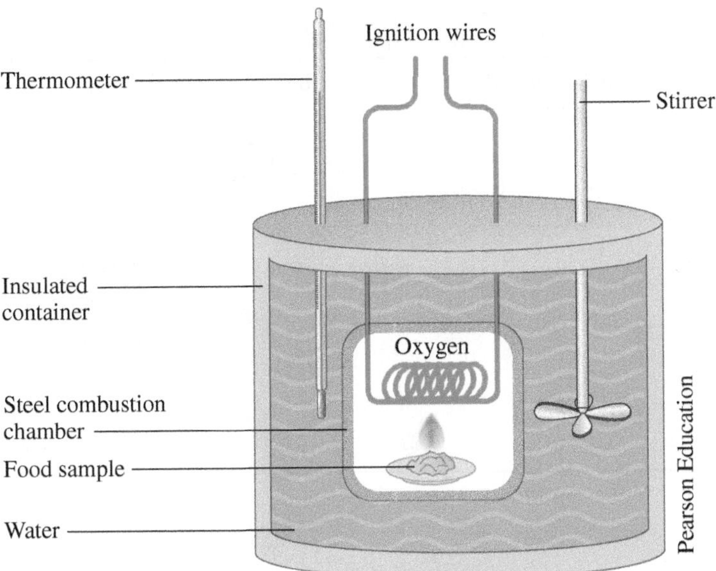

FIGURE 7 Heat released from burning a food sample in a calorimeter is used to determine the energy value of the food.

Q What happens to the temperature of water in a calorimeter during the combustion of a food sample?

CONCEPT CHECK 6 **Energy Values of Food**

When 55 g of pasta is burned in a calorimeter, 220 Cal of heat is released. What is the energy value of pasta in kcal/g?

ANSWER

Using the equality of 1 Cal = 1 kcal, we can calculate the energy value of the pasta.

$$\frac{220\ \cancel{\text{Cal}}}{55\ \text{g}} \times \frac{1\ \text{kcal}}{1\ \cancel{\text{Cal}}} = 4.0\ \text{kcal/g}$$

Energy Values for Foods

The **energy (caloric) values** of food are the kilojoules or kilocalories obtained from burning 1 g of a carbohydrate, fat, or protein (see Table 9).

Using the energy values in Table 9, we can calculate the total energy of a food if the mass of each food type is known.

$$\text{kilojoules} = \cancel{g} \times \frac{\text{kJ}}{\cancel{g}} \qquad \text{kilocalories} = \cancel{g} \times \frac{\text{kcal}}{\cancel{g}}$$

On packaged food, the energy content is listed in the Nutrition Facts label on the package, usually in terms of the number of Calories for one serving. The general composition and caloric content of some foods are given in Table 10.

TABLE 9 Typical Energy (Caloric) Values for the Three Food Types

Food Type	kJ/g	kcal/g
Carbohydrate	17	4
Fat	38	9
Protein	17	4

Snack Crackers

Nutrition Facts
Serving Size 14 crackers (31g)
Servings Per Container About 7

Amount Per Serving
Calories 120 Calories from Fat 35
Kilojoules 500 kJ from Fat 150

	% Daily Value*
Total Fat 4g	6%
Saturated Fat 0.5g	3%
Trans Fat 0g	
Polyunsaturated Fat 0.5%	
Monounsaturated Fat 1.5g	
Cholesterol 0mg	0%
Sodium 310mg	13%
Total Carbohydrate 19g	6%
Dietary Fiber Less than 1g	4%
Sugars 2g	
Proteins 2g	

Vitamin A 0% • Vitamin C 0%
Calcium 4% • Iron 6%

*Percent Daily Values are based on a 2,000 calorie diet. Your daily values may be higher or lower depending on your calorie needs.

	Calories:	2,000	2,500
Total Fat	Less than	65g	80g
Sat Fat	Less than	20g	25g
Cholesterol	Less than	300mg	300mg
Sodium	Less than	2,400mg	2,400mg
Total Carbohydrate		300g	375g
Dietary Fiber		25g	30g

Calories per gram:
Fat 9 • Carbohydrate 4 • Protein 4

The nutrition facts include the total Calories, Calories from fat, and total grams of carbohydrate.

TABLE 10 General Composition and Energy Content of Some Foods

Food	Carbohydrate (g)	Fat (g)	Protein (g)	Energy*
Banana, 1 medium	26	0	1	460 kJ (110 kcal)
Beef, ground, 3 oz	0	14	22	910 kJ (220 kcal)
Carrots, raw, 1 cup	11	0	1	200 kJ (50 kcal)
Chicken, no skin, 3 oz	0	3	20	460 kJ (110 kcal)
Egg, 1 large	0	6	6	330 kJ (80 kcal)
Milk, 4% fat, 1 cup	12	9	9	700 kJ (170 kcal)
Milk, nonfat, 1 cup	12	0	9	360 kJ (90 kcal)
Potato, baked	23	0	3	440 kJ (100 kcal)
Salmon, 3 oz	0	5	16	460 kJ (110 kcal)
Steak, 3 oz	0	27	19	1350 kJ (320 kcal)

*Energy values are rounded off to the tens place.

Guide to Calculating the Energy Content for a Food

1 State the given and needed quantities.

2 Use the energy value of each food type and calculate the kJ or kcal rounded off to the tens place.

3 Add the energy for each food type to give the total energy for the food.

SAMPLE PROBLEM 9 Energy Content for a Food

At a fast-food restaurant, a hamburger contains 37 g of carbohydrate, 19 g of fat, and 24 g of protein. What is the energy content for each food type and the total energy content, in kcal? Round off the kilocalories for each food type to the tens place.

SOLUTION

Step 1 State the given and needed quantities.

Analyze the Problem

Given	Need
Carbohydrate, 37 g	kilocalories for each food and the total number of kilocalories
Fat, 19 g	
Protein, 24 g	

Using the energy values for carbohydrate, fat, and protein (see Table 9), we can calculate the energy for each type of food.

Step 2 Use the energy value of each food type and calculate the kJ or kcal rounded off to the tens place.

Food Type	Mass	Energy Value	Energy
Carbohydrate	$37\ \cancel{g}\ \times$	$\frac{4\ \text{kcal}}{1\ \cancel{g}}$ =	150 kcal
Fat	$19\ \cancel{g}\ \times$	$\frac{9\ \text{kcal}}{1\ \cancel{g}}$ =	170 kcal
Protein	$24\ \cancel{g}\ \times$	$\frac{4\ \text{kcal}}{1\ \cancel{g}}$ =	100 kcal

Step 3 Add the energy for each food type to give the total energy for the food.

$$\text{Total energy content} = 150\ \text{kcal} + 170\ \text{kcal} + 100\ \text{kcal}$$
$$= 420\ \text{kcal}$$

STUDY CHECK 9

If you buy the same hamburger as described in Sample Problem 9 at a fast-food restaurant in Canada, what is the energy content for each food type and the total energy content, in kJ? Round off the kilojoules for each food type to the tens place.

Explore Your World

COUNTING CALORIES

Obtain a food item that has a nutrition label. From the information on the label, determine the number of grams of carbohydrate, fat, and protein in one serving. Using energy values, calculate the total Calories for one serving. (For most products, the kilocalories for each food type are rounded off to the tens place.)

QUESTION

How does your total for the Calories in one serving compare to the Calories stated on the label for a single serving?

Chemistry Link to Health

LOSING AND GAINING WEIGHT

The number of kilocalories or kilojoules needed in the daily diet of an adult depends on gender, age, and level of physical activity. Some general levels of energy needs are given in Table 11.

The amount of food a person eats is regulated by the hunger center in the hypothalamus, located in the brain. Food intake is normally proportional to the nutrient stores in the body. If these nutrient stores are low, you feel hungry; if they are high, you do not feel like eating. The hunger signal is governed by blood sugar (and insulin).

A person gains weight when food intake exceeds energy output, and loses weight when food intake is less than energy output. Many diet products contain cellulose, which has no nutritive value but provides bulk and makes you feel full. Some diet drugs depress the hunger center and must be used with caution, because they excite the nervous system and can elevate blood pressure. Because muscular exercise is an important way to expend energy, an increase in daily exercise aids weight loss. Table 12 lists some activities and the amount of energy they require.

Stockbyte/Getty Images

One hour of swimming uses 2100 kJ of energy.

TABLE 11 Typical Energy Requirements for Adults

Gender	Age	Moderately Active kJ (kcal)	Highly Active kJ (kcal)
Female	19–30	8800 (2100)	10 000 (2400)
	31–50	8400 (2000)	9200 (2200)
Male	19–30	11 300 (2700)	12 600 (3000)
	31–50	10 500 (2500)	12 100 (2900)

TABLE 12 Energy Expended by a 70.0-kg (154-lb) Adult

Activity	Energy (kJ/h)	Energy (kcal/h)
Sleeping	250	60
Sitting	420	100
Walking	840	200
Swimming	2100	500
Running	3100	750

QUESTIONS AND PROBLEMS

6 Energy and Nutrition

LEARNING GOAL: *Use the energy values to calculate the kilojoules (kJ) or kilocalories (kcal) in a food.*

39 Using the following data, determine the kilojoules and kilocalories for each food burned in a calorimeter:

a. one stalk of celery that produces energy to heat 505 g of water from 25.2 °C to 35.7 °C

b. a waffle that produces energy to heat 4980 g of water from 20.6 °C to 62.4 °C

40 Using the following data, calculate the kilojoules and kilocalories for each food burned in a calorimeter:

a. 1 cup of popcorn that produces energy to change the temperature of 1250 g of water from 25.5 °C to 50.8 °C

b. a sample of butter that produces energy to increase the temperature of 357 g of water from 22.7 °C to 38.8 °C

41 Using the energy values for foods (see Table 9), determine each of the following (round off the answers for kilojoules and kilocalories to the tens place):

a. the kilojoules for 1 cup of orange juice that contains 26 g of carbohydrate, no fat, and 2 g of protein

b. the grams of carbohydrate in one apple if the apple has no fat and no protein and provides 72 kcal of energy

c. the kilocalories in 1 tablespoon of vegetable oil, which contains 14 g of fat and no carbohydrate or protein

d. the kilocalories for a diet that consists of 68 g of carbohydrate, 9.0 g of fat, and 150 g of protein

42 Using the energy values for foods (see Table 9), determine each of the following (round off the answers for kilojoules and kilocalories to the tens place):

a. the kilojoules in 2 tablespoons of crunchy peanut butter that contains 6 g of carbohydrate, 16 g of fat, and 7 g of protein

b. the grams of protein in a cup of soup that has 110 kcal with 9 g of carbohydrate and 7 g of fat

c. the grams of sugar (carbohydrate) in a can of cola if it has 140 Cal and no fat and no protein

d. the grams of fat in one avocado if it has 405 kcal, 13 g of carbohydrate, and 5 g of protein

43 One cup of clam chowder contains 16 g of carbohydrate, 12 g of fat, and 9 g of protein. How much energy, in kilojoules and kilocalories, is in the clam chowder? (Round off the kilojoules and kilocalories to the tens place.)

44 A high-protein diet contains 70. g of carbohydrate, 5.0 g of fat, and 150 g of protein. How much energy, in kilojoules and kilocalories, does this diet provide? (Round off the kilojoules or kilocalories to the tens place.)

CONCEPT MAP

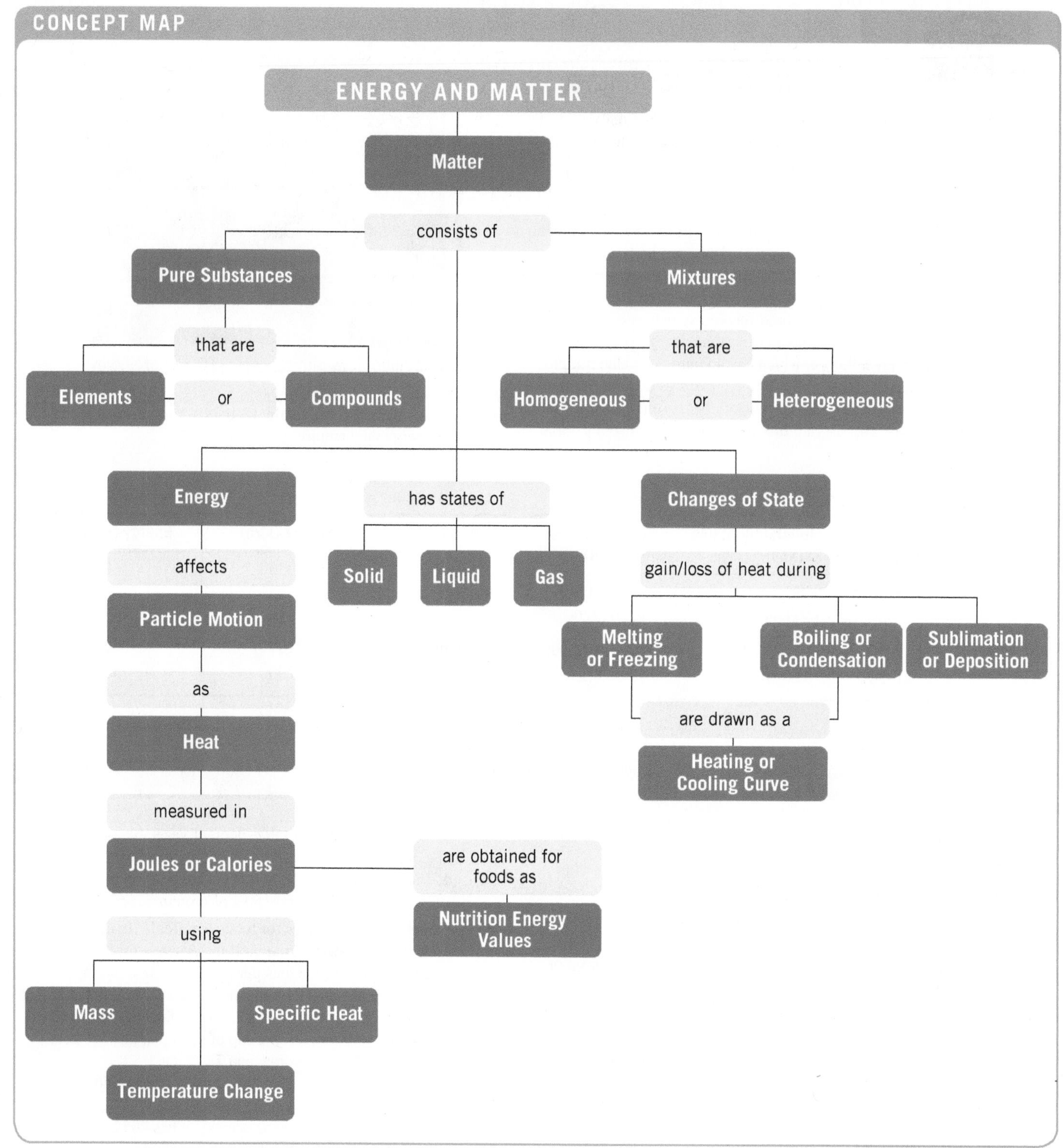
ENERGY AND MATTER
Matter
consists of
Pure Substances
Mixtures
that are
Elements
or
Compounds
that are
Homogeneous
or
Heterogeneous
Energy
has states of
Changes of State
affects
Solid
Liquid
Gas
gain/loss of heat during
Particle Motion
Melting or Freezing
Boiling or Condensation
Sublimation or Deposition
as
are drawn as a
Heat
Heating or Cooling Curve
measured in
Joules or Calories
are obtained for foods as
Nutrition Energy Values
using
Mass
Specific Heat
Temperature Change

CHAPTER REVIEW

1 Energy

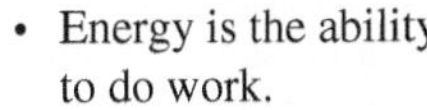

LEARNING GOAL: *Identify energy as potential or kinetic; convert between units of energy.*

Jennifer Photography Imaging/iStockphoto

- Energy is the ability to do work.
- Potential energy is stored energy; kinetic energy is the energy of motion.

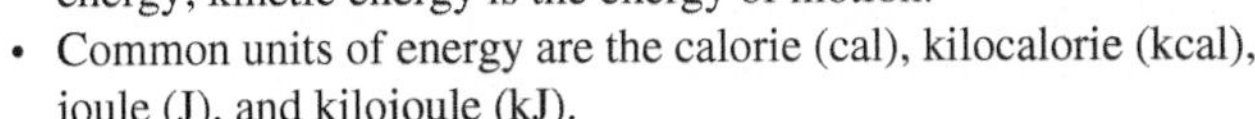

- Common units of energy are the calorie (cal), kilocalorie (kcal), joule (J), and kilojoule (kJ).
- One cal is equal to 4.184 J.

2 Temperature

LEARNING GOAL: *Given a temperature, calculate a corresponding value on another temperature scale.*

- In science, temperature is measured in degrees Celsius (°C) or kelvins (K).
- On the Celsius scale, there are 100 units between the freezing point (0 °C) and the boiling point (100 °C) of water.
- On the Fahrenheit scale used in the United States, there are 180 units between the freezing point (32 °F) and the boiling point (212 °F) of water.
- A Fahrenheit temperature is related to its Celsius temperature by the equation $T_F = 1.8\,T_C + 32$.
- The SI unit, kelvin, is related to the Celsius temperature by the equation $T_K = T_C + 273$.

3 Classification of Matter

LEARNING GOAL: *Classify examples of matter as pure substances or mixtures.*

Richard Megna/ Fundamental Photographs

- Matter is anything that has mass and occupies space.
- Matter is classified as pure substances or mixtures.
- Pure substances, which are elements or compounds, have fixed compositions, and mixtures have variable compositions.
- The substances in mixtures can be separated using physical methods.

4 States and Properties of Matter

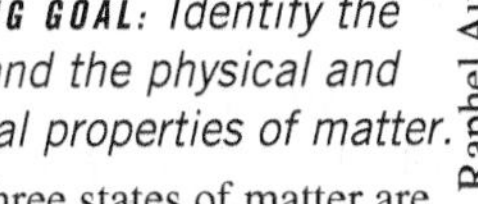

LEARNING GOAL: *Identify the states and the physical and chemical properties of matter.*

Raphel Auvray/ SuperStock

- The three states of matter are solid, liquid, and gas.
- A physical property is a characteristic of a substance in which the identity of the substance does not change.
- A physical change occurs when physical properties change, but not the identity of the substance.
- A chemical property indicates the ability of a substance to change into another substance.
- A chemical change occurs when one or more substances react to form a substance with new physical and chemical properties.

5 Specific Heat

LEARNING GOAL: *Use specific heat to calculate the quantity of heat lost or gained during a temperature change.*

Joe Potato/iStockphoto

- Specific heat is the amount of energy required to raise the temperature of exactly 1 g of a substance by exactly 1 °C.
- The heat gained or lost by a substance is calculated by multiplying its mass, its temperature change, and its specific heat (cal/g °C or J/g °C).

6 Energy and Nutrition

LEARNING GOAL: *Use the energy values to calculate the kilojoules (kJ) or kilocalories (kcal) in a food.*

- The nutritional Calorie is the same amount of energy as 1 kcal or 1000 cal.
- The energy content of a food is the sum of kilojoules or kilocalories from carbohydrate, fat, and protein.

TABLE 9 Typical Energy (Caloric) Values for the Three Food Types

Food Type	kJ/g	kcal/g
Carbohydrate	17	4
Fat	38	9
Protein	17	4

KEY TERMS

boiling The formation of bubbles of gas throughout a liquid.

boiling point (bp) The temperature at which a liquid changes to gas (boils) and gas changes to liquid (condenses).

calorie (cal) The amount of heat energy that raises the temperature of exactly 1 g of water exactly 1 °C; 1 cal = 4.184 J.

Calorie (Cal) A nutritional unit of energy equal to 1000 cal, or 1 kcal.

change of state The transformation of one state of matter to another; for example, from solid to liquid, liquid to solid, and liquid to gas.

chemical change A change during which the original substance is converted into a new substance with a different composition and new physical and chemical properties.

chemical properties The properties that indicate the ability of a substance to change to a new substance.

compound A pure substance consisting of two or more elements, with a definite composition, that can be broken down into a simpler substance only by chemical methods.

condensation The change of state of a gas to a liquid.
deposition The reverse process of sublimation, with gas particles changing directly into a solid.
element A pure substance containing only one type of matter, which cannot be broken down by chemical methods.
energy The ability to do work.
energy (caloric) value The kilojoules or kilocalories obtained per gram of the three food types: carbohydrate, fat, and protein.
evaporation The formation of a gas (vapor) by the escape of high-energy molecules from the surface of a liquid.
freezing A change of state from liquid to solid.
freezing point (fp) The temperature at which a liquid changes to a solid (freezes) and a solid changes to a liquid (melts).
gas A state of matter characterized by no definite shape or volume. Particles in a gas move rapidly.
heat The energy associated with the motion of particles in a substance.
joule (J) The SI unit of heat energy; 4.184 J = 1 cal.
kinetic energy The energy of motion.
liquid A state of matter that takes the shape of its container but has a definite volume.
matter Anything that has mass and occupies space.
melting A change of state that involves the conversion of a solid to a liquid.
melting point (mp) The temperature at which a solid becomes a liquid (melts). It is the same temperature as the freezing point.
mixture The physical combination of two or more substances that does not change the identities of the substances.
physical change The change in which the physical appearance of a substance changes, but the chemical composition stays the same.
physical properties The properties that can be observed or measured without affecting the identity of a substance.
potential energy An inactive type of energy that is stored for future use.
pure substance Matter composed of elements or compounds that has a definite composition.
solid A state of matter that has its own shape and volume.
specific heat (*SH*) A quantity of heat that changes the temperature of exactly 1 g of a substance by exactly 1 °C.
sublimation The change of state in which a solid is transformed directly to a gas without forming a liquid first.
work An activity that requires energy.

UNDERSTANDING THE CONCEPTS

The chapter sections to review are shown in parentheses at the end of each question.

45 Select the warmer temperature in each of the following pairs: (2)
a. 10 °C or 10 °F **b.** 30 °C or 15 °F
c. −10 °C or 32 °F **d.** 200 °C or 200 K

46 State the temperature, including the estimated digit, on each of the following Celsius thermometers: (2)

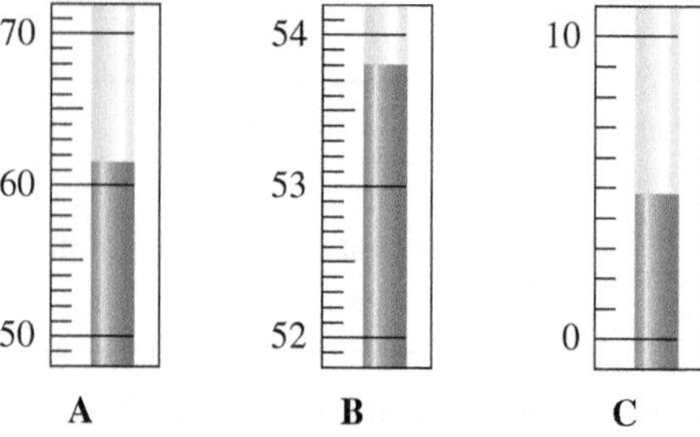

47 Compost can be made at home from grass clippings, some kitchen scraps, and dry leaves. As microbes break down organic matter, heat is generated and the compost can reach a temperature of 155 °F, which kills most pathogens. What is this temperature in degrees Celsius and kelvins? (2)

48 After a week, biochemical reactions in compost slow, and the temperature drops to 45 °C. The dark brown organic-rich mixture is ready for use in the garden. What is this temperature in Fahrenheit degrees and kelvins? (2)

starfotograf/iStockphoto

Compost produced from decayed plant material is used to enrich the soil.

49 Identify each of the following as an element, compound, or mixture: (3)

a.
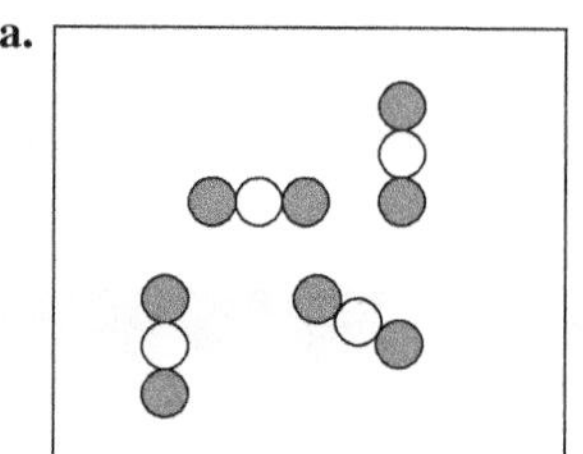
b.
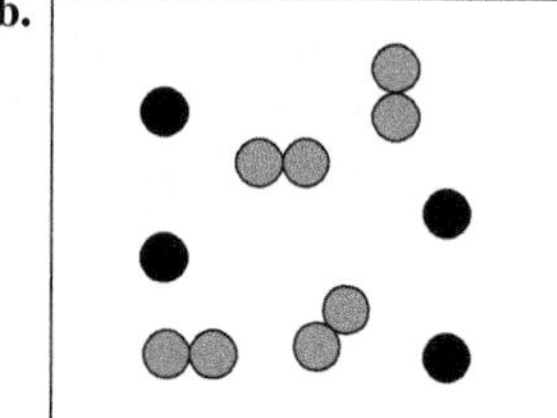
c.
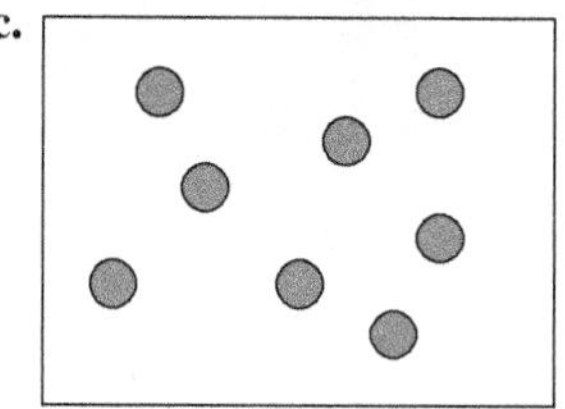

50 Which diagram illustrates a heterogeneous mixture? Explain your choice. Which diagrams illustrate a homogeneous mixture? Explain your choice. (3)

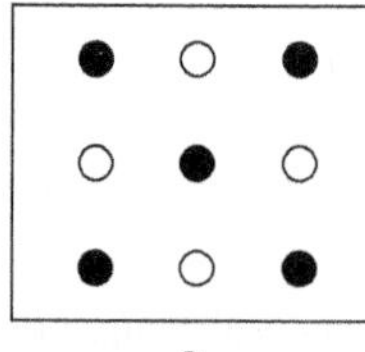
a.
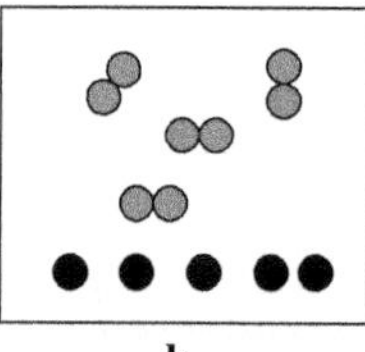
b.
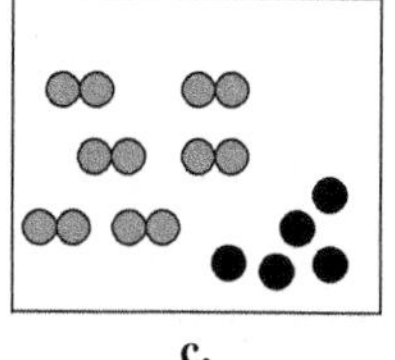
c.

51 Classify each of the following as a homogeneous or heterogeneous mixture: (3)
a. lemon-flavored water **b.** stuffed mushrooms
c. eye drops

52 Classify each of the following as a homogeneous or heterogeneous mixture: (3)
a. ketchup **b.** tortilla soup **c.** hard-boiled egg

Pearson Education

Masterfile Royalty Free Division

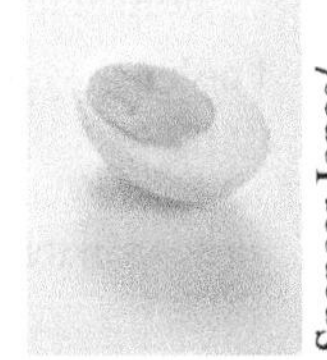
Spencer Jones/ Photodisc/ Getty Images

53 Indicate if heat is added or removed in each of the following: (4)
a. water freezing **b.** copper melting
c. dry ice subliming

54 Indicate if heat is added or removed in each of the following: (4)
a. water boiling **b.** water condensing
c. alcohol evaporating

55 Use your knowledge of changes of state to explain the following: (4)
a. How does perspiration during heavy exercise cool the body?
b. Why do towels dry more quickly on a hot summer day than on a cold winter day?

AP Photo/ Alessandro Trovati

Perspiration forms on the skin during heavy exercise.

56 Use your knowledge of changes of state to explain the following: (4)
a. When a sports injury occurs during a game, a spray such as ethyl chloride (chloroethane) may be used to numb an area of the skin. Explain how a substance such as ethyl chloride that evaporates quickly can numb the skin.
b. Why does water in a wide, flat, shallow dish evaporate more quickly than the same amount of water in a tall, narrow glass?

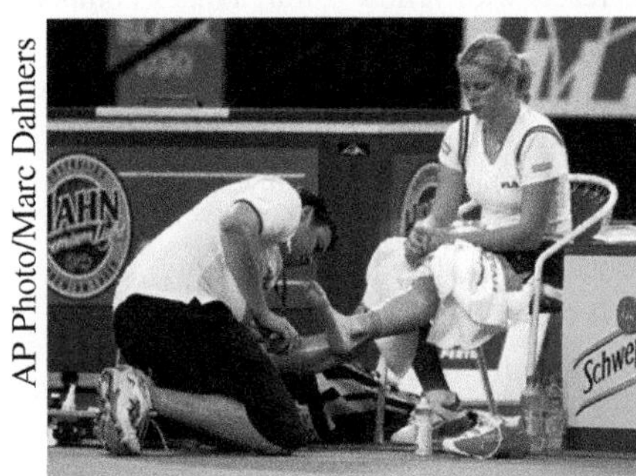
AP Photo/Marc Dahners

A spray is used to numb a sports injury.

57 The following is a heating curve for chloroform, a solvent for fats, oils, and waxes. (4)

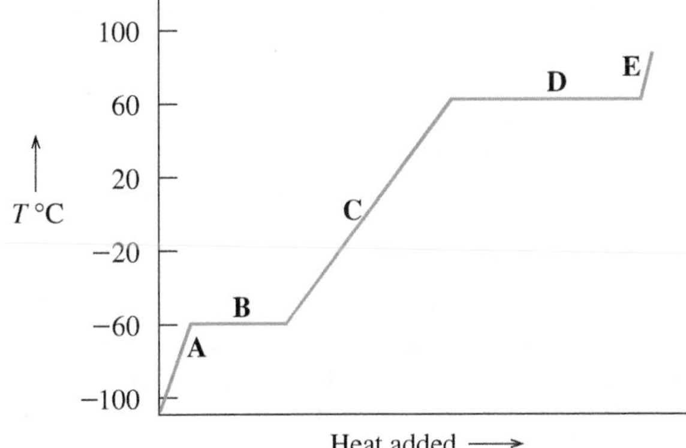

a. What is the melting point of chloroform?
b. What is the boiling point of chloroform?
c. On the heating curve, identify the segments **A**, **B**, **C**, **D**, and **E** as solid, liquid, gas, melting, or boiling.
d. At the following temperatures, is chloroform a solid, liquid, or gas? −80 °C; −40 °C; 25 °C; 80 °C

58 Match the contents of the beakers (**1–5**) with segments (**A–E**) on the heating curve for water. (4)

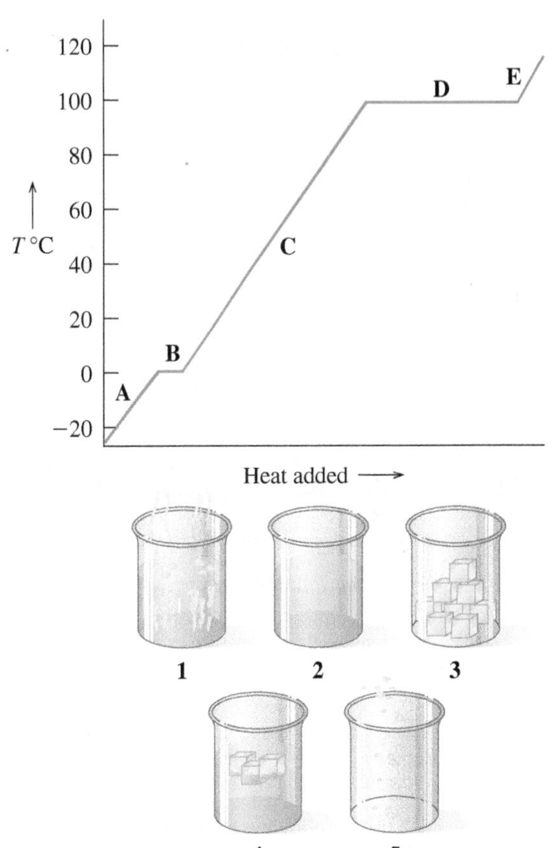

59 On a hot day, the beach sand gets hot, but the water stays cool. Would you predict the specific heat of sand is higher or lower than that of water? Explain. (5)

Khoroshunova Olga/ Shutterstock

The water, sand, and air gain energy from the Sun.

60 Determine the energy to heat three cubes (gold, aluminum, and silver), each with a volume of 10.0 cm^3, from 15 °C to 25 °C. What do you notice about the energy needed for each? (5)

61 A 70.0-kg person has just eaten a quarter-pound cheeseburger, french fries, and a chocolate shake. (6)

a. Using Table 9, calculate the total kilocalories for each food type in this meal (round off the kilocalories to the tens place).

FuatKose/iStockphoto

Item	Carbohydrate (g)	Fat (g)	Protein (g)
Cheeseburger	34	29	31
French fries	26	11	3
Chocolate shake	60	9	11

b. Using Table 12, determine the number of hours of sleeping needed to burn off the kilocalories in this meal.

c. Using Table 12, determine the number of hours of running needed to burn off the kilocalories in this meal.

62 For lunch, your friend, who has a mass of 70.0 kg, has a slice of pizza, a cola soft drink, and ice cream. (6)

a. Using Table 9, calculate the total kilocalories for each food type in this meal (round off the kilocalories to the tens place).

Item	Carbohydrate (g)	Fat (g)	Protein (g)
Pizza	29	10	13
Cola	51	0	0
Ice cream	44	28	8

b. Using Table 12, determine the number of hours of sitting needed to burn off the kilocalories in this meal.

c. Using Table 12, determine the number of hours of swimming needed to burn off the kilocalories in this meal.

ADDITIONAL QUESTIONS AND PROBLEMS

For instructor-assigned homework, go to www.masteringchemistry.com.

63 Calculate each of the following temperatures in degrees Celsius: (2)

a. The highest recorded temperature in the continental United States was 134 °F in Death Valley, California, on July 10, 1913.

b. The lowest recorded temperature in the continental United States was −69.7 °F in Rodgers Pass, Montana, January 20, 1954.

64 Calculate each of the following temperatures in degrees Fahrenheit: (2)

a. The highest recorded temperature in the world was 58.0 °C in El Azizia, Libya, on September 13, 1922.

b. The lowest recorded temperature in the world was −89.2 °C in Vostok, Antarctica, on July 21, 1983.

65 What is −15 °F in degrees Celsius and in kelvins? (2)

66 The highest recorded body temperature that a person has survived is 46.5 °C. Calculate that temperature in degrees Fahrenheit and in kelvins. (2)

67 Classify each of the following as an element, a compound, or a mixture: (3)

a. carbon in pencils
b. carbon dioxide (CO_2) we exhale
c. orange juice
d. neon gas in lights
e. salad dressing of oil and vinegar

68 Classify each of the following as a homogeneous or heterogeneous mixture: (3)

a. hot fudge sundae **b.** herbal tea
c. vegetable oil **d.** water and sand
e. mustard

69 Identify each of the following as a solid, a liquid, or a gas: (4)

a. vitamin tablets in a bottle **b.** helium in a balloon
c. milk in a glass **d.** the air you breathe
e. charcoal briquettes on a barbecue

70 Identify each of the following as a solid, a liquid, or a gas: (4)

a. popcorn in a bag **b.** water in a garden hose
c. a computer mouse **d.** air in a tire
e. hot tea

71 Identify each of the following as a physical or chemical property: (4)

a. Gold is shiny.
b. Gold melts at 1064 °C.
c. Gold is a good conductor of electricity.
d. When gold reacts with yellow sulfur, a black compound forms.

72 Identify each of the following as a physical or chemical property of a candle: (4)

a. The candle is 20 cm high with a diameter of 3 cm.
b. The candle burns.
c. The wax of the candle softens on a hot day.
d. The candle is blue.

73 Identify each of the following as a physical or chemical change: (4)

a. A plant grows a new leaf.
b. Chocolate is melted for a dessert.
c. Wood is chopped for the fireplace.
d. Wood burns in a fireplace.

74 Identify each of the following as a physical or chemical change: (4)

a. A medication tablet is broken in two.
b. Carrots are grated for use in a salad.
c. Malt undergoes fermentation to make beer.
d. A copper pipe reacts with air and turns green.

75 A hot-water bottle contains 725 g of water at 65 °C. If the water cools to body temperature (37 °C), how many kilocalories of heat could be transferred to sore muscles? (5)

76 A pitcher containing 0.75 L of water at 4 °C is removed from the refrigerator. How many kilojoules are needed to warm the water to a room temperature of 22 °C? (5)

77 Calculate the Cal (kcal) in 1 cup of whole milk: 12 g of carbohydrate, 8 g of fat, and 8 g of protein. (Round off the answers to the tens place). (6)

78 Calculate the Cal (kcal) in 1/2 cup of soft ice cream that contains 18 g of carbohydrate, 11 g of fat, and 4 g of protein. (Round off the answers to the tens place). (6)

CHALLENGE QUESTIONS

79 The combustion of 1.0 g of gasoline releases 11 kcal of heat (density of gasoline = 0.74 g/mL). (5)

a. How many megajoules are released when 1.0 gal of gasoline burns?

b. When a color television is on for 2.0 h, 300 kJ are used. How long can a color television run on the energy from 1.0 gal of gasoline?

80 In a large building, oil is used in a steam boiler heating system. The combustion of 1.0 lb of oil provides 2.4×10^7 J. How many kilograms of oil are needed to heat 150 kg of water from 22 °C to 100 °C? (5)

81 The melting point of carbon tetrachloride is −23 °C and its boiling point is 77 °C. Sketch a heating curve for carbon tetrachloride from −100 °C to 100 °C. (4)

a. What is the state of carbon tetrachloride at −50 °C?

b. What happens on the curve at −23 °C?

c. What is the state of carbon tetrachloride at 20 °C?

d. What is the state of carbon tetrachloride at 90 °C?

e. At what temperature will both solid and liquid be present?

82 The melting point of benzene is 5.5 °C and its boiling point is 80.1 °C. Sketch a heating curve for benzene from 0 °C to 100 °C. (4)

a. What is the state of benzene at 15 °C?

b. What happens on the curve at 5.5 °C?

c. What is the state of benzene at 63 °C?

d. What is the state of benzene at 98 °C?

e. At what temperature will both liquid and gas be present?

83 A 70.0-g piece of copper metal at 86.0 °C is placed in 50.0 g of water at 16.0 °C. The metal and water come to the same temperature of 24.0 °C. What is the specific heat, in J/g °C, of copper? (5)

84 A 125-g piece of metal is heated to 288 °C and dropped into 85.0 g of water at 26 °C. If the final temperature of the water and metal is 58.0 °C, what is the specific heat (J/g °C) of the metal? (5)

85 A metal is thought to be titanium or aluminum. When 4.7 g of the metal absorbs 11 J, its temperature rises by 4.5 °C. (5)

a. What is the specific heat, in J/g °C, of the metal?

b. Would you identify the metal as titanium or aluminum (see Table 8)?

86 A metal is thought to be copper or gold. When 18 g of the metal absorbs 58 cal, its temperature rises by 35 °C. (5)

a. What is the specific heat, in cal/g °C, of the metal?

b. Would you identify the metal as copper or gold (see Table 8)?

87 When a 0.660-g sample of olive oil is burned in a calorimeter, the heat released increases the temperature of 370. g of water in the calorimeter from 22.7 °C to 38.8 °C. What is the energy value, in kJ/g and kcal/g, of the olive oil? (6)

88 When a 1.30-g sample of ethanol (alcohol) is burned in a calorimeter, the heat released increases the temperature of 870. g of water in the calorimeter from 18.5 °C to 28.9 °C. What is the energy value, in kJ/g and kcal/g, of ethanol? (6)

89 If you want to lose 1 pound of "fat," which is 15% water, how many kilocalories do you need to expend? (6)

90 A patient receives 2500 mL of an IV solution containing 5 g of glucose per 100 mL. How much energy, in kilojoules and kilocalories, does the patient obtain from glucose, a carbohydrate? (6)

ANSWERS

Answers to Study Checks

1 35 kJ

2 12 °F

3 39.8 °C

4 night −260. °C; day 410. °C

5 This salad dressing is a heterogeneous mixture with a nonuniform composition.

6 **a** and **c** are chemical changes.

7 SH = 1.23 J/g °C

8 14.6 kJ

9 carbohydrate 630 kJ, fat 720 kJ, protein 410 kJ; total = 1760 kJ

Answers to Selected Questions and Problems

1 a. potential **b.** kinetic
c. potential **d.** potential

3 a. increase **b.** decrease **c.** decrease

5 a. 8.1×10^5 J **b.** 190 kcal

7 In the United States, the Fahrenheit scale is in common use. On a Fahrenheit thermometer, normal body temperature is 98.6 °F. A temperature of 99.8 °F would indicate a mild fever. On the Celsius scale, her temperature is 37.7 °C.

9 a. 98.6 °F **b.** 18.5 °C **c.** 246 K
d. −49 °C **e.** 46 °C

11 a. 41 °C
b. No. The temperature is equivalent to 39 °C.

13 a. compound; contains four elements in a definite composition
b. mixture
c. compound; consists of two elements in a definite composition
d. element; consists of one type of pure substance
e. mixture

15 a. heterogeneous **b.** homogeneous
c. homogeneous **d.** heterogeneous
e. heterogeneous

17 a. gas **b.** gas **c.** solid

19 a. physical **b.** chemical
c. physical **d.** chemical

21 a. physical **b.** chemical **c.** physical
d. physical **e.** physical

23 a. chemical **b.** physical **c.** physical
d. chemical **e.** physical

25 a. melting **b.** sublimation
c. freezing **d.** deposition

27 a. condensation **b.** evaporation
c. boiling **d.** condensation

29

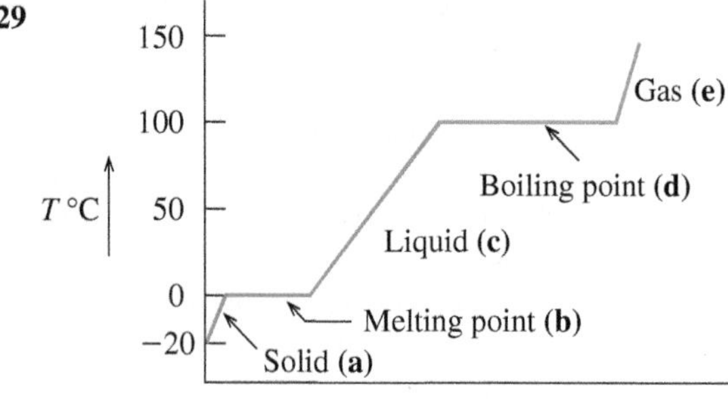

31 Copper has the lowest specific heat of the samples and will reach the highest temperature.

33 a. 0.389 J/g °C **b.** 0.313 J/g °C

35 a. 250 cal **b.** 3300 J **c.** 9.3 kcal

37 a. 1380 J; 330. cal **b.** 1810 J; 434 cal
c. 3780 J; 904 cal **d.** 3200 J; 760 cal

39 a. 5.30 kcal; 22.2 kJ **b.** 208 kcal; 871 kJ

41 a. 470 kJ **b.** 18 g
c. 130 kcal **d.** 950 kcal

43 880 kJ; 210 kcal

45 a. 10 °C **b.** 30 °C
c. 32 °F **d.** 200 °C

47 68.3 °C; 341 K

49 a. compound **b.** mixture **c.** element

51 a. homogeneous **b.** heterogeneous
c. homogeneous

53 a. removed **b.** added **c.** added

55 a. The heat from the skin is used to evaporate the water (perspiration). Therefore, the skin is cooled.
b. On a hot day, there are more molecules with sufficient energy to become water vapor.

57 a. about −60 °C
b. about 60 °C
c. A is solid. **B** is melting. **C** is liquid. **D** is boiling. **E** is gas.
d. At −80 °C, it is solid; at −40 °C, it is liquid; at 25 °C, it is liquid; at 80 °C, it is gas.

59 Sand must have a lower specific heat than water. When both substances absorb the same amount of heat, the final temperature of the sand will be higher than that of water.

61 a. 1100 kcal
b. 18 h of sleeping
c. 1.5 h of running

63 a. 56.7 °C **b.** −56.5 °C

65 a. −26 °C, 247 K

67 a. element **b.** compound **c.** mixture
d. element **e.** mixture

69 a. solid **b.** gas **c.** liquid
d. gas **e.** solid

71 a. physical property **b.** physical property
c. physical property **d.** chemical property

73 a. chemical change **b.** physical change
c. physical change **d.** chemical change

75 20. kcal

77 150 Cal

79 a. 130 MJ **b.** 860 h

81 a. solid **b.** solid carbon tetrachloride melts
c. liquid **d.** gas **e.** −23 °C

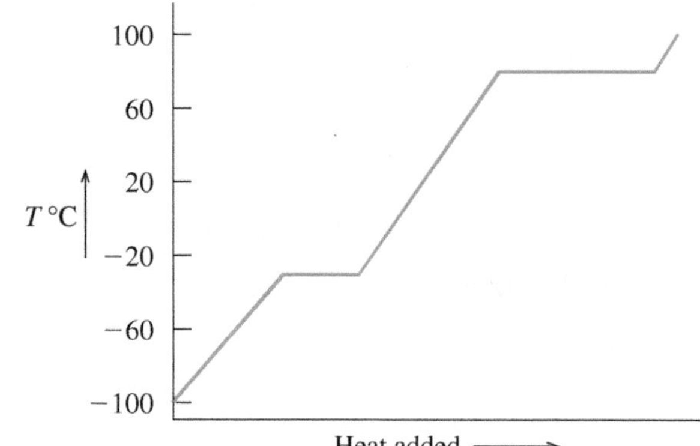

83 Specific heat = 0.39 J/g °C

85 a. 0.52 J/g °C
b. titanium

87 37.8 kJ/g; 9.03 kcal/g

89 3500 kcal

Combining Ideas 1

CI.1 Gold, one of the most sought-after metals in the world, has a density of 19.3 g/cm^3, a melting point of 1064 °C, and a specific heat of 0.129 J/g °C. A gold nugget found in Alaska in 1998 weighs 20.17 lb.

Gold nuggets, also called native gold, can be found in streams and mines.

Photolibrary RF / Photolibrary

a. How many significant figures are in the measurement of weight of the nugget?
b. What is the mass of the nugget in kilograms?
c. If the nugget were pure gold, what would its volume be in cm^3 ?
d. What is the melting point of gold in degrees Fahrenheit and kelvins?
e. How many kilojoules are required to heat the nugget from 27 °C to 358 °C? How many kilocalories is that?
f. In 2010, the price of gold was \$61.08 per gram. What was the nugget worth, in dollars, in 2010?

CI.2 The mileage for a motorcycle with a fuel-tank capacity of 22 L is 35 mi/gal. The density of gasoline is 0.74 g/mL.
a. How long a trip, in kilometers, can be made on one full tank of gasoline?
b. If the price of gasoline is \$3.59 per gallon, what would be the cost of fuel for the trip?
c. If the average speed during the trip is 44 mi/h, how many hours will it take to reach the destination?
d. What is the mass, in grams, of the fuel in the tank?
e. When 1.0 g of gasoline burns, 47 kJ of energy is released. How many kilojoules are produced when the fuel in one full tank is completely burned?

Shalom Ormsby / Getty Images

When 1.0 g of gasoline burns in a motorcycle, 47 kJ of energy is released.

CI.3

Answer the following for diagrams **A** and **B**:
a. In which sample (**A** or **B**) does the water have its own shape?
b. Which diagram (**1**, **2**, or **3**) represents the arrangement of particles in water sample **A**?
c. Which diagram (**1**, **2**, or **3**) represents the arrangement of particles in water sample **B**?

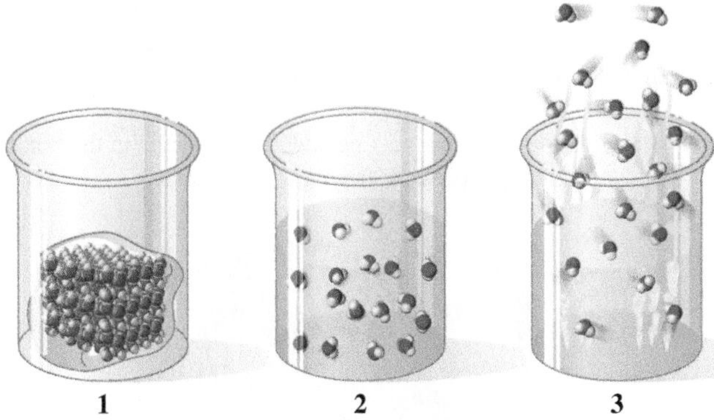

Answer the following for diagrams **1**, **2**, and **3**:
d. The state of matter indicated in diagram **1** is a ________; in diagram **2**, it is a ________; and in diagram **3**, it is a ________.
e. The motion of the particles is slowest in diagram ________.
f. The arrangement of particles is farthest apart in diagram ________.
g. The particles fill the volume of the container in diagram ________.
h. If the water in diagram **2** has a mass of 19 g and a temperature of 45 °C, how much heat, in kilojoules, is removed to cool the liquid to 0 °C?

CI.4 The label of a black cherry almond energy bar with a mass of 68 g lists the "nutrition facts" as 39 g of carbohydrate, 5 g of fat, and 10 g of protein.
a. Using the energy values of carbohydrates, fats, and proteins, what are the kilocalories (Calories) listed for the black cherry almond bar? (Round off answers for each food type to the tens place.)
b. What are the kilojoules for the black cherry almond bar? (Round off answers for each food type to the tens place.)
c. If you obtain 160 kJ, how many grams of the black cherry almond bar did you eat?
d. If you are walking and using energy at a rate of 840 kJ/h, how many minutes will you need to walk to expend the energy from two bars?

Pearson Education / Eric Schrader

An energy bar contains carbohydrate, fat, and protein.

CI.5 In a box of nails, there are 75 iron nails weighing 0.250 lb. The density of iron is 7.86 g/cm^3. The specific heat of iron is 0.452 J/g °C.

a. What is the volume, in cm^3, of the iron nails in the box?

b. If 30 nails are added to a graduated cylinder containing 17.6 mL of water, what is the new level of water in the cylinder?

c. How many joules must be added to the nails in the box to raise their temperature from 16 °C to 125 °C?

Photolibrary RF / Photolibrary

Nails made of iron have a density of 7.86 g/cm^3.

CI.6 A hot tub is filled with 450 gal of water.

a. What is the volume, in liters, of water in the tub?

b. What is the mass, in kilograms, of water in the tub?

c. How many kilocalories are needed to heat the water from 62 °F to 105 °F?

d. If the hot tub heater provides 1400 kcal/min, how long, in minutes, will it take to heat the water in the hot tub from 62 °F to 105 °F?

Masterfile

A hot tub filled with water is heated to 105 °F.

ANSWERS

CI.1 **a.** Four significant figures are in the measurement.
b. 9.17 kg
c. 475 cm^3
d. 1947 °F; 1337 K
e. 392 kJ; 93.6 kcal
f. \$560 000 or \$5.60 × 10^5

CI.3 **a.** B
b. A is represented by diagram 2.
c. B is represented by diagram 1.
d. solid, liquid, gas
e. diagram 1
f. diagram 3
g. diagram 3
h. 3.6 kJ

CI.5 **a.** 14.4 cm^3
b. 23.4 mL
c. 5590 J or 5.59 × 10^3 J

Atoms and Elements

LOOKING AHEAD

Visit **www.masteringchemistry.com** for self-study materials and instructor-assigned homework.

Martin Harvey/Alamy

John is preparing for the next growing season as he decides how much of each crop should be planted and their location on his farm. Part of this decision is determined by the quality of the soil including the pH, the amount of moisture, and the nutrient content in the soil. He begins by sampling the soil and performing a few chemical tests on the samples. John determines that several of his fields need additional fertilizer before the crops can be planted.

John considers several different types of fertilizers, as each kind supplies nutrients to the soil to help increase crop production. Plants need three basic elements for plant growth. These elements are potassium, nitrogen, and phosphorus. Potassium (K on the periodic table) is a metal, while nitrogen (N) and phosphorus (P) are nonmetals. Fertilizers may also contain several other elements including calcium (Ca), magnesium (Mg), and sulfur (S). John applies a fertilizer containing a mixture of all of these elements to his soil, and plans to retest the soil nutrient content in a few days.

Career: Farmer

Farming involves much more than growing crops and raising animals. Farmers must understand how to perform chemical tests, apply fertilizer to soil, and pesticides or herbicides to crops. Pesticides are chemicals used to kill insects that could destroy the crop, while herbicides are chemicals used to kill weeds that would compete for the crop's water and nutrient supply. This requires a knowledge of how these chemicals work, their safety, effectiveness, and their storage. In using this information, farmers are able to grow crops that produce a higher yield, greater nutritional value, and better taste.

From Chapter 3 of *General, Organic, and Biological Chemistry: Structures of Life*, Fourth Edition. Karen C. Timberlake.

All matter is composed of *elements*, of which there are 118 different kinds. Of these, 88 elements occur naturally and make up all the substances in our world. Many elements are already familiar to you. Perhaps you use aluminum in the form of foil or drink soft drinks from aluminum cans. You may have a ring or necklace made of gold, silver, or perhaps platinum. If you play tennis or golf, your racket or clubs may be made from the elements titanium or carbon. In our bodies, compounds of calcium and phosphorus form the structure of bones and teeth, iron and copper are needed for the formation of red blood cells, and iodine is required for the proper functioning of the thyroid.

The amounts of certain elements are crucial for the proper growth and function of the body. Low levels of iron can lead to anemia, while lack of iodine can cause hypothyroidism and goiter. Some elements known as microminerals, such as chromium, cobalt, and selenium, are needed in our bodies in very small amounts. Laboratory tests are used to confirm that these elements are within normal ranges in our bodies.

LEARNING GOAL

Given the name of an element, write its correct symbol; from the symbol, write the correct name.

TUTORIAL
Elements and Symbols in the Periodic Table

1 Elements and Symbols

Elements are pure substances from which all other things are built. Elements cannot be broken down into simpler substances. Over the centuries, elements have been named for planets, mythological figures, colors, minerals, geographic locations, and famous people. Some sources of names of elements are listed in Table 1. A complete list of all the elements and their symbols appears on the inside front cover of this text.

TABLE 1 Some Elements, Symbols, Sources of Names, and Atomic Numbers

Element	Symbol	Source of Name	Atomic Number
Uranium	U	The planet Uranus	92
Titanium	Ti	Titans (mythology)	22
Chlorine	Cl	*Chloros*: "greenish yellow" (Greek)	17
Iodine	I	*Ioeides*: "violet" (Greek)	53
Magnesium	Mg	Magnesia, a mineral	12
Californium	Cf	California	98
Curium	Cm	Marie and Pierre Curie	96
Copernicium	Cn	Nicolaus Copernicus	112

One-Letter Symbols		Two-Letter Symbols	
C	carbon	Co	cobalt
S	sulfur	Si	silicon
N	nitrogen	Ne	neon
I	iodine	Ni	nickel

Chemical symbols are one- and two-letter abbreviations for the names of the elements. Only the first letter of an element's symbol is capitalized. If the symbol has a second letter, it is lowercase so that we know when a different element is indicated. If two letters are capitalized, they represent the symbols of two different elements. For example, the element cobalt has the symbol Co. However, the two capital letters CO specify two elements, carbon (C) and oxygen (O).

Chemistry Link to Industry

MANY FORMS OF CARBON

Carbon has the symbol C and atomic number 6. However, carbon atoms can be arranged in different ways to give several different kinds of carbon substances. Two forms—diamond and graphite—have been known since prehistoric times. A diamond is transparent and harder than any other substance, whereas graphite is black and soft. In diamond, carbon atoms are arranged in a rigid structure, while in graphite, carbon atoms are arranged in sheets that slide easily over each other. Graphite is used as pencil lead, as a lubricant, and in the manufacture of carbon fibers used for lightweight golf clubs and tennis rackets.

Two other forms of carbon have been discovered more recently. In the form called *buckminsterfullerene* or *buckyball* (named after R. Buckminster "Bucky" Fuller, who popularized the geodesic dome), 60 carbon atoms are arranged as rings of 5 and 6 atoms to give a spherical, cage-like structure. When the buckyball structure is stretched out, it produces a cylinder called a *nanotube*, which has a diameter of a few nanometers. Practical uses for buckyballs and nanotubes have not yet been developed, but they are expected to find use in lightweight structural materials, heat conductors, computer parts, and medicine.

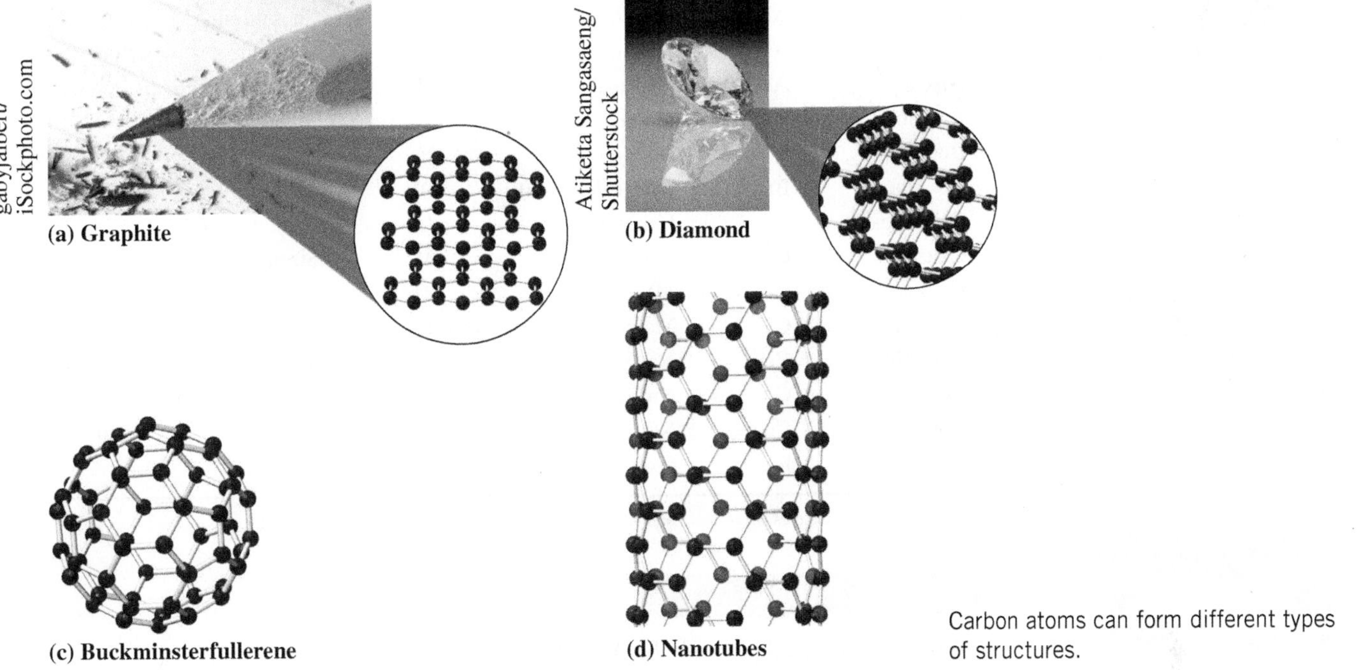

Carbon atoms can form different types of structures.

Although most of the symbols use letters from their English names, some are derived from their ancient names. For example, Na, the symbol for sodium, comes from the Latin word *natrium*. The symbol for iron, Fe, is derived from the Latin name *ferrum*. Table 2 lists the names and symbols of some common elements. Learning their names and symbols will greatly help your learning of chemistry.

Chemistry Link to Health

LATIN NAMES FOR ELEMENTS IN CLINICAL USAGE

In medicine, the Latin name *natrium* is often used for sodium, an important electrolyte in body fluids and cells. An increase in serum sodium, a condition called *hypernatremia*, may occur when water is lost because of profuse sweating, severe diarrhea, or vomiting, or when there is inadequate water intake. A decrease in sodium, a condition called *hyponatremia*, may occur when a person takes in a large amount of water or fluid-replacement solutions. Conditions that occur in cardiac failure, liver failure, and malnutrition can also cause hyponatremia.

The Latin name *kalium* is often used for potassium, the most common electrolyte inside the cells. Potassium regulates osmotic pressure, acid–base balance, nerve and muscle excitability, and the function of cellular enzymes. Serum potassium measures potassium outside the cells, which amounts to only 2% of total body potassium. An increase in serum potassium (*hyperkalemia* or *hyperpotassemia*) may occur when cells are severely injured, in renal failure when potassium is not properly excreted, and in Addison's disease. A severe loss of potassium (*hypokalemia* or *hypopotassemia*) may occur during excessive vomiting, diarrhea, renal tubular defects, and glucose or insulin therapy.

Aluminum

Pearson Education

Carbon

Pearson Education

Gold

Pearson Education

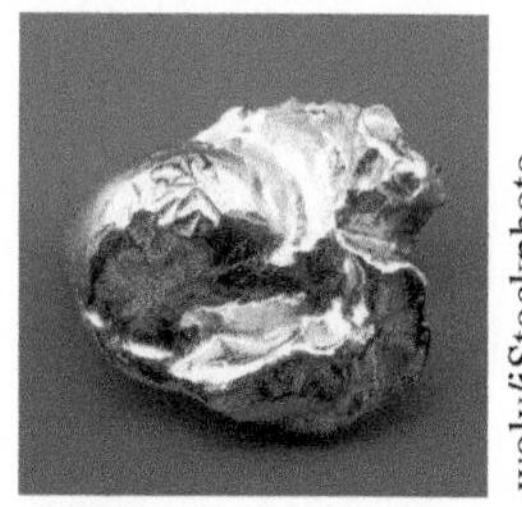
Silver

wolv/iStockphoto

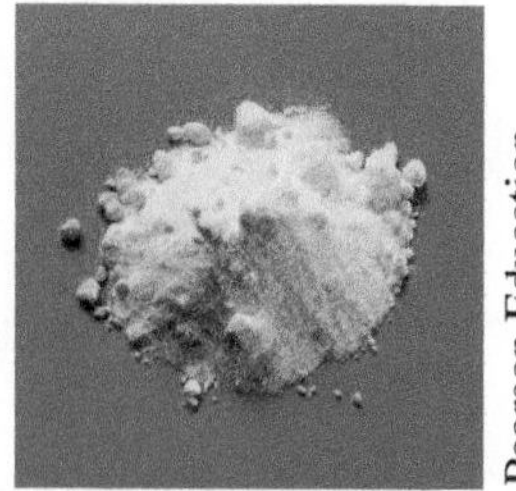
Sulfur

Pearson Education

CONCEPT CHECK 1 **Symbols of the Elements**

The symbol for carbon is C, and the symbol for sulfur is S. However, the symbol for cesium is Cs, not CS. Why?

ANSWER

When the symbol for an element has two letters, the first letter is capitalized, but the second letter is lowercase. If both letters are capitalized such as in CS, then two elements—carbon and sulfur—are indicated.

TABLE 2 Names and Symbols of Some Common Elements

Name*	Symbol	Name*	Symbol	Name*	Symbol
Aluminum	Al	Gold (*aurum*)	Au	Phosphorus	P
Argon	Ar	Helium	He	Platinum	Pt
Arsenic	As	Hydrogen	H	Potassium (*kalium*)	K
Barium	Ba	Iodine	I	Radium	Ra
Boron	B	Iron (*ferrum*)	Fe	Silicon	Si
Bromine	Br	Lead (*plumbum*)	Pb	Silver (*argentum*)	Ag
Cadmium	Cd	Lithium	Li	Sodium (*natrium*)	Na
Calcium	Ca	Magnesium	Mg	Strontium	Sr
Carbon	C	Manganese	Mn	Sulfur	S
Chlorine	Cl	Mercury (*hydrargyrum*)	Hg	Tin (*stannum*)	Sn
Chromium	Cr	Neon	Ne	Titanium	Ti
Cobalt	Co	Nickel	Ni	Uranium	U
Copper (*cuprum*)	Cu	Nitrogen	N	Zinc	Zn
Fluorine	F	Oxygen	O		

*Names given in parentheses are ancient Latin or Greek words from which the symbols are derived.

SAMPLE PROBLEM 1 **Writing Chemical Symbols**

What are the chemical symbols for each of the following elements?

a. nickel **b.** nitrogen **c.** neon

SOLUTION

a. Ni **b.** N **c.** Ne

STUDY CHECK 1

What are the chemical symbols for silicon, sulfur, and silver?

SAMPLE PROBLEM 2 **Names and Symbols of Chemical Elements**

Give the name of the element that corresponds to each of the following chemical symbols:

a. Zn **b.** K **c.** H **d.** Fe

SOLUTION

a. zinc **b.** potassium **c.** hydrogen **d.** iron

STUDY CHECK 2

What are the names of the elements with the chemical symbols Mg, Al, and F?

Chemistry Link to the Environment

TOXICITY OF MERCURY

Mercury is a silvery, shiny element that is a liquid at room temperature. Mercury can enter the body through inhalation as a vapor, contact with the skin, or foods or water that have been contaminated with mercury. In the body, mercury destroys proteins and disrupts cell function. Long-term exposure to mercury can damage the brain and kidneys, cause mental retardation, and decrease physical development. Blood, urine, and hair samples are used to test for mercury.

In both freshwater and seawater, bacteria convert mercury into toxic methylmercury, which attacks the central nervous system (CNS). Because fish absorb methylmercury, we are exposed to mercury when we eat mercury-contaminated fish. The Food and Drug Administration (FDA) has set a maximum level of one part mercury per million parts seafood (1 ppm), which is the same as 1 mg of mercury in every kilogram of seafood. Fish higher in the food chain such as swordfish, tuna, and shark can have such high levels of mercury that the Environmental Protection Agency (EPA) recommends they be consumed no more than once a week.

One of the worst incidents of mercury poisoning occurred in Minamata and Niigata, Japan, in 1950. At that time, the ocean was polluted with high levels of mercury from industrial wastes. Because fish were a major food in the Japanese diet, more than 2000 people were affected with mercury poisoning and many died or developed neural damage. In the United States, between 1988 and 1997, the use of mercury decreased by 75% when mercury was banned in paints and pesticides, and regulated in batteries and other products. Certain batteries and CFL bulbs contain mercury and instructions for their safe disposal should be followed.

Mary Ann Sullivan

This mercury fountain, housed in glass, was designed by Alexander Calder for the 1937 World's Fair in Paris.

QUESTIONS AND PROBLEMS

1 Elements and Symbols

LEARNING GOAL: *Given the name of an element, write its correct symbol; from the symbol, write the correct name.*

1 Write the symbols for the following elements:
a. copper **b.** platinum **c.** calcium
d. manganese **e.** iron **f.** barium
g. lead **h.** strontium

2 Write the symbols for the following elements:
a. oxygen **b.** lithium **c.** uranium
d. titanium **e.** hydrogen **f.** chromium
g. tin **h.** gold

3 Write the name of the element for each of the following symbols:
a. C **b.** Cl **c.** I **d.** Hg
e. Ag **f.** Ar **g.** B **h.** Ni

4 Write the name of the element for each of the following symbols:
a. He **b.** P **c.** Na **d.** As
e. Ca **f.** Br **g.** Cd **h.** Si

5 What elements are represented by the symbols in each of the following substances?
a. table salt, NaCl
b. plaster cast, $CaSO_4$
c. Demerol, $C_{15}H_{22}ClNO_2$
d. antacid, $CaCO_3$

6 What elements are represented by the symbols in each of the following substances?
a. water, H_2O
b. baking soda, $NaHCO_3$
c. lye, NaOH
d. sugar, $C_{12}H_{22}O_{11}$

2 The Periodic Table

LEARNING GOAL

Use the periodic table to identify the group and the period of an element; identify the element as a metal, nonmetal, or metalloid.

As more elements were discovered, it became necessary to organize them into some type of classification system. By the late 1800s, scientists recognized that certain elements looked alike and behaved in much the same way. In 1872, a Russian chemist, Dmitri Mendeleev, arranged the 60 elements known at that time into groups with similar properties and placed them in order of increasing mass. Today, this arrangement of 118 elements is known as the **periodic table** (see Figure 1).

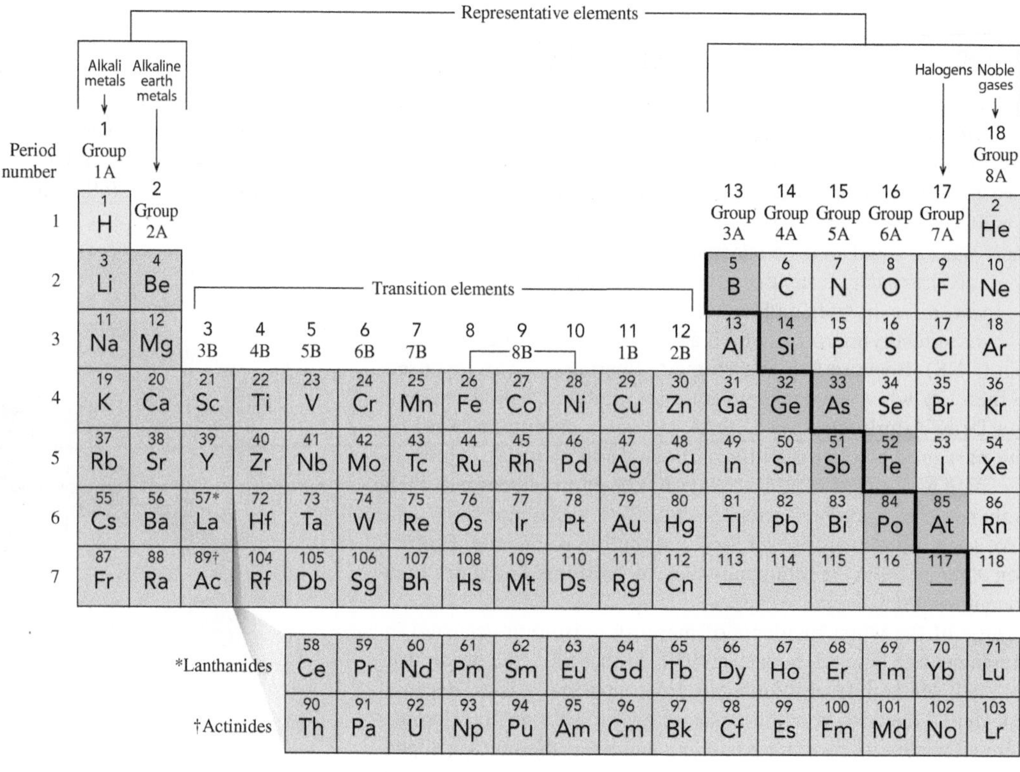

FIGURE 1 On the periodic table, groups are elements arranged as vertical columns, and periods are the elements in each horizontal row.

Q What is the symbol and name of the alkali metal in Period 3?

Periods and Groups

Each horizontal row in the periodic table is a **period** (see Figure 2). The periods are counted from the top of the table as Period 1 to Period 7. The first period contains two elements: hydrogen (H) and helium (He). The second period contains eight elements: lithium (Li), beryllium (Be), boron (B), carbon (C), nitrogen (N), oxygen (O), fluorine (F), and neon (Ne). The third period also contains eight elements, beginning with sodium (Na) and ending with argon (Ar). The fourth period, which begins with potassium (K), and the fifth period, which begins with rubidium (Rb), have 18 elements each. The sixth period, which begins with cesium (Cs), has 32 elements. The seventh period contains 32 elements, for a total of 118 elements.

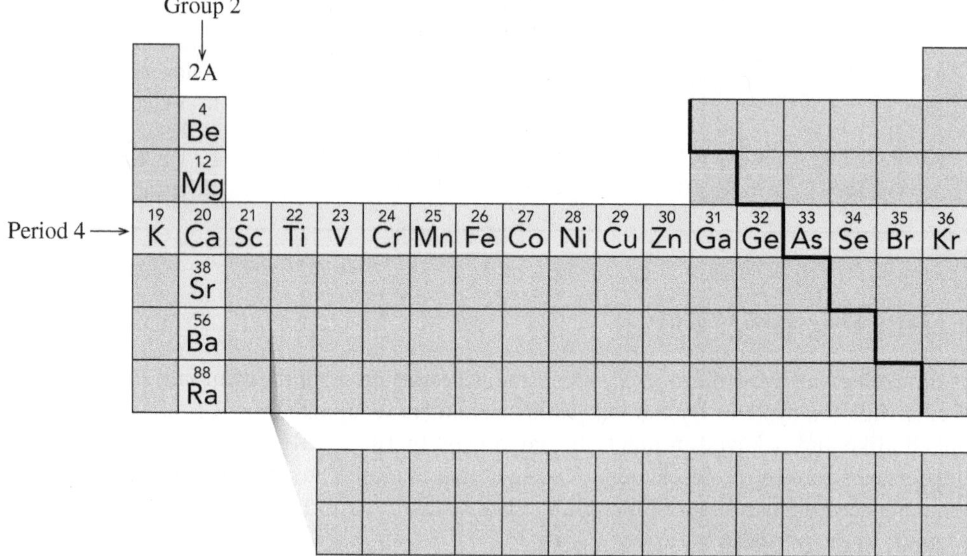

FIGURE 2 On the periodic table, each vertical column represents a group of elements, and each horizontal row of elements represents a period.

Q Are the elements Si, P, and S part of a group or a period?

Each vertical column on the periodic table contains a **group** (or family) of elements that have similar properties. At the top of each column is a number that is assigned to each group. The elements in the first two columns on the left of the periodic table and the last six columns on the right are called the **representative elements**. For many years, they have been given **group numbers** 1A–8A. In the center of the periodic table is a block of elements known as the **transition elements**, which are designated with the letter "B." A newer system assigns numbers 1 to 18 to the groups going left to right across the periodic table. Because both systems of group numbers are currently in use, they are both shown on the periodic table in this text and are included in our discussions of elements and group numbers. Below the periodic table, there are two rows of 14 elements, which are part of Periods 6 and 7. These elements, called the lanthanides and actinides (or the inner transition elements), are placed below the periodic table to allow it to fit on a page.

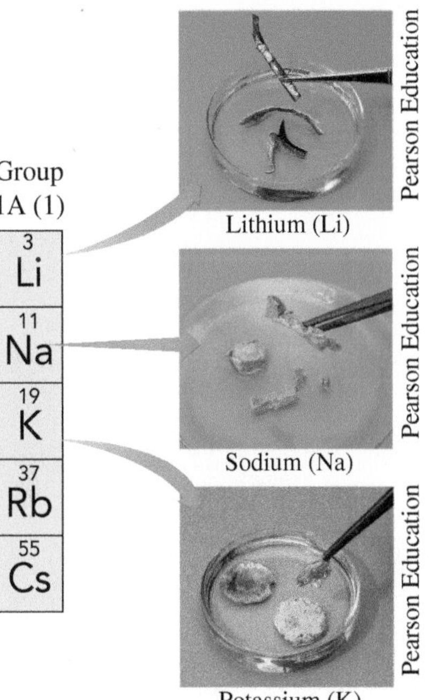

FIGURE 4 Lithium (Li), sodium (Na), and potassium (K) are some alkali metals from Group 1A (1).

Q What physical properties do these alkali metals have in common?

Names of Groups

Several groups in the periodic table have special names (see Figure 3). Group 1A (1) elements—lithium (Li), sodium (Na), potassium (K), rubidium (Rb), cesium (Cs), and francium (Fr)—are a family of elements known as the **alkali metals** (see Figure 4). The elements within this group are soft, shiny metals that are good conductors of heat and electricity, and have relatively low melting points. Alkali metals react vigorously with water and form white products when they combine with oxygen.

Although hydrogen (H) is at the top of Group 1A (1), it is not an alkali metal and has very different properties than the rest of the elements in this group. Thus, hydrogen is not included in the classification of alkali metals.

The **alkaline earth metals** are found in Group 2A (2). They include the elements beryllium (Be), magnesium (Mg), calcium (Ca), strontium (Sr), barium (Ba), and radium (Ra). The alkaline earth metals are shiny metals like those in Group 1A (1), but they are not as reactive.

The **halogens** are found on the right side of the periodic table in Group 7A (17). They include the elements fluorine (F), chlorine (Cl), bromine (Br), iodine (I), and astatine (At) (see Figure 5). The halogens, especially fluorine and chlorine, are highly reactive and form compounds with most of the elements.

The **noble gases** are found in Group 8A (18). They include helium (He), neon (Ne), argon (Ar), krypton (Kr), xenon (Xe), and radon (Rn). The noble gases are quite unreactive and are seldom found in combination with other elements.

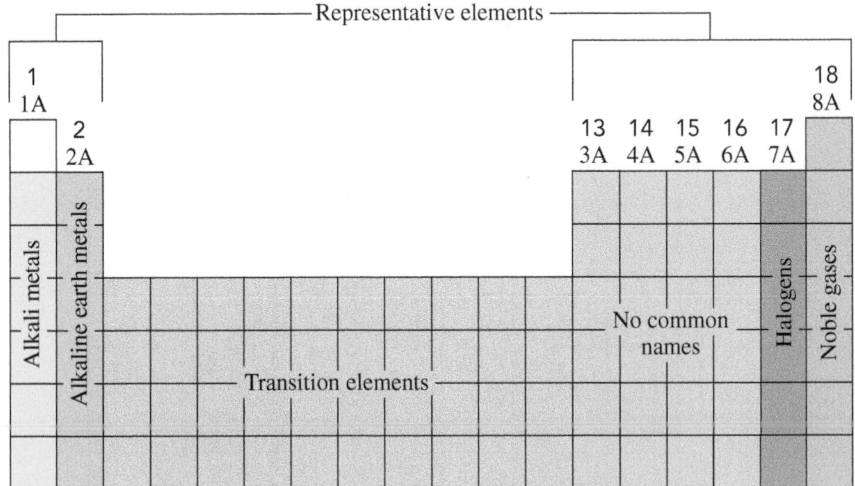

FIGURE 3 Certain groups on the periodic table have common names.

Q What is the common name for the group of elements that includes helium and argon?

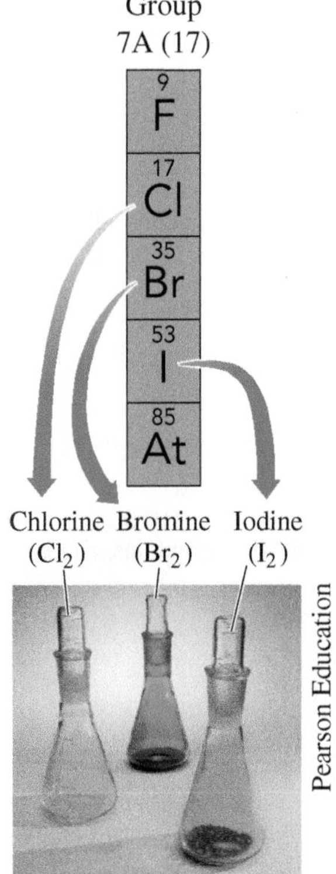

FIGURE 5 Chlorine (Cl_2), bromine (Br_2), and iodine (I_2) are examples of halogens from Group 7A (17).

Q What elements are in the halogen group?

SAMPLE PROBLEM 3 **Period and Group Numbers of Some Elements**

Give the period and group number for each of the following elements, and identify each as a representative or transition element:

a. iodine **b.** manganese **c.** barium **d.** gold

SOLUTION

a. Iodine (I), Period 5, Group 7A (17), is a representative element.
b. Manganese (Mn), Period 4, Group 7B (7), is a transition element.
c. Barium (Ba), Period 6, Group 2A (2), is a representative element.
d. Gold (Au), Period 6, Group 1B (11), is a transition element.

STUDY CHECK 3

Strontium is an element that gives a brilliant red color to fireworks.

a. In what group is strontium found?
b. In what chemical family is strontium found?
c. In what period is strontium found?
d. What is the name and symbol of the element in Period 3 that is in the same group as strontium?
e. What alkali metal, halogen, and noble gas are in the same period as strontium?

Polushkin Ivan Nikolaevich/Shutterstock

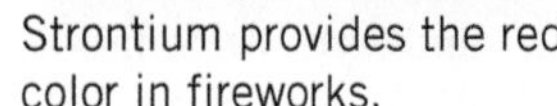

Strontium provides the red color in fireworks.

Metals, Nonmetals, and Metalloids

The heavy zigzag line on the periodic table separates the *metals* from the *nonmetals. Except for hydrogen*, the metals are to the left of the line with the nonmetals to the right (see Figure 6). In general, most **metals** are shiny solids, such as copper (Cu), gold (Au), and silver (Ag). Metals can be shaped into wires (ductile) or hammered into flat sheets (malleable). Metals are good conductors of heat and electricity. They usually melt at higher temperatures than nonmetals. All of the metals are solids at room temperature, except for mercury (Hg), which is a liquid.

Nonmetals are not especially shiny, ductile, or malleable, and they are often poor conductors of heat and electricity. They typically have low melting points and low densities. Some examples of nonmetals are hydrogen (H), carbon (C), nitrogen (N), oxygen (O), chlorine (Cl), and sulfur (S).

Except for aluminum, the elements located along the heavy zigzag line are **metalloids**: B, Si, Ge, As, Sb, Te, Po, and At. Metalloids exhibit some properties that are typical

TUTORIAL
Metals, Nonmetals, and Metalloids

5 B, 14 Si, 32 Ge, 33 As, 51 Sb, 52 Te, 84 Po, 85 At, 117 —

Metals Metalloids Nonmetals

FIGURE 6 The metalloids that border the heavy zigzag line on the periodic table exhibit characteristics of both metals and nonmetals.

Q On which side of the heavy zigzag line are the nonmetals located?

of the metals, and other properties that are characteristic of the nonmetals. For example, metalloids are better conductors of heat and electricity than the nonmetals, but not as good as the metals. The metalloids are semiconductors because they can be modified to function as conductors or insulators. Table 3 compares some characteristics of silver, a metal, with those of antimony, a metalloid, and sulfur, a nonmetal.

TABLE 3 Some Characteristics of a Metal, a Metalloid, and a Nonmetal

Silver (Ag)	Antimony (Sb)	Sulfur (S)
Metal	Metalloid	Nonmetal
Shiny	Blue-gray, shiny	Dull, yellow
Extremely ductile	Brittle	Brittle
Can be hammered into sheets (malleable)	Shatters when hammered	Shatters when hammered
Good conductor of heat and electricity	Poor conductor of heat and electricity	Poor conductor, good insulator
Used in coins, jewelry, tableware	Used to harden lead, color glass and plastics	Used in gunpowder, rubber, fungicides
Density 10.5 g/mL	Density 6.7 g/mL	Density 2.1 g/mL
Melting point 962 °C	Melting point 630 °C	Melting point 113 °C

Pearson Education

A silver cup is shiny, antimony is a blue-gray solid, and sulfur is a dull, yellow color.

SAMPLE PROBLEM 4 **Names and Classification of Elements**

Use the periodic table to classify each of the following elements by its group, group name (if any), and as a metal, nonmetal, or metalloid:

a. Na **b.** I **c.** B

SOLUTION

a. Na (sodium), Group 1A (1), an alkali metal, is a metal.
b. I (iodine), Group 7A (17), a halogen, is a nonmetal.
c. B (boron), Group 3A (13), is a metalloid.

STUDY CHECK 4

Identify each of the following as a metal, nonmetal, or metalloid:

a. germanium **b.** radon **c.** chromium

Chemistry Link to Health

ELEMENTS ESSENTIAL TO HEALTH

Of all the elements, only about 20 are essential for the well-being and survival of the human body. Of those, four elements—oxygen, carbon, hydrogen, and nitrogen—which are representative elements in Period 1 and Period 2 on the periodic table, make up 96% of our body mass. Most of the food in our daily diet consists of these elements, which are found in carbohydrates, fats, and proteins. Much of the hydrogen and oxygen is found in water, which makes up 55–60% of our body mass.

The *macrominerals*—Ca, P, K, Cl, S, Na, and Mg—are representative elements located in Period 3 and Period 4 of the periodic table. They are involved in the formation of bones and teeth, maintenance of heart and blood vessels, muscle contraction, nerve impulses, acid–base balance of body fluids, and regulation of cellular metabolism. The macrominerals are present in lower amounts than the major elements, so that smaller amounts are required in our daily diets.

The other essential elements, called *microminerals* or *trace elements*, are mostly transition elements in Period 4 along with Mo and I in Period 5. They are present in the human body in small amounts, some less than 100 mg. In recent years, the detection of such small amounts has improved so that researchers can more easily identify the roles of trace elements. Some trace elements such as arsenic, chromium, and selenium are toxic at higher levels in the body, but are still required by the body. Other elements such as tin and nickel are thought to be essential, but their metabolic role has not yet been determined. Some examples and the amounts present in a 60-kg person are listed in Table 4.

TABLE 4 Typical Amounts of Essential Elements in a 60-kg Adult

Element	Quantity	Function
Major Elements		
Oxygen (O)	39 kg	Building block of biomolecules and water (H_2O)
Carbon (C)	11 kg	Building block of organic molecules and biomolecules
Hydrogen (H)	6 kg	Component of biomolecules, water (H_2O), and pH of body fluids, stomach acid (HCl)
Nitrogen (N)	1.5 kg	Component of proteins and nucleic acids
Macrominerals		
Calcium (Ca)	1000 g	Needed for bone and teeth, muscle contraction, nerve impulses
Phosphorus (P)	600 g	Needed for bone and teeth, nucleic acids, ATP
Potassium (K)	120 g	Most abundant positive ion (K^+) in cells, muscle contraction, nerve impulses
Chlorine (Cl)	100 g	Most abundant negative ion (Cl^-) in fluids outside cells, stomach acid (HCl)
Sulfur (S)	86 g	Component of proteins, liver, vitamin B_1, insulin
Sodium (Na)	60 g	Most abundant positive ion (Na^+) in fluids outside cells, water balance, functions in muscle contraction, nerve impulses
Magnesium (Mg)	36 g	Component of bone, required for metabolic reactions
Microminerals (trace elements)		
Iron (Fe)	3600 mg	Component of oxygen carrier hemoglobin
Silicon (Si)	3000 mg	Needed for growth and maintenance of bone and teeth, tendons and ligaments, hair and skin
Zinc (Zn)	2000 mg	Used in metabolic reactions in cells, DNA synthesis, growth of bone, teeth, connective tissue, immune system
Copper (Cu)	240 mg	Needed for blood vessels, blood pressure, immune system
Manganese (Mn)	60 mg	Needed for bone growth, blood clotting, necessary for metabolic reactions
Iodine (I)	20 mg	Needed for proper thyroid function
Molybdenum (Mo)	12 mg	Needed to process Fe and N from diets
Arsenic (As)	3 mg	Needed for growth and reproduction
Chromium (Cr)	3 mg	Needed for maintenance of blood sugar levels, synthesis of biomolecules
Cobalt (Co)	3 mg	Component of vitamin B_{12}, red blood cells
Selenium (Se)	2 mg	Used in the immune system, health of heart and pancreas
Vanadium (V)	2 mg	Needed in the formation of bone and teeth, energy from food

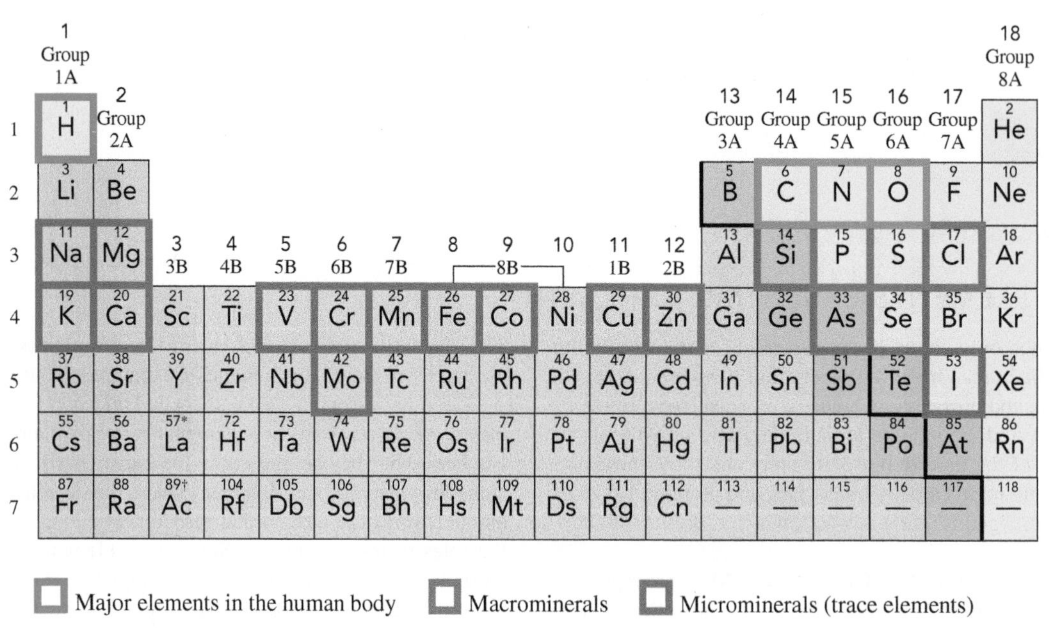

QUESTIONS AND PROBLEMS

2 The Periodic Table

LEARNING GOAL: *Use the periodic table to identify the group and the period of an element; identify the element as a metal, nonmetal, or metalloid.*

7 Identify the period or group number described by each of the following:
a. contains the elements C, N, and O
b. begins with helium
c. contains the alkali metals
d. ends with neon

8 Identify the period or group number described by each of the following:
a. contains Na, K, and Rb
b. the row that begins with Li
c. the noble gases
d. contains F, Cl, Br, and I

9 Classify each of the following as an alkali metal, alkaline earth metal, transition element, halogen, or noble gas:
a. Ca **b.** Fe **c.** Xe
d. K **e.** Cl

10 Classify each of the following as an alkali metal, alkaline earth metal, transition element, halogen, or noble gas:
a. Ne **b.** Mg **c.** Cu
d. Br **e.** Cs

11 Give the symbol of the element described by each of the following:
a. Group 4A (14), Period 2
b. a noble gas in Period 1
c. an alkali metal in Period 3
d. Group 2A (2), Period 4
e. Group 3A (13), Period 3

12 Give the symbol of the element described by each of the following:
a. an alkaline earth metal in Period 2
b. Group 5A (15), Period 3
c. a noble gas in Period 4
d. a halogen in Period 5
e. Group 4A (14), Period 4

13 Is each of the following elements a metal, nonmetal, or metalloid?
a. calcium
b. sulfur
c. a shiny element
d. an element that is a gas at room temperature
e. located in Group 8A (18)
f. bromine
g. tellurium
h. silver

14 Is each of the following elements a metal, nonmetal, or metalloid?
a. located in Group 2A (2)
b. a good conductor of electricity
c. chlorine
d. silicon
e. an element that is not shiny
f. oxygen
g. nitrogen
h. tin

3 The Atom

LEARNING GOAL

Describe the electrical charge and location in an atom for a proton, a neutron, and an electron.

All the elements listed in the periodic table are made up of atoms. We described an **atom** as the smallest particle of an element. Imagine that you are dividing a piece of aluminum foil into smaller and smaller pieces. Now imagine that you have a piece so small that you cannot divide it further. Then you would have a single atom of aluminum.

SELF-STUDY ACTIVITY
Atoms and Isotopes

TUTORIAL
The Anatomy of Atoms

Russ Lappa/Pearson

Aluminum foil consists of atoms of aluminum.

The concept of the atom is relatively recent. Although the Greek philosophers in 500 B.C.E. reasoned that everything must contain minute particles they called *atomos*, the idea of atoms did not become a scientific theory until 1808. Then John Dalton

(1766–1844) developed an atomic theory that proposed that atoms were responsible for the combinations of elements found in compounds.

IBM Research, Almaden Research Center

FIGURE 7 Images of nickel atoms are produced when nickel is magnified millions of times by a scanning tunneling microscope (STM). This instrument generates an image of the atomic structure.

Q Why is a microscope with extremely high magnification needed to see these atoms?

Dalton's Atomic Theory

1. All matter is made up of tiny particles called atoms.
2. All atoms of a given element are similar to one another and different from atoms of other elements.
3. Atoms of two or more different elements combine to form compounds. A particular compound is always made up of the same kinds of atoms and always has the same number of each kind of atom.
4. A chemical reaction involves the rearrangement, separation, or combination of atoms. Atoms are never created or destroyed during a chemical reaction.

Dalton's atomic theory formed the basis of current atomic theory, although we have modified some of Dalton's statements. We now know that atoms of the same element are not completely identical to each other and consist of even smaller particles. However, an atom is still the smallest particle of any element.

Although atoms are the building blocks of everything we see around us, we cannot see an atom or even a billion atoms with the naked eye. However, when billions and billions of atoms are packed together, the characteristics of each atom are added to those of the next until we can see the characteristics we associate with the element. For example, a small piece of the shiny element nickel consists of many, many nickel atoms. A special kind of microscope called a *scanning tunneling microscope* (STM) produces images of individual atoms (see Figure 7).

Electrical Charges in an Atom

By the end of the 1800s, experiments with electricity showed that atoms were not solid spheres, but were composed of even smaller bits of matter called **subatomic particles**, three of which are the proton, electron, and neutron. Some of these subatomic particles were discovered because they have electrical charges.

An electrical charge can be positive or negative. Experiments show that like charges repel, or push away from each other. When you brush your hair on a dry day, electrical charges that are alike build up on the brush and in your hair. As a result, your hair flies away from the brush. Opposite or unlike charges attract. The crackle of clothes taken from the clothes dryer indicates the presence of electrical charges. The clinginess of the clothing results from the attraction of opposite, unlike charges, as shown in Figure 8.

Positive charges repel

Negative charges repel

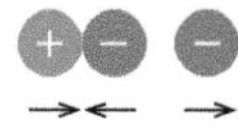

Unlike charges attract

FIGURE 8 Like charges repel, and unlike charges attract.

Q Why are electrons attracted to the protons in the nucleus of an atom?

Structure of the Atom

In 1897, J. J. Thomson, an English physicist, applied electricity to a glass tube and produced streams of small particles called *cathode rays*. Because these rays were attracted to a positively charged electrode, Thomson realized that these particles must be negatively charged. In further experiments, these particles called **electrons** were found to be much smaller than the atom and to have an extremely small mass. Because atoms are neutral, scientists soon discovered that atoms contain positively charged particles called **protons** that are much heavier than the electrons.

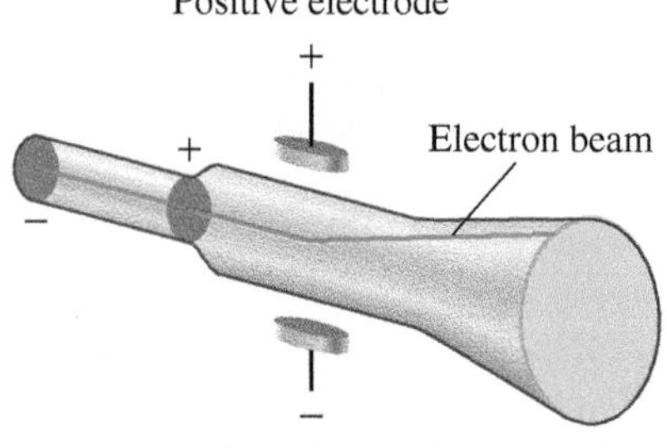

Negatively charged cathode rays (electrons) are attracted to the positive electrode.

Thomson proposed a model for the atom in which the electrons and protons were randomly distributed through the atom. In 1911, Ernest Rutherford worked with Thomson to test this model. In Rutherford's experiment, positively charged particles were aimed at a thin sheet of gold foil (see Figure 9). If the Thomson model was correct, the particles would travel in straight paths through the gold foil. Rutherford was greatly surprised to find that some of the particles were deflected slightly as they passed through the gold foil, and a few particles were deflected so much that they went back in the opposite direction. According to Rutherford, it was as though he had shot a cannonball at a piece of tissue paper, and it bounced back at him.

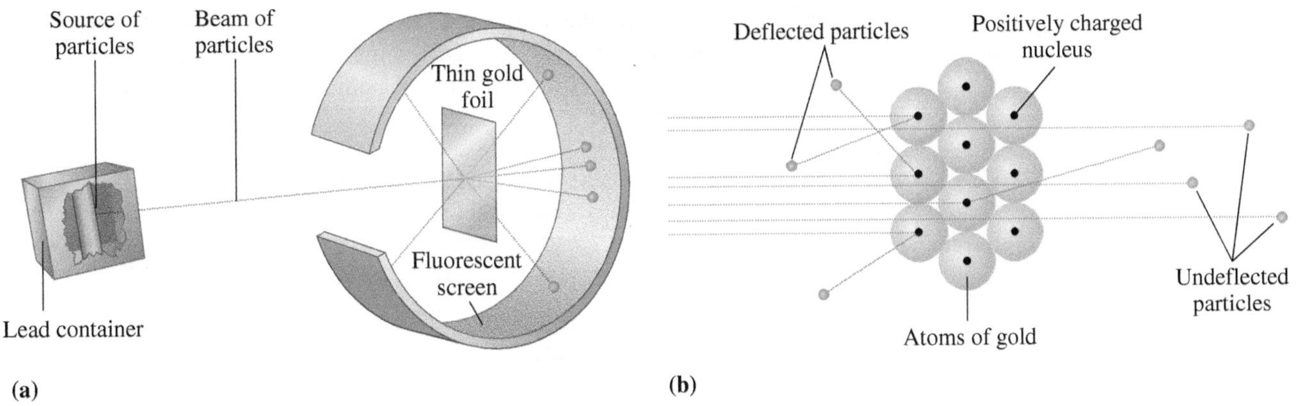

FIGURE 9 **(a)** Positive particles are aimed at a piece of gold foil. **(b)** Particles that come close to the atomic nuclei of gold are deflected from their straight path.

Q Why are some particles deflected while most pass through the gold foil undeflected?

From his gold-foil experiments, Rutherford realized that the protons must be contained in a small, positively charged region at the center of the atom, which he called the **nucleus**. He proposed that the electrons in the atom occupy the space surrounding the nucleus through which most of the particles traveled undisturbed. Only the particles that came near this dense, positive center within the gold atoms were deflected. If an atom were the size of a football stadium, the nucleus would be about the size of a golf ball placed in the center of the field.

Scientists knew that the nucleus was heavier than the mass of the protons and looked for another subatomic particle. Eventually, James Chadwick, in 1932, discovered that the nucleus also contained a particle called a **neutron**, which is neutral. Thus, the masses of the protons and neutrons in the nucleus determine its mass (see Figure 10).

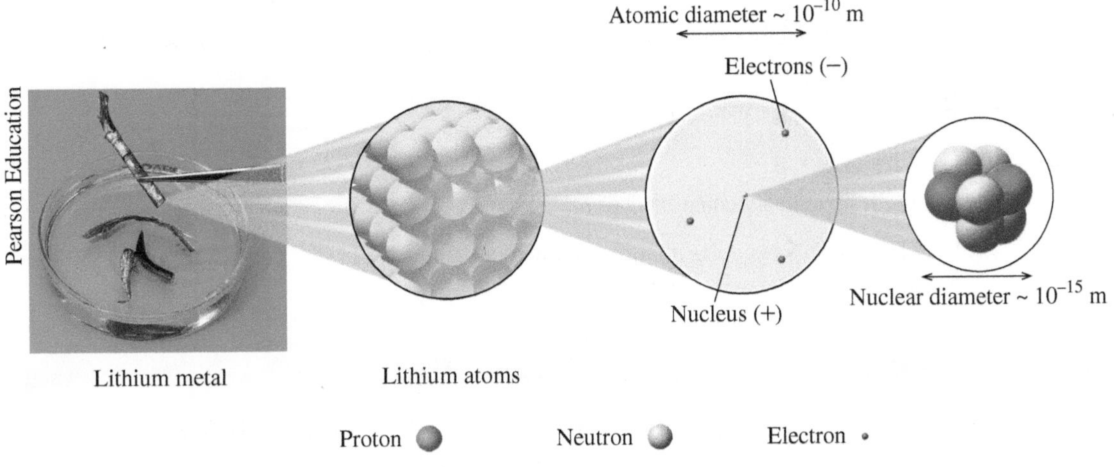

FIGURE 10 In an atom, the protons and neutrons that make up almost all the mass of the atom are packed into the tiny volume of the nucleus. The rapidly moving electrons surround the nucleus and account for the large volume of the atom.

Q Why can we say that an atom is mostly empty space?

Mass of the Atom

TUTORIAL
Atomic Structure and Properties of Subatomic Particles

All the subatomic particles are extremely small compared with the things you see around you. One proton has a mass of 1.7×10^{-24} g, and the neutron is about the same. The mass of the electron is 9.1×10^{-28} g, which is about 1/2000th of the mass of either a proton or a neutron. Because the masses of subatomic particles are so small, chemists use a unit called an **atomic mass unit (amu)**. An amu is defined as one-twelfth of the mass of the carbon atom with six protons and six neutrons, a standard with which the mass of every other atom is compared. In biology, the atomic mass unit is called a *Dalton* (Da) in honor of

John Dalton. On the amu scale, the proton and neutron each have a mass of about 1 amu. Because the electron mass is so small, it is usually ignored in atomic mass calculations. Table 5 summarizes some information about the subatomic particles in an atom.

TABLE 5 Particles in the Atom

Subatomic Particle	Symbol	Electrical Charge	Mass (amu)	Location in Atom
Proton	p or p^+	1+	1.007	Nucleus
Neutron	n or n^0	0	1.008	Nucleus
Electron	e^-	1−	0.000 55	Outside nucleus

CONCEPT CHECK 2 **Subatomic Particles**

Is each of the following statements *true* or *false*? If false, explain your reason.

a. Protons are heavier than electrons.
b. Protons are attracted to neutrons.
c. Electrons are so small that they have no electrical charge.
d. The nucleus contains all the protons and neutrons of an atom.

ANSWER

a. True
b. False; protons are attracted to electrons.
c. False; electrons have a 1− charge.
d. True

SAMPLE PROBLEM 5 **Identifying Subatomic Particles**

Identify the subatomic particle that has the following characteristics:

a. no charge
b. a mass of 0.000 55 amu
c. a mass about the same as a neutron

SOLUTION

a. neutron **b.** electron **c.** proton

STUDY CHECK 5

Is the following statement *true* or *false*?

The nucleus occupies a large volume in an atom.

QUESTIONS AND PROBLEMS

3 The Atom

LEARNING GOAL: *Describe the electrical charge and location in an atom for a proton, a neutron, and an electron.*

15 Identify each of the following as describing a proton, a neutron, or an electron:
a. has the smallest mass
b. has a 1+ charge
c. is found outside the nucleus
d. is electrically neutral

16 Identify each of the following as describing a proton, a neutron, or an electron:
a. has a mass about the same as a proton
b. is found in the nucleus
c. is attracted to the protons
d. has a 1− charge

17 Is each of the following statements *true* or *false*?
a. A proton and an electron have opposite charges.
b. The nucleus contains most of the mass of an atom.
c. Electrons repel each other.
d. A proton is attracted to a neutron.

18 Is each of the following statements *true* or *false*?
a. A proton is attracted to an electron.
b. A neutron has twice the mass of a proton.
c. Neutrons repel each other.
d. Electrons and neutrons have opposite charges.

19 How did Thomson determine that the electrons have a negative charge?

20 What did Rutherford determine about the structure of the atom from his gold-foil experiment?

4 Atomic Number and Mass Number

LEARNING GOAL

Given the atomic number and the mass number of an atom, state the number of protons, neutrons, and electrons.

TUTORIAL
Atomic Number and Mass Number

All of the atoms of the same element always have the same number of protons. This feature distinguishes atoms of one element from atoms of all the other elements.

Atomic Number

The **atomic number** of an element is equal to the number of protons in every atom of that element. The atomic number is the whole number that appears above the symbol of each element on the periodic table.

Atomic number = number of protons in an atom

The periodic table on the inside front cover of this text shows the elements in order of atomic number from 1 to 118. We can use an atomic number to identify the number of protons in an atom of any element. For example, a lithium atom, with atomic number 3, has 3 protons. Every lithium atom has 3 and only 3 protons. Any atom with 3 protons is always a lithium atom. In the same way, we determine that a carbon atom, with atomic number 6, has 6 protons. Every carbon atom has 6 protons and any atom with 6 protons is carbon.

An atom is electrically neutral. That means that the number of protons in an atom is equal to the number of electrons, which gives every atom an overall electrical charge of zero. Thus, for any atom, the atomic number also gives the number of electrons.

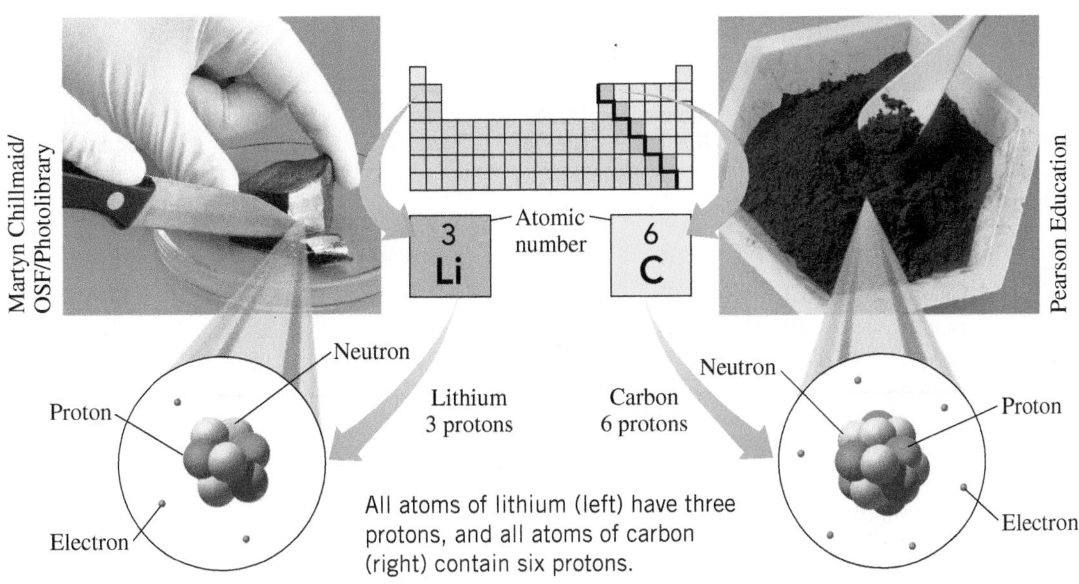

All atoms of lithium (left) have three protons, and all atoms of carbon (right) contain six protons.

SAMPLE PROBLEM 6 **Atomic Number, Protons, and Electrons**

Using the periodic table, state the atomic number, number of protons, and number of electrons for an atom of each of the following elements:

a. nitrogen **b.** magnesium **c.** bromine

SOLUTION

a. atomic number 7; 7 protons and 7 electrons
b. atomic number 12; 12 protons and 12 electrons
c. atomic number 35; 35 protons and 35 electrons

STUDY CHECK 6

Consider an atom that has 79 electrons.

a. How many protons are in its nucleus?
b. What is its atomic number?
c. What is its name, and what is its symbol?

Career Focus

OPTICIAN

Opticians fit and adjust eyewear for patients who have had their eyesight tested by an ophthalmologist or optometrist. Optics and mathematics are used to select materials for frames and lenses that are compatible with patients' facial measurements and lifestyles.

Mass Number

We now know that protons and neutrons determine the mass of any nucleus. Thus, a **mass number** is written for any single atom, which is the total number of protons and neutrons in its nucleus. However, the mass number of a single atom does not appear on the periodic table.

Mass number = number of protons + number of neutrons in a nucleus

For example, the nucleus of a single oxygen atom that contains 8 protons and 8 neutrons has a mass number of 16. If the nucleus of a single iron atom contains 26 protons and 32 neutrons, it would have a mass number of 58.

If we are given the mass number of an atom and its atomic number, we can calculate the number of neutrons in its nucleus.

Number of neutrons in a nucleus = mass number − number of protons

For example, if we are given a mass number of 37 for an atom of chlorine (atomic number 17), we can calculate the number of neutrons in its nucleus.

Number of neutrons = 37 (mass number) − 17 (protons) = 20 neutrons

Table 6 illustrates these relationships between atomic number, mass number, and the number of protons, neutrons, and electrons in examples of single atoms for different elements.

TABLE 6 Composition of Some Atoms of Different Elements

Element	Symbol	Atomic Number	Mass Number	Number of Protons	Number of Neutrons	Number of Electrons
Hydrogen	H	1	1	1	0	1
Nitrogen	N	7	14	7	7	7
Oxygen	O	8	16	8	8	8
Chlorine	Cl	17	37	17	20	17
Iron	Fe	26	58	26	32	26
Gold	Au	79	197	79	118	79

CONCEPT CHECK 3 Subatomic Particles in Atoms

An atom of silver has a mass number of 109.

a. How many protons are in the nucleus?
b. How many neutrons are in the nucleus?
c. How many electrons are in the atom?

ANSWER

a. Silver (Ag), with atomic number 47, has 47 protons.
b. The number of neutrons is calculated by subtracting the number of protons from the mass number.

109 − 47 = 62 neutrons for an atom of Ag with a mass number of 109.

c. In a neutral atom, the number of electrons is equal to the number of protons. An atom of silver with 47 protons has 47 electrons.

SAMPLE PROBLEM 7 Calculating Numbers of Protons, Neutrons, and Electrons

For an atom of zinc that has a mass number of 68, determine the following:

a. the number of protons
b. the number of neutrons
c. the number of electrons

SOLUTION

Analyze the Problem

Element	Atomic Number	Number of Protons	Mass Number	Number of Neutrons	Number of Electrons
Zinc (Zn)	30	Equal to atomic number	68	Mass number – number of protons	Equal to number of protons

a. Zinc (Zn), with an atomic number of 30, has 30 protons.
b. The number of neutrons in this zinc atom is found by subtracting the number of protons (atomic number) from the mass number.

$$\begin{array}{ccccc} \text{Mass number} & - & \text{atomic number} & = & \text{number of neutrons} \\ 68 & - & 30 & = & 38 \end{array}$$

c. Because the zinc atom is neutral, the number of electrons is equal to the number of protons. A zinc atom has 30 electrons.

STUDY CHECK 7

How many neutrons are in the nucleus of a bromine atom that has a mass number of 80?

QUESTIONS AND PROBLEMS

4 Atomic Number and Mass Number

LEARNING GOAL: *Given the atomic number and the mass number of an atom, state the number of protons, neutrons, and electrons.*

21 Would you use atomic number, mass number, or both to obtain the following?
a. number of protons in an atom
b. number of neutrons in an atom
c. number of particles in the nucleus
d. number of electrons in a neutral atom

22 What do you know about the subatomic particles from the following?
a. atomic number **b.** mass number
c. mass number − atomic number
d. mass number + atomic number

23 Write the names and symbols of the elements with the following atomic numbers:
a. 3 **b.** 9 **c.** 20 **d.** 30
e. 10 **f.** 14 **g.** 53 **h.** 8

24 Write the names and symbols of the elements with the following atomic numbers:
a. 1 **b.** 11 **c.** 19 **d.** 82
e. 35 **f.** 47 **g.** 15 **h.** 2

25 How many protons and electrons are there in a neutral atom of the following?
a. argon **b.** zinc
c. iodine **d.** cadmium

26 How many protons and electrons are there in a neutral atom of the following?
a. carbon **b.** fluorine
c. tin **d.** nickel

27 Complete the following table for each neutral atom:

Name of the Element	Symbol	Atomic Number	Mass Number	Number of Protons	Number of Neutrons	Number of Electrons
	Al		27			
		12			12	
Potassium					20	
				16	15	
			56			26

28 Complete the following table for each neutral atom:

Name of the Element	Symbol	Atomic Number	Mass Number	Number of Protons	Number of Neutrons	Number of Electrons
	N		15			
Calcium			42			
				38	50	
		14			16	
		56	138			

5 Isotopes and Atomic Mass

LEARNING GOAL

Give the number of protons, neutrons, and electrons in one or more of the isotopes of an element; calculate the atomic mass of an element using the abundance and mass of its naturally occurring isotopes.

We have seen that all atoms of the same element have the same number of protons and electrons. Although Dalton could not know it at the time, scientists eventually discovered in 1913 that atoms of any one element are not entirely identical because the atoms of most elements have different numbers of neutrons. When a sample of an element consists of

SELF-STUDY ACTIVITY
Atoms and Isotopes

TUTORIAL
Isotopes

two or more atoms with differing numbers of neutrons, those atoms are called *isotopes*. We will see that some isotopes of an element are stable, whereas others are radioactive, breaking down and emitting radiation particles.

Isotopes

Isotopes are atoms of the same element that have the same atomic number but different numbers of neutrons. For example, all atoms of the element magnesium (Mg) have an atomic number of 12. Thus every magnesium atom always has 12 protons. However, some of the magnesium atoms have 12 neutrons, others have 13 neutrons, and still others have 14 neutrons. These different numbers of neutrons give the magnesium atoms different mass numbers but do not change their chemical behavior.

To distinguish between the different isotopes of an element, we write an **atomic symbol** for a particular isotope with its mass number in the upper left corner and its atomic number in the lower left corner.

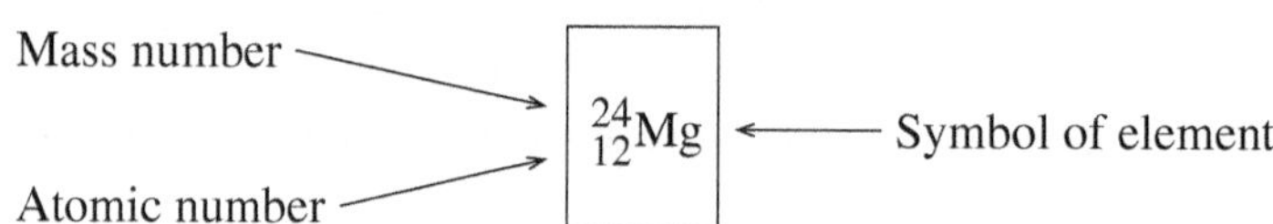

Atomic symbol for an isotope of magnesium, Mg-24.

Pearson Education

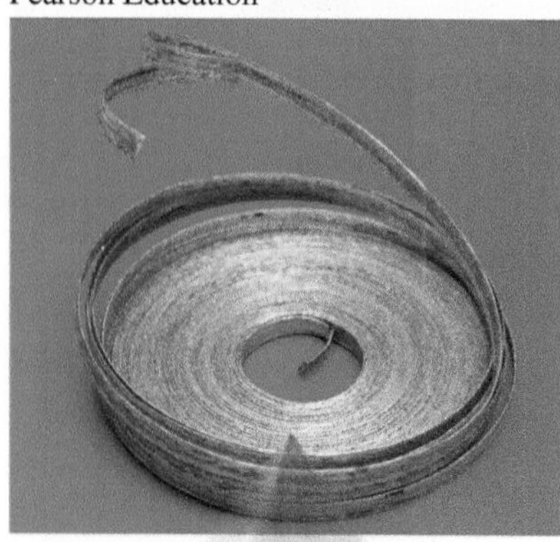

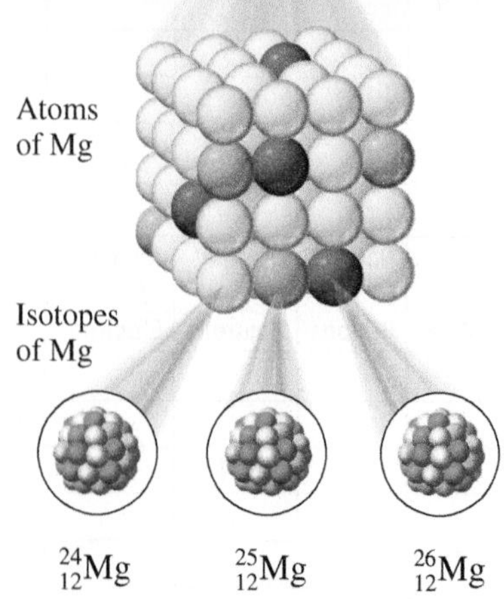

The nuclei of the three naturally occurring magnesium isotopes have the same number of protons, but different numbers of neutrons.

An isotope may be referred to by its name or symbol, followed by the mass number, such as magnesium-24 or Mg-24. Magnesium has three naturally occurring isotopes, as shown in Table 7.

TABLE 7 Isotopes of Magnesium

Atomic Symbol	$^{24}_{12}Mg$	$^{25}_{12}Mg$	$^{26}_{12}Mg$
Name	Mg-24	Mg-25	Mg-26
Number of Protons	12	12	12
Number of Electrons	12	12	12
Mass Number	**24**	**25**	**26**
Number of Neutrons	**12**	**13**	**14**
Mass of Isotope (amu)	23.99	24.99	25.98
% Abundance	78.70	10.13	11.17

SAMPLE PROBLEM 8 **Identifying Protons and Neutrons in Isotopes**

The element neon has three naturally occurring stable isotopes: Ne-20, Ne-21, and Ne-22. State the number of protons and neutrons in the stable isotopes of neon (Ne):

a. $^{20}_{10}Ne$ **b.** $^{21}_{10}Ne$ **c.** $^{22}_{10}Ne$

SOLUTION

The atomic number of Ne is 10, which means that each isotope has 10 protons. The number of neutrons in each isotope is found by subtracting the number of protons (10) from each of their mass numbers.

a. 10 protons; 10 neutrons $(20 - 10)$
b. 10 protons; 11 neutrons $(21 - 10)$
c. 10 protons; 12 neutrons $(22 - 10)$

STUDY CHECK 8

Write an atomic symbol for each of the following isotopes:

a. a nitrogen atom with 8 neutrons
b. an atom with 35 protons and 46 neutrons
c. an atom with mass number 27 and 13 neutrons

Atomic Mass

In laboratory work, a chemist generally uses samples with many atoms that contain all the different isotopes of an element. Because each kind of isotope has a different mass, chemists have calculated an **atomic mass** for an "average atom," which is a *weighted average* of the masses of all the naturally occurring isotopes of that element. On the periodic table, the atomic mass is the number including decimal places that is shown below the symbol of each element. Most of the elements consist of two or more isotopes, which is one reason why atomic masses on the periodic table are seldom whole numbers.

Calculating Atomic Mass Using Isotopes

To calculate the atomic mass of an element, we need to know the percent abundance of each isotope and its mass, which are determined experimentally. For example, a large sample of naturally occurring chlorine consists of 75.76% of ${}^{35}_{17}\text{Cl}$ atoms and 24.24% of ${}^{37}_{17}\text{Cl}$ atoms. The atomic mass is a *weighted average* because it is calculated from the percent abundance of each isotope and its mass: the isotope ${}^{35}_{17}\text{Cl}$ has a mass of 34.97 amu, and the isotope ${}^{37}_{17}\text{Cl}$ has a mass of 36.97 amu.

$$\text{Atomic mass of Cl} = \underbrace{\text{mass of } {}^{35}_{17}\text{Cl} \times \frac{{}^{35}_{17}\text{Cl}\%}{100\%}}_{\text{mass from } {}^{35}_{17}\text{Cl}} + \underbrace{\text{mass of } {}^{37}_{17}\text{Cl} \times \frac{{}^{37}_{17}\text{Cl}\%}{100\%}}_{\text{mass from } {}^{37}_{17}\text{Cl}}$$

Isotope	Mass (amu)		Abundance (%)		Contribution to Average Cl Atom
${}^{35}_{17}\text{Cl}$	34.97	$\times$	$\frac{75.76}{100}$	=	26.49 amu
${}^{37}_{17}\text{Cl}$	36.97	$\times$	$\frac{24.24}{100}$	=	8.962 amu
			Atomic mass of Cl	=	35.45 amu (weighted average mass)

The atomic mass of 35.45 amu is the weighted average mass of a sample of Cl atoms, although no individual Cl atom actually has this mass. An atomic mass of 35.45, which is closer to the mass number of Cl-35, indicates there is a higher percentage of ${}^{35}_{17}\text{Cl}$ atoms in the chlorine sample. In fact, there are about three atoms of ${}^{35}_{17}\text{Cl}$ for every one atom of ${}^{37}_{17}\text{Cl}$ in a sample of chlorine atoms.

Table 8 lists the naturally occurring isotopes of selected elements, their atomic mass, and their most prevalent isotope.

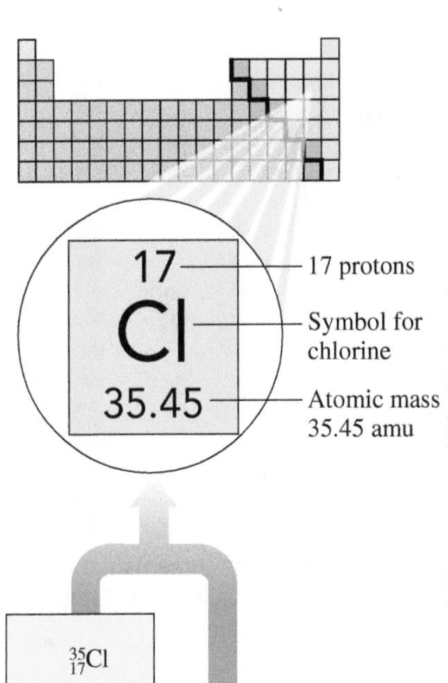

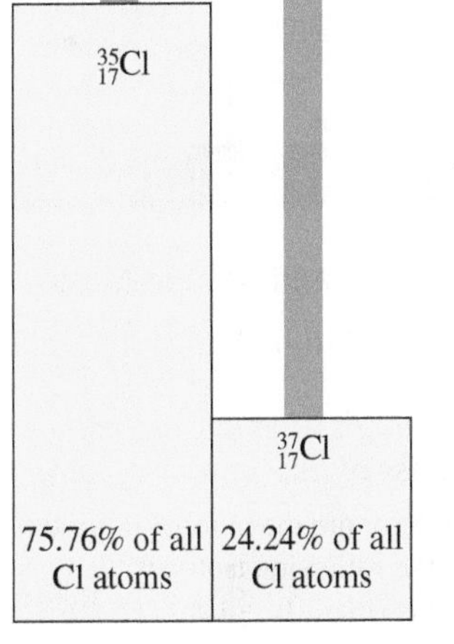

Chlorine, with two naturally occurring isotopes, has an atomic mass of 35.45 amu.

TUTORIAL
Atomic Mass Calculations

TABLE 8 The Atomic Mass of Some Elements

Element	Stable Isotopes	Atomic Mass (weighted average)	Most Prevalent Isotope
Lithium	${}^{6}_{3}\text{Li}$, ${}^{7}_{3}\text{Li}$	6.941 amu	${}^{7}_{3}\text{Li}$
Carbon	${}^{12}_{6}\text{C}$, ${}^{13}_{6}\text{C}$, ${}^{14}_{6}\text{C}$	12.01 amu	${}^{12}_{6}\text{C}$
Oxygen	${}^{16}_{8}\text{O}$, ${}^{17}_{8}\text{O}$, ${}^{18}_{8}\text{O}$	16.00 amu	${}^{16}_{8}\text{O}$
Fluorine	${}^{19}_{9}\text{F}$	19.00 amu	${}^{19}_{9}\text{F}$
Sulfur	${}^{32}_{16}\text{S}$, ${}^{33}_{16}\text{S}$, ${}^{34}_{16}\text{S}$, ${}^{36}_{16}\text{S}$	32.07 amu	${}^{32}_{16}\text{S}$
Copper	${}^{63}_{29}\text{Cu}$, ${}^{65}_{29}\text{Cu}$	63.55 amu	${}^{63}_{29}\text{Cu}$

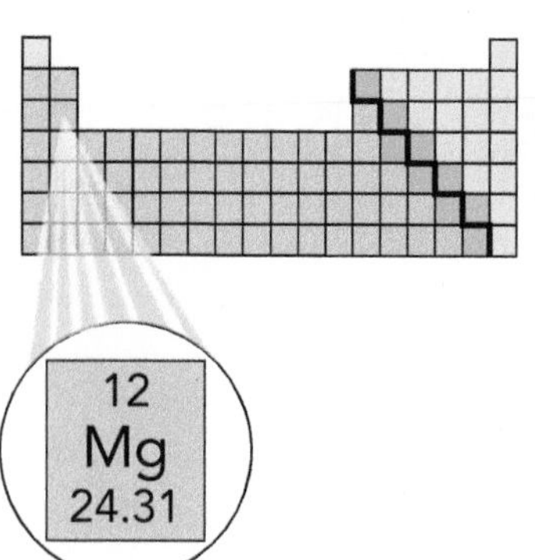

Magnesium, with three naturally occuring isotopes, has an atomic mass of 24.31 amu.

CONCEPT CHECK 4 **Average Atomic Mass**

Neon consists of three naturally occurring isotopes: $^{20}_{10}Ne$, $^{21}_{10}Ne$, and $^{22}_{10}Ne$. Using the atomic mass on the periodic table, which isotope of neon is likely to be the most prevalent?

ANSWER

Using the periodic table, we find that the atomic mass for all the naturally occurring isotopes of neon is 20.18 amu. Since this number is very close to the mass number of 20, the isotope Ne-20 is the most prevalent isotope in a naturally occurring sample of neon atoms.

SAMPLE PROBLEM 9 **Calculating Atomic Mass**

Using Table 7, calculate the atomic mass for magnesium.

SOLUTION

Isotope	Mass (amu)		Abundance (%)		Contribution to the Atomic Mass
$^{24}_{12}Mg$	23.99	×	$\frac{78.70}{100}$	=	18.88 amu
$^{25}_{12}Mg$	24.99	×	$\frac{10.13}{100}$	=	2.531 amu
$^{26}_{12}Mg$	25.98	×	$\frac{11.17}{100}$	=	2.902 amu
			Atomic mass of Mg	=	24.31 amu (weighted average mass)

STUDY CHECK 9

There are two naturally occurring isotopes of boron. The isotope $^{10}_{5}B$ has a mass of 10.01 amu with an abundance of 19.80%, and the isotope $^{11}_{5}B$ has a mass of 11.01 amu with an abundance of 80.20%. What is the atomic mass of boron?

QUESTIONS AND PROBLEMS

5 Isotopes and Atomic Mass

LEARNING GOAL: *Give the number of protons, neutrons, and electrons in one or more of the isotopes of an element; calculate the atomic mass of an element using the abundance and mass of its naturally occurring isotopes.*

29 What are the number of protons, neutrons, and electrons in the following isotopes?
a. $^{89}_{38}Sr$ **b.** $^{52}_{24}Cr$ **c.** $^{34}_{16}S$ **d.** $^{81}_{35}Br$

30 What are the number of protons, neutrons, and electrons in the following isotopes?
a. $^{2}_{1}H$ **b.** $^{14}_{7}N$ **c.** $^{26}_{14}Si$ **d.** $^{70}_{30}Zn$

31 Write the atomic symbols for isotopes with the following:
a. 15 protons and 16 neutrons
b. 35 protons and 45 neutrons
c. 50 electrons and 72 neutrons
d. a chlorine atom with 18 neutrons
e. a mercury atom with 122 neutrons

32 Write the atomic symbols for isotopes with the following:
a. an oxygen atom with 10 neutrons
b. 4 protons and 5 neutrons
c. 25 electrons and 28 neutrons
d. a mass number of 24 and 13 neutrons
e. a nickel atom with 32 neutrons

33 Argon has three naturally occurring isotopes, with mass numbers 36, 38, and 40.
a. Write the atomic symbol for each of these atoms.
b. How are these isotopes alike?
c. How are they different?
d. Why is the atomic mass of argon on the periodic table not a whole number?
e. Which isotope is most prevalent in a sample of argon?

34 Strontium has four naturally occurring isotopes, with mass numbers 84, 86, 87, and 88.
a. Write the atomic symbol for each of these atoms.
b. How are these isotopes alike?
c. How are they different?
d. Why is the atomic mass of strontium on the periodic table not a whole number?
e. Which isotope is the most prevalent in a sample of strontium?

35 Two isotopes of gallium are naturally occurring. The isotope $^{69}_{31}Ga$ has a percent abundance of 60.11% and a mass of 68.93 amu, and the isotope $^{71}_{31}Ga$ has a percent abundance of 39.89% and a mass of 70.92 amu. Calculate the atomic mass of gallium.

36 Two isotopes of copper are naturally occurring. The isotope $^{63}_{29}Cu$ has a percent abundance of 69.09% and a mass of 62.93 amu, and the isotope $^{65}_{29}Cu$ has a percent abundance of 30.91% and a mass of 64.93 amu. Calculate the atomic mass of copper.

6 Electron Arrangement in Atoms

LEARNING GOAL

Describe the energy levels, sublevels, and orbitals for the electrons in an atom.

We have seen that the protons and neutrons are contained in the small, dense nucleus of an atom. However, it is the electrons within the atoms that determine the physical and chemical properties of the elements. Therefore, we need to understand how electrons are arranged within the large volume of space surrounding the nucleus.

Electron Energy Levels

Scientists have now determined that every electron occupies an **energy level**, which has a specific energy. Each energy level has a *principal quantum number* (n), starting with the lowest energy level $n = 1$ up to the highest energy level $n = 7$.

Electrons in the lower energy levels are usually closer to the nucleus, while electrons in the higher energy levels are farther away. As an analogy, we can think of the energy levels of an atom as similar to the shelves in a bookcase (see Figure 11). The first shelf is the lowest energy level; the second shelf would be the second energy level. If we are arranging books on the shelves, it would take less energy to fill the bottom shelf first, and then the second shelf, and so on. However, we could never put a book in the space between any of the shelves. Similarly, an electron must be at one of the specific energy levels, and not between them.

Unlike bookcases, there is a large difference between the energy of the first and second energy levels, but then the higher levels are closer together. Another difference is that the higher electron energy levels hold more electrons than the lower energy levels.

Increasing Energy

$n = 5$

$n = 4$

$n = 3$

$n = 2$

$n = 1$

Nucleus

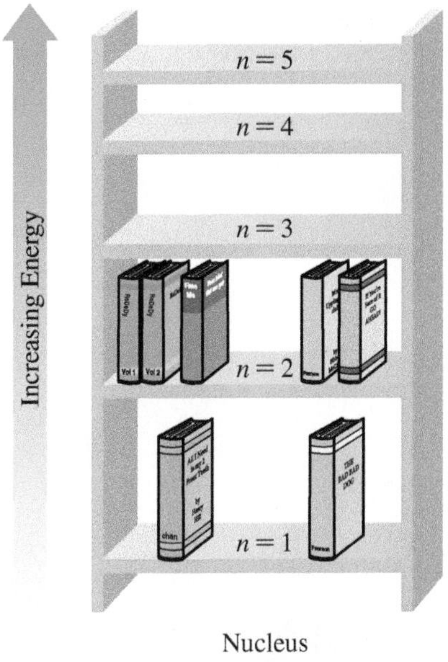

FIGURE 11 An electron can have the energy of only one of the energy levels in an atom.

Q Does an electron in $n = 3$ have less or greater energy than an electron in $n = 1$?

Electron Sublevels

Each of the energy levels consists of one or more **sublevels**, in which electrons with identical energy are found. The sublevels are identified by the letters *s*, *p*, *d*, and *f*. The number of sublevels within each energy level is equal to its principal quantum number, n (see Figure 12). For example, the first energy level ($n = 1$) has one sublevel, 1*s*. The second energy level ($n = 2$) has two sublevels, 2*s* and 2*p*. The third energy level ($n = 3$) has three sublevels, 3*s*, 3*p*, and 3*d*. The fourth energy level ($n = 4$) has four sublevels: 4*s*, 4*p*, 4*d*, and 4*f*. Energy levels $n = 5$, $n = 6$, and $n = 7$ also have as many sublevels as the value of n, but only *s*, *p*, *d*, and *f* sublevels are utilized to hold the electrons of atoms of the 118 elements known today. Within each energy level, the *s* sublevel has the lowest energy, the *p* sublevel has the next lowest energy, then the *d* sublevel, and finally the *f* sublevel.

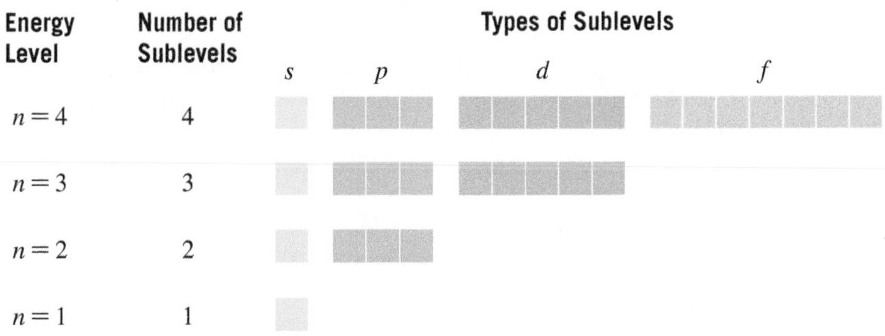

Energy Level	Number of Sublevels	Types of Sublevels
		s *p* *d* *f*
$n = 4$	4	
$n = 3$	3	
$n = 2$	2	
$n = 1$	1	

FIGURE 12 The number of sublevels in an energy level is the same as the principal quantum number n.

Q How many sublevels are in energy level $n = 5$?

Chemistry Link to the Environment

ENERGY-SAVING FLUORESCENT BULBS

The compact fluorescent light (CFL) is replacing the standard lightbulb we use in our homes and workplaces. Compared to a standard lightbulb, the CFL has a longer life and uses less electricity. Within about 20 days of use, the fluorescent bulb saves enough money in electricity costs to pay for its higher initial cost.

A standard incandescent lightbulb has a thin tungsten filament inside a sealed glass bulb. When the light is switched on, electricity flows through this filament, and electrical energy is converted to heat energy. When the filament reaches a temperature around 2300 °C, we see white light.

A fluorescent bulb produces light in a different way. When the switch is turned on, electrons move between two electrodes and collide with mercury atoms in a mixture of mercury and argon gas inside the bulb. When the electrons in the mercury atoms absorb energy from the collisions, electrons are raised to higher energy levels. As electrons fall to lower levels, energy is emitted that leads to the emission of visible light (fluorescence) by the phosphor coating inside the tube.

The production of light in a fluorescent bulb is more efficient than in an incandescent lightbulb. A 75-watt incandescent bulb can be replaced by a 20-watt CFL that gives the same amount of light, providing a 70% reduction in electricity costs. A typical incandescent lightbulb lasts for one to two months, whereas a CFL lasts from one to two years. One drawback of the CFL is that each contains about 4 mg of mercury. As long as the bulb stays intact, no mercury is released. However, used CFL bulbs should not be disposed of in household trash, but should be taken to a recycling center.

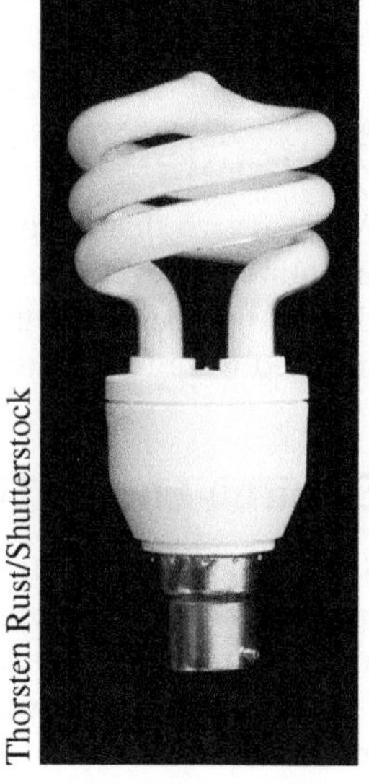

A compact fluorescent light (CFL) uses up to 70% less energy.

Thorsten Rust/Shutterstock

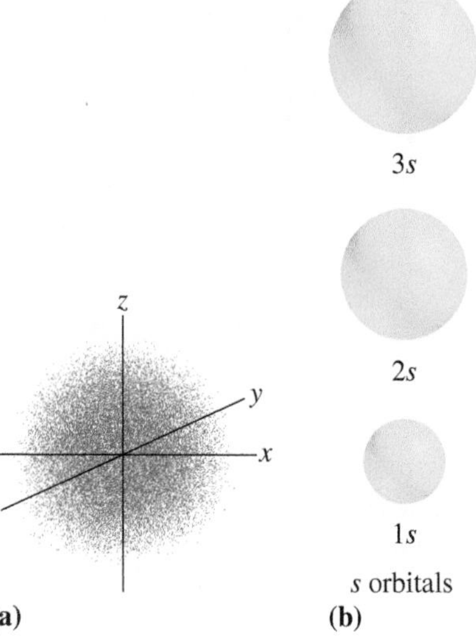

FIGURE 13 **(a)** The electron cloud of an *s* orbital represents the highest probability of finding an *s* electron. **(b)** The *s* orbitals are shown as spheres. The sizes of the *s* orbitals increase because they contain electrons at higher energy levels.

Q Is the probability high or low of finding an *s* electron outside an *s* orbital?

Orbitals

Imagine that you could draw a circle with a 100-m radius around your chemistry classroom. There is a high probability of finding you within that circle when your chemistry class is in session. But once in a while, you may be found outside that circle because you were sick or your car did not start. In a similar way, we do not know the exact location of an electron in an atom at any given time. However, we can describe a three-dimensional space called an **orbital** in which there is a high probability of finding an electron.

Each type of orbital has a unique three-dimensional shape. Electrons in *s* orbitals are most likely found in a region with a spherical shape. Imagine that you take a picture of the electron in an *s* orbital every second for an hour. When all these photos are overlaid, the result would look like the electron cloud shown in Figure 13a. For convenience, we draw this type of electron cloud as a sphere called an *s* orbital. There is one *s* orbital for every energy level starting with $n = 1$. For example, in the first, second, and third energy levels, there are *s* orbitals designated as 1*s*, 2*s*, and 3*s*. As the principal quantum number increases, there is an increase in the size of the *s* orbitals (see Figure13b). For all energy levels, a single orbital can hold up to two electrons, which allows an *s* orbital in any energy level to hold two electrons.

The orbitals occupied by *p*, *d*, and *f* electrons have different three-dimensional shapes than that of the *s* electrons. There are three *p* orbitals in each sublevel, starting with $n = 2$. Each *p* orbital has two lobes like a balloon tied in the middle. The three *p* orbitals in each *p* sublevel are arranged along the *x*, *y*, and *z* axes around the nucleus (see Figure 14). As with the *s* orbital, each *p* orbital can hold two electrons, which means that three *p* orbitals can hold up to six electrons. At higher energy levels, the shape of *p* orbitals is the same, but their volume increases.

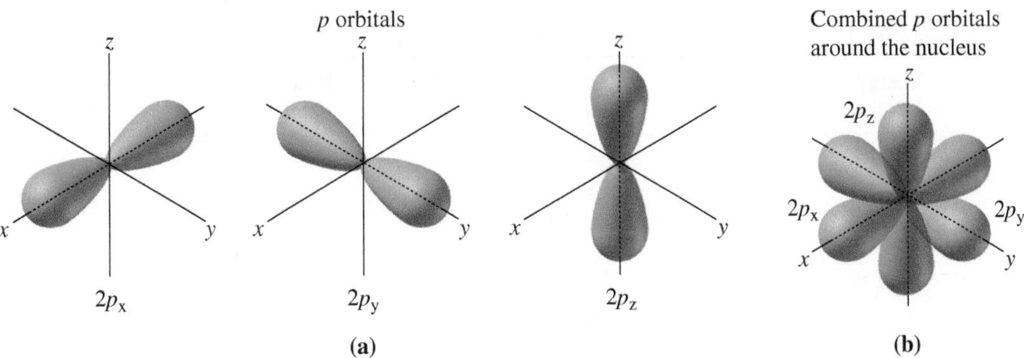

FIGURE 14 A *p* orbital has two regions of high probability, which gives a "dumb-bell" shape. **(a)** Each of the *p* orbitals is aligned along a different axis from other *p* orbitals. **(b)** All three *p* orbitals are shown around the nucleus.

Q What is the maximum number of electrons possible in a *p* sublevel?

In summary, energy level $n = 2$, which has $2s$ and $2p$ sublevels, contains one *s* orbital and three *p* orbitals. Thus, the $n = 2$ energy level can hold a maximum of eight electrons.

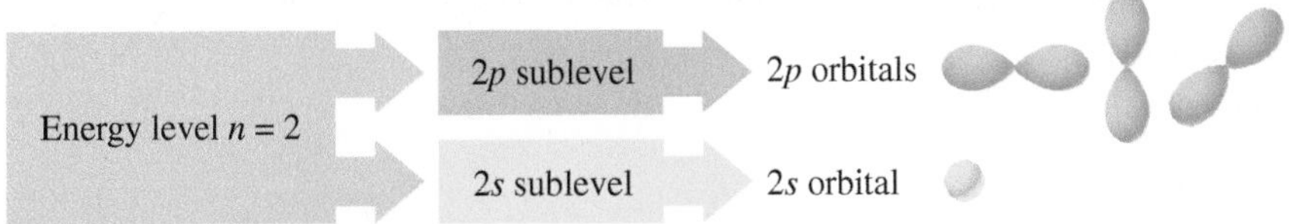

Energy level $n = 2$ is made up of one $2s$ orbital and three $2p$ orbitals.

Energy level $n = 3$ consists of three sublevels *s*, *p*, and *d*. A *d* sublevel consists of five *d* orbitals. Because each *d* orbital can hold two electrons, a *d* sublevel can have a maximum of ten electrons (see Figure 15).

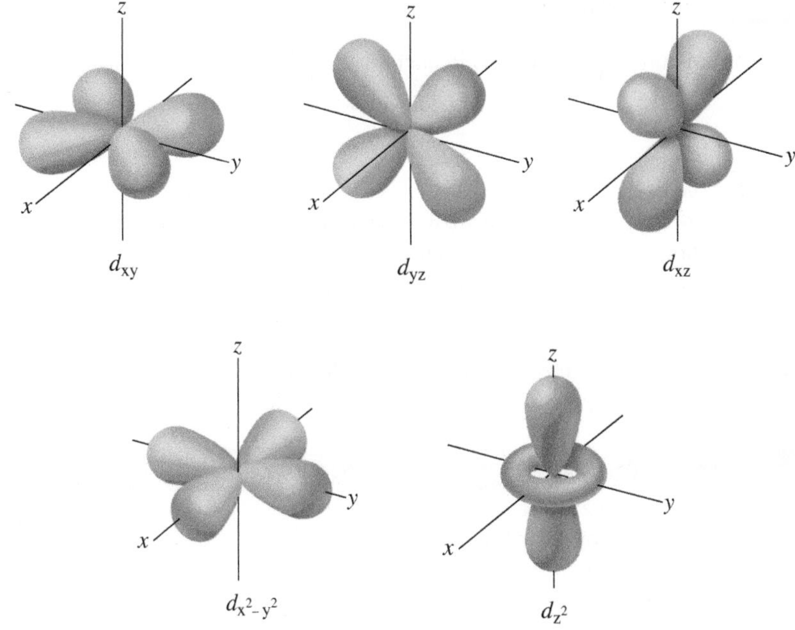

FIGURE 15 Four of the five *d* orbitals consist of four lobes that are aligned along or between different axes. One *d* orbital consists of two lobes and a doughnut-shaped ring around its center.

Q What is the maximum number of electrons possible in the $5d$ sublevel?

Energy level $n = 4$ consists of four sublevels *s*, *p*, *d*, and *f*. In the *f* sublevel, there are seven *f* orbitals. Because each *f* orbital can hold two electrons, the *f* sublevel can have a maximum of 14 electrons (see Table 9). The shapes of *f* orbitals are more complex, and we have not included them in this text.

TABLE 9 Electron Capacity in Sublevels for Energy Levels 1–4

Energy Level (n)	Number of Sublevels	Type of Sublevel	Number of Orbitals	Maximum Number of Electrons	Total Electrons
4	4	$4f$	7	14	32
		$4d$	5	10	
		$4p$	3	6	
		$4s$	1	2	
3	3	$3d$	5	10	18
		$3p$	3	6	
		$3s$	1	2	
2	2	$2p$	3	6	8
		$2s$	1	2	
1	1	$1s$	1	2	2

CONCEPT CHECK 5 **Energy Levels, Sublevels, and Orbitals**

Indicate the type and number of orbitals available in each of the following:

a. $3p$ sublevel **b.** $n = 2$
c. $1s$ sublevel **d.** $4d$ sublevel

ANSWER

a. The $3p$ sublevel contains three $3p$ orbitals.
b. The $n = 2$ energy level consists of one $2s$ orbital and three $2p$ orbitals.
c. The $1s$ sublevel consists of one s orbital.
d. The $4d$ sublevel contains five $4d$ orbitals.

SAMPLE PROBLEM 10 **Electrons**

Indicate the maximum number of electrons in each of the following:

a. $2p$ orbital **b.** $n = 2$ **c.** $3d$ sublevel

SOLUTION

a. A $2p$ orbital can hold two electrons.
b. The $n = 2$ energy level with one $2s$ orbital (two electrons) and three $2p$ orbitals (six electrons) can hold a maximum of 8 electrons.
c. The $3d$ sublevel with five d orbitals can hold 10 electrons.

STUDY CHECK 10

What is the maximum number of electrons in the $4s$ sublevel?

QUESTIONS AND PROBLEMS

6 Electron Arrangement in Atoms

LEARNING GOAL: *Describe the energy levels, sublevels, and orbitals for the electrons in an atom.*

37 Describe the shape of each of the following orbitals:
a. $1s$ **b.** $2p$ **c.** $5s$

38 Describe the shape of each of the following orbitals:
a. $3p$ **b.** $6s$ **c.** $4p$

39 Identify what is the same for **a–d**:
1. They have the same shape.
2. The maximum number of electrons is the same.
3. They are in the same energy level.

a. $1s$ and $2s$ orbitals
b. $3s$ and $3p$ sublevels
c. $3p$ and $4p$ sublevels
d. three $3p$ orbitals

40 Identify what is the same for **a–d**:
1. They have the same shape.
2. The maximum number of electrons is the same.
3. They are in the same energy level.

a. $5s$ and $6s$ orbitals
b. $3p$ and $4p$ orbitals
c. $3s$ and $4s$ sublevels
d. $2s$ and $2p$ orbitals

41 Indicate the number of each in the following:
a. orbitals in the 3*d* sublevel
b. sublevels in the $n = 1$ energy level
c. orbitals in the 6*s* sublevel
d. orbitals in the $n = 3$ energy level

42 Indicate the number of each in the following:
a. orbitals in the $n = 2$ energy level
b. sublevels in the $n = 4$ energy level
c. orbitals in the 5*f* sublevel
d. orbitals in the 6*p* sublevel

43 Indicate the maximum number of electrons in the following:
a. 3*p* orbital
b. 3*p* sublevel
c. $n = 4$ energy level
d. 5*d* sublevel

44 Indicate the maximum number of electrons in the following:
a. 3*s* sublevel
b. 4*p* orbital
c. $n = 3$ energy level
d. 4*f* sublevel

7 Orbital Diagrams and Electron Configurations

LEARNING GOAL

Draw the orbital diagram and write the electron configuration for an element.

We can now look at how electrons are arranged in the orbitals within an atom. An **electron configuration** shows the placement of the electrons in the orbitals in order of increasing energy (see Figure 16). In this energy diagram, we see that the electrons in the 1*s* orbital have the lowest energy level. The energy level is higher for the 2*s* orbital and is even higher for the 2*p* orbitals.

We can begin our discussion of electron configuration by using **orbital diagrams** in which boxes represent the orbitals. Any orbital can have a maximum of two electrons.

To draw an orbital diagram, the lowest energy orbitals are filled in first. For example, in the diagram for a carbon atom with six electrons, the first two electrons fill the 1*s* orbital; the next two electrons go into the 2*s* orbital. When an orbital contains two electrons, the arrows representing the electrons are drawn in opposite directions, one up and one down.

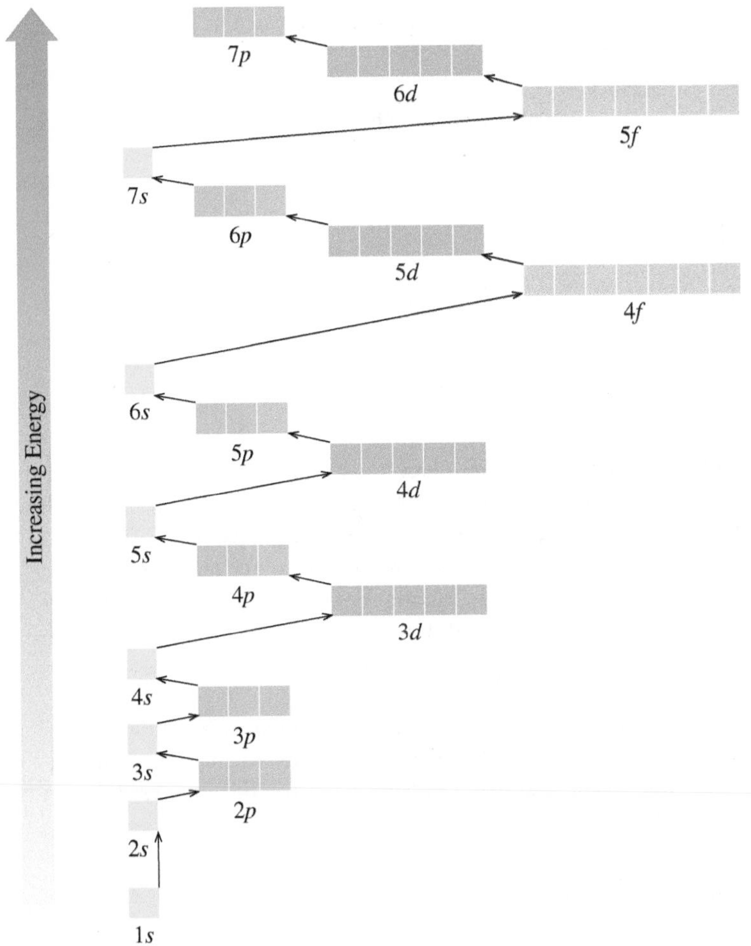

FIGURE 16 The orbitals in an atom fill in order of increasing energy, beginning with 1*s*.

Q Why does the 3*d* sublevel fill after the 4*s* sublevel?

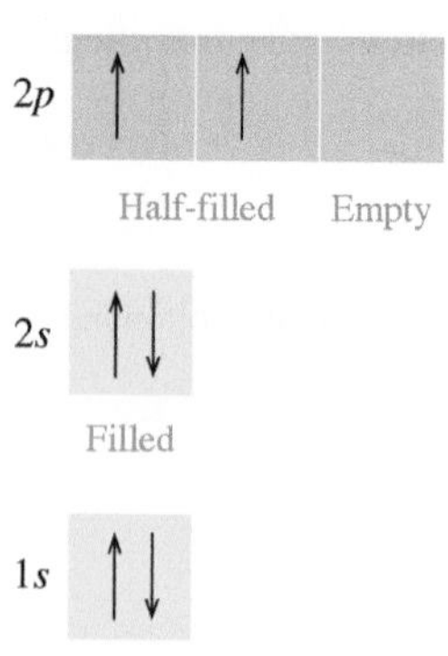

Orbital diagram for carbon

The last two electrons in carbon begin to fill the 2*p* orbitals, which have the next lowest energy. However, there are three 2*p* orbitals of equal energy. Because the negatively charged electrons repel each other, they go into separate 2*p* orbitals.

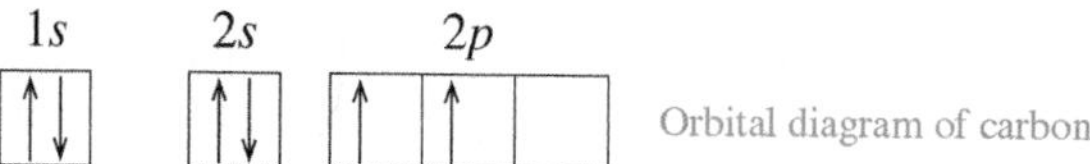

Orbital diagram of carbon

Electron Configurations

Chemists use a notation called the **electron configuration** to indicate the placement of the electrons of an atom in order of increasing energy. For example, the electron configuration for carbon is obtained by writing the lowest energy orbital first, followed by the orbitals of the next lower energy sublevel. The total number of electrons in each orbital is shown as a superscript.

Electron Configuration for Carbon

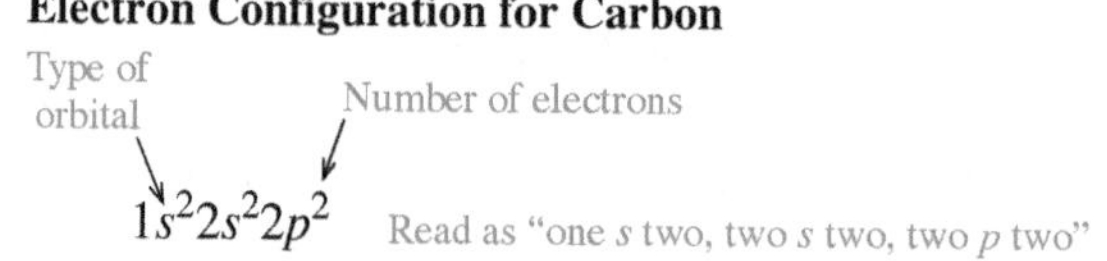

TUTORIAL
Electron Configurations

Period 1 Hydrogen and Helium

We can now draw the orbital diagrams and write the electron configurations for the elements H and He in Period 1. The 1*s* orbital (which is also the 1*s* sublevel) is written first because it has the lowest energy. Hydrogen has one electron in the 1*s* sublevel; helium has two. In the orbital diagram, the electrons for helium are drawn as arrows in opposite directions.

Atomic Number	Element	Orbital Diagram 1s	Electron Configuration
1	H	↑	$1s^1$
2	He	↑↓	$1s^2$

Period 2 Lithium to Neon

Period 2 begins with lithium, which has three electrons. The first two electrons fill the 1*s* orbital, while the third electron goes into the 2*s* orbital, the sublevel with the next lowest energy. In beryllium, another electron is added to complete the 2*s* orbital. The next six electrons are used to fill the 2*p* orbitals. The electrons are added one at a time from boron to nitrogen, which gives three half-filled 2*p* orbitals. From oxygen to neon, the remaining three electrons pair up to complete the 2*p* sublevel. In writing the complete electron configurations for the elements in Period 2, begin with the 1*s* followed by the 2*s* and the 2*p* orbitals.

An electron configuration can also be written in an *abbreviated configuration*. The electron configuration of the preceding noble gas is replaced by writing its symbol inside square brackets. For example, the electron configuration for lithium, $1s^2 2s^1$, can be abbreviated as $[He]2s^1$, where $[He]$ replaces $1s^2$.

Atomic Number	Element	Orbital Diagram	Electron Configuration	Abbreviated Electron Configuration
		1s 2s		
3	Li	[↑↓] [↑]	$1s^22s^1$	$[He]2s^1$
4	Be	[↑↓] [↑↓]	$1s^22s^2$	$[He]2s^2$
		2p		
5	B	[↑↓] [↑↓] [↑| |]	$1s^22s^22p^1$	$[He]2s^22p^1$
6	C	[↑↓] [↑↓] [↑|↑|]	$1s^22s^22p^2$	$[He]2s^22p^2$
		Unpaired electrons		
7	N	[↑↓] [↑↓] [↑|↑|↑]	$1s^22s^22p^3$	$[He]2s^22p^3$
8	O	[↑↓] [↑↓] [↑↓|↑|↑]	$1s^22s^22p^4$	$[He]2s^22p^4$
9	F	[↑↓] [↑↓] [↑↓|↑↓|↑]	$1s^22s^22p^5$	$[He]2s^22p^5$
10	Ne	[↑↓] [↑↓] [↑↓|↑↓|↑↓]	$1s^22s^22p^6$	$[He]2s^22p^6$

CONCEPT CHECK 6 **Orbital Diagrams and Electron Configurations**

Draw or write each of the following for a nitrogen atom:

a. orbital diagram **b.** electron configuration
c. abbreviated electron configuration

ANSWER

On the periodic table, nitrogen has atomic number 7, which means it has seven electrons.

a. For the orbital diagram, we draw boxes to represent the 1*s*, 2*s*, and 2*p* orbitals.

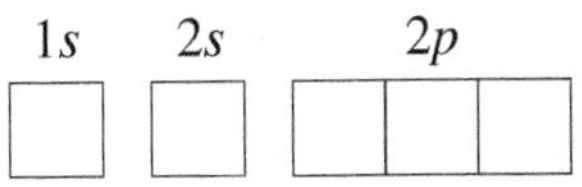

1s 2s 2p
[ ] [ ] [| |]

First, we place a pair of electrons in both the 1*s* and 2*s* orbitals. Then, we place the three remaining electrons in three separate 2*p* orbitals with arrows drawn in the same direction.

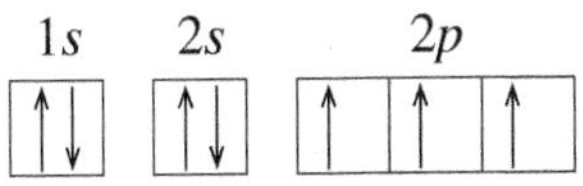

1s 2s 2p
[↑↓] [↑↓] [↑|↑|↑] Orbital diagram for nitrogen (N)

b. The electron configuration for nitrogen is written to show the orbitals and electrons in order of increasing energy.

$1s^22s^22p^3$ Electron configuration for nitrogen (N)

c. The abbreviated electron configuration for nitrogen is written by substituting the symbol of [He], the noble gas that precedes Period 2, for the $1s^2$ notation in the electron configuration.

$[He]2s^22p^3$ Abbreviated electron configuration for nitrogen (N)

Period 3 Sodium to Argon

In Period 3, electrons enter the orbitals of the 3*s* and 3*p* sublevels, but not the 3*d* sublevel. We notice that the elements sodium to argon, which are directly below the elements lithium to neon in Period 2, have a similar pattern of filling their *s* and *p* orbitals. In sodium and magnesium, one and two electrons go into the 3*s* orbital. The electrons for aluminum, silicon, and phosphorus go into separate 3*p* orbitals. We can draw the orbital diagram for phosphorus with three half-filled 3*p* orbitals as follows:

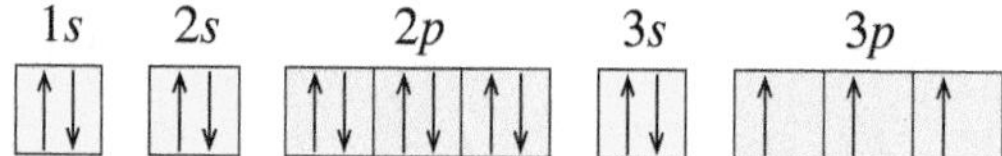

For elements in Period 3 through Period 7, we abbreviate the orbital diagram by using the symbol from the preceding noble gas followed by the boxes for the remaining electrons in the last filled period. In Period 3, the symbol [Ne] replaces the electron configuration of neon, $1s^22s^22p^6$. The abbreviated orbital diagram for phosphorus is as follows:

3*s* 3*p*

[Ne] [↑↓] [↑][↑][↑]

Atomic Number	Element	Orbital Diagram (3*s* and 3*p* orbitals only) 3*s* 3*p*	Electron Configuration	Abbreviated Electron Configuration
11	Na	[Ne] [↑] [ ][ ][ ]	$1s^22s^22p^63s^1$	$[Ne]3s^1$
12	Mg	[Ne] [↑↓] [ ][ ][ ]	$1s^22s^22p^63s^2$	$[Ne]3s^2$
13	Al	[Ne] [↑↓] [↑][ ][ ]	$1s^22s^22p^63s^23p^1$	$[Ne]3s^23p^1$
14	Si	[Ne] [↑↓] [↑][↑][ ]	$1s^22s^22p^63s^23p^2$	$[Ne]3s^23p^2$
15	P	[Ne] [↑↓] [↑][↑][↑]	$1s^22s^22p^63s^23p^3$	$[Ne]3s^23p^3$
16	S	[Ne] [↑↓] [↑↓][↑][↑]	$1s^22s^22p^63s^23p^4$	$[Ne]3s^23p^4$
17	Cl	[Ne] [↑↓] [↑↓][↑↓][↑]	$1s^22s^22p^63s^23p^5$	$[Ne]3s^23p^5$
18	Ar	[Ne] [↑↓] [↑↓][↑↓][↑↓]	$1s^22s^22p^63s^23p^6$	$[Ne]3s^23p^6$

SAMPLE PROBLEM 11 Drawing Orbital Diagrams and Writing Electron Configurations

For the element silicon, draw or write each of the following:

a. orbital diagram
b. electron configuration
c. abbreviated electron configuration

SOLUTION

Analyze the Problem

Given	Atomic Number	Orbital Diagram	Electron Configuration	Abbreviated Electron Configuration
Silicon (Si)	14	Use the order of filling, placing two electrons in separate boxes, and single electrons in highest level.	List the sublevels in order of filling.	Substitute the symbol of the noble gas followed by the remaining order of filling.

a. Starting with the $1s$ orbital, add paired electrons through the $3s$ orbital. Then, place the last two electrons in separate $3p$ orbitals.

$1s$	$2s$	$2p$	$3s$	$3p$	
↑↓	↑↓	↑↓ ↑↓ ↑↓	↑↓	↑ ↑	Complete orbital diagram for Si

b. The electron configuration shows the electrons that fill the orbitals, which are listed in order of increasing energy.

$1s^22s^22p^63s^23p^2$ Electron configuration for Si

c. For silicon, the preceding noble gas is neon. For the abbreviated electron configuration of silicon, we replace $1s^22s^22p^6$ with [Ne].

$[Ne]3s^23p^2$ Abbreviated electron configuration for Si

STUDY CHECK 11

Write the complete and abbreviated electron configurations for sulfur.

Electron Configurations and the Periodic Table

MC™ SELF-STUDY ACTIVITY Bohr's Shell Model

The position of the elements on the periodic table is also related to their electron configurations. Different sections or blocks within the table correspond to the *s*, *p*, *d*, and *f* sublevels and the filling of their orbitals (see Figure 17). Thus, we can also write the electron configuration of an element by reading the periodic table from left to right across each period.

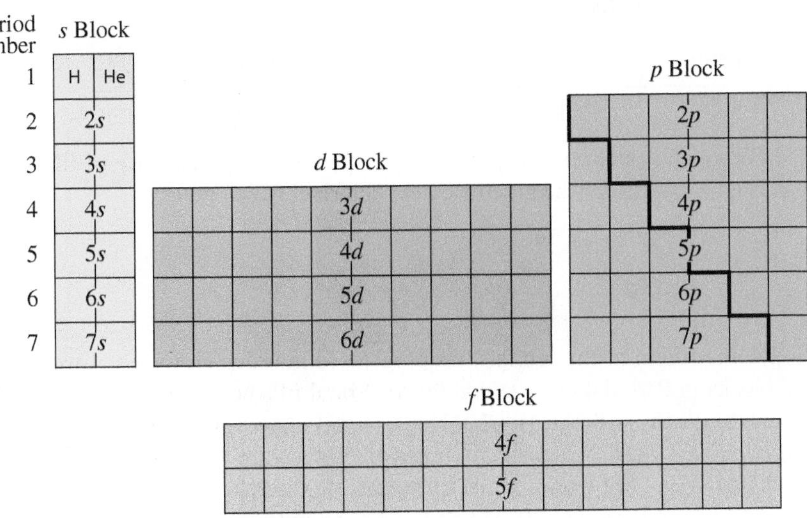

FIGURE 17 Electron configuration follows the order of sublevels on the periodic table.

Q How many electrons are in the $1s$, $2s$, and $2p$ sublevels of neon?

Blocks on the Periodic Table

1. The ***s* block** includes hydrogen and helium as well as the elements in Group 1A (1) and Group 2A (2). This means that the final one or two electrons in the elements of the *s* block are located in an *s* orbital. The period number indicates the particular *s* orbital that is filling: $1s$, $2s$, and so on.
2. The ***p* block** consists of the elements in Group 3A (13) to Group 8A (18). There are six *p* block elements in each period because three *p* orbitals can hold up to six electrons. The period number indicates the particular *p* sublevel that is filling: $2p$, $3p$, and so on.
3. The ***d* block**, which contains the transition elements, first appears after calcium (atomic number 20). There are 10 elements in each period of the *d* block because five *d* orbitals can hold up to 10 electrons. The particular *d* sublevel is one less $(n - 1)$ than the period number. For example, in Period 4, the first *d* block is the $3d$ sublevel. In Period 5, the second *d* block is the $4d$ sublevel.
4. The ***f* block** includes the inner transition elements in the two rows at the bottom of the periodic table. There are 14 elements in each *f* block because seven *f* orbitals can hold up to 14 electrons. Elements that have atomic numbers higher than 57 (La) have electrons in the $4f$ block. The particular *f* sublevel is two less $(n - 2)$ than the period number. For example, in Period 6, the first *f* block is the $4f$ sublevel. In Period 7, the second *f* block is the $5f$ sublevel.

Writing Electron Configurations Using Sublevel Blocks

Now we can write electron configurations using the sublevel blocks on the periodic table as a guide. As before, each configuration begins at H. But now we move across the table, writing down each sublevel block we come to until we reach the element for which we are writing an electron configuration. For example, we will write the electron configuration for chlorine (atomic number 17) from the sublevel blocks on the periodic table.

Step 1 **Locate the element on the periodic table.**
Chlorine (atomic number 17) is in Group 7A (17) and Period 3.

Step 2 **Write the filled sublevels in order, going across each period.** Beginning with 1*s*, and reading from left to right across the periodic table, write the electron configuration for each filled sublevel block as follows:

Period		Sublevel Blocks Filled
1	1*s* sublevel $(\mathrm{H} \rightarrow \mathrm{He})$	$1s^2$
2	2*s* sublevel $(\mathrm{Li} \rightarrow \mathrm{Be})$	$2s^2$
	2*p* sublevel $(\mathrm{B} \rightarrow \mathrm{Ne})$	$2p^6$
3	3*s* sublevel $(\mathrm{Na} \rightarrow \mathrm{Mg})$	$3s^2$

Step 3 **Complete the configuration by counting the electrons in the unfilled block.** Because chlorine is the fifth element in the 3*p* block, there are five electrons in the 3*p* sublevel.

Period		Last Sublevel Block
3	3*p* sublevel $(\mathrm{Al} \rightarrow \mathrm{Cl})$	$3p^5$

The electron configuration is written with the sequence of filled sublevel blocks for the given element chlorine, which gives:

$1s^2 2s^2 2p^6 3s^2 3p^5$

Period 4

Up to Period 4, the filling of the orbitals has progressed in order. However, if we look at the sublevel blocks in Period 4, we see that the 4*s* orbital fills before the 3*d* orbitals. This occurs because the electrons in the 4*s* orbital have slightly lower energy than the electrons in the 3*d* orbitals. This order occurs again in Period 5 when the 5*s* orbital fills before the 4*d* orbitals, and again in Period 6 when the 6*s* fills before the 5*d*.

At the beginning of Period 4, the one and two remaining electrons in potassium (19) and calcium (20) go into the 4*s* orbital. In scandium, the electron following the filled 4*s* orbital goes into the 3*d* block. The 3*d* block continues to fill until it is complete with 10 electrons at zinc (30). Once the 3*d* block is complete, the next six electrons, gallium to krypton, go into the orbitals in the 4*p* block.

CONCEPT CHECK 7 **Electron Configurations**

Give the symbol and name of the element with each of the following electron configurations:

a. $1s^2 2s^2 2p^5$ **b.** $1s^2 2s^2 2p^6 3s^2 3p^6 4s^2 3d^{10} 4p^2$ **c.** $[\mathrm{Ar}]\, 4s^2 3d^6$

ANSWER

a. In the *p* block, Period 2, the fifth element across is F, fluorine.
b. In the *p* block, Period 4, the second element across is Ge, germanium.
c. In the *d* block, Period 4, the sixth element across is Fe, iron.

Atomic Number	Element	Electron Configuration	Abbreviated Electron Configuration
4*s* Block			
19	K	$1s^22s^22p^63s^23p^64s^1$	$[Ar]4s^1$
20	Ca	$1s^22s^22p^63s^23p^64s^2$	$[Ar]4s^2$
3*d* Block			
21	Sc	$1s^22s^22p^63s^23p^64s^23d^1$	$[Ar]4s^23d^1$
22	Ti	$1s^22s^22p^63s^23p^64s^23d^2$	$[Ar]4s^23d^2$
23	V	$1s^22s^22p^63s^23p^64s^23d^3$	$[Ar]4s^23d^3$
24	Cr*	$1s^22s^22p^63s^23p^64s^13d^5$	$[Ar]4s^13d^5$ (half-filled *d* sublevel is stable)
25	Mn	$1s^22s^22p^63s^23p^64s^23d^5$	$[Ar]4s^23d^5$
26	Fe	$1s^22s^22p^63s^23p^64s^23d^6$	$[Ar]4s^23d^6$
27	Co	$1s^22s^22p^63s^23p^64s^23d^7$	$[Ar]4s^23d^7$
28	Ni	$1s^22s^22p^63s^23p^64s^23d^8$	$[Ar]4s^23d^8$
29	Cu*	$1s^22s^22p^63s^23p^64s^13d^{10}$	$[Ar]4s^13d^{10}$ (filled *d* sublevel is stable)
30	Zn	$1s^22s^22p^63s^23p^64s^23d^{10}$	$[Ar]4s^23d^{10}$
4*p* Block			
31	Ga	$1s^22s^22p^63s^23p^64s^23d^{10}4p^1$	$[Ar]4s^23d^{10}4p^1$
32	Ge	$1s^22s^22p^63s^23p^64s^23d^{10}4p^2$	$[Ar]4s^23d^{10}4p^2$
33	As	$1s^22s^22p^63s^23p^64s^23d^{10}4p^3$	$[Ar]4s^23d^{10}4p^3$
34	Se	$1s^22s^22p^63s^23p^64s^23d^{10}4p^4$	$[Ar]4s^23d^{10}4p^4$
35	Br	$1s^22s^22p^63s^23p^64s^23d^{10}4p^5$	$[Ar]4s^23d^{10}4p^5$
36	Kr	$1s^22s^22p^63s^23p^64s^23d^{10}4p^6$	$[Ar]4s^23d^{10}4p^6$

*Exceptions to the order of filling.

SAMPLE PROBLEM 12 **Using Sublevel Blocks to Write Electron Configurations**

Use the sublevel blocks on the periodic table to write the complete electron configuration for selenium.

SOLUTION

Step 1 **Locate the element on the periodic table.** Selenium is in Period 4 and Group 6A (16), which is in the fourth column of the *p* block.

Step 2 **Write the filled sublevels in order, going across each period.** Beginning with 1*s*, and reading from left to right across the periodic table, write the electron configuration for each filled sublevel block as follows:

Period 1 $1s^2$
Period 2 $2s^2 \rightarrow 2p^6$
Period 3 $3s^2 \rightarrow 3p^6$
Period 4 $4s^2 \rightarrow 3d^{10}$

Step 3 **Complete the configuration by counting the electrons in the unfilled block.** There are four electrons in the 4*p* sublevel for Se $(4p^4)$, which completes the electron configuration for Se: $1s^22s^22p^63s^23p^64s^23d^{10}4p^4$.

STUDY CHECK 12

Write the complete electron configuration for tin.

Guide to Writing Electron Configurations using Sublevel Blocks

1 Locate the element on the periodic table.

2 Write the filled sublevels in order, going across each period.

3 Complete the configuration by counting the electrons in the unfilled block.

Exceptions in Sublevel Block Order

Within the filling of the $3d$ sublevel, exceptions occur for chromium and copper. In Cr and Cu, the $3d$ sublevel is close to being a half-filled or filled sublevel, which is particularly stable. Thus, the electron configuration of chromium has only one electron in the $4s$ and five electrons in the $3d$ sublevel, which gives the added stability of a half-filled d sublevel. This is shown in the abbreviated orbital diagram for chromium that follows:

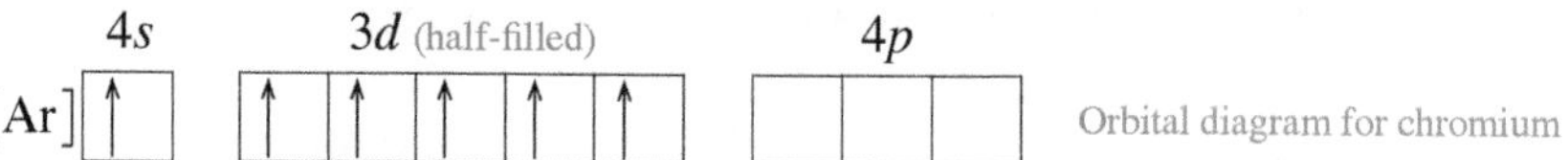

Orbital diagram for chromium

A similar exception occurs for copper, which achieves a stable, filled $3d$ sublevel with ten electrons and only one electron in the $4s$ orbital. This is shown in the abbreviated orbital diagram for copper that follows:

$4s$ $3d$ (filled) $4p$

[Ar] [↑] [↑↓][↑↓][↑↓][↑↓][↑↓] [ ][ ][ ]

Orbital diagram for copper

After the $4s$ and $3d$ sublevels are completed, the $4p$ sublevel fills as expected from gallium to krypton, the noble gas that completes Period 4.

QUESTIONS AND PROBLEMS

7 Orbital Diagrams and Electron Configurations

LEARNING GOAL: *Draw the orbital diagram and write the electron configuration for an element.*

45 Draw an orbital diagram for an atom of each of the following:
a. boron **b.** aluminum
c. phosphorus **d.** argon

46 Draw an orbital diagram for an atom of each of the following:
a. fluorine **b.** sodium
c. magnesium **d.** sulfur

47 Write a complete electron configuration for an atom of each of the following:
a. iron **b.** sodium
c. rubidium **d.** arsenic

48 Write a complete electron configuration for an atom of each of the following:
a. gallium **b.** fluorine
c. phosphorus **d.** cobalt

49 Write an abbreviated electron configuration for an atom of each of the following:
a. magnesium **b.** barium
c. aluminum **d.** titanium

50 Write an abbreviated electron configuration for an atom of each of the following:
a. sodium
b. oxygen
c. nickel
d. silver

51 Give the symbol of the element with each of the following electron configurations:
a. $1s^22s^22p^63s^23p^4$ **b.** $1s^22s^22p^63s^23p^64s^23d^7$
c. $[Ne]3s^23p^2$ **d.** $[Ar]4s^23d^{10}4p^5$

52 Give the symbol of the element with each of the following electron configurations:
a. $1s^22s^22p^4$ **b.** $1s^22s^22p^63s^23p^6$
c. $[Ne]3s^23p^1$ **d.** $[Ar]4s^23d^4$

53 Give the symbol of the element that meets the following conditions:
a. has three electrons in the $n = 3$ energy level
b. has two $2p$ electrons
c. completes the $3p$ sublevel
d. has two electrons in the $4d$ sublevel

54 Give the symbol of the element that meets the following conditions:
a. has five electrons in the $3p$ sublevel
b. has three $2p$ electrons
c. completes the $3s$ sublevel
d. has four $5p$ electrons

55 Give the number of electrons in the indicated orbitals for the following:
a. $3d$ in zinc **b.** $2p$ in sodium
c. $4p$ in arsenic **d.** $5s$ in rubidium

56 Give the number of electrons in the indicated orbitals for the following:
a. $3d$ in manganese **b.** $5p$ in antimony
c. $6p$ in lead **d.** $3s$ in magnesium

LEARNING GOAL

Use the electron configurations of elements to explain the trends in periodic properties.

8 Trends in Periodic Properties

The electron configurations of atoms are an important factor in the physical and chemical properties of the elements. Now we will look at the *valence electrons* in atoms, *atomic size*, *ionization energy*, and *metallic character*. Known as *periodic properties*, each increases or decreases across a period, and then the trend is repeated again in each successive period. We can use the seasonal changes in temperatures as an analogy for periodic properties. In the winter, temperatures are cold and become warmer in the spring. By summer, the outdoor temperatures are high, but begin to cool in the fall. By winter, we expect low temperatures again as the pattern of decreasing and increasing temperatures repeats for another year.

MC TUTORIAL Periodic Trends

TUTORIAL Electron Configurations and the Periodic Table

Group Number and Valence Electrons

The chemical properties of representative elements are mostly due to the **valence electrons**, which are the electrons in the outermost energy level. The *group number* gives the number of valence electrons for each group (vertical column) of representative elements. These valence electrons occupy the *s* and *p* orbitals with the highest principal quantum number *n*. For example, all the elements in Group 1A (1) have one valence electron in an *s* orbital. All the elements in Group 2A (2) have two (2) valence electrons in an *s* orbital. The halogens in Group 7A (17) all have seven valence electrons in *s* and *p* orbitals.

We can see the repetition of the outermost *s* and *p* electrons for the representative elements in Periods 1 to 4 in Table 10. Helium is included in Group 8A (18) because it is a noble gas, but it has only two electrons in its complete energy level.

TABLE 10 Valence Electrons for Representative Elements in Periods 1–4

1A (1)	2A (2)	3A (13)	4A (14)	5A (15)	6A (16)	7A (17)	8A (18)
1 H $1s^1$							2 He $1s^2$
3 Li $2s^1$	4 Be $2s^2$	5 B $2s^22p^1$	6 C $2s^22p^2$	7 N $2s^22p^3$	8 O $2s^22p^4$	9 F $2s^22p^5$	10 Ne $2s^22p^6$
11 Na $3s^1$	12 Mg $3s^2$	13 Al $3s^23p^1$	14 Si $3s^23p^2$	15 P $3s^23p^3$	16 S $3s^23p^4$	17 Cl $3s^23p^5$	18 Ar $3s^23p^6$
19 K $4s^1$	20 Ca $4s^2$	31 Ga $4s^24p^1$	32 Ge $4s^24p^2$	33 As $4s^24p^3$	34 Se $4s^24p^4$	35 Br $4s^24p^5$	36 Kr $4s^24p^6$

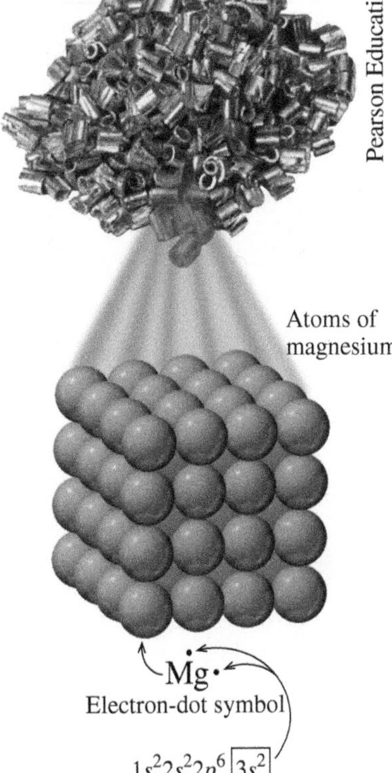

CONCEPT CHECK 8 Using Group Numbers

Using the periodic table, write the group number and the number of valence electrons for each of the following:

a. cesium **b.** iodine **c.** magnesium

ANSWER

a. Cesium (Cs) is in Group 1A (1). Because the group number is the same as the number of valence electrons, cesium has one valence electron.

b. Iodine (I) is in Group 7A (17). Because the group number is the same as the number of valence electrons, iodine has seven valence electrons.

c. Magnesium (Mg) is in Group 2A (2). Because the group number is the same as the number of valence electrons, magnesium has two valence electrons.

Electron-Dot Symbols

TUTORIAL Electron-Dot Symbols for Elements

An **electron-dot symbol** is a convenient way to represent the valence electrons, which are shown as dots placed on the sides, top, or bottom of the symbol for the element. One to four valence electrons are arranged as single dots. When there are five to eight electrons, one or more electrons are paired. Any of the following would be an acceptable electron-dot symbol for magnesium, which has two valence electrons:

Possible Electron-Dot Symbols for the Two Valence Electrons in Magnesium

Ṁg· Mg̣ ·Ṁg ·Mg· Mg̣· ·Mg̣

Electron-dot symbols for selected elements are given in Table 11.

Increasing Number of Valence Electrons →

TABLE 11 Electron-Dot Symbols for Selected Elements in Periods 1–4

	Group Number							
	1A (1)	2A (2)	3A (13)	4A (14)	5A (15)	6A (16)	7A (17)	8A (18)
Number of Valence Electrons	1	2	3	4	5	6	7	8*
Electron-Dot Symbol	H·							He:
	Li·	Ḃe·	·Ḃ·	·Ċ̣·	·N̈̇·	·Ö:	·F̤̈:	:N̤̈e:
	Na·	Ṁg·	·Ȧl·	·Ṩi·	·P̈̇·	·S̤̈:	·C̤̈l:	:Ä̤r:
	K·	Ċa·	·Ġa·	·Ġ̣e·	·Äṣ·	·S̤̈e:	·B̤̈r:	:K̤̈r:

* Helium (He) is stable with 2 valence electrons.

SAMPLE PROBLEM 13 **Writing Electron-Dot Symbols**

Write the electron-dot symbol for each of the following elements:

a. bromine **b.** aluminum

SOLUTION

a. Because the group number for bromine is 7A (17), bromine has seven valence electrons, which are drawn as seven dots, three pairs and one single dot, around the symbol Br.

·B̤̈r:

b. Aluminum, in Group 3A (13), has three valence electrons, which are drawn as three single dots around the symbol Al.

·Ȧl·

STUDY CHECK 13

What is the electron-dot symbol for phosphorus?

Atomic Size

The size of an atom is determined by its *atomic radius*, which is the distance of the valence electrons from the nucleus. For each group of representative elements, the atomic size *increases* going from the top to the bottom because the outermost electrons in each energy level are farther from the nucleus. For example, in Group 1A (1), Li has a valence electron in energy level 2; Na has a valence electron in energy level 3; and K has a valence electron in energy level 4. This means that a K atom is larger than a Na atom, and a Na atom is larger than a Li atom (see Figure 18).

The atomic radius of representative elements is affected by the attractive forces of the protons in the nucleus on the valence electrons. For the elements going across a period, the increase in the number of protons in the nucleus increases the positive charge of the nucleus.

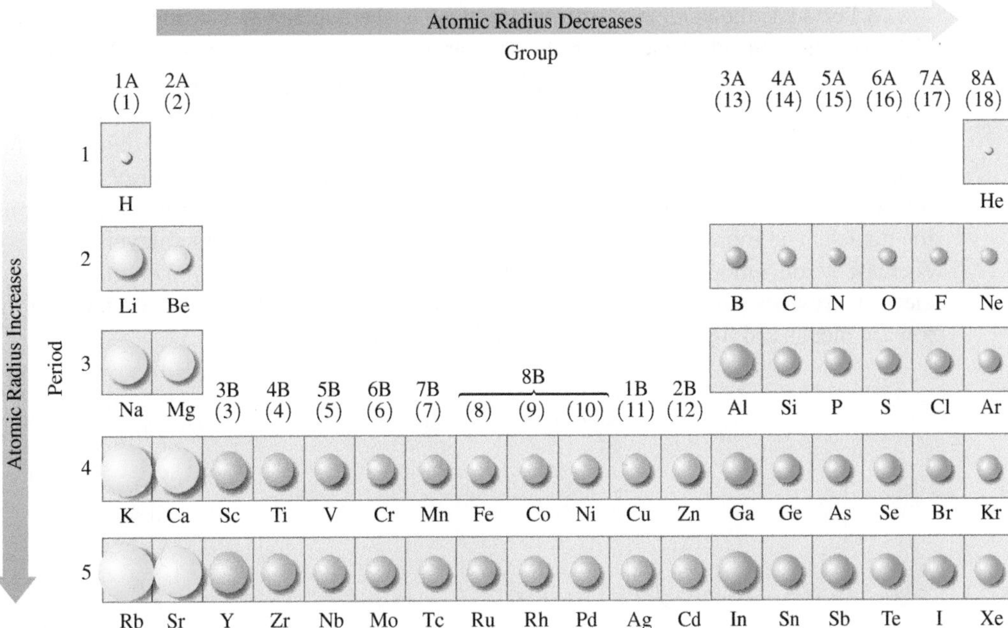

FIGURE 18 The atomic radius increases going down a group but decreases going from left to right across a period.

Q Why does the atomic radius increase going down a group?

As a result, the electrons are pulled closer to the nucleus, which means that the atomic sizes of representative elements decrease going from left to right across a period.

The atomic radii of the transition elements within a period change only slightly because electrons add to *d* orbitals rather than to the outermost energy level. Because the increase in nuclear charge is canceled by an increase in *d* electrons, the attraction of the nucleus for the outermost electrons remains about the same. Thus, the atomic radii of the transition elements are fairly constant.

CONCEPT CHECK 9 **Atomic Radius**

Why is the radius of a phosphorus atom larger than the radius of a nitrogen atom but smaller than the radius of a silicon atom?

ANSWER

The radius of a phosphorus atom is larger than the radius of a nitrogen atom because phosphorus has valence electrons in a higher energy level, which is farther from the nucleus. A phosphorus atom has one more proton than a silicon atom, which makes its nucleus more positive. This gives the nucleus in phosphorus a stronger attraction for the valence electrons, which decreases its radius compared to a silicon atom.

Ionization Energy

In an atom, negatively charged electrons are attracted to the positive charge of the protons in the nucleus. Therefore, energy is required to remove an electron from an atom. The **ionization energy** is the energy needed to remove the least tightly bound electron from an atom in the gaseous (g) state. When an electron is removed from a neutral atom, a particle called a *cation*, with a 1+ charge, is formed.

$$Na(g) + \text{energy (ionization)} \rightarrow Na^{+}(g) + e^{-}$$

The ionization energy decreases going down a group. Less energy is needed to remove an electron because nuclear attraction decreases when electrons are farther from the nucleus. Going across a period from left to right, the ionization energy increases. As the positive charge of the nucleus increases, more energy is needed to remove an electron (see Figure 19).

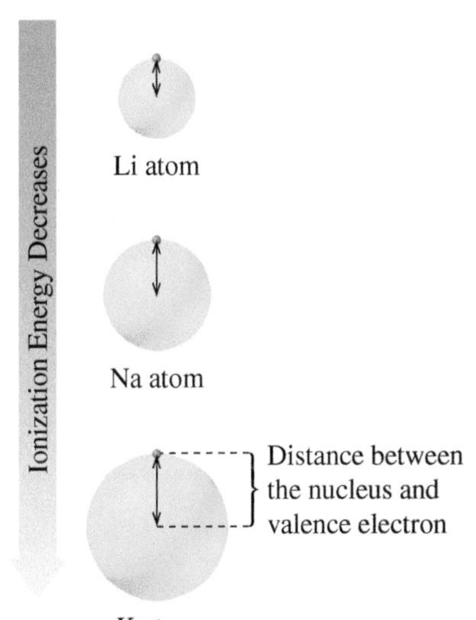

FIGURE 19 As the distance from the nucleus to a valence electron increases in Group 1A (1), the ionization energy decreases.

Q Is it easier to remove an electron from a K atom or from a Li atom?

TUTORIAL
Ionization Energy

In Period 1, the valence electrons are close to the nucleus and strongly held. H and He have high ionization energies because a large amount of energy is required to remove an electron. The ionization energy for He is the highest of any element because He has a full, stable, energy level that requires a very large amount of energy in order to remove an electron. The high ionization energies of the noble gases indicate that their electron arrangements are especially stable. The slight decrease in ionization energy for Group 3A (13) compared to Group 2A (2), occurs because the single *p* electron is farther from the nucleus and more easily removed than the electrons in the full *s* sublevel. The next decrease in ionization energy occurs for Group 6A (16) because the removal of a single *p* electron provides a half-filled, more stable *p* sublevel. In general, the ionization energy is low for metals and high for nonmetals (see Figure 20).

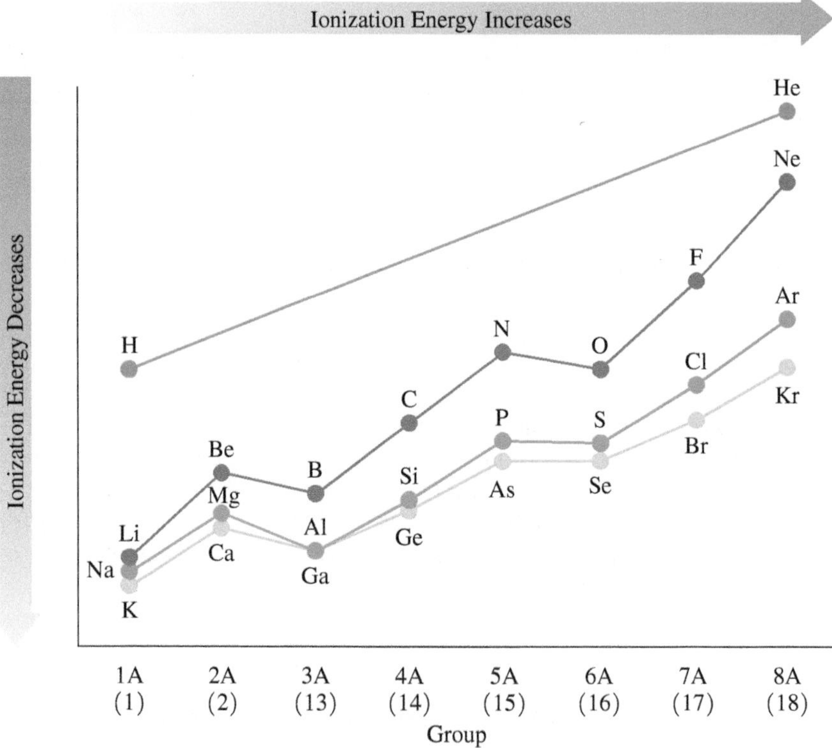

FIGURE 20 Ionization energies for the representative elements tend to decrease going down a group and increase going left to right across a period.

Q Why is the ionization energy for Li less than that for O?

SAMPLE PROBLEM 14 **Ionization Energy**

Indicate the element in each set that has the higher ionization energy and explain your choice.

a. K or Na **b.** Mg or Cl **c.** F, N, or C

SOLUTION

a. Na. In Na, the valence electron is closer to the nucleus.
b. Cl. Attraction for the valence electrons increases across a period, going left to right.
c. F. Because fluorine has more protons than nitrogen or carbon, more energy is needed to remove a valence electron from the fluorine atom.

STUDY CHECK 14

Arrange Sn, Sr, and I in order of increasing ionization energy.

Metallic Character

In Section 2, we identified elements as metals, nonmetals, and metalloids. An element that has **metallic character** is an element that loses valence electrons easily. Metallic character is more prevalent in the elements (metals) on the left side of the periodic table, and decreases going from the left side to the right side of the periodic table. The elements (nonmetals) on the right side of the periodic table do not easily lose electrons, which means they are the least metallic. Most of the metalloids between the metals and nonmetals tend to lose electrons, but not as easily as the metals. Thus, in Period 3, sodium, which loses electrons most easily, would be the most metallic. Going across from left to right in Period 3, metallic character decreases to argon, which has the least metallic character.

For elements in the same group of representative elements, metallic character increases going from top to bottom. Atoms at the bottom of any group have more electron levels, which makes it easier to lose electrons. Thus, the elements at the bottom of a group on the periodic table have lower ionization energy and are more metallic compared to the elements at the top (see Figure 21).

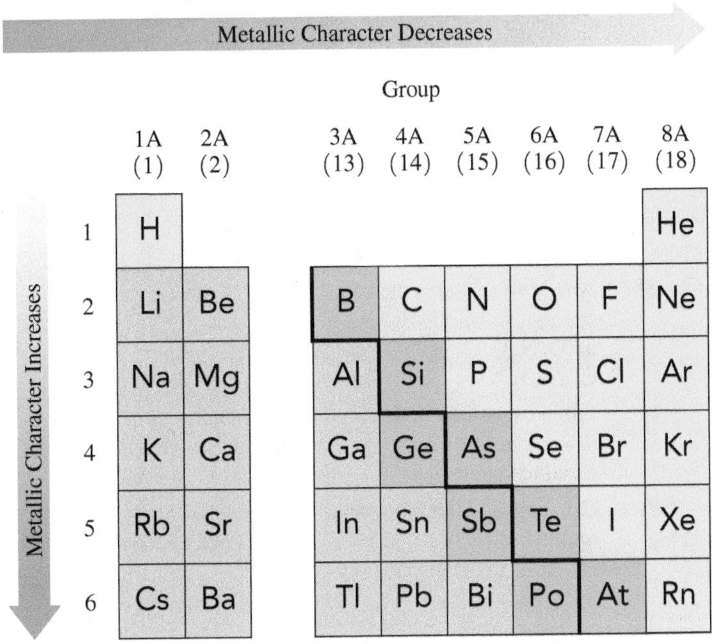

Metallic Character Decreases →

Group

Period	1A (1)	2A (2)	3A (13)	4A (14)	5A (15)	6A (16)	7A (17)	8A (18)
1	H							He
2	Li	Be	B	C	N	O	F	Ne
3	Na	Mg	Al	Si	P	S	Cl	Ar
4	K	Ca	Ga	Ge	As	Se	Br	Kr
5	Rb	Sr	In	Sn	Sb	Te	I	Xe
6	Cs	Ba	Tl	Pb	Bi	Po	At	Rn

Metallic Character Increases ↓

FIGURE 21 Metallic character of the representative elements increases going down a group and decreases going from left to right across a period.

Q Why is the metallic character greater for Rb than for Li?

A summary of the trends in periodic properties we have discussed is given in Table 12.

TABLE 12 Summary of Trends in Periodic Properties of Representative Elements

Periodic Property	Top to Bottom of a Group	Left to Right Across a Period
Valence Electrons	Remains the same	Increases
Atomic Radius	Increases due to the increase in the number of energy levels	Decreases as the increase of protons strengthens the attraction of the nucleus for the valence electrons, and pulls them closer to the nucleus
Ionization Energy	Decreases because the valence electrons are easier to remove when they are farther from the nucleus	Increases as the increase of protons strengthens the attraction between the nucleus for the valence electrons, and more energy is needed to remove an electron
Metallic Character	Increases because the valence electrons are easier to remove when they are farther from the nucleus	Decreases as the attraction of the protons makes it more difficult to remove a valence electron

CONCEPT CHECK 10 **Metallic Character**

Identify the element that has more metallic character in each of the following:

a. Mg or Al **b.** Na or K

ANSWER

a. Mg is more metallic than Al because metallic character decreases going from left to right across a period.
b. K is more metallic than Na because metallic character increases going down a group.

QUESTIONS AND PROBLEMS

8 Trends in Periodic Properties

LEARNING GOAL: *Use the electron configurations of elements to explain the trends in periodic properties.*

57 Indicate the number of valence electrons in each of the following:
a. aluminum
b. Group 5A
c. F, Cl, Br, and I

58 Indicate the number of valence electrons in each of the following:
a. Li, Na, K, Rb, and Cs
b. C, Si, Ge, Sn, and Pb
c. Group 8A

59 Write the group number and electron-dot symbol for each element:
a. sulfur **b.** nitrogen
c. calcium **d.** sodium
e. gallium

60 Write the group number and electron-dot symbol for each element:
a. carbon **b.** oxygen
c. argon **d.** lithium
e. chlorine

61 Select the larger atom in each pair.
a. Na or Cl **b.** Na or Rb
c. Na or Mg **d.** Rb or I

62 Select the larger atom in each pair.
a. S or Ar **b.** S or O
c. S or K **d.** S or Mg

63 Place the elements in each set in order of decreasing atomic radius.
a. Al, Si, Mg **b.** Cl, Br, I
c. Sr, Sb, I **d.** P, Si, Na

64 Place the elements in each set in order of decreasing atomic radius.
a. Cl, S, P **b.** Ge, Si, C
c. Ba, Ca, Sr **d.** S, O, Se

65 Select the element in each pair with the higher ionization energy.
a. Br or I
b. Mg or Sr
c. Si or P
d. I or Xe

66 Select the element in each pair with the higher ionization energy.
a. O or Ne **b.** K or Br
c. Ca or Ba **d.** N or Ne

67 Arrange each set of elements in order of increasing ionization energy.
a. F, Cl, Br **b.** Na, Cl, Al
c. Na, K, Cs **d.** As, Ca, Br

68 Arrange each set of elements in order of increasing ionization energy.
a. O, N, C **b.** S, P, Cl
c. As, P, N **d.** Al, Si, P

69 Fill in each of the following blanks using *larger* or *smaller*, *more* or *less*: Na has a ________ atomic size and is ________ metallic than P.

70 Fill in each of the following blanks using *larger* or *smaller*, *lower* or *higher:* Mg has a ________ atomic size and a ________ ionization energy than Ba.

71 Place the following in order of decreasing metallic character: Br, Ge, Ca, Ga

72 Place the following in order of increasing metallic character: Na, P, Al, Ar

73 Fill in each of the following blanks using *higher* or *lower*, *more* or *less*: Sr has a ________ ionization energy and is ________ metallic than Sb.

74 Fill in each of the following blanks using *higher* or *lower*, *more* or *less*: N has a ________ ionization energy and is ________ metallic than As.

75 Complete each of the statements **a–d** using **1**, **2**, or **3**:
1. decreases **2.** increases **3.** remains the same

Going down Group 6A (16),
a. the ionization energy ________
b. the atomic size ________
c. the metallic character ________
d. the number of valence electrons ________

76 Complete each of the statements **a–d** using **1**, **2**, or **3**:
1. decreases **2.** increases **3.** remains the same

Going from left to right across Period 4,
a. the ionization energy ________
b. the atomic size ________
c. the metallic character ________
d. the number of valence electrons ________

77 Which statements completed with **a–e** will be *true* and which will be *false*?

In Period 2, an atom of N compared to an atom of Li has a larger (greater)

a. atomic size
b. ionization energy
c. number of protons
d. metallic character
e. number of valence electrons

78 Which statements completed with **a–e** will be *true* and which will be *false*?

In Group 4A (14), an atom of C compared to an atom of Sn has a larger (greater)

a. atomic size
b. ionization energy
c. number of protons
d. metallic character
e. number of valence electrons

CONCEPT MAP

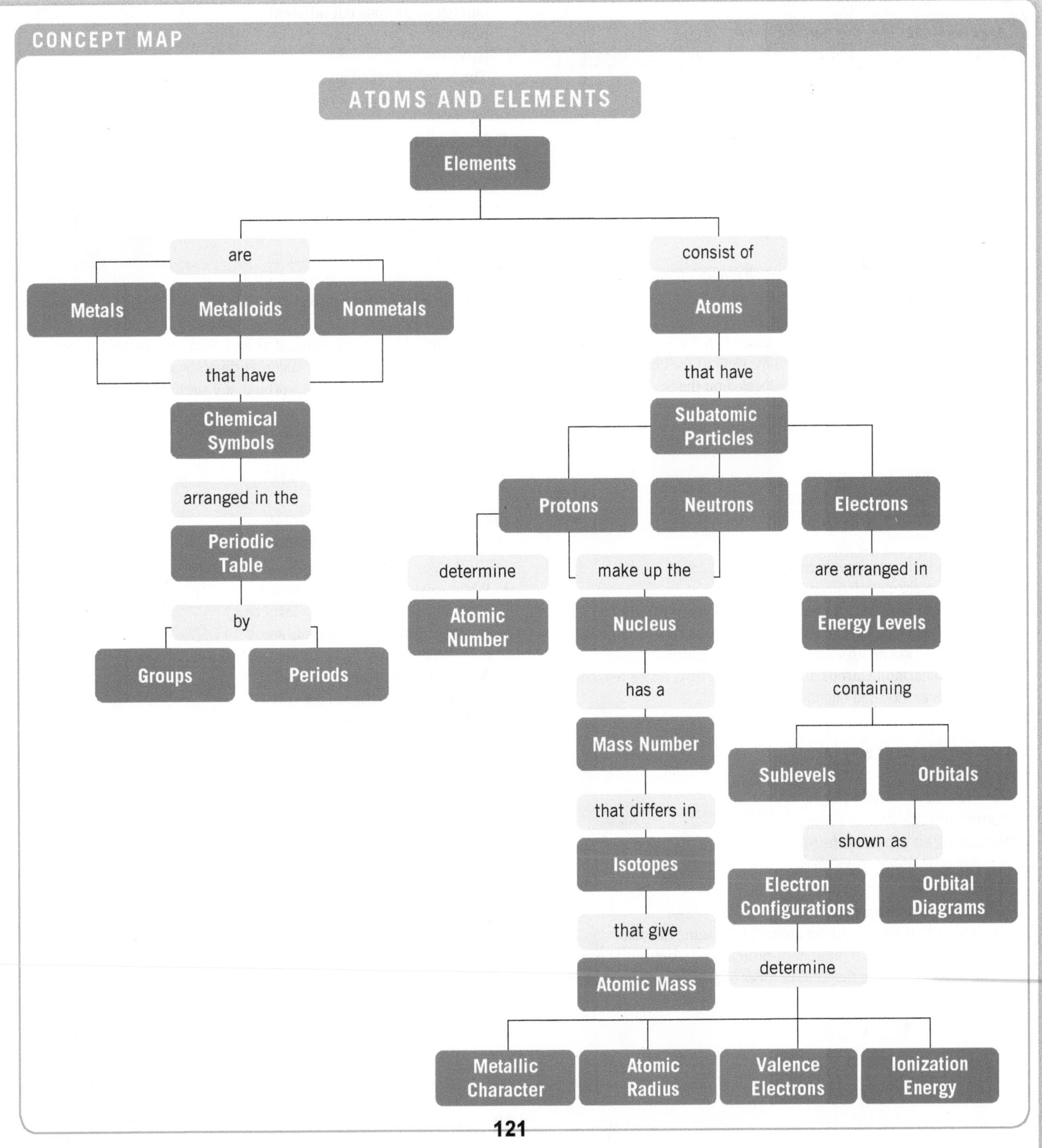

CHAPTER REVIEW

1 Elements and Symbols

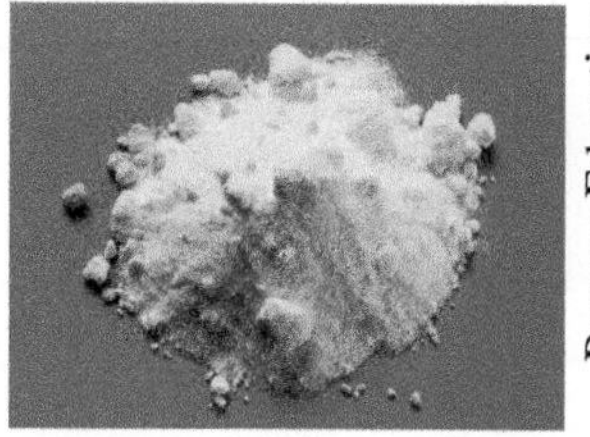

Pearson Education

LEARNING GOAL: *Given the name of an element, write its correct symbol; from the symbol, write the correct name.*

- Elements are the primary substances of matter.
- Chemical symbols are one- or two-letter abbreviations of the names of the elements.

2 The Periodic Table

LEARNING GOAL: *Use the periodic table to identify the group and the period of an element; identify the element as a metal, nonmetal, or metalloid.*

- The periodic table is an arrangement of the elements by increasing atomic number.
- A vertical column on the periodic table containing elements with similar properties is called a *group*. A horizontal row is called a *period*.
- Elements in Group 1A (1) are called the *alkali metals*; Group 2A (2), the *alkaline earth metals*; Group 7A (17), the *halogens*; and Group 8A (18), the *noble gases*.
- On the periodic table, metals are located on the left of the heavy zigzag line, and nonmetals are to the right of the heavy zigzag line.
- Except for aluminum, elements located on the heavy zigzag line are called *metalloids*.

3 The Atom

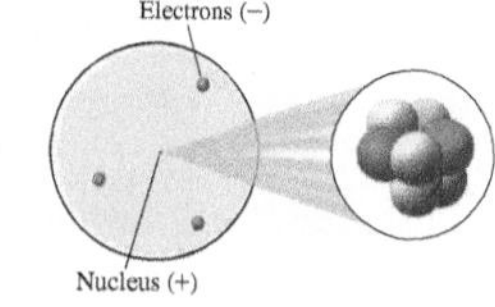

LEARNING GOAL: *Describe the electrical charge and location in an atom for a proton, a neutron, and an electron.*

- An atom is the smallest particle that retains the characteristics of an element.
- Atoms are composed of three types of subatomic particles.
- Protons have a positive charge (+), electrons carry a negative charge (−), and neutrons are electrically neutral.
- The protons and neutrons are found in the tiny, dense nucleus. Electrons are located outside the nucleus.

4 Atomic Number and Mass Number

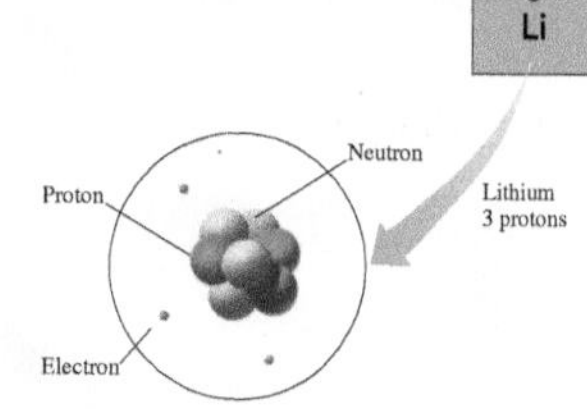

LEARNING GOAL: *Given the atomic number and the mass number of an atom, state the number of protons, neutrons, and electrons.*

- The atomic number gives the number of protons in all the atoms of the same element.
- In a neutral atom, the number of protons and electrons is equal.
- The mass number is the total number of protons and neutrons in an atom.

5 Isotopes and Atomic Mass

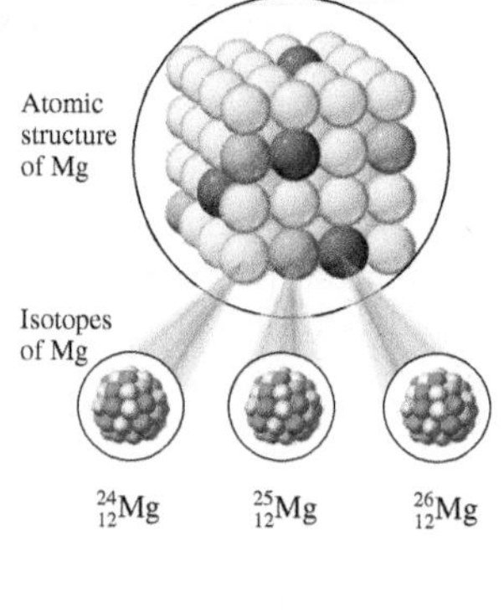

LEARNING GOAL: *Give the number of protons, neutrons, and electrons in one or more of the isotopes of an element; calculate the atomic mass of an element using the abundance and mass of its naturally occurring isotopes.*

- Atoms that have the same number of protons but different numbers of neutrons are called *isotopes*.
- The atomic mass of an element is the weighted average mass of all the atoms in a naturally occurring sample of that element.

6 Electron Arrangement in Atoms

LEARNING GOAL: *Describe the energy levels, sublevels, and orbitals for the electrons in an atom.*

- An orbital is a region around the nucleus in which an electron with a specific energy is most likely to be found.
- Each orbital holds a maximum of two electrons. In each principal energy level (n), electrons occupy orbitals within sublevels.
- An s sublevel contains one s orbital, a p sublevel contains three p orbitals, a d sublevel contains five d orbitals, and an f sublevel contains seven f orbitals. Each type of orbital has a unique shape.

7 Orbital Diagrams and Electron Configurations

LEARNING GOAL: *Draw the orbital diagram and write the electron configuration for an element.*

- Within a sublevel, electrons enter orbitals in the same energy level one at a time until all the orbitals are half-filled.
- Additional electrons enter until the orbitals in that sublevel are filled with two electrons each.
- The electron arrangement in an atom can be drawn as an orbital diagram, which shows the orbitals that are occupied by paired and unpaired electrons.
- The electron configuration shows the number of electrons in each sublevel. In an abbreviated electron configuration, the symbol of a noble gas in brackets represents the filled sublevels.
- The periodic table consists of s, p, d, and f sublevel blocks. Beginning with 1s, an electron configuration is obtained by writing the sublevel blocks in order going across the periodic table until the element is reached.

8 Trends in Periodic Properties

LEARNING GOAL: *Use the electron configurations of elements to explain the trends in periodic properties.*

- The properties of elements are related to the valence electrons of the atoms.
- With only a few minor exceptions, each group of elements has the same number of valence electrons, differing only in the energy level.

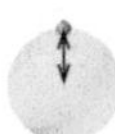
Li atom

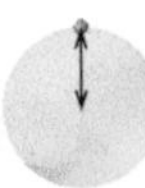
Na atom

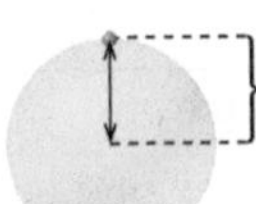

K atom

- Valence electrons are represented as dots around the symbol of the element.
- The radius of an atom increases going down a group and decreases going left to right across a period.
- The energy required to remove a valence electron is the ionization energy, which generally decreases going down a group and generally increases going left to right across a period.
- The metallic character increases going down a group and decreases going left to right across a period.

KEY TERMS

alkali metal An element in Group 1A (1), except hydrogen, that is a soft, shiny metal with one electron in its outermost energy level.

alkaline earth metal An element in Group 2A (2) that has two electrons in its outermost energy level.

atom The smallest particle of an element that retains the characteristics of the element.

atomic mass The weighted average mass of all the naturally occurring isotopes of an element.

atomic mass unit (amu) A small mass unit used to describe the mass of extremely small particles such as atoms and subatomic particles; 1 amu is equal to one-twelfth the mass of a ${}^{12}_{6}C$ atom.

atomic number A number that is equal to the number of protons in an atom.

atomic symbol An abbreviation used to indicate the mass number and atomic number of an isotope.

chemical symbol An abbreviation that represents the name of an element.

***d* block** The block of ten elements from Groups 3B (3) to 2B (12) in which electrons fill the five *d* orbitals in the *d* sublevels.

electron A negatively charged subatomic particle having a minute mass that is usually ignored in mass calculations; its symbol is e^-.

electron configuration A list of the number of electrons in each sublevel within an atom, arranged by increasing energy.

electron-dot symbol The representation of an atom that shows valence electrons as dots around the symbol of the element.

energy level A group of electrons with similar energy.

***f* block** The block of 14 elements in the rows at the bottom of the periodic table in which electrons fill the seven *f* orbitals in the 4*f* and 5*f* sublevels.

group A vertical column in the periodic table that contains elements having similar physical and chemical properties.

group number A number that appears at the top of each vertical column (group) in the periodic table and indicates the number of electrons in the outermost energy level.

halogen An element in Group 7A (17)—fluorine, chlorine, bromine, iodine, and astatine—that has seven electrons in its outermost energy level.

ionization energy The energy needed to remove the least tightly bound electron from the outermost energy level of an atom.

isotope An atom that differs only in mass number from another atom of the same element. Isotopes have the same atomic number (number of protons) but different numbers of neutrons.

mass number The total number of protons and neutrons in the nucleus of an atom.

metal An element that is shiny, malleable, ductile, and a good conductor of heat and electricity. The metals are located to the left of the heavy zigzag line on the periodic table.

metallic character A measure of how easily an element loses a valence electron.

metalloid Elements with properties of both metals and nonmetals located along the heavy zigzag line on the periodic table.

neutron A neutral subatomic particle having a mass of about 1 amu and found in the nucleus of an atom; its symbol is n or n^0.

noble gas An element in Group 8A (18) of the periodic table, generally unreactive and seldom found in combination with other elements, that has eight electrons (helium has two electrons) in its outermost energy level.

nonmetal An element with little or no luster that is a poor conductor of heat and electricity. The nonmetals are located to the right of the heavy zigzag line on the periodic table.

nucleus The compact, extremely dense center of an atom, containing the protons and neutrons of the atom.

orbital The region around the nucleus where electrons of a certain energy are more likely to be found. The *s* orbitals are spherical; the *p* orbitals have two lobes.

orbital diagram A diagram that shows the distribution of electrons in the orbitals of the energy levels.

***p* block** The elements in Groups 3A (13) to 8A (18) in which electrons fill the *p* orbitals in the *p* sublevels.

period A horizontal row of elements in the periodic table.

periodic table An arrangement of elements by increasing atomic number such that elements having similar chemical behavior are grouped in vertical columns.

proton A positively charged subatomic particle having a mass of about 1 amu and found in the nucleus of an atom; its symbol is p or p^+.

representative element An element in the first two columns on the left of the periodic table and the last six columns on the right that has a group number of 1A through 8A or 1, 2, and 13 through 18.

***s* block** The elements in Groups 1A (1) and 2A (2) in which electrons fill the *s* orbitals.

subatomic particle A particle within an atom; protons, neutrons, and electrons are subatomic particles.

sublevel A group of orbitals of equal energy within principal energy levels. The number of sublevels in each energy level is the same as the principal quantum number (n).

transition element An element in the center of the periodic table that is designated with the letter "B" or the group number of 3 through 12.

valence electrons Electrons in the highest energy level of an atom.

UNDERSTANDING THE CONCEPTS

The chapter sections to review are shown in parentheses at the end of each question.

79 According to Dalton's atomic theory, which of the following are *true*? (3)
- **a.** Atoms of an element are identical to atoms of other elements.
- **b.** Every element is made of atoms.
- **c.** Atoms of two different elements combine to form compounds.
- **d.** In a chemical reaction, some atoms disappear and new atoms appear.

80 Use Rutherford's gold-foil experiment to answer each of the following: (3)
- **a.** What did Rutherford expect to happen when he aimed particles at the gold foil?
- **b.** How did the results differ from what he expected?
- **c.** How did he use the results to propose a model of the atom?

81 Match the subatomic particles (**1–3**) to each of the descriptions below: (3)

1. protons **2.** neutrons **3.** electrons
- **a.** atomic mass
- **b.** atomic number
- **c.** positive charge
- **d.** negative charge
- **e.** mass number – atomic number

82 Match the subatomic particles (**1–3**) to each of the descriptions below: (3)

1. protons **2.** neutrons **3.** electrons
- **a.** mass number
- **b.** surround the nucleus
- **c.** nucleus
- **d.** charge of 0
- **e.** equal to number of electrons

83 Consider the following atoms in which X represents the chemical symbol of the element: $^{16}_{8}X$ $^{16}_{9}X$ $^{18}_{10}X$ $^{17}_{8}X$ $^{18}_{8}X$ (4, 5)
- **a.** What atoms have the same number of protons?
- **b.** Which atoms are isotopes? Of what element?
- **c.** Which atoms have the same mass number?
- **d.** What atoms have the same number of neutrons?

84 For each of the following, write the symbol and name for X and the number of protons and neutrons. Which are isotopes of each other? (4, 5)
- **a.** $^{80}_{35}X$
- **b.** $^{56}_{26}X$
- **c.** $^{116}_{50}X$
- **d.** $^{124}_{50}X$
- **e.** $^{116}_{48}X$

85 Indicate if the atoms in each pair have the same number of protons, neutrons, and electrons. (4)
- **a.** $^{37}_{17}Cl$, $^{38}_{18}Ar$
- **b.** $^{36}_{14}Si$, $^{35}_{14}Si$
- **c.** $^{40}_{18}Ar$, $^{39}_{17}Cl$

86 Complete the following table for the three naturally occurring isotopes of silicon, the major component in computer chips: (5)

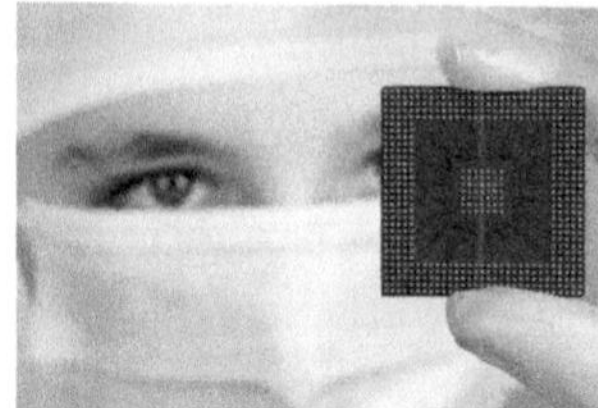

Computer chips consist primarily of the element silicon.

iStockphoto

	Isotope		
	$^{28}_{14}Si$	$^{29}_{14}Si$	$^{30}_{14}Si$
Number of protons			
Number of neutrons			
Number of electrons			
Atomic number			
Mass number			

87 For each representation of a nucleus **A–E**, write the atomic symbol, and identify which are isotopes. (4, 5)

Proton ●
Neutron ●

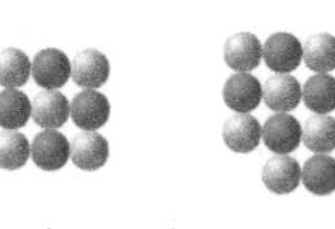

A B C D E

88 Identify the element represented by each nucleus **A–E** in Problem 87 as a metal, nonmetal, or metalloid. (2)

89 Match the spheres **A–D** with atoms of Li, Na, K, and Rb. (8)

A B C D

90 Match the spheres **A–D** with atoms of K, Ge, Ca, and Kr. (8)

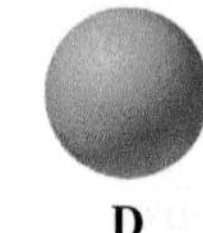

A B C D

91 Of the elements Na, Mg, Si, S, Cl, and Ar, identify one that fits each of the following: (2, 7, 8)
- **a.** largest atomic size
- **b.** a halogen
- **c.** electron configuration $1s^22s^22p^63s^23p^4$
- **d.** highest ionization energy
- **e.** is a metalloid
- **f.** most metallic character
- **g.** two valence electrons

92 Of the elements Sn, Xe, Te, Sr, I, and Rb, identify one that fits each of the following: (2, 8)
- **a.** smallest atomic size
- **b.** in Group 2A (2)
- **c.** a metalloid
- **d.** lowest ionization energy
- **e.** in Group 4A (14)
- **f.** least metallic character
- **g.** seven valence electrons

ADDITIONAL QUESTIONS AND PROBLEMS

For instructor-assigned homework, go to www.masteringchemistry.com.

93 Give the period and group number for each of the following elements: (2)

a. bromine **b.** argon
c. potassium **d.** radium

94 Give the period and group number for each of the following elements: (2)

a. radon **b.** lead
c. carbon **d.** neon

95 The following trace elements have been found to be crucial to the functions of the body. Indicate each as a metal, nonmetal, or metalloid. (2)

a. zinc **b.** cobalt
c. manganese **d.** iodine

96 The following trace elements have been found to be crucial to the functions of the body. Indicate each as a metal, nonmetal, or metalloid. (2)

a. copper **b.** selenium
c. arsenic **d.** chromium

97 Indicate if each of the following statements is *true* or *false*: (3)

a. The proton is a negatively charged particle.
b. The neutron is 2000 times as heavy as a proton.
c. The atomic mass unit is based on a carbon atom with 6 protons and 6 neutrons.
d. The nucleus is the largest part of the atom.
e. The electrons are located outside the nucleus.

98 Indicate if each of the following statements is *true* or *false*: (3)

a. The neutron is electrically neutral.
b. Most of the mass of an atom is due to the protons and neutrons.
c. The charge of an electron is equal, but opposite, to the charge of a neutron.
d. The proton and the electron have about the same mass.
e. The mass number is the number of protons.

99 For the following atoms, give the number of protons, neutrons, and electrons: (3)

a. ${}^{114}_{48}Cd$ **b.** ${}^{98}_{43}Tc$
c. ${}^{199}_{79}Au$ **d.** ${}^{222}_{86}Rn$
e. ${}^{136}_{54}Xe$

100 For the following atoms, give the number of protons, neutrons, and electrons: (3)

a. ${}^{202}_{80}Hg$ **b.** ${}^{127}_{53}I$
c. ${}^{75}_{35}Br$ **d.** ${}^{133}_{55}Cs$
e. ${}^{195}_{78}Pt$

101 Complete the following table: (3)

Name of the Element	Atomic Symbol	Number of Protons	Number of Neutrons	Number of Electrons
	${}^{34}_{16}S$			
		28	34	
Magnesium			14	
	${}^{228}_{88}Ra$			

102 Complete the following table: (3)

Name of the Element	Atomic Symbol	Number of Protons	Number of Neutrons	Number of Electrons
Potassium			22	
	${}^{51}_{23}V$			
		48	64	
Barium			82	

103 **a.** What electron sublevel starts to fill after completion of the 3*s* sublevel? (7)
b. What electron sublevel starts to fill after completion of the 4*p* sublevel?
c. What electron sublevel starts to fill after completion of the 3*d* sublevel?
d. What electron sublevel starts to fill after completion of the 3*p* sublevel?

104 **a.** What electron sublevel starts to fill after completion of the 5*s* sublevel? (7)
b. What electron sublevel starts to fill after completion of the 4*d* sublevel?
c. What electron sublevel starts to fill after completion of the 4*f* sublevel?
d. What electron sublevel starts to fill after completion of the 5*p* sublevel?

105 **a.** How many 3*d* electrons are in Fe? (7)
b. How many 5*p* electrons are in Ba?
c. How many 4*d* electrons are in I?
d. How many 7*s* electrons are in Ra?

106 **a.** How many 4*d* electrons are in Cd? (7)
b. How many 4*p* electrons are in Br?
c. How many 6*p* electrons are in Bi?
d. How many 5*s* electrons are in Zn?

107 Name the element that corresponds to each of the following: (7, 8)

a. $1s^22s^22p^63s^23p^3$
b. alkali metal with the smallest atomic radius
c. $[Kr]5s^24d^{10}$
d. Group 5A (15) element with the highest ionization energy
e. Period 3 element with the largest atomic radius

108 Name the element that corresponds to each of the following: (7, 8)

a. $1s^22s^22p^63s^23p^64s^13d^5$
b. $[Xe]6s^24f^{14}5d^{10}6p^5$
c. halogen with the highest ionization energy
d. Group 2A (2) element with the smallest ionization energy
e. Period 4 element with the smallest atomic radius

109 Of the elements Na, P, Cl, and F, which (2, 8)

a. is a metal?
b. is in Group 5A (15)?
c. has the highest ionization energy?
d. loses an electron most easily?
e. is found in Group 7A (17), Period 3?

110 Of the elements K, Ca, Br, and Kr, which (2, 8)
a. is a noble gas?
b. has the smallest atomic radius?
c. has the lowest ionization energy?
d. requires the most energy to remove an electron?
e. is found in Group 2A (2), Period 4?

CHALLENGE QUESTIONS

111 The most abundant isotope of lead is $^{208}_{82}Pb$. (4)
a. How many protons, neutrons, and electrons are in $^{208}_{82}Pb$?
b. What is the atomic symbol of another isotope of lead with 132 neutrons?
c. What is the name and symbol of an atom with the same mass number as in part **b** and 131 neutrons?

112 The most abundant isotope of silver is $^{107}_{47}Ag$. (4)
a. How many protons, neutrons, and electrons are in $^{107}_{47}Ag$?
b. What is the symbol of another isotope of silver with 62 neutrons?
c. What is the name and symbol of an atom with the same mass number as in part **b** and 61 neutrons?

113 Give the symbol of the element that has the (8)
a. smallest atomic size in Group 6A (16)
b. smallest atomic size in Period 3
c. highest ionization energy in Group 4A (14)
d. lowest ionization energy in Period 3
e. most metallic character in Group 2A (2)

114 Give the symbol of the element that has the (8)
a. largest atomic size in Group 1A (1)
b. largest atomic size in Period 4
c. highest ionization energy in Group 2A (2)
d. lowest ionization energy in Group 7A (17)
e. least metallic character in Group 4A (14)

115 Silicon has three naturally occurring isotopes: Si-28 that has a percent abundance of 92.23% and a mass of 27.977 amu, Si-29 that has a 4.68% abundance and a mass of 28.976 amu, and Si-30 that has a percent abundance of 3.09% and a mass of 29.974 amu. What is the atomic mass of silicon? (5)

116 Antimony (Sb), has two naturally occurring isotopes: Sb-121 that has a percent abundance of 57.30% and a mass of 120.9 amu, and Sb-123 that has a percent abundance of 42.70% and a mass of 122.9 amu. What is the atomic mass of antimony? (5)

117 Consider three elements with the following abbreviated electron configurations: (2, 8)

$X = [Ar]4s^2$ $\quad Y = [Ne]3s^23p^4$

$Z = [Ar]4s^23d^{10}4p^4$

a. Identify each element as a metal, nonmetal, or metalloid.
b. Which element has the largest atomic radius?
c. Which elements have similar properties?
d. Which element has the highest ionization energy?
e. Which element has the smallest atomic radius?

118 Consider three elements with the following abbreviated electron configurations: (2, 8)

$X = [Ar]4s^23d^5$ $\quad Y = [Ar]4s^23d^{10}4p^1$

$Z = [Ar]4s^23d^{10}4p^6$

a. Identify each element as a metal, nonmetal, or metalloid.
b. Which element has the smallest atomic radius?
c. Which elements have similar properties?
d. Which element has the highest ionization energy?
e. Which element has a half-filled sublevel?

ANSWERS

Answers to Study Checks

1 Si, S, Ag

2 magnesium, aluminum, fluorine

3 a. Group 2A (2) **b.** alkaline earth metals
c. Period 5 **d.** magnesium, Mg
e. alkali metal, Rb; halogen, I; noble gas, Xe

4 a. metalloid **b.** nonmetal **c.** metal

5 False; most of the volume in an atom is outside the nucleus.

6 a. 79 **b.** 79 **c.** gold, Au

7 45 neutrons

8 a. $^{15}_{7}N$ **b.** $^{81}_{35}Br$ **c.** $^{27}_{14}Si$

9 10.81 amu

10 The 4*s* sublevel can hold a maximum of 2 electrons.

11 $1s^22s^22p^63s^23p^4$ Complete electron configuration for sulfur (S)
$[Ne]3s^23p^4$ Abbreviated electron configuration for sulfur (S)

12 Tin has the electron configuration:
$1s^22s^22p^63s^23p^64s^23d^{10}4p^65s^24d^{10}5p^2$

13 $\cdot\ddot{P}\cdot$ (with one dot below)

14 Ionization energy increases going across a period from left to right: Sr is lowest, Sn is higher, and I is the highest of this set.

Answers to Selected Questions and Problems

1 a. Cu **b.** Pt **c.** Ca **d.** Mn
e. Fe **f.** Ba **g.** Pb **h.** Sr

3 a. carbon **b.** chlorine **c.** iodine **d.** mercury
e. silver **f.** argon **g.** boron **h.** nickel

5 a. sodium, chlorine
b. calcium, sulfur, oxygen
c. carbon, hydrogen, chlorine, nitrogen, oxygen
d. calcium, carbon, oxygen

7 a. Period 2 **b.** Group 8A (18)
c. Group 1A (1) **d.** Period 2

9 a. alkaline earth metal **b.** transition element
c. noble gas **d.** alkali metal
e. halogen

11 a. C **b.** He **c.** Na
d. Ca **e.** Al

13 a. metal **b.** nonmetal **c.** metal
d. nonmetal **e.** nonmetal **f.** nonmetal
g. metalloid **h.** metal

15 a. electron
b. proton
c. electron
d. neutron

17 a, b, and **c** are *true*, but **d** is *false*. A proton is attracted to an electron, not a neutron.

19 Thomson determined that electrons had a negative charge when he observed they were attracted to a positive electrode in a cathode ray tube.

21 a. atomic number
b. both
c. mass number
d. atomic number

23 a. lithium, Li **b.** fluorine, F
c. calcium, Ca **d.** zinc, Zn
e. neon, Ne **f.** silicon, Si
g. iodine, I **h.** oxygen, O

25 a. 18 protons and 18 electrons
b. 30 protons and 30 electrons
c. 53 protons and 53 electrons
d. 48 protons and 48 electrons

27 See the table at the bottom of the page.

29 a. 38 protons, 51 neutrons, 38 electrons
b. 24 protons, 28 neutrons, 24 electrons
c. 16 protons, 18 neutrons, 16 electrons
d. 35 protons, 46 neutrons, 35 electrons

31 a. $^{31}_{15}P$ **b.** $^{80}_{35}Br$ **c.** $^{122}_{50}Sn$
d. $^{35}_{17}Cl$ **e.** $^{202}_{80}Hg$

33 a. $^{36}_{18}Ar$ $^{38}_{18}Ar$ $^{40}_{18}Ar$
b. They all have the same number of protons and electrons.
c. They have different numbers of neutrons, which gives them different mass numbers.
d. The atomic mass of Ar listed on the periodic table is the average atomic mass of all the isotopes.
e. Because argon has an atomic mass of 39.95, the isotope $^{40}_{18}Ar$ would be the most prevalent.

35 69.72 amu

37 a. spherical **b.** two lobes
c. spherical

39 a. 1 and 2 **b.** 3
c. 1 and 2 **d.** 1, 2, and 3

41 a. There are five orbitals in the 3*d* sublevel.
b. There is one sublevel in the $n = 1$ energy level.
c. There is one orbital in the 6*s* sublevel.
d. There are nine orbitals in the $n = 3$ energy level.

43 a. There is a maximum of two electrons in a 3*p* orbital.
b. There is a maximum of six electrons in the 3*p* sublevel.
c. There is a maximum of 32 electrons in the $n = 4$ energy level.
d. There is a maximum of 10 electrons in the 5*d* sublevel.

45 a. 1*s* [↑↓] 2*s* [↑↓] 2*p* [↑][ ][ ]

b. 1*s* [↑↓] 2*s* [↑↓] 2*p* [↑↓][↑↓][↑↓] 3*s* [↑↓] 3*p* [↑][ ][ ]

c. 1*s* [↑↓] 2*s* [↑↓] 2*p* [↑↓][↑↓][↑↓] 3*s* 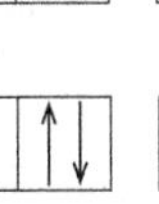 [↑↓] 3*p* 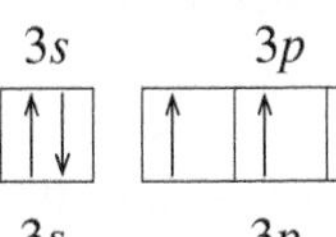 [↑][↑][↑]

d. 1*s* [↑↓] 2*s* [↑↓] 2*p* [↑↓][↑↓][↑↓] 3*s* [↑↓] 3*p* [↑↓][↑↓][↑↓]

47 a. $1s^22s^22p^63s^23p^64s^23d^6$
b. $1s^22s^22p^63s^1$
c. $1s^22s^22p^63s^23p^64s^23d^{10}4p^65s^1$
d. $1s^22s^22p^63s^23p^64s^23d^{10}4p^3$

49 a. $[Ne]3s^2$ **b.** $[Xe]6s^2$
c. $[Ne]3s^23p^1$ **d.** $[Ar]4s^23d^2$

51 a. S **b.** Co **c.** Si **d.** Br

53 a. Al **b.** C **c.** Ar **d.** Zr

55 a. 10 **b.** 6 **c.** 3 **d.** 1

57 a. 3 **b.** 5 **c.** 7

59 a. Group 6A (16) $\cdot\ddot{\underset{\cdot}{S}}:$ **b.** Group 5A (15) $\cdot\ddot{\underset{\cdot}{N}}\cdot$
c. Group 2A (2) $Ca\cdot$ **d.** Group 1A (1) $Na\cdot$
e. Group 3A (13) $\cdot\dot{Ga}\cdot$

61 a. Na **b.** Rb **c.** Na **d.** Rb

63 a. Mg, Al, Si **b.** I, Br, Cl
c. Sr, Sb, I **d.** Na, Si, P

65 a. Br **b.** Mg
c. P **d.** Xe

67 a. Br, Cl, F **b.** Na, Al, Cl
c. Cs, K, Na **d.** Ca, As, Br

69 larger, more

71 Ca, Ga, Ge, Br

Answer to 27

Name of the Element	Symbol	Atomic Number	Mass Number	Number of Protons	Number of Neutrons	Number of Electrons
Aluminum	Al	13	27	13	14	13
Magnesium	Mg	12	24	12	12	12
Potassium	K	19	39	19	20	19
Sulfur	S	16	31	16	15	16
Iron	Fe	26	56	26	30	26

73 lower, more

75 **a.** 1 **b.** 2 **c.** 2 **d.** 3

77 **a.** false **b.** true **c.** true
d. false **e.** true

79 Statements **b** and **c** are true.

81 **a.** 1 and 2 **b.** 1 **c.** 1
d. 3 **e.** 2

83 **a.** ${}^{16}_{8}X$, ${}^{17}_{8}X$, and ${}^{18}_{8}X$ have eight protons.
b. ${}^{16}_{8}X$, ${}^{17}_{8}X$, and ${}^{18}_{8}X$ are isotopes of oxygen.
c. ${}^{16}_{8}X$ and ${}^{16}_{9}X$ have mass number 16, whereas ${}^{18}_{8}X$ and ${}^{18}_{10}X$ have mass number 18.
d. ${}^{16}_{8}X$ and ${}^{18}_{10}X$ both have eight neutrons.

85 **a.** Both atoms have 20 neutrons.
b. Both atoms have 14 protons and 14 electrons.
c. Both atoms have 22 neutrons.

87 **a.** ${}^{9}_{4}Be$ **b.** ${}^{11}_{5}B$ **c.** ${}^{13}_{6}C$
d. ${}^{10}_{5}B$ **e.** ${}^{12}_{6}C$
Representations **B** and **D** are isotopes of boron; **C** and **E** are isotopes of carbon.

89 **A** is Na, **B** is Rb, **C** is K, and **D** is Li.

91 **a.** Na **b.** Cl **c.** S **d.** Ar
e. Si **f.** Na **g.** Mg

93 **a.** Period 4, Group 7A (17)
b. Period 3, Group 8A (18)
c. Period 4, Group 1A (1)
d. Period 7, Group 2A (2)

95 **a.** metal **b.** metal **c.** metal **d.** nonmetal

97 **a.** false **b.** false **c.** true
d. false **e.** true

99 **a.** 48 protons, 66 neutrons, 48 electrons
b. 43 protons, 55 neutrons, 43 electrons
c. 79 protons, 120 neutrons, 79 electrons
d. 86 protons, 136 neutrons, 86 electrons
e. 54 protons, 82 neutrons, 54 electrons

101 See the table at the bottom of the page.

103 **a.** 3*p* **b.** 5*s* **c.** 4*p* **d.** 4*s*

105 **a.** 6 **b.** 6 **c.** 10 **d.** 2

107 **a.** phosphorus **b.** lithium (H is a nonmetal)
c. cadmium **d.** nitrogen
e. sodium

109 **a.** Na **b.** Na **c.** F
d. Na **e.** Cl

111 **a.** 82 protons, 126 neutrons, 82 electrons
b. ${}^{214}_{82}Pb$ **c.** ${}^{214}_{83}Bi$

113 **a.** O **b.** Ar **c.** C
d. Na **e.** Ra

115 28.09 amu

117 **a.** X is a metal; Y and Z are nonmetals.
b. X has the largest atomic radius.
c. Y and Z have six valence electrons and are in Group 6A (16).
d. Y has the highest ionization energy.
e. Y has the smallest atomic radius.

Answer to 101

Name of the Element	Atomic Symbol	Number of Protons	Number of Neutrons	Number of Electrons
Sulfur	${}^{34}_{16}S$	16	18	16
Nickel	${}^{62}_{28}Ni$	28	34	28
Magnesium	${}^{26}_{12}Mg$	12	14	12
Radon	${}^{228}_{88}Ra$	88	140	88

Nuclear Chemistry

LOOKING AHEAD

Visit **www.masteringchemistry.com** for self-study materials and instructor-assigned homework.

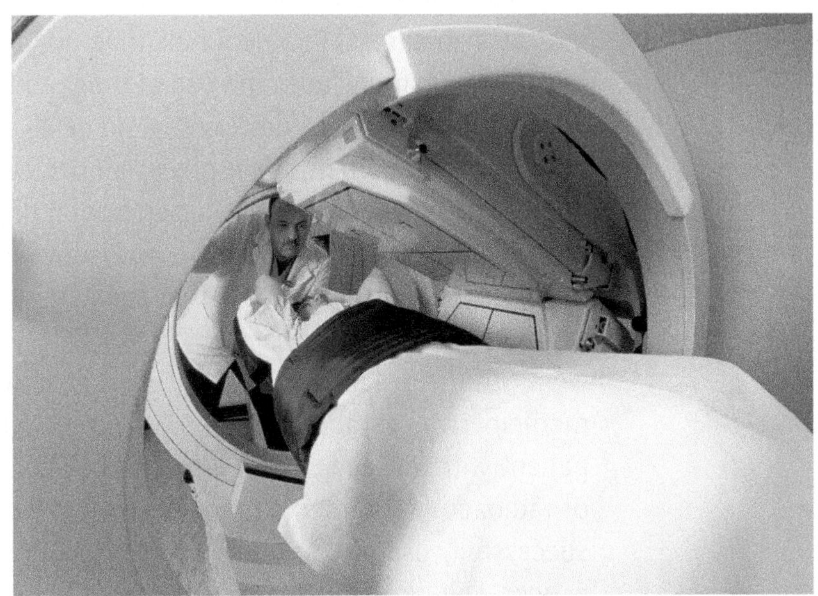

Larry Mulvehill/SPL/Photo Researchers, Inc.

Simone's doctor is concerned about her elevated cholesterol, which could lead to coronary heart disease and a heart attack. He sends her to a nuclear medicine center to undergo a cardiac stress test.

Paul, the nuclear medicine technician, explains to Simone that he will inject Technetium-99m (Tc-99m) into her bloodstream. He explains that Tc-99m is a radioactive isotope that has a half-life of 6 h and is a gamma emitter. Simone is curious about the term "half-life". Paul explains that a half-life is the amount of time it takes for one-half of a radioactive sample to break down. He assures her that after four half-lives (one day), the radiation emitted will be almost zero.

Paul tells Simone that when the Tc-99m reaches her heart that any area with restricted blood supply will pick up only small amounts of the radioisotope, which can indicate coronary heart disease. Later, Simone will undergo an active stress test to compare her cardiac blood flow during rest and under stress.

Career: Nuclear Medicine Technician

Nuclear medicine is frequently used to diagnose and treat a variety of medical conditions. A variety of techniques are employed for imaging, including Computed Tomography (CT), Magnetic Resonance Imaging (MRI), and Positron Emission Tomography (PET). Nuclear medicine technicians operate the instrumentation and computers associated with the various techniques in nuclear medicine. Nuclear medicine technicians safely handle radioisotopes, employ the necessary type of shielding, and administer radioactive isotopes to patients. In addition, they must physically and mentally prepare patients for imaging by explaining the procedure to them.

From Chapter 4 of *General, Organic, and Biological Chemistry: Structures of Life*, Fourth Edition. Karen C. Timberlake.

A female patient, age 50, complains of nervousness, irritability, increased perspiration, brittle hair, and muscle weakness. Her hands are shaky at times, and her heart often beats rapidly. She has been experiencing weight loss. The doctor decides to test her thyroid. To get a detailed look, a thyroid scan is ordered. The patient is given a small amount of an iodine radioisotope, which will be taken up by the thyroid. The scan shows a higher than normal rate of uptake of the radioactive iodine, which indicates an overactive thyroid gland, a condition called *hyperthyroidism*. Treatment for hyperthyroidism includes the use of drugs to lower the level of thyroid hormone, the use of radioactive iodine to destroy thyroid cells, or surgical removal of part or the entire thyroid. In our case, the nuclear physician decides to use radioactive iodine. To begin treatment, the patient drinks a solution containing radioactive iodine. In the following few weeks, the cells that take up the radioactive iodine are destroyed by the radiation. After treatment, further tests show that the patient's thyroid is smaller and the blood level of thyroid hormone is normal.

With the production of artificial radioactive substances in 1934, the field of nuclear medicine was established. In 1937, the first radioactive isotope was used to treat a patient with leukemia at the University of California at Berkeley. Major strides in the use of radioactivity in medicine occurred in 1946, when a radioactive iodine isotope was successfully used to diagnose thyroid function and to treat hyperthyroidism and thyroid cancer. During the 1970s and 1980s, a variety of radioactive substances were used to produce images of organs such as the liver, spleen, thyroid, kidney, and brain, and to detect heart disease. Today, procedures in nuclear medicine provide information about the function and structure of every organ in the body, allowing physicians to diagnose and treat diseases early.

LEARNING GOAL

Describe alpha, beta, positron, and gamma radiation.

1 Natural Radioactivity

Most naturally occurring isotopes of elements up to atomic number 19 have stable nuclei. An atom has a stable nucleus when the forces of attraction and repulsion are balanced. Elements with atomic numbers 20 and higher usually have one or more isotopes that have unstable nuclei. An unstable nucleus has too many or too few protons compared to the number of neutrons, which means the forces between protons and neutrons are unbalanced. An unstable nucleus is *radioactive*, which means that it spontaneously emits small particles of energy called **radiation**, to become more stable.

Radiation may take the form of alpha (α) and beta (β) particles, positrons (β^+), or pure energy such as gamma (γ) rays. An isotope that emits radiation is called a *radioisotope*. For most types of radiation, there is a change in the number of protons in the nucleus. This change, called *transmutation*, occurs when an atom of one element is converted into an atom of a different element. This kind of nuclear change was not evident to Dalton when he made his predictions about atoms. Elements with atomic numbers of 93 and higher are produced artificially in nuclear laboratories and consist only of radioactive isotopes.

We wrote symbols for the different isotopes of an element. These symbols had their mass numbers written in the upper left corner and their atomic number in the lower left corner. Recall that the mass number is equal to the number of protons and neutrons in the nucleus, and that the atomic number is equal to the number of protons. For example, a radioactive isotope of iodine used in the diagnosis and treatment of thyroid conditions has a symbol with a mass number of 131 and an atomic number of 53.

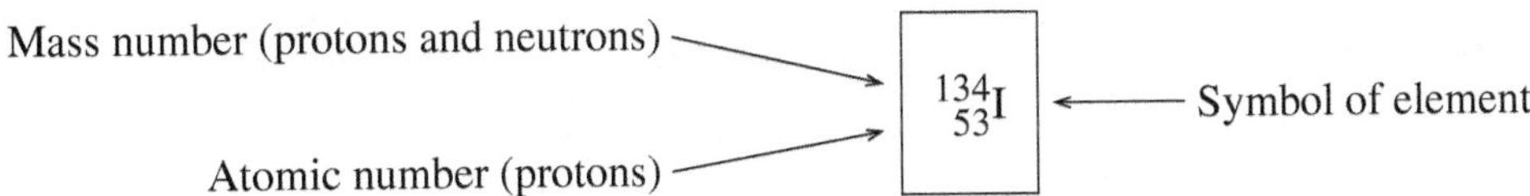

Radioactive isotopes are identified by writing the mass number after the element's name or symbol. Thus, in this example, the isotope is called iodine-131 or I-131. Table 1 compares some stable, nonradioactive isotopes with some radioactive isotopes.

TABLE 1 Stable and Radioactive Isotopes of Some Elements

Magnesium	Iodine	Uranium
Stable Isotopes		
$^{24}_{12}Mg$	$^{127}_{53}I$	None
Magnesium-24	Iodine-127	
Radioactive Isotopes		
$^{23}_{12}Mg$	$^{125}_{53}I$	$^{235}_{92}U$
Magnesium-23	Iodine-125	Uranium-235
$^{27}_{12}Mg$	$^{131}_{53}I$	$^{238}_{92}U$
Magnesium-27	Iodine-131	Uranium-238

Types of Radiation

By emitting radiation, an unstable nucleus forms a more stable, lower energy nucleus. One type of radiation consists of *alpha particles*. An **alpha particle** is identical to a helium (He) nucleus, which has two protons and two neutrons. An alpha particle has a mass number of 4, an atomic number of 2, and a charge of 2+. It is represented as the Greek letter alpha (α) or the atomic symbol of a helium nucleus.

Another type of radiation occurs when a radioisotope emits a *beta particle*. A **beta particle** is a high-energy electron with a charge of 1−, and because its mass is so much less than the mass of a proton, it has a mass number of 0. It is represented by the Greek letter beta (β) or by the symbol for the electron including the mass number and the charge, $^{0}_{-1}e$. A beta particle forms when a neutron in an unstable nucleus changes to a proton and an electron.

A **positron**, similar to a beta particle, has a positive (1+) charge with a mass number of 0. It is represented by the Greek letter beta with a 1+ charge, β^+, or by the symbol for the electron, which includes the mass number and the charge, $^{0}_{+1}e$. A positron is produced by an unstable nucleus when a proton is transformed into a neutron and a positron.

A positron is an example of *antimatter*, a term physicists use to describe a particle that is the exact opposite of another particle, in this case, an electron. When an electron and a positron collide, their minute masses are completely converted to energy in the form of gamma rays.

$$^{0}_{-1}e + ^{0}_{+1}e \longrightarrow 2\,^{0}_{0}\gamma$$

Gamma rays are high-energy radiation, released when an unstable nucleus undergoes a rearrangement of its particles to give a more stable, lower-energy nucleus. Gamma rays are often emitted along with other types of radiation. A gamma ray is represented by the Greek letter gamma (γ). Because gamma rays are energy only, zeros are used to show that a gamma ray has no mass or charge.

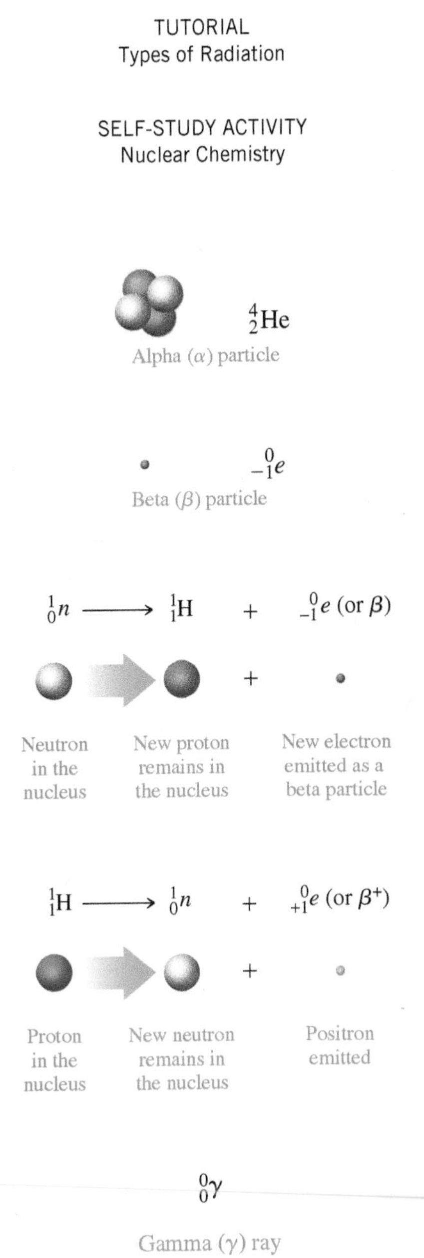

Table 2 summarizes the types of radiation we will use in nuclear equations.

TABLE 2 Some Forms of Radiation

Type of Radiation	Symbol		Change in Nucleus	Mass Number	Charge
Alpha particle	α	$^{4}_{2}He$	Two protons and two neutrons are emitted as an alpha particle.	4	2+
Beta particle	β	$^{0}_{-1}e$	A neutron changes to a proton and an electron is emitted.	0	1−
Positron	β^+	$^{0}_{+1}e$	A proton changes to a neutron and a positron is emitted.	0	1+
Gamma ray	γ	$^{0}_{0}\gamma$	Energy is lost to stabilize the nucleus.	0	0
Proton	p	$^{1}_{1}H$	A proton is emitted.	1	1+
Neutron	n	$^{1}_{0}n$	A neutron is emitted.	1	0

CONCEPT CHECK 1 **Radiation Particles**

Give the name and write the symbol for each of the following types of radiation:

a. contains two protons and two neutrons
b. has a mass number of 0 and a 1− charge

ANSWER

a. An alpha (α) particle, $^{4}_{2}He$, has two protons and two neutrons.
b. A beta (β) particle, $^{0}_{-1}e$, is like an electron with a mass number of 0 and a 1− charge.

SELF-STUDY ACTIVITY
Radiation and Its Biological Effects

Biological Effects of Radiation

When radiation strikes molecules in its path, electrons may be knocked away, forming unstable ions. If this *ionizing radiation* passes through the human body, it may interact with water molecules, removing electrons, and producing H_2O^+, which can cause undesirable chemical reactions.

The cells most sensitive to ionizing radiation are the ones undergoing rapid division—those of the bone marrow, skin, reproductive organs, and intestinal lining, as well as all cells of growing children. Damaged cells may lose their ability to produce necessary materials. For example, if radiation damages cells of the bone marrow, red blood cells may no longer be produced. If sperm cells, ova, or the cells of a fetus are damaged, birth defects may result. In contrast, cells of the nerves, muscles, liver, and adult bones are much less sensitive to radiation because they undergo little or no cellular division.

Cancer cells are another example of rapidly dividing cells. Because cancer cells are highly sensitive to radiation, large doses of radiation are used to destroy them. The normal tissue that surrounds cancer cells divides at a slower rate and suffers less damage from radiation. However, radiation, due to its high penetrating energy, may itself cause malignant tumors, leukemia, anemia, and genetic mutations.

Radiation Protection

Radiologists, chemists, doctors, and nurses who work with radioactive isotopes must use proper radiation protection. Proper **shielding** is necessary to prevent exposure. Alpha particles, which have the largest mass and charge of the radiation particles, travel only a few centimeters in the air before they collide with air molecules, acquire electrons, and become helium atoms. A piece of paper, clothing, and our skin are protection against alpha particles. Lab coats and gloves will also provide sufficient shielding. However, if alpha emitters are ingested or inhaled, the alpha particles they give off can cause serious internal damage.

Beta particles have a very small mass and move much faster and farther than alpha particles, traveling as far as several meters through air. They can pass through paper and penetrate as far as 4–5 mm into body tissue. External exposure to beta particles can burn the surface of the skin, but they do not travel far enough to reach the internal organs. Heavy clothing such as lab coats and gloves are needed to protect the skin from beta particles.

Gamma rays travel great distances through the air and pass through many materials, including body tissues. Because gamma rays penetrate so deeply, exposure to these rays is extremely hazardous. Only very dense shielding from substances such as lead and concrete will stop them. Syringes used for injections of radioactive materials use shielding made of lead or heavy-weight materials such as tungsten and plastic composites.

When working with radioactive materials, medical personnel wear protective clothing and gloves and stand behind a shield (see Figure 1). Long tongs may be used to pick up vials of radioactive material, keeping them away from the hands and body.

Table 3 summarizes the shielding materials required for the various types of radiation.

If you work in an environment where radioactive materials are present, such as a nuclear medicine facility, try to keep the time you must spend in a radioactive area to a minimum. Remaining in a radioactive area twice as long exposes you to twice as much radiation.

Keep your distance! The greater the distance from the radioactive source, the lower the intensity of radiation you receive. Just by doubling your distance from the radiation source, the intensity of the radiation drops to $\left(\frac{1}{2}\right)^2$ or one-fourth of its previous value.

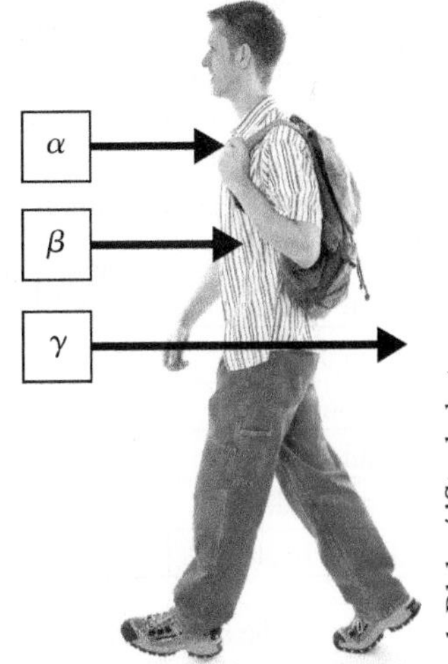

Health Protection Agency/
Photo Researchers, Inc.

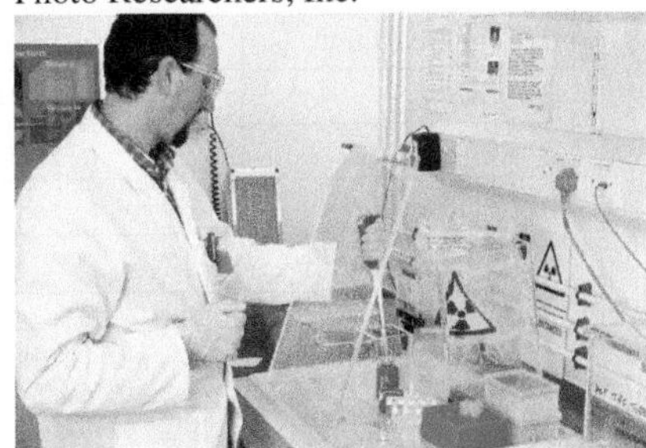

FIGURE 1 A person working with radioisotopes wears protective clothing and gloves and stands behind a shield.

Q What types of radiation does a lead shield block?

TABLE 3 Properties of Ionizing Radiation and Shielding Required

Property	Alpha (α) Particle	Beta (β) Particle	Gamma (γ) Ray
Travel Distance in Air	2–4 cm	200–300 cm	500 m
Tissue Depth	0.05 mm	4–5 mm	50 cm or more
Shielding	Paper, clothing	Heavy clothing, lab coats, gloves	Lead, thick concrete
Typical Source	Radium-226	Carbon-14	Technetium-99m

SAMPLE PROBLEM 1 Radiation Protection

How does the type of shielding for alpha radiation differ from that used for gamma radiation?

SOLUTION

Alpha radiation is stopped by paper and clothing. However, lead or concrete is needed for protection from gamma radiation.

STUDY CHECK 1

Besides shielding, what other methods help reduce exposure to radiation?

QUESTIONS AND PROBLEMS

1 Natural Radioactivity

LEARNING GOAL: *Describe alpha, beta, positron, and gamma radiation.*

1 Identify the type of particle or radiation for each of the following:
a. ${}^{4}_{2}He$ **b.** ${}^{0}_{+1}e$ **c.** ${}^{0}_{0}\gamma$

2 Identify the type of particle or radiation for each of the following:
a. ${}^{0}_{-1}e$ **b.** ${}^{1}_{1}H$ **c.** ${}^{1}_{0}n$

3 Naturally occurring potassium consists of three isotopes: potassium-39, potassium-40, and potassium-41.
a. Write the atomic symbol for each isotope.
b. In what ways are the isotopes similar and in what ways do they differ?

4 Naturally occurring iodine is iodine-127. Medically, radioactive isotopes of iodine-125 and iodine-130 are used.
   a. Write the atomic symbol for each isotope.
   b. In what ways are the isotopes similar and in what ways do they differ?

5 Supply the missing information in the following table:

Medical Use	Atomic Symbol	Mass Number	Number of Protons	Number of Neutrons
Heart imaging	$^{201}_{81}Tl$			
Radiation therapy		60	27	
Abdominal scan			31	36
Hyperthyroidism	$^{131}_{53}I$			
Leukemia treatment		32		17

6 Supply the missing information in the following table:

Medical Use	Atomic Symbol	Mass Number	Number of Protons	Number of Neutrons
Cancer treatment	$^{131}_{55}Cs$			
Brain scan		99	43	
Blood flow		141	58	
Bone scan		85		47
Lung function	$^{133}_{54}Xe$			

7 Write the symbol for each of the following isotopes used in nuclear medicine:
   a. copper-64 **b.** selenium-75
   c. sodium-24 **d.** nitrogen-15

8 Write the symbol for each of the following isotopes used in nuclear medicine:
   a. indium-111 **b.** palladium-103
   c. barium-131 **d.** rubidium-82

9 Identify each of the following:
   a. $^{0}_{-1}X$ **b.** $^{4}_{2}X$ **c.** $^{1}_{0}X$
   d. $^{38}_{18}X$ **e.** $^{14}_{6}X$

10 Identify each of the following:
   a. $^{1}_{1}X$ **b.** $^{81}_{35}X$ **c.** $^{0}_{0}X$
   d. $^{59}_{26}X$ **e.** $^{0}_{+1}X$

11 Match the type of radiation with each of the following statements:
   1. alpha particle
   2. beta particle
   3. gamma radiation

   a. does not penetrate skin
   b. shielding protection includes lead or thick concrete
   c. can be very harmful if ingested

12 Match the type of radiation with each of the following statements:
   1. alpha particle
   2. beta particle
   3. gamma radiation

   a. penetrates farthest into skin and body tissues
   b. shielding protection includes lab coats and gloves
   c. travels only a short distance in air

LEARNING GOAL

Write a balanced nuclear equation showing mass numbers and atomic numbers for radioactive decay.

2 Nuclear Reactions

In a process called **radioactive decay**, a nucleus spontaneously breaks down by emitting radiation. This process can be written as a nuclear equation with the atomic symbols of the original radioactive nucleus on the left, an arrow, and the new nucleus and radiation emitted on the right.

$$\text{Radioactive nucleus} \longrightarrow \text{new nucleus} + \text{radiation}(\alpha, \beta, \beta^+, \gamma)$$

In a nuclear equation, the total of the mass numbers and the total of the atomic numbers on one side of the arrow must equal the total of the mass numbers and the total of the atomic numbers on the other side.

Alpha Decay

In alpha decay, an unstable nucleus emits an alpha particle, which consists of 2 protons and 2 neutrons. Thus, the mass number of the radioactive nucleus decreases by 4, and its atomic number decreases by 2. For example, when uranium-238 emits an alpha particle, the new nucleus that forms has a mass number of 234. Compared to uranium with 92 protons, the new nucleus has 90 protons, which is thorium.

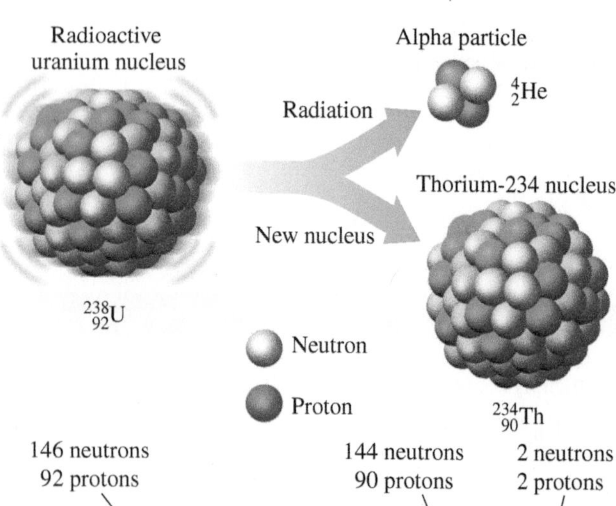

In alpha decay, the mass number of the new nucleus decreases by 4 and its atomic number decreases by 2.

CONCEPT CHECK 2 **Alpha Decay**

When francium-221 undergoes alpha decay, an alpha particle is emitted.

a. Does the new nucleus have a larger or smaller mass number? By how much?
b. Does the new nucleus have a larger or smaller atomic number? By how much?

ANSWER

a. The loss of an alpha particle will give the new nucleus a smaller mass number. Because an alpha particle is a helium nucleus, ${}^{4}_{2}\text{He}$, the mass number of the new nucleus will decrease by four from 221 to 217.
b. The loss of an alpha particle will give the new nucleus a smaller atomic number. Because an alpha particle is a helium nucleus, ${}^{4}_{2}\text{He}$, the atomic number of the new nucleus will decrease by two from 87 to 85.

We can look at writing a balanced nuclear equation for americium-241, which undergoes alpha decay as shown in Sample Problem 2.

SAMPLE PROBLEM 2 **Writing an Equation for Alpha Decay**

Smoke detectors that are used in homes and apartments contain americium-241, which undergoes alpha decay. When alpha particles collide with air molecules, charged particles are produced that generate an electrical current. If smoke particles enter the detector, they interfere with the formation of charged particles in the air, and the electrical current is interrupted. This causes the alarm to sound and warns the occupants of the danger of fire. Complete the following nuclear equation for the decay of americium-241:

$${}^{241}_{95}\text{Am} \longrightarrow ? + {}^{4}_{2}\text{He}$$

Uberphotos/iStockphoto

A smoke detector sounds an alarm when smoke enters its ionization chamber.

SOLUTION

Step 1 **Write the incomplete nuclear equation.**

$${}^{241}_{95}\text{Am} \longrightarrow ? + {}^{4}_{2}\text{He}$$

Step 2 **Determine the missing mass number.** In the equation, the mass number of the americium, 241, is equal to the sum of the mass numbers of the new nucleus and the alpha particle.

$$241 = ? + 4$$
$$241 - 4 = ?$$
$$241 - 4 = 237 \text{ (mass number of new nucleus)}$$

Step 3 **Determine the missing atomic number.** The atomic number of americium, 95, must equal the sum of the atomic numbers of the new nucleus and the alpha particle.

$$95 = ? + 2$$
$$95 - 2 = ?$$
$$95 - 2 = 93 \text{ (atomic number of new nucleus)}$$

Step 4 **Determine the symbol of the new nucleus.** On the periodic table, the element that has atomic number 93 is neptunium, Np. The nucleus of this isotope of Np is written as ${}^{237}_{93}\text{Np}$.

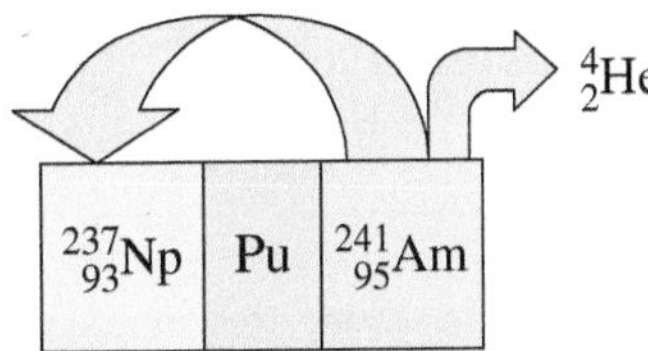

Step 5 **Complete the nuclear equation.**

$${}^{241}_{95}\text{Am} \longrightarrow {}^{237}_{93}\text{Np} + {}^{4}_{2}\text{He}$$

STUDY CHECK 2

Write a balanced nuclear equation for the alpha decay of Po-214.

Guide to Completing a Nuclear Equation

1. Write the incomplete nuclear equation.
2. Determine the missing mass number.
3. Determine the missing atomic number.
4. Determine the symbol of the new nucleus.
5. Complete the nuclear equation.

Beta Decay

As we learned in Section 1, the formation of a beta particle is the result of the breakdown of a neutron into a proton and an electron (beta particle). Because the proton remains in the nucleus, the number of protons increases by one, while the number of neutrons decreases by one. Thus, in a nuclear equation for beta decay, the mass number of the radioactive nucleus and the mass number of the new nucleus are the same. However, the atomic number of the new nucleus increases by one, which makes it a nucleus of a different element (*transmutation*). For example, the beta decay of a carbon-14 nucleus produces a nitrogen-14 nucleus.

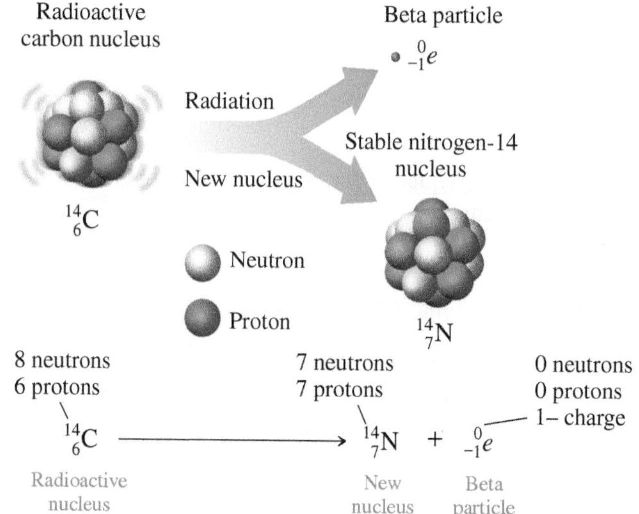

In beta decay, the mass number of the new nucleus remains the same and its atomic number increases by 1.

8 neutrons, 6 protons; 7 neutrons, 7 protons; 0 neutrons, 0 protons, 1– charge

$$^{14}_{6}C \longrightarrow \, ^{14}_{7}N + \, ^{0}_{-1}e$$

Radioactive nucleus — New nucleus — Beta particle

Chemistry Link to the Environment

RADON IN OUR HOMES

The presence of radon has become a much publicized environmental and health issue because of the radiation danger it poses. Radioactive isotopes such as radium-226 are naturally present in many types of rocks and soils. Radium-226 emits an alpha particle and is converted into radon gas, which diffuses out of the rocks and soil.

$$^{226}_{88}Ra \longrightarrow \, ^{222}_{86}Rn + \, ^{4}_{2}He$$

Outdoors, radon gas poses little danger because it disperses in the air. However, if the radioactive source is under a house or building, the radon gas can enter the house through cracks in the foundation or other openings. Those who live or work there may inhale the radon. Inside the lungs, radon-222 emits alpha particles to form polonium-218, which is known to cause lung cancer.

$$^{222}_{86}Rn \longrightarrow \, ^{218}_{84}Po + \, ^{4}_{2}He$$

The Environmental Protection Agency (EPA) estimates that in 2003, exposure to radon caused 21 000 lung cancer deaths in the United States. The EPA recommends that the maximum level of radon not exceed 4 picocuries (pCi) per liter of air in a home. One picocurie (pCi) is equal to 1×10^{-12} curies (Ci); curies are described in Section 3. In California, 1 percent of all the houses surveyed exceeded the EPA's recommended maximum radon level.

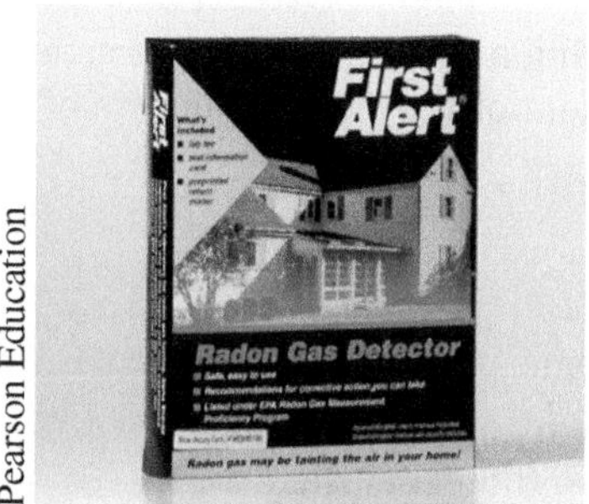

Pearson Education

A radon gas detector is used to determine radon levels in buildings.

TUTORIAL
Writing Nuclear Equations

SAMPLE PROBLEM 3 **Writing an Equation for Beta Decay**

Write the balanced nuclear equation for the beta decay of cobalt-60.

SOLUTION

Step 1 **Write the incomplete nuclear equation.**

$$^{60}_{27}Co \longrightarrow ? + \, ^{0}_{-1}e$$

Step 2 **Determine the missing mass number.** In the equation, the mass number of the cobalt, 60, is equal to the sum of the mass numbers of the new nucleus and the beta particle.

$$60 \quad = ? + 0$$
$$60 - 0 = ?$$
$$60 - 0 = 60 \text{ (mass number of new nucleus)}$$

Step 3 **Determine the missing atomic number.** The atomic number of cobalt, 27, must equal the sum of the atomic numbers of the new nucleus and the beta particle.

$$27 \quad = ? - 1$$
$$27 + 1 = ?$$
$$27 + 1 = 28 \text{ (atomic number of new nucleus)}$$

Step 4 **Determine the symbol of the new nucleus.** On the periodic table, the element that has atomic number 28 is nickel (Ni). The nucleus of this isotope of Ni is written as ${}^{60}_{28}\text{Ni}$.

Step 5 **Complete the nuclear equation.**

$${}^{60}_{27}\text{Co} \longrightarrow {}^{60}_{28}\text{Ni} + {}^{0}_{-1}e$$

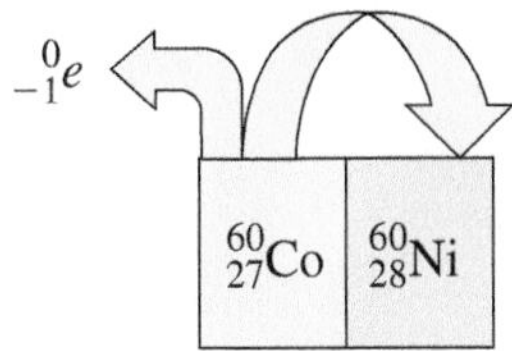

STUDY CHECK 3

Write the balanced nuclear equation for the beta decay of chromium-51.

Positron Emission

As we learned in Section 1, positron emission occurs when a proton in an unstable nucleus is converted to a neutron and a positron. The neutron remains in the nucleus, but the positron is emitted. In a nuclear equation for positron emission, the mass number of the radioactive nucleus and the mass number of the new nucleus are the same. However, the atomic number of the new nucleus decreases by one, indicating a change of one element into another (*transmutation*). For example, an aluminum-24 nucleus undergoes positron emission to produce a magnesium-24 nucleus. The atomic number of magnesium, 12, and the charge of the positron (1+) give the atomic number of aluminum, 13.

$${}^{24}_{13}\text{Al} \longrightarrow {}^{24}_{12}\text{Mg} + {}^{0}_{+1}e$$

SAMPLE PROBLEM 4 **Writing an Equation for Positron Emission**

Write the balanced nuclear equation for manganese-49, which decays by emitting a positron.

SOLUTION

Step 1 **Write the incomplete nuclear equation.**

$${}^{49}_{25}\text{Mn} \longrightarrow ? + {}^{0}_{+1}e$$

Step 2 **Determine the missing mass number.** In the equation, the mass number of the manganese, 49, is equal to the sum of the mass numbers of the new nucleus and the positron.

$$49 \quad = ? + 0$$
$$49 - 0 = ?$$
$$49 - 0 = 49 \text{ (mass number of new nucleus)}$$

Step 3 **Determine the missing atomic number.** The atomic number of manganese, 25, must equal the sum of the atomic numbers of the new nucleus and the positron.

$$25 \quad = ? + 1$$
$$25 - 1 = ?$$
$$25 - 1 = 24 \text{ (atomic number of new nucleus)}$$

BETA EMITTERS IN MEDICINE

The radioactive isotopes of several biologically important elements are beta emitters. When a radiologist wants to treat a malignancy within the body, a beta emitter may be used. The short range of penetration into the tissue by beta particles is advantageous for certain conditions. For example, some malignant tumors increase the fluid within the body tissues. A compound containing phosphorus-32, a beta emitter, is injected into the tumor. The beta particles travel only a few millimeters through the tissue, so only the malignancy and any tissue within that range are affected. The growth of the tumor is slowed or stopped, and the production of fluid decreases. Phosphorus-32 is also used to treat leukemia, polycythemia vera (an excessive production of red blood cells), and lymphomas.

$${}^{32}_{15}\text{P} \longrightarrow {}^{32}_{16}\text{S} + {}^{0}_{-1}e$$

Another beta emitter, iron-59, is used in blood tests to determine the level of iron in the blood and the rate of production of red blood cells by the bone marrow.

$${}^{59}_{26}\text{Fe} \longrightarrow {}^{59}_{27}\text{Co} + {}^{0}_{-1}e$$

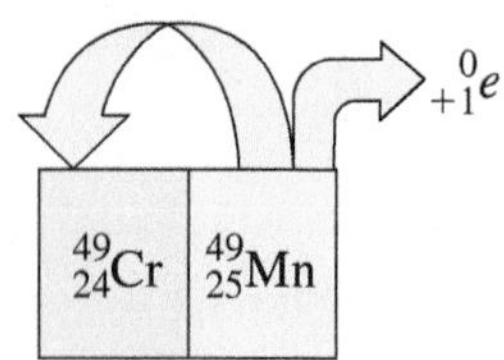

Step 4 **Determine the symbol of the new nucleus.** On the periodic table, the element that has atomic number 24 is chromium, Cr. The nucleus of this isotope of Cr is written as $^{49}_{24}Cr$.

Step 5 **Complete the nuclear equation.**

$$^{49}_{25}Mn \longrightarrow ^{49}_{24}Cr + ^{0}_{+1}e$$

STUDY CHECK 4

Write the balanced nuclear equation for xenon-118, which undergoes positron emission.

Radiation Source	Radiation		New Nucleus
Alpha emitter	$^{4}_{2}He$	+	New element Mass number −4 Atomic number −2
Beta emitter	$^{0}_{-1}e$	+	New element Mass number same Atomic number +1
Positron emitter	$^{0}_{+1}e$	+	New element Mass number same Atomic number −1
Gamma emitter	$^{0}_{0}\gamma$	+	Stable nucleus of the same element Mass number same Atomic number same

FIGURE 2 When the nuclei of alpha, beta, positron, and gamma emitters emit radiation, new and more stable nuclei are produced.

Q What changes occur in the number of protons and neutrons of an unstable nucleus that undergoes alpha decay?

Gamma Emission

Pure gamma emitters are rare, although some gamma radiation accompanies most alpha and beta radiation. In radiology, one of the most commonly used gamma emitters is technetium (Tc). The unstable isotope of technetium is written as the *metastable* (symbol m) isotope technetium-99m, Tc-99m, or $^{99m}_{43}Tc$. By emitting energy in the form of gamma rays, the unstable nucleus becomes more stable.

$$^{99m}_{43}Tc \longrightarrow ^{99}_{43}Tc + ^{0}_{0}\gamma$$

Figure 2 summarizes the changes in the nucleus for alpha, beta, positron, and gamma radiation.

Producing Radioactive Isotopes

Today, many radioisotopes are produced in small amounts by converting stable, nonradioactive isotopes into radioactive ones. In the process called *transmutation*, a stable nucleus is bombarded by high-speed particles such as alpha particles, protons, neutrons, and small nuclei. When one of these particles is absorbed, the stable nucleus is converted to a radioactive isotope and usually some type of radiation particle.

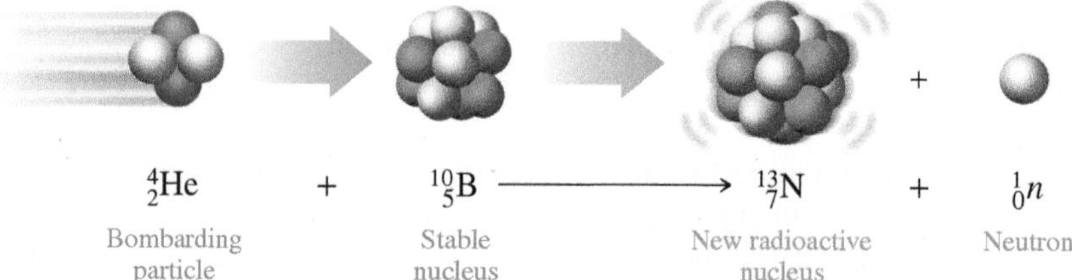

When nonradioactive B-10 is bombarded by an alpha particle, the products are radioactive N-13 and a neutron.

All elements that have an atomic number greater than 92 have been produced artificially by bombardment. Most have been produced in small amounts and exist for only a short time, making it difficult to study their properties. For example, when californium-249 is bombarded with nitrogen-15, the radioactive element 105, dubnium (Db), and some neutrons are produced.

$$^{15}_{7}N + ^{249}_{98}Cf \longrightarrow ^{260}_{105}Db + 4^{1}_{0}n$$

Technetium-99m is a radioisotope used in nuclear medicine for several diagnostic procedures, including the detection of brain tumors and examinations of the liver and spleen. The source of technetium-99m is molybdenum-99, which is produced in a nuclear reactor by neutron bombardment of molybdenum-98.

$$^{1}_{0}n + ^{98}_{42}\text{Mo} \longrightarrow ^{99}_{42}\text{Mo}$$

Many radiology laboratories have small generators containing molybdenum-99, which decays to technetium-99m.

$$^{99}_{42}\text{Mo} \longrightarrow ^{99m}_{43}\text{Tc} + ^{0}_{-1}e$$

The technetium-99m radioisotope decays by emitting gamma rays. Gamma emission is desirable for diagnostic work because the gamma rays pass through the body to the detection equipment.

$$^{99m}_{43}\text{Tc} \longrightarrow ^{99}_{43}\text{Tc} + ^{0}_{0}\gamma$$

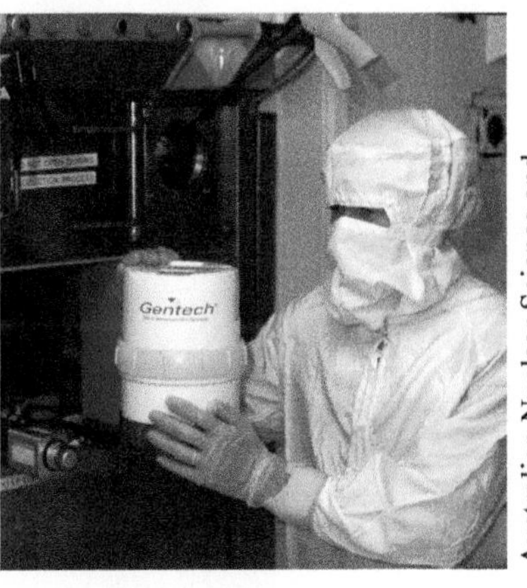

Australian Nuclear Science and Technology Organisation

A generator is used to prepare technetium-99m.

TUTORIAL
Alpha, Beta, and Gamma Emitters

CONCEPT CHECK 3 Writing an Isotope Produced by Bombardment

Sulfur-32 is bombarded with a neutron to produce a new radioactive isotope and an alpha particle. What is the symbol for the new isotope?

$$^{1}_{0}n + ^{32}_{16}\text{S} \longrightarrow ? + ^{4}_{2}\text{He}$$

ANSWER

To determine the new isotope, we need to calculate its mass number and atomic number. On the left side of the equation, the sum of the mass numbers of one neutron, 1, and the sulfur isotope, 32, gives a total of 33. On the right side, the sum of the mass number of the new isotope and that of the alpha particle, 4, must equal 33. Thus, the new isotope has a mass number of 29.

$$^{1}_{0}n + ^{32}_{16}\text{S} \longrightarrow ^{29}_{?}? + ^{4}_{2}\text{He}$$

On the left side of the equation, the sum of the atomic numbers of a neutron, 0, and the sulfur, 16, gives a total of 16. On the right side, the sum of the atomic number of the new isotope and the atomic number of the alpha particle, 2, must equal 16. Thus, the new isotope has an atomic number of 14. On the periodic table, the element that has atomic number 14 is silicon. Thus, the symbol for the new isotope is $^{29}_{14}\text{Si}$.

$$^{1}_{0}n + ^{32}_{16}\text{S} \longrightarrow ^{29}_{14}\text{Si} + ^{4}_{2}\text{He}$$

SAMPLE PROBLEM 5 Writing Equations for Isotope Production

Write the balanced nuclear equation for the bombardment of nickel-58 by a proton ($^{1}_{1}\text{H}$), which produces a radioactive isotope and an alpha particle.

SOLUTION

Step 1 **Write the incomplete nuclear equation.**

$$^{1}_{1}\text{H} + ^{58}_{28}\text{Ni} \longrightarrow ? + ^{4}_{2}\text{He}$$

Step 2 **Determine the missing mass number.** In the equation, the sum of the mass numbers of the proton, 1, and the nickel, 58, gives a total of 59, which must equal the sum of the mass numbers of the new nucleus and the alpha particle, 4.

$1 + 58 = ? + 4$

$59 - 4 = ?$

$59 - 4 = 55$ (mass number of new nucleus)

$^{4}_{2}He$ $^{1}_{1}H$ $^{55}_{27}Co$ $^{58}_{28}Ni$

Step 3 **Determine the missing atomic number.** The sum of the atomic numbers of the proton, 1, and nickel, 28, gives a total of 29, which must equal the sum of the atomic numbers of the new nucleus and the alpha particle, 2.

$$1 + 28 = ? + 2$$
$$29 - 2 = ?$$
$$29 - 2 = 27 \text{ (atomic number of new nucleus)}$$

Step 4 **Determine the symbol of the new nucleus.** On the periodic table, the element that has atomic number 27 is cobalt, Co. The nucleus of this isotope is written as $^{55}_{27}Co$.

Step 5 **Complete the nuclear equation.**

$$^{1}_{1}H + ^{58}_{28}Ni \longrightarrow ^{55}_{27}Co + ^{4}_{2}He$$

STUDY CHECK 5

The first radioactive isotope was produced in 1934 by the bombardment of aluminum-27 by an alpha particle to produce a radioactive isotope and one neutron. What is the balanced nuclear equation for this transmutation?

QUESTIONS AND PROBLEMS

2 Nuclear Reactions

LEARNING GOAL: *Write a balanced nuclear equation showing mass numbers and atomic numbers for radioactive decay.*

13 Write a balanced nuclear equation for the alpha decay of each of the following radioactive isotopes:
a. $^{208}_{84}Po$ **b.** $^{232}_{90}Th$
c. $^{251}_{102}No$ **d.** radon-220

14 Write a balanced nuclear equation for the alpha decay of each of the following radioactive isotopes:
a. curium-243 **b.** $^{252}_{99}Es$
c. $^{251}_{98}Cf$ **d.** $^{261}_{107}Bh$

15 Write a balanced nuclear equation for the beta decay of each of the following radioactive isotopes:
a. $^{25}_{11}Na$ **b.** $^{20}_{8}O$
c. strontium-92 **d.** iron-60

16 Write a balanced nuclear equation for the beta decay of each of the following radioactive isotopes:
a. $^{44}_{19}K$ **b.** iron-59
c. potassium-42 **d.** $^{141}_{56}Ba$

17 Write a balanced nuclear equation for the positron emission of each of the following radioactive isotopes:
a. silicon-26 **b.** cobalt-54
c. $^{77}_{37}Rb$ **d.** $^{93}_{45}Rh$

18 Write a balanced nuclear equation for the positron emission of each of the following radioactive isotopes:
a. boron-8 **b.** $^{15}_{8}O$
c. $^{40}_{19}K$ **d.** nitrogen-13

19 Complete each of the following nuclear equations and describe the type of radiation:
a. $^{28}_{13}Al \longrightarrow ? + ^{0}_{-1}e$ **b.** $^{180m}_{73}Ta \longrightarrow ^{180}_{73}Ta + ?$
c. $^{66}_{29}Cu \longrightarrow ^{66}_{30}Zn + ?$ **d.** $? \longrightarrow ^{234}_{90}Th + ^{4}_{2}He$
e. $^{188}_{80}Hg \longrightarrow ? + ^{0}_{+1}e$

20 Complete each of the following nuclear equations and describe the type of radiation:
a. $^{11}_{6}C \longrightarrow ^{11}_{5}B + ?$ **b.** $^{35}_{16}S \longrightarrow ? + ^{0}_{-1}e$
c. $? \longrightarrow ^{90}_{39}Y + ^{0}_{-1}e$ **d.** $^{210}_{83}Bi \longrightarrow ? + ^{4}_{2}He$
e. $? \longrightarrow ^{89}_{39}Y + ^{0}_{+1}e$

21 Complete each of the following bombardment reactions:
a. $^{1}_{0}n + ^{9}_{4}Be \longrightarrow ?$
b. $^{1}_{0}n + ^{131}_{52}Te \longrightarrow ? + ^{0}_{-1}e$
c. $^{1}_{0}n + ? \longrightarrow ^{24}_{11}Na + ^{4}_{2}He$
d. $^{4}_{2}He + ^{27}_{13}Al \longrightarrow ? + ^{1}_{0}n$

22 Complete each of the following bombardment reactions:
a. $? + ^{40}_{18}Ar \longrightarrow ^{43}_{19}K + ^{1}_{1}H$
b. $^{1}_{0}n + ^{238}_{92}U \longrightarrow ?$
c. $^{1}_{0}n + ? \longrightarrow ^{14}_{6}C + ^{1}_{1}H$
d. $? + ^{64}_{28}Ni \longrightarrow ^{272}_{111}Rg + ^{1}_{0}n$

LEARNING GOAL

Describe the detection and measurement of radiation.

3 Radiation Measurement

One of the most common instruments for detecting beta and gamma radiation is the Geiger counter. It consists of a metal tube filled with a gas such as argon. When radiation enters a window on the end of the tube, it produces charged particles in the gas, which produce an electrical current. Each burst of current is amplified to give a click and a reading on a meter.

$$Ar + \text{radiation} \longrightarrow Ar^{+} + e^{-}$$

AP Photo/James McPherson

Don Farrall/PhotoDisc/Getty Images

A radiation technician uses a Geiger counter to check radiation levels.

Measuring Radiation

TUTORIAL
Measuring Radiation

SELF-STUDY ACTIVITY
Nuclear Chemistry

Radiation is measured in several different ways. When a radiology laboratory obtains a radioisotope, the *activity* of the sample is measured in terms of the number of nuclear disintegrations per second. The **curie (Ci)**, the original unit of activity, was defined as the number of disintegrations that occur in 1 second for 1 gram of radium, which is equal to 3.7×10^{10} disintegrations/s. The unit was named for the Polish scientist Marie Curie, who along with her husband, Pierre, discovered the radioactive elements radium and polonium. The SI unit of radiation activity is the **becquerel (Bq)**, which is 1 disintegration/s.

The **rad (radiation absorbed dose)** is a unit that measures the amount of radiation absorbed by a gram of material such as body tissue. The SI unit for absorbed dose is the **gray (Gy)**, which is defined as the joules of energy absorbed by 1 kilogram of body tissue. The gray is equal to 100 rad.

The **rem (radiation equivalent in humans)** is a unit that measures the biological effects of different kinds of radiation. Although alpha particles do not penetrate the skin, if they should enter the body by some other route, they can cause extensive damage within a short distance in tissue. High-energy radiation, such as beta particles, high-energy protons, and neutrons that penetrate the skin and travel into tissue cause more damage. Gamma rays are damaging because they travel a long way through body tissue.

To determine the **equivalent dose** or rem dose, the absorbed dose (rads) is multiplied by a factor that adjusts for biological damage caused by a particular form of radiation. For beta and gamma radiation, the factor is 1, so the biological damage in rems is the same as the absorbed radiation (rads). For high-energy protons and neutrons, the factor is about 10, and for alpha particles it is 20.

$$\text{Biological damage (rems)} = \text{absorbed dose (rads)} \times \text{factor}$$

Often the measurement for an equivalent dose will be in units of millirems (mrems). One rem is equal to 1000 mrem. The SI unit is the **sievert (Sv)**. One sievert is equal to 100 rem. Table 4 summarizes the units used to measure radiation.

TABLE 4 Some Units of Radiation Measurement

Measurement	Common Unit	SI Unit	Relationship
Activity	curie (Ci)	becquerel (Bq)	$1 \text{ Ci} = 3.7 \times 10^{10} \text{ Bq}$
Absorbed Dose	rad	gray (Gy)	1 Gy = 100 rad
Biological Damage	rem	sievert (Sv)	1 Sv = 100 rem

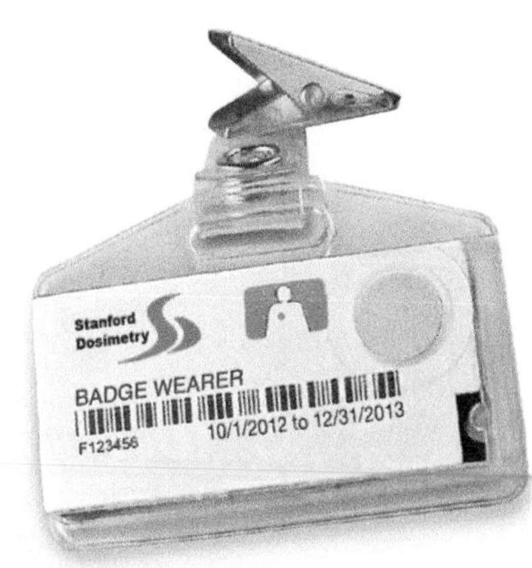

Stanford Dosimetry, LLC

A film badge measures radiation exposure.

CASE STUDY
Food Irradiation

People who work in radiology laboratories wear film badges to monitor their exposure to radiation. A film badge consists of radiation-sensitive film in a holder that is attached to clothing. If gamma rays, X-rays, or beta particles strike the film, it appears darker upon development. Periodically, the film is collected to determine if any exposure to radiation has occurred.

Chemistry Link to Health

RADIATION AND FOOD

Food-borne illnesses caused by pathogenic bacteria such as *Salmonella*, *Listeria*, and *Escherichia coli* have become a major health concern in the United States. The Centers for Disease Control and Prevention (CDC) estimates that each year, *E. coli* in contaminated foods infects 20 000 people in the United States, and that 500 people die. *E. coli* has been responsible for outbreaks of illness from contaminated ground beef, eggs, fruit juices, lettuce, spinach, and alfalfa sprouts.

The Food and Drug Administration (FDA) has approved the use of 0.3 kGy to 1 kGy of radiation produced by cobalt-60 or cesium-137 for the treatment of foods. The irradiation technology is much like that used to sterilize medical supplies. Cobalt pellets are placed in stainless steel tubes, which are arranged in racks. When food moves through the series of racks, the gamma rays pass through the food and kill the bacteria.

It is important for consumers to understand that when food is irradiated, it never comes into contact with the radioactive source. The gamma rays pass through the food to kill bacteria, but that does not make the food radioactive. The radiation kills bacteria because it stops their ability to divide and grow. We cook or heat food thoroughly for the same purpose. Radiation has little effect on the food itself because its cells are no longer dividing or growing. Thus, irradiated food is not harmed although small amounts of vitamins B_1 and C may be lost.

Currently, tomatoes, blueberries, strawberries, and mushrooms are being irradiated to allow them to be harvested when completely ripe and extend their shelf life (see Figure 3). The FDA has also approved the irradiation of pork, poultry, and beef to decrease potential infections and to extend shelf life. Currently, irradiated vegetable and meat products are available in more than 40 countries. In the United States, irradiated foods such as tropical fruits, spinach, and ground meats are found in some stores. *Apollo 17* astronauts ate irradiated foods on the Moon, and some U.S. hospitals and nursing homes now use irradiated poultry to reduce the possibility of salmonella infections among patients. The extended shelf life of irradiated food also makes it useful for campers and military personnel. Soon, consumers concerned about food safety will have a choice of irradiated meats, fruits, and vegetables at the market.

FIGURE 3 **(a)** The FDA requires this symbol to appear on irradiated retail foods. **(b)** After two weeks, the irradiated strawberries on the right show no spoilage. Mold is growing on the nonirradiated ones on the left.

Q Why are irradiated foods used on spaceships and in nursing homes?

SAMPLE PROBLEM 6 **Radiation Measurement**

One treatment for bone pain involves intravenous administration of the radioisotope phosphorus-32, which is primarily incorporated into bone. A typical dose of 7 mCi can produce up to 450 rad in the bone. What is the difference between the units of mCi and rad?

SOLUTION

The millicuries (mCi) indicate the activity of the P-32 in terms of nuclei that break down in 1 second. The radiation absorbed dose (rads) is a measure of the amount of radiation absorbed by the bone.

STUDY CHECK 6

If P-32 is a beta emitter, how do the number of rems compare to the rads?

Exposure to Radiation

Every day, we are exposed to low levels of radiation from naturally occurring radioactive isotopes in the buildings where we live and work, in our food and water, and in the air we breathe. For example, potassium-40 is a naturally occurring isotope that is present in any potassium-containing food. Other naturally occurring radioisotopes in air and food are carbon-14, radon-222, strontium-90, and iodine-131. The average person in the United States is exposed to about 360 mrem of radiation annually. Medical sources of radiation, including dental, hip, spine, and chest X-rays and mammograms, add to our radiation exposure. Table 5 lists some common sources of radiation.

Another source of background radiation is cosmic radiation produced in space by the Sun. People who live at high altitudes or travel by airplane receive a greater amount of cosmic radiation because there are fewer molecules in the atmosphere to absorb the radiation. For example, a person living in Denver receives about twice the cosmic radiation as a person living in Los Angeles. A person living close to a nuclear power plant normally does not receive much additional radiation, perhaps 0.1 mrem in one year. (One rem equals 1000 mrem.) However, in the accident at the Chernobyl nuclear power plant in 1986 in Ukraine, it is estimated that people in a nearby town received as much as 1 rem/h.

TABLE 5 Average Annual Radiation Received by a Person in the United States

Source	Dose (mrem)
Natural	
Ground	20
Air, water, food	30
Cosmic rays	40
Wood, concrete, brick	50
Medical	
Chest X-ray	20
Dental X-ray	20
Mammogram	40
Hip X-ray	60
Lumbar spine X-ray	70
Upper gastrointestinal tract X-ray	200
Other	
Nuclear power plants	0.1
Air travel	10
Television	20
Radon	200*

*Varies widely.

Radiation Sickness

The larger the amount of radiation received at one time, the greater the effect on the body. Exposure to radiation of less than 25 rem is usually not detected. Whole-body exposure of 100 rem produces a temporary decrease in the number of white blood cells. If the exposure to radiation is greater than 100 rem, a person may experience symptoms of radiation sickness: nausea, vomiting, fatigue, and a reduction in white-cell count. A whole-body dosage greater than 300 rem can decrease the white-cell count to zero. The victim may have diarrhea, hair loss, and infection. Exposure to radiation of 500 rem is expected to cause death in 50% of the people receiving that dose. This amount of radiation to the whole body is called the *lethal dose for one-half the population*, or the LD_{50}. The LD_{50} varies for different life forms, as Table 6 shows. Whole body radiation of 600 rem or greater would be fatal to all humans within a few weeks.

TABLE 6 Lethal Doses of Whole-Body Radiation for Some Life Forms

Life Form	LD_{50} (rem)
Insect	100 000
Bacterium	50 000
Rat	800
Human	500
Dog	300

QUESTIONS AND PROBLEMS

3 Radiation Measurement

LEARNING GOAL: *Describe the detection and measurement of radiation.*

23 Match each property (**1–3**) with its unit of measurement.
1. activity
2. absorbed dose
3. biological damage

a. rad **b.** mrem
c. μCi **d.** Gy

24 Match each property (**1–3**) with its unit of measurement.
1. activity
2. absorbed dose
3. biological damage

a. mrad **b.** gray
c. becquerel **d.** Sv

25 Two technicians in a nuclear laboratory were accidentally exposed to radiation. If one was exposed to 8 mGy and the other to 5 rad, which technician received more radiation?

26 Two samples of a radioisotope were spilled in a nuclear laboratory. The activity of one sample was 8 kBq and the other 15 μCi. Which sample produced the higher amount of radiation?

27 **a.** The recommended dosage of iodine-131 is 4.20 μCi/kg of body mass. How many microcuries of iodine-131 are needed for a 70.0-kg patient with hyperthyroidism?
b. A person receives 50 rad of gamma radiation. What is that amount in grays?

28 **a.** The dosage of technetium-99m for a lung scan is 20. μCi/kg of body mass. How many millicuries of technetium-99m are needed for a 50.0-kg patient?
b. Suppose a person absorbed 50 mrad of alpha radiation. What would be the equivalent dose in millirems?

4 Half-Life of a Radioisotope

LEARNING GOAL

Given the half-life of a radioisotope, calculate the amount of radioisotope remaining after one or more half-lives.

The **half-life** of a radioisotope is the amount of time it takes for one-half of a sample to decay. For example, $^{131}_{53}I$ has a half-life of 8.0 days. As $^{131}_{53}I$ decays, it produces the nonradioactive isotope $^{131}_{54}Xe$ and a beta particle.

$$^{131}_{53}I \longrightarrow ^{131}_{54}Xe + ^{0}_{-1}e$$

SELF-STUDY ACTIVITY
Nuclear Chemistry

Suppose we have a sample that initially contains 20. mg of $^{131}_{53}I$. In 8.0 days, one-half (10. mg) of the I-131 nuclei in the sample will decay, which leaves 10. mg of I-131. After 16 days (two half-lives), 5.0 mg of the remaining I-131 decays, which leaves 5.0 mg of I-131. After 24 days (three half-lives), 2.5 mg of the remaining I-131 decays, which leaves 2.5 mg of I-131 still capable of producing radiation.

As the I-131 undergoes beta decay, there is a buildup of the decay product Xe-131. That means that after the first half-life, the decay process produces 10. mg of Xe-131, and after a second half-life, there is a total of 15. mg of the product Xe-131. After the third half-life, there is a total of 17.5 mg of Xe-131.

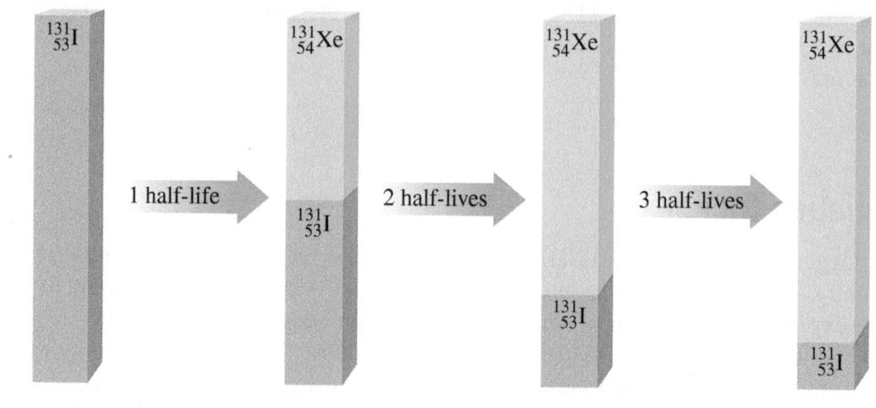

$$20.\text{ mg of } ^{131}_{53}I \xrightarrow{\text{1 half-life}} 10.\text{ mg of } ^{131}_{53}I \xrightarrow{\text{2 half-lives}} 5.0\text{ mg of } ^{131}_{53}I \xrightarrow{\text{3 half-lives}} 2.5\text{ mg of } ^{131}_{53}I$$

A **decay curve** is a diagram of the decay of a radioactive isotope. Figure 4 shows such a curve for the $^{131}_{53}I$ we have discussed.

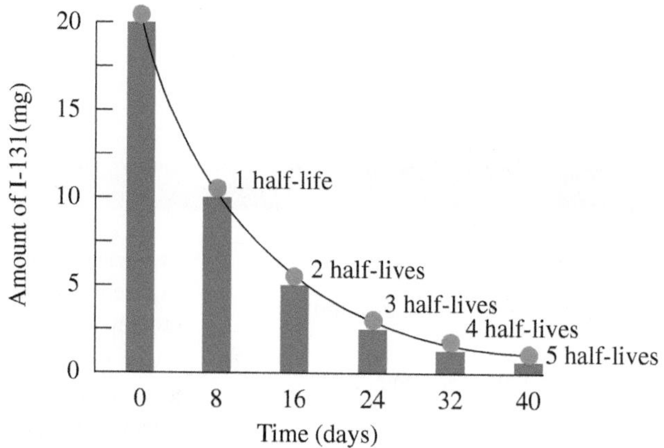

FIGURE 4 The decay curve for iodine-131 shows that one-half of the radioactive sample decays and one-half remains radioactive, after each half-life of 8.0 days.

Q How many milligrams of the 20.-mg sample remain radioactive after 2 half-lives?

TUTORIAL
Radioactive Half-Lives

CONCEPT CHECK 4 **Half-Lives**

Iridium-192, used to treat breast and prostate cancer, has a half-life of 74 days. What is the activity of the Ir-192 after 74 days if the activity of the initial sample of Ir-192 is 8×10^4 Bq?

ANSWER

In 74 days, which is one half-life of iridium-192, one-half of the iridium-192 atoms will decay. Thus, after 74 days, the activity is half of the initial activity of 8×10^4 Bq, which is 4×10^4 Bq.

SAMPLE PROBLEM 7 Using Half-Lives of a Radioisotope

Phosphorus-32, a radioisotope used in the treatment of leukemia, has a half-life of 14.3 days. If a sample contains 8.0 mg of phosphorus-32, how many milligrams of phosphorus-32 remain after 42.9 days?

SOLUTION

Step 1 **State the given and needed quantities.**

Analyze the Problem

Given	Equality	Need
8.0 mg of P-32 42.9 days elapsed	1 half-life = 14.3 days	milligrams of P-32 remaining

Step 2 **Write a plan to calculate the unknown quantity.**

days → Half-life → number of half-lives

milligrams of $^{32}_{15}P$ → Number of half-lives → milligrams of $^{32}_{15}P$ remaining

Step 3 **Write the half-life equality and conversion factors.**

1 half-life = 14.3 days

$$\frac{14.3 \text{ days}}{1 \text{ half-life}} \quad \text{and} \quad \frac{1 \text{ half-life}}{14.3 \text{ days}}$$

Step 4 **Set up the problem to calculate the needed quantity.** First, we determine the number of half-lives in the amount of time that has elapsed.

$$\text{Number of half-lives} = 42.9 \text{ days} \times \frac{1 \text{ half-life}}{14.3 \text{ days}} = 3 \text{ half-lives}$$

Now we can calculate how much of the sample decays in 3 half-lives, and how many milligrams of the phosphorus remain.

$$8.0 \text{ mg of } ^{32}_{15}P \xrightarrow{\text{1 half-life}} 4.0 \text{ mg of } ^{32}_{15}P \xrightarrow{\text{2 half-lives}} 2.0 \text{ mg of } ^{32}_{15}P \xrightarrow{\text{3 half-lives}} 1.0 \text{ mg of } ^{32}_{15}P$$

STUDY CHECK 7

Fe-59 has a half-life of 44 days. If a laboratory received 8.0 μg of Fe-59, how many micrograms of Fe-59 are still active after 176 days?

Guide to Using Half-Lives

1. State the given and needed quantities.
2. Write a plan to calculate the unknown quantity.
3. Write the half-life equality and conversion factors.
4. Set up the problem to calculate the needed quantity.

MODELING HALF-LIVES

Obtain a piece of paper and a licorice stick or celery stalk. Draw a vertical and a horizontal axis on the paper. Label the vertical axis as radioactive atoms and the horizontal axis as minutes. Place the licorice stick or celery against the vertical axis and mark its height at zero minutes. In the next minute, cut the licorice stick or celery in two. (You can eat the half if you are hungry.) Place the shortened licorice stick or celery at 1 minute on the horizontal axis and mark its height. Every minute, cut the licorice stick or celery in half again and mark the height at the corresponding time. Keep reducing the length by half until you cannot divide the licorice or celery in half any more. Connect the points you made for each minute. What does the curve look like? How does this curve represent the concept of a half-life for a radioisotope?

Naturally occurring isotopes of the elements usually have long half-lives, as shown in Table 7. They disintegrate slowly and produce radiation over a long period of time, even hundreds or millions of years. In contrast, the radioisotopes used in nuclear medicine have much shorter half-lives. They disintegrate rapidly and produce almost all their radiation in a short period of time. For example, technetium-99m emits half of its radiation in the first six hours. This means that a small amount of the radioisotope given to a patient is essentially gone within two days. The decay products of technetium-99m are totally eliminated by the body.

TABLE 7 Half-Lives of Some Radioisotopes

Element	Radioisotope	Half-Life	Type of Radiation
Naturally Occurring Radioisotopes			
Carbon-14	$^{14}_{6}C$	5730 y	Beta
Potassium-40	$^{40}_{19}K$	1.3×10^9 y	Beta, gamma
Radium-226	$^{226}_{88}Ra$	1600 y	Alpha
Strontium-90	$^{90}_{38}Sr$	38.1 y	Alpha
Uranium-238	$^{238}_{92}U$	4.5×10^9 y	Alpha
Some Medical Radioisotopes			
Chromium-51	$^{51}_{24}Cr$	28 d	Gamma
Iodine-131	$^{131}_{53}I$	8.0 d	Beta, gamma
Iridium-192	$^{192}_{77}Ir$	74 d	Beta, gamma
Iron-59	$^{59}_{26}Fe$	44 d	Beta, gamma
Radon-222	$^{222}_{86}Rn$	3.8 d	Alpha
Technetium-99m	$^{99m}_{43}Tc$	6.0 h	Gamma

TUTORIAL
Radiocarbon Dating

Chemistry Link to the Environment

DATING ANCIENT OBJECTS

Radiological dating is a technique used by geologists, archaeologists, and historians to determine the age of ancient objects. The age of an object derived from plants or animals (such as wood, fiber, natural pigments, bone, and cotton and woolen clothing) is determined by measuring the amount of carbon-14, a naturally occurring radioactive form of carbon. In 1960, Willard Libby received the Nobel Prize for his work developing carbon-14 dating techniques during the 1940s. Carbon-14 is produced in the upper atmosphere by the bombardment of $^{14}_{7}N$ by high-energy neutrons from cosmic rays.

$$^{1}_{0}n + {}^{14}_{7}N \longrightarrow {}^{14}_{6}C + {}^{1}_{1}H$$

Neutron from cosmic rays; Nitrogen in atmosphere; Radioactive carbon-14; Proton

The carbon-14 reacts with oxygen to form radioactive carbon dioxide, $^{14}_{6}CO_2$. Living plants continuously absorb carbon dioxide, which incorporates carbon-14 into the plant material. The uptake of carbon-14 stops when the plant dies.

$$^{14}_{6}C \longrightarrow {}^{14}_{7}N + {}^{0}_{-1}e$$

As the carbon-14 decays, the amount of radioactive carbon-14 in the plant material steadily decreases. In a process called **carbon dating**, scientists use the half-life of carbon-14 (5730 years) to calculate the length of time since the plant died. For example, a wooden beam found in an ancient dwelling might have one-half of the carbon-14 found in a living tree. Because one half-life of carbon-14 is 5730 years, this tells us that the tree was cut down about 5730 years ago. Carbon-14 dating was used to determine that the Dead Sea Scrolls are about 2000 years old.

A radiological dating method used for determining the age of much older items is based on the radioisotope uranium-238, which decays through a series of reactions to lead-206. The uranium-238 isotope has an incredibly long half-life, about 4×10^9 (4 billion) years. Measurements of the amounts of uranium-238 and lead-206 enable geologists to determine the age of rock samples. The older rocks will have a higher percentage of lead-206 because more of the uranium-238 has decayed. The age of rocks brought back from the moon by the *Apollo* missions, for example, was determined using uranium-238. They were found to be about 4×10^9 years old, approximately the same age calculated for Earth.

Library of Congress

The age of the Dead Sea Scrolls was determined using carbon-14 dating.

SAMPLE PROBLEM 8 Carbon Dating Using Half-Lives

Carbon material in the bones of humans and animals assimilates carbon until death. Using radiocarbon dating, the number of half-lives of carbon-14 from a bone sample determine the age of the bone. Suppose a sample is obtained from a prehistoric animal and used for radiocarbon dating. We can calculate the age of the bone or the years elapsed since the animal died by using the half-life of carbon-14, which is 5730 years. If the sample shows that four half-lives have passed, how much time has elapsed since the animal died?

JIHAD SIQLAWI/AFP/ Getty Images/Newscom

The age of a bone sample from a skeleton can be determined by carbon dating.

SOLUTION

Step 1 State the given and needed quantities.

Analyze the Problem

Given	Equality	Need
4 half-lives elapsed	1 half-life = 5730 y	years elapsed

Step 2 Write a plan to calculate the unknown quantity.

4 half-lives → Half-life → years elapsed

Step 3 Write the half-life equality and conversion factors.

$$1 \text{ half-life} = 5730 \text{ y}$$

$$\frac{5730 \text{ y}}{1 \text{ half-life}} \quad \text{and} \quad \frac{1 \text{ half-life}}{5730 \text{ y}}$$

Step 4 Set up the problem to calculate the needed quantity.

$$\text{Years elapsed} = 4.0 \cancel{\text{half-lives}} \times \frac{5730 \text{ y}}{1 \cancel{\text{half-life}}} = 23\,000 \text{ y}$$

We would estimate that the animal lived 23 000 years ago.

STUDY CHECK 8

Suppose that a piece of wood found in a tomb had $\frac{1}{8}$ of its original carbon-14 activity. About how many years ago was the wood part of a living tree?

QUESTIONS AND PROBLEMS

4 Half-Life of a Radioisotope

LEARNING GOAL: *Given the half-life of a radioisotope, calculate the amount of radioisotope remaining after one or more half-lives.*

29 For each of the following, indicate if the number of half-lives elapsed is:
1. one half-life **2.** two half-lives **3.** three half-lives
- **a.** a sample of Pd-103 with a half-life of 17 days after 34 days
- **b.** a sample of C-11 with a half-life of 20 min after 20 min
- **c.** a sample of At-211 with a half-life of 7 h after 21 h

30 For each of the following, indicate if the number of half-lives elapsed is:
1. one half-life **2.** two half-lives **3.** three half-lives
- **a.** a sample of Ce-141 with a half-life of 32.5 days after 32.5 days
- **b.** a sample of F-18 with a half-life of 110 min after 330 min
- **c.** a sample of Au-198 with a half-life of 2.7 days after 5.4 days

31 Technetium-99m is an ideal radioisotope for scanning organs because it has a half-life of 6.0 h and is a pure gamma emitter. Suppose that 80.0 mg were prepared in the technetium generator this morning. How many milligrams of technetium-99m would remain active after the following intervals?
- **a.** one half-life **b.** two half-lives
- **c.** 18 h **d.** 24 h

32 A sample of sodium-24 with an activity of 12 mCi is used to study the rate of blood flow in the circulatory system. If sodium-24 has a half-life of 15 h, what is the activity of the sodium after 2.5 days?

33 Strontium-85, used for bone scans, has a half-life of 65 days. How long will it take for the radiation level of strontium-85 to drop to one-fourth of its original level? To one-eighth?

34 Fluorine-18, which has a half-life of 110 min, is used in PET scans (see Section 5). If 100. mg of fluorine-18 is shipped at 8 A.M., how many milligrams of the radioisotope are still active if the sample arrives at the radiology laboratory at 1:30 P.M.?

LEARNING GOAL

Describe the use of radioisotopes in medicine.

5 Medical Applications Using Radioactivity

To determine the condition of an organ in the body, a radiologist may use a radioisotope that concentrates in that organ. The cells in the body cannot differentiate between a nonradioactive atom and a radioactive one, so these radioisotopes are easily incorporated. Then the radioactive atoms can be detected because they emit radiation. Some radioisotopes used in nuclear medicine are listed in Table 8.

TABLE 8 Medical Applications of Some Common Radioisotopes

Isotope	Half-Life	Radiation	Medical Application
Au-198	2.7 d	Beta	Liver imaging; treatment of abdominal carcinoma
Ce-141	32.5 d	Gamma	Gastrointestinal tract diagnosis; measuring blood flow to the heart
Cs-131	9.7 d	Gamma	Prostate brachytherapy
F-18	110 min	Positron	Positron emission tomography (PET)
Ga-67	78 h	Gamma	Abdominal imaging; tumor detection
Ga-68	68 min	Gamma	Detection of pancreatic cancer
I-123	13.2 h	Gamma	Treatment of thyroid, brain, and prostate cancer
I-131	8.0 d	Beta	Treatment of Graves' disease, goiter, hyperthyroidism, thyroid and prostate cancer
Ir-192	74 d	Gamma	Treatment of breast and prostate cancer
P-32	14.3 d	Beta	Treatment of leukemia, excess red blood cells, pancreatic cancer
Pd-103	17 d	Gamma	Prostate brachytherapy
Sr-85	65 d	Gamma	Detection of bone lesions; brain scans
Tc-99m	6 h	Gamma	Imaging of skeleton and heart muscle, brain, liver, heart, lungs, bone, spleen, kidney, and thyroid; most widely used radioisotope in nuclear medicine
Y-90	2.7 d	Beta	Treatment of liver cancer

Chemistry Link to Health

RADIATION DOSES IN DIAGNOSTIC AND THERAPEUTIC PROCEDURES

We can compare the levels of radiation exposure commonly used during diagnostic and therapeutic procedures in nuclear medicine. In diagnostic procedures, the radiologist uses the minimum amount of radioactive isotope needed to evaluate the condition of an organ or tissue. The doses used in radiation therapy are much greater than those used for diagnostic procedures. For example, a therapeutic dose would be used to destroy the cells in a malignant tumor. Although there will be some damage to surrounding tissue, the healthy cells are more resistant to radiation and can repair themselves (see Table 9).

TABLE 9 Radiation Doses Used for Diagnostic and Therapeutic Procedures

Organ/Condition	Dose (rem)
Diagnostic	
Liver	0.3
Lung	2.0
Thyroid	50.0
Therapeutic	
Lymphoma	4500
Skin cancer	5000–6000
Lung cancer	6000
Brain tumor	6000–7000

Scans with Radioisotopes

After a person receives a radioisotope, the radiologist determines the level and location of radioactivity emitted by the radioisotope. An apparatus called a *scanner* is used to produce an image of the organ. The scanner moves slowly across the patient's body above the region where the organ containing the radioisotope is located. The gamma rays emitted from the radioisotope in the organ can be used to expose a photographic plate, producing a **scan** of the organ. On a scan, an area of decreased or increased radiation can indicate conditions such as a disease of the organ, a tumor, a blood clot, or edema.

A common method of determining thyroid function is the use of *radioactive iodine uptake* (*RAIU*). Taken orally, the radioisotope iodine-131 mixes with the iodine already present in the thyroid. Twenty-four hours later, the amount of iodine taken up by the thyroid is determined. A detection tube held up to the area of the thyroid gland detects the radiation coming from the iodine-131 that has located there (see Figure 5).

A person with a hyperactive thyroid will have a higher than normal level of radioactive iodine, whereas a person with a hypoactive thyroid will have low values. If the person has hyperthyroidism, treatment is begun to lower the activity of the thyroid. One treatment involves giving a therapeutic dosage of radioactive iodine, which has a higher radiation level than the diagnostic dose. The radioactive iodine accumulates in the thyroid, where its radiation permanently destroys some of the thyroid cells. The thyroid produces less thyroid hormone, bringing the hyperthyroid condition under control.

Positron Emission Tomography (PET)

Positron emitters with short half-lives such as carbon-11, nitrogen-13, oxygen-15, and fluorine-18 are used in an imaging method called *positron emission tomography* (*PET*). A positron-emitting isotope such as fluorine-18 is used to study brain function, metabolism, and blood flow.

$$^{18}_{9}\text{F} \longrightarrow {}^{18}_{8}\text{O} + {}^{0}_{+1}e$$

As positrons are emitted, they combine with electrons to produce gamma rays that are detected by computerized equipment to create a three-dimensional image of the organ (see Figure 6).

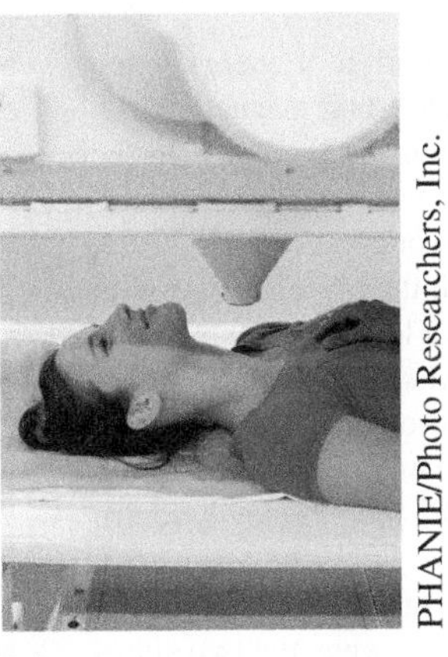

PHANIE/Photo Researchers, Inc.

(a)

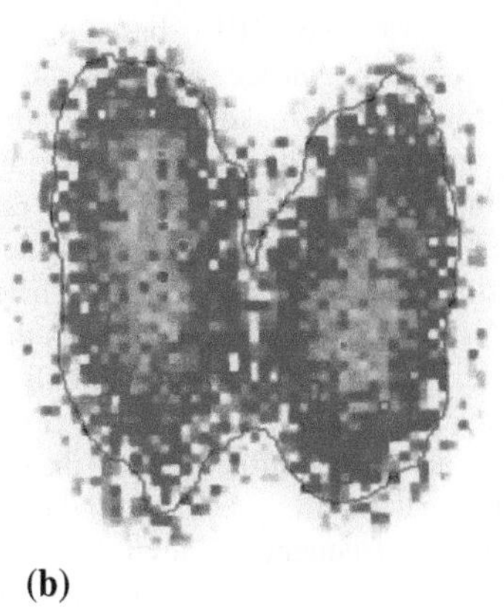

Pasieka/Photo Researchers, Inc.

(b)

FIGURE 5 **(a)** A scanner is used to detect radiation from a radioisotope that has accumulated in an organ. **(b)** A scan of the thyroid shows the accumulation of radioactive iodine-131 in the thyroid.

Q What type of radiation would move through body tissues, exposing a photographic plate and creating a scan?

SAMPLE PROBLEM 9 Medical Applications of Radioisotopes

In the treatment of abdominal carcinoma, a person is treated with gold-198, a beta emitter. Write the balanced nuclear equation for the beta decay of gold-198.

SOLUTION

We can write the incomplete nuclear equation starting with gold-198.

$$^{198}_{79}\text{Au} \longrightarrow ? + {}^{0}_{-1}e$$

In beta decay, the mass number, 198, does not change, but the atomic number of the new nucleus increases by one. The new atomic number is 80, which is mercury, Hg.

$$^{198}_{79}\text{Au} \longrightarrow {}^{198}_{80}\text{Hg} + {}^{0}_{-1}e$$

STUDY CHECK 9

An experimental treatment uses boron-10, which is taken up by malignant tumors. When bombarded with neutrons, boron-10 decays by emitting alpha particles that destroy the surrounding tumor cells. Write the balanced equation for the nuclear reaction for this experimental procedure.

Lawrence Berkeley National Laboratory

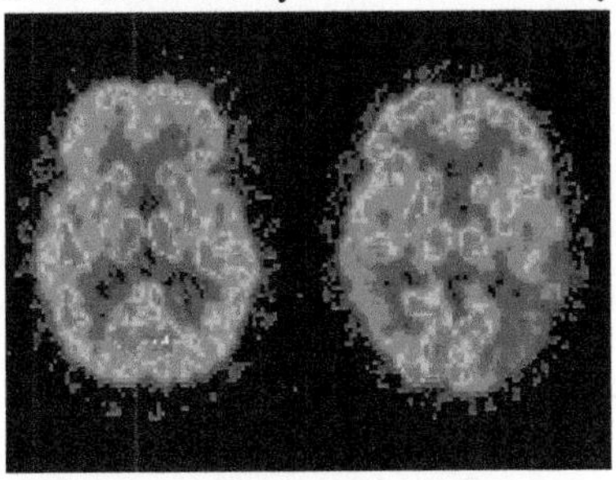

FIGURE 6 These PET scans of the brain show a normal brain on the left and a brain affected by Alzheimer's disease on the right.

Q When positrons collide with electrons, what type of radiation is produced that gives an image of an organ?

Chemistry Link to Health

OTHER IMAGING METHODS

Computed Tomography (CT)

Another medical imaging method used to scan organs such as the brain, lungs, and heart is *computed tomography* (*CT*). A computer monitors the degree of absorption of 30 000 X-ray beams directed at successive layers of the target organ. Based on the densities of the tissues and fluids in the organ, the differences in absorption of the X-rays provide a series of images of the organ. This technique is successful in the identification of brain hemorrhages, tumors, and atrophy (see Figure 7).

Magnetic Resonance Imaging (MRI)

Magnetic resonance imaging (*MRI*) is a powerful imaging technique that does not involve X-ray radiation. It is the least invasive imaging

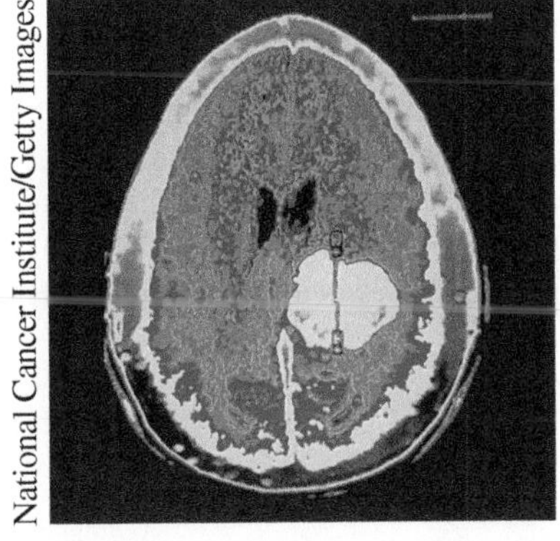

National Cancer Institute/Getty Images

FIGURE 7 A CT scan shows a tumor (yellow) in the brain.

Q What is the type of radiation used to give a CT scan?

method available. MRI is based on the absorption of energy when the protons in hydrogen atoms are placed in a strong magnetic field. Hydrogen atoms make up 63% of all the atoms in the body. In the hydrogen nuclei, the protons act like tiny bar magnets. With no external magnetic field, the protons have random orientations. However, when placed within a strong magnetic field, the protons align with the field. A proton aligned with the field has a lower energy than one that is aligned against the field. As the MRI scan proceeds, pulses of radio waves that are specific only to hydrogen are applied, and the hydrogen nuclei resonate at a certain frequency. Then the radio waves are quickly turned off and the hydrogen protons slowly return to their natural alignment within the magnetic field, and resonate at a different frequency. They release the energy absorbed from the radio wave pulses. The difference in energy between the two states is released as photons, which produce the electromagnetic signal that the scanner detects. These signals are sent to a computer system, where a color image of the body is generated. Because hydrogen atoms in the body are in different chemical environments, different energies are absorbed. MRI is particularly useful in obtaining images of soft tissues, which contain large amounts of hydrogen atoms in the form of water (see Figure 8).

GJLP/Photo Reseatchers, Inc.

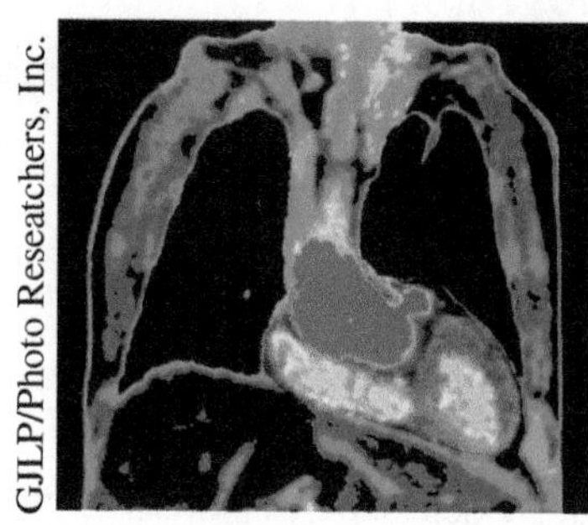

FIGURE 8 An MRI scan of the heart and lungs, with the left ventricle shown in red.

Q What is the source of energy in an MRI?

Chemistry Link to Health

BRACHYTHERAPY

The process called *brachytherapy*, or seed implantation, uses an internal form of radiation therapy. The prefix *brachy* is from the Greek word for short distance. With internal radiation, a high dose of radiation is delivered to a cancerous area, while normal tissue sustains minimal damage. Because higher doses are used, fewer treatments of shorter duration are needed. Conventional external treatment delivers a lower dose per treatment but requires six to eight weeks of treatments.

Permanent Brachytherapy

One of the most common forms of cancer in males is prostate cancer. In addition to surgery and chemotherapy, one treatment option is to place 40 or more titanium capsules, or "seeds," in the malignant area. Each seed, which is the size of a small grain of rice, contains radioactive iodine-125, palladium-103, or cesium-131. The radiation from the seeds interferes with the reproduction of cancer cells with minimal damage to adjacent normal tissues. Ninety percent (90%) of the radioisotopes decay within a few months because they have short half-lives.

Isotope	I-125	Pd-103	Cs-131
Radiation	Gamma	Gamma	Gamma
Half-Life	60 days	17 days	10 days
Time to Deliver 90% of Radiation	7 months	2 months	1 month

Almost no radiation passes out of the patient's body. The amount of radiation received by a family member is no greater than that received on a long plane flight. Because the radioisotopes decay to products that are not radioactive, the inert titanium capsules can be left in the body.

Temporary Brachytherapy

In another type of treatment for prostate cancer, long needles containing iridium-192 are placed in the tumor. However, the needles are removed after 5 to 10 minutes, depending on the activity of the iridium isotope. Compared to permanent brachytherapy, temporary brachytherapy can deliver a higher dose of radiation over a shorter time. The procedure may be repeated in a few days.

Brachytherapy is also used following breast cancer lumpectomy. An iridium-192 isotope is inserted into a catheter that is implanted in the space left by the removal of the tumor. The isotope is removed after 5 to 10 minutes, depending on the activity of the iridium source. Radiation is delivered primarily to the tissue surrounding the cavity that contained the tumor and where the cancer is most likely to reoccur. The procedure is repeated twice a day for five days to give an absorbed dose of 34 Gy (3400 rad). The catheter is then removed, and no radioactive material remains in the body.

In conventional external beam therapy for breast cancer, a patient is given 2 Gy once a day for six to seven weeks, which gives a total absorbed dose of about 80 Gy or 8000 rad. The external beam therapy irradiates the entire breast, including the tumor cavity.

Cytyc Hologic Corporation

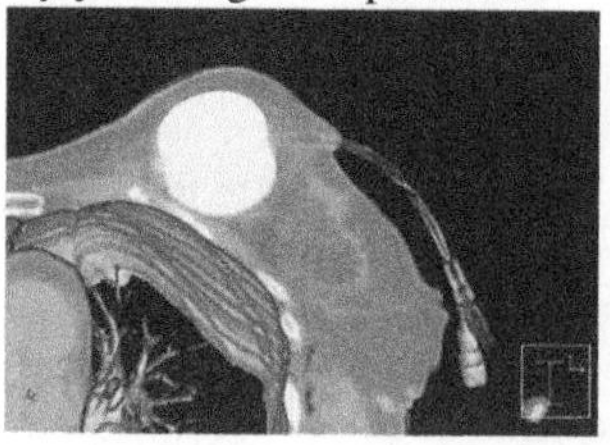

Cytyc Hologic Corporation

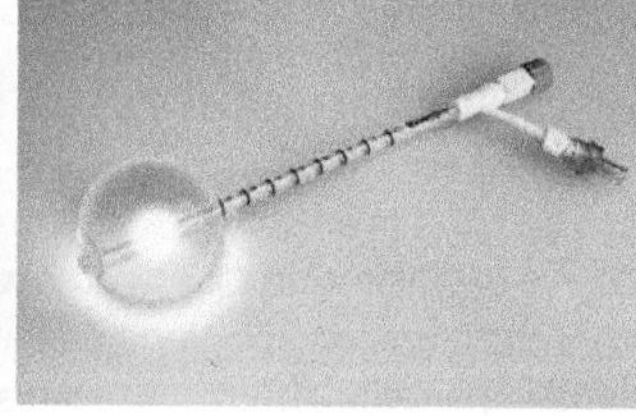

A catheter placed temporarily in the breast supplies radiation from Ir-192.

QUESTIONS AND PROBLEMS

5 Medical Applications Using Radioactivity

LEARNING GOAL: *Describe the use of radioisotopes in medicine.*

35 Bone and bony structures contain calcium and phosphorus.
  a. Why would the radioisotopes calcium-47 and phosphorus-32 be used in the diagnosis and treatment of bone diseases?
  b. The radioisotope strontium-89, a beta emitter, is used to treat bone cancer. Write the balanced nuclear equation and explain why a strontium radioisotope would be used to treat bone cancer.

36 **a.** Technetium-99m emits only gamma radiation. Why would this type of radiation be used in diagnostic imaging rather than an isotope that also emits beta or alpha radiation?
  b. A patient with polycythemia vera (excess production of red blood cells) receives radioactive phosphorus-32. Why would this treatment reduce the production of red blood cells in the bone marrow of the patient?

37 In a diagnostic test for leukemia, a patient receives 4.0 mL of a solution containing selenium-75. If the activity of the selenium-75 is 45 μCi/mL, what is the dose received by the patient?

38 A vial contains radioactive iodine-131 with an activity of 2.0 mCi/mL. If a thyroid test requires 3.0 mCi in an "atomic cocktail," how many milliliters are used to prepare the iodine-131 solution?

6 Nuclear Fission and Fusion

LEARNING GOAL

Describe the processes of nuclear fission and fusion.

TUTORIAL
Fission and Fusion

TUTORIAL
Nuclear Fission and Fusion Reactions

During the 1930s, scientists bombarding uranium-235 with neutrons discovered that the U-235 nucleus splits into two medium-weight nuclei and produces a great amount of energy. This was the discovery of nuclear **fission**. The energy generated by splitting the atom was called *atomic* energy. A typical equation for nuclear fission is:

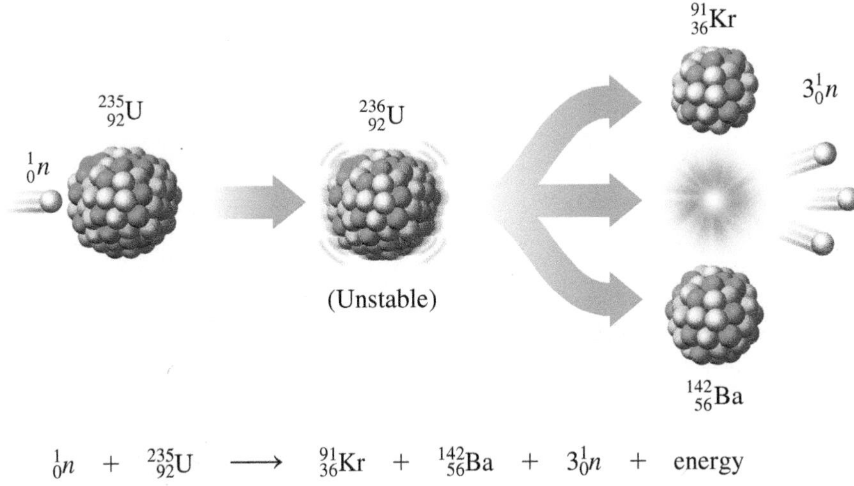

$$^{1}_{0}n + ^{235}_{92}U \longrightarrow ^{91}_{36}Kr + ^{142}_{56}Ba + 3^{1}_{0}n + \text{energy}$$

If we could determine the mass of the products, krypton, barium, and 3 neutrons, with great accuracy, we would find that their total mass is slightly less than the mass of the starting materials. The missing mass has been converted into an enormous amount of energy, consistent with the famous equation derived by Albert Einstein:

$$E = mc^2$$

where E is the energy released, m is the mass lost, and c is the speed of light, 3×10^8 m/s. Even though the mass loss is very small, when it is multiplied by the speed of light squared, the result is a large value for the energy released. The fission of 1 g of uranium-235 produces about as much energy as the burning of 3 tons of coal.

Chain Reaction

Fission begins when a neutron collides with the nucleus of a uranium atom. The resulting nucleus is unstable and splits into smaller nuclei. This fission process also releases neutrons and large amounts of gamma radiation and energy. The neutrons emitted have high energies

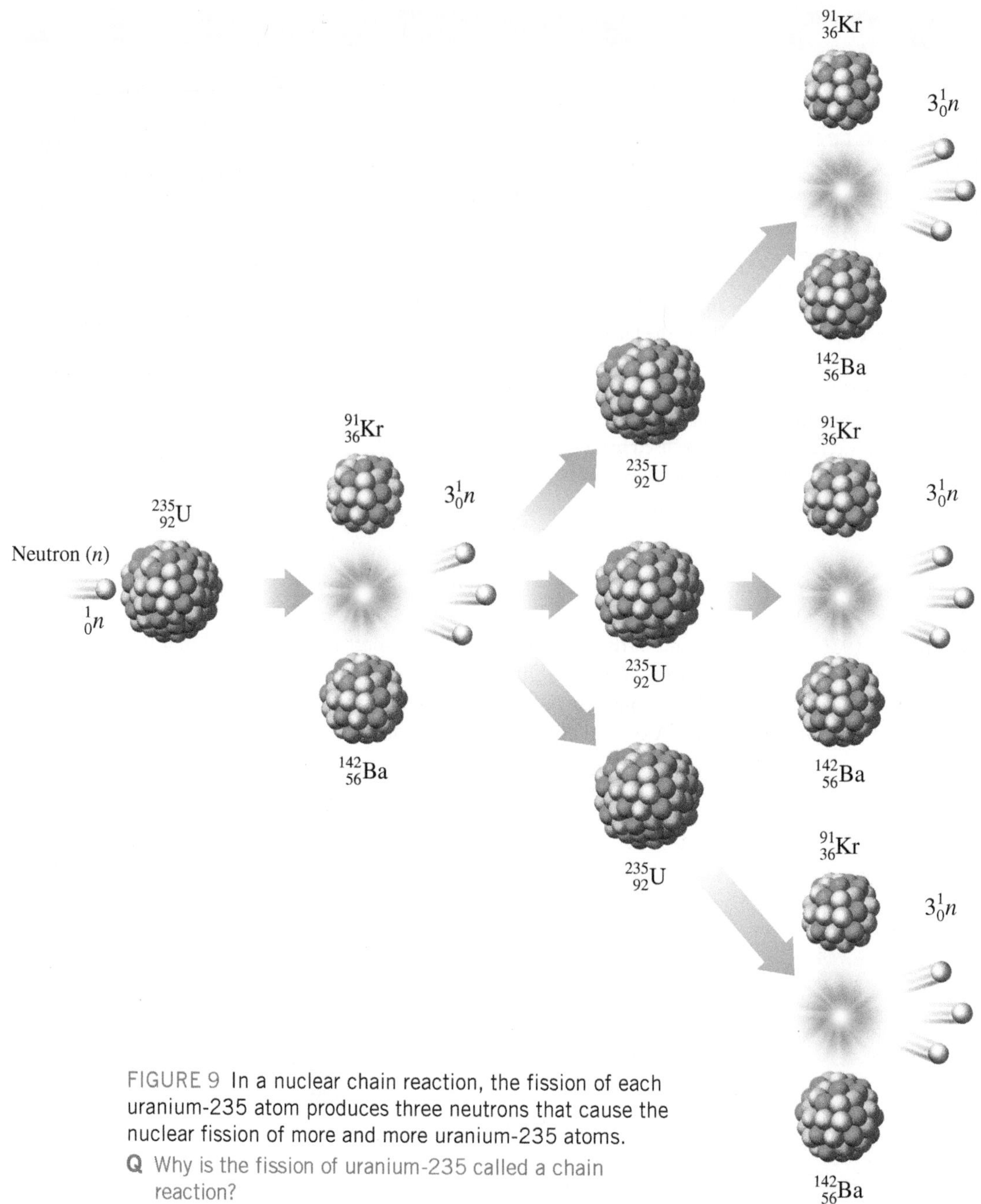

FIGURE 9 In a nuclear chain reaction, the fission of each uranium-235 atom produces three neutrons that cause the nuclear fission of more and more uranium-235 atoms.

Q Why is the fission of uranium-235 called a chain reaction?

and bombard other uranium-235 nuclei. In a **chain reaction**, there is a rapid increase in the number of high-energy neutrons available to react with more uranium. To sustain a nuclear chain reaction, sufficient quantities of uranium-235 must be brought together to provide a *critical mass* in which almost all the neutrons collide with more uranium-235 nuclei. So much heat and energy are released that an atomic explosion can occur (see Figure 9).

Nuclear Fusion

In **fusion**, two small nuclei such as those in hydrogen combine to form a larger nucleus. Mass is lost, and a tremendous amount of energy is released, even more than the energy released from nuclear fission. However, a fusion reaction requires a temperature of 100 000 000 °C to overcome the repulsion of the hydrogen nuclei and cause them to undergo fusion. Fusion reactions occur continuously in the Sun and other stars, providing us with heat and light. The huge amounts of energy produced by our Sun come from the fusion of 6×10^{11} kg of hydrogen every second. The following fusion reaction involves the combination of two isotopes of hydrogen:

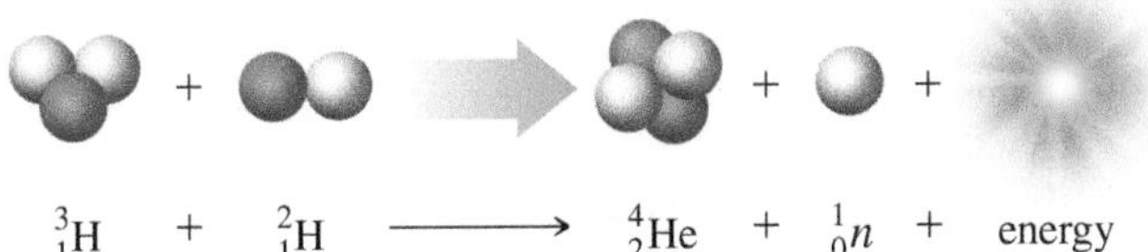

$${}^{3}_{1}\text{H} + {}^{2}_{1}\text{H} \longrightarrow {}^{4}_{2}\text{He} + {}^{1}_{0}n + \text{energy}$$

Scientists expect less radioactive waste with shorter half-lives from fusion reactors. However, fusion is still in the experimental stage because the extremely high temperatures needed have been difficult to reach and even more difficult to maintain. Research groups around the world are attempting to develop the technology needed to make the harnessing of the fusion reaction for energy a reality in our lifetime.

CONCEPT CHECK 5 **Identifying Fission and Fusion**

Classify the following as pertaining to nuclear fission, nuclear fusion, or both:

a. Small nuclei combine to form larger nuclei.
b. Large amounts of energy are released.
c. Extremely high temperatures are needed for reaction.

ANSWER

a. When small nuclei are combined, the process is fusion.
b. Large amounts of energy are generated in both the fission and fusion processes.
c. An extremely high temperature is required for fusion.

Chemistry Link to the Environment

NUCLEAR POWER PLANTS

In a nuclear power plant, the quantity of uranium-235 is held below a critical mass so that it cannot sustain a chain reaction. The fission reactions are slowed by placing control rods among the uranium samples to absorb some of the fast-moving neutrons. In this way, there is a slower, controlled production of energy. The heat from the controlled fission is used to produce steam. The steam drives a generator, which produces electricity. Approximately 10% of the electrical energy produced in the United States is generated by nuclear power plants.

Although nuclear power plants help meet our energy needs, there are some problems. One of the most serious is the production of radioactive by-products that have long half-lives, such as plutonium-239 with a half-life of 24 000 y. It is essential that these waste products be stored safely in a place where they do not contaminate the environment. Several countries are now in the process of selecting areas where nuclear waste can be placed in caverns 1000 m below the surface of the Earth. In the United States, a current proposed repository site for nuclear waste is Yucca Mountain, Nevada.

foto-rolf/iStockphoto

Nuclear power plants supply about 10% of the electricity in the United States.

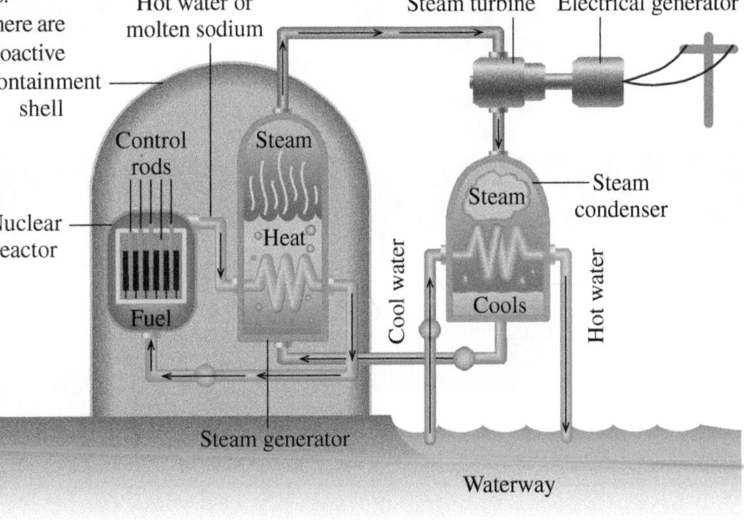

Heat from nuclear fission is used to generate electricity.

QUESTIONS AND PROBLEMS

6 Nuclear Fission and Fusion

LEARNING GOAL: *Describe the processes of nuclear fission and fusion.*

39 What is nuclear fission?

40 How does a chain reaction occur in nuclear fission?

41 Complete the following fission reaction:

$$^{1}_{0}n + ^{235}_{92}U \longrightarrow ^{131}_{50}Sn + ? + 2^{1}_{0}n + \text{energy}$$

42 In another fission reaction, uranium-235 bombarded with a neutron produces strontium-94, another nucleus, and 3 neutrons. Write the balanced equation for the fission reaction.

43 Indicate whether each of the following is characteristic of the fission process, the fusion process, or both:
a. Neutrons bombard a nucleus.
b. The nuclear process occurring in the Sun.
c. A large nucleus splits into smaller nuclei.
d. Small nuclei combine to form larger nuclei.

44 Indicate whether each of the following is characteristic of the fission process, the fusion process, or both:
a. Extremely high temperatures are required to initiate the reaction.
b. Less radioactive waste is produced.
c. Hydrogen nuclei are the reactants.
d. Large amounts of energy are released when the nuclear reaction occurs.

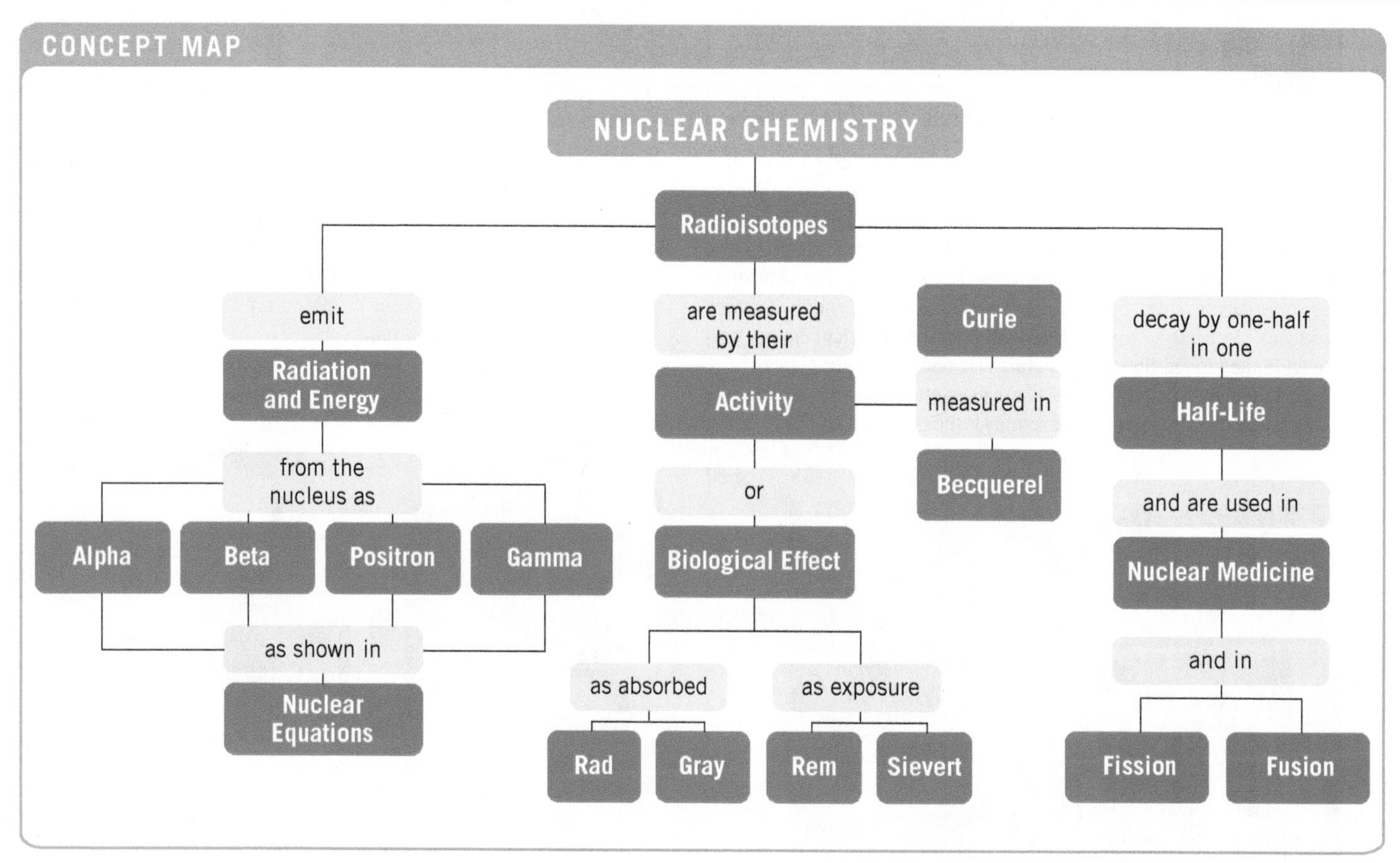

CHAPTER REVIEW

1 Natural Radioactivity

LEARNING GOAL: *Describe alpha, beta, positron, and gamma radiation.*

Alpha (α) particle

- Radioactive isotopes have unstable nuclei that break down (decay), spontaneously emitting alpha (α), beta (β), positron (β^+), and gamma (γ) radiation.
- Because radiation can damage the cells in the body, proper protection must be used: shielding, limiting the time of exposure, and distance.

2 Nuclear Reactions

LEARNING GOAL: *Write a balanced nuclear equation showing mass numbers and atomic numbers for radioactive decay.*

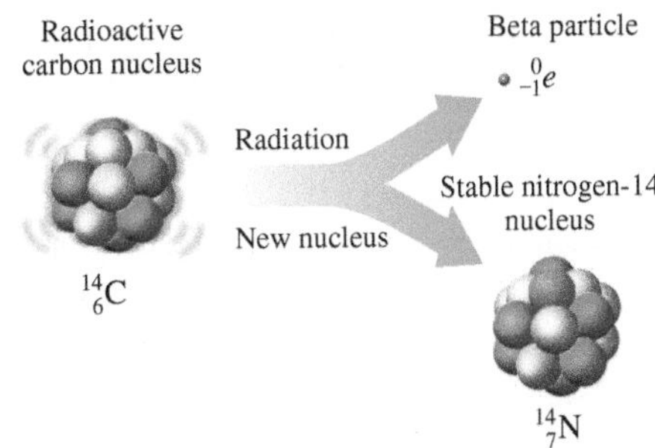

- A balanced equation is used to represent the changes that take place in the nuclei of the reactants and products.
- The new isotopes and the type of radiation emitted can be determined from the symbols that show the mass numbers and atomic numbers of the isotopes in the nuclear reaction.
- A radioisotope is produced artificially when a nonradioactive isotope is bombarded by a small particle.

3 Radiation Measurement

LEARNING GOAL: *Describe the detection and measurement of radiation.*

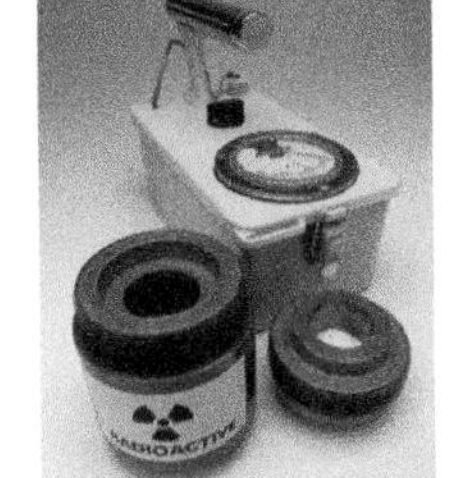
Don Farrall/PhotoDisc/ Getty Images

- In a Geiger counter, radiation produces charged particles in the gas contained in the tube, which generates an electrical current.
- The curie (Ci) measures the number of nuclear transformations of a radioactive sample. Activity is also measured in becquerel (Bq) units.
- The amount of radiation absorbed by a substance is measured in rads or the gray (Gy).
- The rem and the sievert (Sv) are units used to determine the biological damage from the different types of radiation.

4 Half-Life of a Radioisotope

LEARNING GOAL: *Given the half-life of a radioisotope, calculate the amount of radioisotope remaining after one or more half-lives.*

- Every radioisotope has its own rate of emitting radiation.
- The time it takes for one-half of a radioactive sample to decay is called its half-life.
- For many medical radioisotopes, such as Tc-99m and I-131, half-lives are short.
- For other isotopes, usually naturally occurring ones such as C-14, Ra-226, and U-238, half-lives are extremely long.

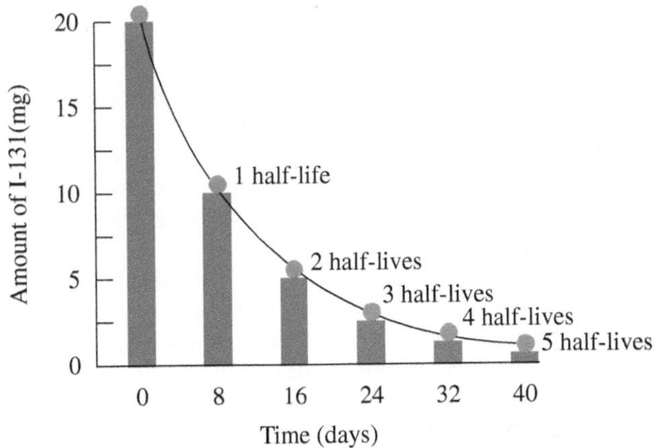

5 Medical Applications Using Radioactivity

LEARNING GOAL: *Describe the use of radioisotopes in medicine.*

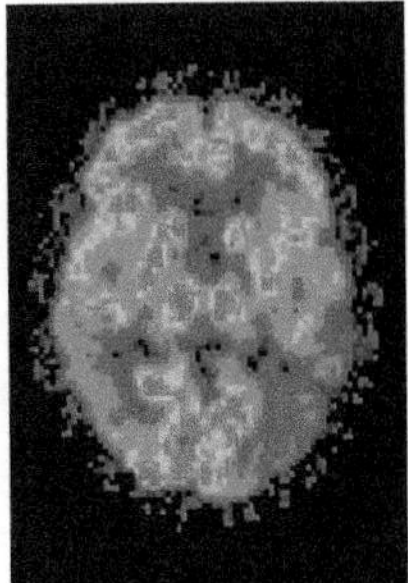
Lawrence Berkeley National Laboratory/ Getty Images

- In nuclear medicine, radioisotopes that go to specific sites in the body are given to the patient.
- By detecting the radiation they emit, an evaluation can be made about the location and extent of an injury, disease, tumor, or the level of function of a particular organ.
- Higher levels of radiation are used to treat or destroy tumors.

6 Nuclear Fission and Fusion

LEARNING GOAL: *Describe the processes of nuclear fission and fusion.*

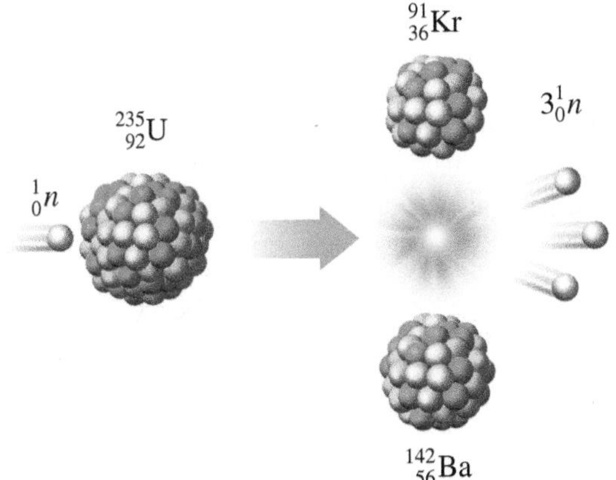

- In fission, a large nucleus breaks apart into smaller pieces, releasing one or more types of radiation and a great amount of energy.
- In fusion, small nuclei combine to form a larger nucleus while great amounts of energy are released.

KEY TERMS

alpha particle A nuclear particle identical to a helium nucleus, symbol α or ${}^{4}_{2}He$.

becquerel (Bq) A unit of activity of a radioactive sample equal to one disintegration per second.

beta particle A particle identical to an electron, symbol β or ${}^{0}_{-1}e$, that forms in the nucleus when a neutron changes to a proton and an electron.

carbon dating A technique used to date ancient specimens that contain carbon. The age is determined by the amount of active carbon-14 that remains in the samples.

chain reaction A fission reaction that will continue once it has been initiated by a high-energy neutron bombarding a heavy nucleus such as uranium-235.

curie (Ci) A unit of radiation equal to 3.7×10^{10} disintegrations/s.

decay curve A diagram of the decay of a radioactive element.

equivalent dose The measure of biological damage from an absorbed dose that has been adjusted for the type of radiation.

fission A process in which large nuclei are split into smaller pieces, releasing large amounts of energy.

fusion A reaction in which large amounts of energy are released when small nuclei combine to form larger nuclei.

gamma ray High-energy radiation, symbol ${}^{0}_{0}\gamma$, that is emitted by an unstable nucleus.

gray (Gy) A unit of absorbed dose equal to 100 rad.

half-life The length of time it takes for one-half of a radioactive sample to decay.

positron A particle with no mass and a positive charge, symbol β^{+} or ${}^{0}_{+1}e$, produced when a proton is transformed into a neutron and a positron.

rad (radiation absorbed dose) A measure of an amount of radiation absorbed by the body.

radiation Energy or particles released by radioactive atoms.

radioactive decay The process by which an unstable nucleus breaks down and releases high-energy radiation.

rem (radiation equivalent in humans) A measure of the biological damage caused by the various kinds of radiation (rad $\times$ radiation biological factor).

scan The image of a site in the body created by the detection of radiation from radioactive isotopes that have accumulated in that site.

shielding Materials used to provide protection from radioactive sources.

sievert (Sv) A unit of biological damage (equivalent dose) equal to 100 rem.

UNDERSTANDING THE CONCEPTS

The chapter sections to review are shown in parentheses at the end of each question.

In Problems 45 to 48, a nucleus is shown with protons and neutrons.

proton

neutron

45 Draw the new nucleus when this isotope emits a positron to complete the following figure: (2)

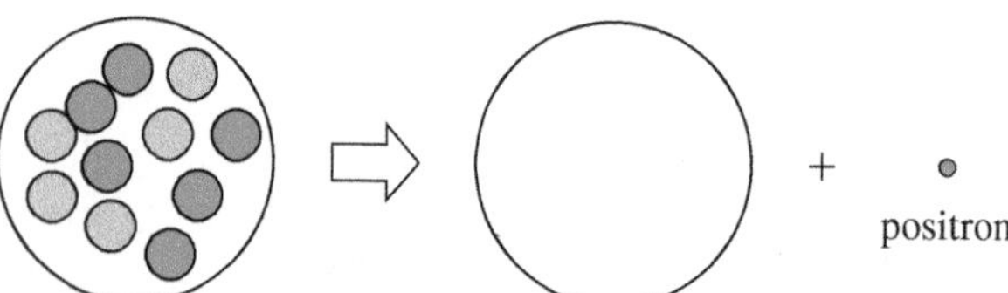

46 Draw the nucleus of an isotope that emits a beta particle to complete the following figure: (2)

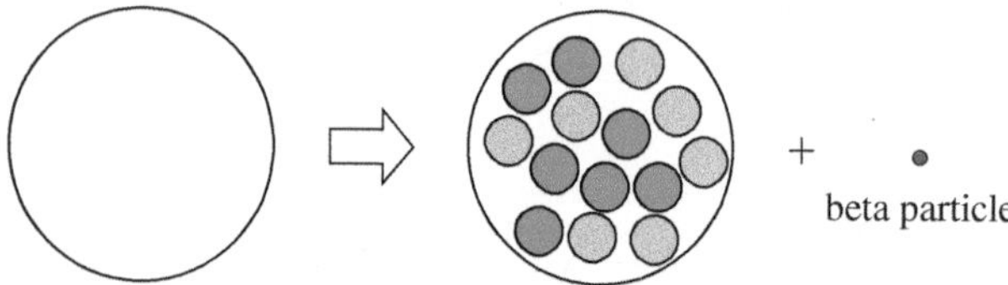

47 Draw the nucleus of the isotope that is bombarded in the following figure: (2)

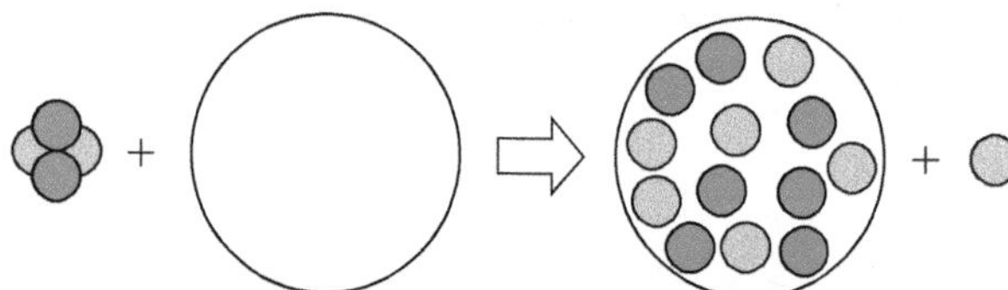

48 Complete the following bombardment reaction by drawing the nucleus of the new isotope that is produced in the following figure: (2)

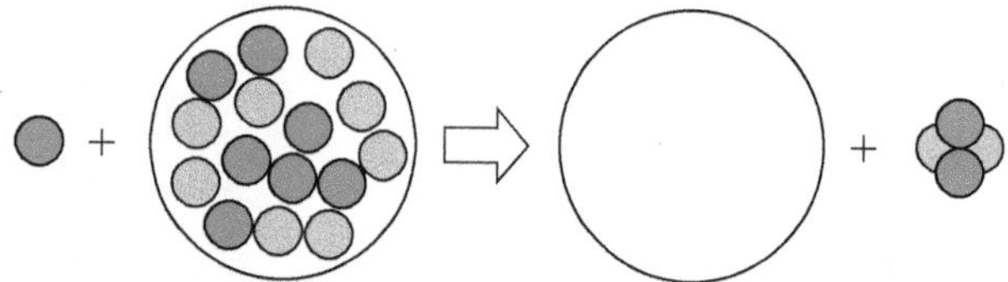

49 Carbon dating of small bits of charcoal used in cave paintings has determined that some of the paintings are from 10 000 to 30 000 y old. Carbon-14 has a half-life of 5730 y. In a 1 μg-sample of carbon from a live tree, the activity of ${}^{14}_{6}C$ is 6.4 μCi. If researchers determine that 1 μg of charcoal from a prehistoric cave painting in France has an activity of 0.80 μCi, what is the age of the painting? (4)

The technique of carbon dating is used to determine the age of ancient cave paintings.

50 Use the following decay curve for iodine-131 to answer Questions **a–c**: (4)

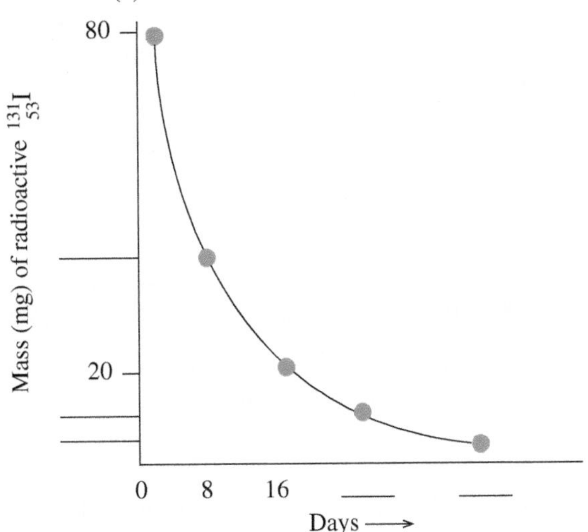

a. Complete the values for the mass of radioactive $^{131}_{53}I$ on the vertical axis.
b. Complete the number of days on the horizontal axis.
c. Use the graph to determine the half-life, in days, of iodine-131.

ADDITIONAL QUESTIONS AND PROBLEMS

For instructor-assigned homework, go to www.masteringchemistry.com.

51 State the number of protons and number of neutrons in the nucleus of each of the following: (1)
a. sodium-25 **b.** nickel-61
c. rubidium-84 **d.** silver-110

52 State the number of protons and number of neutrons in the nucleus of each of the following: (1)
a. boron-10 **b.** zinc-72
c. iron-59 **d.** gold-198

53 Identify each of the following as alpha decay, beta decay, positron emission, or gamma emission: (1)
a. $^{27m}_{13}Al \longrightarrow ^{27}_{13}Al + ^{0}_{0}\gamma$
b. $^{8}_{5}B \longrightarrow ^{8}_{4}Be + ^{0}_{+1}e$
c. $^{220}_{86}Rn \longrightarrow ^{216}_{84}Po + ^{4}_{2}He$

54 Identify each of the following as alpha decay, beta decay, positron emission, or gamma emission: (1)
a. $^{127}_{55}Cs \longrightarrow ^{127}_{54}Xe + ^{0}_{+1}e$
b. $^{90}_{38}Sr \longrightarrow ^{90}_{39}Y + ^{0}_{-1}e$
c. $^{218}_{85}At \longrightarrow ^{214}_{83}Bi + ^{4}_{2}He$

55 Write a balanced nuclear equation for each of the following: (2)
a. Th-225 (α decay) **b.** Bi-210 (α decay)
c. cesium-137 (β decay) **d.** tin-126 (β decay)
e. F-18 (β^{+} emission)

56 Write a balanced nuclear equation for each of the following: (2)
a. potassium-40 (β decay)
b. sulfur-35 (β decay)
c. platinum-190 (α decay)
d. Ra-210 (α decay)
e. In-113m (γ emission)

57 Complete each of the following nuclear equations: (2)
a. $^{4}_{2}He + ^{14}_{7}N \longrightarrow ? + ^{1}_{1}H$
b. $^{4}_{2}He + ^{27}_{13}Al \longrightarrow ^{30}_{14}Si + ?$
c. $^{1}_{0}n + ^{235}_{92}U \longrightarrow ^{90}_{38}Sr + 3^{1}_{0}n + ?$
d. $^{23m}_{12}Mg \longrightarrow ? + ^{0}_{0}\gamma$

58 Complete each of the following nuclear equations: (2)
a. $? + ^{59}_{27}Co \longrightarrow ^{56}_{25}Mn + ^{4}_{2}He$
b. $? \longrightarrow ^{14}_{7}N + ^{0}_{-1}e$
c. $^{0}_{-1}e + ^{76}_{36}Kr \longrightarrow ?$
d. $^{4}_{2}He + ^{241}_{95}Am \longrightarrow ? + 2^{1}_{0}n$

59 Write the balanced nuclear equation for each of the following: (2)
a. When two oxygen-16 atoms collide, one of the products is an alpha particle.
b. When californium-249 is bombarded by oxygen-18, a new isotope and four neutrons are produced.
c. Radon-222 undergoes alpha decay.

60 Write the balanced nuclear equation for each of the following: (2)
a. Polonium-210 decays to give lead-206.
b. Bismuth-211 emits an alpha particle.
c. A radioisotope emits a positron to form titanium-48.

61 If the amount of radioactive phosphorus-32 in a sample decreases from 1.2 mg to 0.30 mg in 28.6 days, what is the half-life, in days, of phosphorus-32? (4)

62 If the amount of radioactive iodine-123 in a sample decreases from 0.4 g to 0.1 g in 26.4 h, what is the half-life, in hours, of iodine-123? (4)

63 Calcium-47, a beta emitter, has a half-life of 4.5 days. (2, 4)
a. Write the balanced nuclear equation for the beta decay of calcium-47.
b. How much, in milligrams, of a 16-mg sample of calcium-47 remains after 18 days?
c. How many days have passed if 4.8 mg of calcium-47 decayed to 1.2 mg of calcium-47?

64 Cesium-137, a beta emitter, has a half-life of 30 y. (2, 4)
a. Write the balanced nuclear equation for the beta decay of cesium-137.
b. How many grams of a 16-mg sample of cesium-137 would remain after 90 y?
c. How many years are required for 28 mg of cesium-137 to decay to 3.5 mg of cesium-137?

65 A thyroid scan used 320 mCi of I-123, which has a half-life of 13.2 h. How long, in hours, would it take for the activity to be reduced to 40. mCi? (4)

66 A wooden object from the site of an ancient temple has a carbon-14 activity of 10 counts/min, compared with a reference piece of wood cut today that has an activity of 40 counts/min. If the half-life for carbon-14 is 5730 y, what is the age of the object? (4)

67 A 120-mg sample of technetium-99m is used for a diagnostic test. If technetium-99m has a half-life of 6.0 h, how much of the technetium-99m sample remains 24 h after the test? (4)

68 The half-life of oxygen-15 is 124 s. If a sample of oxygen-15 has an activity of 4000 Bq, how many minutes will elapse before it reaches an activity of 500 Bq? (4)

CHALLENGE QUESTIONS

69 Uranium-238 decays in a series of nuclear changes until stable ${}^{206}_{82}\text{Pb}$ is produced. Complete the following nuclear equations that are part of the ${}^{238}_{92}\text{U}$ decay series: (2)

a. ${}^{238}_{92}\text{U} \longrightarrow {}^{234}_{90}\text{Th} + ?$ **b.** ${}^{234}_{90}\text{Th} \longrightarrow ? + {}^{0}_{-1}e$

c. $? \longrightarrow {}^{222}_{86}\text{Rn} + {}^{4}_{2}\text{He}$

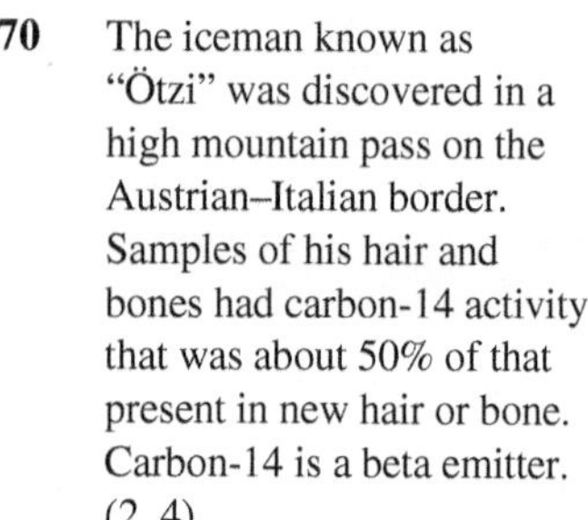

70 The iceman known as "Ötzi" was discovered in a high mountain pass on the Austrian–Italian border. Samples of his hair and bones had carbon-14 activity that was about 50% of that present in new hair or bone. Carbon-14 is a beta emitter. (2, 4)

AP Photo/Augustin Ochsenreite

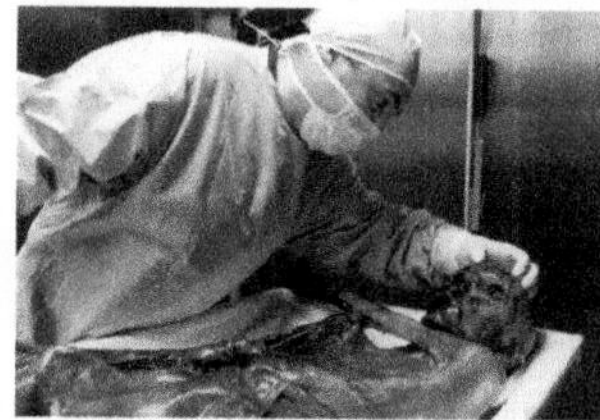

The mummified remains of "Ötzi" were discovered in 1991.

a. How long ago did "Ötzi" live if the half-life for C-14 is 5730 y?

b. Write a balanced nuclear equation for the decay of carbon-14.

71 The half-life for the radioactive decay of Ce-141 is 32.5 days. If a sample has an activity of 4.0 μCi after 130 days have elapsed, what was the initial activity, in microcuries, of the sample? (4)

72 A technician was accidentally exposed to potassium-42 while doing some brain scans for possible tumors. The error was not discovered until 36 h later when the activity of the potassium-42 sample was 2.0 μCi. If potassium-42 has a half-life of 12 h, what was the activity of the sample at the time the technician was exposed? (4)

73 A 64-μCi sample of Tl-201 decays to 4.0 μCi in 12 days. What is the half-life, in days, of Tl-201? (4)

74 A 16-μg sample of sodium-24 decays to 2.0 μg in 45 h. What is the half-life, in hours, of sodium-24? (4)

75 The activity of K-40 in a 70.-kg human body is estimated to be 120 nCi. What is this activity in becquerels? (3)

76 The activity of C-14 in a 70.-kg human body is estimated to be 3.7 kBq. What is this activity in microcuries? (3)

77 Write a balanced equation for each of the following radioactive emissions: (2)

a. an alpha particle from Hg-180

b. a beta particle from Au-198

c. a positron from Rb-82

78 Write a balanced equation for each of the following radioactive emissions: (2)

a. an alpha particle from Gd-148

b. a beta particle from Ni-64

c. a positron from Al-25

79 All the elements beyond uranium, the transuranium elements, have been prepared by bombardment and are not naturally occurring elements. The first transuranium element, neptunium, Np, was prepared by bombarding U-238 with neutrons to form a neptunium atom and a beta particle. Complete the following equation: (2)

$${}^{1}_{0}n + {}^{238}_{92}\text{U} \longrightarrow ? + ?$$

80 One of the most recent transuranium elements, ununoctium-294 (Uuo-294), atomic number 118, was prepared by bombarding californium-249 with another isotope. Complete the following equation for the preparation of this new element: (2)

$$? + {}^{249}_{98}\text{Cf} \longrightarrow {}^{294}_{118}\text{Uuo} + 3{}^{1}_{0}n$$

ANSWERS

Answers to Study Checks

1 distance from the radioactive source and minimizing the time of exposure

2 ${}^{214}_{84}\text{Po} \longrightarrow {}^{210}_{82}\text{Pb} + {}^{4}_{2}\text{He}$

3 ${}^{51}_{24}\text{Cr} \longrightarrow {}^{51}_{25}\text{Mn} + {}^{0}_{-1}e$

4 ${}^{118}_{54}\text{Xe} \longrightarrow {}^{118}_{53}\text{I} + {}^{0}_{+1}e$

5 ${}^{4}_{2}\text{He} + {}^{27}_{13}\text{Al} \longrightarrow {}^{30}_{15}\text{P} + {}^{1}_{0}n$

6 For β, the factor is 1; rads and rems are equal.

7 0.50 μg

8 17 200 y

9 ${}^{1}_{0}n + {}^{10}_{5}\text{B} \longrightarrow {}^{7}_{3}\text{Li} + {}^{4}_{2}\text{He}$

Answers to Selected Questions and Problems

1 **a.** alpha particle
b. positron
c. gamma radiation

3 **a.** ${}^{39}_{19}\text{K}$, ${}^{40}_{19}\text{K}$, ${}^{41}_{19}\text{K}$
b. They all have 19 protons and 19 electrons, but they differ in the number of neutrons.

5

Medical Use	Atomic Symbol	Mass Number	Number of Protons	Number of Neutrons
Heart imaging	${}^{201}_{81}\text{Tl}$	201	81	120
Radiation therapy	${}^{60}_{27}\text{Co}$	60	27	33
Abdominal scan	${}^{67}_{31}\text{Ga}$	67	31	36
Hyperthyroidism	${}^{131}_{53}\text{I}$	131	53	78
Leukemia treatment	${}^{32}_{15}\text{P}$	32	15	17

7 a. ${}^{64}_{29}\text{Cu}$ **b.** ${}^{75}_{34}\text{Se}$ **c.** ${}^{24}_{11}\text{Na}$ **d.** ${}^{15}_{7}\text{N}$

9 a. β or ${}^{0}_{-1}e$ **b.** α or ${}^{4}_{2}\text{He}$ **c.** n or ${}^{1}_{0}n$
d. ${}^{38}_{18}\text{Ar}$ **e.** ${}^{14}_{6}\text{C}$

11 a. 1. alpha particle
b. 3. gamma radiation
c. 1. alpha particle

13 a. ${}^{208}_{84}\text{Po} \longrightarrow {}^{204}_{82}\text{Pb} + {}^{4}_{2}\text{He}$
b. ${}^{232}_{90}\text{Th} \longrightarrow {}^{228}_{88}\text{Ra} + {}^{4}_{2}\text{He}$
c. ${}^{251}_{102}\text{No} \longrightarrow {}^{247}_{100}\text{Fm} + {}^{4}_{2}\text{He}$
d. ${}^{220}_{86}\text{Rn} \longrightarrow {}^{216}_{84}\text{Po} + {}^{4}_{2}\text{He}$

15 a. ${}^{25}_{11}\text{Na} \longrightarrow {}^{25}_{12}\text{Mg} + {}^{0}_{-1}e$
b. ${}^{20}_{8}\text{O} \longrightarrow {}^{20}_{9}\text{F} + {}^{0}_{-1}e$
c. ${}^{92}_{38}\text{Sr} \longrightarrow {}^{92}_{39}\text{Y} + {}^{0}_{-1}e$
d. ${}^{60}_{26}\text{Fe} \longrightarrow {}^{60}_{27}\text{Co} + {}^{0}_{-1}e$

17 a. ${}^{26}_{14}\text{Si} \longrightarrow {}^{26}_{13}\text{Al} + {}^{0}_{+1}e$
b. ${}^{54}_{27}\text{Co} \longrightarrow {}^{54}_{26}\text{Fe} + {}^{0}_{+1}e$
c. ${}^{77}_{37}\text{Rb} \longrightarrow {}^{77}_{36}\text{Kr} + {}^{0}_{+1}e$
d. ${}^{93}_{45}\text{Rh} \longrightarrow {}^{93}_{44}\text{Ru} + {}^{0}_{+1}e$

19 a. ${}^{28}_{14}\text{Si}$, beta decay
b. ${}^{0}_{0}\gamma$, gamma emission
c. ${}^{0}_{-1}e$, beta decay
d. ${}^{238}_{92}\text{U}$, alpha decay
e. ${}^{188}_{79}\text{Au}$, positron emission

21 a. ${}^{10}_{4}\text{Be}$ **b.** ${}^{132}_{53}\text{I}$ **c.** ${}^{27}_{13}\text{Al}$ **d.** ${}^{30}_{15}\text{P}$

23 a. 2 **b.** 3 **c.** 1 **d.** 2

25 The technician exposed to 5 rad received the higher amount of radiation.

27 a. 294 μCi **b.** 0.5 Gy

29 a. two half-lives **b.** one half-life
c. three half-lives

31 a. 40.0 mg **b.** 20.0 mg
c. 10.0 mg **d.** 5.00 mg

33 130 days, 195 days

35 a. Because the elements Ca and P are part of bone, their radioactive isotopes will also become part of the bony structures of the body, where their radiation can be used to diagnose or treat bone diseases.
b. ${}^{89}_{38}\text{Sr} \longrightarrow {}^{89}_{39}\text{Y} + {}^{0}_{-1}e$
Strontium (Sr) acts much like calcium (Ca) because both are Group 2A (2) elements. The body will accumulate radioactive strontium in bones in the same way that it incorporates calcium. Once the strontium isotope is absorbed by the bone, the beta radiation will destroy cancer cells.

37 180 μCi

39 Nuclear fission is the splitting of a large atom into smaller fragments with the release of large amounts of energy.

41 ${}^{103}_{42}\text{Mo}$

43 a. fission **b.** fusion
c. fission **d.** fusion

45

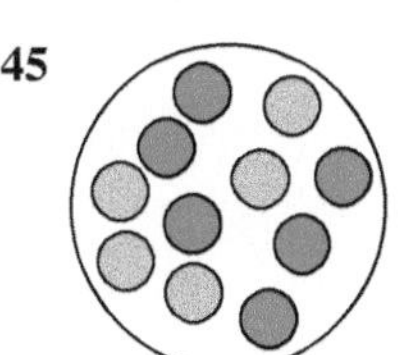

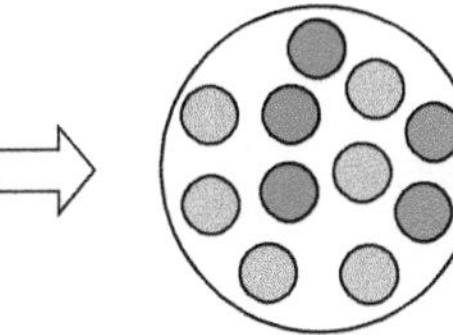

+ positron

47

+ ⇨ +

49 17 200 y old

51 a. 11 protons and 14 neutrons
b. 28 protons and 33 neutrons
c. 37 protons and 47 neutrons
d. 47 protons and 63 neutrons

53 a. gamma emission
b. positron emission
c. alpha decay

55 a. ${}^{225}_{90}\text{Th} \longrightarrow {}^{221}_{88}\text{Ra} + {}^{4}_{2}\text{He}$
b. ${}^{210}_{83}\text{Bi} \longrightarrow {}^{206}_{81}\text{Tl} + {}^{4}_{2}\text{He}$
c. ${}^{137}_{55}\text{Cs} \longrightarrow {}^{137}_{56}\text{Ba} + {}^{0}_{-1}e$
d. ${}^{126}_{50}\text{Sn} \longrightarrow {}^{126}_{51}\text{Sb} + {}^{0}_{-1}e$
e. ${}^{18}_{9}\text{F} \longrightarrow {}^{18}_{8}\text{O} + {}^{0}_{+1}e$

57 a. ${}^{17}_{8}\text{O}$ **b.** ${}^{1}_{1}\text{H}$ **c.** ${}^{143}_{54}\text{Xe}$ **d.** ${}^{23}_{12}\text{Mg}$

59 a. ${}^{16}_{8}\text{O} + {}^{16}_{8}\text{O} \longrightarrow {}^{28}_{14}\text{Si} + {}^{4}_{2}\text{He}$
b. ${}^{18}_{8}\text{O} + {}^{249}_{98}\text{Cf} \longrightarrow {}^{263}_{106}\text{Sg} + 4{}^{1}_{0}n$
c. ${}^{222}_{86}\text{Rn} \longrightarrow {}^{218}_{84}\text{Po} + {}^{4}_{2}\text{He}$

61 14.3 days

63 a. ${}^{47}_{20}\text{Ca} \longrightarrow {}^{47}_{21}\text{Sc} + {}^{0}_{-1}e$
b. 1.0 mg of Ca-47 **c.** 9.0 days

65 39.6 h

67 7.5 mg

69 a. ${}^{238}_{92}\text{U} \longrightarrow {}^{234}_{90}\text{Th} + {}^{4}_{2}\text{He}$
b. ${}^{234}_{90}\text{Th} \longrightarrow {}^{234}_{91}\text{Pa} + {}^{0}_{-1}e$
c. ${}^{226}_{88}\text{Ra} \longrightarrow {}^{222}_{86}\text{Rn} + {}^{4}_{2}\text{He}$

71 64 μCi

73 3.0 days

75 4.4×10^3 Bq

77 a. ${}^{180}_{80}\text{Hg} \longrightarrow {}^{176}_{78}\text{Pt} + {}^{4}_{2}\text{He}$
b. ${}^{198}_{79}\text{Au} \longrightarrow {}^{198}_{80}\text{Hg} + {}^{0}_{-1}e$
c. ${}^{82}_{37}\text{Rb} \longrightarrow {}^{82}_{36}\text{Kr} + {}^{0}_{+1}e$

79 ${}^{1}_{0}n + {}^{238}_{92}\text{U} \longrightarrow {}^{239}_{93}\text{Np} + {}^{0}_{-1}e$

Compounds and Their Bonds

Compounds and Their Bonds

Don Hammond/Design Pics Inc./Alamy

LOOKING AHEAD

1 Ions: Transfer of Electrons
2 Ionic Compounds
3 Naming and Writing Ionic Formulas
4 Polyatomic Ions
5 Covalent Compounds: Sharing Electrons
6 Naming and Writing Covalent Formulas
7 Electronegativity and Bond Polarity
8 Shapes and Polarity of Molecules
9 Attractive Forces in Compounds

Sarah, a pharmacy technician, is working at a local drug store. A customer asks Sarah about the effects of aspirin, as his doctor has recommended that he take a low-dose aspirin (81 mg) every day to prevent a heart attack or stroke.

Sarah informs her customer that aspirin is acetylsalicylic acid, and has the chemical formula, $C_9H_8O_4$. Aspirin is a covalent compound, often referred to as an organic molecule because it contains the nonmetals carbon (C), hydrogen (H), and oxygen (O). Sarah shows the customer the chemical structure of aspirin, and explains that aspirin is used to relieve minor pains, to reduce inflammation and fever, and to slow blood clotting. Some potential side effects of aspirin may include heartburn, upset stomach, nausea, and an increased risk of a stomach ulcer. Sarah then refers the customer to the licensed pharmacist on duty for additional information.

Visit **www.masteringchemistry.com** for self-study materials and instructor-assigned homework.

Career: Pharmacy Technician

Pharmacy technicians work under the supervision of a pharmacist, and their main responsibility is to fill prescriptions by preparing pharmaceutical medications. They obtain the proper medication, calculate, measure, and label the patient's medication, which is then approved by the pharmacist. After the prescription is filled, the technicians price and file the prescription. Pharmacy technicians also provide customer service by receiving prescription requests, interacting with customers, and answering any questions they may have about the drugs and their health condition. Pharmacy technicians may also prepare insurance claims, and create and maintain patient profiles.

Aspirin

In nature, atoms of almost all the elements on the periodic table are found in combination with other atoms. Only the atoms of the noble gases—He, Ne, Ar, Kr, Xe, and Rn—do not combine in nature with other atoms. A compound is a pure substance, composed of two or more elements, with a definite composition. Compounds are either ionic or covalent. In an ionic compound, one or more electrons are transferred from the atoms of metals to atoms of nonmetals. The attractions that result are called *ionic bonds*.

We use many ionic compounds every day, such as salt ($NaCl$) and baking soda ($NaHCO_3$). Milk of magnesia ($Mg(OH)_2$) or calcium carbonate ($CaCO_3$) may be taken to settle an upset stomach. In a mineral supplement, iron may be present as iron(II) sulfate ($FeSO_4$), iodine as potassium iodide (KI), and manganese as manganese(II) sulfate ($MnSO_4$). Some sunscreens contain zinc oxide (ZnO), and the tin(II) fluoride (SnF_2) in toothpaste provides fluoride to help prevent tooth decay.

Precious and semiprecious gemstones are examples of ionic compounds called minerals that are cut and polished to make jewelry. Sapphires and rubies are made of a crystalline form of aluminum oxide (Al_2O_3). Impurities of chromium make rubies red, and iron and titanium make sapphires blue.

buckarooh/iStockphoto

Small amounts of metals cause the different colors of gemstones.

In compounds of nonmetals, *covalent bonds* occur when atoms share one or more valence electrons. There are many more covalent compounds than there are ionic ones, and many simple covalent compounds are present in our everyday lives. For example, water (H_2O), oxygen (O_2), and carbon dioxide (CO_2) are covalent compounds.

Covalent compounds consist of molecules, which are discrete groups of atoms. A molecule of water (H_2O) consists of two atoms of hydrogen and one atom of oxygen. When you have iced tea, perhaps you add molecules of sugar ($C_{12}H_{22}O_{11}$). Other covalent compounds include propane (C_3H_8), alcohol (C_2H_6O), and the antibiotic amoxicillin ($C_{16}H_{19}N_3O_5S$).

1 Ions: Transfer of Electrons

LEARNING GOAL

Using the octet rule, write the symbols for the simple ions of the representative elements.

Most of the elements, except the noble gases, are found in nature combined as compounds. The noble gases are so stable that they form compounds only under extreme conditions. One explanation for their stability is that they have a filled valence energy level. Helium is stable with two valence electrons that fill its outermost electron level. All the other noble gases are stable because they have eight valence electrons, called an *octet*.

TUTORIAL
Octet Rule and Ions

Compounds are the result of a transfer or sharing of electrons to give the atoms in the compound stable electron configurations. A few atoms, such as hydrogen, are stable with two electrons, but most are stable when they have eight electrons. *Ionic bonds* occur when the electrons of atoms of a metal are transferred to atoms of nonmetals. *Covalent bonds* form when atoms of nonmetals share valence electrons. This tendency for the atoms to obtain a stable electron configuration is called the

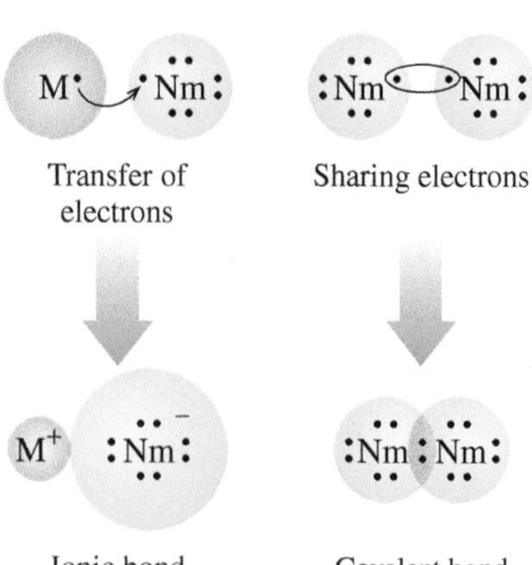

M is a metal
Nm is a nonmetal

octet rule and provides a key to our understanding of the ways in which atoms of representative elements bond and form compounds. The octet rule does not apply to transition elements.

Positive Ions: Loss of Electrons

In ionic bonding, **ions**, which have electrical charges, form when atoms lose or gain electrons to obtain a stable electron configuration. The ionization energies of metals of Groups 1A (1), 2A (2), and 3A (13) are low. Thus, metal atoms readily lose their valence electrons. In doing so, they form ions with positive charges. For example, when a sodium atom loses its one valence electron, the remaining electrons have a stable electron configuration. By losing an electron, sodium has 10 electrons instead of 11. Because there are still 11 protons in its nucleus, the atom is no longer neutral. It is now a sodium ion with an electrical charge, called an **ionic charge**, of 1+. In the symbol for the sodium ion, the ionic charge of 1+ is written in the upper right-hand corner, Na^+, where the 1 is understood. The sodium ion is smaller than the sodium atom because the ion has lost its outermost electron from the third energy level. The positively charged ions of metals are called **cations** (pronounced ***cat**-eye-uns*) and use the name of the element.

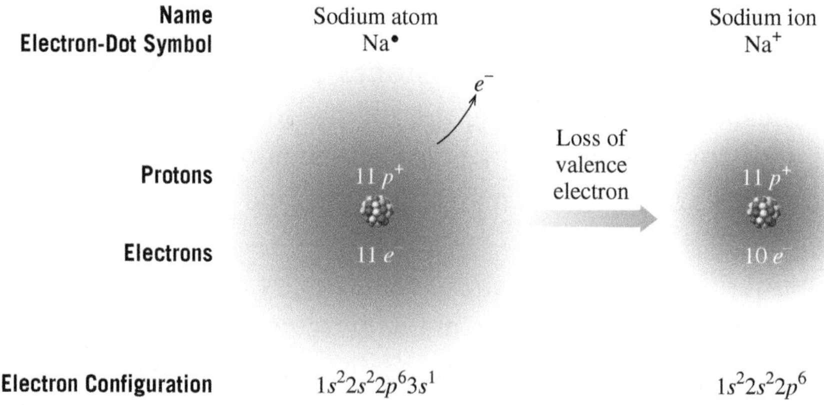

Magnesium, a metal in Group 2A (2), obtains a stable electron configuration by losing two valence electrons to form a magnesium ion with a 2+ ionic charge, Mg^{2+}. The magnesium ion is smaller than the magnesium atom because the outermost electrons

Chemistry Link to Health

SOME USES FOR NOBLE GASES

Noble gases may be used when it is necessary to have a substance that is unreactive. Scuba divers normally use a pressurized mixture of nitrogen and oxygen gases for breathing under water. However, when the air mixture is used at depths where pressure is high, the nitrogen gas is absorbed into the blood, where it can cause mental disorientation. To avoid nitrogen narcosis, a breathing mixture of oxygen and helium may be substituted. The diver still obtains the necessary oxygen, but the unreactive helium that dissolves in the blood does not cause mental disorientation. However, its lower density does change the vibrations of the vocal cords, and the diver will sound like Donald Duck.

Helium is also used to fill blimps and balloons. When dirigibles were first designed, they were filled with hydrogen, a very light gas. However, when they came in contact with any type of spark or heating source, they exploded violently because of the extreme reactivity of hydrogen gas with oxygen present in the air. Today, blimps are filled with unreactive helium gas, which presents no danger of explosion.

Lighting tubes are generally filled with a noble gas such as neon or argon. While the electrically heated filaments that produce the light get very hot, the surrounding noble gases do not react with the hot filament. If heated in air, the elements that constitute the filament will quickly burn out when oxygen is present.

Karl R. Martin/Shutterstock

The helium in a blimp is much less dense than air, which allows the blimp to fly above the ground.

in the third energy level were removed. The octet in the magnesium ion is made up of electrons that fill its second energy level.

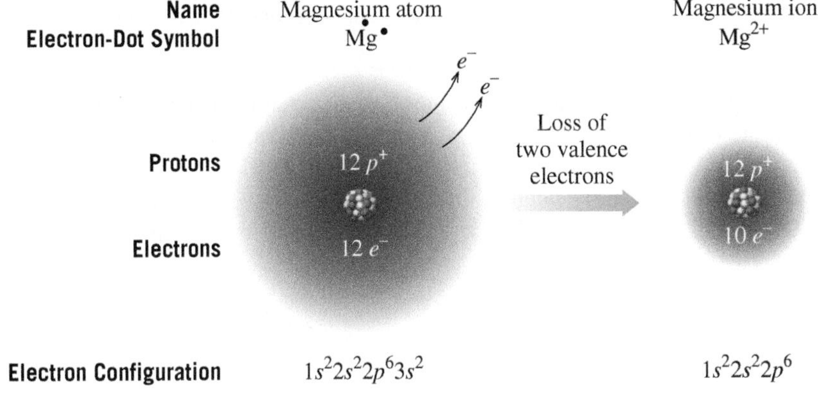

Negative Ions: Gain of Electrons

The ionization energy of a nonmetal atom in Group 5A (15), 6A (16), or 7A (17) is high. Rather than lose electrons to form ions, a nonmetal atom gains one or more valence electrons to obtain a stable electron configuration. For example, an atom of chlorine with seven valence electrons gains one more electron to form an octet. Because there are now 18 electrons and 17 protons, the chlorine atom is no longer neutral. It becomes a chloride ion with an ionic charge of 1−, which is written as Cl^-. A negatively charged ion, called an **anion** (pronounced ***an**-eye-un*), is named by using the first syllable of its element name followed by *ide*. The chloride ion is larger than a chlorine atom because the ion has an additional electron, which completes its outermost energy level.

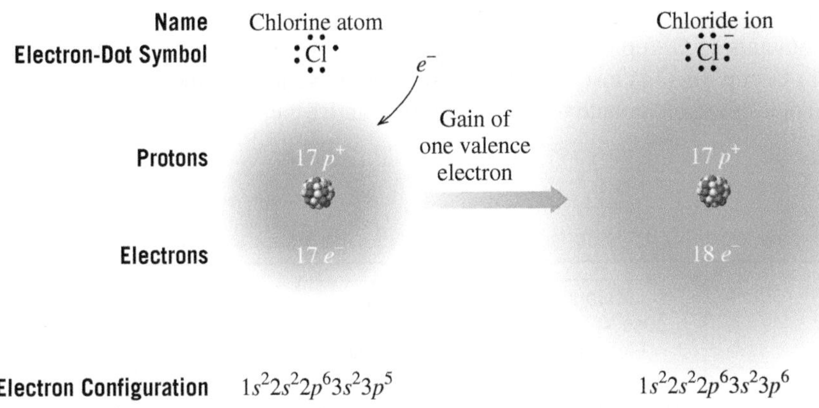

Table 1 lists the names of some important metal and nonmetal ions.

TABLE 1 Symbols and Names of Some Common Ions

Group Number	Cation	Name of Cation	Group Number	Anion	Name of Anion
	Metals			**Nonmetals**	
1A (1)	Li^+	Lithium	5A (15)	N^{3-}	Nitride
	Na^+	Sodium		P^{3-}	Phosphide
	K^+	Potassium	6A (16)	O^{2-}	Oxide
2A (2)	Mg^{2+}	Magnesium		S^{2-}	Sulfide
	Ca^{2+}	Calcium	7A (17)	F^-	Fluoride
	Ba^{2+}	Barium		Cl^-	Chloride
3A (13)	Al^{3+}	Aluminum		Br^-	Bromide
				I^-	Iodide

TUTORIAL
Ions

CONCEPT CHECK 1 **Ions**

a. Write the symbol and name for the ion that has 7 protons and 10 electrons.
b. Write the symbol and name for the ion that has 20 protons and 18 electrons.

ANSWER

a. The element with 7 protons is nitrogen. In an ion of nitrogen with 10 electrons, the ionic charge is 3−, (7+) + (10−) = 3−. The ion, written as N^{3-}, is the *nitride* ion.
b. The element with 20 protons is calcium. In an ion of calcium with 18 electrons, the ionic charge is 2+, (20+) + (18−) = 2+. The ion, written as Ca^{2+}, is the *calcium* ion.

Ionic Charges from Group Numbers

We can obtain the number of valence electrons of the representative elements from their group numbers on the periodic table. Now we can use group numbers to determine the charges for their ions, which acquire eight valence electrons like the nearest noble gas, or two for helium. The elements in Group 1A (1) lose one electron to form ions with a 1+ charge. The atoms of the elements in Group 2A (2) lose two electrons to form ions with a 2+ charge. The atoms of the elements in Group 3A (13) lose three electrons to form ions with a 3+ charge. In this text, we do not use the group numbers of the transition elements to determine their ionic charges.

In ionic compounds, the atoms of the nonmetals in Group 7A (17) gain one electron to form ions with a 1− charge. The atoms of the elements in Group 6A (16) gain two electrons to form ions with a 2− charge. The atoms of the elements in Group 5A (15) typically gain three electrons to form ions with a 3− charge.

The nonmetals of Group 4A (14) do not typically form ions. However, the metals Sn and Pb in Group 4A (14) lose electrons to form positive ions. Table 2 lists the ionic charges for some common monatomic ions of representative elements.

TABLE 2 Examples of Monatomic Ions and Their Nearest Noble Gases

		Metals Lose Valence Electrons			Nonmetals Gain Valence Electrons				
Noble Gases		1A (1)	2A (2)	3A (13)	5A (15)	6A (16)	7A (17)		**Noble Gases**
He	⇦	Li^+							
Ne	⇦	Na^+	Mg^{2+}	Al^{3+}	N^{3-}	O^{2-}	F^-	⇨	**Ne**
Ar	⇦	K^+	Ca^{2+}		P^{3-}	S^{2-}	Cl^-	⇨	**Ar**
Kr	⇦	Rb^+	Sr^{2+}				Br^-	⇨	**Kr**
Xe	⇦	Cs^+	Ba^{2+}				I^-	⇨	**Xe**

Chemistry Link to Health

SOME IMPORTANT IONS IN THE BODY

Several ions in body fluids have important physiological and metabolic functions. Some of them are listed in Table 3.

Foods such as bananas, milk, cheese, and potatoes provide the body with ions that are important in regulating body functions.

Pearson Education

TABLE 3 Ions in the Body

Ion	Occurrence	Function	Source	Result of Too Little	Result of Too Much
Na^+	Principal cation outside the cell	Regulates and controls body fluids	Salt, cheese, pickles, potato chips, pretzels	Hyponatremia, anxiety, diarrhea, circulatory failure, decrease in body fluid	Hypernatremia, little urine, thirst, edema
K^+	Principal cation inside the cell	Regulates body fluids and cellular functions	Bananas, orange juice, milk, prunes, potatoes	Hypokalemia (hypopotassemia), lethargy, muscle weakness, failure of neurological impulses	Hyperkalemia (hyperpotassemia), irritability, nausea, little urine, cardiac arrest
Ca^{2+}	Cation outside the cell; 90% of calcium in the body in bone occurs as $Ca_3(PO_4)_2$ or $CaCO_3$	Major cation of bone; needed for muscle contraction	Milk, yogurt, cheese, greens, spinach	Hypocalcemia, tingling fingertips, muscle cramps, osteoporosis	Hypercalcemia, relaxed muscles, kidney stones, deep bone pain
Mg^{2+}	Cation outside the cell; 70% of magnesium in the body is in the bones	Essential for certain enzymes, muscles, nerve control	Widely distributed (part of chlorophyll of all green plants), nuts, whole grains	Disorientation, hypertension, tremors, slow pulse	Drowsiness
Cl^-	Principal anion outside the cell	Major anion of gastric juice, regulates body fluids	Salt	Same as for Na^+	Same as for Na^+

QUESTIONS AND PROBLEMS

1 Ions: Transfer of Electrons

LEARNING GOAL: *Using the octet rule, write the symbols for the simple ions of the representative elements.*

1 State the number of electrons that must be lost by atoms of each of the following to obtain a stable electron configuration:
a. Li **b.** Ca **c.** Ga
d. Cs **e.** Ba

2 State the number of electrons that must be gained by atoms of each of the following to obtain a stable electron configuration:
a. Cl **b.** Se **c.** N
d. I **e.** S

3 Write the symbols for the ions with the following number of protons and electrons:
a. 3 protons, 2 electrons
b. 9 protons, 10 electrons
c. 12 protons, 10 electrons
d. 26 protons, 23 electrons

4 Write the symbols for the ions with the following number of protons and electrons:
a. 30 protons, 28 electrons
b. 53 protons, 54 electrons
c. 82 protons, 78 electrons
d. 15 protons, 18 electrons

5 How many protons and electrons are in each of the following ions?
a. O^{2-} **b.** K^+ **c.** Br^- **d.** S^{2-}

6 How many protons and electrons are in each of the following ions?
a. Sr^{2+} **b.** F^- **c.** Au^{3+} **d.** Cs^+

7 Write the symbol for the ion of each of the following:
a. chlorine **b.** potassium **c.** oxygen
d. aluminum **e.** selenium

8 Write the symbol for the ion of each of the following:
a. fluorine **b.** calcium **c.** sodium
d. iodine **e.** barium

LEARNING GOAL

Using charge balance, write the correct formula for an ionic compound.

TUTORIAL
Ionic Compounds

2 Ionic Compounds

Ionic compounds consist of positive and negative ions. The ions are held together by strong attractions between the oppositely charged ions, called **ionic bonds**.

Properties of Ionic Compounds

The physical and chemical properties of an ionic compound such as NaCl are very different from those of the original elements. For example, the original elements of NaCl were sodium, which is a soft, shiny metal, and chlorine, which is a yellow-green poisonous gas. However, when they react and form positive and negative ions, they produce ordinary table salt, NaCl, a hard, white, crystalline substance that is important in our diet.

In a crystal of NaCl, every Na^+ ion (shown in purple) is surrounded by six Cl^- ions (shown in green), and every Cl^- ion is surrounded by six Na^+ ions (see Figure 1). Thus,

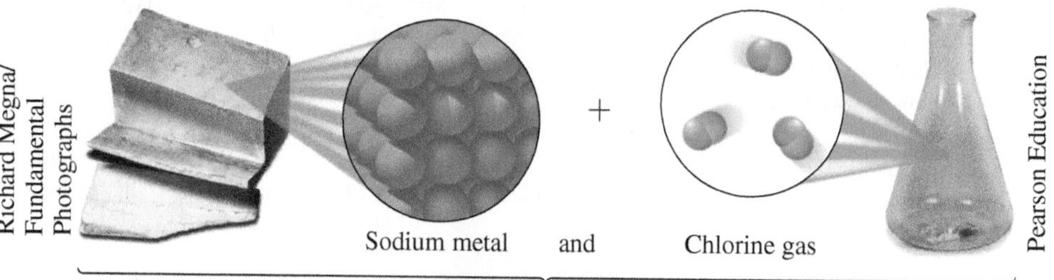

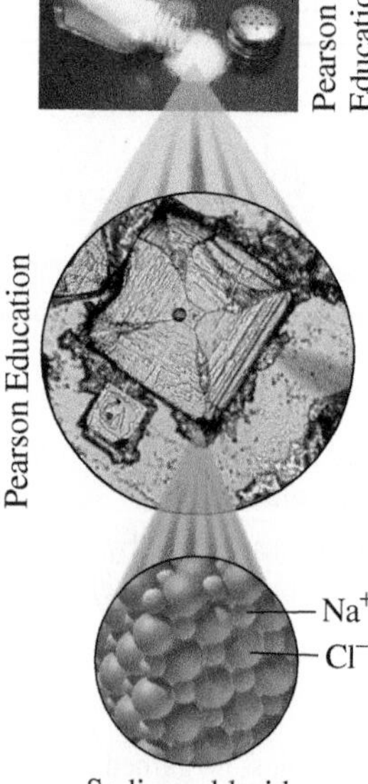

FIGURE 1 The elements sodium and chlorine react to form the ionic compound sodium chloride, which makes up table salt. The magnification of NaCl crystals shows the arrangements of Na^+ and Cl^- ions in a NaCl crystal.

Q What is the type of bonding between Na^+ and Cl^- ions in NaCl?

there are many strong attractions between the positive and negative ions, which account for the high melting points of ionic compounds. For example, the melting point of NaCl is 801 °C. At room temperature, ionic compounds are solids.

Formulas of Ionic Compounds

The **chemical formula** of a compound represents the symbols and subscripts in the lowest whole-number ratio of the atoms or ions. In the formula of an ionic compound, the sum of the ionic charges is always zero, which means that the total amount of positive charge is equal to the total amount of negative charge. For example, the formula NaCl indicates that this compound consists of one sodium ion, Na^+, for every chloride ion, Cl^-. Although the ions have positive or negative charges, their ionic charges are not shown in the formula of the compound.

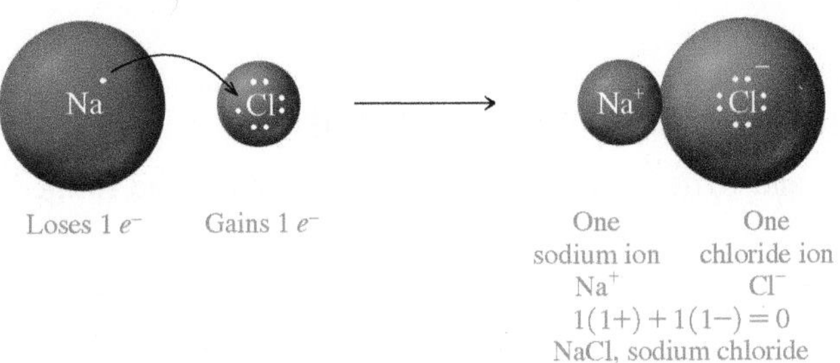

One sodium ion Na^+ One chloride ion Cl^-

$1(1+) + 1(1-) = 0$

NaCl, sodium chloride

Subscripts in Formulas

Consider a compound of magnesium and chlorine. To achieve an octet, a Mg atom loses its two valence electrons to form Mg^{2+}. Two Cl atoms each gain one electron to form two Cl^- ions. The two Cl^- ions are needed to balance the positive charge of Mg^{2+}. This gives the formula $MgCl_2$, magnesium chloride, in which the subscript 2 shows that two Cl^- ions are needed for charge balance.

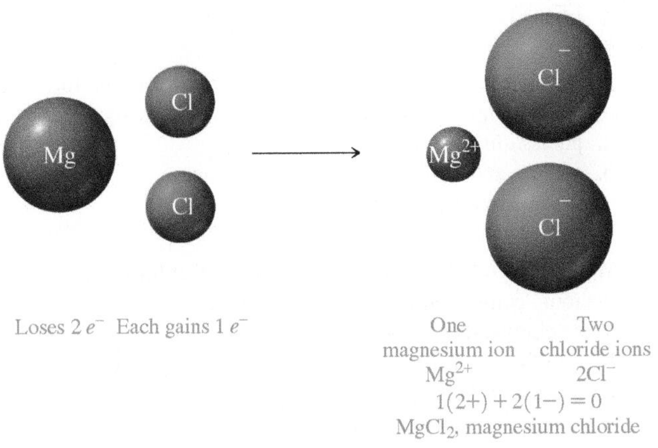

One magnesium ion Mg^{2+} Two chloride ions $2Cl^-$

$1(2+) + 2(1-) = 0$

$MgCl_2$, magnesium chloride

Writing Ionic Formulas from Ionic Charges

The subscripts in the formula of an ionic compound represent the number of positive and negative ions that give an overall charge of zero. Thus, we can now write a formula directly from the ionic charges of the positive and negative ions. In the formula of an ionic compound, the cation is written first and is followed by the anion. Suppose we wish to write the formula for the ionic compound containing Na^+ and S^{2-} ions. To balance the ionic charge of the S^{2-} ion, we show two Na^+ ions by using a subscript 2 in the formula. This gives the formula Na_2S, which has an overall charge of zero. When there is no subscript for a symbol such as the S in Na_2S, it assumed to be 1.

The group of ions that has the lowest ratio of the ions in an ionic compound is called a *formula unit*.

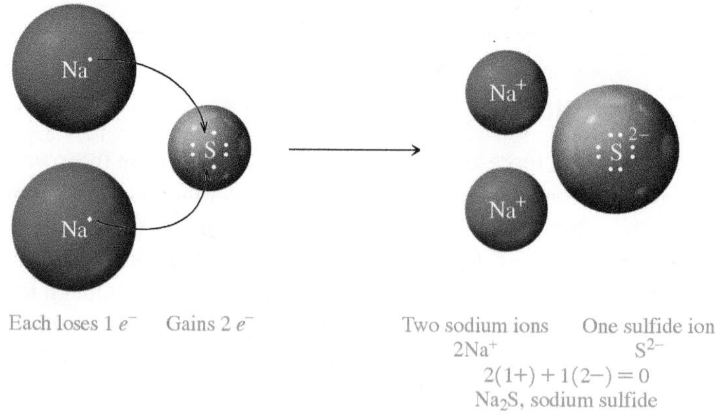

CONCEPT CHECK 2 **Writing Formulas from Ionic Charges**

Determine the ionic charges, and write the formula for the ionic compound formed when lithium and nitrogen react.

ANSWER

Lithium in Group 1A (1) forms Li^+; nitrogen in Group 5A (15) forms N^{3-}. The charge of 3− for N^{3-} is balanced by three Li^+ ions. Writing the positive ion first gives the formula Li_3N.

QUESTIONS AND PROBLEMS

2 Ionic Compounds

LEARNING GOAL: *Using charge balance, write the correct formula for an ionic compound.*

9 Which of the following pairs of elements are likely to form ionic compounds?
a. lithium and chlorine **b.** oxygen and bromine
c. potassium and oxygen **d.** sodium and neon
e. cesium and magnesium **f.** nitrogen and fluorine

10 Which of the following pairs of elements are likely to form ionic compounds?
a. helium and oxygen **b.** magnesium and chlorine
c. chlorine and bromine **d.** potassium and sulfur
e. sodium and potassium **f.** nitrogen and iodine

11 Write the correct ionic formula for the compound formed between the following:
a. Na^+ and O^{2-} **b.** Al^{3+} and Br^-
c. Ba^{2+} and N^{3-} **d.** Mg^{2+} and F^-
e. Al^{3+} and S^{2-}

12 Write the correct ionic formula for the compound formed between the following:
a. Al^{3+} and Cl^- **b.** Ca^{2+} and S^{2-}
c. Li^+ and S^{2-} **d.** Rb^+ and P^{3-}
e. Cs^+ and I^-

13 Write the symbols for the ions and the correct formula for the ionic compound formed by each of the following:
a. potassium and sulfur
b. sodium and nitrogen
c. aluminum and iodine
d. gallium and oxygen

14 Write the symbols for the ions and the correct formula for the ionic compound formed by each of the following:
a. calcium and chlorine
b. rubidium and sulfur
c. sodium and phosphorus
d. magnesium and oxygen

LEARNING GOAL

Given the formula of an ionic compound, write the correct name; given the name of an ionic compound, write the correct formula.

3 Naming and Writing Ionic Formulas

In the name of an ionic compound made up of two elements, the name of the metal ion, which is written first, is the same as its element name. The name of the nonmetal ion is obtained by using the first syllable of its element name followed by *ide*. In the name of any ionic compound, a space separates the name of the cation from the name of the anion.

Subscripts are not used; they are understood because of the charge balance of the ions in the compound (see Table 4).

TABLE 4 Names of Some Ionic Compounds

Compound	Metal Ion	Nonmetal Ion	Name of Ionic Compound
KI	K^+ Potassium	I^- Iodide	Potassium iodide
$MgBr_2$	Mg^{2+} Magnesium	Br^- Bromide	Magnesium bromide
Al_2O_3	Al^{3+} Aluminum	O^{2-} Oxide	Aluminum oxide

Iodized salt contains KI to prevent iodine deficiency.

SAMPLE PROBLEM 1 **Naming Ionic Compounds**

Write the name for the ionic compound Mg_3N_2.

SOLUTION

Step 1 **Identify the cation and anion.** The cation from Group 2A (2) is Mg^{2+}, and the anion from Group 5A (15) is N^{3-}.

Step 2 **Name the cation by its element name.** The cation Mg^{2+} is magnesium.

Step 3 **Name the anion by using the first syllable of its element name followed by *ide*.** The anion N^{3-} is nitride.

Step 4 **Write the name for the cation first and the name for the anion second.** Mg_3N_2 is magnesium nitride.

STUDY CHECK 1

Name the compound Ga_2S_3.

Guide to Naming Ionic Compounds with Metals That Form a Single Ion

1. Identify the cation and anion.
2. Name the cation by its element name.
3. Name the anion by using the first syllable of its element name followed by *ide*.
4. Write the name for the cation first and the name for the anion second.

Metals with Variable Charge

We have seen that the charge of an ion of a representative element can be obtained from its group number. However, it is not as easy to determine the charge of a transition element because they typically form two or more positive ions. The transition elements can lose *s* electrons from the highest energy level as well as *d* electrons from a lower energy level. This is also true for metals of representative elements in Groups 4A (14) and 5A (15), such as Pb, Sn, and Bi.

In some ionic compounds, iron is in the Fe^{2+} form; but in other compounds, it has the Fe^{3+} form. Copper also forms two different ions: Cu^+ and Cu^{2+}. When a metal can form two or more ions, it has a *variable charge*. Thus, for these metals, we cannot predict the ionic charge from the group number.

When different ions are possible, a naming system is used to identify the particular cation. To do this, a Roman numeral that is equal to the ionic charge is placed in parentheses immediately after its element name. For example, Fe^{2+} is named iron(II), and Fe^{3+} is named iron(III). Table 5 lists the ions of some transition elements that have two or more ions.

Figure 2 shows some ions and their location on the periodic table. The transition elements form more than one positive ion except for zinc (Zn^{2+}), cadmium (Cd^{2+}), and silver (Ag^+), which form only one ion. Thus, the names of zinc, cadmium, and silver are sufficient when naming their cations in ionic compounds. Metals in Group 4A (14) also form more than one positive ion. For example, lead and tin in Group 4A (14) form cations with charges of 2+ and 4+.

TUTORIAL
Writing Ionic Formulas

TABLE 5 Some Metals That Form More Than One Positive Ion

Element	Ions	Name of Ion	Element	Ions	Name of Ion
Chromium	Cr^{2+}	Chromium(II)	Lead	Pb^{2+}	Lead(II)
	Cr^{3+}	Chromium(III)		Pb^{4+}	Lead(IV)
Cobalt	Co^{2+}	Cobalt(II)	Manganese	Mn^{2+}	Manganese(II)
	Co^{3+}	Cobalt(III)		Mn^{3+}	Manganese(III)
Copper	Cu^{+}	Copper(I)	Mercury	Hg_2^{2+}	Mercury(I)*
	Cu^{2+}	Copper(II)		Hg^{2+}	Mercury(II)
Gold	Au^{+}	Gold(I)	Nickel	Ni^{2+}	Nickel(II)
	Au^{3+}	Gold(III)		Ni^{3+}	Nickel(III)
Iron	Fe^{2+}	Iron(II)	Tin	Sn^{2+}	Tin(II)
	Fe^{3+}	Iron(III)		Sn^{4+}	Tin(IV)

*Mercury(I) ions form an ion pair with a 2+ charge.

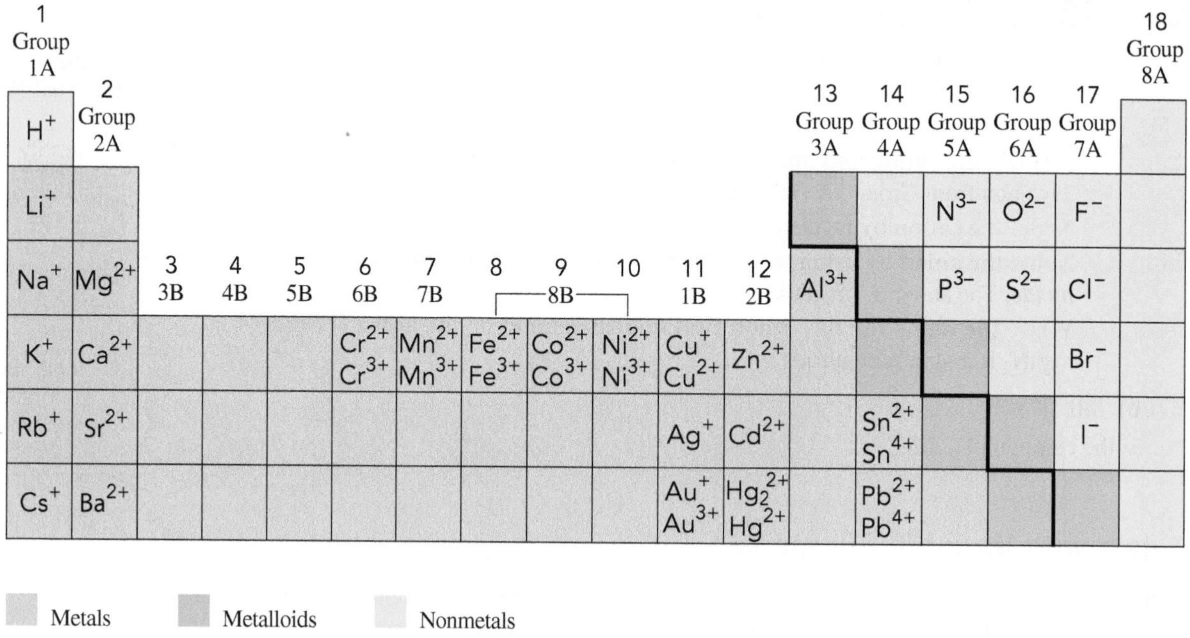

1 Group 1A	2 Group 2A	3 3B	4 4B	5 5B	6 6B	7 7B	8 8B	9 8B	10 8B	11 1B	12 2B	13 Group 3A	14 Group 4A	15 Group 5A	16 Group 6A	17 Group 7A	18 Group 8A
H^+																	
Li^+														N^{3-}	O^{2-}	F^-	
Na^+	Mg^{2+}											Al^{3+}		P^{3-}	S^{2-}	Cl^-	
K^+	Ca^{2+}				Cr^{2+} Cr^{3+}	Mn^{2+} Mn^{3+}	Fe^{2+} Fe^{3+}	Co^{2+} Co^{3+}	Ni^{2+} Ni^{3+}	Cu^+ Cu^{2+}	Zn^{2+}					Br^-	
Rb^+	Sr^{2+}									Ag^+	Cd^{2+}		Sn^{2+} Sn^{4+}			I^-	
Cs^+	Ba^{2+}									Au^+ Au^{3+}	Hg_2^{2+} Hg^{2+}		Pb^{2+} Pb^{4+}				

Metals Metalloids Nonmetals

FIGURE 2 On the periodic table, positive ions are produced from metals and negative ions are produced from nonmetals.

Q What are the ions produced by calcium, copper, and oxygen?

Determination of Variable Charge

When you name an ionic compound, you need to determine if the metal is a representative element or a transition element. If it is a transition element, except for zinc, cadmium, or silver, you will need to write its ionic charge as a Roman numeral for part of its name. The calculation of ionic charge depends on the negative charge of the anions in the formula. For example, we use charge balance to calculate the charge of the copper cation in the formula $CuCl_2$. Because there are two chloride ions, each with a 1− charge, the total negative charge is 2−. To balance the 2− charge, the copper ion must have a charge of 2+, which is a Cu^{2+} ion:

$CuCl_2$

Cu charge + $2Cl^-$ charge = 0

? + 2(1−) = 0

2+ + 2− = 0

To indicate the 2+ charge for the copper ion Cu^{2+}, we place the Roman numeral (II) immediately after copper when naming the compound: copper(II) chloride.

Table 6 lists the names of some ionic compounds in which the transition elements and metals from Group 4A (14) have more than one positive ion.

TABLE 6 Some Ionic Compounds of Metals That Form Two Kinds of Positive Ions

Compound	Systematic Name
$FeCl_2$	Iron(II) chloride
Fe_2O_3	Iron(III) oxide
Cu_3P	Copper(I) phosphide
$CuBr_2$	Copper(II) bromide
$SnCl_2$	Tin(II) chloride
PbS_2	Lead(IV) sulfide

SAMPLE PROBLEM 2 Naming Ionic Compounds with Variable Charge Metal Ions

Antifouling paint contains Cu_2O, which prevents the growth of barnacles and algae on the bottoms of boats. What is the name of Cu_2O?

Gary Blakeley/Shutterstock

SOLUTION

Step 1 **Determine the charge of the cation from the anion.** The nonmetal O in Group 6A (16) forms the O^{2-} ion. Because there are two Cu ions to balance the O^{2-}, the charge of each Cu ion must be 1+.

Analyze the Problem

	Metal	Nonmetal
Element	Copper	Oxygen
Location on the Periodic Table	Transition element	Group 6A (16)
Ion	Cu?	O^{2-}
Charge balance	$2(1+)$ +	$(2-) = 0$
Ion	Cu^+	O^{2-}

Step 2 **Name the cation by its element name, and use a Roman numeral in parentheses for the charge.** copper(I)

Step 3 **Name the anion by using the first syllable of its element name followed by *ide*.** oxide

Step 4 **Write the name for the cation first and the name for the anion second.** copper(I) oxide

STUDY CHECK 2

Write the name for the compound with the formula Mn_2S_3.

Guide to Naming Ionic Compounds with Variable Charge Metals

1 Determine the charge of the cation from the anion.

2 Name the cation by its element name, and use a Roman numeral in parentheses for the charge.

3 Name the anion by using the first syllable of its element name followed by *ide*.

4 Write the name for the cation first and the name for the anion second.

SAMPLE PROBLEM 3 Writing Formulas for Ionic Compounds

Write the formula for iron(III) chloride.

SOLUTION

Step 1 **Identify the cation and anion.** The Roman numeral (III) indicates that the charge of the iron ion is 3+, Fe^{3+}.

Analyze the Problem

	Metal	Nonmetal
Ion	Iron(III)	Chloride
Group	Transition	7A (17)
Symbol	Fe^{3+}	Cl^-

Step 2 **Balance the charges.**

Fe^{3+} Cl^-
Cl^-
Cl^-

$$\mathbf{1}(3+) + \mathbf{3}(1-) = 0$$

Becomes a subscript in the formula

Guide to Writing Formulas from the Name of an Ionic Compound

1 Identify the cation and anion.

2 Balance the charges.

3 Write the formula, cation first, using subscripts from the charge balance.

Step 3 **Write the formula, cation first, using subscripts from the charge balance.**

$FeCl_3$

STUDY CHECK 3

Write the correct formula for chromium(III) oxide.

Mark Huls/Fotolia

The pigment chrome oxide green contains chromium(III) oxide.

QUESTIONS AND PROBLEMS

3 Naming and Writing Ionic Formulas

LEARNING GOAL: *Given the formula of an ionic compound, write the correct name; given the name of an ionic compound, write the correct formula.*

15 Write the name for each of the following:
a. Al_2O_3 b. $CaCl_2$ c. Na_2O
d. Mg_3P_2 e. KI f. BaF_2

16 Write the name for each of the following:
a. $MgCl_2$ b. K_3P c. Li_2S
d. CsF e. MgO f. $SrBr_2$

17 Why is a Roman numeral placed after the name of the ions of most transition elements?

18 The compound $CaCl_2$ is named calcium chloride; the compound $CuCl_2$ is named copper(II) chloride. Explain why a Roman numeral is used in one name but not in the other.

19 Write the name for each of the following (include the Roman numeral when necessary):
a. Fe^{2+} b. Cu^{2+} c. Zn^{2+}
d. Pb^{4+} e. Cr^{3+} f. Mn^{2+}

20 Write the name for each of the following (include the Roman numeral when necessary):
a. Ag^{+} b. Cu^{+} c. Fe^{3+}
d. Sn^{2+} e. Au^{3+} f. Ni^{2+}

21 Write the name for each of the following:
a. $SnCl_2$ b. FeO c. Cu_2S
d. CuS e. $CrBr_3$ f. $ZnCl_2$

22 Write the name for each of the following:
a. Ag_3P b. PbS
c. SnO_2 d. $MnCl_3$
e. FeS f. $CoCl_2$

23 Write the symbol for the cation in each of the following:
a. $AuCl_3$ b. Fe_2O_3
c. PbI_4 d. $SnCl_2$

24 Write the symbol for the cation in each of the following:
a. $FeCl_2$ b. CrO
c. Ni_2S_3 d. AlP

25 Write formulas for the following ionic compounds:
a. magnesium chloride
b. sodium sulfide
c. copper(I) oxide
d. zinc phosphide
e. gold(III) nitride
f. chromium(II) chloride

26 Write formulas for the following ionic compounds:
a. nickel(III) oxide
b. barium fluoride
c. tin(IV) chloride
d. silver sulfide
e. copper(II) chloride
f. lithium nitride

LEARNING GOAL

Write the name and formula for a compound containing a polyatomic ion.

TUTORIAL
Polyatomic Ions

4 Polyatomic Ions

A **polyatomic ion** is a group of covalently bonded atoms that has an overall ionic charge. Most polyatomic ions consist of a nonmetal such as phosphorus, sulfur, carbon, or nitrogen bonded to oxygen atoms.

Almost all of the polyatomic ions are anions with charges of 1−, 2−, or 3−, which indicate that the group of atoms has gained 1, 2, or 3 electrons to complete a stable electron configuration, usually an octet. Only one common polyatomic ion, NH_4^+, has a positive charge. Some models of common polyatomic ions are shown in Figure 3.

Names of Polyatomic Ions

The names of the most common negatively charged polyatomic ions end in *ate* such as nitrate and sulfate. When a related ion has one less oxygen atom, the *ite* ending is used for its name such as nitrite and sulfite. Recognizing these endings will help you identify polyatomic ions in the names of compounds. The hydroxide ion (OH^-) and cyanide ion (CN^-) are exceptions to this naming pattern.

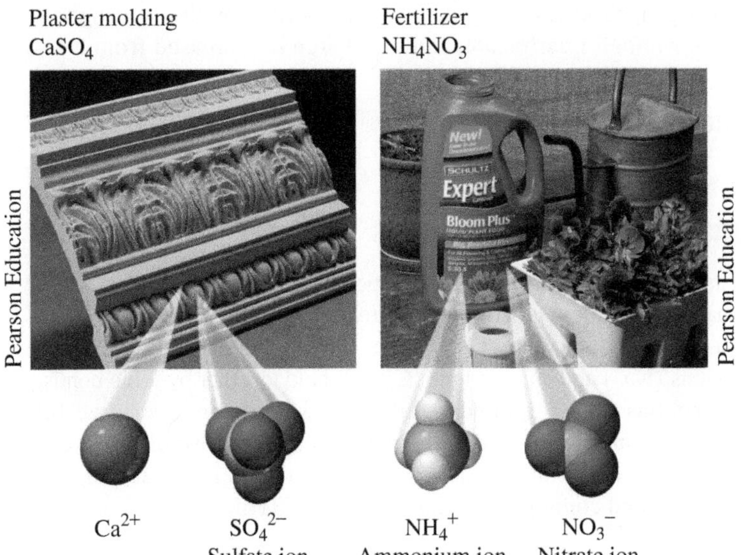

FIGURE 3 Many products contain polyatomic ions, which are groups of bonded atoms that carry an ionic charge.

Q Why does the sulfate ion have a 2− charge?

By learning the formulas, charges, and the names of the polyatomic ions shown in bold type in Table 7, you can derive the related ions. Note that the *ate* and *ite* ions of a particular nonmetal have the same ionic charge. For example, the sulfate ion is SO_4^{2-}, and the sulfite ion, which has one less oxygen atom, is SO_3^{2-}. Phosphate and phosphite ions each have a 3− charge; nitrate and nitrite each have a 1− charge. The elements in Group 7A (17) form four different polyatomic ions with oxygen. Prefixes are added to the names, and the ending is changed to distinguish among these ions. The prefix *per* is used for the polyatomic ion that has one more oxygen than the *ate* form. The prefix *hypo* is used for the polyatomic ion that has one oxygen less than the *ite* form. For example, the polyatomic ions of chlorine—perchlorate, chlorate, chlorite, and hypochlorite—each have a 1− charge.

TABLE 7 Names and Formulas of Some Common Polyatomic Ions

Nonmetal	Formula of Ion*	Name of Ion
Hydrogen	OH^-	Hydroxide
Nitrogen	NH_4^+	Ammonium
	$\mathbf{NO_3^-}$	**Nitrate**
	NO_2^-	Nitrite
Chlorine	ClO_4^-	Perchlorate
	$\mathbf{ClO_3^-}$	**Chlorate**
	ClO_2^-	Chlorite
	ClO^-	Hypochlorite
Carbon	$\mathbf{CO_3^{2-}}$	**Carbonate**
	HCO_3^-	Hydrogen carbonate (or bicarbonate)
	CN^-	Cyanide
	$H_2C_3O_2^-$	Acetate
Sulfur	$\mathbf{SO_4^{2-}}$	**Sulfate**
	HSO_4^-	Hydrogen sulfate (or bisulfate)
	SO_3^{2-}	Sulfite
	HSO_3^-	Hydrogen sulfite (or bisulfite)
Phosphorus	$\mathbf{PO_4^{3-}}$	**Phosphate**
	HPO_4^{2-}	Hydrogen phosphate
	$H_2PO_4^-$	Dihydrogen phosphate
	PO_3^{3-}	Phosphite

*Formulas and names in bold show the most common polyatomic ion for that element.

AP Photo/Eckehard Schulz

Sodium chlorite is used in the processing and bleaching of pulp from wood fibers and recycled cardboard.

The formula of hydrogen carbonate, or *bicarbonate*, is written with a hydrogen in front of the polyatomic formula for carbonate, and the charge is decreased from 2− to 1− to give HCO_3^-.

$$CO_3^{2-} + H^+ = HCO_3^-$$

Compounds Containing Polyatomic Ions

No polyatomic ion exists by itself. Like any other ion, a polyatomic ion must be associated with ions of opposite charge. The bonding between polyatomic ions and other ions is one of electrical attraction. For example, the compound sodium chlorite, used in bleaching wood pulp, consists of sodium ions (Na^+) and chlorite ions (ClO_2^-) held together by ionic bonds.

To write correct formulas for compounds containing a polyatomic ion, we follow the same rules of charge balance that we used when writing the formulas for ionic compounds. The total negative and positive charges must equal zero. For example, consider the formula for a compound containing sodium ions and chlorite ions. The ions are written:

	Na^+	ClO_2^-	
	Sodium ion	Chlorite ion	
Ionic charge	(1+)	+ (1−)	= 0

Because it takes one ion of each to balance the charge, the formula is written:

$NaClO_2$
Sodium chlorite

When more than one polyatomic ion is needed for charge balance, parentheses are used to enclose the formula of the ion. A subscript is written outside the closing parenthesis of the polyatomic ion to indicate the number needed for charge balance. The formula for magnesium nitrate contains the magnesium ion and the polyatomic nitrate ion.

Mg^{2+}	NO_3^-
Magnesium ion	Nitrate ion

To balance the positive charge of 2+ on the magnesium ion, two nitrate ions are needed. In the formula of the compound, parentheses are placed around the nitrate ion, and the subscript 2 is written outside the closing parenthesis.

Mg^{2+} NO_3^- NO_3^-

$(2+) + 2(1-) = 0$

Magnesium nitrate
$Mg(NO_3)_2$

Parentheses enclose the formula of the nitrate ion

Subscript outside the parenthesis indicates the use of two nitrate ions

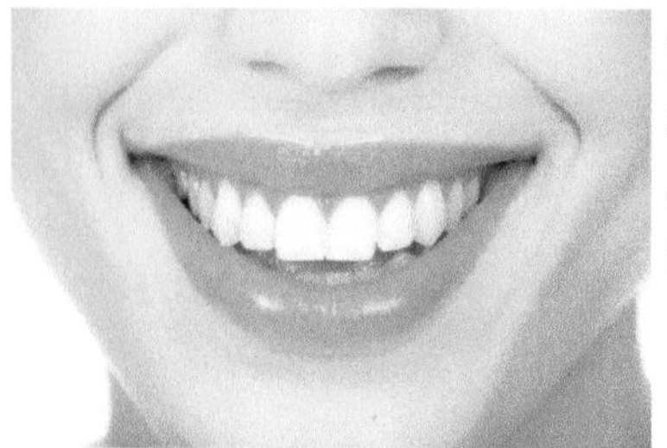
Kurhan/Fotolia

The mineral substance in teeth contains phosphate and hydroxide ions.

CONCEPT CHECK 3 **Polyatomic Ions in Bones and Teeth**

Bones and teeth contain a solid mineral substance called hydroxyapatite, $Ca_{10}(PO_4)_6(OH)_2$. What are the names and formulas of the polyatomic ions contained in the mineral substance of bones and teeth?

ANSWER

The polyatomic ions are phosphate, PO_4^{3-}, and hydroxide, OH^-.

Naming Compounds Containing Polyatomic Ions

When naming ionic compounds containing polyatomic ions, we first write the positive ion, usually a metal, and then we write the name for the polyatomic ion. It is important that you learn to recognize the polyatomic ion in the formula and name it correctly. As with other ionic compounds, no prefixes are used.

Na_2SO_4	$FePO_4$	$Al_2(CO_3)_3$
$Na_2\boxed{SO_4}$	$Fe\boxed{PO_4}$	$Al_2(\boxed{CO_3})_3$
Sodium sulfate	Iron(III) phosphate	Aluminum carbonate

Table 8 lists the formulas and names of some ionic compounds that include polyatomic ions and also gives their uses in medicine and industry.

TABLE 8 Some Compounds That Contain Polyatomic Ions

Formula	Name	Use
$BaSO_4$	Barium sulfate	Contrast medium for X-rays
$CaCO_3$	Calcium carbonate	Antacid, calcium supplement
$Ca_3(PO_4)_2$	Calcium phosphate	Calcium dietary supplement
$CaSO_3$	Calcium sulfite	Preservative in cider and fruit juices
$CaSO_4$	Calcium sulfate	Plaster casts
$AgNO_3$	Silver nitrate	Topical anti-infective
$NaHCO_3$	Sodium bicarbonate *or* Sodium hydrogen carbonate	Antacid
$Zn_3(PO_4)_2$	Zinc phosphate	Dental cement
$FePO_4$	Iron(III) phosphate	Food additive
K_2CO_3	Potassium carbonate	Alkalizer, diuretic
$Al_2(SO_4)_3$	Aluminum sulfate	Antiperspirant, anti-infective
$AlPO_4$	Aluminum phosphate	Antacid
$MgSO_4$	Magnesium sulfate	Cathartic, Epsom salts

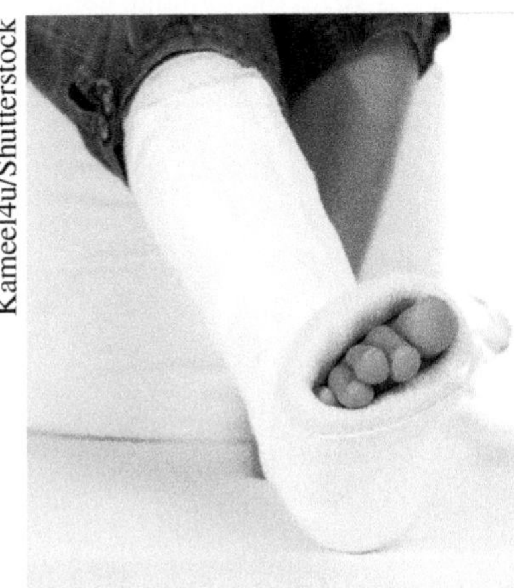
Kameel4u/Shutterstock

A plaster cast made of $CaSO_4$ immobilizes a broken leg.

SAMPLE PROBLEM 4 Naming Compounds Containing Polyatomic Ions

Name the following ionic compounds:

a. $KClO_3$
b. $Cu(NO_2)_2$

SOLUTION

Formula	Step 1 Cation	Step 1 Anion	Step 2 Name of Cation	Step 3 Name of Polyatomic Ion	Step 4 Name of Compound
a. $KClO_3$	K^+	ClO_3^-	Potassium ion	Chlorate ion	Potassium chlorate
b. $Cu(NO_2)_2$	Cu^{2+}	NO_2^-	Copper(II) ion	Nitrite ion	Copper(II) nitrite

STUDY CHECK 4

What is the name of $Co_3(PO_4)_2$?

Guide to Naming Ionic Compounds with Polyatomic Ions

1. Identify the cation and polyatomic ion (anion).
2. Name the cation using a Roman numeral, if needed.
3. Name the polyatomic ion.
4. Write the name for the compound, cation first and the polyatomic ion second.

SAMPLE PROBLEM 5 Writing Formulas for Ionic Compounds Containing Polyatomic Ions

Write the formula for aluminum bicarbonate.

Guide to Writing Formulas with Polyatomic Ions

1. Identify the cation and polyatomic ion (anion).
2. Balance the charges.
3. Write the formula, cation first, using the subscripts from charge balance.

SOLUTION

Step 1 Identify the cation and polyatomic ion (anion).

Cation	Polyatomic Ion (Anion)
Al^{3+}	HCO_3^-

Step 2 Balance the charges.

Al^{3+} HCO_3^- HCO_3^- HCO_3^-

$1(3+) + 3(1-) = 0$

Becomes a subscript in the formula (the 3)

Step 3 Write the formula, cation first, using the subscripts from charge balance. The formula for the compound is written by enclosing the formula of the bicarbonate ion, HCO_3^-, in parentheses, and writing the subscript 3 outside the closing parenthesis.

$Al(HCO_3)_3$

STUDY CHECK 5

Write the formula for a compound containing ammonium ion(s) and phosphate ion(s).

QUESTIONS AND PROBLEMS

4 Polyatomic Ions

LEARNING GOAL: *Write the name and formula for a compound containing a polyatomic ion.*

27 Write the formula, including the charge, for each of the following polyatomic ions:
- **a.** hydrogen carbonate (bicarbonate)
- **b.** ammonium
- **c.** phosphate
- **d.** hydrogen sulfate
- **e.** perchlorate

28 Write the formula, including the charge, for each of the following polyatomic ions:
a. nitrite **b.** sulfite **c.** hydroxide **d.** hypophosphite **e.** bromate

29 Name each of the following polyatomic ions:
a. SO_4^{2-} **b.** ClO^- **c.** PO_4^{3-} **d.** NO_3^-

30 Name each of the following polyatomic ions:
a. OH^- **b.** HSO_3^- **c.** CN^- **d.** NO_2^-

31 Complete the following table with the formula of the compound that forms between each pair of ions:

	NO_2^-	CO_3^{2-}	HSO_4^-	PO_4^{3-}
Li^+				
Cu^{2+}				
Ba^{2+}				

32 Complete the following table with the formula of the compound that forms between each pair of ions:

	NO_3^-	HCO_3^-	SO_3^{2-}	HPO_4^{2-}
NH_4^+				
Al^{3+}				
Pb^{4+}				

33 Write the formula for the polyatomic ion in each of the following and name each compound:
a. Na_2CO_3 **b.** NH_4Cl **c.** K_3PO_4 **d.** $Cr(NO_2)_2$ **e.** $FeSO_3$

34 Write the formula for the polyatomic ion in each of the following and name each compound:
a. KOH **b.** $NaNO_3$ **c.** Au_2CO_3 **d.** $NaHCO_3$ **e.** $BaSO_4$

35 Write the correct formula for each of the following compounds:
a. barium hydroxide **b.** sodium sulfate **c.** iron(II) nitrate **d.** zinc phosphate **e.** iron(III) carbonate

36 Write the correct formula for each of the following compounds:
a. aluminum chlorate **b.** ammonium oxide **c.** magnesium bicarbonate **d.** sodium nitrite **e.** copper(I) sulfate

5 Covalent Compounds: Sharing Electrons

A **covalent compound** forms when atoms of two nonmetals share electrons. Because of the high ionization energies of the nonmetals, electrons are not transferred between atoms of nonmetals, but are shared to achieve stability. When nonmetal atoms share electrons, the bond is a **covalent bond**. When two or more atoms share electrons, they form a **molecule**.

LEARNING GOAL

Draw the electron-dot formulas for covalent compounds, including multiple bonds and resonance structures.

SELF-STUDY ACTIVITY
Covalent Bonds

Formation of a Hydrogen Molecule

The simplest covalent molecule is hydrogen, H_2. When two H atoms are far apart, there are no attractions between them. As the H atoms move closer, the positive charge of each nucleus attracts the electron of the other atom. This attraction, which is greater than the repulsion between the valence electrons, pulls the atoms closer until they share a pair of valence electrons. The result is called a *covalent bond*, in which each H atom has a stable electron configuration. The atoms bonded in H_2 are more stable than two individual H atoms.

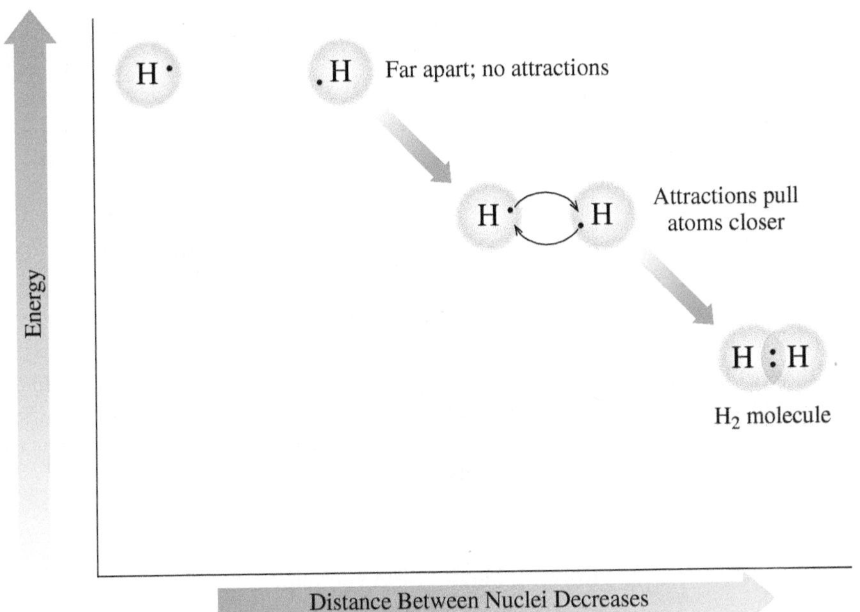

Electron-Dot Formulas of Covalent Molecules

The valence electrons in covalent molecules are shown using an electron-dot formula, also called a Lewis structure. The shared electrons, or *bonding pairs*, are shown as two dots or a single line between atoms. The nonbonding pairs of electrons, or *lone pairs*, are placed on the outside. For example, a fluorine molecule, F_2, consists of two fluorine atoms, Group 7A (17), each with seven valence electrons. In the F_2 molecule, each F atom achieves an octet by sharing its unpaired valence electron.

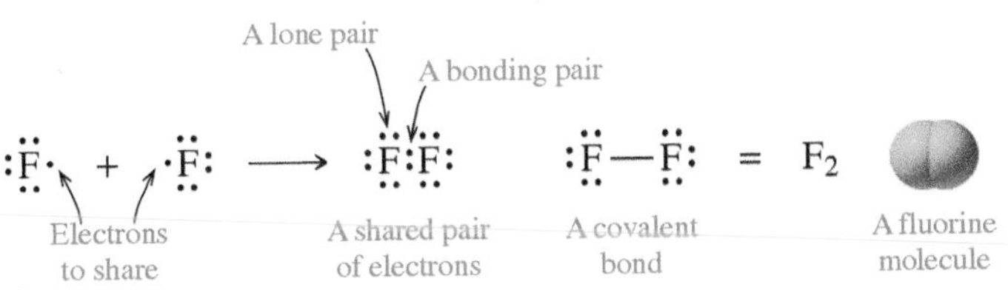

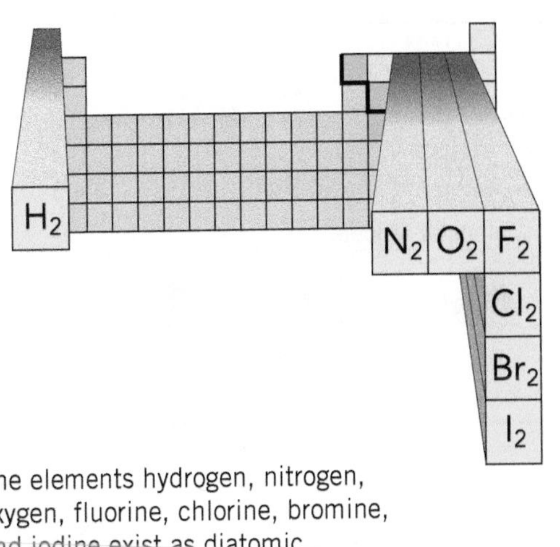

The elements hydrogen, nitrogen, oxygen, fluorine, chlorine, bromine, and iodine exist as diatomic molecules.

TABLE 9 Elements That Exist as Diatomic, Covalent Molecules

Diatomic Molecule	Name
H_2	Hydrogen
N_2	Nitrogen
O_2	Oxygen
F_2	Fluorine
Cl_2	Chlorine
Br_2	Bromine
I_2	Iodine

Hydrogen (H_2) and fluorine (F_2) are examples of nonmetal elements whose natural state is diatomic; that is, they contain two like atoms. The elements that exist as diatomic molecules are listed in Table 9.

Sharing Electrons between Atoms of Different Elements

The number of covalent bonds that a nonmetal forms is usually equal to the number of electrons it needs to acquire a stable electron configuration. Table 10 gives the most typical bonding patterns for several of the nonmetals.

TABLE 10 Typical Bonding Patterns of Some Nonmetals in Covalent Compounds

1A (1)	3A (13)	4A (14)	5A (15)	6A (16)	7A (17)
*H 1 bond					
	*B 3 bonds	C 4 bonds	N 3 bonds	O 2 bonds	F 1 bond
		Si 4 bonds	P 3 bonds	S 2 bonds	Cl, Br, I 1 bond

*H and B do not form eight-electron octets. H atoms share one electron pair; B atoms share three electron pairs for a set of 6 electrons.

TUTORIAL
Covalent Molecules and the Octet Rule

TUTORIAL
Writing Electron-Dot Formulas

TUTORIAL
Covalent Lewis-Dot Formulas

Methane, CH_4, a component of natural gas, is a compound of carbon and hydrogen. By sharing electrons, each carbon atom forms four bonds, and each hydrogen atom forms one bond. The carbon atom obtains an octet and each hydrogen atom is complete with two shared electrons. As seen in Table 11, the electron-dot formula for methane is drawn with the carbon atom as the center atom with the hydrogen atoms on all four sides. The bonding pairs of electrons, which are single covalent bonds, may also be shown as single lines between the carbon atom and each of the hydrogen atoms. Table 11 gives the formulas of some covalent molecules for Period 2 elements.

TABLE 11 Electron-Dot Formulas for Some Covalent Compounds

CH_4	NH_3	H_2O

Formulas Using Electron Dots

```
    H
    ••
H : C : H    H : N̈ : H    : Ö : H
    ••           ••           ••
    H            H            H
```

Formulas Using Bonds and Electron Dots

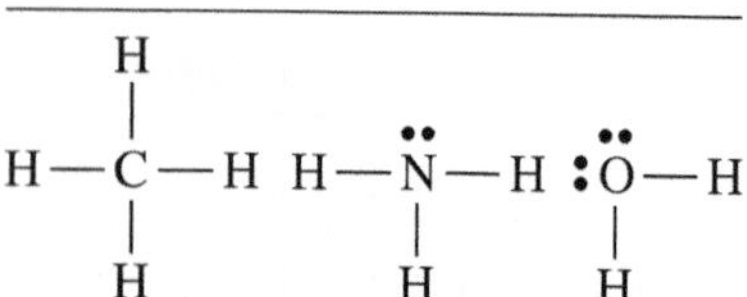

Molecular Models

Methane molecule

Ammonia molecule

Water molecule

CONCEPT CHECK 4 **Drawing Electron-Dot Formulas**

Use the electron-dot symbols of S and F to draw the electron-dot formula for SF_2, sulfur difluoride, in which sulfur is the central atom.

ANSWER

To draw the electron-dot formula for SF_2, we need the electron-dot symbols of sulfur with six valence electrons, and fluorine with seven valence electrons.

```
:S̈·      ·F̈:
```

A sulfur atom will form two bonds by sharing each of its two unpaired electrons with the unpaired electron in each of two fluorine atoms. In this way, both the S atom and the two F atoms obtain stable electron configurations. The electron-dot formula for SF_2 shows the central S atom attached to two fluorine atoms using electron pairs or single bonds.

```
:S̈:F̈:        :S̈—F̈:
:F̈:    or     |
              :F̈:
```

SAMPLE PROBLEM 6 **Drawing Electron-Dot Formulas for Covalent Compounds**

Draw the electron-dot formula for PCl_3, phosphorus trichloride.

SOLUTION

Step 1 **Determine the arrangement of atoms.** In PCl_3, the central atom is P because it needs the most electrons.

```
Cl  P  Cl
   Cl
```

Step 2 **Determine the total number of valence electrons.** We use the group numbers to determine the valence electrons for each of the atoms in the molecule.

Element	Group	Atoms	Valence Electrons	=	Total
P	5A (15)	1 P	$\times 5\ e^-$	=	$5\ e^-$
Cl	7A (17)	3 Cl	$\times 7\ e^-$	=	$21\ e^-$
	Total valence electrons for PCl_3			=	$26\ e^-$

Step 3 **Attach each bonded atom to the central atom with a pair of electrons.**

```
Cl:P:Cl    or    Cl—P—Cl
   ··               |
   Cl               Cl
```

Step 4 **Place the remaining electrons using single or multiple bonds to complete the octets.** A total of six electrons $(3 \times 2\ e^-)$ are needed to bond the central P atom to three Cl atoms. Twenty valence electrons are left:

$$26 \text{ valence } e^- - 6 \text{ bonding } e^- = 20\ e^- \text{ remaining}$$

The remaining electrons are placed as lone pairs of electrons around the outer Cl atoms first, which uses 18 more electrons.

```
 ··   ··               ··       ··
:Cl:P:Cl:     or      :Cl—P—Cl:
 ·· ·· ··              ··  |    ··
   :Cl:                   :Cl:
    ··                     ··
```

Use the remaining two electrons to complete the octet for the P atom.

P has an octet

```
 ·· ·· ··              ··  ··  ··
:Cl:P:Cl:     or      :Cl—P—Cl:
 ·· ·· ··              ··  |   ··
   :Cl:                   :Cl:
    ··                     ··
```

STUDY CHECK 6

Draw the electron-dot formula for Cl_2O (O is the central atom).

Guide to Drawing Electron-Dot Formulas

1. Determine the arrangement of atoms.
2. Determine the total number of valence electrons.
3. Attach each bonded atom to the central atom with a pair of electrons.
4. Place the remaining electrons using single or multiple bonds to complete the octets (two for H, six for B).

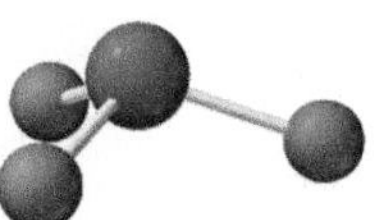

The ball-and-stick model of PCl_3 consists of P (blue) and Cl atoms (green).

Exceptions to the Octet Rule

While the octet rule is useful, there are exceptions. We have already seen that a hydrogen (H_2) molecule requires just two electrons or a single bond to achieve stability. In $BeCl_2$, Be forms only two covalent bonds. In BCl_3, the B atom has only three valence electrons to share. Boron compounds typically have three electron groups around the central B atom and form three covalent bonds. Although the nonmetals typically form octets, atoms such as P, S, Cl, Br, and I can form compounds with 10, 12, or even 14 valence electrons. For example, in PCl_3, the P atom has an octet, but in PCl_5, the P atom has 10 valence electrons or five covalent bonds. In H_2S, the S atom has an octet, but in SF_6, there are 12 valence electrons or six bonds to the sulfur atom. In this text, we will encounter formulas with expanded octets, but we do not represent them with electron-dot formulas.

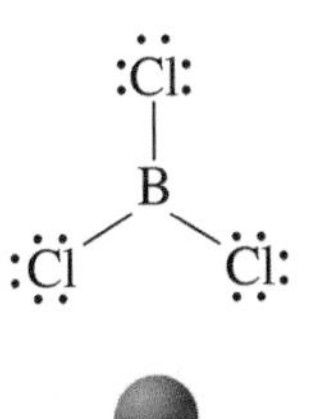

In BCl_3, the central B atom (purple) is bonded to three Cl atoms (green).

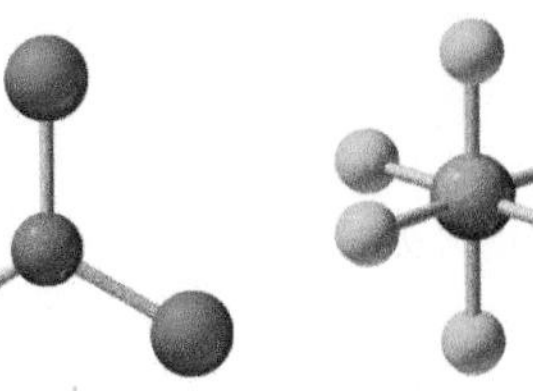

In SF_6, the central S atom (yellow) is bonded to six F atoms (yellow-green).

Double and Triple Covalent Bonds

Up to now, we have looked at covalent bonding in molecules having only single bonds. In many covalent compounds, atoms share two or three pairs of electrons to complete their octets. A **double bond** occurs when two pairs of electrons are shared; in a **triple bond**, three pairs of electrons are shared. Atoms of carbon, oxygen, nitrogen, and sulfur are most likely to form multiple bonds. Atoms of hydrogen and the halogens do not form double or triple bonds.

Double or triple bonds form when there are not enough valence electrons to complete the octets of some of the atoms in the molecule. Then one or more lone pairs of electrons from the atoms attached to the central atom are shared with the central atom.

For example, there are double bonds in CO_2 because two pairs of electrons are shared between the carbon atom and each oxygen atom to give octets. The process of drawing an electron-dot formula for CO_2 is shown in Sample Problem 7.

SAMPLE PROBLEM 7 Drawing Electron-Dot Formulas with Multiple Bonds

Draw the electron-dot formula for carbon dioxide, CO_2, in which the central atom is C.

SOLUTION

Step 1 **Determine the arrangement of atoms.** O C O

Step 2 **Determine the total number of valence electrons.** Using the group numbers to determine valence electrons, each oxygen atom has six valence electrons, and one carbon atom has four valence electrons, which gives a total of 16 valence electrons for the molecule.

Element	Group	Atoms	Valence Electrons		Total
O	6A (16)	2 O	$\times 6\,e^-$	=	$12\,e^-$
C	4A (14)	1 C	$\times 4\,e^-$	=	$4\,e^-$
	Total valence electrons for CO_2			=	$16\,e^-$

Step 3 **Attach each bonded atom to the central atom by a pair of electrons.** A pair of bonding electrons (single bond) is placed between each O atom and the central C atom.

O:C:O or O—C—O

Step 4 **Place the remaining electrons using single or multiple bonds to complete the octets.** Because we used four valence electrons to attach the C atom to two O atoms, there are 12 valence electrons remaining.

16 valence e^- − 4 bonding e^- = 12 e^- remaining

The remaining 12 electrons are placed as six lone pairs of electrons on the O atoms. However, this does not complete the octet for the C atom.

:Ö:C:Ö: or :Ö—C—Ö:

To complete the octet for the C atom, it shares a lone pair of electrons from each of the O atoms. When two bonding pairs occur between atoms, it is a double bond.

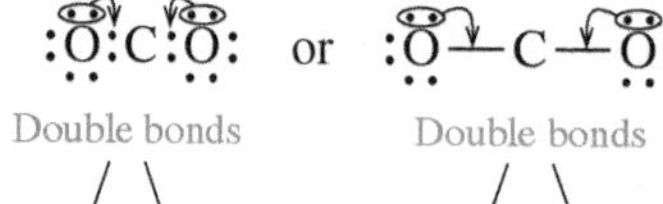

Molecule of carbon dioxide

Double bonds Double bonds

:O::C::O: or :O=C=O:

STUDY CHECK 7

Draw the electron-dot formula for HCN (atoms arranged as H C N).

To draw the electron-dot formula for the covalent compound N_2, an octet is achieved when each nitrogen atom shares three pairs of electrons. Three covalent bonds between atoms is a triple bond as shown in Concept Check 5.

CONCEPT CHECK 5 **Drawing Triple Bonds in Covalent Molecules**

The covalent molecule N_2 contains a triple bond. Show how the atoms of N achieve octets to form a triple bond.

ANSWER

Step 1 **Determine the arrangement of atoms.** N N

Step 2 **Determine the total number of valence electrons.** Because nitrogen is in Group 5A (15), each N atom has five valence electrons.

Element	Group	Atoms	Valence Electrons	=	Total
N	5A (15)	2 N	$\times 5\ e^-$	=	$10\ e^-$

Step 3 **Attach each bonded atom to the central atom by a pair of electrons.** A pair of bonding electrons (single bond) is placed between the N atoms. However, this does not provide an octet for each N atom.

·N̈:N̈· or ·N̈—N̈·

Step 4 **Place the remaining electrons using single or multiple bonds to complete the octets.** Each N atom achieves an octet by sharing three bonding pairs of electrons to form a triple bond.

Octets

·N̈:N̈· ⟶ :N⋮⋮N: :N≡N: N_2

Three shared pairs — Triple bond — Nitrogen molecule

Resonance Structures

When a molecule contains multiple bonds, it may be possible to draw more than one electron-dot formula. We can see how this happens when we try to draw the electron-dot formula for ozone, O_3, a component in the stratosphere that protects us from the ultraviolet rays of the Sun.

To draw the electron-dot formula, we need to determine the number of valence electrons for an O atom, and then the total number of valence electrons for O_3. Because O is in Group 6A (16), it has six valence electrons. Therefore, the compound O_3 would have a total of 18 valence electrons. To draw the electron-dot formula for O_3, we place three O atoms in a row and identify the O atom in the middle as the central atom.

Using four of the available valence electrons, we draw a bonding pair between the O atoms on the end and the central O atom.

O—O—O

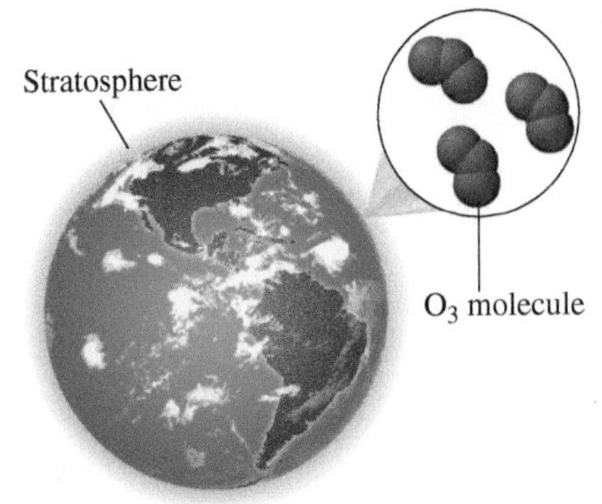

Ozone, O_3, is a component in the stratosphere that protects us from the ultraviolet rays of the Sun.

These bonding pairs use four valence electrons and 14 valence electrons remain. We now place three lone pairs of electrons around the O atoms on both ends of the electron-dot formula, which uses 12 more valence electrons. The two remaining valence electrons are placed as a lone pair of electrons on the central O atom.

:Ö—Ö—Ö:

However, this use of all the remaining valence electrons does not complete an octet for the central O atom. To achieve an octet for the central O atom, one lone pair of electrons from an end O atom is shared. But which one should be used? One possibility is to form a double bond on the left and the other possibility is to form a double bond on the right.

$$:\ddot{\underset{..}{O}}-\ddot{O}-\ddot{\underset{..}{O}}: \quad \text{or} \quad :\ddot{\underset{..}{O}}-\ddot{O}-\ddot{\underset{..}{O}}:$$

Now we see that we can draw more than one electron-dot formula for O_3. When this happens, all the possible electron-dot formulas are called **resonance structures**, which are shown with a double-headed arrow. Because the electrons in resonance structures are delocalized, they are not associated with a single atom. Thus, the bonding of these electrons is drawn with more than one electron-dot formula.

$$:\ddot{O}=\ddot{O}-\ddot{\underset{..}{O}}: \longleftrightarrow :\ddot{\underset{..}{O}}-\ddot{O}=\ddot{O}:$$

Resonance structures

Experiments show that the actual bond lengths are equivalent to a molecule with a "one and a half" bond between the central O atom and each outside O atom. In the actual ozone molecules, the electrons are shown spread equally over all the O atoms. When we draw resonance structures, the true structure is really an average of those structures.

CONCEPT CHECK 6 Resonance Structures

Explain why SCl_2 does not have resonance structures, but SO_2 does.

ANSWER

In the electron-dot formula of SCl_2, the unpaired valence electrons of each chlorine atom complete the octet of the sulfur atom. However, in SO_2, the central sulfur atom must form a double bond with one of the oxygen atoms. Thus, two electron-dot formulas, or resonance structures, are possible.

SAMPLE PROBLEM 8 Drawing Resonance Structures

Sulfur dioxide is produced naturally from volcanic activity and the burning of sulfur-containing coal. Once in the atmosphere, the SO_2 is converted to SO_3, which combines with water to form sulfuric acid, H_2SO_4, a component of acid rain. Draw two resonance structures for sulfur dioxide, SO_2.

SOLUTION

Step 1 **Determine the arrangement of atoms.** In SO_2, the S atom is the central atom.

O S O

Step 2 **Determine the total number of valence electrons.**

Element	Group	Atoms	Valence Electrons	=	Total
S	6A (16)	1 S	$\times 6\,e^-$	=	$6\,e^-$
O	6A (16)	2 O	$\times 6\,e^-$	=	$12\,e^-$
	Total valence electrons for SO_2			=	$18\,e^-$

Step 3 **Attach each bonded atom to the central atom with a pair of electrons.**

O—S—O

Step 4 **Place the remaining electrons using single or multiple bonds to complete the octets.** After four electrons are used to form single bonds between the

S atom and the O atoms, the remaining 14 electrons are drawn as lone pairs of electrons to complete the octets of the O atoms but not the S atom.

$$:\underset{\cdot\cdot}{\ddot{O}}-\ddot{S}-\underset{\cdot\cdot}{\ddot{O}}:$$

To complete the octet for S, one lone pair of electrons from one of the O atoms is shared to form a double bond. Because the lone pair of electrons that is shared can come from either O atom, two resonance structures can be drawn.

$$:\underset{\cdot\cdot}{O}=\ddot{S}-\underset{\cdot\cdot}{\ddot{O}}: \longleftrightarrow :\underset{\cdot\cdot}{\ddot{O}}-\ddot{S}=\underset{\cdot\cdot}{O}:$$

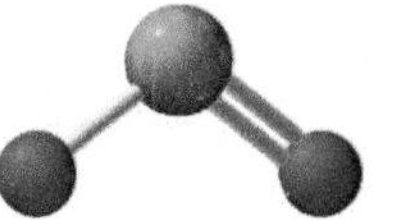

The ball-and-stick model of SO_2, which consists of S (yellow) and O atoms (red).

STUDY CHECK 8

Draw three resonance structures for SO_3.

QUESTIONS AND PROBLEMS

5 Covalent Compounds: Sharing Electrons

LEARNING GOAL: *Draw the electron-dot formulas for covalent compounds, including multiple bonds and resonance structures.*

37 Which of the following pairs of elements are most likely to form covalent compounds?
- **a.** oxygen and chlorine
- **b.** calcium and bromine
- **c.** nitrogen and oxygen
- **d.** iodine and iodine
- **e.** sodium and iodine
- **f.** carbon and sulfur

38 Which of the following pairs of elements are most likely to form covalent compounds?
- **a.** chlorine and bromine
- **b.** phosphorus and oxygen
- **c.** cesium and fluorine
- **d.** barium and iodine
- **e.** nitrogen and bromine
- **f.** potassium and sulfur

39 State the number of valence electrons, bonding pairs, and lone pairs in each of the following electron-dot formulas:

a. H:H **b.** $H:\underset{\cdot\cdot}{\ddot{Br}}:$ **c.** $:\underset{\cdot\cdot}{\ddot{Br}}:\underset{\cdot\cdot}{\ddot{Br}}:$

40 State the number of valence electrons, bonding pairs, and lone pairs in each of the following electron-dot formulas:

a. H:Ö: (with H above O) **b.** H:N̈:H (with H below N) **c.** :B̈r:Ö: (with :B̈r: above O)

41 Draw the electron-dot formula for each of the following molecules:
- **a.** HF
- **b.** NBr_3
- **c.** CH_3OH (methyl alcohol)

```
  H
H C O H
  H
```

- **d.** N_2H_4 (hydrazine)

```
  H H
H N N H
```

42 Draw the electron-dot formula for each of the following molecules:
- **a.** H_2O
- **b.** SiF_4
- **c.** CF_2Cl_2
- **d.** C_2H_6 (ethane)

```
  H H
H C C H
  H H
```

43 Draw the electron-dot formula, including multiple bonds, for each of the following molecules:
- **a.** CO (carbon monoxide)
- **b.** H_2CCH_2 (ethylene)
- **c.** H_2CO (C is the central atom)

44 Draw the electron-dot formula, including multiple bonds, for each of the following molecules:
- **a.** HCCH (acetylene)
- **b.** CS_2 (C is the central atom)
- **c.** $COCl_2$ (C is the central atom)

45 Draw resonance structures for $ClNO_2$ (N is the central atom).

46 Draw resonance structures for N_2O (N N O).

6 Naming and Writing Covalent Formulas

LEARNING GOAL

Given the formula of a covalent compound, write its correct name; given the name of a covalent compound, write its formula.

When naming a covalent compound, the first nonmetal in the formula is named by its element name; the second nonmetal is named using the first syllable of its element name, followed by *ide*. When a subscript indicates two or more atoms of an element, a prefix is shown in front of its name. Table 12 lists prefixes used in naming covalent compounds. The names of covalent compounds need prefixes because it is possible for atoms of two nonmetals to form two or more different compounds. For example, atoms of carbon and

TUTORIAL
Naming Covalent Compounds

TUTORIAL
Naming Molecular Compounds

oxygen form carbon monoxide (CO) and carbon dioxide (CO_2), in which the number of atoms of oxygen in each compound is indicated by the prefixes *mono* or *di* in their names.

When the vowels *o* and *o* or *a* and *o* appear together, the first vowel is omitted as in carbon monoxide. In the name of a covalent compound, the prefix *mono* is usually omitted, as in NO, nitrogen oxide. Traditionally, however, CO is named carbon monoxide. Table 13 lists the formulas, names, and commercial uses of some covalent compounds.

TABLE 12 Prefixes Used in Naming Covalent Compounds

1	mono	6	hexa
2	di	7	hepta
3	tri	8	octa
4	tetra	9	nona
5	penta	10	deca

TABLE 13 Some Common Covalent Compounds

Formula	Name	Commercial Uses
CS_2	Carbon disulfide	Manufacture of rayon
CO_2	Carbon dioxide	Carbonation of beverages; fire extinguishers; propellant in aerosols; dry ice
NO	Nitrogen oxide	Stabilizer
N_2O	Dinitrogen oxide	Inhalation anesthetic: "laughing gas"
SiO_2	Silicon dioxide	Manufacture of glass
SO_2	Sulfur dioxide	Preserving fruits, vegetables; disinfectant in breweries; bleaching textiles
SF_6	Sulfur hexafluoride	Electrical circuits

CONCEPT CHECK 7 **Naming Covalent Compounds**

Why is it that the name of the covalent compound BrCl, bromine chloride, does not include a prefix, but the name of OCl_2, oxygen dichloride, does?

ANSWER

When a formula has one atom of each element, the prefix (*mono*) is not used in the name. Thus, the name of BrCl is bromine chloride. However, two or more atoms of an element are indicated by using a prefix. Thus, the name of OCl_2 contains the prefix *di*, oxygen dichloride.

SAMPLE PROBLEM 9 **Naming Covalent Compounds**

Name the covalent compound NCl_3.

SOLUTION

Analyze the Problem

Symbol of Element	N	Cl
Name	Nitrogen	Chloride
Subscript	1	3
Prefix	none (understood)	tri

Guide to Naming Covalent Compounds

1 Name the first nonmetal by its element name.

2 Name the second nonmetal by using the first syllable of its name followed by *ide*.

3 Add prefixes to indicate the number of atoms (subscripts).

Step 1 **Name the first nonmetal by its element name.** In NCl_3, the first nonmetal (N) is nitrogen.

Step 2 **Name the second nonmetal by using the first syllable of its name followed by *ide*.** The second nonmetal (Cl) is named chloride.

Step 3 **Add prefixes to indicate the number of atoms (subscripts).** Because there is one nitrogen atom, no prefix is needed. The subscript 3 for the Cl atoms is written as the prefix *tri*. The name of NCl_3 is nitrogen trichloride.

STUDY CHECK 9

Write the name for each of the following compounds:

a. $SiBr_4$ **b.** Br_2O

Writing Formulas from the Names of Covalent Compounds

In the name of a covalent compound, the names of two nonmetals are given along with prefixes for the number of atoms of each. To write its formula, we use the element symbol for each element and a subscript when a prefix indicates two or more atoms, as shown in Sample Problem 10.

SAMPLE PROBLEM 10 **Writing Formulas for Covalent Compounds**

Write the formula for diboron trioxide.

SOLUTION

Analyze the Problem

Name	Diboron	Trioxide
Symbol of Element	B	O
Subscript	2 (from *di*)	3 (from *tri*)

Step 1 **Write the symbols in order of the elements in the name.** In this covalent compound of two nonmetals, the first nonmetal is boron (B) and the second nonmetal is oxygen (O).

B O

Step 2 **Write any prefixes as subscripts.** The prefix *di* in *diboron* indicates that there are two atoms of boron, shown as a subscript 2 in the formula. The prefix *tri* in *trioxide* indicates that there are three atoms of oxygen, shown as a subscript 3 in the formula.

B_2O_3

STUDY CHECK 10

What is the formula of iodine heptafluoride?

Guide to Writing Formulas for Covalent Compounds

1 Write the symbols in the order of the elements in the name.

2 Write any prefixes as subscripts.

Summary of Naming Ionic and Covalent Compounds

We have now examined strategies for naming ionic and covalent compounds. In general, compounds having two elements are named by stating the first element name, followed by the name of the second element with an *ide* ending. If the first element is a metal, the compound is usually ionic; if the first element is a nonmetal, the compound is usually covalent. For ionic compounds, it is necessary to determine whether the metal can form more than one type of positive ion; if so, a Roman numeral following the name of the metal indicates the particular ionic charge. One exception is the ammonium ion, NH_4^+, which is also written first as a positively charged polyatomic ion. Ionic compounds having three or more elements include some type of polyatomic ion. They are named by ionic rules but have an *ate* or *ite* ending when the polyatomic ion has a negative charge.

In naming covalent compounds having two elements, prefixes are necessary to indicate two or more atoms of each nonmetal as shown in that particular formula (see Figure 4). Organic compounds of C and H, such as CH_4 and C_2H_6, use a different system of naming.

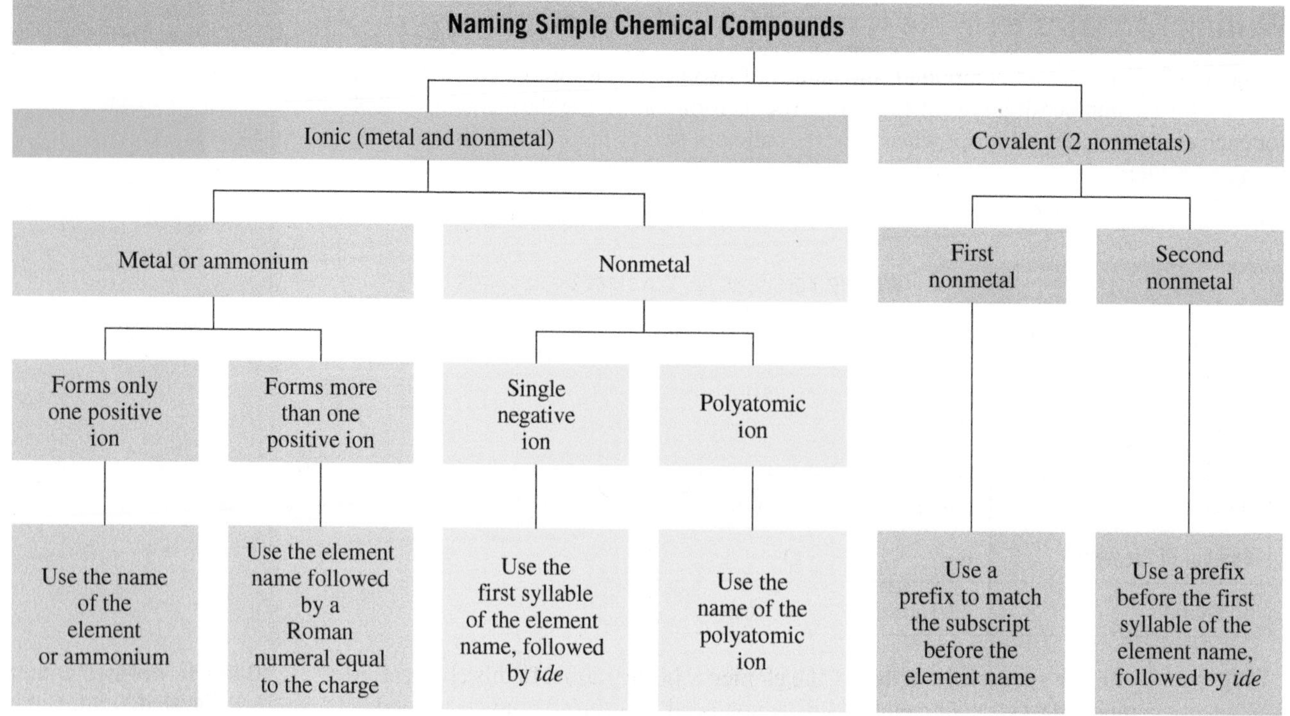

FIGURE 4 A flowchart shows a strategy for naming ionic and covalent compounds.
Q Why does the name sulfur dichloride have a prefix but the name magnesium chloride does not?

CONCEPT CHECK 8 **Naming Ionic and Covalent Compounds**

Identify each of the following compounds as ionic or covalent and give its name:

a. Na_3P **b.** $NiSO_4$ **c.** SO_3

ANSWER

a. Na_3P, consisting of a metal and nonmetal, is an ionic compound. As a representative element in Group 1A (1), Na forms the sodium ion, Na^+. Phosphorus, as a representative element in Group 5A (15), forms a phosphide ion, P^{3-}. Writing the name for the cation followed by the name for the anion gives the name sodium phosphide.

b. $NiSO_4$, consisting of a cation of a transition element and an anion, SO_4^{2-}, of a polyatomic ion is an ionic compound. As a transition element, Ni forms more than one type of ion. In this formula, the 2− charge of SO_4^{2-} is balanced by one nickel ion, Ni^{2+}. In the name, a Roman numeral written after the metal name, nickel(II), specifies the 2+ charge. The anion SO_4^{2-} is a polyatomic ion named sulfate. The compound is named nickel(II) sulfate.

c. SO_3 consists of two nonmetals, which indicates that it is a covalent compound. The first element, S, is *sulfur* (no prefix is needed). The second element O, *oxide*, has a subscript 3, which requires a prefix of *tri* in the name. The compound is named sulfur trioxide.

QUESTIONS AND PROBLEMS

6 Naming and Writing Covalent Formulas

LEARNING GOAL: *Given the formula of a covalent compound, write its correct name; given the name of a covalent compound, write its formula.*

47 Name each of the following:
a. PBr_3 **b.** CBr_4 **c.** SiO_2 **d.** N_2O_3 **e.** PCl_5

48 Name each of the following:
a. CS_2 **b.** P_2O_5 **c.** Cl_2O **d.** PCl_3 **e.** IBr_3

49 Write the formula for each of the following:
a. carbon tetrachloride
b. carbon monoxide
c. phosphorus trichloride
d. dinitrogen tetroxide
e. boron trifluoride
f. sulfur hexafluoride

50 Write the formula for each of the following:
a. sulfur dioxide
b. silicon tetrachloride
c. iodine pentafluoride
d. dinitrogen oxide
e. tetraphosphorus hexoxide
f. dinitrogen pentoxide

51 Name each of the following ionic or covalent compounds:
a. $Al_2(SO_4)_3$ antiperspirant
b. $CaCO_3$ antacid
c. N_2O "laughing gas" (inhaled anesthetic)
d. Na_3PO_4 cathartic
e. $(NH_4)_2SO_4$ fertilizer
f. Fe_2O_3 pigment

52 Name each of the following ionic or covalent compounds:
a. N_2 Earth's atmosphere
b. $Mg_3(PO_4)_2$ antacid
c. $FeSO_4$ iron supplement in vitamins
d. N_2O_4 rocket fuel
e. Cu_2O fungicide
f. NI_3 contact explosive

7 Electronegativity and Bond Polarity

LEARNING GOAL

Use electronegativity to determine the polarity of a bond.

We can learn more about the chemistry of compounds by looking at how electrons are shared between atoms. Although we have discussed covalent bonds as one or more bonding pairs of electrons, we do not know if those electrons are shared equally or unequally.

To do this, we use **electronegativity**, which is the ability of an atom to attract the shared electrons in a chemical bond (see Figure 5). Nonmetals have higher electronegativities than do metals, because nonmetals have a great attraction for electrons. The nonmetal fluorine, which has the highest electronegativity (4.0), is located in the upper right corner of the periodic table. The metal cesium, which has the lowest electronegativity (0.7), is located in the lower left corner of the periodic table. Note that there are no electronegativity values for the noble gases because they do not typically form bonds. The electronegativity values for transition elements are also low, but we have not included them in our discussion.

TUTORIAL
Electronegativity

SELF-STUDY ACTIVITY
Bonds and Bond Polarities

Electronegativity Increases →

Electronegativity Decreases ↓

H 2.1

1 Group 1A	2 Group 2A	13 Group 3A	14 Group 4A	15 Group 5A	16 Group 6A	17 Group 7A	18 Group 8A
Li 1.0	Be 1.5	B 2.0	C 2.5	N 3.0	O 3.5	F 4.0	
Na 0.9	Mg 1.2	Al 1.5	Si 1.8	P 2.1	S 2.5	Cl 3.0	
K 0.8	Ca 1.0	Ga 1.6	Ge 1.8	As 2.0	Se 2.4	Br 2.8	
Rb 0.8	Sr 1.0	In 1.7	Sn 1.8	Sb 1.9	Te 2.1	I 2.5	
Cs 0.7	Ba 0.9	Tl 1.8	Pb 1.9	Bi 1.9	Po 2.0	At 2.1	

FIGURE 5 The electronegativities of the representative elements in Group 1A (1) to Group 7A (17), which indicate the ability of atoms to attract shared electrons, increase across a period and decrease going down a group.

Q What element on the periodic table has the strongest attraction for shared electrons?

Types of Bonding

The difference in the electronegativity of two atoms can be used to predict the type of bond, ionic or covalent, that forms. For the H—H bond, the electronegativity difference is zero $(2.1 - 2.1 = 0.0)$, which means that the bonding electrons are shared equally. Thus, we see a symmetrical electron cloud around the H atoms. A covalent bond between atoms with identical or very similar electronegativity values is a **nonpolar covalent bond**. However, when bonds are between atoms with different electronegativity values, the electrons are shared unequally; the bond is a **polar covalent bond**. The electron cloud for a polar covalent bond is unsymmetrical. For the H—Cl bond, there is an electronegativity difference of 0.9 $(3.0 - 2.1 = 0.9)$, which means that the H—Cl bond is polar covalent (see Figure 6).

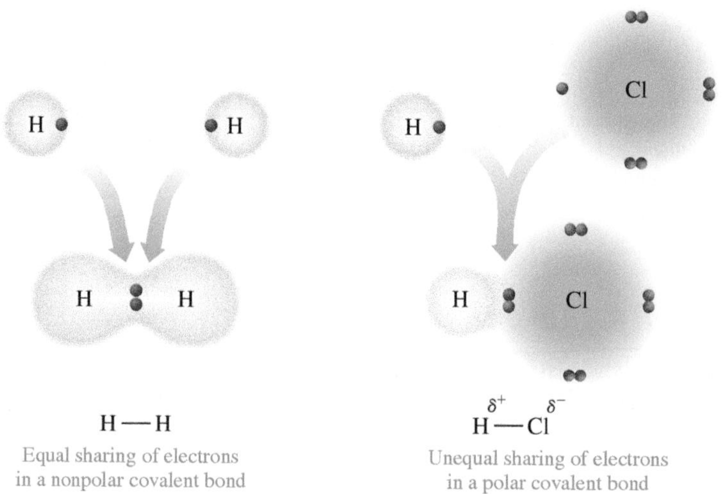

FIGURE 6 In the nonpolar covalent bond of H_2, electrons are shared equally. In the polar covalent bond of HCl, electrons are shared unequally.

Q H_2 has a nonpolar covalent bond, but HCl has a polar covalent bond. Explain.

Dipoles and Bond Polarity

The *polarity* of a bond depends on its electronegativity difference. In a polar covalent bond, the shared electrons are attracted to the more electronegative atom, which makes it partially negative, due to the negatively charged electrons around that atom. At the other end of the bond, the atom with the lower electronegativity becomes partially positive due to a lack of electrons around that atom. A bond becomes more *polar* as the electronegativity difference increases. A polar covalent bond that has a separation of charges is called a **dipole**. The positive and negative ends of the dipole are indicated by the lowercase Greek letter delta with a positive or negative sign, δ^+ and δ^-. Sometimes we use an arrow that points from the positive charge to the negative charge (⟶) to indicate the dipole.

Examples of Dipoles in Polar Covalent Bonds

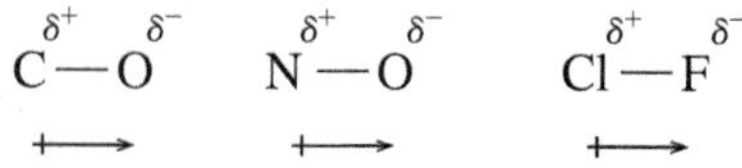

Variations in Bonding

The variations in bonding are continuous; there is no definite point at which one type of bond stops and the next starts. When the electronegativity difference is from 0.0 to 0.4, the electrons are considered to be shared equally in a *nonpolar covalent bond*. For example, the H—H bond with an electronegativity difference of 0.0 $(2.1 - 2.1 = 0.0)$ and the C—H bond with an electronegativity difference of 0.4 $(2.5 - 2.1 = 0.4)$ are classified as nonpolar covalent bonds. As the electronegativity difference increases, the shared electrons are attracted more closely to the more electronegative atom, which increases the polarity of the bond. When the electronegativity difference is from 0.5 to 1.8, the bond is classified as a *polar covalent bond* (see Table 14).

TABLE 14 Electronegativity Difference and Types of Bonds

Electronegativity Difference	0 — 0.4	0.4 — 1.8	1.8 — 3.3
Bond Type	Covalent nonpolar	Covalent polar	Ionic
Electron Bonding	Electrons shared equally	Electrons shared unequally	Electron transfer
		δ^+ δ^-	+ −

When the electronegativity difference is greater than 1.8, electrons are transferred from one atom to another, which results in an ionic bond. For example, the electronegativity difference for the ionic compound NaCl is 2.1 $(3.0 - 0.9 = 2.1)$. Thus, for large differences in electronegativity, we would predict an ionic bond (see Table 15).

TABLE 15 Predicting Bond Type from Electronegativity Differences

Molecule	Bond	Type of Electron Sharing	Electronegativity Difference*	Type of Bond	Reason
H_2	H—H	Shared equally	$2.1 - 2.1 = 0.0$	Nonpolar covalent	Less than 0.4
Cl_2	Cl—Cl	Shared equally	$3.0 - 3.0 = 0.0$	Nonpolar covalent	Less than 0.4
HBr	$\overset{\delta^+}{H}$—$\overset{\delta^-}{Br}$	Shared unequally	$2.8 - 2.1 = 0.7$	Polar covalent	Greater than 0.4, but less than 1.8
HCl	$\overset{\delta^+}{H}$—$\overset{\delta^-}{Cl}$	Shared unequally	$3.0 - 2.1 = 0.9$	Polar covalent	Greater than 0.4, but less than 1.8
NaCl	$Na^+ Cl^-$	Electron transfer	$3.0 - 0.9 = 2.1$	Ionic	Greater than 1.8
MgO	$Mg^{2+} O^{2-}$	Electron transfer	$3.5 - 1.2 = 2.3$	Ionic	Greater than 1.8

*Values are taken from Figure 5.

CONCEPT CHECK 9 **Using Electronegativity to Determine the Polarity of Bonds**

Complete the following table for each of the bonds indicated:

Bond	Electronegativity Difference	Type of Bond	Reason
Si—P			
Si—S			
Cs—Cl			

ANSWER

Bond	Electronegativity Difference	Type of Bond	Reason
Si—P	$2.1 - 1.8 = 0.3$	Nonpolar covalent	Less than 0.4
Si—S	$2.5 - 1.8 = 0.7$	Polar covalent	Greater than 0.4, but less than 1.8
Cs—Cl	$3.0 - 0.7 = 2.3$	Ionic	Greater than 1.8

SAMPLE PROBLEM 11 **Bond Polarity**

Using electronegativity values, classify each bond as nonpolar covalent, polar covalent, or ionic:

N—N, O—H, Cl—As, O—K

SOLUTION

For each bond, we obtain the electronegativity values and calculate the difference.

Bond	Electronegativity Difference	Type of Bond
N—N	$3.0 - 3.0 = 0.0$	Nonpolar covalent
O—H	$3.5 - 2.1 = 1.4$	Polar covalent
Cl—As	$3.0 - 2.0 = 1.0$	Polar covalent
O—K	$3.5 - 0.8 = 2.7$	Ionic

STUDY CHECK 11

Using electronegativity values, classify each bond as nonpolar covalent, polar covalent, or ionic:

a. P—Cl **b.** Br—Br **c.** Na—O

QUESTIONS AND PROBLEMS

7 Electronegativity and Bond Polarity

LEARNING GOAL: *Use electronegativity to determine the polarity of a bond.*

53 Using the periodic table, describe the trend in electronegativity as *increases* or *decreases* for each of the following:
a. from B to F **b.** from Mg to Ba
c. from F to I

54 Using the periodic table, describe the trend in electronegativity as *increases* or *decreases* for each of the following:
a. from Al to Cl **b.** from N to Bi
c. from Li to Cs

55 State the electronegativity difference for each of the following pairs of elements:
a. Rb and Cl **b.** Cl and Cl
c. N and O **d.** C and H

56 State the electronegativity difference for each of the following pairs of elements:
a. Sr and S **b.** N and S
c. Cl and Br **d.** K and F

57 Using the periodic table, arrange the atoms in each set in order of increasing electronegativity:
a. Li, Na, K **b.** Na, Cl, P **c.** Se, Ca, O

58 Using the periodic table, arrange the atoms in each set in order of increasing electronegativity:
a. Cl, F, Br **b.** B, O, N **c.** Mg, F, S

59 Predict whether each of the following bonds is nonpolar covalent, polar covalent, or ionic:
a. Si—Br **b.** Li—F **c.** Br—F
d. I—I **e.** N—P **f.** C—O

60 Predict whether each of the following bonds is nonpolar covalent, polar covalent, or ionic:
a. Si—O **b.** K—Cl **c.** S—F
d. P—Br **e.** Li—S **f.** N—S

61 For each of the following bonds, indicate the positive end with δ^+ and the negative end with δ^-. Draw an arrow to show the dipole for each.
a. N—F **b.** Si—Br **c.** C—O
d. P—Br **e.** N—P

62 For each of the following bonds, indicate the positive end with δ^+ and the negative end with δ^-. Draw an arrow to show the dipole for each.
a. P—Cl **b.** Se—F **c.** Br—F
d. N—H **e.** B—Cl

LEARNING GOAL

Predict the three-dimensional structure of a molecule and classify it as polar or nonpolar.

8 Shapes and Polarity of Molecules

Using the information in Section 7, we can now predict the three-dimensional shapes of many molecules. The shape is important to our understanding of how molecules interact with enzymes and certain antibiotics, or produce our sense of taste and smell.

The three-dimensional shape of a molecule is determined by drawing an electron-dot formula and identifying the number of electron groups and their geometry around a central atom. In the **valence-shell electron-pair repulsion (VSEPR) theory**, the electron groups are arranged as far apart as possible to minimize the repulsion between them. The specific shape of the molecule is determined from the number of atoms attached to the central atom.

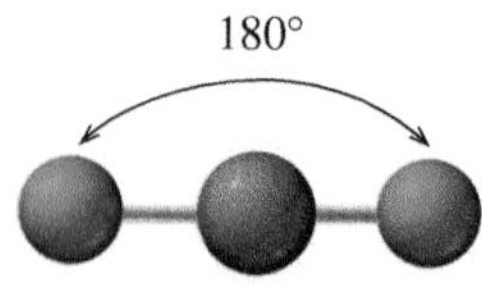

Linear shape

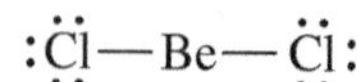

Linear electron-group geometry

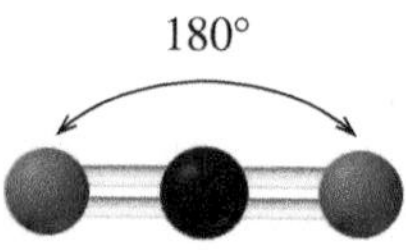

Linear shape

:O=C=O:

Linear electron-group geometry

Central Atoms with Two Electron Groups

In $BeCl_2$, two chlorine atoms are bonded to a central Be atom. Because an atom of Be has a strong attraction for valence electrons, it forms a covalent rather than ionic compound. With only two electron groups (two electron pairs) around the central atom, the electron-dot formula of $BeCl_2$ is an exception to the octet rule. The best geometry for two electron groups for minimal repulsion is to place them on opposite sides of the central Be atom. This gives the $BeCl_2$ molecule a linear electron-group geometry and a **linear** shape with a bond angle of 180°.

Another example of a linear molecule is CO_2. To predict geometry, we count a double or triple bond as *one electron group*. In the electron-dot formula of CO_2, the two electron groups (two double bonds) are on opposite sides of the central C atom, which is a linear electron-group geometry. With two atoms attached to the central C, the shape of the CO_2 molecule is *linear* with a bond angle of 180°.

Central Atoms with Three Electron Groups

In the electron-dot formula for BF_3, the central B atom has three electron groups attached to three fluorine atoms, which is another exception to the octet rule. In the electron-group geometry, the three electron groups are placed as far apart as possible around

TUTORIAL
Molecular Shape

TUTORIAL
Shapes of Molecules

the central B atom at 120° bond angles. This type of electron-group geometry is *trigonal planar*. In BF_3, the three electron groups around the central B atom are each bonded to a fluorine atom, which gives a shape called **trigonal planar** with bond angles of 120°.

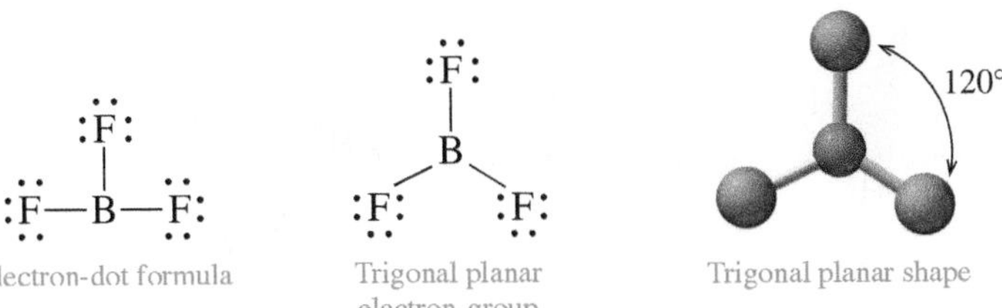

Electron-dot formula

Trigonal planar electron-group geometry

120°

Trigonal planar shape

In the electron-dot formula for SO_2, there are also three electron groups around the central S atom: a single bond, a double bond, and a lone pair of electrons. As in BF_3, three electron groups have minimal repulsion by forming a trigonal planar electron-group geometry. However, in SO_2 one of the electron groups is a lone pair of electrons. Therefore, the shape of SO_2 is determined by the two oxygen atoms bonded to the central S atom, which gives the SO_2 molecule a **bent** shape with a bond angle of 120°. When there are one or more lone pairs on the central atom, the shape of the molecule is different than that of the electron-group geometry.

Electron-dot formula

Lone pair of electrons

Trigonal planar electron-group geometry

120°

Bent shape

Central Atoms with Four Electron Groups

In a molecule of CH_4, the central C atom is bonded to four H atoms. From the electron-dot formula, you may think that CH_4 is planar with 90° bond angles. However, the best geometry for minimal repulsion is *tetrahedral*, which places the bonded atoms at the corners of a tetrahedron, giving bond angles of 109°. When there are four atoms attached to four electron groups, the shape of the molecule is **tetrahedral**.

A way to represent the three-dimensional structure of methane is to use the wedge–dash notation. In this notation, the two bonds connecting carbon to hydrogen by solid lines are in the plane of the paper. The wedge represents a carbon-to-hydrogen bond coming out of the page towards us, whereas the dash represents a carbon-to-hydrogen bond going into the page away from us.

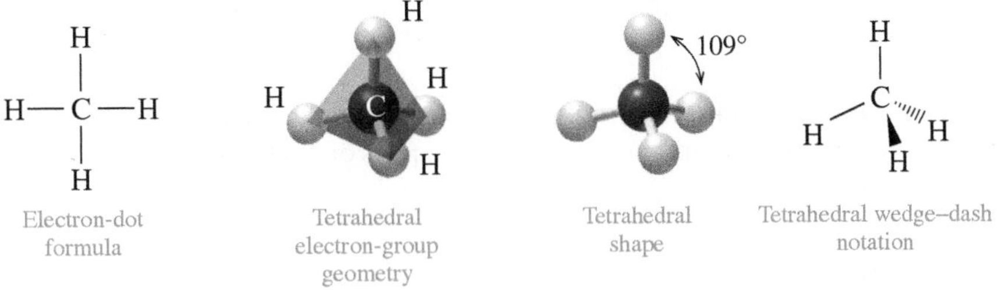

Electron-dot formula

Tetrahedral electron-group geometry

109°

Tetrahedral shape

Tetrahedral wedge–dash notation

Now we can look at molecules that also have four electron groups of which one or more are lone pairs. Then the central atom is attached to only two or three atoms. For example, in the electron-dot formula of ammonia, NH_3, four electron groups have a tetrahedral electron-group geometry. However, in NH_3 one of the electron groups is a lone pair of electrons. Therefore, the shape of NH_3 is determined by the three hydrogen atoms bonded to the central N atom, which gives the NH_3 molecule a **trigonal pyramidal** shape with a bond angle of 109°. The wedge–dash notation can also represent this three-dimensional structure of ammonia with one N—H bond in the plane, one N—H bond coming towards us, and one N—H bond going away from us.

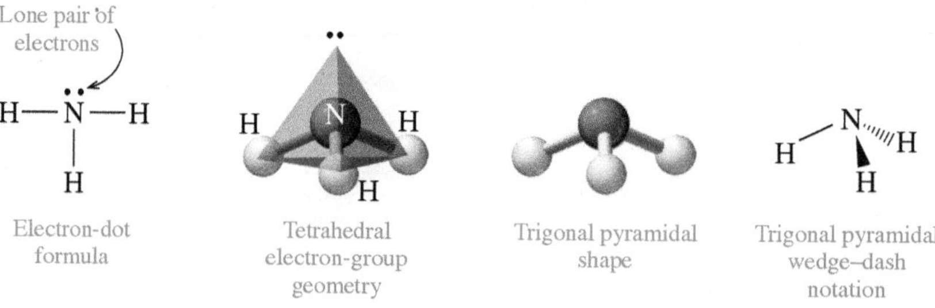

In the electron-dot formula of water, H_2O, there are also four electron groups, which have minimal repulsion when the electron-group geometry is tetrahedral. However, in H_2O, two of the electron groups are lone pairs of electrons. Because the shape of H_2O is determined by the two hydrogen atoms bonded to the central O atom, the H_2O molecule has a **bent** shape with a bond angle of 109°. Table 16 gives the molecular shapes for molecules with two, three, and four electron groups.

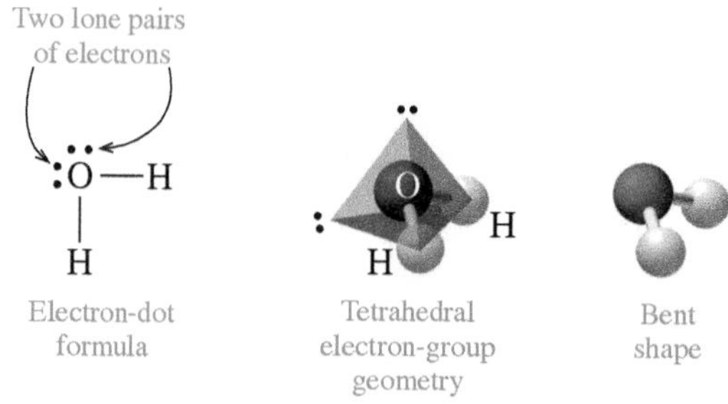

CONCEPT CHECK 10 **Shapes of Molecules**

If the four electron groups in a PH_3 molecule form a tetrahedron, why does a PH_3 molecule have a trigonal pyramidal shape?

ANSWER

Four electron groups achieve minimal repulsion when the electron-group geometry is a tetrahedron. However, one of the electron groups is a lone pair of electrons. Because the shape of the PH_3 molecule is determined by the three H atoms bonded to the central P atom, the shape of PH_3 is trigonal pyramidal.

SAMPLE PROBLEM 12 **Predicting Shapes**

Predict the shape of a molecule of H_2Se.

SOLUTION

Step 1 **Draw the electron-dot formula.** In the electron-dot formula for H_2Se, there are four electron groups, including two lone pairs of electrons.

:Se—H
|
H

Step 2 **Arrange the electron groups around the central atom to minimize repulsion.** The four electron groups around Se would have a tetrahedral arrangement.

Step 3 **Use the atoms bonded to the central atom to determine the molecular shape.** Two bonded atoms give H_2Se a bent shape with a bond angle of 109°.

STUDY CHECK 12

Predict the shape of CBr_4.

Guide to Predicting Molecular Shape (VSEPR Theory)

1. Draw the electron-dot formula.
2. Arrange the electron groups around the central atom to minimize repulsion.
3. Use the atoms bonded to the central atom to determine the molecular shape.

TABLE 16 Molecular Shapes for a Central Atom with Two, Three, and Four Bonded Atoms

Electron Groups	Electron-Group Arrangement	Bonded Atoms	Lone Pairs	Bond Angle	Molecular Shape	Example	Three-Dimensional Model
2	**Linear**	2	0	180°	Linear	$BeCl_2$	
3	**Trigonal planar**	3	0	120°	Trigonal planar	BF_3	
		2	1	120°	Bent	SO_2	
4	**Tetrahedral**	4	0	109°	Tetrahedral	CH_4	
		3	1	109°	Trigonal pyramidal	NH_3	
		2	2	109°	Bent	H_2O	

Polarity of Molecules

We have seen that covalent bonds can be polar or nonpolar. The bond polarities and shape of a molecule determines whether that molecule is polar or nonpolar.

TUTORIAL
Distinguishing Polar and Nonpolar Molecules

Nonpolar Molecules

In a **nonpolar molecule**, all the bonds are nonpolar or the polar bonds cancel each other out. Molecules such as H_2, Cl_2, and CH_4 are nonpolar because they contain only nonpolar covalent bonds.

H—H   Cl—Cl   H—C(H)(H)—H

Nonpolar

A *nonpolar molecule* also occurs when polar bonds or dipoles in a molecule cancel each other because they are in a symmetrical arrangement. For example, CO_2, a linear molecule, contains two polar covalent bonds whose dipoles point in opposite directions. As a result, the dipoles cancel out, which makes a CO_2 molecule nonpolar.

O=C=O

Dipoles cancel

CO_2 is a nonpolar molecule.

Other examples of nonpolar molecules with symmetrical arrangements of polar bonds include BF_3 and CCl_4. In BF_3, the dipoles of three polar bonds in a trigonal planar shape cancel out to give a nonpolar molecule. The CCl_4 molecule is also nonpolar because its four polar bonds are symmetrically arranged around the central C atom with the dipoles pointing away from each other and canceling out.

BF_3 is a nonpolar molecule.

CCl_4 is a nonpolar molecule.

Polar Molecules

H—Cl

A single dipole does not cancel.

In a **polar molecule**, one end of the molecule is more negatively charged than another end. Polarity in a molecule occurs when the polar bonds or dipoles do not cancel out. For example, the HCl molecule is polar because electrons are shared unequally in the polar H—Cl bond.

In polar molecules with three or more atoms, the shape of the molecule determines whether the dipoles cancel or not. Often, there are lone pairs of electrons around the central atom. In H_2O, the dipoles point in the same direction, which means they do not cancel, but add together. The result is a molecule positive at one end and negative at the other end. Thus, water is a polar molecule.

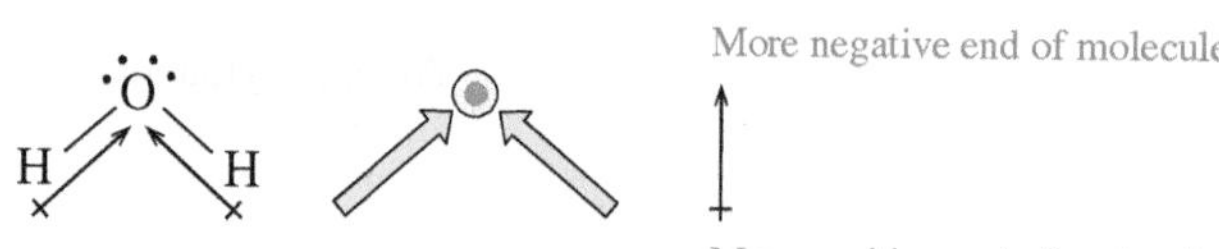

More positive end of molecule

H_2O is a polar molecule because its dipoles do not cancel.

In the molecule NH_3, there are three dipoles, but they do not cancel.

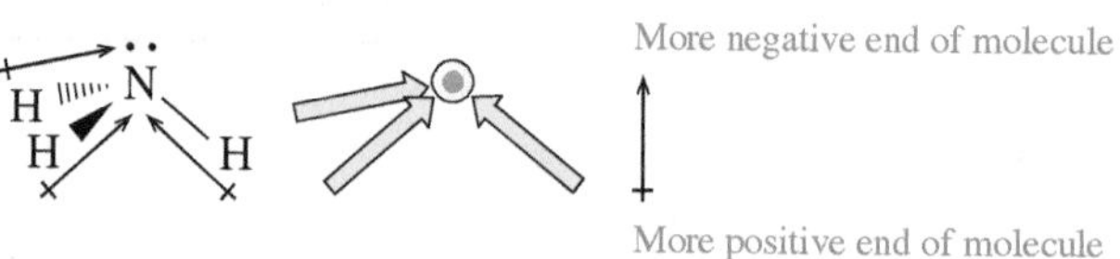

NH_3 is a polar molecule because its dipoles do not cancel.

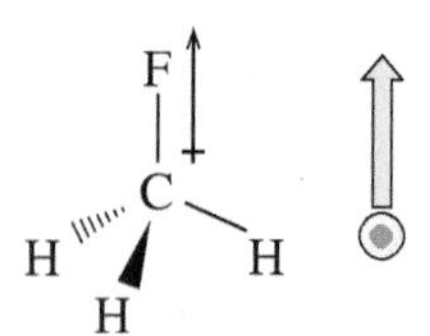

CH_3F is a polar molecule.

In the molecule CH_3F, the C—F bond is polar but the three C—H bonds are nonpolar, which makes CH_3F a polar molecule.

Guide to Determination of Polarity of a Molecule

1 Determine if the bonds are polar covalent or nonpolar covalent.

2 If the bonds are polar covalent, draw the electron-dot formula and determine if the dipoles cancel or not.

SAMPLE PROBLEM 13 **Polarity of Molecules**

Determine whether each of the following molecules is polar or nonpolar:

a. $SiCl_4$ **b.** OF_2

SOLUTION

a. Step 1 **Determine if the bonds are polar covalent or nonpolar covalent.** From the electronegativity table, Cl 3.0 and Si 1.8 gives a difference of 1.2, which makes the Si—Cl bonds polar covalent.

Step 2 **If the bonds are polar covalent, draw the electron-dot formula and determine if the dipoles cancel or not.** The electron-dot formula for $SiCl_4$ has four electron groups and four bonded atoms. The molecule has a tetrahedral shape. The dipoles of the Si—Cl bonds point away from each other and cancel out, which makes $SiCl_4$ a nonpolar molecule.

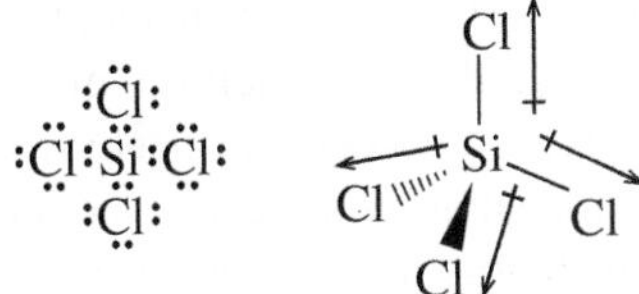

$SiCl_4$ is a nonpolar molecule.

b. Step 1 **Determine if the bonds are polar covalent or nonpolar covalent.** From the electronegativity table, F 4.0 and O 3.5 gives a difference of 0.5, which makes the O—F bonds polar covalent.

Step 2 **If the bonds are polar covalent, draw the electron-dot formula and determine if the dipoles cancel or not.** The electron-dot formula for OF_2 has four electron groups and two bonded atoms. The molecule has a bent shape in which the dipoles of the O—F bonds point in the same direction. This makes one end of the molecule positive and the other end negative. The OF_2 molecule would be a polar molecule.

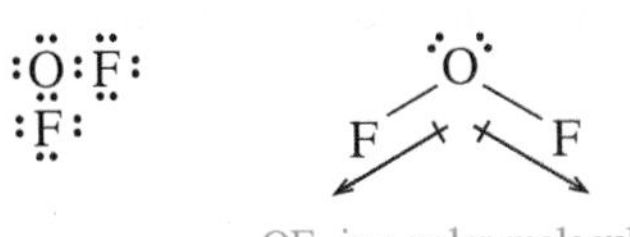

OF_2 is a polar molecule.

STUDY CHECK 13

Would PCl_3 be a polar or nonpolar molecule?

QUESTIONS AND PROBLEMS

8 Shapes and Polarity of Molecules

LEARNING GOAL: *Predict the three-dimensional structure of a molecule and classify it as polar or nonpolar.*

63 Choose the shape (**1–6**) that matches with each of the following three descriptions:

1. linear **2.** bent (109°) **3.** trigonal planar
4. bent (120°) **5.** trigonal pyramidal **6.** tetrahedral

a. a molecule with a central atom that has four electron groups and four bonded atoms
b. a molecule with a central atom that has four electron groups and three bonded atoms
c. a molecule with a central atom that has three electron groups and three bonded atoms

64 Choose the shape (**1–6**) that matches with each of the following three descriptions:

1. linear **2.** bent (109°) **3.** trigonal planar
4. bent (120°) **5.** trigonal pyramidal **6.** tetrahedral

a. a molecule with a central atom that has four electron groups and two bonded atoms
b. a molecule with a central atom that has two electron groups and two bonded atoms
c. a molecule with a central atom that has three electron groups and two bonded atoms

65 Complete each of the following statements for a molecule of SeO_3:

a. There are ______ electron groups around the central atom.
b. The electron-group geometry is ______________.
c. The shape of the molecule is ______________.
d. The molecule is (polar/nonpolar) ______________.

66 Complete each of the following statements for a molecule of $SeCl_2$:

a. There are ______ electron groups around the central atom.
b. The electron-group geometry is ______________.
c. The shape of the molecule is ______________.
d. The molecule is (polar/nonpolar) ______________.

67 Which of the following molecules has the same shape as PH_3?
a. NCl_3 **b.** PCl_3 **c.** BF_3

68 Which of the following molecules has the same shape as CO_2?
a. BeF_2 **b.** H_2O **c.** OF_2

69 Use the VSEPR theory to predict the shape of each molecule:
a. OF_2 **b.** CCl_4
c. $GaCl_3$ **d.** SeO_2

70 Use the VSEPR theory to predict the shape of each molecule:
a. NCl_3 **b.** SCl_2
c. SiF_2Cl_2 **d.** $BeBr_2$

71 The molecule Cl_2 is nonpolar, but HCl is polar. Explain.

72 The molecules CH_4 and CH_3Cl both contain four bonds. Why is CH_4 nonpolar whereas CH_3Cl is polar?

73 Identify each of the following molecules as polar or nonpolar:
a. HBr **b.** NF_3
c. CHF_3 **d.** SO_3

74 Identify each of the following molecules as polar or nonpolar:
a. SeF_2 **b.** PBr_3
c. SiF_4 **d.** SeO_2

LEARNING GOAL

Describe the attractive forces between ions, polar molecules, and nonpolar molecules.

TUTORIAL
Intermolecular Forces

TUTORIAL
Forces between Molecules

9 Attractive Forces in Compounds

Now we will look at the attractive forces that hold molecules and ions close together in liquids and solids. A solid melts and a liquid boils when the quantity of heat added exceeds the strength of the attractive forces between the particles. When attractive forces are weak, the substance undergoes a change of state at relatively low melting and boiling points. If the attractive forces are strong, the substance changes state at higher temperatures.

In gases, the attractions between particles are minimal, which allows gas molecules to move far apart from each other. In solids and liquids, there are sufficient attractions between the particles to hold them close together, although some solids have low melting points whereas others have extremely high melting points. Such differences in properties are explained by looking at the various kinds of attractive forces between particles.

Ionic compounds typically have high melting points. Large amounts of energy are needed to overcome the strong attractive forces between positive and negative ions and to melt the ionic solid. For example, solid NaCl melts at 801 °C. In solids containing molecules with covalent bonds, there are also attractive forces, but they are weaker than those of ionic compounds. The attractive forces we will discuss are *dipole–dipole attractions, hydrogen bonds*, and *dispersion forces.*

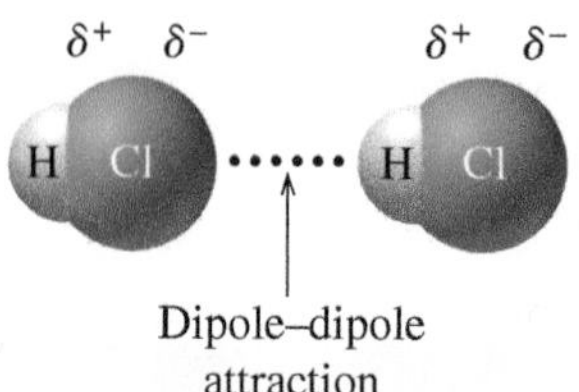

Dipole–Dipole Attractions and Hydrogen Bonds

Attractive forces called **dipole–dipole attractions** occur between polar molecules in which a partially positive charge of one molecule is attracted to the partially negative charge in another molecule. For example, in the polar molecule HCl, the partially positive H atom of one HCl molecule attracts the partially negative Cl atom in another molecule.

When a hydrogen atom is attached to a highly electronegative atom of fluorine, oxygen, or nitrogen, there are strong dipole–dipole attractions between the polar molecules. This type of attraction, called a **hydrogen bond**, occurs between the partially positive hydrogen atom of one molecule and a lone pair of electrons on a nitrogen, oxygen, or fluorine atom in another molecule. Hydrogen bonds are not true chemical bonds, but represent the strongest type of dipole–dipole attraction. They are a major factor in the formation and structure of biological molecules such as proteins and DNA.

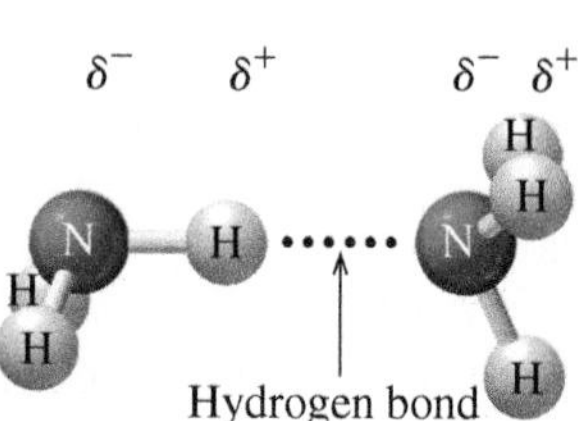

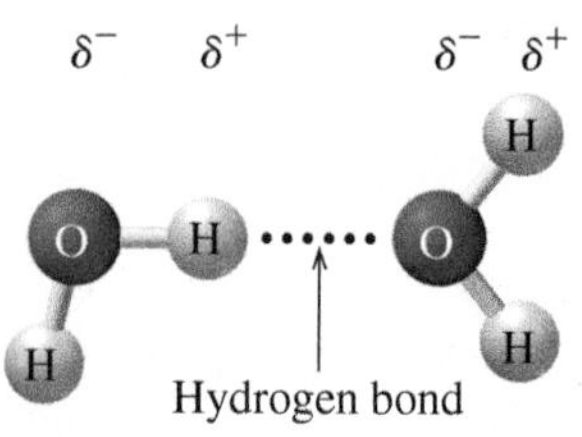

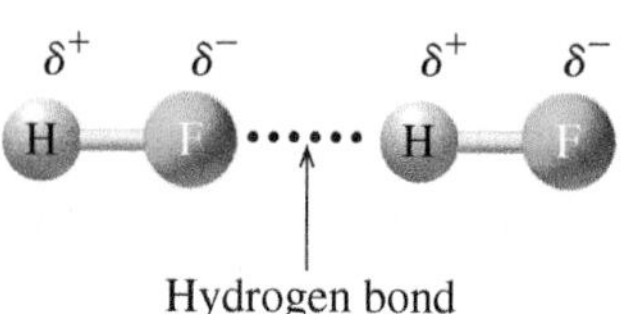

Dispersion Forces

Nonpolar compounds can form solids or liquids, but only at low temperatures. Very weak attractions called **dispersion forces** occur between nonpolar molecules. Usually, the electrons in a nonpolar molecule are distributed symmetrically. However, electrons may accumulate more in one part of the molecule than another, which forms a temporary dipole. Although dispersion forces are especially weak, they make it possible for nonpolar molecules to form liquids and solids.

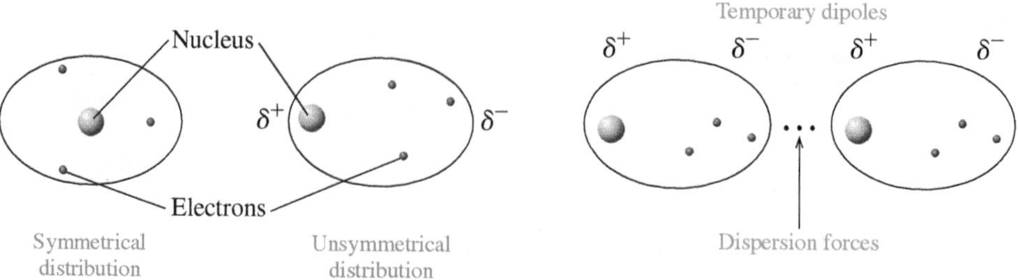

Nonpolar molecules form attractions when they form temporary dipoles.

The various types of attractions within ionic and covalent compounds, and between the particles in solids and liquids are summarized in Table 17.

TABLE 17 Comparison of Bonding and Attractive Forces

Type of Force	Particle Arrangement	Example	Strength
Between Atoms or Ions			
Ionic bond	+ − + / − + −	Na^+Cl^-	Strong
Covalent bond (X = nonmetal)	X:X	Cl—Cl	
Between Molecules			
Hydrogen bond (X = F, O, or N)	$\delta^+ \delta^-$ H X ··· $\delta^+ \delta^-$ H X	δ^+ H—δ^- F···δ^+ H—δ^- F	
Dipole–dipole attractions (X and Y = nonmetals)	$\delta^+ \delta^-$ Y X ··· $\delta^+ \delta^-$ Y X	δ^+ Br—δ^- Cl···δ^+ Br—δ^- Cl	
Dispersion forces (temporary shift of electrons in nonpolar bonds)	$\delta^+ \delta^-$ X :X ··· $\delta^+ \delta^-$ X :X (temporary dipoles)	δ^+ F—δ^- F···δ^+ F—δ^- F	Weak

CONCEPT CHECK 11 **Attractive Forces between Particles**

Indicate the major type of molecular interaction expected of each of the following:

1. dipole–dipole attractions **2.** hydrogen bonding **3.** dispersion forces

a. HF **b.** Br_2 **c.** PCl_3

ANSWER

a. 2; HF is a polar molecule that interacts with other HF molecules by hydrogen bonding.
b. 3; Br_2 is nonpolar; the only molecular interactions would be from dispersion forces.
c. 1; The polarity of the PCl_3 molecules provides dipole–dipole attractions.

Attractive Forces and Melting Point

The melting point of a substance is related to the strength of the attractive forces between its particles. A compound with weak attractive forces such as dispersion forces has a low melting point because only a small amount of energy is needed to separate its molecules and form a liquid. A compound with dipole–dipole attractions requires more energy to break the attractive forces that hold its particles together. A compound that forms hydrogen bonds requires even more energy to overcome the attractive forces that exist between its molecules. The highest melting points are seen with ionic compounds that have very strong attractions between positive and negative ions. Table 18 compares the melting points of some substances with different kinds of attractive forces.

TABLE 18 Melting Points of Selected Substances

Substance	Melting Point (°C)
Ionic Bonds	
MgF_2	1248
NaCl	801
Hydrogen Bonds	
H_2O	0
NH_3	−78
Dipole–Dipole Attractions	
HI	−51
HBr	−89
HCl	−115
Dispersion Forces	
Br_2	−7
Cl_2	−101
F_2	−220
CH_4	−182

QUESTIONS AND PROBLEMS

9 Attractive Forces in Compounds

LEARNING GOAL: *Describe the attractive forces between ions, polar molecules, and nonpolar molecules.*

75 Identify the major type of interactive force between particles in each of the following:
a. BrF **b.** KCl **c.** CCl_4 **d.** Cl_2

76 Identify the major type of interactive force between particles in each of the following:
a. HCl **b.** MgF_2 **c.** PBr_3 **d.** NH_3

77 Identify the strongest attractive forces between molecules of each of the following:
a. CH_3OH **b.** N_2 **c.** HBr
d. CH_4 **e.** CH_3CH_3

78 Identify the strongest attractive forces between molecules of each of the following:
a. O_2 **b.** CBr_4
c. CH_3Cl **d.** H_2O
e. NF_3

79 Identify the substance in each of the following pairs that would have the higher boiling point and explain your choice:
a. HF or HBr **b.** HF or NaF
c. $MgBr_2$ or PBr_3 **d.** CH_4 or CH_3OH

80 Identify the substance in each of the following pairs that would have the higher boiling point and explain your choice:
a. NaCl or HCl **b.** H_2O or H_2Se
c. NH_3 or PH_3 **d.** F_2 or HF

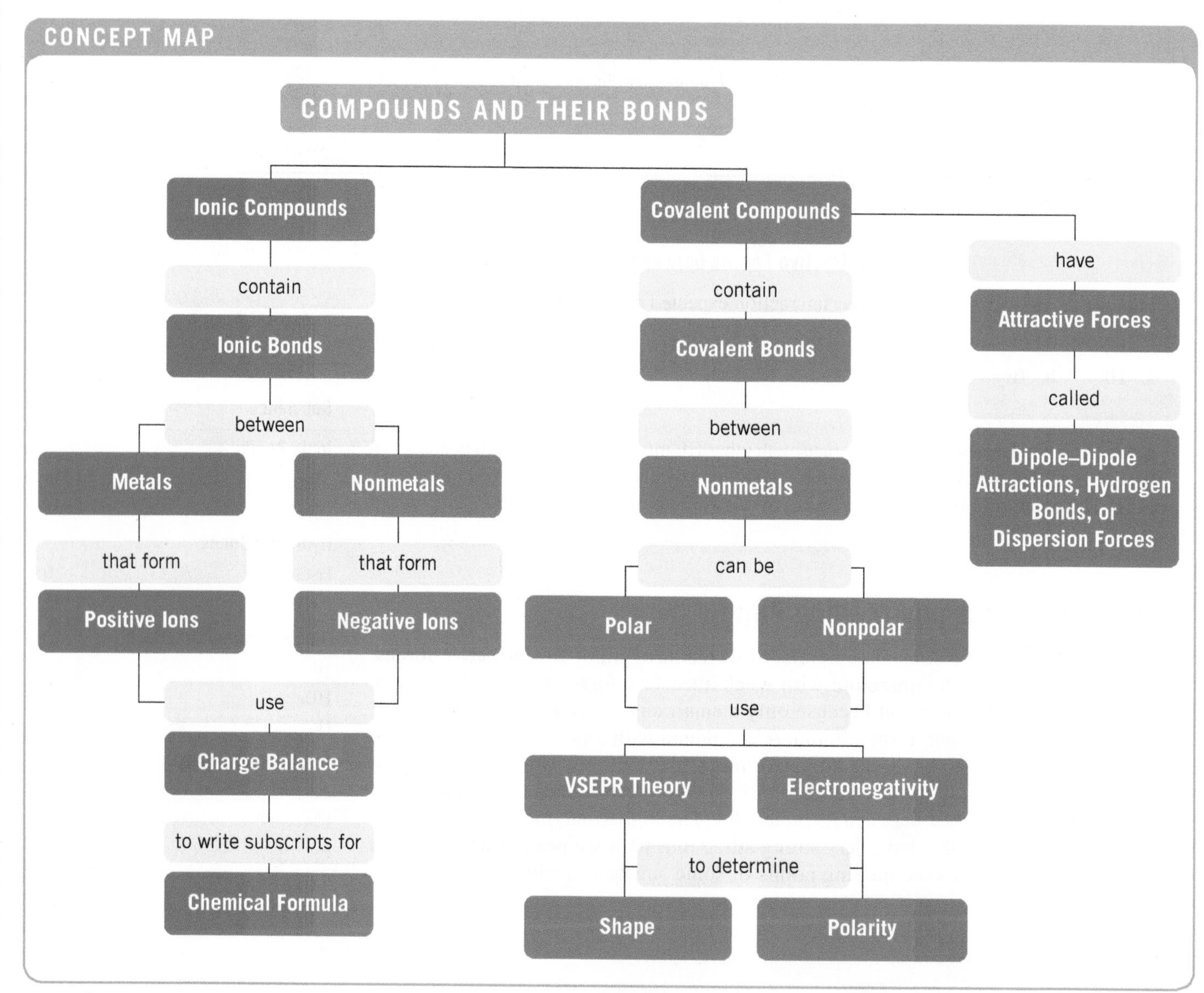

CHAPTER REVIEW

1 Ions: Transfer of Electrons

LEARNING GOAL: *Using the octet rule, write the symbols for the simple ions of the representative elements.*

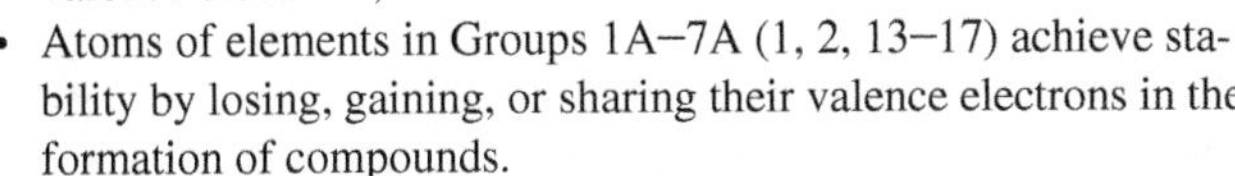

- The stability of the noble gases is associated with a complete electron configuration in the outermost energy level.
- With the exception of helium, which needs two electrons for stability, noble gases have eight valence electrons, which is an octet.
- Atoms of elements in Groups 1A–7A (1, 2, 13–17) achieve stability by losing, gaining, or sharing their valence electrons in the formation of compounds.
- Metals of the representative elements lose valence electrons to form positively charged ions (cations): Group 1A (1), 1+; Group 2A (2), 2+; and Group 3A (13), 3+.
- When reacting with metals, nonmetals gain electrons to form octets and form negatively charged ions (anions): Group 5A (15), 3−; Group 6A (16), 2−; and Group 7A (17), 1−.

2 Ionic Compounds

LEARNING GOAL: *Using charge balance, write the correct formula for an ionic compound.*

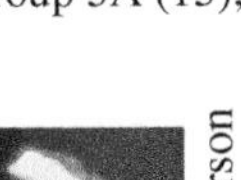
Pearson Education

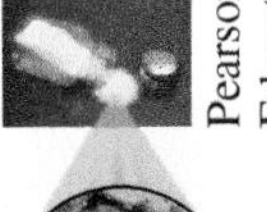
Pearson Education

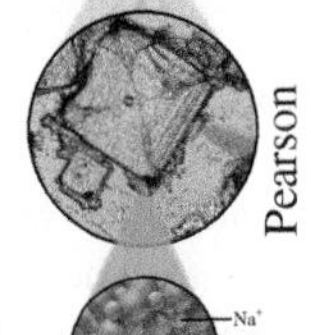

Sodium chloride

- The total positive and negative ionic charge is balanced in the formula for an ionic compound.
- Charge balance in a formula is achieved by using subscripts after each symbol so that the overall charge is zero.

3 Naming and Writing Ionic Formulas

LEARNING GOAL: *Given the formula of an ionic compound, write the correct name; given the name of an ionic compound, write the correct formula.*

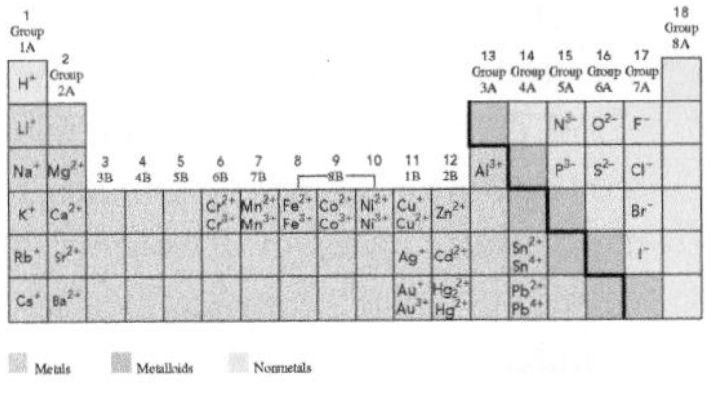

- In naming ionic compounds, the name of the positive ion is given first, followed by the name of the negative ion.
- Ionic compounds containing two elements end with *ide*.
- Except for Ag, Cd, and Zn, transition elements form cations with two or more ionic charges.
- The charge of a cation of a transition element is determined from the total negative charge in the formula and included as a Roman numeral following the name.

4 Polyatomic Ions

LEARNING GOAL: *Write the name and formula for a compound containing a polyatomic ion.*

- A polyatomic ion is a group of nonmetal atoms that carries an electrical charge; for example, the carbonate ion has the formula CO_3^{2-}.
- Most polyatomic ions have names that end with *ate* or *ite*.

Pearson Education

5 Covalent Compounds: Sharing Electrons

LEARNING GOAL: *Draw the electron-dot formulas for covalent compounds, including multiple bonds and resonance structures.*

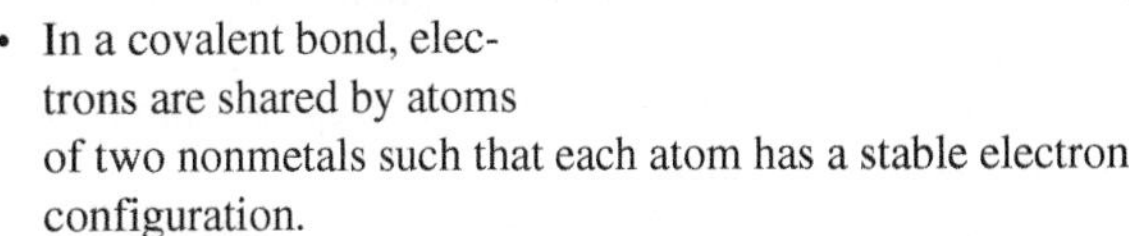

- In a covalent bond, electrons are shared by atoms of two nonmetals such that each atom has a stable electron configuration.
- In some covalent compounds, double or triple bonds provide an octet (or a pair of electrons for H.)
- Resonance structures are possible when more than one electron-dot formula can be drawn for a molecule with a multiple bond.

6 Naming and Writing Covalent Formulas

LEARNING GOAL: *Given the formula of a covalent compound, write its correct name; given the name of a covalent compound, write its formula.*

1	mono	6	hexa
2	di	7	hepta
3	tri	8	octa
4	tetra	9	nona
5	penta	10	deca

- The first nonmetal in a covalent compound uses its element name; the second nonmetal uses the first syllable of its element name followed by *ide*.
- The name of a covalent compound with two different atoms uses prefixes to indicate the number of atoms of each nonmetal in the formula.

7 Electronegativity and Bond Polarity

LEARNING GOAL: *Use electronegativity to determine the polarity of a bond.*

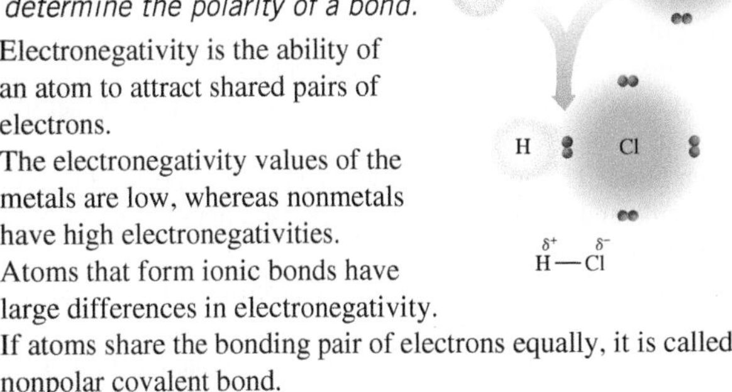

- Electronegativity is the ability of an atom to attract shared pairs of electrons.
- The electronegativity values of the metals are low, whereas nonmetals have high electronegativities.
- Atoms that form ionic bonds have large differences in electronegativity.
- If atoms share the bonding pair of electrons equally, it is called a nonpolar covalent bond.
- If the bonding electrons in a covalent bond are unequally shared, it is called a polar covalent bond.
- In polar covalent bonds, the atom with the lower electronegativity is partially positive and the atom with the higher electronegativity is partially negative.

8 Shapes and Polarity of Molecules

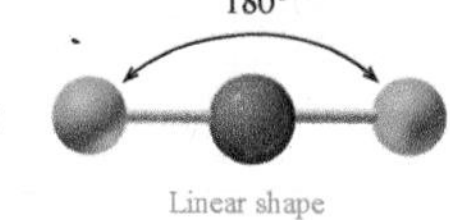

LEARNING GOAL: *Predict the three-dimensional structure of a molecule and classify it as polar or nonpolar.*

- The VSEPR theory indicates that the arrangement of electron groups around a central atom is minimized when the electron groups are as far apart as possible.
- The shape of a molecule with two electron groups and two bonded atoms is linear.
- The shape of a molecule with three electron groups and three bonded atoms is trigonal planar.
- The shape of a molecule with three electron groups and two bonded atoms is bent, 120°.
- The shape of a molecule with four electron groups and four bonded atoms is tetrahedral.
- The shape of a molecule with four electron groups and three bonded atoms is trigonal pyramidal.
- The shape of a molecule with four electron groups and two bonded atoms is bent, 109°.
- Molecules are nonpolar if they contain nonpolar covalent bonds or have an arrangement of polar covalent bonds with dipoles that cancel out.
- In polar molecules, the dipoles do not cancel.

9 Attractive Forces in Compounds

LEARNING GOAL: *Describe the attractive forces between ions, polar molecules, and nonpolar molecules.*

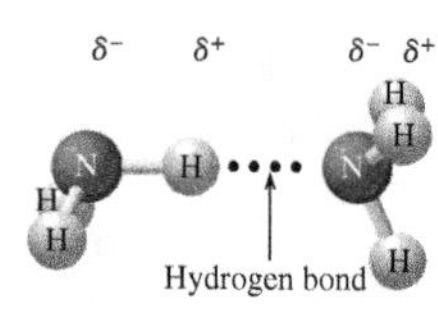

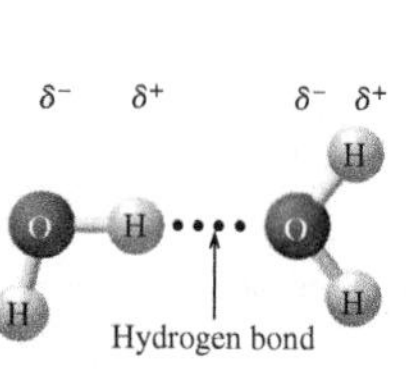

- Ionic bonds consist of very strong attractive forces between oppositely charged ions.
- Attractive forces in polar covalent compounds are weaker than ionic bonds and include dipole–dipole attractions and hydrogen bonds.
- Nonpolar covalent compounds form solids using temporary dipoles called dispersion forces.

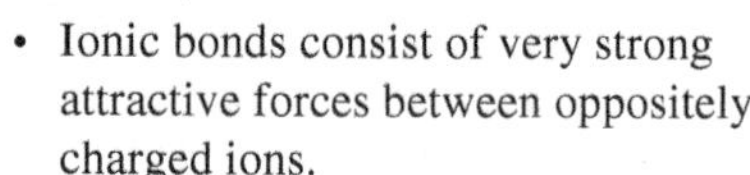

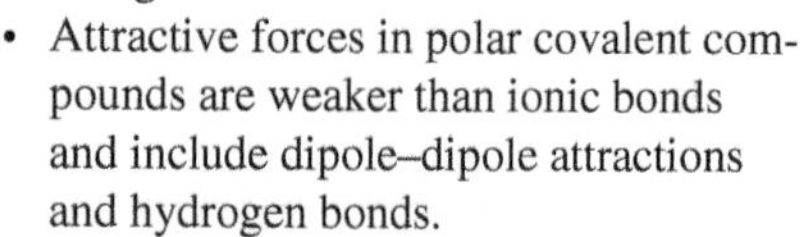

KEY TERMS

anion A negatively charged ion such as Cl^-, O^{2-}, or SO_4^{2-}.

bent The shape of a molecule with four electron groups, but only two bonded atoms; or three electron groups but only two bonded atoms.

cation A positively charged ion such as Na^+, Mg^{2+}, Al^{3+}, or NH_4^+.

chemical formula The symbols and subscripts that represent the lowest whole-number ratio of the atoms or ions in a compound.

covalent bond A bond created by the sharing of valence electrons by two nonmetal atoms.

covalent compound A combination of nonmetals that share electrons to obtain a stable electron configuration.

dipole The separation of positive and negative charge in a polar bond indicated by an arrow that is drawn from the more positive atom to the more negative atom.

dipole–dipole attractions Attractive forces between oppositely charged ends of polar molecules.

dispersion forces Weak dipole attractions that result from a momentary polarization of nonpolar molecules.

double bond A sharing of two pairs of electrons by two atoms.

electronegativity The relative ability of an element to attract electrons in a bond.

hydrogen bond The attraction between a partially positive H in one molecule and a strongly electronegative atom of F, O, or N in a nearby molecule.

ion An atom or group of atoms having an electrical charge because of a loss or gain of electrons.

ionic bond The attraction between positively charged metal ions and negatively charged nonmetal ions.

ionic charge The difference between the number of protons (positive) and the number of electrons (negative) written in the upper right corner of the symbol for the element or polyatomic ion.

ionic compound A compound of positive and negative ions held together by ionic bonds.

linear The shape of a molecule that has two electron groups and two bonded atoms.

molecule The smallest unit of two or more nonmetal atoms held together by covalent bonds.

nonpolar covalent bond A covalent bond in which the electrons are shared equally between atoms.

nonpolar molecule A molecule that has only nonpolar bonds or in which the bond dipoles cancel.

octet rule The tendency for elements in Groups 1A–7A (1, 2, 13–17) to react with other elements to produce a stable electron configuration, usually eight electrons in the outer shell.

polar covalent bond A covalent bond in which the electrons are shared unequally between two nonmetal atoms.

polar molecule A molecule containing polar bonds with dipoles that do not cancel.

polyatomic ion A group of covalently bonded nonmetal atoms that has an overall electrical charge.

resonance structures Two or more electron-dot formulas that can be drawn for a molecule by placing a multiple bond between different atoms.

tetrahedral The shape of a molecule with four electron groups and four bonded atoms.

trigonal planar The shape of a molecule with three electron groups and three bonded atoms.

trigonal pyramidal The shape of a molecule that has four electron groups, but only three bonded atoms.

triple bond A sharing of three pairs of electrons by two nonmetal atoms.

valence-shell electron-pair repulsion (VSEPR) theory A theory that predicts the shape of a molecule by placing the electron pairs on a central atom as far apart as possible to minimize the mutual repulsion of the electrons.

UNDERSTANDING THE CONCEPTS

The chapter sections to review are shown in parentheses at the end of each question.

81 Identify each of the following atoms or ions: (1)

a. 18 e^-, 15 p^+, 16 n
b. 8 e^-, 8 p^+, 8 n
c. 28 e^-, 30 p^+, 35 n
d. 23 e^-, 26 p^+, 28 n

82 Identify each of the following atoms or ions: (1)

a. 2 e^-, 3 p^+, 4 n
b. 0 e^-, 1 p^+
c. 3 e^-, 3 p^+, 4 n
d. 10 e^-, 7 p^+, 8 n

83 Identify each of the following atoms or ions: (1)
a. 35 protons, 45 neutrons, and 36 electrons
b. 47 protons, 60 neutrons, and 46 electrons
c. 50 protons, 68 neutrons, and 46 electrons

84 Identify each of the following atoms or ions: (1)
a. 28 protons, 31 neutrons, and 26 electrons
b. 82 protons, 126 neutrons, and 82 electrons
c. 34 protons, 46 neutrons, and 36 electrons

85 Consider an ion with the symbol X^{2+} formed from a representative element. (2, 3)
a. What is the group number of the element?
b. What is the electron-dot symbol of the element?
c. If X is in Period 3, what is the element?
d. What is the formula of the compound formed from X and the nitride ion?

86 Consider an ion with the symbol Y^{3-} formed from a representative element. (2, 3)
a. What is the group number of the element?
b. What is the electron-dot symbol of the element?
c. If Y is in Period 3, what is the element?
d. What is the formula of the compound formed from the barium ion and Y?

87 Match each of the electron-dot formulas (**a–c**) with the correct diagram (**1–3**) of its shape, and name the shape; indicate if each molecule is polar or nonpolar. Assume X and Y are nonmetals and all bonds are polar covalent. (7, 8)

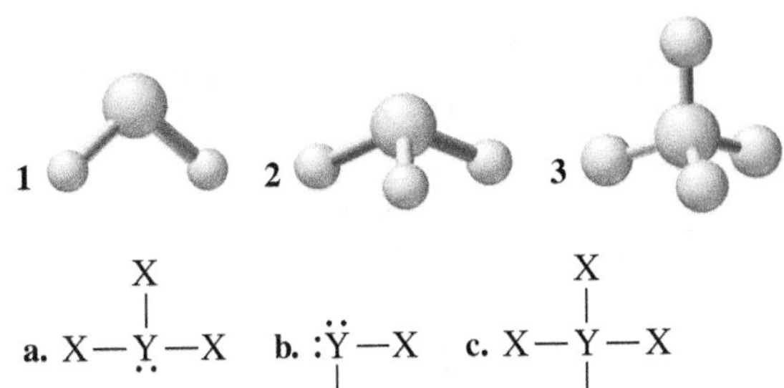

88 Match each of the formulas (**a–c**) with the correct diagram (**1–3**) of its shape, and name the shape; indicate if each molecule is polar or nonpolar. (7, 8)

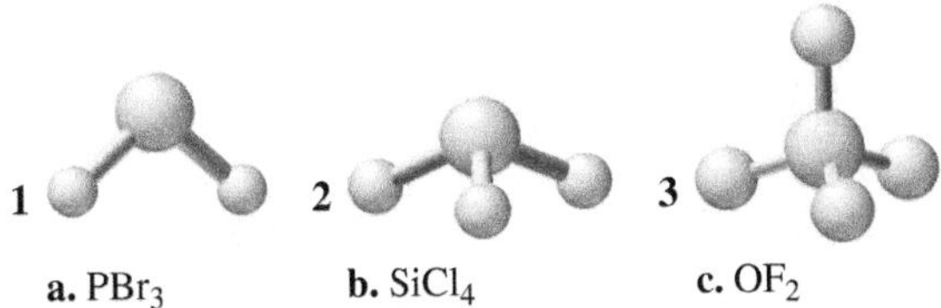

89 Consider the following bonds: Ca—O, C—O, K—O, O—O, and N—O. (7)
a. Which bonds are polar covalent?
b. Which bonds are nonpolar covalent?
c. Which bonds are ionic?
d. Arrange the covalent bonds in order of decreasing polarity.

90 Consider the following bonds: F—Cl, Cl—Cl, Cs—Cl, O—Cl, and Ca—Cl. (7)
a. Which bonds are polar covalent?
b. Which bonds are nonpolar covalent?
c. Which bonds are ionic?
d. Arrange the covalent bonds in order of decreasing polarity.

ADDITIONAL QUESTIONS AND PROBLEMS

For instructor-assigned homework, go to www.masteringchemistry.com.

91 Write the electron configuration for each of the following: (1)
a. N^{3-} **b.** Mg^{2+} **c.** P^{3-}
d. Al^{3+} **e.** Li^+

92 Write the electron configuration for each of the following: (1)
a. K^+ **b.** Na^+ **c.** S^{2-}
d. Cl^- **e.** Ca^{2+}

93 One of the ions of tin is tin(IV). (1, 2, 3, 4)
a. What is the symbol for this ion?
b. How many protons and electrons are in the ion?
c. What is the formula of tin(IV) oxide?
d. What is the formula of tin(IV) phosphate?

94 One of the ions of gold is gold(III). (1, 2, 3, 4)
a. What is the symbol for this ion?
b. How many protons and electrons are in the ion?
c. What is the formula of gold(III) sulfate?
d. What is the formula of gold(III) nitrate?

95 Write the symbol for the ion of each of the following: (1)
a. chloride **b.** potassium
c. oxide **d.** aluminum

96 Write the symbol for the ion of each of the following: (1)
a. fluoride **b.** calcium
c. sodium **d.** phosphide

97 What is the name of each of the following ions? (1)
a. K^+ **b.** S^{2-} **c.** Ca^{2+} **d.** N^{3-}

98 What is the name of each of the following ions? (1)
a. Mg^{2+} **b.** Ba^{2+} **c.** I^- **d.** Cl^-

99 Write the formula for each of the following ionic compounds: (3)
a. tin(II) sulfide **b.** lead(IV) oxide
c. silver chloride **d.** calcium nitride
e. copper(I) phosphide **f.** chromium(II) bromide

100 Write the formula for each of the following ionic compounds: (3)
a. nickel(III) oxide **b.** iron(III) sulfide
c. lead(II) sulfide **d.** chromium(III) iodide
e. lithium nitride **f.** gold(I) oxide

101 Draw the electron-dot formula for each of the following: (5)
a. Cl_2O **b.** CF_4
c. H_2NOH (N is the central atom)
d. H_2CCCl_2

102 Draw the electron-dot formula for each of the following: (5)
a. H_3COCH_3; the atoms are in the order C O C
b. CS_2; the atoms are in the order S C S
c. NH_3
d. H_2CCHCN; the atoms are in the order C C C N

103 Name each of the following covalent compounds: (6)
a. NCl_3 **b.** N_2S_3 **c.** N_2O
d. F_2 **e.** SO_2 **f.** P_2O_5

104 Name each of the following covalent compounds: (6)
a. CBr_4 **b.** SF_6 **c.** Br_2
d. N_2O_4 **e.** PCl_5 **f.** CS_2

105 Write the formula for each of the following: (6)
a. carbon monoxide **b.** diphosphorus pentoxide
c. dihydrogen sulfide **d.** sulfur dichloride

106 Write the formula for each of the following: (6)
a. silicon dioxide
b. carbon tetrabromide
c. diphosphorus tetraiodide
d. dinitrogen oxide

107 Classify each of the following compounds as ionic or covalent, and give its name: (2, 3, 4, 6)
a. $FeCl_3$ **b.** Na_2SO_4 **c.** NO_2
d. N_2 **e.** PF_5 **f.** CF_4

108 Classify each of the following compounds as ionic or covalent, and give its name: (2, 3, 4, 6)
a. $Al_2(CO_3)_3$ **b.** ClF_5 **c.** H_2
d. Mg_3N_2 **e.** ClO_2 **f.** $CrPO_4$

109 Write the formulas for the following: (2, 3, 4, 6)
a. tin(II) carbonate **b.** lithium phosphide
c. silicon tetrachloride **d.** manganese(III) oxide
e. iodine **f.** calcium bromide

110 Write the formulas for the following: (2, 3, 4, 6)
a. sodium carbonate **b.** nitrogen dioxide
c. aluminum nitrate **d.** copper(I) nitride
e. potassium phosphate **f.** cobalt(III) sulfate

111 Select the more polar bond in each of the following pairs: (7)
a. C—N or C—O
b. N—F or N—Br
c. Br—Cl or S—Cl
d. Br—Cl or Br—I
e. N—F or N—O

112 Select the more polar bond in each of the following pairs: (7)
a. C—C or C—O
b. P—Cl or P—Br
c. Si—S or Si—Cl
d. F—Cl or F—Br
e. P—O or P—S

113 Show the dipole arrow for each of the following bonds: (7)
a. Si—Cl **b.** C—N **c.** F—Cl
d. C—F **e.** N—O

114 Show the dipole arrow for each of the following bonds: (7)
a. C—O **b.** N—F **c.** O—Cl
d. S—Cl **e.** P—F

115 Classify each of the following bonds as nonpolar covalent, polar covalent, or ionic: (7)
a. Si—Cl **b.** C—C **c.** Na—Cl
d. C—H **e.** F—F

116 Classify each of the following bonds as nonpolar covalent, polar covalent, or ionic: (7)
a. C—N **b.** Cl—Cl **c.** K—Br
d. H—H **e.** N—F

117 For each of the following, draw the electron-dot formula and determine the shape of the molecule: (8)
a. NF_3 **b.** $SiBr_4$ **c.** $BeCl_2$ **d.** SO_2

118 For each of the following, draw the electron-dot formula and determine the shape of the molecule: (8)
a. SiH_4 **b.** HCCH
c. $COCl_2$ (C is the central atom) **d.** BCl_3

CHALLENGE QUESTIONS

119 Write the formula and name for the compound that forms for each pair of elements (X = metal, Y = nonmetal) indicated by the period and electron-dot symbols in the following table: (2, 3, 5, 6)

Period	Electron-Dot Symbols	Formula of Compound	Name of Compound
3	·X· and ·Ÿ·		
3	·Ẋ· and ·Ÿ:		
3	·Ÿ: and ·Ÿ:		
3	·Ÿ· and ·Ÿ:		

120 Write the formula and name for the compound that forms for each pair of elements (X = metal, Y = nonmetal) indicated by the period and electron-dot symbols in the following table: (2, 3, 5, 6)

Period	Electron-Dot Symbols	Formula of Compound	Name of Compound
2	X· and ·Ÿ·		
2	·Ẏ· and ·Ÿ:		
4	·X· and ·Ÿ:		
4	·Ẋ· and ·Ÿ:		

121 Write the symbols of ions, formulas, and names for their ionic compounds using their electron configurations. (2, 3)

Electron Configurations		Symbols of Ions			
Metal	Nonmetal	Cation	Anion	Formula of Compound	Name of Compound
$1s^22s^1$	$1s^22s^22p^63s^23p^4$				
$1s^22s^22p^63s^23p^64s^2$	$1s^22s^22p^63s^23p^3$				
$1s^22s^22p^63s^1$	$1s^22s^22p^63s^23p^5$				

122 Write the symbols of ions, formulas, and names for their ionic compounds using the electron configurations. (2, 3)

Electron Configurations		Symbols of Ions			
Metal	Nonmetal	Cation	Anion	Formula of Compound	Name of Compound
$1s^22s^22p^63s^2$	$1s^22s^22p^3$				
$1s^22s^22p^63s^23p^64s^1$	$1s^22s^22p^4$				
$1s^22s^22p^63s^23p^1$	$1s^22s^22p^5$				

123 Consider the following electron-dot formulas for elements X and Y: (2, 3, 5, 6)

X· ·Ÿ:

a. What are the group numbers of X and Y?
b. Will a compound of X and Y be ionic or covalent?
c. What ions would be formed by X and Y?
d. What would be the formula of a compound of X and Y?
e. What would be the formula of a compound of X and chlorine?
f. What would be the formula of a compound of Y and sodium?
g. Is the compound in part **f** ionic or covalent?

124 Consider the following electron-dot formulas for elements X and Y: (2, 3, 5, 6)

·X· and ·Ÿ·

a. What are the group numbers of X and Y?
b. Will a compound of X and Y be ionic or covalent?
c. What ions would be formed by X and Y?
d. What would be the formula of a compound of X and Y?
e. What would be the formula of a compound of X and chlorine?
f. What would be the formula of a compound of Y and sulfur?
g. Is the compound in part **f** ionic or covalent?

125 Classify the following compounds as ionic or covalent and name each: (2, 3, 5, 6)
a. Li_2O **b.** N_2O
c. CF_4 **d.** Cl_2O

126 Classify the following compounds as ionic or covalent and name each: (2, 3, 5, 6)
a. MgF_2 **b.** CO **c.** $CaCl_2$ **d.** K_3PO_4

127 Name the following compounds: (3, 4, 6)
a. $FeCl_2$ **b.** Cl_2O_7 **c.** N_2
d. $Ca_3(PO_4)_2$ **e.** PCl_3 **f.** $Ca(ClO)_2$

128 Name the following compounds: (3, 4, 6)
a. $PbCl_4$ **b.** $MgCO_3$ **c.** NO_2
d. $SnSO_4$ **e.** $Ba(NO_3)_2$ **f.** CuS

129 Predict the shape and polarity of each of the following molecules: (8)
a. H_2S **b.** NF_3 **c.** NH_3
d. CH_3Cl **e.** SiF_4

130 Predict the shape and polarity of each of the following molecules: (8)
a. H_2O **b.** CF_4 **c.** GeH_4
d. PCl_3 **e.** SCl_2

131 Indicate the major type of attractive forces—(1) ionic bonds, (2) dipole–dipole attractions, (3) hydrogen bonds, (4) dispersion forces—that occurs between particles of the following: (9)
a. NH_3 **b.** ClF **c.** Br_2
d. Cs_2O **e.** C_3H_8 **f.** CH_3OH

132 Indicate the major type of attractive force—(1) ionic bonds, (2) dipole–dipole attraction, (3) hydrogen bonds, (4) dispersion forces—that occurs between particles of the following: (9)
a. $CHCl_3$ **b.** H_2O **c.** LiCl
d. Cl_2 **e.** HBr **f.** IBr

ANSWERS

Answers to Study Checks

1 gallium sulfide

2 manganese(III) sulfide

3 Cr_2O_3

4 cobalt(II) phosphate

5 $(NH_4)_3PO_4$

6 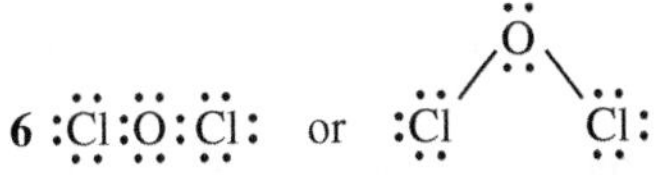

7 H:C:::N: or H—C≡N:
In HCN, there is a triple bond between C and N atoms.

8 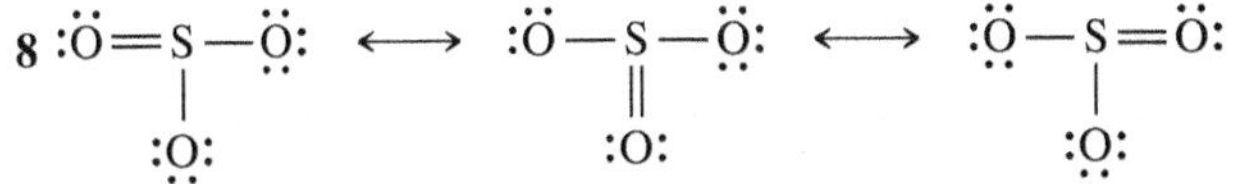

9 **a.** silicon tetrabromide **b.** dibromine oxide

10 IF_7

11 **a.** polar covalent **b.** nonpolar covalent **c.** ionic

12 tetrahedral

13 polar

Answers to Selected Questions and Problems

1 a. 1 **b.** 2 **c.** 3 **d.** 1 **e.** 2

3 a. Li^+ **b.** F^- **c.** Mg^{2+} **d.** Fe^{3+}

5 a. 8 protons, 10 electrons **b.** 19 protons, 18 electrons
c. 35 protons, 36 electrons **d.** 16 protons, 18 electrons

7 a. Cl^- **b.** K^+ **c.** O^{2-} **d.** Al^{3+} **e.** Se^{2-}

9 a and c

11 a. Na_2O **b.** $AlBr_3$ **c.** Ba_3N_2 **d.** MgF_2 **e.** Al_2S_3

13 a. K^+, S^{2-} K_2S **b.** Na^+, N^{3-} Na_3N
c. Al^{3+}, I^- AlI_3 **d.** Ga^{3+}, O^{2-} Ga_2O_3

15 a. aluminum oxide **b.** calcium chloride
c. sodium oxide **d.** magnesium phosphide
e. potassium iodide **f.** barium fluoride

17 Most of the transition elements form more than one positive ion. The specific ion is indicated in the name by writing a Roman numeral that is the same as the ionic charge. For example, iron forms Fe^{2+} and Fe^{3+} ions, which are named iron(II) and iron(III).

19 a. iron(II) **b.** copper(II) **c.** zinc
d. lead(IV) **e.** chromium(III) **f.** manganese(II)

21 a. tin(II) chloride **b.** iron(II) oxide
c. copper(I) sulfide **d.** copper(II) sulfide
e. chromium(III) bromide **f.** zinc chloride

23 a. Au^{3+} **b.** Fe^{3+} **c.** Pb^{4+} **d.** Sn^{2+}

25 a. $MgCl_2$ **b.** Na_2S **c.** Cu_2O
d. Zn_3P_2 **e.** AuN **f.** $CrCl_2$

27 a. HCO_3^- **b.** NH_4^+ **c.** PO_4^{3-}
d. HSO_4^- **e.** ClO_4^-

29 a. sulfate **b.** hypochlorite
c. phosphate **d.** nitrate

31

	NO_2^-	CO_3^{2-}	HSO_4^-	PO_4^{3-}
Li^+	$LiNO_2$	Li_2CO_3	$LiHSO_4$	Li_3PO_4
Cu^{2+}	$Cu(NO_2)_2$	$CuCO_3$	$Cu(HSO_4)_2$	$Cu_3(PO_4)_2$
Ba^{2+}	$Ba(NO_2)_2$	$BaCO_3$	$Ba(HSO_4)_2$	$Ba_3(PO_4)_2$

33 a. CO_3^{2-}, sodium carbonate
b. NH_4^+, ammonium chloride
c. PO_4^{3-}, potassium phosphate
d. NO_2^-, chromium(II) nitrite
e. SO_3^{2-}, iron(II) sulfite

35 a. $Ba(OH)_2$ **b.** Na_2SO_4 **c.** $Fe(NO_3)_2$
d. $Zn_3(PO_4)_2$ **e.** $Fe_2(CO_3)_3$

37 a, c, d, and f

39 a. 2 valence electrons: 1 bonding pair and 0 lone pairs
b. 8 valence electrons: 1 bonding pair and 3 lone pairs
c. 14 valence electrons: 1 bonding pair and 6 lone pairs

41 a. HF (8 e^-) H:F: or H—F:

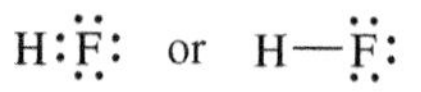

b. NBr_3 (26 e^-) :Br:N:Br: (with :Br: above N) or :Br—N—Br: (with :Br: bonded above N)

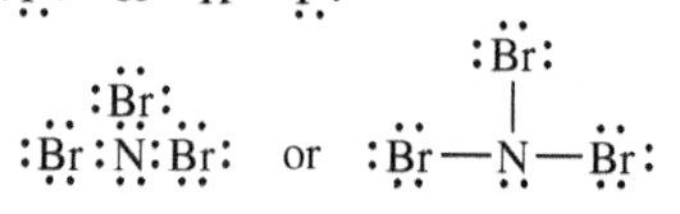

c. CH_3OH (14 e^-) H:C:O:H (with H above and below C) or H—C—O—H (with H above and below C)

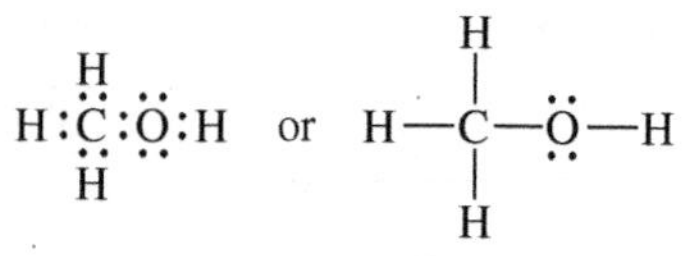

d. N_2H_4 (14 e^-) H:N:N:H (with H above each N) or H—N—N—H (with H above each N)

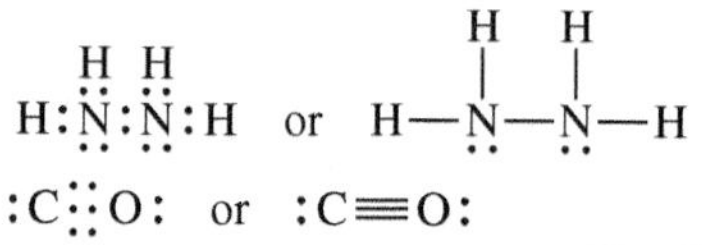

43 a. CO (10 e^-) :C:::O: or :C≡O:

b. H_2CCH_2 (12 e^-) H:C::C:H (with H above each C) or H—C=C—H (with H above each C)

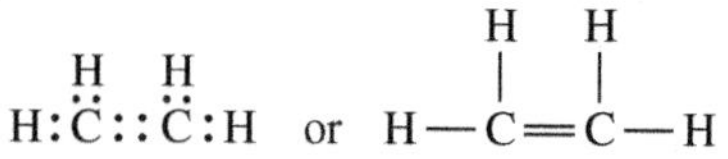

c. H_2CO (12 e^-) H:C:H (with :O: above C) or H—C—H (with :O: double-bonded above C)

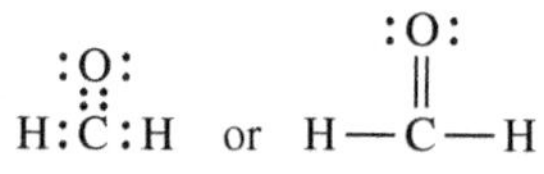

45 $ClNO_2$ (24 e^-) :Cl—N—O: (with :O: double-bonded above N) ⟷ :Cl—N=O: (with :O: single-bonded above N)

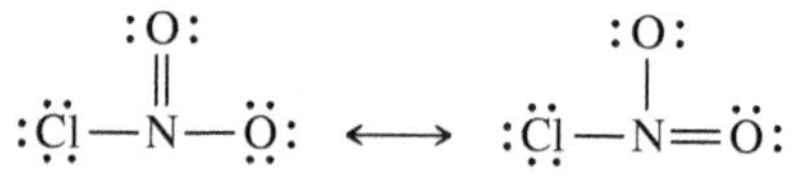

47 a. phosphorus tribromide **b.** carbon tetrabromide
c. silicon dioxide **d.** dinitrogen trioxide
e. phosphorus pentachloride

49 a. CCl_4 **b.** CO **c.** PCl_3
d. N_2O_4 **e.** BF_3 **f.** SF_6

51 a. aluminum sulfate **b.** calcium carbonate
c. dinitrogen oxide **d.** sodium phosphate
e. ammonium sulfate **f.** iron(III) oxide

53 a. increases **b.** decreases **c.** decreases

55 a. 2.2 **b.** 0.0 **c.** 0.5 **d.** 0.4

57 a. K, Na, Li **b.** Na, P, Cl **c.** Ca, Se, O

59 a. polar covalent **b.** ionic
c. polar covalent **d.** nonpolar covalent
e. polar covalent **f.** polar covalent

61 a. $\overset{\delta^+}{N}—\overset{\delta^-}{F}$ (⟶) **b.** $\overset{\delta^+}{Si}—\overset{\delta^-}{Br}$ (⟶) **c.** $\overset{\delta^+}{C}—\overset{\delta^-}{O}$ (⟶)
d. $\overset{\delta^+}{P}—\overset{\delta^-}{Br}$ (⟶) **e.** $\overset{\delta^-}{N}—\overset{\delta^+}{P}$ (⟵)

63 a. 6 **b.** 5 **c.** 3

65 a. 3 **b.** trigonal planar
c. trigonal planar **d.** nonpolar

67 a and b

69 a. bent (109°) **b.** tetrahedral
c. trigonal planar **d.** bent (120°)

71 Cl_2 is a nonpolar molecule because there is a nonpolar covalent bond between Cl atoms, which have identical electronegativity values. In HCl, the bond is a polar bond because there is a large electronegativity difference, which makes HCl a polar molecule.

73 a. polar **b.** polar **c.** polar **d.** nonpolar

75 a. dipole–dipole attractions **b.** ionic bonds
c. dispersion forces **d.** dispersion forces

77 a. hydrogen bonding **b.** dispersion forces
c. dipole–dipole attractions **d.** dispersion forces
e. dispersion forces

79 a. HF; hydrogen bonds are stronger than the dipole–dipole attractions in HBr.
b. NaF; ionic bonds are stronger than the hydrogen bonds in HF.

c. $MgBr_2$; ionic bonds are stronger than the dipole–dipole attractions in PBr_3.
d. CH_3OH; hydrogen bonds are stronger than the dispersion forces in CH_4.

81 a. P^{3-} **b.** O atom **c.** Zn^{2+} **d.** Fe^{3+}

83 a. Br^- **b.** Ag^+ **c.** Sn^{4+}

85 a. 2A (2) **b.** $\dot{X}\cdot$ **c.** Mg **d.** X_3N_2

87 a. 2, trigonal pyramidal, polar
b. 1, bent (109°), polar
c. 3, tetrahedral, nonpolar

89 a. C—O and N—O **b.** O—O
c. Ca—O and K—O **d.** C—O, N—O, O—O

91 a. $1s^22s^22p^6$ **b.** $1s^22s^22p^6$ **c.** $1s^22s^22p^63s^23p^6$
d. $1s^22s^22p^6$ **e.** $1s^2$

93 a. Sn^{4+} **b.** 50 protons, 46 electrons
c. SnO_2 **d.** $Sn_3(PO_4)_4$

95 a. Cl^- **b.** K^+ **c.** O^{2-} **d.** Al^{3+}

97 a. potassium **b.** sulfide **c.** calcium **d.** nitride

99 a. SnS **b.** PbO_2 **c.** AgCl
d. Ca_3N_2 **e.** Cu_3P **f.** $CrBr_2$

101 a. Cl_2O ($20\ e^-$)

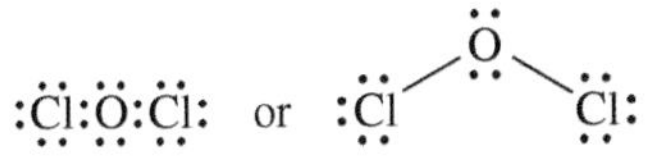

b. CF_4 ($32\ e^-$)

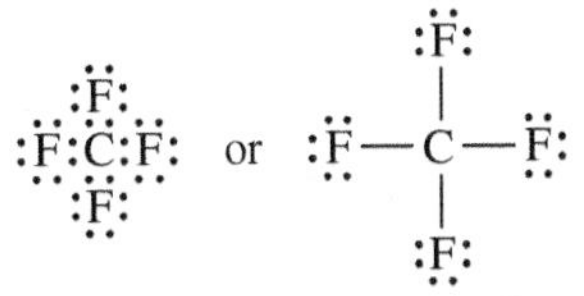

c. H_2NOH ($14\ e^-$)

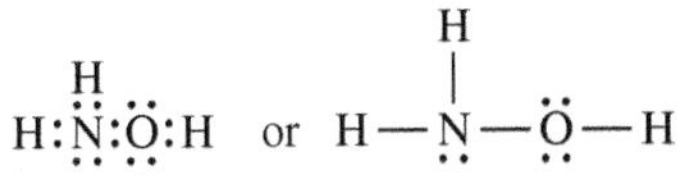

d. H_2CCCl_2 ($24\ e^-$)

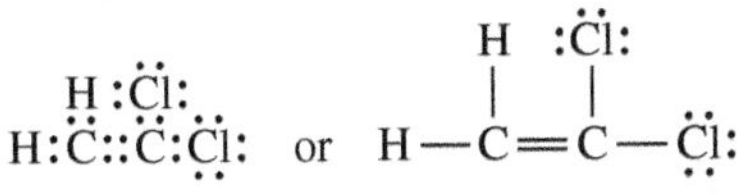

103 a. nitrogen trichloride **b.** dinitrogen trisulfide
c. dinitrogen oxide **d.** fluorine
e. sulfur dioxide **f.** diphosphorus pentoxide

105 a. CO **b.** P_2O_5 **c.** H_2S **d.** SCl_2

107 a. ionic, iron(III) chloride
b. ionic, sodium sulfate
c. covalent, nitrogen dioxide
d. covalent, nitrogen
e. covalent, phosphorus pentafluoride
f. covalent, carbon tetrafluoride

109 a. $SnCO_3$ **b.** Li_3P **c.** $SiCl_4$
d. Mn_2O_3 **e.** I_2 **f.** $CaBr_2$

111 a. C—O **b.** N—F **c.** S—Cl
d. Br—I **e.** N—F

113 a. Si—Cl **b.** C—N **c.** F—Cl
d. C—F **e.** N—O

115 a. polar covalent **b.** nonpolar covalent
c. ionic **d.** nonpolar covalent
e. nonpolar covalent

117 a. NF_3 ($26\ e^-$)

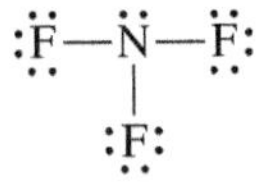

trigonal pyramidal

b. $SiBr_4$ ($32\ e^-$)

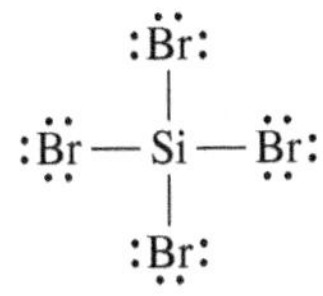

tetrahedral

c. $BeCl_2$ ($16\ e^-$)

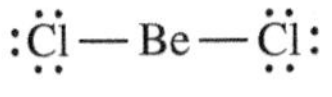

linear

d.

SO_2 ($18\ e^-$)

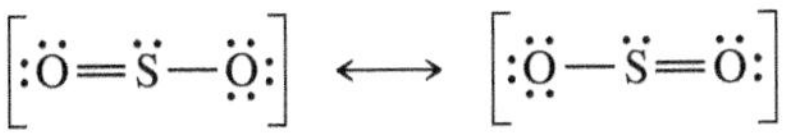

bent (120°)

119

Period	Electron-Dot Symbols	Formula of Compound	Name of Compound
3	$\cdot$X$\cdot$ and $\cdot\ddot{Y}\cdot$	Mg_3P_2	Magnesium phosphide
3	$\cdot\dot{X}\cdot$ and $\cdot\ddot{Y}:$	Al_2S_3	Aluminum sulfide
3	$\cdot\ddot{Y}:$ and $\cdot\ddot{Y}:$	Cl_2	Chlorine
3	$\cdot\ddot{Y}\cdot$ and $\cdot\ddot{Y}:$	PCl_3	Phosphorus trichloride

121 See the table at the bottom of the page.

123 a. X is in Group 1A (1); Y is in Group 6A (16)
b. ionic **c.** X^+, Y^{2-} **d.** X_2Y
e. XCl **f.** Na_2Y **g.** ionic

125 a. ionic, lithium oxide
b. covalent, dinitrogen oxide
c. covalent, carbon tetrafluoride
d. covalent, dichlorine oxide

127 a. iron(II) chloride **b.** dichlorine heptoxide
c. nitrogen **d.** calcium phosphate
e. phosphorus trichloride **f.** calcium hypochlorite

129 a. bent (109°), nonpolar **b.** trigonal pyramidal, polar
c. trigonal pyramidal, polar **d.** tetrahedral, polar
e. tetrahedral, nonpolar

131 a. (3) hydrogen bonds **b.** (2) dipole–dipole attractions
c. (4) dispersion forces **d.** (1) ionic bonds
e. (4) dispersion forces **f.** (3) hydrogen bonds

Answer to 121

Electron Configurations		Symbols of Ions			
Metal	Nonmetal	Cation	Anion	Formula of Compound	Name of Compound
$1s^22s^1$	$1s^22s^22p^63s^23p^4$	Li^+	S^{2-}	Li_2S	Lithium sulfide
$1s^22s^22p^63s^23p^64s^2$	$1s^22s^22p^63s^23p^3$	Ca^{2+}	P^{3-}	Ca_3P_2	Calcium phosphide
$1s^22s^22p^63s^1$	$1s^22s^22p^63s^23p^5$	Na^+	Cl^-	NaCl	Sodium chloride

Chemical Reactions and Quantities

From Chapter 6 of *General, Organic, and Biological Chemistry: Structures of Life*, Fourth Edition. Karen C. Timberlake.

Chemical Reactions and Quantities

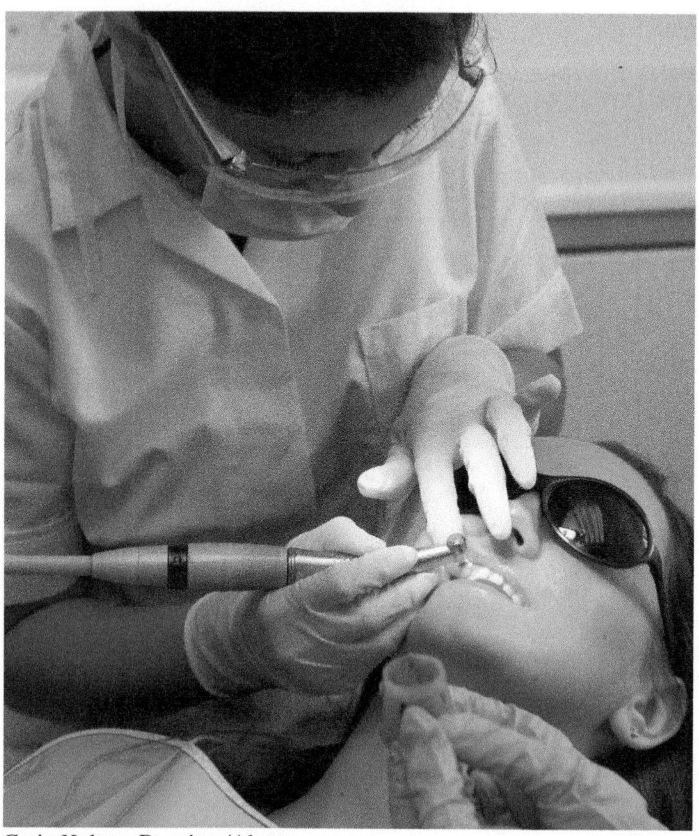

Craig Holmes Premium/Alamy

LOOKING AHEAD

Visit **www.masteringchemistry.com** for self-study materials and instructor-assigned homework.

Kimberly's teeth have become badly stained due to drinking excessive amounts of coffee. She makes an appointment to have her teeth whitened with her dental hygienist. First, Kimberly's teeth are cleaned by the dental hygienist, and the dentist then checks her teeth for any cavities.

After that, the hygienist begins the process of whitening Kimberly's teeth. She explains to Kimberly that she uses a gel of 15–35% hydrogen peroxide which penetrates into the enamel of the tooth, where it causes a chemical reaction that whitens the teeth. The chemical reaction is referred to as a redox reaction where one chemical (hydrogen peroxide) is reduced and the other chemical (the coffee stain) is oxidized. During the oxidation, the coffee stains on the teeth become lighter or colorless, and therefore, the teeth are whiter.

Career: Dental Hygienist

A visit to the dentist frequently begins with a dental hygienist who cleans and polishes the patient's teeth by removing tartar, stains and plaque. This requires the hygienist to use a variety of tools, including hand and rotary instruments, as well as ultrasonic equipment. The hygienist also discusses the proper technique for brushing and flossing with each patient. The dental hygienist may also take X-rays of a patient's teeth in order to detect any abnormalities. A dental hygienist must be knowledgeable about the proper safety procedures for taking X-rays and how to protect themselves from disease transmission by wearing the proper safety attire like safety glasses, surgical masks and gloves.

The fuel in our cars burns with oxygen to provide energy to make the car move or run the air conditioner. When we cook our food or bleach our hair, chemical reactions take place. In our bodies, chemical reactions convert food substances into molecules to build muscles and move them. In the leaves of trees and plants, carbon dioxide and water are converted into carbohydrates.

Some chemical reactions are simple, whereas others are quite complex. However, they can all be written with equations used to describe chemical reactions. In every chemical reaction, the atoms in the reacting substances, called *reactants*, are rearranged to give new substances called *products*.

In this chapter, we will see how equations are written and how we can determine the amount of reactant or product involved. When we cook, we follow a recipe that gives the correct amounts of ingredients (reactants) to mix together and how much bread or cookies (products) we will obtain. At the automotive repair shop, a mechanic does essentially the same thing when adjusting the fuel system of an engine to allow for the correct amounts of fuel and oxygen. In the hospital, a respiratory therapist evaluates the levels of CO_2 and O_2 in the blood. A certain amount of O_2 must reach the tissues for efficient metabolic reactions. If the oxygenation of the blood is low, then the therapist will oxygenate the patient and recheck the blood oxygen levels.

1 Equations for Chemical Reactions

LEARNING GOAL

Write a balanced chemical equation from the formulas of the reactants and products for a chemical reaction.

A *chemical change* occurs when a substance is converted into one or more new substances. There may be a change in color or the formation of bubbles or a solid. For example, when silver tarnishes, the shiny silver metal (Ag) reacts with sulfur (S) to form the dull, black substance we call tarnish (Ag_2S) (see Figure 1).

MC™

SELF-STUDY ACTIVITY
Chemical Reactions and Equations

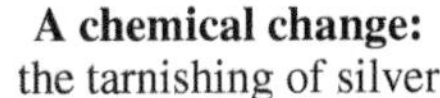

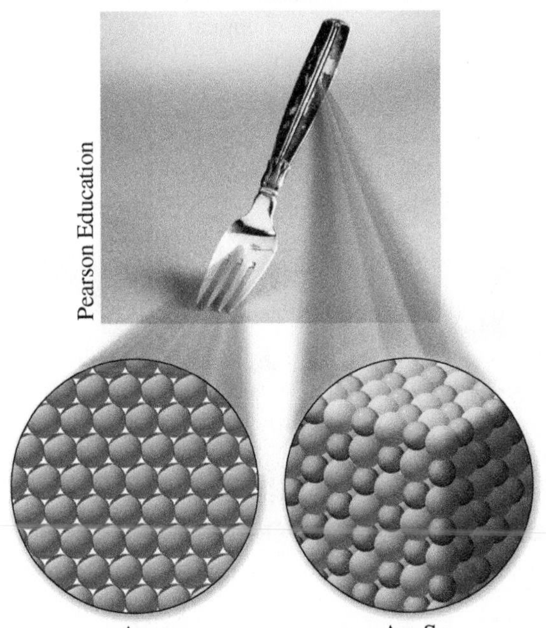

FIGURE 1 A chemical change produces new substances.

Q Why is the formation of tarnish a chemical change?

FIGURE 2 A chemical reaction forms new products with different properties. An antacid ($NaHCO_3$) tablet in water forms bubbles of carbon dioxide (CO_2).

Q What is the evidence for chemical change in this chemical reaction?

A Chemical Equation Describes a Chemical Reaction

A **chemical reaction** always involves chemical change because atoms of the reacting substances form new combinations with new properties. For example, a chemical reaction takes place when an antacid tablet is dropped into a glass of water. The tablet fizzes and bubbles as $NaHCO_3$ and citric acid ($C_6H_8O_7$) in the tablet react to form carbon dioxide (CO_2) gas (see Figure 2). During a chemical change, new properties become visible, which are an indication that a chemical reaction has taken place (see Table 1).

CONCEPT CHECK 1 **Evidence of a Chemical Reaction**

Indicate why each of the following is a chemical reaction:

a. burning propane fuel in a barbecue
b. using peroxide to change the color of hair

ANSWER

a. The production of heat during the burning of propane fuel is evidence of a chemical reaction.
b. The change in hair color is evidence of a chemical reaction.

TABLE 1 Types of Visible Evidence of a Chemical Reaction

1. Change in the color
2. Formation of a gas (bubbles)
3. Formation of a solid (precipitate)
4. Heat (or a flame) produced or heat absorbed

When you install a new computer program, cook using a recipe, or prepare a medication, you follow a set of directions. These directions tell you what materials to use and the products you will obtain. In chemistry, a *chemical equation* tells us the materials we need and the products that will form in a chemical reaction.

SELF-STUDY ACTIVITY
What is Chemistry?

Writing a Chemical Equation

Suppose you work in a bicycle shop, assembling wheels and frames into bicycles. You could represent this process by an equation:

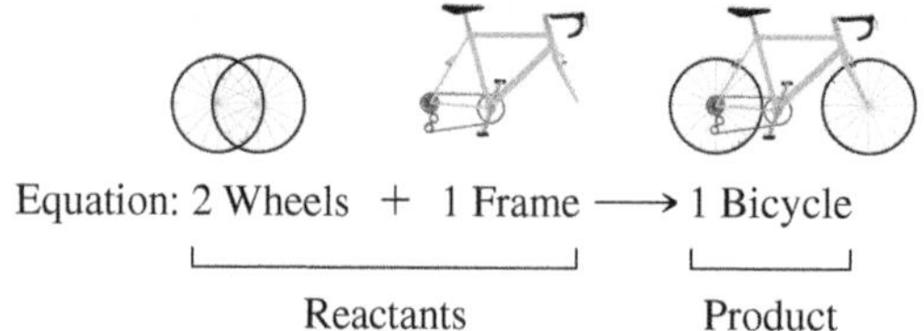

Equation: 2 Wheels + 1 Frame ⟶ 1 Bicycle

Reactants — Product

When you burn charcoal in a grill, the carbon in the charcoal combines with oxygen to form carbon dioxide. We can represent this reaction by a chemical equation that is much like the one for the bicycle:

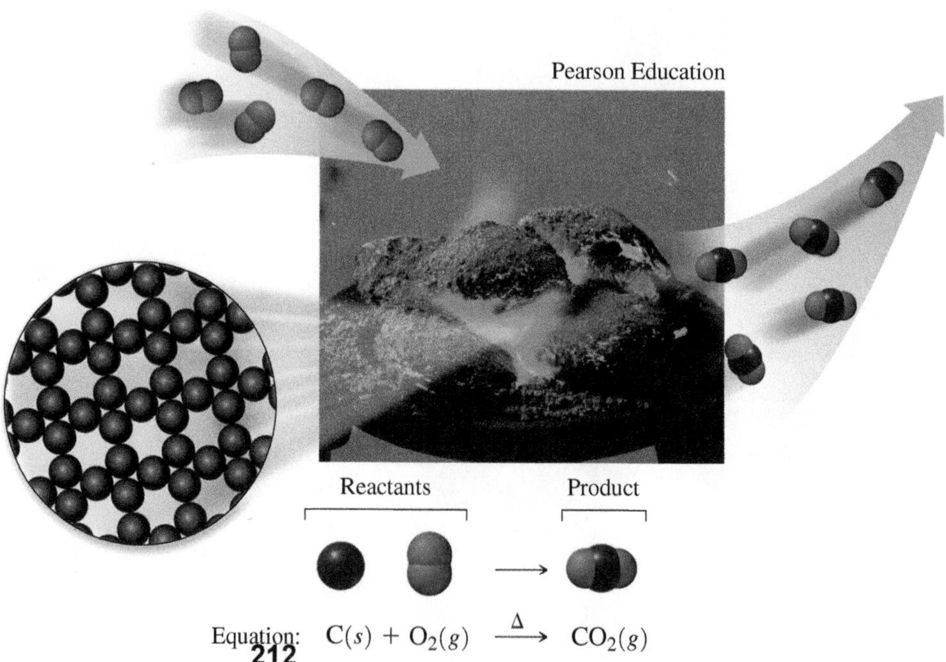

Equation: $C(s) + O_2(g) \xrightarrow{\Delta} CO_2(g)$

TUTORIAL
Chemical Reactions and Equations

In a **chemical equation**, the formulas of the **reactants** are written on the left of the arrow and the formulas of the **products** on the right. When there are two or more formulas on the same side, they are separated by plus (+) signs. The delta sign (Δ) over the reaction arrow indicates that heat was used to start the reaction.

Generally, each formula in an equation is followed by an abbreviation, in parentheses, that gives the physical state of the substance: solid (s), liquid (l), or gas or vapor (g). If a substance is dissolved in water, it is an aqueous (aq) solution. Table 2 summarizes some of the symbols used in equations.

TABLE 2 Some Symbols Used in Writing Equations

Symbol	Meaning
$+$	Separates two or more formulas
$\longrightarrow$	Reacts to form products
$\xrightarrow{\Delta}$	Reactants are heated
(s)	Solid
(l)	Liquid
(g)	Gas or vapor
(aq)	Aqueous

Identifying a Balanced Chemical Equation

When a chemical reaction takes place, the bonds between the atoms of the reactants are broken, and new bonds are formed to give the products. All atoms are conserved, which means that atoms cannot be gained, lost, or changed into other types of atoms during the reaction. Every chemical reaction must be written as a **balanced equation**, which shows the same number of atoms for each element in the reactants as well as in the products.

Now consider the reaction in which hydrogen reacts with oxygen to form water. The formulas of the reactants and products are written as follows:

$$H_2(g) + O_2(g) \longrightarrow H_2O(g)$$

When we add up the atoms of each element on each side, we find that the equation is *not balanced*. There are two oxygen atoms to the left side of the arrow, but only one to the right. To balance this equation, we place whole numbers called **coefficients** in front of the formulas. If we write a coefficient of 2 in front of the H_2O formula, it represents two molecules of water. Because the coefficient multiplies all the atoms in H_2O, there are now four hydrogen atoms and two oxygen atoms in the products. To obtain four hydrogen atoms in the reactants, we must write a coefficient of 2 in front of H_2. However, we *do not change any subscripts*, which would alter the chemical identity of a reactant or product. Now the number of hydrogen atoms and the number of oxygen atoms are the same in the reactants as in the products. The equation is *balanced*.

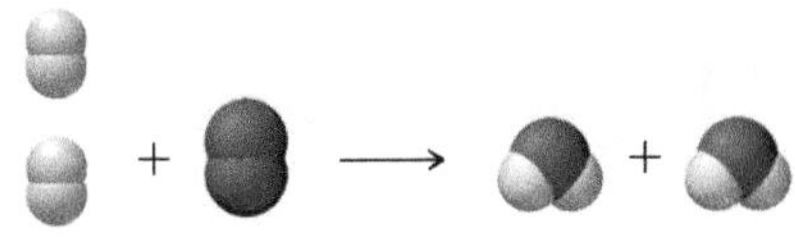

$$2H_2(g) + O_2(g) \longrightarrow 2H_2O(g)$$

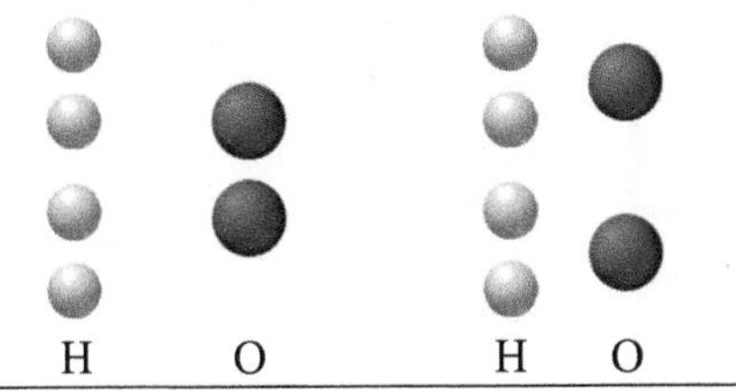

Reactant atoms = Product atoms

CONCEPT CHECK 2 **Balancing Chemical Equations**

Indicate the number of each atom in the reactants and in the products for the following equation:

$$Fe_2S_3(s) + 6HCl(aq) \longrightarrow 2FeCl_3(aq) + 3H_2S(g)$$

	Reactants	Products
Atoms of Fe		
Atoms of S		
Atoms of H		
Atoms of Cl		

ANSWER

The total number of atoms in each formula is obtained by multiplying through by its coefficient.

	Reactants	Products
Atoms of Fe	2	2
Atoms of S	3	3
Atoms of H	6	6
Atoms of Cl	6	6

TUTORIAL
Balancing Chemical Equations

TUTORIAL
Signs of a Chemical Reaction

Balancing a Chemical Equation

The chemical reaction that occurs in the flame of a gas burner you use in the laboratory or a gas cooktop is the reaction of methane gas, CH_4, and oxygen to produce carbon dioxide and water. We show the process of balancing a chemical equation in Sample Problem 1.

Guide to Balancing a Chemical Equation

1. Write an equation using the correct formulas of the reactants and products.
2. Count the atoms of each element in the reactants and products.
3. Use coefficients to balance each element.
4. Check the final equation to confirm it is balanced.

SAMPLE PROBLEM 1 Balancing a Chemical Equation

The chemical reaction of methane, CH_4, and oxygen gas, O_2, produces carbon dioxide, CO_2, and water, H_2O. Write a balanced chemical equation for this reaction.

SOLUTION

Step 1 **Write an equation using the correct formulas of the reactants and products.**

$$CH_4(g) + O_2(g) \xrightarrow{\Delta} CO_2(g) + H_2O(g)$$

Pearson Education

Step 2 **Count the atoms of each element in the reactants and products.** In the initial unbalanced equation, a coefficient of 1 is understood and not usually written. When we compare the atoms on the reactant side with the atoms on the product side, we see that there are more H atoms in the reactants and more O atoms in the products.

$$CH_4(g) + O_2(g) \xrightarrow{\Delta} CO_2(g) + H_2O(g)$$

Reactants	Products	
1 C atom	1 C atom	Balanced
4 H atoms	2 H atoms	Not balanced
2 O atoms	3 O atoms	Not balanced

Step 3 **Use coefficients to balance each element.** We will start by balancing the H atoms in CH_4 because it has the most atoms. By placing a coefficient of 2 in front of the formula for water, a total of 4 H atoms in the products is obtained.

$$CH_4(g) + O_2(g) \xrightarrow{\Delta} CO_2(g) + 2H_2O(g)$$

Reactants	Products	
1 C atom	1 C atom	Balanced
4 H atoms	4 H atoms	Balanced
2 O atoms	4 O atoms	Not balanced

We can balance the O atoms on the reactant side by placing a coefficient of 2 in front of the formula O_2. There are now 4 O atoms and 4 H atoms in both the reactants and products.

$$CH_4(g) + 2O_2(g) \xrightarrow{\Delta} CO_2(g) + 2H_2O(g)$$ Balanced

Step 4 **Check the final equation to confirm it is balanced.** In the final equation, the numbers of C, H, and O atoms are the same in both the reactants and products. The equation is balanced.

$$CH_4(g) + 2O_2(g) \xrightarrow{\Delta} CO_2(g) + 2H_2O(g)$$

Reactants	Products	
1 C atom	1 C atom	Balanced
4 H atoms	4 H atoms	Balanced
4 O atoms	4 O atoms	Balanced

In a balanced equation, the coefficients must be the lowest whole numbers possible. Suppose you had obtained the following:

$$2CH_4(g) + 4O_2(g) \xrightarrow{\Delta} 2CO_2(g) + 4H_2O(g)$$ Incorrect

Although there are equal numbers of atoms in the reactants and in the products, this is not balanced correctly. The correctly balanced equation is obtained by dividing all the coefficients by 2.

STUDY CHECK 1

Balance the following equation:

$$Al(s) + Cl_2(g) \longrightarrow AlCl_3(s)$$

SAMPLE PROBLEM 2 Balancing Chemical Equations with Polyatomic Ions

Balance the following equation:

$$Na_3PO_4(aq) + MgCl_2(aq) \longrightarrow Mg_3(PO_4)_2(s) + NaCl(aq)$$

SOLUTION

Step 1 **Write an equation using the correct formulas of the reactants and products.**

$$Na_3PO_4(aq) + MgCl_2(aq) \longrightarrow Mg_3(PO_4)_2(s) + NaCl(aq)$$

Step 2 **Count the atoms of each element in the reactants and products.** When we compare the number of ions on the reactant and product sides, we find they are not balanced. In this equation, we can balance the phosphate ion as a group because it appears on both sides of the equation.

$$Na_3PO_4(aq) + MgCl_2(aq) \longrightarrow Mg_3(PO_4)_2(s) + NaCl(aq)$$

Reactants	Products	
3 Na^+	1 Na^+	Not balanced
1 PO_4^{3-}	2 PO_4^{3-}	Not balanced
1 Mg^{2+}	3 Mg^{2+}	Not balanced
2 Cl^-	1 Cl^-	Not balanced

Step 3 **Use coefficients to balance each element.** We begin with the formula that has the highest subscript values, which in this equation is $Mg_3(PO_4)_2$. The subscript 3 in $Mg_3(PO_4)_2$ is used as a coefficient for $MgCl_2$ to balance magnesium. The subscript 2 in $Mg_3(PO_4)_2$ is used as a coefficient for Na_3PO_4 to balance the phosphate ion.

$$2Na_3PO_4(aq) + 3MgCl_2(aq) \longrightarrow Mg_3(PO_4)_2(s) + NaCl(aq)$$

Reactants	Products	
6 Na^+	1 Na^+	Not balanced
2 PO_4^{3-}	2 PO_4^{3-}	Balanced
3 Mg^{2+}	3 Mg^{2+}	Balanced
6 Cl^-	1 Cl^-	Not balanced

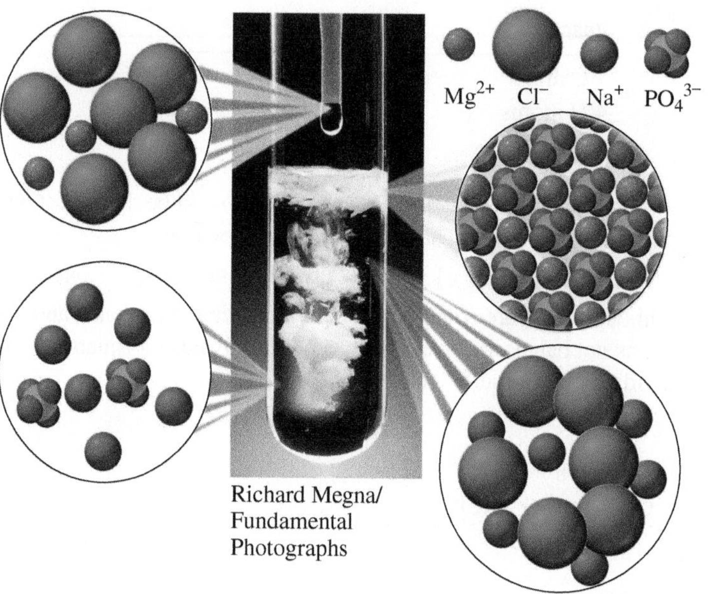

Richard Megna/ Fundamental Photographs

Looking again at each of the ions in the reactants and products, we see that the sodium and chloride ions are not yet equal. A coefficient of 6 for the NaCl balances the equation.

$$2Na_3PO_4(aq) + 3MgCl_2(aq) \longrightarrow Mg_3(PO_4)_2(s) + 6NaCl(aq)$$

Step 4 **Check the final equation to confirm it is balanced.** A check of the total number of atoms indicates that the equation is balanced. A coefficient of 1 is understood and not usually written.

$$2Na_3PO_4(aq) + 3MgCl_2(aq) \longrightarrow Mg_3(PO_4)_2(s) + 6NaCl(aq)$$ Balanced

Reactants	Products	
6 Na^+	6 Na^+	Balanced
2 PO_4^{3-}	2 PO_4^{3-}	Balanced
3 Mg^{2+}	3 Mg^{2+}	Balanced
6 Cl^-	6 Cl^-	Balanced

STUDY CHECK 2

Balance the following equation:

$$Sb_2S_3(s) + HCl(aq) \longrightarrow SbCl_3(s) + H_2S(g)$$

QUESTIONS AND PROBLEMS

1 Equations for Chemical Reactions

LEARNING GOAL: *Write a balanced chemical equation from the formulas of the reactants and products for a chemical reaction.*

1 Determine whether each of the following equations is balanced or not balanced:

a. $S(s) + O_2(g) \longrightarrow SO_3(g)$
b. $2Al(s) + 3Cl_2(g) \longrightarrow 2AlCl_3(s)$
c. $2NaOH(s) + H_2SO_4(aq) \longrightarrow Na_2SO_4(aq) + H_2O(l)$
d. $C_3H_8(g) + 5O_2(g) \xrightarrow{\Delta} 3CO_2(g) + 4H_2O(g)$

2 Determine whether each of the following equations is balanced or not balanced:

a. $PCl_3(s) + Cl_2(g) \longrightarrow PCl_5(s)$
b. $CO(g) + 2H_2(g) \longrightarrow CH_3OH(g)$
c. $2KClO_3(s) \xrightarrow{\Delta} 2KCl(s) + O_2(g)$
d. $Mg(s) + N_2(g) \longrightarrow Mg_3N_2(s)$

3 Balance each of the following equations:

a. $N_2(g) + O_2(g) \longrightarrow NO(g)$
b. $HgO(s) \longrightarrow Hg(l) + O_2(g)$
c. $Fe(s) + O_2(g) \longrightarrow Fe_2O_3(s)$
d. $Na(s) + Cl_2(g) \longrightarrow NaCl(s)$
e. $Cu_2O(s) + O_2(g) \longrightarrow CuO(s)$

4 Balance each of the following equations:

a. $Ca(s) + Br_2(l) \longrightarrow CaBr_2(s)$
b. $P_4(s) + O_2(g) \longrightarrow P_4O_{10}(s)$
c. $C_4H_8(g) + O_2(g) \xrightarrow{\Delta} CO_2(g) + H_2O(g)$
d. $Sb_2S_3(s) + HCl(aq) \longrightarrow SbCl_3(s) + H_2S(g)$
e. $Fe_2O_3(s) + C(s) \longrightarrow Fe(s) + CO(g)$

5 Balance each of the following equations:

a. $Mg(s) + AgNO_3(aq) \longrightarrow Mg(NO_3)_2(aq) + Ag(s)$
b. $CuCO_3(s) \longrightarrow CuO(s) + CO_2(g)$
c. $C_5H_{12}(g) + O_2(g) \xrightarrow{\Delta} CO_2(g) + H_2O(g)$
d. $Pb(NO_3)_2(aq) + NaCl(aq) \longrightarrow PbCl_2(s) + NaNO_3(aq)$
e. $Al(s) + HCl(aq) \longrightarrow AlCl_3(aq) + H_2(g)$

6 Balance each of the following equations:

a. $Zn(s) + H_2SO_4(aq) \longrightarrow ZnSO_4(aq) + H_2(g)$
b. $N_2(g) + I_2(g) \longrightarrow NI_3(g)$
c. $K_2SO_4(aq) + BaCl_2(aq) \longrightarrow BaSO_4(s) + KCl(aq)$
d. $CaCO_3(s) \xrightarrow{\Delta} CaO(s) + CO_2(g)$
e. $Al_2(SO_4)_3(aq) + KOH(aq) \longrightarrow Al(OH)_3(s) + K_2SO_4(aq)$

2 Types of Reactions

LEARNING GOAL

Identify a chemical reaction as a combination, decomposition, single replacement, double replacement, or combustion reaction.

A great number of reactions occur in nature, in biological systems, and in the laboratory. However, some general patterns among all reactions help us to classify them. Most fit into five general reaction types.

Combination Reactions

TUTORIAL
Classifying Chemical Reactions by What Atoms Do

In a **combination reaction**, two or more elements or compounds bond to form one product. For example, sulfur and oxygen combine to form the product sulfur dioxide.

$$S(s) + O_2(g) \longrightarrow SO_2(g)$$

Combination

Two or more reactants | combine to yield | a single product

+

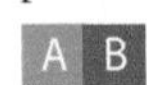

In Figure 3, the elements magnesium and oxygen combine to form a single product, magnesium oxide.

$$2Mg(s) + O_2(g) \xrightarrow{\Delta} 2MgO(s)$$

In other examples of combination reactions, elements or compounds combine to form a single product.

$$N_2(g) + 3H_2(g) \longrightarrow \underset{\text{Ammonia}}{2NH_3(g)}$$

$$Cu(s) + S(s) \longrightarrow CuS(s)$$

$$MgO(s) + CO_2(g) \longrightarrow MgCO_3(s)$$

Pearson Education
O_2
Pearson Education
Pearson Education
Mg Mg
Mg Mg
Mg^{2+} Mg^{2+}
O^{2-} O^{2-}
$2Mg(s)$
Magnesium
+
$O_2(g)$
Oxygen
Δ
$2MgO(s)$
Magnesium oxide

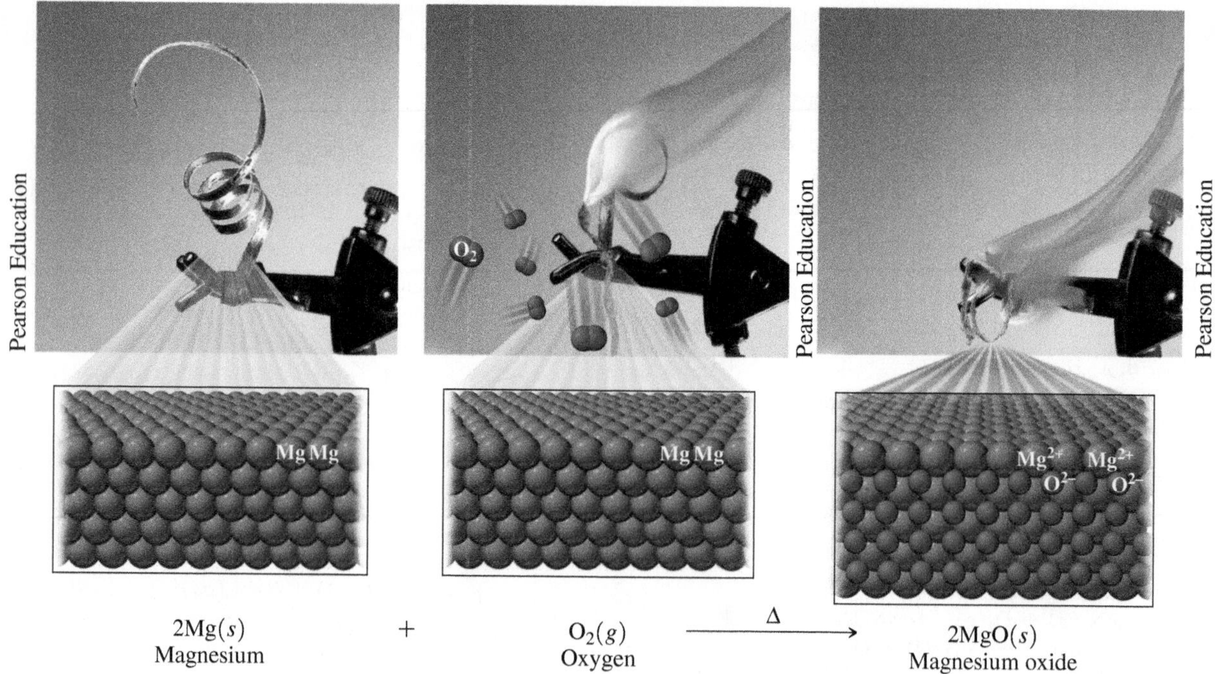

FIGURE 3 In a combination reaction, two or more substances combine to form one substance as product.

Q What happens to the atoms of the reactants in a combination reaction?

Decomposition

A reactant splits into two or more products

AB ⟶ A + B

Decomposition Reactions

In a **decomposition reaction**, a reactant splits into two or more simpler products. For example, when mercury(II) oxide is heated, the compound breaks apart into mercury atoms and oxygen (see Figure 4).

$$2HgO(s) \xrightarrow{\Delta} 2Hg(l) + O_2(g)$$

FIGURE 4 In a decomposition reaction, one reactant breaks down into two or more products.

Q How do the differences in the reactant and products classify this as a decomposition reaction?

Pearson Education/Tom Bochsler
Hg^{2+} Hg^{2+}
O^{2-} O^{2-}
Hg
Hg
Hg
Hg
Hg
Hg
O_2
$2HgO(s)$
Mercury(II) oxide
Δ
$2Hg(l)$
Mercury
+
$O_2(g)$
Oxygen

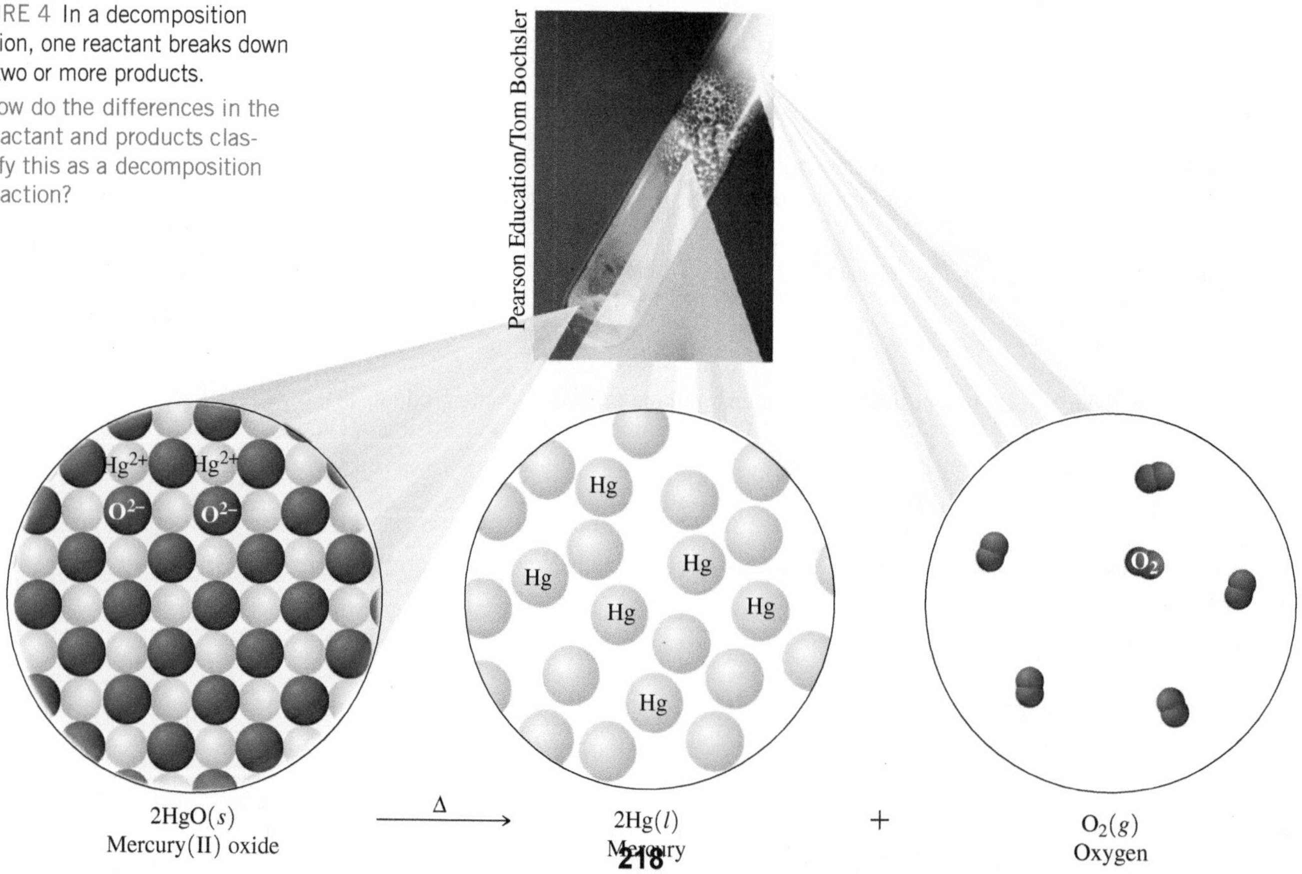

In another example of a decomposition reaction, calcium carbonate breaks apart into simpler compounds of calcium oxide and carbon dioxide.

$$CaCO_3(s) \xrightarrow{\Delta} CaO(s) + CO_2(g)$$

Single Replacement Reactions

In a replacement reaction, elements in a compound are replaced by other elements. In a **single replacement reaction**, a reacting element switches place with an element in the other reacting compound. In the single replacement reaction shown in Figure 5, zinc replaces hydrogen in hydrochloric acid, $HCl(aq)$.

Single replacement

One element replaces another element

A + BC ⟶ AC + B

$$Zn(s) + 2HCl(aq) \longrightarrow ZnCl_2(aq) + H_2(g)$$

In another single replacement reaction, chlorine replaces bromine in the compound potassium bromide.

$$Cl_2(g) + 2KBr(aq) \longrightarrow 2KCl(s) + Br_2(l)$$

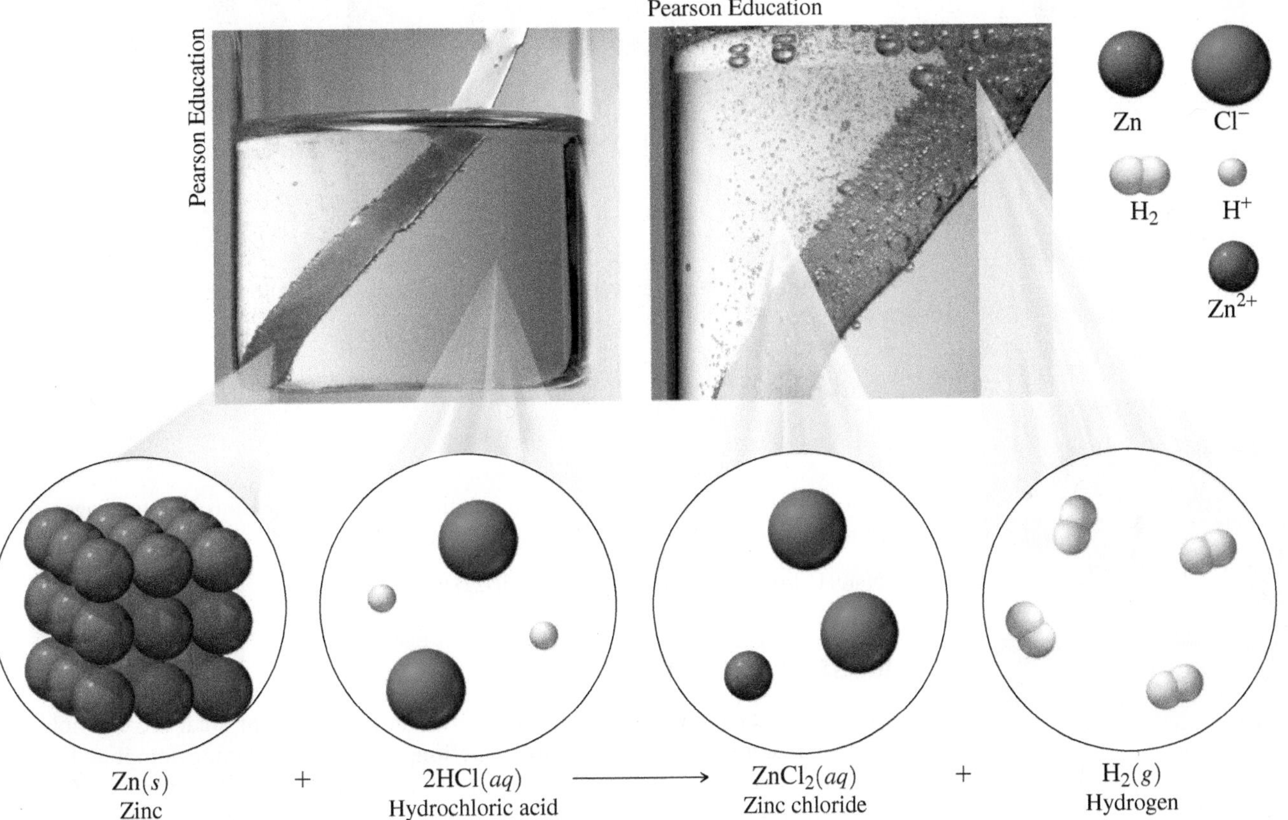

FIGURE 5 In a single replacement reaction, an atom or ion replaces an atom or ion in a compound.

Q What changes in the formulas of the reactants identify this equation as a single replacement?

Double Replacement Reactions

Double replacement

Two elements replace each other

AB + CD ⟶ AD + CB

In a **double replacement reaction**, the positive ions in the reacting compounds switch places.

In the reaction shown in Figure 6, barium ions change places with sodium ions in the reactants to form sodium chloride and a white solid precipitate of barium sulfate. The formulas of the products depend on the charges of the ions.

$$BaCl_2(aq) + Na_2SO_4(aq) \longrightarrow BaSO_4(s) + 2NaCl(aq)$$

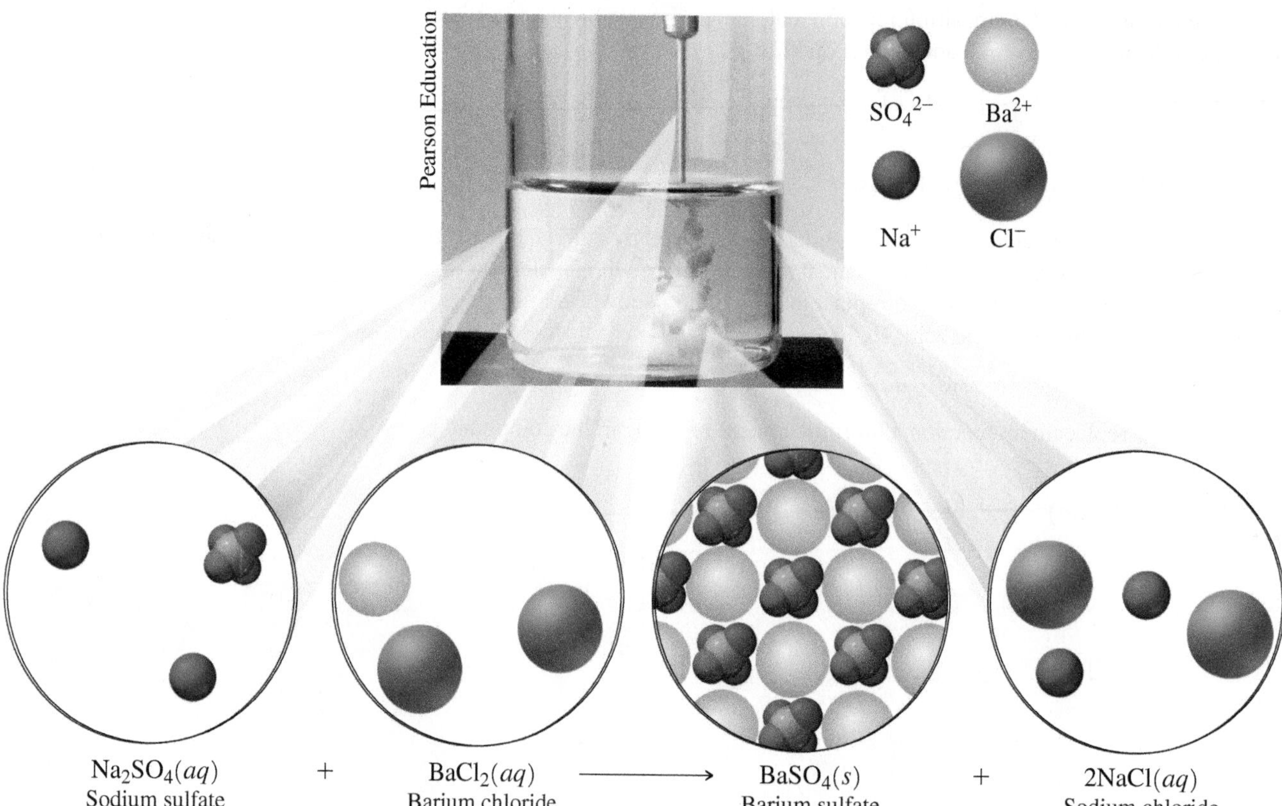

FIGURE 6 In a double replacement reaction, the positive ions in the reactants replace each other.

Q How do the changes in the formulas of the reactants identify this equation as a double replacement reaction?

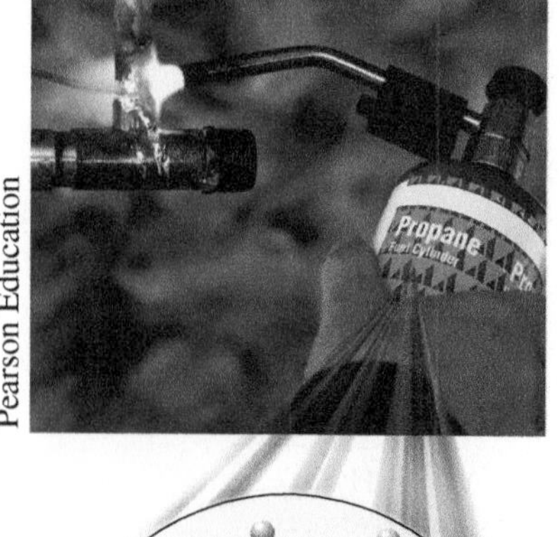

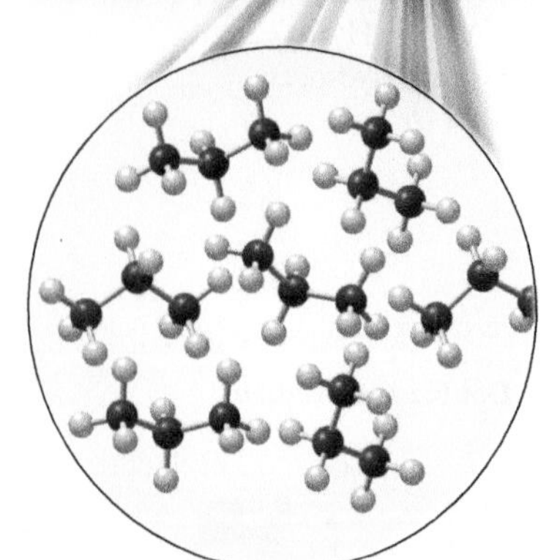

The propane from the torch undergoes combustion, which provides energy to solder metals.

When sodium hydroxide and hydrochloric acid (HCl) react, sodium and hydrogen ions switch places, forming sodium chloride and water.

$$NaOH(aq) + HCl(aq) \longrightarrow NaCl(aq) + HOH(l)$$

Combustion Reactions

The burning of a candle and the burning of fuel in the engine of a car are examples of combustion reactions. In a **combustion reaction**, a carbon-containing compound that is the fuel burns in oxygen from the air to produce carbon dioxide (CO_2), water (H_2O), and energy in the form of heat or a flame. For example, methane gas (CH_4) undergoes combustion when used to cook our food on a gas cooktop and to heat our homes. In the equation for the combustion of methane, each element in the fuel (CH_4) forms a compound with oxygen.

$$\underset{\text{Methane}}{CH_4(g)} + 2O_2(g) \xrightarrow{\Delta} CO_2(g) + 2H_2O(g) + \text{energy}$$

The balanced equation for the combustion of propane (C_3H_8) is:

$$C_3H_8(g) + 5O_2(g) \xrightarrow{\Delta} 3CO_2(g) + 4H_2O(g) + \text{energy}$$

Propane is the fuel used in portable heaters and gas barbecues. Gasoline, a mixture of liquid hydrocarbons, is the fuel that powers our cars, lawn mowers, and snow blowers.

Table 3 summarizes the reaction types and gives examples.

CONCEPT CHECK 3 **Identifying the Type of Reaction**

Classify the following reactions as combination, decomposition, single replacement, double replacement, or combustion:

a. $2Fe_2O_3(s) + 3C(s) \longrightarrow 3CO_2(g) + 4Fe(s)$

b. $2KClO_3(s) \xrightarrow{\Delta} 2KCl(s) + 3O_2(g)$

c. $C_2H_4(g) + 3O_2(g) \xrightarrow{\Delta} 2CO_2(g) + 2H_2O(g) + \text{energy}$

ANSWER

a. In this single replacement reaction, a C atom replaces Fe in Fe_2O_3 to form the compound CO_2 and Fe atoms.

b. When one reactant breaks down to produce two products, the reaction is decomposition.

c. The reaction of a carbon compound with oxygen to produce carbon dioxide, water, and energy makes this a combustion reaction.

Richard Megna/Fundamental Photographs

In a combustion reaction, a candle burns using the oxygen in the air.

TABLE 3 **Summary of Reaction Types**

Reaction Type	Example
Combination	
$A + B \longrightarrow AB$	$Ca(s) + Cl_2(g) \longrightarrow CaCl_2(s)$
Decomposition	
$AB \longrightarrow A + B$	$Fe_2S_3(s) \longrightarrow 2Fe(s) + 3S(s)$
Single Replacement	
$A + BC \longrightarrow AC + B$	$Cu(s) + 2AgNO_3(aq) \longrightarrow Cu(NO_3)_2(aq) + 2Ag(s)$
Double Replacement	
$AB + CD \longrightarrow AD + CB$	$BaCl_2(aq) + K_2SO_4(aq) \longrightarrow BaSO_4(s) + 2KCl(aq)$
Combustion	
$C_XH_Y + ZO_2(g) \xrightarrow{\Delta} XCO_2(g) + Y/2\,H_2O(g) + \text{energy}$	$CH_4(g) + 2O_2(g) \xrightarrow{\Delta} CO_2(g) + 2H_2O(g) + \text{energy}$

Chemistry Link to Health

SMOG AND HEALTH CONCERNS

There are two types of smog. One, photochemical smog, requires sunlight to initiate reactions that produce pollutants such as nitrogen oxides and ozone. The other type of smog, industrial or London smog, occurs in areas where coal that contains sulfur is burned and the unwanted product, sulfur dioxide, is emitted.

Photochemical smog is most prevalent in cities where people are dependent on cars for transportation. On a typical day in Los Angeles, for example, nitrogen oxide (NO) emissions from car exhausts increase as traffic increases on the roads. When N_2 and O_2 react at high temperatures in car and truck engines, the product is nitrogen oxide.

$$N_2(g) + O_2(g) \xrightarrow{\Delta} 2NO(g)$$

Then NO reacts with oxygen in the air to produce NO_2, a reddish-brown gas that is irritating to the eyes and damaging to the respiratory tract.

$$2NO(g) + O_2(g) \xrightarrow{\Delta} 2NO_2(g)$$

Patrick Clark/Getty Images

The reddish-brown color of smog is due to nitrogen dioxide.

When NO_2 molecules are exposed to sunlight, they are converted into NO and an oxygen atom (O).

$$NO_2(g) \xrightarrow{\text{Sunlight}} NO(g) + \underset{\text{Oxygen atom}}{O(g)}$$

Oxygen atoms are so reactive that they combine with oxygen molecules in the atmosphere, forming ozone.

$$O(g) + O_2(g) \longrightarrow \underset{\text{Ozone}}{O_3(g)}$$

In the upper atmosphere (the stratosphere), ozone is beneficial because it protects us from harmful ultraviolet radiation that comes from the Sun. However, in the lower atmosphere, ozone irritates the eyes and respiratory tract, where it causes coughing, decreased lung function, and fatigue. It also causes deterioration of fabrics, cracks rubber, and damages trees and crops.

Industrial smog is prevalent in areas where sulfur is converted to sulfur dioxide during the burning of coal or other sulfur-containing fuels.

$$S(s) + O_2(g) \longrightarrow SO_2(g)$$

The SO_2 is damaging to plants and is corrosive to metals such as steel. SO_2 is also damaging to humans and can cause lung impairment and respiratory difficulties. In the air, the SO_2 reacts with more oxygen to form SO_3, which can combine with water to form sulfuric acid. When rain falls, it absorbs the sulfuric acid, which makes acid rain.

$$2SO_2(g) + O_2(g) \longrightarrow 2SO_3(g)$$

$$SO_3(g) + H_2O(l) \longrightarrow \underset{\text{Sulfuric acid}}{H_2SO_4(aq)}$$

The presence of sulfuric acid in rivers and lakes causes an increase in the acidity of the water, reducing the ability of animals and plants to survive.

QUESTIONS AND PROBLEMS

2 Types of Reactions

LEARNING GOAL: *Identify a chemical reaction as a combination, decomposition, single replacement, double replacement, or combustion reaction.*

7 Classify each of the following as a combination, decomposition, single replacement, double replacement, or combustion reaction:

a. $2Al_2O_3(s) \xrightarrow{\Delta} 4Al(s) + 3O_2(g)$
b. $Br_2(g) + BaI_2(s) \longrightarrow BaBr_2(s) + I_2(g)$
c. $2C_2H_2(g) + 5O_2(g) \xrightarrow{\Delta} 4CO_2(g) + 2H_2O(g)$
d. $BaCl_2(aq) + K_2CO_3(aq) \longrightarrow BaCO_3(s) + 2KCl(aq)$

8 Classify each of the following as a combination, decomposition, single replacement, double replacement, or combustion reaction:

a. $H_2(g) + Br_2(g) \longrightarrow 2HBr(g)$
b. $AgNO_3(aq) + NaCl(aq) \longrightarrow AgCl(s) + NaNO_3(aq)$
c. $2H_2O_2(aq) \longrightarrow 2H_2O(g) + O_2(g)$
d. $Zn(s) + CuCl_2(aq) \longrightarrow Cu(s) + ZnCl_2(aq)$

9 Classify each of the following as a combination, decomposition, single replacement, double replacement, or combustion reaction:

a. $Mg(s) + 2AgNO_3(aq) \longrightarrow Mg(NO_3)_2(aq) + 2Ag(s)$
b. $4Fe(s) + 3O_2(g) \longrightarrow 2Fe_2O_3(s)$
c. $CuCO_3(s) \xrightarrow{\Delta} CuO(s) + CO_2(g)$
d. $2C_6H_6(l) + 15O_2(g) \xrightarrow{\Delta} 12CO_2(g) + 6H_2O(g)$
e. $Al_2(SO_4)_3(aq) + 6KOH(aq) \longrightarrow 2Al(OH)_3(s) + 3K_2SO_4(aq)$
f. $KOH(aq) + HBr(aq) \longrightarrow KBr(aq) + H_2O(l)$

10 Classify each of the following as a combination, decomposition, single replacement, double replacement or combustion reaction:

a. $CuO(s) + 2HCl(aq) \longrightarrow CuCl_2(aq) + H_2O(l)$
b. $2Al(s) + 3Br_2(g) \longrightarrow 2AlBr_3(s)$
c. $Pb(NO_3)_2(aq) + 2NaCl(aq) \longrightarrow PbCl_2(s) + 2NaNO_3(aq)$
d. $C_6H_{12}O_6(aq) \longrightarrow 2C_2H_6O(aq) + 2CO_2(g)$
e. $NaOH(aq) + HCl(aq) \longrightarrow NaCl(aq) + H_2O(l)$
f. $C_6H_{12}(l) + 9O_2(g) \xrightarrow{\Delta} 6CO_2(g) + 6H_2O(g)$

11 Complete the equation for each of the following types of reactions, and then balance:

a. combination: $Mg(s) + Cl_2(g) \longrightarrow$ ______
b. decomposition: $HBr(g) \longrightarrow$ ______ $+ Br_2(g)$
c. single replacement: $Mg(s) + Zn(NO_3)_2(aq) \longrightarrow$ ______ + ______
d. double replacement: $K_2S(aq) + Pb(NO_3)_2(aq) \longrightarrow$ ______ + ______
e. combustion: $C_5H_{10}(l) + O_2(g) \xrightarrow{\Delta} CO_2(g) +$ ______

12 Complete the equation for each of the following types of reactions, and then balance:

a. combination: $Ca(s) + O_2(g) \longrightarrow$ ______
b. combustion: $C_3H_4(g) + O_2(g) \xrightarrow{\Delta}$ ______ $+ H_2O(g)$
c. decomposition: $PbO_2(s) \longrightarrow$ ______ + ______
d. single replacement: $KI(s) + Cl_2(g) \longrightarrow$ ______ + ______
e. double replacement: $CuCl_2(aq) + Na_2S(aq) \longrightarrow$ ______ $+ NaCl(aq)$

LEARNING GOAL

Define the terms oxidation and reduction; identify the reactant that is oxidized and the reactant that is reduced.

3 Oxidation–Reduction Reactions

Perhaps you have never heard of an oxidation and reduction reaction. However, this type of reaction has many important applications in your everyday life. When you see a rusty nail, tarnish on a silver spoon, or corrosion on iron metal, you are observing oxidation.

$$4Fe(s) + 3O_2(g) \longrightarrow \underset{\text{Rust}}{2Fe_2O_3(s)}$$

When we turn the lights on in our automobiles, an oxidation–reduction reaction within the car battery provides the electricity. On a cold, wintry day, we might build a fire. As the wood burns, oxygen combines with carbon and hydrogen to produce carbon dioxide, water, and heat. In the last section, we called this a combustion reaction, but it is also an oxidation–reduction reaction. When we eat foods with starches in them, the starches break down to give glucose, which is oxidized in our cells to give us energy along with carbon dioxide and water. Every breath we take provides oxygen to carry out oxidation in our cells.

$$C_6H_{12}O_6(aq) + 6O_2(g) \longrightarrow 6CO_2(g) + 6H_2O(l) + \text{energy}$$

Rust forms when the oxygen in the air reacts with iron.

Oxidation–Reduction Reactions

In an **oxidation–reduction reaction** (*redox*), electrons are transferred from one substance to another. If one substance loses electrons, another substance must gain electrons. **Oxidation** is defined as the *loss* of electrons; **reduction** is defined as the *gain* of electrons.

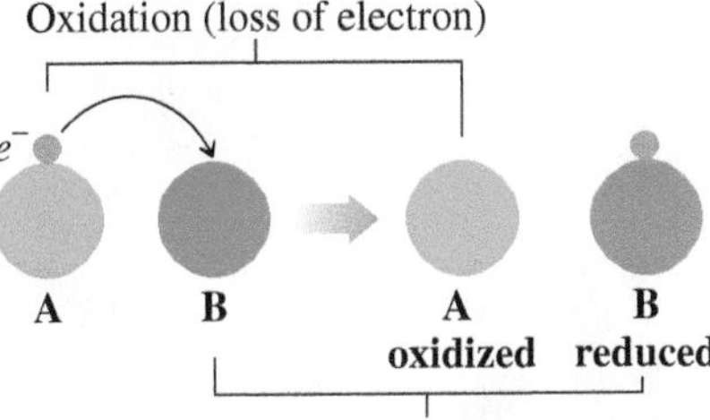

TUTORIAL
Identifying Oxidation–Reduction Reactions

One way to remember these definitions is to use the following:

OIL RIG

Oxidation **I**s **L**oss of electrons.

Reduction **I**s **G**ain of electrons.

In the formation of ionic compounds, we have seen that metals lose electrons to become positive ions and nonmetals gain electrons to become negative ions. We can identify oxidation and reduction by looking at their charges in the reactants and the products. We can write a number line that goes from 0 up to 4+ and down from 0 to 4−. Using the value of 0 for any element by itself, we can determine whether each change is an oxidation or reduction reaction.

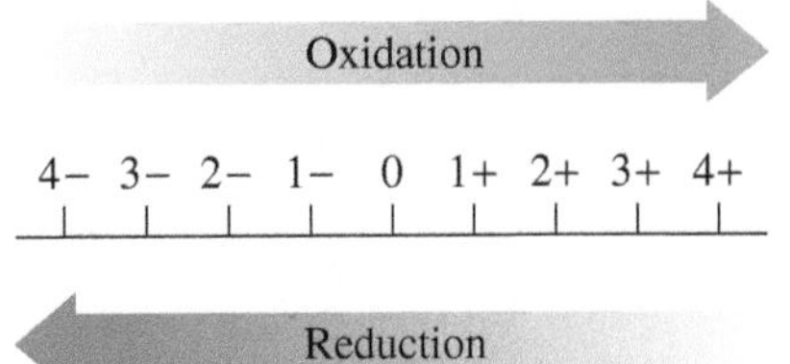

An oxidation reaction occurs when the charge becomes more positive. A reduction reaction occurs when the charge becomes more negative.

Let's look at the formation of the ionic compound CaS from its elements Ca and S.

$$Ca(s) + S(s) \longrightarrow CaS(s)$$

The element Ca in the reactants has a charge of 0, but in the CaS product, it is present as a Ca^{2+} ion. Because the charge is more positive, we know that the calcium atom lost two electrons, which means that an oxidation reaction took place.

$$Ca^0(s) \longrightarrow Ca^{2+}(s) + 2\,e^- \quad \text{Oxidation; loss of electrons}$$

At the same time, the element S in the reactants has a charge of 0, but in the CaS product, it is present as a S^{2-} ion. Because the charge is more negative, we know that the sulfur atom gained two electrons, which means that a reduction reaction took place.

$$S^0(s) + 2\,e^- \longrightarrow S^{2-}(s) \quad \text{Reduction; gain of electrons}$$

Thus, the overall equation for the formation of CaS involves an oxidation and a reduction reaction that occur simultaneously. In every oxidation and reduction, the number of electrons lost must be equal to the number of electrons gained. Because each shows a loss or gain of two electrons, we can add them and write the overall equation for the formation of CaS.

$$\begin{array}{lll} Ca^0(s) & \longrightarrow & Ca^{2+}(s) + \cancel{2e^-} \\ S^0(s) + \cancel{2e^-} & \longrightarrow & S^{2-}(s) \\ \hline Ca^0(s) + S^0(s) & \longrightarrow & Ca^{2+}S^{2-}(s) \end{array}$$

The overall equation without the charges is written as:

$$Ca(s) + S(s) \longrightarrow CaS(s)$$

As we can see in the next reaction between zinc and copper(II) sulfate, there is always an oxidation with every reduction (see Figure 7).

$$Zn(s) + CuSO_4(aq) \longrightarrow ZnSO_4(aq) + Cu(s)$$

We can rewrite the equation to show the atoms and ions that react as:

$$Zn^0(s) + Cu^{2+}(aq) + SO_4^{2-}(aq) \longrightarrow Zn^{2+}(aq) + SO_4^{2-}(aq) + Cu^0(s)$$

FIGURE 7 In this single replacement reaction, $Zn^0(s)$ is oxidized to Zn^{2+} when it provides two electrons to reduce Cu^{2+} to $Cu^0(s)$:

$$Zn^0(s) + Cu^{2+}(aq) \longrightarrow Cu^0(s) + Zn^{2+}(aq)$$

Q In the oxidation, does Zn(*s*) lose or gain electrons?

In this reaction, Zn atoms lose two electrons to form Zn^{2+}. The increase in positive charge indicates that Zn(*s*) is oxidized. At the same time, Cu^{2+} gains two electrons to form Cu(*s*). The decrease in charge indicates that Cu^{2+} is reduced. The SO_4^{2-} ions are *spectator ions*, which means they are present in both the reactants and products and do not change.

$$Zn^0(s) \longrightarrow Zn^{2+}(aq) + 2\,e^- \quad \text{Oxidation of Zn}$$
$$Cu^{2+}(aq) + 2\,e^- \longrightarrow Cu^0(s) \quad \text{Reduction of } Cu^{2+}$$

Pearson Education/
Creative Digital Vision

Batteries come in many shapes and sizes.

CONCEPT CHECK 4 **Oxidation and Reduction**

The following unbalanced reaction takes place in a NiCad battery used in cameras and toys:

$$Cd^0(s) \longrightarrow Cd^{2+}(aq)$$

a. Complete the equation by showing the electron loss or gain.
b. Is this reaction an oxidation or a reduction? Why?

ANSWER

a. Cd(*s*) loses electrons to form $Cd^{2+}(aq)$.

$$Cd^0(s) \longrightarrow Cd^{2+}(aq) + 2\,e^-$$

b. There is an increase in the positive charge, which means that the reaction of Cd is an oxidation.

CONCEPT CHECK 5 **Identifying Oxidation–Reduction Reactions**

In photographic film, the following decomposition reaction occurs in the presence of light. What is oxidized, and what is reduced?

$$2AgBr(s) \xrightarrow{\text{Light}} 2Ag(s) + Br_2(g)$$

ANSWER

To determine the substances oxidized and reduced, we need to look at the ions and charges in the reactants and products. In AgBr, there is a silver ion (Ag^+) with a 1+ charge and a bromide ion (Br^-) with a charge of 1−. By writing AgBr as ions, we obtain the following reaction:

$$2Ag^+(s) + 2Br^-(s) \longrightarrow 2Ag^0(s) + Br_2{}^0(g)$$

Now we can compare Ag^+ with the product Ag atom. We see that each Ag^+ gained an electron; Ag^+ is reduced.

$$2Ag^+(s) + 2\,e^- \longrightarrow 2Ag^0(s) \quad \text{Reduction}$$

When we compare Br^- in the reactant with the Br atom in the product Br_2, we see that each Br^- lost an electron; Br_2 is oxidized.

$$2Br^-(s) \longrightarrow Br_2{}^0(g) + 2\,e^- \quad \text{Oxidation}$$

Chris Price/iStockphoto

A vintage photograph has a sepia tone that is caused by the reaction of light with silver in the film.

Explore Your World

OXIDATION OF FRUITS AND VEGETABLES

Freshly cut surfaces of fruits and vegetables discolor when exposed to oxygen in the air. Cut three slices of a fruit or vegetable such as apple, potato, avocado, or banana. Leave one piece on the kitchen counter (uncovered). Wrap one piece in plastic wrap and leave on the kitchen counter. Dip one piece in lemon juice and leave uncovered.

QUESTIONS

1. What changes take place in each sample after 1–2 h?
2. Why would wrapping fruits and vegetables slow the rate of discoloration?
3. If lemon juice contains vitamin C (an antioxidant), why would dipping a fruit or vegetable in lemon juice affect the oxidation reaction on its surface?
4. Other kinds of antioxidants are vitamin E, citric acid, and BHT. Look for these antioxidants on the labels of cereals, potato chips, and other foods in your kitchen. Why are antioxidants added to food products that will be stored on our kitchen shelves?

Oxidation and Reduction in Biological Systems

Oxidation may also involve the addition of oxygen or the loss of hydrogen, whereas reduction may involve the loss of oxygen or the gain of hydrogen. In the cells of the body, oxidation of organic (carbon) compounds involves the transfer of hydrogen atoms (H), which are composed of electrons and protons. For example, the oxidation of a typical biological molecule can involve the transfer of two hydrogen atoms (or $2H^+$ and $2\,e^-$) to a proton acceptor such as the coenzyme FAD (flavin adenine dinucleotide). The coenzyme is reduced to $FADH_2$.

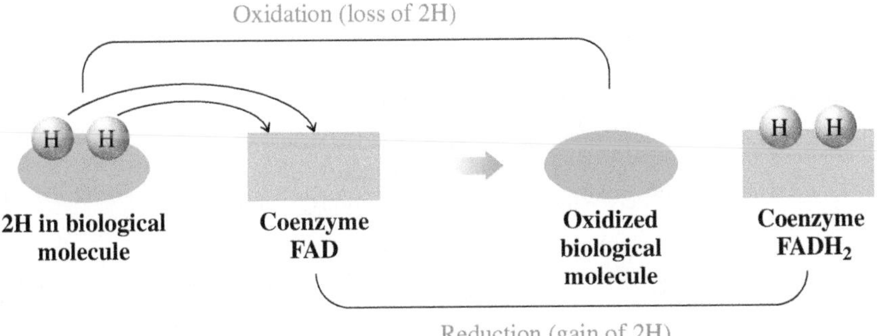

In biological systems, oxidation is identified as a gain of O atoms or a loss of H atoms; reduction is identified as a loss of O atoms or a gain of H atoms.

In many biochemical oxidation–reduction reactions, the transfer of hydrogen atoms is necessary for the production of energy in the cells. For example, when methanol (CH_3OH), a poisonous substance, is metabolized in the body, it loses two H atoms to form the oxidized product methanal. The H atoms reduce the coenzyme NAD^+ to NADH and H^+.

$$\underset{\text{Methanol}}{CH_3OH} \longrightarrow \underset{\text{Methanal}}{H_2CO} + 2H \qquad NAD^+ + 2H \longrightarrow NADH + H^+$$

The methanal is oxidized further to methanoic acid by gaining oxygen, which is itself reduced.

$$\underset{\text{Methanal}}{2H_2CO} + O_2 \longrightarrow \underset{\text{Methanoic acid}}{2H_2CO_2}$$

Finally, methanoic acid is oxidized to carbon dioxide and water as O_2 is reduced.

$$\underset{\text{Methanoic acid}}{2H_2CO_2} + O_2 \longrightarrow 2CO_2 + 2H_2O$$

The intermediate products of the oxidation of methanol are quite toxic, causing blindness and possibly death as they interfere with key reactions in the cells of the body.

In summary, we find that the particular definition of oxidation and reduction we use depends on the process that occurs in the reaction. All of these definitions are summarized in Table 4. Oxidation always involves a loss of electrons, but it may also be seen as an addition of oxygen, or the loss of hydrogen atoms. A reduction always involves a gain of electrons and may also be seen as the loss of oxygen, or the gain of hydrogen.

TABLE 4 Characteristics of Oxidation and Reduction

Oxidation	
Always Involves	**May Involve**
Loss of electrons	Addition of oxygen Loss of hydrogen
Reduction	
Always Involves	**May Involve**
Gain of electrons	Loss of oxygen Gain of hydrogen

QUESTIONS AND PROBLEMS

3 Oxidation–Reduction Reactions

LEARNING GOAL: *Define the terms oxidation and reduction; identify the reactant that is oxidized and the reactant that is reduced.*

13 Indicate whether each of the following is an oxidation or a reduction reaction:

a. $Na^+(aq) + e^- \longrightarrow Na(s)$
b. $Ni(s) \longrightarrow Ni^{2+}(aq) + 2\,e^-$
c. $Cr^{3+}(aq) + 3\,e^- \longrightarrow Cr(s)$
d. $2H^+(aq) + 2\,e^- \longrightarrow H_2(g)$

14 Indicate whether each of the following is an oxidation or a reduction reaction:

a. $O_2(g) + 4\,e^- \longrightarrow 2O^{2-}(aq)$
b. $Al(s) \longrightarrow Al^{3+}(aq) + 3\,e^-$
c. $Fe^{3+}(aq) + e^- \longrightarrow Fe^{2+}(aq)$
d. $2Br^-(aq) \longrightarrow Br_2(l) + 2\,e^-$

15 In the following reactions, identify which reactant is oxidized and which is reduced:

a. $Zn(s) + Cl_2(g) \longrightarrow ZnCl_2(s)$
b. $Cl_2(g) + 2NaBr(aq) \longrightarrow 2NaCl(aq) + Br_2(l)$
c. $2PbO(s) \longrightarrow 2Pb(s) + O_2(g)$
d. $2Fe^{3+}(aq) + Sn^{2+}(aq) \longrightarrow 2Fe^{2+}(aq) + Sn^{4+}(aq)$

16 In the following reactions, identify which reactant is oxidized and which is reduced:

a. $2Li(s) + F_2(g) \longrightarrow 2LiF(s)$
b. $Cl_2(g) + 2KI(aq) \longrightarrow 2KCl(aq) + I_2(s)$
c. $Mg(s) + Cu^{2+}(aq) \longrightarrow Mg^{2+}(aq) + Cu(s)$
d. $Fe(s) + CuSO_4(aq) \longrightarrow FeSO_4(aq) + Cu(s)$

17 In the mitochondria of human cells, energy for the production of ATP is provided by the oxidation and reduction reactions of the iron ions in the cytochromes that function in electron transport. Identify each of the following reactions as an oxidation or reduction:

a. $Fe^{3+} + e^- \longrightarrow Fe^{2+}$
b. $Fe^{2+} \longrightarrow Fe^{3+} + e^-$

18 Chlorine (Cl_2) is a strong germicide used to disinfect drinking water and to kill microbes in swimming pools. If the product is Cl^-, was the Cl_2 oxidized or reduced?

19 When linoleic acid, an unsaturated fatty acid, reacts with hydrogen, it forms a saturated fatty acid. Is linoleic acid oxidized or reduced in the hydrogenation reaction?

$$\underset{\text{Linoleic acid}}{C_{18}H_{32}O_2} + 2H_2 \longrightarrow C_{18}H_{36}O_2$$

20 In one of the reactions in the citric acid cycle, which provides energy for ATP synthesis, succinic acid is converted to fumaric acid.

$$\underset{\text{Succinic acid}}{C_4H_6O_4} \longrightarrow \underset{\text{Fumaric acid}}{C_4H_4O_4} + 2H$$

The reaction is accompanied by a coenzyme, flavin adenine dinucleotide (FAD):

$$FAD + 2H \longrightarrow FADH_2$$

a. Is succinic acid oxidized or reduced?
b. Is FAD oxidized or reduced?
c. Why would the two reactions occur together?

Chemistry Link to the Environment

FUEL CELLS: CLEAN ENERGY FOR THE FUTURE

Fuel cells are of interest to scientists because they provide an alternative source of electrical energy that is more efficient, does not use up oil reserves, and generates products that do not pollute the atmosphere. Fuel cells are considered a clean way to produce energy.

In a fuel cell, the reactants continuously enter the cell, which generates an electrical current. One type of hydrogen–oxygen fuel cell has been used in automobile prototypes. In this cell, hydrogen gas enters the fuel cell and comes in contact with platinum embedded in a plastic membrane. The platinum assists in the oxidation of hydrogen atoms to hydrogen ions and electrons.

The electrons produce an electric current as they travel through the wire. The hydrogen ions move through the plastic membrane to react with oxygen molecules. The oxygen molecules are reduced to oxide ions that combine with the hydrogen ions to form water.

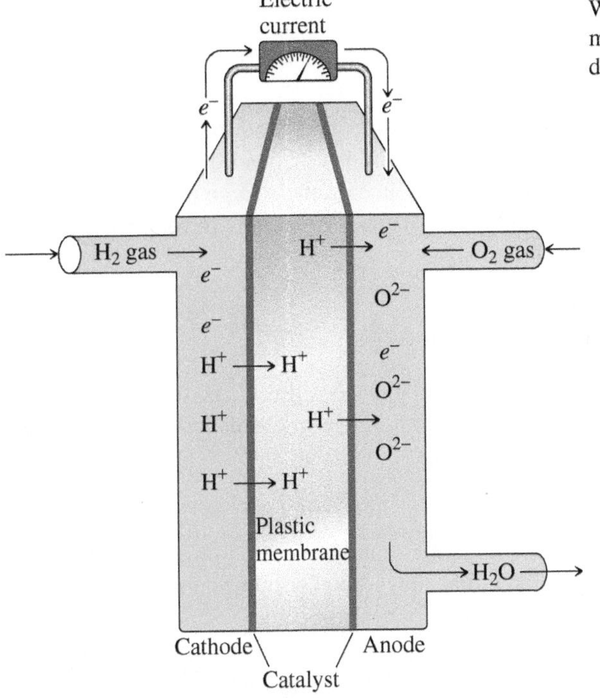

Oxidation

$2H_2(g) \longrightarrow 4H^+(aq) + 4\,e^-$

Reduction

$O_2(g) + 4H^+(aq) + 4\,e^- \longrightarrow 2H_2O(l)$

A fuel cell uses a continuous supply of hydrogen and oxygen to generate electricity.

The overall hydrogen–oxygen fuel cell reaction can be written as:

$$2H_2(g) + O_2(g) \longrightarrow 2H_2O(l)$$

Fuel cells have already been used to power the space shuttle. A major drawback to the practical use of fuel cells is the economic impact of converting cars to fuel cell operation. The storage and cost of producing hydrogen are also problems. Some manufacturers are experimenting with systems that convert gasoline or methanol to hydrogen for use in fuel cells. Energy must be expended to produce the hydrogen fuel for these cells. However, this can be accomplished using solar or wind power, which means there is a minimum of pollution and fossil fuels are not needed. In addition, the output from the fuel cell is water, a nonpollutant.

In homes, fuel cells may one day replace the batteries currently used to provide electrical power for cell phones, CD and DVD players, and laptop computers. Fuel cell design is still in the prototype phase, although there is much interest in development of these cells. We already know they can work, but modifications must still be made before they become reasonably priced and part of our everyday lives.

Fuel cells are used to supply power on the space shuttle orbiter.

LEARNING GOAL

Use Avogadro's number to determine the number of particles in a given amount of moles.

4 The Mole

At the grocery store, you buy eggs by the dozen or soda by the case. In an office-supply store, pencils are ordered by the gross and paper by the ream. The terms such as dozen, gross, ream, and case are used to count the number of items present. For example, when you buy a dozen eggs, you know you will get 12 eggs in the carton.

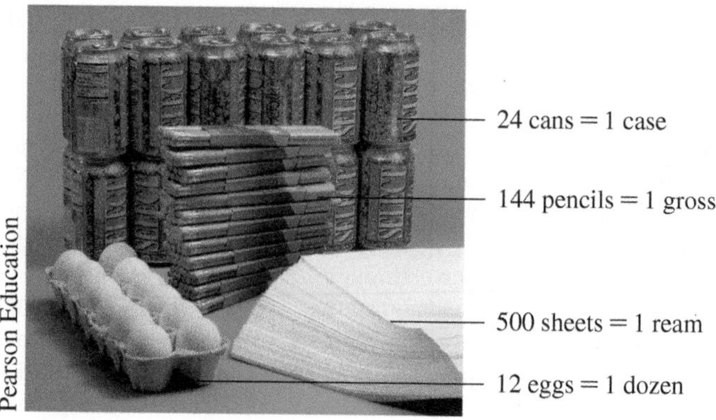

Collections of items include dozen, gross, and mole.

TUTORIAL
Using Avogadro's Number

TUTORIAL
The Mole as a Counting Unit

One mole of sulfur contains 6.02×10^{23} sulfur atoms.

Avogadro's Number

In chemistry, particles such as atoms, molecules, and ions are counted by the **mole**, a unit that contains 6.02×10^{23} of those particles. Avogadro's number is a very big number because atoms are so small that it takes an extremely large number of atoms to provide a sufficient amount to weigh and use in chemical reactions. **Avogadro's number** is named for Amedeo Avogadro, an Italian physicist.

Avogadro's number

$$602\,000\,000\,000\,000\,000\,000\,000 = 6.02 \times 10^{23}$$

One mole of any element always contains Avogadro's number of atoms. In one mole of carbon, there are 6.02×10^{23} carbon atoms; in one mole of aluminum, there are 6.02×10^{23} aluminum atoms; and in one mole of sulfur, there are 6.02×10^{23} sulfur atoms.

$$1 \text{ mole of an element} = 6.02 \times 10^{23} \text{ atoms of that element}$$

Avogadro's number tells us that one mole of a compound contains 6.02×10^{23} of the particular type of particles that make up that compound. One mole of a covalent compound contains Avogadro's number of molecules. For example, one mole of CO_2 contains 6.02×10^{23} molecules of CO_2. One mole of an ionic compound contains Avogadro's number of **formula units**, which are the groups of ions represented by the formula of an ionic compound. One mole of NaCl contains 6.02×10^{23} formula units of NaCl (Na^+, Cl^-). Table 5 gives examples of the number of particles in some one-mole quantities.

TABLE 5 Number of Particles in One-Mole Samples

Substance	Number and Type of Particles
1 mole of Al	6.02×10^{23} atoms of Al
1 mole of S	6.02×10^{23} atoms of S
1 mole of water (H_2O)	6.02×10^{23} molecules of H_2O
1 mole of vitamin C ($C_6H_8O_6$)	6.02×10^{23} molecules of vitamin C
1 mole of NaCl	6.02×10^{23} formula units of NaCl

We can use Avogadro's number as a conversion factor to convert between the moles of a substance and the number of particles it contains.

$$\frac{6.02 \times 10^{23} \text{ particles}}{1 \text{ mole}} \quad \text{and} \quad \frac{1 \text{ mole}}{6.02 \times 10^{23} \text{ particles}}$$

For example, we use Avogadro's number to convert 4.00 moles of iron to atoms of iron.

$$4.00 \text{ moles Fe atoms} \times \frac{6.02 \times 10^{23} \text{ Fe atoms}}{1 \text{ mole Fe atoms}} = 2.41 \times 10^{24} \text{ Fe atoms}$$

Avogadro's number as a conversion factor

We can also use Avogadro's number to convert 3.01×10^{24} molecules of CO_2 to moles of CO_2.

$$3.01 \times 10^{24} \text{ } CO_2 \text{ molecules} \times \frac{1 \text{ mole } CO_2 \text{ molecules}}{6.02 \times 10^{23} \text{ } CO_2 \text{ molecules}} = 5.00 \text{ moles of } CO_2 \text{ molecules}$$

Avogadro's number as a conversion factor

Generally, in calculations that convert between moles and particles, the number of moles will be a small number compared to the number of atoms or molecules, which will be a large number.

CONCEPT CHECK 6 **Moles and Particles**

Explain why 0.20 mole of aluminum is a small number, but the number of atoms in 0.20 mole is a large number: 1.2×10^{23} atoms of aluminum.

ANSWER

The term *mole* is used as a collection term that represents 6.02×10^{23} particles. Because atoms are submicroscopic particles, a large number of atoms are in one mole of aluminum.

SAMPLE PROBLEM 3 **Calculating the Number of Molecules**

How many molecules are present in 1.75 moles of carbon dioxide, CO_2?

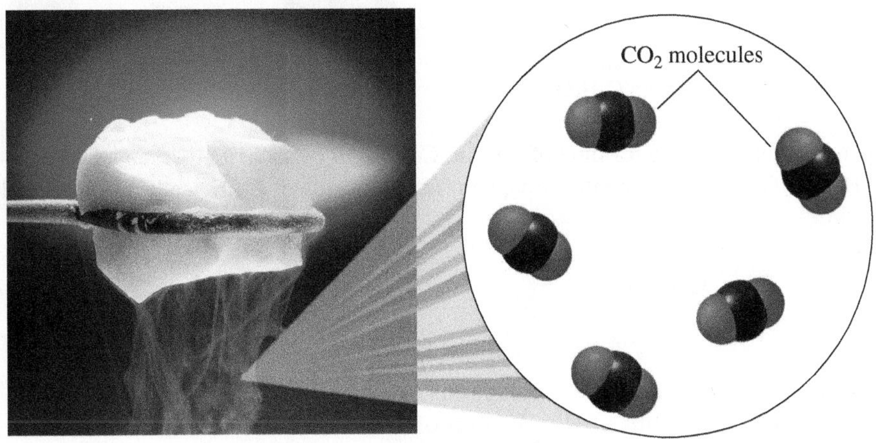

The solid form of carbon dioxide is known as "dry ice."

SOLUTION

Step 1 **State the given and needed quantities.**

Analyze the Problem

Given	Need
1.75 moles of CO_2	molecules of CO_2

Guide to Calculating the Atoms or Molecules of a Substance

1 State the given and needed quantities.

2 Write a plan to convert moles to atoms or molecules.

3 Use Avogadro's number to write conversion factors.

4 Set up the problem to calculate the number of particles.

Step 2 Write a plan to convert moles to atoms or molecules.

moles of CO_2 → Avogadro's number → molecules of CO_2

Step 3 Use Avogadro's number to write conversion factors.

$$1 \text{ mole of } CO_2 = 6.02 \times 10^{23} \text{ molecules of } CO_2$$

$$\frac{6.02 \times 10^{23} \text{ molecules } CO_2}{1 \text{ mole } CO_2} \quad \text{and} \quad \frac{1 \text{ mole } CO_2}{6.02 \times 10^{23} \text{ molecules } CO_2}$$

Step 4 Set up the problem to calculate the number of particles.

$$1.75 \cancel{\text{moles } CO_2} \times \frac{6.02 \times 10^{23} \text{ molecules } CO_2}{1 \cancel{\text{mole } CO_2}} = 1.05 \times 10^{24} \text{ molecules of } CO_2$$

STUDY CHECK 3

How many moles of water, H_2O, contain 2.60×10^{23} molecules of water?

TUTORIAL
Moles and the Chemical Formula

Moles of Elements in a Formula

We have seen that the subscripts in a chemical formula of a compound indicate the number of atoms of each type of element. For example, in a molecule of aspirin, chemical formula $C_9H_8O_4$, there are 9 carbon atoms, 8 hydrogen atoms, and 4 oxygen atoms. The subscripts also state the number of moles of each element in one mole of aspirin: 9 moles of C atoms, 8 moles of H atoms, and 4 moles of O atoms.

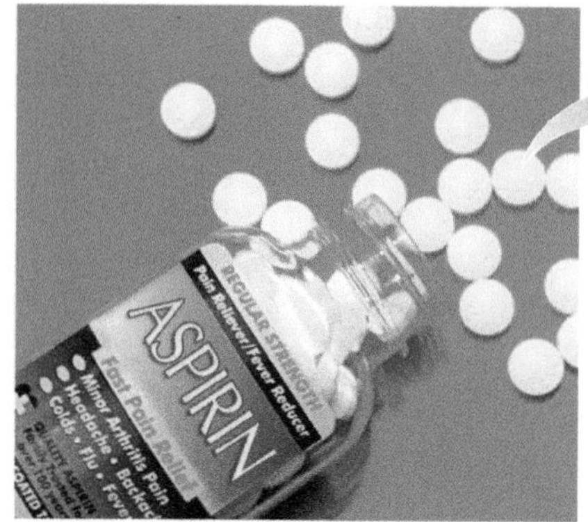

Pearson Education

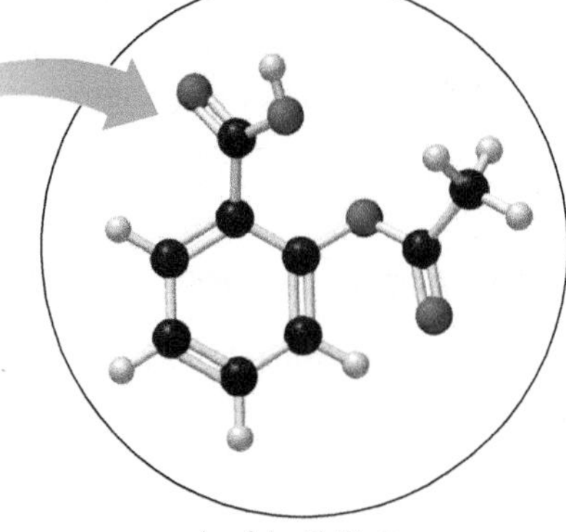

Aspirin $C_9H_8O_4$

Number of atoms in one molecule

Carbon (C) Hydrogen (H) Oxygen (O)

Using the subscripts in the formula of aspirin, $C_9H_8O_4$, we can write the number of atoms of C, H, and O in one molecule of aspirin, or the moles of C, H, and O in one mole of aspirin.

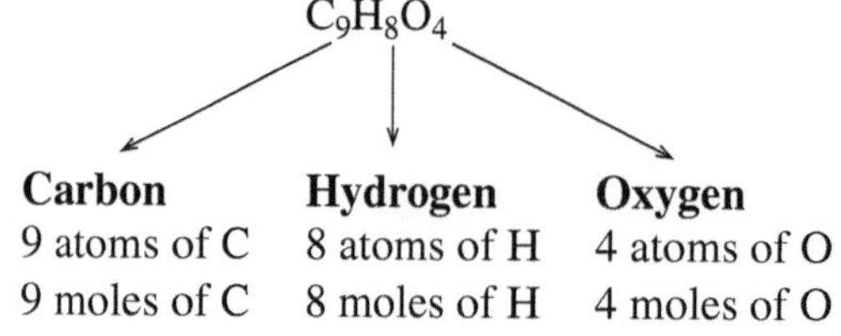

$C_9H_8O_4$

Carbon	**Hydrogen**	**Oxygen**
9 atoms of C	8 atoms of H	4 atoms of O
9 moles of C	8 moles of H	4 moles of O

Using the subscripts from the formula, $C_9H_8O_4$, we can write the conversion factors for each of the elements in one mole of aspirin:

$$\frac{9 \text{ moles C}}{1 \text{ mole } C_9H_8O_4} \quad \frac{8 \text{ moles H}}{1 \text{ mole } C_9H_8O_4} \quad \frac{4 \text{ moles O}}{1 \text{ mole } C_9H_8O_4}$$

$$\frac{1 \text{ mole } C_9H_8O_4}{9 \text{ moles C}} \quad \frac{1 \text{ mole } C_9H_8O_4}{8 \text{ moles H}} \quad \frac{1 \text{ mole } C_9H_8O_4}{4 \text{ moles O}}$$

CONCEPT CHECK 7 **Using Subscripts of a Formula**

Indicate the moles of each type of atom in one mole of each of the following:

a. $C_5H_{10}O_2$, propyl acetate, odor and taste of pears
b. $Zn(C_2H_3O_2)_2$, zinc dietary supplement

ANSWER

a. The subscripts in the formula indicate that there are 5 moles of C atoms, 10 moles of H atoms, and 2 moles of O atoms in 1 mole of propyl acetate.
b. The subscript 2 outside the parentheses indicates there are 2 moles of the ion $C_2H_3O_2^-$ in the formula. Thus, there is 1 mole of Zn^{2+} ions, 4 (2×2) moles of C atoms, 6 (2×3) moles of H atoms, and 4 (2×2) moles of O atoms in 1 mole of $Zn(C_2H_3O_2)_2$.

Michael Hill/iStockphoto

The compound propyl acetate provides the odor and taste of pears.

SAMPLE PROBLEM 4 **Calculating the Moles of an Element**

How many moles of carbon are present in 1.50 moles of aspirin, $C_9H_8O_4$?

SOLUTION

Step 1 **State the given and needed quantities.**

Analyze the Problem

Given	Need
1.50 moles of aspirin	moles of C
molecular formula $C_9H_8O_4$	

Step 2 **Write a plan to convert moles of compound to moles of an element.**

moles of $C_9H_8O_4$ → Subscript → moles of C atoms

Step 3 **Write equalities and conversion factors using subscripts.**

1 mole of $C_9H_8O_4$ = 9 moles of C atoms

$$\frac{9 \text{ moles C}}{1 \text{ mole } C_9H_8O_4} \quad \text{and} \quad \frac{1 \text{ mole } C_9H_8O_4}{9 \text{ moles C}}$$

Step 4 **Set up the problem to calculate the moles of an element.**

$$1.50 \cancel{\text{moles } C_9H_8O_4} \times \frac{9 \text{ moles C}}{1 \cancel{\text{mole } C_9H_8O_4}} = 13.5 \text{ moles of C}$$

STUDY CHECK 4

How many moles of aspirin, $C_9H_8O_4$, contain 0.480 mole of O?

Guide to Calculating Moles

1. State the given and needed quantities.
2. Write a plan to convert moles of compound to moles of an element.
3. Write equalities and conversion factors using subscripts.
4. Set up the problem to calculate the moles of an element.

QUESTIONS AND PROBLEMS

4 The Mole

LEARNING GOAL: *Use Avogadro's number to determine the number of particles in a given amount of moles.*

21 Calculate each of the following:
a. number of Ag atoms in 0.200 mole of Ag
b. number of C_3H_8O molecules in 0.750 mole of C_3H_8O
c. number of Cr atoms in 1.25 moles of Cr

22 Calculate each of the following:
a. number of Ni atoms in 3.4 moles of Ni
b. number of $Mg(OH)_2$ formula units in 1.20 moles of $Mg(OH)_2$
c. number of Li atoms in 4.5 moles of Li

23 Calculate each of the following:
a. moles of Al in 3.26×10^{24} atoms of Al
b. moles of C_2H_5OH in 8.50×10^{24} molecules of C_2H_5OH
c. moles of Au in 2.88×10^{23} atoms of Au

24 Calculate each of the following:
a. moles of Cu in 7.8×10^{21} atoms of Cu
b. moles of C_2H_6 in 3.75×10^{23} molecules of C_2H_6
c. moles of Zn in 5.6×10^{24} atoms of Zn

25 Quinine, $C_{20}H_{24}N_2O_2$, is a component of tonic water and bitter lemon.
a. How many moles of hydrogen are in 1.0 mole of quinine?
b. How many moles of carbon are in 5.0 moles of quinine?
c. How many moles of nitrogen are in 0.020 mole of quinine?

26 Aluminum sulfate, $Al_2(SO_4)_3$, is used in some antiperspirants.

a. How many moles of sulfur are present in 3.0 moles of $Al_2(SO_4)_3$?

b. How many moles of aluminum ions are present in 0.40 mole of $Al_2(SO_4)_3$?

c. How many moles of sulfate ions (SO_4^{2-}) are present in 1.5 moles of $Al_2(SO_4)_3$?

27 Calculate each of the following:

a. number of C atoms in 0.500 mole of C

b. number of SO_2 molecules in 1.28 moles of SO_2

c. moles of Fe in 5.22×10^{22} atoms of Fe

28 Calculate each of the following:

a. number of Co atoms in 2.2 moles of Co

b. number of CO_2 molecules in 0.0180 mole of CO_2

c. moles of Cr in 4.58×10^{23} atoms of Cr

29 Calculate each of the following quantities in 2.00 moles of H_3PO_4:

a. moles of H **b.** moles of O

c. atoms of P **d.** atoms of O

30 Calculate each of the following quantities in 0.185 mole of $(C_3H_7)_2O$:

a. moles of C **b.** moles of O

c. atoms of H **d.** atoms of C

LEARNING GOAL

Determine the molar mass of a substance and use the molar mass to convert between grams and moles.

5 Molar Mass

A single atom or molecule is much too small to weigh, even on the most sensitive laboratory balance. In fact, it takes a huge number of atoms or molecules to make enough of a substance for you to see. An amount of water that contains Avogadro's number of water molecules is only a few sips. In the laboratory, we can use a balance to weigh out Avogadro's number of particles or one mole of a substance.

For any element, the quantity called **molar mass** is the number of grams that equals the atomic mass of that element. We are counting 6.02×10^{23} atoms of an element when we weigh out the number of grams equal to its molar mass. For example, carbon has an atomic mass of 12.01 on the periodic table. Then to obtain one mole of carbon atoms, we would weigh out 12.01 g of carbon. Thus, the molar mass of carbon is found by looking at its atomic mass on the periodic table.

Pearson Education

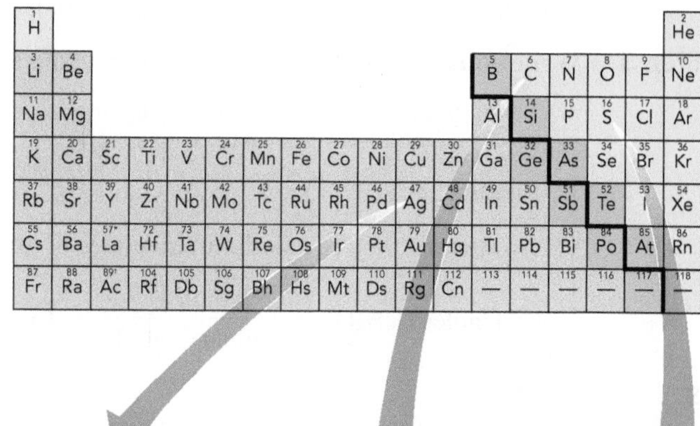

6.02×10^{23} atoms of C

1 mole of C atoms

12.01 g of C atoms

47 Ag 107.9	6 C 12.01	16 S 32.07
1 mole of silver atoms has a mass of 107.9 g	1 mole of carbon atoms has a mass of 12.01 g	1 mole of sulfur atoms has a mass of 32.07 g

Molar Mass of a Compound

To determine the molar mass of a compound, multiply the molar mass of each element by its subscript in the formula, and add the results as shown in Sample Problem 5. ***In this text, we round the molar mass of an element to the tenths (0.1 g) place or use at least three significant figures for calculations.***

SAMPLE PROBLEM 5 **Calculating the Molar Mass of a Compound**

Find the molar mass of Li_2CO_3 used to produce the red color in fireworks.

SOLUTION

Analyze the Problem

Given	Need
molecular formula Li_2CO_3	molar mass of Li_2CO_3

Step 1 **Obtain the molar mass of each element.**

$$\frac{6.94 \text{ g Li}}{1 \text{ mole Li}} \quad \frac{12.0 \text{ g C}}{1 \text{ mole C}} \quad \frac{16.0 \text{ g O}}{1 \text{ mole O}}$$

Step 2 **Multiply each molar mass by the number of moles (subscript) in the formula.**

Grams from 2 moles of Li

$$2 \cancel{\text{moles Li}} \times \frac{6.94 \text{ g Li}}{1 \cancel{\text{mole Li}}} = 13.9 \text{ g of Li}$$

Grams from 1 mole of C

$$1 \cancel{\text{mole C}} \times \frac{12.0 \text{ g C}}{1 \cancel{\text{mole C}}} = 12.0 \text{ g of C}$$

Grams from 3 moles of O

$$3 \cancel{\text{moles O}} \times \frac{16.0 \text{ g O}}{1 \cancel{\text{mole O}}} = 48.0 \text{ g of O}$$

Step 3 **Calculate the molar mass by adding the masses of the elements.**

$$\begin{aligned} 2 \text{ moles of Li} &= 13.9 \text{ g of Li} \\ 1 \text{ mole of C} &= 12.0 \text{ g of C} \\ 3 \text{ moles of O} &= +48.0 \text{ g of O} \\ \hline \text{Molar mass of } Li_2CO_3 &= 73.9 \text{ g} \end{aligned}$$

STUDY CHECK 5

Calculate the molar mass of salicylic acid, $C_7H_6O_3$.

Guide to Calculating Molar Mass

1. Obtain the molar mass of each element.
2. Multiply each molar mass by the number of moles (subscript) in the formula.
3. Calculate the molar mass by adding the masses of the elements.

Polushkin Ivan Nikolaevich/ Shutterstock

Lithium carbonate produces a red color in fireworks.

Calculations Using Molar Mass

The molar mass of an element or a compound is a useful conversion factor because it converts moles of a substance to grams, or grams to moles. For example, 1 mole of magnesium has a mass of 24.3 g. To express its molar mass as an equality, we can write:

$$1 \text{ mole of Mg} = 24.3 \text{ g of Mg}$$

From this equality, two conversion factors can be written.

$$\frac{24.3 \text{ g Mg}}{1 \text{ mole Mg}} \quad \text{and} \quad \frac{1 \text{ mole Mg}}{24.3 \text{ g Mg}}$$

Figure 8 shows some one-mole quantities of substances. Table 6 lists the molar mass for several one-mole samples.

TABLE 6 **The Molar Mass of Selected Elements and Compounds**

Substance	Molar Mass
1 mole of C	12.0 g
1 mole of Na	23.0 g
1 mole of Fe	55.9 g
1 mole of NaF	42.0 g
1 mole of $CaCO_3$	100.1 g
1 mole of $C_6H_{12}O_6$ (glucose)	180.1 g
1 mole of $C_8H_{10}N_4O_2$ (caffeine)	194.1 g

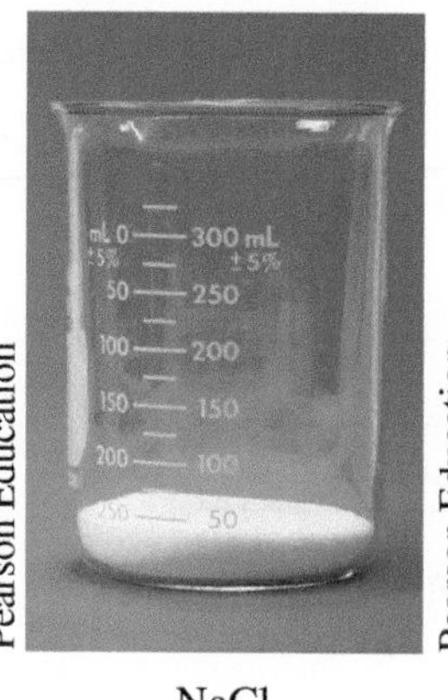

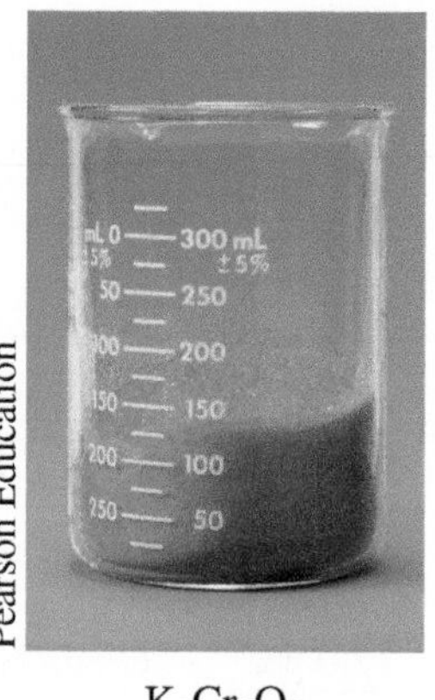

Pearson Education Pearson Education Pearson Education Pearson Education Pearson Education

S Fe NaCl $K_2Cr_2O_7$ $C_{12}H_{22}O_{11}$

FIGURE 8 One-mole samples: sulfur, S (32.1 g); iron, Fe (55.9 g); salt, NaCl (58.5 g); potassium dichromate, $K_2Cr_2O_7$ (294 g); and sugar, sucrose, $C_{12}H_{22}O_{11}$ (342 g).

Q How is the molar mass for $K_2Cr_2O_7$ obtained?

TUTORIAL
Converting Between Grams and Moles

Conversion factors are written for compounds in the same way. For example, the equality for the molar mass of the compound H_2O is written:

$$1 \text{ mole of } H_2O = 18.0 \text{ g of } H_2O$$

From this equality, the conversion factors from the molar mass of H_2O are written as:

$$\frac{18.0 \text{ g } H_2O}{1 \text{ mole } H_2O} \quad \text{and} \quad \frac{1 \text{ mole } H_2O}{18.0 \text{ g } H_2O}$$

We can now change from moles to grams, or grams to moles, using the conversion factors derived from the molar mass as shown in Sample Problem 6. (Remember, you must determine the molar mass of the substance first.)

Guide to Calculating the Moles (or Grams) of a Substance from Grams (or Moles)

1 State the given and needed quantities.

2 Write a plan to convert moles to grams (or grams to moles).

3 Determine the molar mass and write conversion factors.

4 Set up the problem to convert moles to grams (or grams to moles).

SAMPLE PROBLEM 6 Converting Mass of a Compound to Moles

A box of salt contains 737 g of NaCl. How many moles of NaCl are present in the box?

SOLUTION

Step 1 State the given and needed quantities.

Analyze the Problem

Given	Need
737 g of NaCl	moles of NaCl

Step 2 Write a plan to convert grams to moles.

grams of NaCl → Molar mass → moles of NaCl

Step 3 Determine the molar mass and write conversion factors.

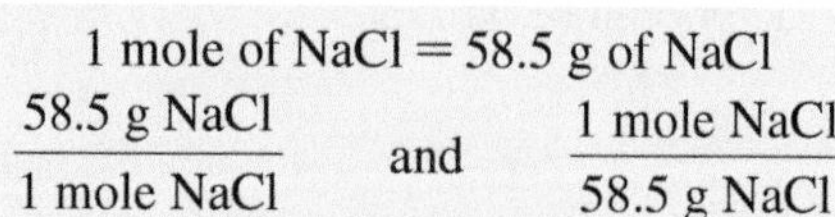

$$1 \text{ mole of NaCl} = 58.5 \text{ g of NaCl}$$

$$\frac{58.5 \text{ g NaCl}}{1 \text{ mole NaCl}} \quad \text{and} \quad \frac{1 \text{ mole NaCl}}{58.5 \text{ g NaCl}}$$

Pearson Education/Eric Schrader

Table salt is sodium chloride, NaCl.

Step 4 Set up the problem to convert grams to moles.

$$737 \cancel{\text{g NaCl}} \times \frac{1 \text{ mole NaCl}}{58.5 \cancel{\text{g NaCl}}} = 12.6 \text{ moles of NaCl}$$

STUDY CHECK 6

Silver metal is used in the manufacture of tableware, mirrors, jewelry, and dental alloys. If the design for a piece of jewelry requires 0.750 mole of silver, how many grams of silver are needed?

Ruzanna/Shutterstock

Silver metal is used to make jewelry.

CALCULATING MOLES IN THE KITCHEN

The labels on food products list the components in grams and milligrams. Read the labels of some products in the kitchen and convert the amounts given in grams or milligrams to moles using molar mass.

QUESTIONS

1. How many moles of NaCl are in a 4-oz salt shaker?
2. How many moles of sugar are contained in a 5-lb bag of sugar if sugar has the formula $C_{12}H_{22}O_{11}$?
3. A serving of cereal contains 90 mg of potassium. If there are 11 servings of cereal in the box, how many moles of K^+ are present in the cereal in the box?

Figure 9 shows the connections between the moles of a compound, its mass in grams, the number of molecules (or formula units if ionic), and the moles and atoms of each element in that compound.

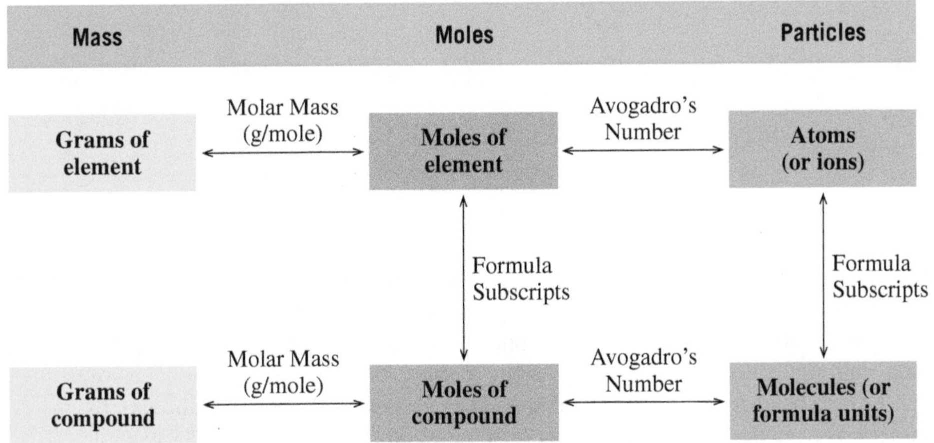

FIGURE 9 The moles of a compound are related to its mass in grams by molar mass, to the number of molecules (or formula units) by Avogadro's number, and to the moles of each element by the subscripts in the formula.

Q What steps are needed to calculate the number of H atoms in 5.00 g of CH_4?

QUESTIONS AND PROBLEMS

5 Molar Mass

LEARNING GOAL: *Determine the molar mass of a substance and use the molar mass to convert between grams and moles.*

31 Calculate the molar mass for each of the following:
- **a.** $KC_4H_5O_6$ (cream of tartar)
- **b.** Fe_2O_3 (rust)
- **c.** $C_{19}H_{20}FNO_3$ (Paxil, an antidepressant)
- **d.** $Al_2(SO_4)_3$ (antiperspirant)
- **e.** $Mg(OH)_2$ (antacid)
- **f.** $C_{16}H_{19}N_3O_5S$ (amoxicillin, an antibiotic)

32 Calculate the molar mass for each of the following:
- **a.** $FeSO_4$ (iron supplement)
- **b.** Al_2O_3 (absorbent and abrasive)
- **c.** $C_7H_5NO_3S$ (saccharin)
- **d.** C_3H_8O (rubbing alcohol)
- **e.** $(NH_4)_2CO_3$ (baking powder)
- **f.** $Zn(C_2H_3O_2)_2$ (dietary supplement)

33 Calculate the mass, in grams, for each of the following:
- **a.** 2.00 moles of Na **b.** 2.80 moles of Ca
- **c.** 0.125 mole of Sn **d.** 1.76 moles of Cu

34 Calculate the mass, in grams, for each of the following:
- **a.** 1.50 moles of K **b.** 2.5 moles of C
- **c.** 0.25 mole of P **d.** 12.5 moles of He

35 Calculate the mass, in grams, for each of the following:
- **a.** 0.500 mole of NaCl **b.** 1.75 moles of Na_2O
- **c.** 0.225 mole of H_2O **d.** 4.42 moles of CO_2

36 Calculate the mass, in grams, for each of the following:
- **a.** 2.0 moles of $MgCl_2$ **b.** 3.5 moles of C_3H_8
- **c.** 5.00 moles of C_2H_6O **d.** 0.488 mole of $C_3H_6O_3$

37
- **a.** The compound $MgSO_4$ is called Epsom salts. How many grams will you need to prepare a bath containing 5.00 moles of Epsom salts?
- **b.** In a bottle of soda, there is 0.25 mole of CO_2. How many grams of CO_2 are in the bottle?

38
- **a.** Cyclopropane, C_3H_6, is an anesthetic given by inhalation. How many grams are in 0.25 mole of cyclopropane?
- **b.** The sedative Demerol hydrochloride has the formula $C_{15}H_{22}ClNO_2$. How many grams are in 0.025 mole of Demerol hydrochloride?

39 How many moles are contained in each of the following?
- **a.** 50.0 g of Ag **b.** 0.200 g of C
- **c.** 15.0 g of NH_3 **d.** 75.0 g of SO_2

40 How many moles are contained in each of the following?
- **a.** 25.0 g of Ca **b.** 5.00 g of S
- **c.** 40.0 g of H_2O **d.** 12.2 g of O_2

41 How many moles of S are in each of the following quantities?
a. 25 g of S b. 125 g of SO_2 c. 30.1 g of Al_2S_3

42 How many moles of C are in each of the following quantities?
a. 75 g of C b. 32.6 g of C_2H_6 c. 88 g of CO_2

43 Caffeine, $C_8H_{10}N_4O_2$, is obtained from tea, coffee, and energy drinks.

Shutterstock

Coffee beans are a source of caffeine.

a. How many grams of caffeine are in 0.850 mole?
b. How many moles of caffeine are in 28.0 g of caffeine?
c. How many moles of carbon are in 28.0 g of caffeine?
d. How many grams of nitrogen are in 28.0 g of caffeine?

44 Fructose, $C_6H_{12}O_6$, a monosaccharide, is found in honey and fruits.
a. How many grams of fructose are in 1.20 moles of fructose?
b. How many moles of fructose are in 15.0 g of fructose?
c. How many moles of carbon are in 15.0 g of fructose?
d. How many grams of oxygen are in 15.0 g of fructose?

LEARNING GOAL

Given a quantity in moles of reactant or product, use a mole–mole factor from the balanced equation to calculate the moles of another substance in the reaction.

6 Mole Relationships in Chemical Equations

In Section 1, we saw that equations are balanced in terms of the numbers of each type of atom in the reactants and products. However, when experiments are done in the laboratory or medications are prepared in the pharmacy, the samples we use contain billions of atoms and molecules, making it impossible to count them. What we can measure is their mass using a balance. Because mass is related to the number of particles through the molar mass, measuring the mass is equivalent to counting the number of particles or moles.

TUTORIAL
Moles of Reactants and Products

TUTORIAL
Law of Conservation of Mass

SELF-STUDY ACTIVITY
Stoichiometry

Conservation of Mass

In any chemical reaction, the total amount of matter in the reactants is equal to the total amount of matter in the products. Thus, the total mass of all the reactants must be equal to the total mass of all the products. This is known as the *law of conservation of mass*, which says that there is no change in the total mass of the substances reacting in a balanced chemical reaction. Thus, no material is lost or gained as original substances are changed to new substances.

For example, tarnish forms when silver reacts with sulfur to form silver sulfide.

$$2Ag(s) + S(s) \longrightarrow Ag_2S(s)$$

Pearson Education

Pearson Education

Pearson Education

$2Ag(s)$ + $S(s)$ $\longrightarrow$ $Ag_2S(s)$

Mass of reactants = Mass of product

The law of conservation of mass states that there is no matter lost or gained in a chemical reaction.

In this reaction, the number of silver atoms that reacts is two times the number of sulfur atoms. When 200 silver atoms react, 100 sulfur atoms are required. However, in the actual chemical reaction, many more atoms of both silver and sulfur would react. If we are dealing with molar amounts, then the coefficients in the equation can be interpreted in terms of moles. Thus, 2 moles of Ag react with 1 mole of S to produce 1 mole of Ag_2S. Because the molar mass of each can be determined, the moles of Ag, S, and Ag_2S can also be stated in terms of mass in grams of each. Thus, 215.8 g of Ag and 32.1 g of S react to form 247.9 g of Ag_2S. The total mass of the reactants (247.9 g) is equal to the mass of the product, 247.9 g. The various ways in which a chemical equation can be interpreted are seen in Table 7.

TABLE 7 Information Available from a Balanced Equation

	Reactants			Product
Equation	$2Ag(s)$	$+ S(s)$	$\longrightarrow$	$Ag_2S(s)$
Atoms	2 Ag atoms	+ 1 S atom	$\longrightarrow$	Ag_2S formula unit
	200 Ag atoms	+ 100 S atoms	$\longrightarrow$	100 Ag_2S formula units
Avogadro's Number of Atoms	$2(6.02 \times 10^{23})$ Ag atoms	$+ 1(6.02 \times 10^{23})$ S atoms	$\longrightarrow$	$1(6.02 \times 10^{23})$ Ag_2S formula units
Moles	2 moles of Ag	+ 1 mole of S	$\longrightarrow$	1 mole of Ag_2S
Mass (g)	2(107.9 g) of Ag	+ 1(32.1 g) of S	$\longrightarrow$	1(247.9 g) of Ag_2S
Total Mass (g)	247.9 g		$\longrightarrow$	247.9 g

Mole–Mole Factors from an Equation

When iron reacts with sulfur, the product is iron(III) sulfide.

$$2Fe(s) + 3S(s) \longrightarrow Fe_2S_3(s)$$

Iron (Fe) $2Fe(s)$ + Sulfur (S) $3S(s)$ $\longrightarrow$ Iron(III) sulfide (Fe_2S_3) $Fe_2S_3(s)$

In the chemical reaction of Fe and S, the mass of the reactants is the same as the mass of the product, Fe_2S_3.

Because the equation is balanced, we know the proportions of iron and sulfur in the reaction. For this reaction, we see that 2 moles of iron react with 3 moles of sulfur to form 1 mole of iron(III) sulfide. Actually, any amount of iron or sulfur may be used but the *ratio* of iron reacting with sulfur will be the same. From the coefficients, we can write **mole–mole factors** between reactants and between reactants and products.

The coefficients used in the mole–mole factors are exact numbers; they do not limit the number of significant figures.

Fe and S: $\frac{2 \text{ moles Fe}}{3 \text{ moles S}}$ and $\frac{3 \text{ moles S}}{2 \text{ moles Fe}}$

Fe and Fe_2S_3: $\frac{2 \text{ moles Fe}}{1 \text{ mole } Fe_2S_3}$ and $\frac{1 \text{ mole } Fe_2S_3}{2 \text{ moles Fe}}$

S and Fe_2S_3: $\frac{3 \text{ moles S}}{1 \text{ mole } Fe_2S_3}$ and $\frac{1 \text{ mole } Fe_2S_3}{3 \text{ moles S}}$

CONCEPT CHECK 8 **Writing Mole–Mole Factors**

Consider the following balanced equation:

$4Na(s) + O_2(g) \longrightarrow 2Na_2O(s)$

Write the mole–mole factors for each of the following relationships:

a. Na and O_2 **b.** Na and Na_2O

ANSWER

a. The mole–mole factors for Na and O_2 use the coefficient of Na to write 4 moles of Na, and the coefficient of 1 (understood) to write 1 mole of O_2.

4 moles of Na = 1 mole of O_2

$\frac{4 \text{ moles Na}}{1 \text{ mole } O_2}$ and $\frac{1 \text{ mole } O_2}{4 \text{ moles Na}}$

b. The mole–mole factors for Na and Na_2O use the coefficient of Na to write 4 moles of Na, and the coefficient of Na_2O to write 2 moles of Na_2O.

4 moles of Na = 2 moles of Na_2O

$\frac{4 \text{ moles Na}}{2 \text{ moles } Na_2O}$ and $\frac{2 \text{ moles } Na_2O}{4 \text{ moles Na}}$

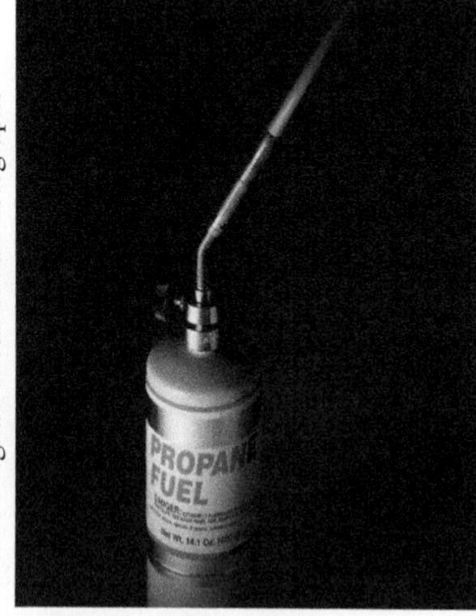

Richard Megna/Fundamental Photographs

Propane fuel reacts with O_2 in the air to produce CO_2, H_2O, and energy.

Using Mole–Mole Factors in Calculations

Whenever you prepare a recipe, adjust an engine for the proper mixture of fuel and air, or prepare medicines in a pharmaceutical laboratory, you need to know the proper amounts of reactants to use and how much of the product will form. Earlier, we wrote all the possible conversion factors that can be obtained from this balanced equation: $2Fe(s) + 3S(s) \longrightarrow Fe_2S_3(s)$. Now we will use mole–mole factors in chemical calculations in Sample Problem 7.

SAMPLE PROBLEM 7 **Using Mole–Mole Factors**

Propane gas (C_3H_8), a fuel used in camp stoves, soldering torches, and specially equipped automobiles, reacts with oxygen to produce carbon dioxide, water, and energy. How many moles of CO_2 can be produced when 2.25 moles of C_3H_8 react?

$\underset{\text{Propane}}{C_3H_8(g)} + 5O_2(g) \xrightarrow{\Delta} 3CO_2(g) + 4H_2O(g) + \text{energy}$

SOLUTION

Step 1 **State the given and needed quantities.**

Analyze the Problem

Given	Need
2.25 moles of C_3H_8	moles of CO_2
Equation	
$C_3H_8(g) + 5O_2(g) \xrightarrow{\Delta} 3CO_2(g) + 4H_2O(g) + \text{energy}$ Propane	

Step 2 **Write a plan to convert the given to the needed quantity (moles or grams).**

moles of C_3H_8 → Mole–mole factor → moles of CO_2

Step 3 **Use coefficients to write mole–mole factors; write molar mass factors if needed.**

1 mole of C_3H_8 = 3 moles of CO_2

$$\frac{1 \text{ mole } C_3H_8}{3 \text{ moles } CO_2} \quad \text{and} \quad \frac{3 \text{ moles } CO_2}{1 \text{ mole } C_3H_8}$$

Step 4 **Set up the problem to give the needed quantity (moles or grams).**

$$2.25 \cancel{\text{moles } C_3H_8} \times \frac{3 \text{ moles } CO_2}{1 \cancel{\text{mole } C_3H_8}} = 6.75 \text{ moles of } CO_2$$

The answer is given with three SFs because the given quantity, 2.25 moles of C_3H_8, has three SFs. The values in the mole–mole factor are exact.

STUDY CHECK 7

Using the equation in Sample Problem 7, calculate the number of moles of oxygen that must react to produce 0.756 mole of water.

Guide to Calculating the Quantities of Reactants and Products in a Chemical Reaction

1. State the given and needed quantities.
2. Write a plan to convert the given to the needed quantity (moles or grams).
3. Use coefficients to write mole–mole factors; write molar mass factors if needed.
4. Set up the problem to give the needed quantity (moles or grams).

QUESTIONS AND PROBLEMS

6 Mole Relationships in Chemical Equations

LEARNING GOAL: *Given a quantity in moles of reactant or product, use a mole–mole factor from the balanced equation to calculate the moles of another substance in the reaction.*

45 Write all of the mole–mole factors for each of the following equations:

a. $2SO_2(g) + O_2(g) \longrightarrow 2SO_3(g)$

b. $4P(s) + 5O_2(s) \longrightarrow 2P_2O_5(s)$

46 Write all of the mole–mole factors for each of the following equations:

a. $2Al(s) + 3Cl_2(g) \longrightarrow 2AlCl_3(s)$

b. $4HCl(g) + O_2(g) \longrightarrow 2Cl_2(g) + 2H_2O(g)$

47 The reaction of hydrogen with oxygen produces water.

$$2H_2(g) + O_2(g) \longrightarrow 2H_2O(g)$$

a. How many moles of O_2 are required to react with 2.0 moles of H_2?

b. If you have 5.0 moles of O_2, how many moles of H_2 are needed for the reaction?

c. How many moles of H_2O form when 2.5 moles of O_2 react?

48 Ammonia is produced by the reaction of hydrogen and nitrogen.

$$N_2(g) + 3H_2(g) \longrightarrow 2NH_3(g)$$

Ammonia

a. How many moles of H_2 are needed to react with 1.0 mole of N_2?

b. How many moles of N_2 reacted if 0.60 mole of NH_3 is produced?

c. How many moles of NH_3 are produced when 1.4 moles of H_2 react?

49 Carbon disulfide and carbon monoxide are produced when carbon is heated with sulfur dioxide.

$$5C(s) + 2SO_2(g) \longrightarrow CS_2(l) + 4CO(g)$$

a. How many moles of C are needed to react with 0.500 mole of SO_2?
b. How many moles of CO are produced when 1.2 moles of C react?
c. How many moles of SO_2 are required to produce 0.50 mole of CS_2?
d. How many moles of CS_2 are produced when 2.5 moles of C react?

50 In the acetylene torch, acetylene gas (C_2H_2) burns in oxygen to produce carbon dioxide and water.

$$2C_2H_2(g) + 5O_2(g) \xrightarrow{\Delta} 4CO_2(g) + 2H_2O(g)$$

a. How many moles of O_2 are needed to react with 2.00 moles of C_2H_2?
b. How many moles of CO_2 are produced when 3.5 moles of C_2H_2 react?
c. How many moles of C_2H_2 are required to produce 0.50 mole of H_2O?
d. How many moles of CO_2 are produced from 0.100 mole of O_2?

LEARNING GOAL

Given the mass in grams of a substance in a reaction, calculate the mass in grams of another substance in the reaction.

7 Mass Calculations for Reactions

When you perform a chemistry experiment in the laboratory, you measure a specific mass of reactant. From the mass in grams, you can calculate the number of moles of reactant. By using mole–mole factors, you can predict the moles of product that can be produced. Then the molar mass of the product is used to convert moles to grams as seen in Sample Problem 8.

TUTORIAL
Masses of Reactants and Products

Thinkstock Images/Getty Images

A mixture of acetylene and oxygen undergoes combustion during the welding of metals.

SAMPLE PROBLEM 8 **Mass of Product from Mass of Reactant**

When acetylene, C_2H_2, burns in oxygen, high temperatures are produced that are used for welding metals.

$$2C_2H_2(g) + 5O_2(g) \xrightarrow{\Delta} 4CO_2(g) + 2H_2O(g)$$

How many grams of CO_2 are produced when 54.6 g of C_2H_2 is burned?

SOLUTION

Step 1 **State the given and needed quantities.**

Analyze the Problem

Given	Need
54.6 g of C_2H_2	grams of CO_2
Equation	
$2C_2H_2(g) + 5O_2(g) \xrightarrow{\Delta} 4CO_2(g) + 2H_2O(g)$ + energy	

Step 2 **Write a plan to convert the given to the needed quantity (mole or grams).**

grams of C_2H_2 → Molar mass → moles of C_2H_2 → Mole–mole factor → moles of CO_2 → Molar mass → grams of CO_2

Step 3 **Use coefficients to write mole–mole factors; write molar mass factors if needed.**

1 mole of C_2H_2 = 26.0 g of C_2H_2

$$\frac{26.0 \text{ g } C_2H_2}{1 \text{ mole } C_2H_2} \quad \text{and} \quad \frac{1 \text{ mole } C_2H_2}{26.0 \text{ g } C_2H_2}$$

2 moles of C_2H_2 = 4 moles of CO_2

$$\frac{2 \text{ moles } C_2H_2}{4 \text{ moles } CO_2} \quad \text{and} \quad \frac{4 \text{ moles } CO_2}{2 \text{ moles } C_2H_2}$$

1 mole of CO_2 = 44.0 g of CO_2

$$\frac{44.0 \text{ g } CO_2}{1 \text{ mole } CO_2} \quad \text{and} \quad \frac{1 \text{ mole } CO_2}{44.0 \text{ g } CO_2}$$

Step 4 **Set up the problem to give the needed quantity (moles or grams).**

$$54.6\,\cancel{g\,C_2H_2} \times \frac{1\,\cancel{mole\,C_2H_2}}{26.0\,\cancel{g\,C_2H_2}} \times \frac{4\,\cancel{moles\,CO_2}}{2\,\cancel{moles\,C_2H_2}} \times \frac{44.0\,g\,CO_2}{1\,\cancel{mole\,CO_2}} = 185\text{ g of }CO_2$$

STUDY CHECK 8

Using the equation in Sample Problem 8, calculate the grams of CO_2 that can be produced when 25.0 g of O_2 reacts.

QUESTIONS AND PROBLEMS

7 Mass Calculations for Reactions

LEARNING GOAL: *Given the mass in grams of a substance in a reaction, calculate the mass in grams of another substance in the reaction.*

51 Sodium reacts with oxygen to produce sodium oxide.

$$4Na(s) + O_2(g) \longrightarrow 2Na_2O(s)$$

a. How many grams of Na_2O are produced when 57.5 g of Na reacts?
b. If you have 18.0 g of Na, how many grams of O_2 are required for reaction?
c. How many grams of O_2 are needed in a reaction that produces 75.0 g of Na_2O?

52 Nitrogen gas reacts with hydrogen gas to produce ammonia by the following equation:

$$N_2(g) + 3H_2(g) \longrightarrow 2NH_3(g)$$

a. If you have 3.64 g of H_2, how many grams of NH_3 can be produced?
b. How many grams of H_2 are needed to react with 2.80 g of N_2?
c. How many grams of NH_3 can be produced from 12.0 g of H_2?

53 Ammonia and oxygen react to form nitrogen and water.

$$4NH_3(g) + 3O_2(g) \longrightarrow 2N_2(g) + 6H_2O(g)$$

a. How many grams of O_2 are needed to react with 13.6 g of NH_3?
b. How many grams of N_2 can be produced when 6.50 g of O_2 reacts?
c. How many grams of water are formed from the reaction of 34.0 g of NH_3?

54 Iron(III) oxide reacts with carbon to give iron and carbon monoxide.

$$Fe_2O_3(s) + 3C(s) \longrightarrow 2Fe(s) + 3CO(g)$$

a. How many grams of C are required to react with 16.5 g of Fe_2O_3?
b. How many grams of CO are produced when 36.0 g of C reacts?
c. How many grams of Fe can be produced when 6.00 g of Fe_2O_3 reacts?

55 Nitrogen dioxide and water react to produce nitric acid, HNO_3, and nitrogen oxide.

$$3NO_2(g) + H_2O(l) \longrightarrow 2HNO_3(aq) + NO(g)$$

a. How many grams of H_2O are required to react with 28.0 g of NO_2?
b. How many grams of NO are obtained from 15.8 g of NO_2?
c. How many grams of HNO_3 are produced from 8.25 g of NO_2?

56 Calcium cyanamide reacts with water to form calcium carbonate and ammonia.

$$CaCN_2(s) + 3H_2O(l) \longrightarrow CaCO_3(s) + 2NH_3(g)$$

a. How many grams of water are needed to react with 75.0 g of $CaCN_2$?
b. How many grams of NH_3 are produced from 5.24 g of $CaCN_2$?
c. How many grams of $CaCO_3$ form if 155 g of water reacts?

57 When the ore lead(II) sulfide burns in oxygen, the products are solid lead(II) oxide and sulfur dioxide gas.

a. Write the balanced equation for the reaction.
b. How many grams of oxygen are required to react with 29.9 g of lead(II) sulfide?
c. How many grams of sulfur dioxide can be produced when 65.0 g of lead(II) sulfide reacts?
d. How many grams of lead(II) sulfide are used to produce 128 g of lead(II) oxide?

58 When the gases dihydrogen sulfide and oxygen react, they form the gases sulfur dioxide and water.

a. Write the balanced equation for the reaction.
b. How many grams of oxygen are required to react with 2.50 g of dihydrogen sulfide?
c. How many grams of sulfur dioxide can be produced when 38.5 g of oxygen reacts?
d. How many grams of oxygen are required to produce 55.8 g of water vapor?

LEARNING GOAL

Given the actual quantity of product, determine the percent yield for a reaction. Identify a limiting reactant when given the quantities of two or more reactants; calculate the amount of product formed from the limiting reactant.

8 Percent Yield and Limiting Reactants

In our problems up to now, we assumed that all of the reactants were changed completely to product. Thus, we have calculated the amount of product as the maximum quantity possible, or 100%. While this would be an ideal situation, it does not usually happen. As we run a reaction and transfer products from one container to another, some product is usually lost. In the lab as well as commercially, the starting materials may not be completely pure, and side reactions may use some of the reactants to give unwanted products. Thus, 100% of the desired product is not actually obtained.

When we run a chemical reaction in the laboratory, we measure out specific quantities of the reactants and place them in a reaction flask. We calculate the **theoretical yield** for the reaction, which is the amount of product (100%) we would expect if all the reactants are converted to the desired product. When the reaction ends, we collect and measure the mass of the product, which is the **actual yield** for the product. Because some product is usually lost, the actual yield is less than the theoretical yield. Using the actual yield and the theoretical yield, we can calculate the **percent yield**.

$$\text{Percent yield } (\%) = \frac{\text{Actual yield}}{\text{Theoretical yield}} \times 100\%$$

CONCEPT CHECK 9 **Calculating Percent Yield**

For your chemistry class party, you have prepared cookie dough from a recipe that makes 5 dozen cookies. You place dough for 12 cookies on a baking sheet, and place it in the oven. But then the phone rings, and you answer. While you are talking, the cookies on the baking sheet burn and you have to throw them out. You proceed to prepare four more baking sheets with 12 cookies each. If the rest of the cookies are edible, what is the percent yield of cookies you provide for the chemistry party?

ANSWER

The theoretical yield of cookies is 5 dozen or 60 cookies, which is the maximum or 100% of the possible number of cookies. The actual yield is 48 edible cookies, which is 60 cookies minus the 12 cookies that burned. The percent yield is the ratio of 48 edible cookies divided by the theoretical yield of 60 cookies that were possible, multiplied by 100%.

Theoretical yield: 60 cookies possible

Actual yield: 48 cookies to eat

Percent yield: $\dfrac{\text{48 cookies (actual)}}{\text{60 cookies (theoretical)}} \times 100\% = 80\%$

Guide to Calculations for Percent Yield

1. State the given and needed quantities.
2. Write a plan to calculate the theoretical yield and the percent yield.
3. Write the molar mass for the reactant and the mole–mole factor from the balanced equation.
4. Solve for the percent yield ratio by dividing the actual yield (given) by the theoretical yield and multiplying the result by 100%.

SAMPLE PROBLEM 9 **Calculating Percent Yield**

On a space shuttle, LiOH is used to absorb exhaled CO_2 from breathing air to form $LiHCO_3$.

$$LiOH(s) + CO_2(g) \longrightarrow LiHCO_3(s)$$

What is the percent yield of the reaction if 50.0 g of LiOH gives 72.8 g of $LiHCO_3$?

NASA

On a space shuttle, the LiOH in the canisters removes CO_2 from the air.

SOLUTION

Step 1 **State the given and needed quantities.**

Analyze the Problem

Given	Need
50.0 g of LiOH (reactant)	theoretical yield of $LiHCO_3$
72.8 g of $LiHCO_3$ (actual product)	percent yield of $LiHCO_3$
Equation	
$LiOH(s) + CO_2(g) \longrightarrow LiHCO_3(s)$	

Step 2 **Write a plan to calculate the theoretical yield and the percent yield.**

Calculation of theoretical yield:

grams of LiOH → (Molar mass) → moles of LiOH → (Mole–mole factor) → moles of $LiHCO_3$ → (Molar mass) → grams of $LiHCO_3$ (theoretical yield)

Calculation of percent yield:

$$\text{Percent yield } (\%) = \frac{\text{Actual yield}}{\text{Theoretical yield}} \times 100\%$$

Step 3 **Write the molar mass for the reactant and the mole–mole factor from the balanced equation.**

1 mole of LiOH = 24.0 g of LiOH

$$\frac{1 \text{ mole LiOH}}{24.0 \text{ g LiOH}} \quad \text{and} \quad \frac{24.0 \text{ g LiOH}}{1 \text{ mole LiOH}}$$

1 mole of $LiHCO_3$ = 1 mole of LiOH

$$\frac{1 \text{ mole } LiHCO_3}{1 \text{ mole LiOH}} \quad \text{and} \quad \frac{1 \text{ mole LiOH}}{1 \text{ mole } LiHCO_3}$$

1 mole of $LiHCO_3$ = 68.0 g of $LiHCO_3$

$$\frac{68.0 \text{ g } LiHCO_3}{1 \text{ mole } LiHCO_3} \quad \text{and} \quad \frac{1 \text{ mole } LiHCO_3}{68.0 \text{ g } LiHCO_3}$$

Step 4 **Solve for the percent yield ratio by dividing the actual yield (given) by the theoretical yield and multiplying the result by 100%.**

Calculation of theoretical yield:

$$50.0 \text{ g LiOH} \times \frac{1 \text{ mole LiOH}}{24.0 \text{ g LiOH}} \times \frac{1 \text{ mole } LiHCO_3}{1 \text{ mole LiOH}} \times \frac{68.0 \text{ g } LiHCO_3}{1 \text{ mole } LiHCO_3} = 142 \text{ g of } LiHCO_3 \text{ (theoretical yield)}$$

Calculation of percent yield:

$$\frac{\text{Actual yield (given)}}{\text{Theoretical yield (calculated)}} \times 100\% = \frac{72.8 \text{ g } LiHCO_3}{142 \text{ g } LiHCO_3} \times 100\% = 51.3\%$$

A percent yield of 51.3% means that 72.8 g of the theoretical amount of 142 g of $LiHCO_3$ was actually produced by the reaction.

STUDY CHECK 9

For the reaction in Sample Problem 9, what is the percent yield if 8.00 g of CO_2 produces 10.5 g of $LiHCO_3$?

Limiting Reactants

When you make peanut butter sandwiches for lunch, you need 2 slices of bread and 1 tablespoon of peanut butter for each sandwich. As an equation, we could write:

2 slices of bread + 1 tablespoon of peanut butter ⟶ 1 peanut butter sandwich

If you have 8 slices of bread and a full jar of peanut butter, you will run out of bread after you make 4 peanut butter sandwiches. You cannot make any more sandwiches once the bread is used up, even though there is a lot of peanut butter left in the jar. The number of slices of bread has limited the number of sandwiches you can make.

On a different day, you might have 8 slices of bread but only a tablespoon of peanut butter left in the peanut butter jar. You will run out of peanut butter after you make just 1 peanut butter sandwich with 6 slices of bread left over. The small amount of peanut butter available has limited the number of sandwiches you can make.

Pearson Education

The reactant that is used up first is the **limiting reactant**. The other reactant, called the **excess reactant**, is left over.

Bread	Peanut Butter	Sandwiches	Limiting Reactant	Excess Reactant
8 slices	1 full jar	4	bread	peanut butter
8 slices	1 tablespoon	1	peanut butter	bread

CONCEPT CHECK 10 **Limiting Reactants**

For a picnic that you are planning, you have 10 spoons, 8 forks, and 6 knives. If each person including yourself requires 1 spoon, 1 fork, and 1 knife, how many people can be served at your picnic?

ANSWER

The relationship of utensils required by each person can be written:

$$1 \text{ person} = 1 \text{ spoon, } 1 \text{ fork, and } 1 \text{ knife}$$

The maximum number of people for each utensil can be calculated as follows:

$$10 \cancel{\text{spoons}} \times \frac{1 \text{ person}}{1 \cancel{\text{spoon}}} = 10 \text{ people}$$

$$8 \cancel{\text{forks}} \times \frac{1 \text{ person}}{1 \cancel{\text{fork}}} = 8 \text{ people}$$

$$6 \cancel{\text{knives}} \times \frac{1 \text{ person}}{1 \cancel{\text{knife}}} = 6 \text{ people} \quad \text{(smallest number of people)}$$

Brian A Jackson/Shutterstock

The limiting utensil is 6 knives, which means that 6 people, including yourself, can be at your picnic.

Calculating Moles of Product from a Limiting Reactant

TUTORIAL
What Will Run Out First?

TUTORIAL
Limiting Reactant and Yield: Mole Calculations

In a similar way, the availability of reactants in a chemical reaction can limit the amount of product that forms. In many reactions, the reactants are not combined in quantities that allow each to be used up at exactly the same time. Consider the reaction in which hydrogen and chlorine form hydrogen chloride:

$$H_2(g) + Cl_2(g) \longrightarrow 2HCl(g)$$

Suppose the reaction mixture contains 2 moles of H_2 and 5 moles of Cl_2. From the equation, we see that 1 mole of hydrogen reacts with 1 mole of chlorine to produce 2 moles of hydrogen chloride. Now we need to calculate the amount of product that is possible from each of the reactants. We are looking for the limiting reactant, which is the one that runs out first, producing the smaller amount of product.

The mole–mole factors from the equation are written as follows:

2 moles of HCl = 1 mole of H_2

$$\frac{2 \text{ moles HCl}}{1 \text{ mole } H_2} \quad \text{and} \quad \frac{1 \text{ mole } H_2}{2 \text{ moles HCl}}$$

2 moles of HCl = 1 mole of Cl_2

$$\frac{2 \text{ moles HCl}}{1 \text{ mole } Cl_2} \quad \text{and} \quad \frac{1 \text{ mole } Cl_2}{2 \text{ moles HCl}}$$

Moles of HCl from H_2:

$$2 \cancel{\text{moles } H_2} \times \frac{2 \text{ moles HCl}}{1 \cancel{\text{mole } H_2}} = 4 \text{ moles of HCl}$$ (smaller amount of product)

Moles of HCl from Cl_2:

$$5 \cancel{\text{moles } Cl_2} \times \frac{2 \text{ moles HCl}}{1 \cancel{\text{mole } Cl_2}} = 10 \text{ moles of HCl}$$ (not possible)

In this reaction mixture, H_2 is the limiting reactant. When 2 moles of H_2 are used up, the reaction stops. The excess reactant, 3 moles of Cl_2, is left over and cannot react. We can show the changes in each reactant and the product as follows:

	Reactants				Product
Equation	H_2	+	Cl_2	$\longrightarrow$	2HCl
Initial Moles	2 moles		5 moles		0 mole
Moles Used/Formed	−2 moles		−2 moles		+4 moles
Moles Left	0 mole (2 − 2)		3 moles (5 − 2)		4 moles (0 + 4)
Identify As	Limiting reactant		Excess reactant		Product possible

CONCEPT CHECK 11 **Moles of Product from Limiting Reactant**

Consider the reaction for the synthesis of methanol (CH_3OH):

$$CO(g) + 2H_2(g) \longrightarrow CH_3OH(g)$$

In the laboratory, 3.00 moles of reactant CO and 5.00 moles of reactant H_2 are combined. Calculate the number of moles of CH_3OH that can form and identify the limiting reactant.

a. What mole–mole equalities will be needed in the calculation?
b. What are the mole–mole factors from the equalities you wrote in **a**?
c. What is the number of moles of CH_3OH from each reactant?
d. What is the liming reactant for the reaction?

ANSWER

a. Two equalities are needed: one for the mole–mole relationship between CO and CH_3OH and another for the mole–mole relationship between H_2 and CH_3OH using the coefficients from the balanced equation.

$$1 \text{ mole of CO} = 1 \text{ mole of } CH_3OH \qquad 2 \text{ moles of } H_2 = 1 \text{ mole of } CH_3OH$$

b. From each equality, two mole–mole factors can be written:

$$\frac{1 \text{ mole } CH_3OH}{1 \text{ mole CO}} \text{ and } \frac{1 \text{ mole CO}}{1 \text{ mole } CH_3OH} \qquad \frac{1 \text{ mole } CH_3OH}{2 \text{ moles } H_2} \text{ and } \frac{2 \text{ moles } H_2}{1 \text{ mole } CH_3OH}$$

c. Using separate calculations, calculate the moles of CH_3OH that are possible from each of the reactants.

$$3.00 \cancel{\text{moles CO}} \times \frac{1 \text{ mole } CH_3OH}{1 \cancel{\text{mole CO}}} = 3.00 \text{ moles of } CH_3OH$$

$$5.00 \cancel{\text{moles } H_2} \times \frac{1 \text{ mole } CH_3OH}{2 \cancel{\text{moles } H_2}} = 2.50 \text{ moles of } CH_3OH$$

d. The smaller amount, which is 2.50 moles of CH_3OH, is the maximum number of moles of methanol that can be produced. Because this smaller quantity is produced from H_2, the limiting reactant is H_2. Thus, H_2 is the limiting reactant and CO is in excess.

	Reactants				Product
Equation	**CO**	+	**$2H_2$**	$\longrightarrow$	**CH_3OH**
Initial Moles	3.0 moles		5.0 moles		0 mole
Moles Used/Formed	−2.5 moles		−5.0 moles		+2.5 moles
Moles Left	0.5 mole		0 mole		2.5 moles
Identify As	Excess reactant		Limiting reactant		Product possible

TUTORIAL
Limiting Reactant and Yield: Mass Calculations

Calculating Mass of Product from a Limiting Reactant

The quantities of the reactants can also be given in grams. The calculations to identify the limiting reactant are the same as before, but the grams of each reactant must first be converted to moles. Once the limiting reactant is determined, the smaller number of moles of product is converted to grams using molar mass. This calculation is shown in Sample Problem 10.

Klaus Schräder/Westend 61 GmbH/Alamy

A ceramic brake disc in a sports car withstands temperatures of 1400 °C.

SAMPLE PROBLEM 10 **Mass of Product from a Limiting Reactant**

When silicon dioxide (sand) and carbon are heated, the products are silicon carbide, SiC, and carbon monoxide. Silicon carbide is a ceramic material, which tolerates extreme temperatures, and is used as an abrasive and in the brake discs of sports cars. How many grams of CO are produced from a mixture of 70.0 g of SiO_2 and 50.0 g of C?

$$SiO_2(s) + 3C(s) \xrightarrow{\text{Heat}} SiC(s) + 2CO(g)$$

SOLUTION

Step 1 **State the given and needed quantities.**

Analyze the Problem

Given	Need
70.0 g of SiO_2	grams of CO from limiting reactant
50.0 g of C	
Equation	
$SiO_2(s) + 3C(s) \xrightarrow{\text{Heat}} SiC(s) + 2CO(g)$	

Step 2 Use coefficients to write mole–mole factors; write molar mass factors, if needed.

1 mole of SiO_2 = 60.1 g of SiO_2

$$\frac{1 \text{ mole } SiO_2}{60.1 \text{ g } SiO_2} \text{ and } \frac{60.1 \text{ g } SiO_2}{1 \text{ mole } SiO_2}$$

1 mole of C = 12.0 g of C

$$\frac{1 \text{ mole C}}{12.0 \text{ g C}} \text{ and } \frac{12.0 \text{ g C}}{1 \text{ mole C}}$$

2 moles of CO = 1 mole of SiO_2

$$\frac{2 \text{ moles CO}}{1 \text{ mole } SiO_2} \text{ and } \frac{1 \text{ mole } SiO_2}{2 \text{ moles CO}}$$

3 moles of C = 2 moles of CO

$$\frac{2 \text{ moles CO}}{3 \text{ moles C}} \text{ and } \frac{3 \text{ moles C}}{2 \text{ moles CO}}$$

Step 3 Calculate the number of moles of product from each reactant and determine the limiting reactant.

$$70.0 \text{ g } SiO_2 \times \frac{1 \text{ mole } SiO_2}{60.1 \text{ g } SiO_2} \times \frac{2 \text{ moles CO}}{1 \text{ mole } SiO_2} = 2.32 \text{ moles of CO} \quad \text{(smaller amount)}$$

$$50.0 \text{ g C} \times \frac{1 \text{ mole C}}{12.0 \text{ g C}} \times \frac{2 \text{ moles CO}}{3 \text{ moles C}} = 2.77 \text{ moles of CO}$$

Step 4 Use the molar mass to convert the smaller number of moles of product to grams.

1 mole of CO = 28.0 g of CO

$$\frac{1 \text{ mole CO}}{28.0 \text{ g CO}} \text{ and } \frac{28.0 \text{ g CO}}{1 \text{ mole CO}}$$

$$2.32 \text{ moles CO} \times \frac{28.0 \text{ g CO}}{1 \text{ mole CO}} = 65.0 \text{ g of CO}$$

STUDY CHECK 10

Hydrogen sulfide burns with oxygen to give sulfur dioxide and water. How many grams of sulfur dioxide can be produced from the reaction of 8.52 g of H_2S and 10.6 g of O_2?

Guide to Calculating Product from a Limiting Reactant

1. State the given and needed quantities.
2. Use coefficients to write mole–mole factors; write molar mass factors, if needed.
3. Calculate the number of moles of product from each reactant and determine the limiting reactant.
4. Use the molar mass to convert the smaller number of moles of product to grams.

QUESTIONS AND PROBLEMS

8 Percent Yield and Limiting Reactants

LEARNING GOAL: *Given the actual quantity of product, determine the percent yield for a reaction. Identify a limiting reactant when given the quantities of two or more reactants; calculate the amount of product formed from the limiting reactant.*

59 Carbon disulfide is produced by the reaction of carbon and sulfur dioxide.

$$5C(s) + 2SO_2(g) \longrightarrow CS_2(g) + 4CO(g)$$

a. What is the percent yield for carbon disulfide if the reaction of 40.0 g of carbon produces 36.0 g of carbon disulfide?

b. What is the percent yield for carbon disulfide if the reaction of 32.0 g of sulfur dioxide produces 12.0 g of carbon disulfide?

60 Iron(III) oxide reacts with carbon monoxide to produce iron and carbon dioxide.

$$Fe_2O_3(s) + 3CO(g) \longrightarrow 2Fe(s) + 3CO_2(g)$$

a. What is the percent yield for iron if the reaction of 65.0 g of iron(III) oxide produces 38.0 g of iron?

b. What is the percent yield for carbon dioxide if a reaction of 75.0 g of carbon monoxide produces 85.0 g of carbon dioxide?

61 Aluminum reacts with oxygen to produce aluminum oxide.

$$4Al(s) + 3O_2(g) \longrightarrow 2Al_2O_3(s)$$

Calculate the mass of Al_2O_3 that can be produced if the reaction of 50.0 g of aluminum and excess oxygen has a 75.0% yield.

62 Propane (C_3H_8) burns in oxygen to produce carbon dioxide and water.

$$C_3H_8(g) + 5O_2(g) \xrightarrow{\Delta} 3CO_2(g) + 4H_2O(g)$$

Calculate the mass of CO_2 that can be produced if the reaction of 45.0 g of propane and excess oxygen has a 60.0% yield.

63 When 30.0 g of carbon is heated with silicon dioxide, 28.2 g of carbon monoxide is produced. What is the percent yield of carbon monoxide for this reaction?

$$3C(s) + SiO_2(s) \xrightarrow{\Delta} SiC(s) + 2CO(g)$$

64 When 56.6 g of calcium is reacted with nitrogen gas, 32.4 g of calcium nitride is produced. What is the percent yield of calcium nitride for this reaction?

$$3Ca(s) + N_2(g) \longrightarrow Ca_3N_2(s)$$

65 A taxi company has 10 taxis.

a. On a certain day, only eight taxi drivers show up for work. How many taxis can be used to pick up passengers?
b. On another day, 10 taxi drivers show up for work but three taxis are in the repair shop. How many taxis can be driven?

66 A clock maker has 15 clock faces. Each clock requires one clock face and two hands.

a. If the clock maker has 42 hands, how many clocks can be produced?
b. If the clock maker has only eight hands, how many clocks can be produced?

67 Nitrogen and hydrogen react to form ammonia.

$$N_2(g) + 3H_2(g) \longrightarrow 2NH_3(g)$$

Determine the limiting reactant in each of the following mixtures of reactants:

a. 3.0 moles of N_2 and 5.0 moles of H_2
b. 8.0 moles of N_2 and 4.0 moles of H_2
c. 3.0 moles of N_2 and 12.0 moles of H_2

68 Iron and oxygen react to form iron(III) oxide.

$$4Fe(s) + 3O_2(g) \longrightarrow 2Fe_2O_3(s)$$

Determine the limiting reactant in each of the following mixtures of reactants:

a. 2.0 moles of Fe and 6.0 moles of O_2
b. 5.0 moles of Fe and 4.0 moles of O_2
c. 16.0 moles of Fe and 20.0 moles of O_2

69 For each of the following reactions, 2.00 moles of each reactant is present initially. Determine the limiting reactant, and calculate the moles of product in parentheses that would form.

a. $2SO_2(g) + O_2(g) \longrightarrow 2SO_3(g)$ (SO_3)
b. $3Fe(s) + 4H_2O(l) \longrightarrow Fe_3O_4(s) + 4H_2(g)$ (Fe_3O_4)
c. $C_7H_{16}(g) + 11O_2(g) \xrightarrow{\Delta} 7CO_2(g) + 8H_2O(g)$ (CO_2)

70 For each of the following reactions, 3.00 moles of each reactant is present initially. Determine the limiting reactant, and calculate the moles of product in parentheses that would form.

a. $4Li(s) + O_2(g) \longrightarrow 2Li_2O(s)$ (Li_2O)
b. $Fe_2O_3(s) + 3H_2(g) \longrightarrow 2Fe(s) + 3H_2O(l)$ (Fe)
c. $Al_2S_3(s) + 6H_2O(l) \longrightarrow 2Al(OH)_3(aq) + 3H_2S(g)$ (H_2S)

71 For each of the following reactions, 20.0 g of each reactant is present initially. Determine the limiting reactant, and calculate the grams of product in parentheses that would be produced.

a. $2Al(s) + 3Cl_2(g) \longrightarrow 2AlCl_3(s)$ $(AlCl_3)$
b. $4NH_3(g) + 5O_2(g) \longrightarrow 4NO(g) + 6H_2O(g)$ (H_2O)
c. $CS_2(g) + 3O_2(g) \longrightarrow CO_2(g) + 2SO_2(g)$ (SO_2)

72 For each of the following reactions, 20.0 g of each reactant is present initially. Determine the limiting reactant, and calculate the grams of product in parentheses that would be produced.

a. $4Al(s) + 3O_2(g) \longrightarrow 2Al_2O_3(s)$ (Al_2O_3)
b. $3NO_2(g) + H_2O(l) \longrightarrow 2HNO_3(aq) + NO(g)$ (HNO_3)
c. $C_2H_5OH(l) + 3O_2(g) \longrightarrow 2CO_2(g) + 3H_2O(g)$ (H_2O)

LEARNING GOAL

Describe the energy changes in exothermic and endothermic reactions.

9 Energy Changes in Chemical Reactions

For a chemical reaction to take place, the molecules of the reactants must collide with each other and have the proper orientation and energy. Even when a collision has the proper orientation, there still must be sufficient energy to break the bonds of the reactants. The **activation energy** is the amount of energy required to break the bonds between atoms of the reactants. If the energy of a collision is less than the activation energy, the molecules bounce apart without reacting. Many collisions occur, but only a few actually lead to the formation of product.

The concept of activation energy is analogous to climbing over a hill. To reach a destination on the other side, we must expend energy to climb to the top of the hill. Once we are at the top, we can easily run down the other side. The energy needed to get us from our starting point to the top of the hill would be the activation energy.

Three Conditions Required for a Reaction to Occur

1. **Collision** The reactants must collide.
2. **Orientation** The reactants must align properly to break and form bonds.
3. **Energy** The collision must provide the energy of activation.

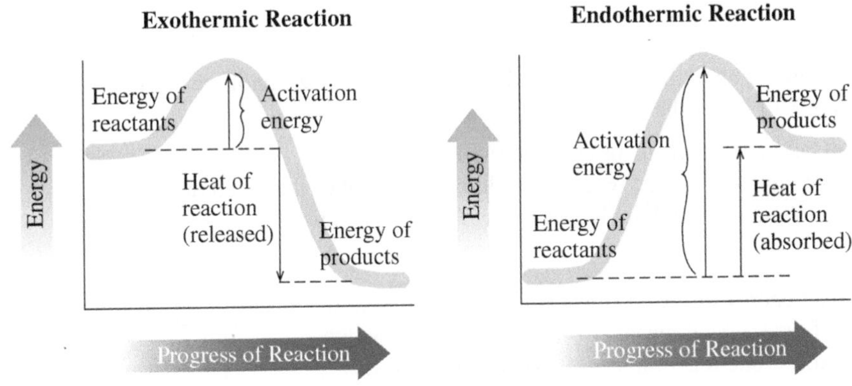

The activation energy is the energy needed to convert reacting molecules into products.

Heat of Reaction

In every chemical reaction, heat is absorbed or released as bonds in the reactants are broken, and new bonds are formed in the products. The **heat of reaction**, symbol ΔH, is the difference between the energy of breaking bonds in the reactants and forming bonds in the products. The direction of heat flow depends on whether the products in the reaction have more or less energy than the reactants.

$$\Delta H = H_{products} - H_{reactants}$$

TUTORIAL
Heat of Reaction

Exothermic Reactions

In an **exothermic reaction** (*exo* means out), the energy of the reactants is greater than that of the products. Thus, heat is released along with the formation of the products. In an exothermic reaction, the heat of reaction (ΔH) value is written with a negative sign ($-$), indicating that heat is emitted or lost. For example, in the thermite reaction, the reaction of aluminum and iron(III) oxide produces so much heat that temperatures of 2500 °C are reached. The thermite reaction has been used to cut or weld railroad tracks.

Richard Megna/Fundamental Photographs

The high temperature of the thermite reaction has been used to cut or weld railroad tracks.

Exothermic, Heat Released (Given Off) **Heat Is a Product**

$$2Al(s) + Fe_2O_3(s) \longrightarrow 2Fe(s) + Al_2O_3(s) + 850\text{ kJ}$$

$$2Al(s) + Fe_2O_3(s) \longrightarrow 2Fe(s) + Al_2O_3(s) \qquad \Delta H = -850\text{ kJ}$$

Negative sign

Endothermic Reactions

In an **endothermic reaction** (*endo* means within), the energy of the reactants is lower than that of the products. Thus, heat is absorbed and used to convert the reactants to products. For an endothermic reaction, the heat of reaction can be written on the same side as the reactants. In an endothermic reaction, the heat of reaction (ΔH) value is written with a positive sign ($+$) indicating that heat is absorbed. For example, in the breakdown of water to hydrogen and oxygen, the ΔH is $+137$ kcal, which is the energy required to break down 2 moles of water into 2 moles of hydrogen and 1 mole of oxygen.

Endothermic, Heat Required **Heat Is a Reactant**

$$2H_2O(l) + 137\text{ kcal} \longrightarrow 2H_2(g) + O_2(g)$$

$$2H_2O(l) \longrightarrow 2H_2(g) + O_2(g) \qquad \Delta H = +137\text{ kcal}$$

Positive sign

Reaction	Energy Change	Heat in the Equation	Sign of ΔH
Exothermic	Heat released	Product side	Negative sign ($-$)
Endothermic	Heat absorbed	Reactant side	Positive sign ($+$)

CONCEPT CHECK 12 **Exothermic and Endothermic Reactions**

In the reaction of one mole of carbon with oxygen gas, the energy of the carbon dioxide product is 393 kJ lower than the energy of the reactants.

a. Is the reaction exothermic or endothermic?
b. Write the equation for the reaction, including the heat of the reaction.
c. What is the value, in kilojoules, of the ΔH for this reaction?

ANSWER

a. When the energy of the products is lower than that of the reactants, the reaction gives off heat, which means it is an exothermic reaction.
b. In an exothermic reaction, heat is written as a product.

$$C(s) + O_2(g) \longrightarrow CO_2(g) + 393 \text{ kJ}$$

c. The heat of reaction for an exothermic reaction has a negative sign: $\Delta H = -393$ kJ

Calculations of Heat in Reactions

The value of ΔH refers to the heat change for the number of moles of each substance in the balanced equation for the reaction. Consider the following decomposition reaction:

$$2H_2O(l) \longrightarrow 2H_2(g) + O_2(g) \qquad \Delta H = +572 \text{ kJ}$$

$$2H_2O(l) + 572 \text{ kJ} \longrightarrow 2H_2(g) + O_2(g)$$

For this reaction, 572 kJ are absorbed by 2 moles of H_2O to produce 2 moles of H_2 and 1 mole of O_2. We can write heat conversion factors for each substance in this reaction:

$$\frac{+572 \text{ kJ}}{2 \text{ moles } H_2O} \quad \frac{+572 \text{ kJ}}{2 \text{ moles } H_2} \quad \frac{+572 \text{ kJ}}{1 \text{ mole } O_2}$$

Suppose in this reaction that 9.00 g of H_2O undergoes reaction. We can calculate the heat absorbed as:

$$9.00 \cancel{\text{g } H_2O} \times \frac{1 \cancel{\text{mole } H_2O}}{18.0 \cancel{\text{g } H_2O}} \times \frac{+572 \text{ kJ}}{2 \cancel{\text{moles } H_2O}} = +143 \text{ kJ}$$

SAMPLE PROBLEM 11 **Calculating the Heat in a Reaction**

In the formation of two moles of ammonia, NH_3, from hydrogen and nitrogen, 92.2 kJ of heat is released.

$$N_2(g) + 3H_2(g) \longrightarrow 2NH_3(g) \quad \Delta H = -92.2 \text{ kJ}$$

How much heat, in kilojoules, is released when 50.0 g of ammonia is produced?

SOLUTION

Step 1 **State the given and needed quantities.**

Analyze the Problem

Given	Need
50.0 g of ammonia, NH_3	kilojoules produced
$\Delta H = -92.2$ kJ	
Equation	
$N_2(g) + 3H_2(g) \longrightarrow 2NH_3(g)$	

Step 2 **Write a plan using heat of reaction and any molar mass needed.**

grams of NH_3 → Molar mass → moles of NH_3 → Heat of reaction → kilojoules

Guide to Calculations Using Heat of Reaction (ΔH)

1 State the given and needed quantities.
2 Write a plan using heat of reaction and any molar mass needed.
3 Write the conversion factors including heat of reaction.
4 Set up the problem to calculate the heat.

Step 3 **Write the conversion factors including heat of reaction.**

1 mole of NH_3 = 17.0 g of NH_3

$$\frac{1 \text{ mole } NH_3}{17.0 \text{ g } NH_3} \text{ and } \frac{17.0 \text{ g } NH_3}{1 \text{ mole } NH_3}$$

2 moles of NH_3 = −92.2 kJ

$$\frac{-92.2 \text{ kJ}}{2 \text{ moles } NH_3} \text{ and } \frac{2 \text{ moles } NH_3}{-92.2 \text{ kJ}}$$

Step 4 **Set up the problem to calculate the heat.**

$$50.0 \text{ g } NH_3 \times \frac{1 \text{ mole } NH_3}{17.0 \text{ g } NH_3} \times \frac{-92.2 \text{ kJ}}{2 \text{ moles } NH_3} = -136 \text{ kJ}$$

STUDY CHECK 11

Mercury(II) oxide decomposes to mercury and oxygen.

$$2HgO(s) \xrightarrow{\Delta} 2Hg(l) + O_2(g) \quad \Delta H = +182 \text{ kJ}$$

a. Is the reaction exothermic or endothermic?
b. How many kilojoules are needed to react 25.0 g of mercury(II) oxide?

Chemistry Link to Health

COLD PACKS AND HOT PACKS

In a hospital, at a first-aid station, or at an athletic event, an instant *cold pack* may be used to reduce swelling from an injury, remove heat from inflammation, or decrease capillary size to lessen the effect of hemorrhaging. Inside the plastic container of a cold pack, there is a compartment containing solid ammonium nitrate (NH_4NO_3) that is separated from a compartment containing water. The pack is activated when it is hit or squeezed hard enough to break the walls between the compartments and cause the ammonium nitrate to mix with the water (shown as H_2O over the reaction arrow). In an endothermic process, one mole of NH_4NO_3 that dissolves absorbs 26 kJ. The temperature drops to about 4–5 °C to give a cold pack that is ready to use.

Endothermic Reaction in a Cold Pack

$$NH_4NO_3(s) + 26 \text{ kJ} \xrightarrow{H_2O} NH_4NO_3(aq)$$

Exothermic Reaction in a Hot Pack

$$CaCl_2(s) \xrightarrow{H_2O} CaCl_2(aq) + 82 \text{ kJ}$$

Hot packs are used to relax muscles, lessen aches and cramps, and increase circulation by expanding capillary size. Constructed in the same way as cold packs, a hot pack contains a salt such as $CaCl_2$. When one mole of $CaCl_2$ dissolves in water, 82 kJ are released. The temperature changes as much as 66 °C to give a hot pack that is ready to use.

Pearson Education

Cold packs use an endothermic reaction.

QUESTIONS AND PROBLEMS

9 Energy Changes in Chemical Reactions

LEARNING GOAL: *Describe the energy changes in exothermic and endothermic reactions.*

73 **a.** Why do chemical reactions require activation energy?
b. In an exothermic reaction, is the energy of the products higher or lower than that of the reactants?
c. Draw an energy diagram for an exothermic reaction.

74 **a.** What is measured by the heat of reaction?
b. In an endothermic reaction, is the energy of the products higher or lower than that of the reactants?
c. Draw an energy diagram for an endothermic reaction.

75 Classify the following as exothermic or endothermic reactions:
a. A reaction releases 550 kJ.
b. The energy level of the products is higher than that of the reactants.
c. The metabolism of glucose in the body provides energy.

76 Classify the following as exothermic or endothermic reactions:
a. The energy level of the products is lower than that of the reactants.
b. In the body, the synthesis of proteins requires energy.
c. A reaction absorbs 125 kJ.

77 Classify the following as exothermic or endothermic reactions and give ΔH for each:

a. $CH_4(g) + 2O_2(g) \xrightarrow{\Delta} CO_2(g) + 2H_2O(g) + 890\text{ kJ}$

b. $Ca(OH)_2(s) + 65.3\text{ kJ} \longrightarrow CaO(s) + H_2O(l)$

c. $2Al(s) + Fe_2O_3(s) \longrightarrow Al_2O_3(s) + 2Fe(s) + 205\text{ kcal}$

78 Classify the following as exothermic or endothermic reactions and give ΔH for each:

a. $C_3H_8(g) + 5O_2(g) \xrightarrow{\Delta} 3CO_2(g) + 4H_2O(g) + 530\text{ kcal}$

b. $2Na(s) + Cl_2(g) \longrightarrow 2NaCl(s) + 819\text{ kJ}$

c. $PCl_5(g) + 67\text{ kJ} \longrightarrow PCl_3(g) + Cl_2(g)$

79 The equation for the formation of silicon tetrachloride from silicon and chlorine is:

$$Si(s) + 2Cl_2(g) \longrightarrow SiCl_4(g) \quad \Delta H = -657\text{ kJ}$$

How many kilojoules are released when 125 g of Cl_2 reacts with silicon?

80 Methanol (CH_3OH), which is used as a cooking fuel, undergoes combustion to produce carbon dioxide and water.

$$2CH_3OH(l) + 3O_2(g) \xrightarrow{\Delta} 2CO_2(g) + 4H_2O(g) \quad \Delta H = -726\text{ kJ}$$

How many kilojoules are released when 75.0 g of methanol is burned?

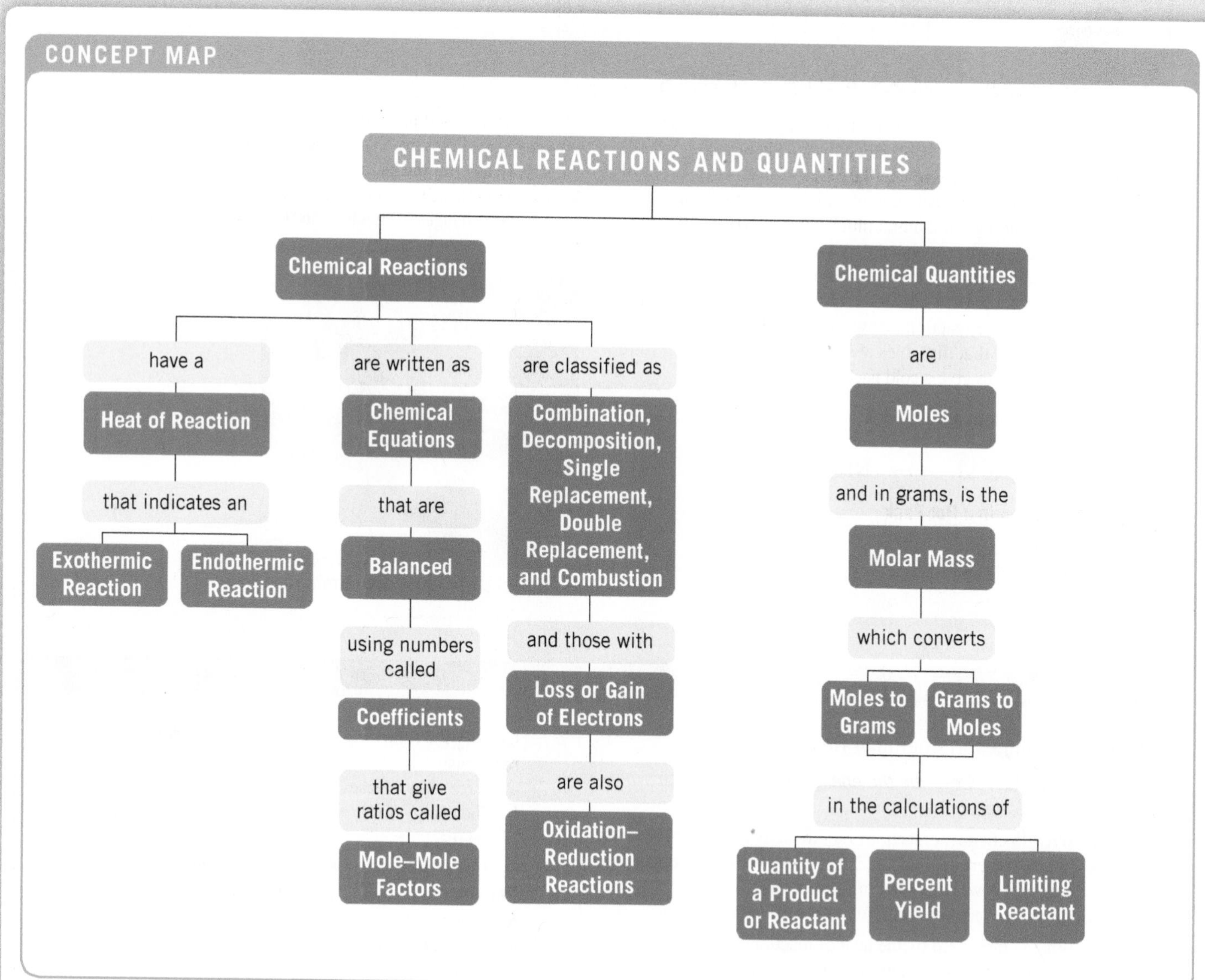

CHAPTER REVIEW

1 Equations for Chemical Reactions

LEARNING GOAL: *Write a balanced chemical equation from the formulas of the reactants and products for a chemical reaction.*

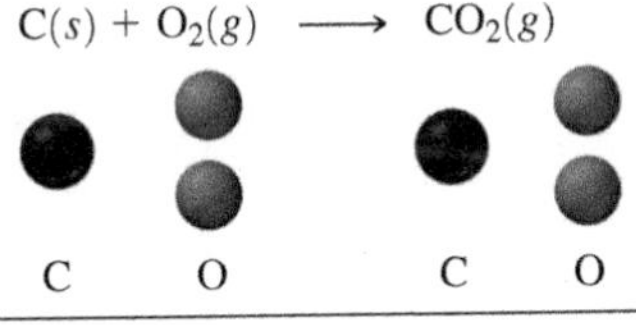

- A chemical change occurs when the atoms of the initial substances rearrange to form new substances.
- A chemical equation shows the formulas of the substances that react on the left side of a reaction arrow and the products that form on the right side of the reaction arrow.
- A chemical equation is balanced by writing coefficients, small whole numbers, in front of formulas to equalize the atoms of each of the elements in the reactants and the products.

2 Types of Reactions

LEARNING GOAL: *Identify a chemical reaction as a combination, decomposition, single replacement, double replacement, or combustion reaction.*

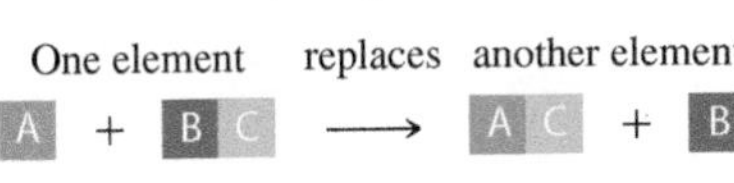

- Many chemical reactions can be organized by reaction type: combination, decomposition, single replacement, double replacement, or combustion.

3 Oxidation–Reduction Reactions

LEARNING GOAL: *Define the terms oxidation and reduction; identify the reactant that is oxidized and the reactant that is reduced.*

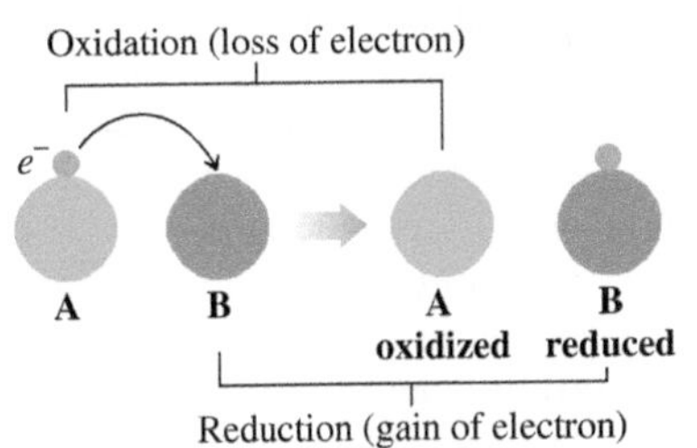

- When electrons are transferred in a reaction, it is an oxidation–reduction reaction.
- The reactant that is oxidized loses electrons, and may also gain oxygen atoms or lose hydrogen atoms.
- The reactant that is reduced gains electrons, and may also lose oxygen atoms or gain hydrogen atoms.
- Overall, the number of electrons lost and gained is equal in any oxidation–reduction reaction.

4 The Mole

LEARNING GOAL: *Use Avogadro's number to determine the number of particles in a given amount of moles.*

TABLE 5 Number of Particles in One-Mole Samples

Substance	Number and Type of Particles
1 mole of Al	6.02×10^{23} atoms of Al
1 mole of S	6.02×10^{23} atoms of S
1 mole of water (H_2O)	6.02×10^{23} molecules of H_2O
1 mole of vitamin C ($C_6H_8O_6$)	6.02×10^{23} molecules of vitamin C
1 mole of NaCl	6.02×10^{23} formula units of NaCl

- One mole of an element contains 6.02×10^{23} atoms.
- One mole of a compound contains 6.02×10^{23} molecules or formula units.

5 Molar Mass

LEARNING GOAL: *Determine the molar mass of a substance and use the molar mass to convert between grams and moles.*

TABLE 6 The Molar Mass of Selected Elements and Compounds

Substance	Molar Mass
1 mole of C	12.0 g
1 mole of Na	23.0 g
1 mole of Fe	55.9 g
1 mole of NaF	42.0 g
1 mole of $CaCO_3$	100.1 g
1 mole of $C_6H_{12}O_6$ (glucose)	180.1 g
1 mole of $C_8H_{10}N_4O_2$ (caffeine)	194.1 g

- The molar mass (g/mole) of any substance is the mass in grams equal numerically to its atomic mass, or the sum of the atomic masses, which have been multiplied by their subscripts in a formula.
- The molar mass is used as a conversion factor to change a quantity in grams to moles or to change a given number of moles to grams.

6 Mole Relationships in Chemical Equations

LEARNING GOAL: *Given a quantity in moles of reactant or product, use a mole–mole factor from the balanced equation to calculate the moles of another substance in the reaction.*

$$1 \text{ mole of } C_3H_8 = 3 \text{ moles of } CO_2$$

$$\frac{1 \text{ mole } C_3H_8}{3 \text{ moles } CO_2} \quad \text{and} \quad \frac{3 \text{ moles } CO_2}{1 \text{ mole } C_3H_8}$$

- In a balanced equation, the total mass of the reactants is equal to the total mass of the products.
- The coefficients in an equation describing the relationship between the moles of any two components are used to write mole–mole factors.
- When the number of moles for one substance is known, a mole–mole factor is used to find the moles of a different substance in the reaction.

7 Mass Calculations for Reactions

LEARNING GOAL: *Given the mass in grams of a substance in a reaction, calculate the mass in grams of another substance in the reaction.*

$$1 \text{ mole of } CO_2 = 44.0 \text{ g of } CO_2$$

$$\frac{44.0 \text{ g } CO_2}{1 \text{ mole } CO_2} \quad \text{and} \quad \frac{1 \text{ mole } CO_2}{44.0 \text{ g } CO_2}$$

- In calculations using equations, molar masses and mole–mole factors are used to change the number of grams of one substance to the corresponding grams of a different substance.

8 Percent Yield and Limiting Reactants

LEARNING GOAL: *Given the actual quantity of product, determine the percent yield for a reaction. Identify a limiting reactant when given the quantities of two or more reactants; calculate the amount of product formed from the limiting reactant.*

$$\text{Percent yield (\%)} = \frac{\text{Actual yield}}{\text{Theoretical yield}} \times 100\%$$

- The percent yield of a reaction indicates the percent of product that is actually produced by a reaction.
- The percent yield is calculated by dividing the actual yield in grams of a product by the theoretical yield in grams, which is expressed as a percent.
- A limiting reactant is the reactant in the reaction that produces the smaller amount of product.
- When the mass of two or more reactants is given, the actual mass of a product is calculated from the limiting reactant.

9 Energy Changes in Chemical Reactions

LEARNING GOAL: *Describe the energy changes in exothermic and endothermic reactions.*

- In a reaction, the reacting particles must collide with energy equal to or greater than the energy of activation.
- The heat of reaction is the energy difference between the initial energy of the reactants and the final energy of the products.

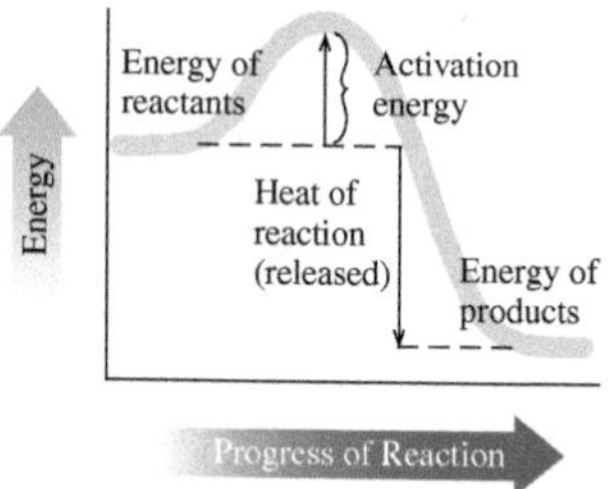

- In an exothermic reaction, the energy of the reactants is greater than that of the products; heat is released and ΔH is negative.
- In an endothermic reaction, the energy of the reactants is lower than that of the products; heat is absorbed and ΔH is positive.

KEY TERMS

activation energy The energy needed upon collision to break the bonds of the reacting molecules.

actual yield The actual amount of product produced by a reaction.

Avogadro's number The number of items in a mole, equal to 6.02×10^{23}.

balanced equation The final form of a chemical equation that shows the same number of atoms of each element in the reactants and products.

chemical equation A shorthand way to represent a chemical reaction using chemical formulas to indicate the reactants and products, and coefficients to show reacting ratios.

chemical reaction The process by which a chemical change takes place.

coefficients Whole numbers placed in front of the formulas to balance the number of atoms or moles of atoms of each element on both sides of an equation.

combination reaction A chemical reaction in which reactants combine to form a single product.

combustion reaction A chemical reaction in which a carbon-containing compound burns in oxygen from the air to produce carbon dioxide, water, and energy.

decomposition reaction A chemical reaction in which a single reactant splits into two or more simpler substances.

double replacement reaction A chemical reaction in which parts of two different reactants exchange places.

endothermic reaction A reaction in which the energy of the reactants is less than that of the products.

excess reactant The reactant that remains when the limiting reactant is used up in a reaction.

exothermic reaction A reaction in which the energy of the reactants is greater than that of the products.

formula unit The group of ions represented by the formula of an ionic compound.

heat of reaction The heat (symbol ΔH) absorbed or released when a reaction takes place.

limiting reactant The reactant used up during a chemical reaction; it limits the amount of product that can form.

molar mass The mass in grams of 1 mole of an element equal numerically to its atomic mass. The molar mass of a compound is equal to the sum of the masses of the elements multiplied by their subscripts in the formula.

mole A group of atoms, molecules, or formula units that contains 6.02×10^{23} of these items.

mole–mole factor A conversion factor that relates the number of moles of two compounds derived from the coefficients in a balanced equation.

oxidation The loss of electrons by a substance. Biological oxidation is indicated by the addition of oxygen or the loss of hydrogen.

oxidation–reduction reaction A reaction in which the oxidation of one reactant is always accompanied by the reduction of another reactant.

percent yield The ratio of the actual yield of a reaction to the theoretical yield possible for the reaction that is multiplied by 100%.

products The substances formed as a result of a chemical reaction.

reactants The initial substances that undergo change in a chemical reaction.

reduction The gain of electrons by a substance. Biological reduction is indicated by the loss of oxygen or the gain of hydrogen.

single replacement reaction A reaction in which an element replaces a different element in a compound.

theoretical yield The maximum amount of product that a reaction can produce from a given amount of reactant.

UNDERSTANDING THE CONCEPTS

The chapter sections to review are shown in parentheses at the end of each question.

81 Balance each of the following by adding coefficients; identify the type of reaction for each: (1, 2)

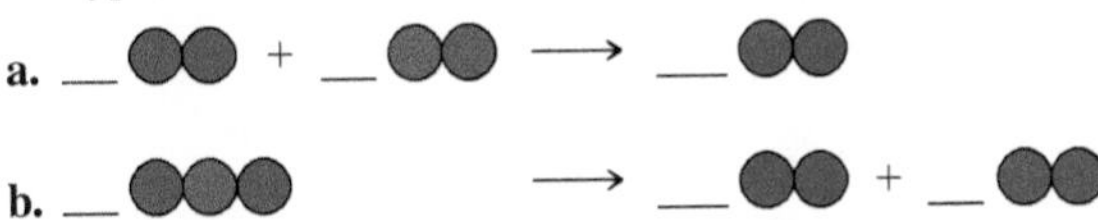

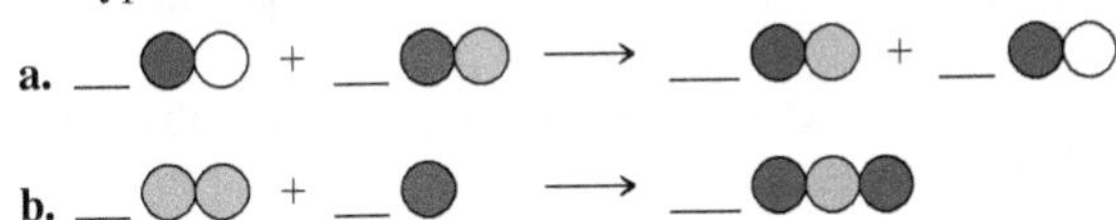

82 Balance each of the following by adding coefficients; identify the type of reaction for each: (1, 2)

83 If red spheres represent oxygen atoms and blue spheres represent nitrogen atoms, (1, 2)

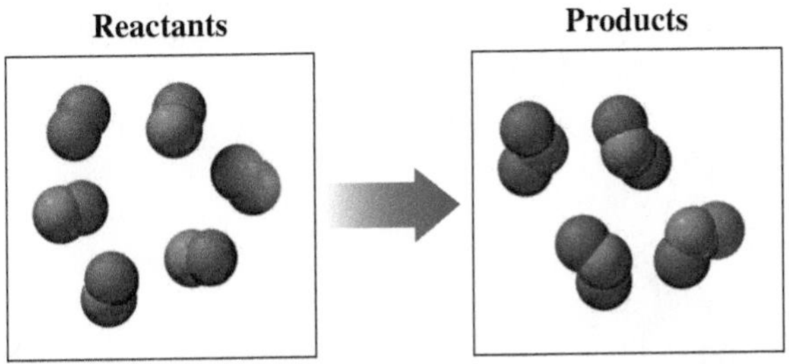

a. write the formula for each of the reactants and products.
b. write the balanced equation for the reaction.
c. indicate the type of reaction as combination, decomposition, single replacement, double replacement, or combustion.

84 If purple spheres represent iodine atoms and white spheres represent hydrogen atoms, (1, 2)

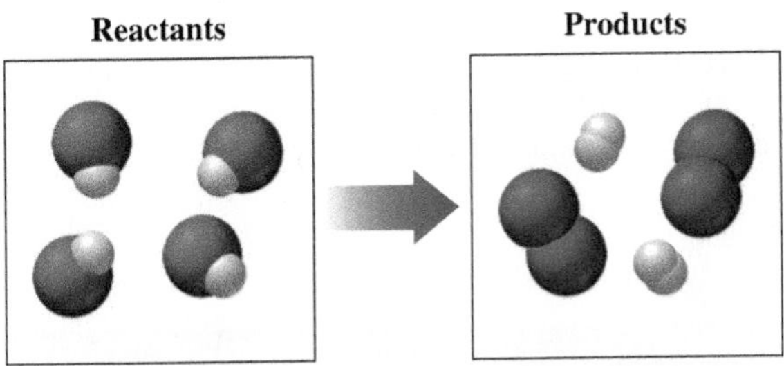

a. write the formula for each of the reactants and products.
b. write the balanced equation for the reaction.
c. indicate the type of reaction as combination, decomposition, single replacement, double replacement, or combustion.

85 If blue spheres represent nitrogen atoms and purple spheres represent iodine atoms, (1, 2)

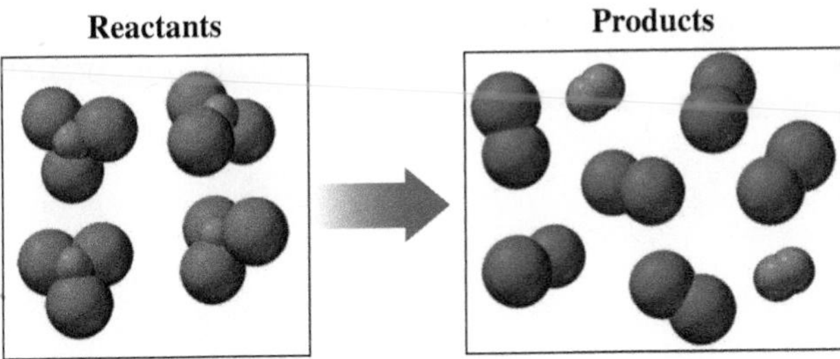

a. write the formula for each of the reactants (solid) and products.
b. write the balanced equation for the reaction.
c. indicate the type of reaction as combination, decomposition, single replacement, double replacement, or combustion.

86 If green spheres represent chlorine atoms, yellow-green spheres represent fluorine atoms, and white spheres represent hydrogen atoms, (1, 2)

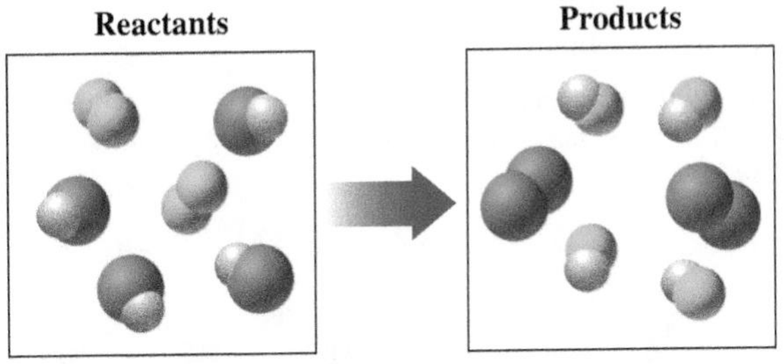

a. write the formula for each of the reactants and products.
b. write the balanced equation for the reaction.
c. indicate the type of reaction as combination, decomposition, single replacement, double replacement, or combustion.

87 If green spheres represent chlorine atoms and red spheres represent oxygen atoms, (1, 2)

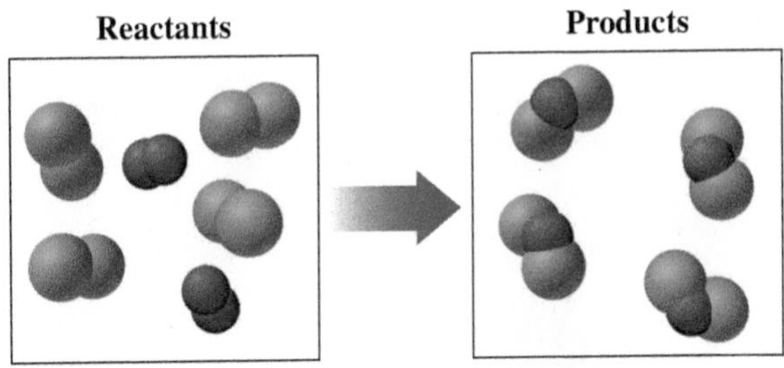

a. write the formula for each of the reactants and products.
b. write the balanced equation for the reaction.
c. indicate the type of reaction as combination, decomposition, single replacement, double replacement, or combustion.

88 If blue spheres represent nitrogen atoms and purple spheres represent iodine atoms, (1, 2)

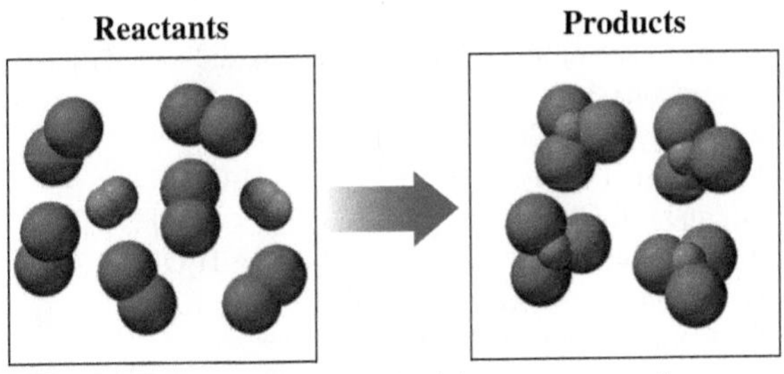

a. write the formula for each of the reactants and products.
b. write the balanced equation for the reaction.
c. indicate the type of reaction as combination, decomposition, single replacement, double replacement, or combustion.

89 Using the models of the molecules, (black = C, white = H, yellow = S, green = Cl), determine each of the following: (4, 5)

1. 

2. 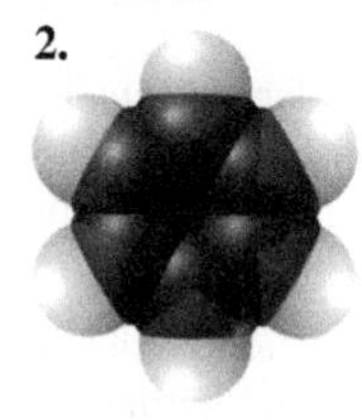

a. molecular formula
b. molar mass
c. number of moles in 10.0 g

90 Using the models of the molecules, (black = C, white = H, yellow = S, red = O), determine each of the following: (4, 5)

1. 

2. 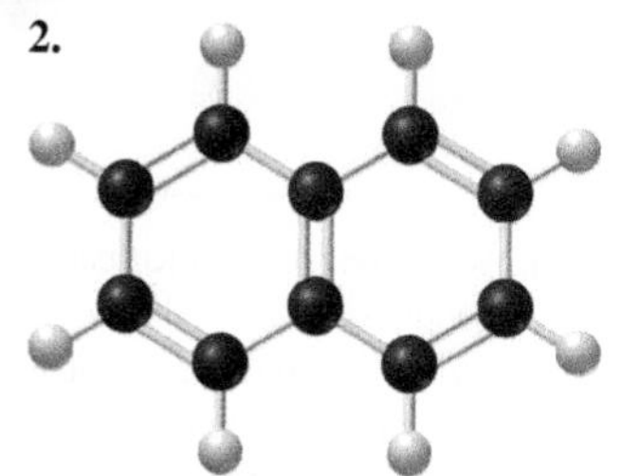

a. molecular formula
b. molar mass
c. number of moles in 10.0 g

91 A dandruff shampoo contains dipyrithione, $C_{10}H_8N_2O_2S_2$, an antibacterial and antifungal agent. (5)

Pearson Education

This dandruff shampoo contains dipyrithione.

a. What is the molar mass of dipyrithione?
b. How many moles of dipyrithione are in 25.0 g?
c. How many moles of carbon are in 25.0 g of dipyrithione?

92 Ammonium sulfate, $(NH_4)_2SO_4$, is used in fertilizers to provide nitrogen for the soil. (4, 5)

a. How many formula units are in 0.200 mole of ammonium sulfate?
b. How many H atoms are in 0.100 mole of ammonium sulfate?
c. How many moles of ammonium sulfate contain 7.4×10^{25} atoms of N?
d. What is the molar mass of ammonium sulfate?

93 Propane gas, C_3H_8, a hydrocarbon, is used as a fuel for many barbecues. (4, 5)

a. How many grams of the compound are in 1.50 moles of propane?
b. How many moles of the compound are in 34.0 g of propane?
c. How many grams of carbon are in 34.0 g of propane?
d. How many atoms of H are in 0.254 g of propane?

94 Allyl sulfide, $(C_3H_5)_2S$, is the substance that gives garlic its characteristic odor. (4, 5)

Tamara Kulikova/iStockphoto

The characteristic odor of garlic is due to a sulfur-containing compound.

a. How many moles of sulfur are in 23.2 g of $(C_3H_5)_2S$?
b. How many atoms of H are in 0.75 mole of $(C_3H_5)_2S$?
c. How many grams of carbon are in 4.20×10^{23} molecules of $(C_3H_5)_2S$?
d. How many atoms of C are in 15.0 g of $(C_3H_5)_2S$?

ADDITIONAL QUESTIONS AND PROBLEMS

For instructor-assigned homework, go to www.masteringchemistry.com.

95 Balance each of the following equations and identify the type of reaction: (1, 2)

a. $NH_3(g) + HCl(g) \longrightarrow NH_4Cl(s)$
b. $Fe_3O_4(s) + H_2(g) \longrightarrow Fe(s) + H_2O(g)$
c. $Sb(s) + Cl_2(g) \longrightarrow SbCl_3(s)$
d. $C_5H_{12}(g) + O_2(g) \xrightarrow{\Delta} CO_2(g) + H_2O(g)$
e. $KBr(aq) + Cl_2(aq) \longrightarrow KCl(aq) + Br_2(l)$
f. $Al_2(SO_4)_3(aq) + NaOH(aq) \longrightarrow Na_2SO_4(aq) + Al(OH)_3(s)$

96 Balance each of the following equations and identify the type of reaction: (1, 2)

a. $Li_3N(s) \longrightarrow Li(s) + N_2(g)$
b. $Mg(s) + N_2(g) \longrightarrow Mg_3N_2(s)$
c. $Mg(s) + H_3PO_4(aq) \longrightarrow Mg_3(PO_4)_2(s) + H_2(g)$
d. $C_4H_6(g) + O_2(g) \xrightarrow{\Delta} CO_2(g) + H_2O(g)$
e. $Al(s) + Cl_2(g) \longrightarrow AlCl_3(s)$
f. $MgCl_2(aq) + AgNO_3(aq) \longrightarrow Mg(NO_3)_2(aq) + AgCl(s)$

97 Predict the products and write a balanced equation for each of the following: (1, 2)
a. single replacement:
$Zn(s) + HCl(aq) \longrightarrow$ _______ + _______
b. decomposition:
$BaCO_3(s) \xrightarrow{\Delta}$ _______ + _______
c. double replacement:
$NaOH(aq) + HCl(aq) \longrightarrow$ _______ + _______
d. combination:
$Al(s) + F_2(g) \longrightarrow$ _______

98 Predict the products and write a balanced equation for each of the following: (1, 2)
a. decomposition:
$NaCl(s) \xrightarrow{\text{Electricity}}$ _______ + _______
b. combination:
$Ca(s) + Br_2(g) \longrightarrow$ _______
c. combustion:
$C_2H_4(g) + O_2(g) \xrightarrow{\Delta}$ _______ + _______
d. double replacement:
$NiCl_2(aq) + NaOH(aq) \longrightarrow Ni(OH)_2(s) +$ _______

99 For each of the following reactions, predict which reactant is oxidized and which reactant is reduced: (3)
a. $Cu(s) + 2H^+(aq) \longrightarrow Cu^{2+}(aq) + H_2(g)$
b. $Ni^{2+}(aq) + Fe(s) \longrightarrow Fe^{2+}(aq) + Ni(s)$
c. $2Ag(s) + Cu^{2+}(aq) \longrightarrow 2Ag^+(aq) + Cu(s)$
d. $3Ni^{2+}(aq) + 2Cr(s) \longrightarrow 3Ni(s) + 2Cr^{3+}(aq)$
e. $Zn(s) + Cu^{2+}(aq) \longrightarrow Zn^{2+}(aq) + Cu(s)$
f. $Pb^{2+}(aq) + Zn(s) \longrightarrow Pb(s) + Zn^{2+}(aq)$

100 For each of the following reactions, predict which reactant is oxidized and which reactant is reduced: (3)
a. $2Ag(s) + 2H^+(aq) \longrightarrow 2Ag^+(aq) + H_2(g)$
b. $Mg(s) + Cu^{2+}(aq) \longrightarrow Mg^{2+}(aq) + Cu(s)$
c. $2Al(s) + 3Cu^{2+}(aq) \longrightarrow 2Al^{3+}(aq) + 3Cu(s)$
d. $Mg^{2+}(aq) + Zn(s) \longrightarrow Mg(s) + Zn^{2+}(aq)$
e. $Al^{3+}(aq) + 3Na(s) \longrightarrow Al(s) + 3Na^+(aq)$
f. $Ni^{2+}(aq) + Mg(s) \longrightarrow Mg^{2+}(aq) + Ni(s)$

101 During heavy exercise and workouts, lactic acid, $C_3H_6O_3$, accumulates in the muscles, where it can cause pain and soreness. (4, 5)

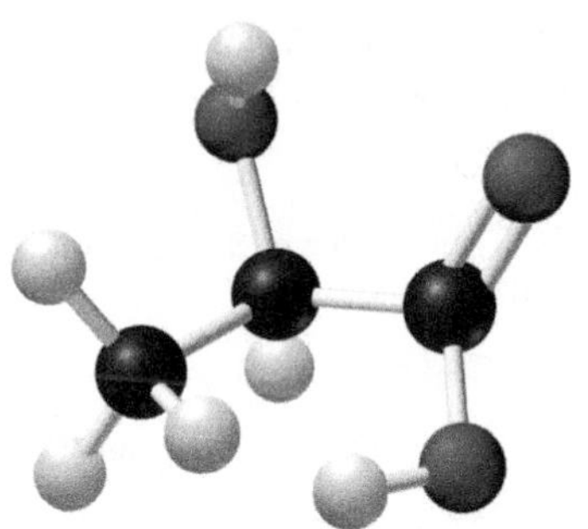

In the ball-and-stick model of lactic acid, black spheres = C, white spheres = H, and red spheres = O.

a. What is the molar mass of lactic acid?
b. How many molecules are in 0.500 mole of lactic acid?
c. How many atoms of C are in 1.50 moles of lactic acid?
d. How many grams of lactic acid contain 4.5×10^{24} atoms of O?

102 Ibuprofen, the anti-inflammatory ingredient in Advil, has the formula $C_{13}H_{18}O_2$. (4, 5)

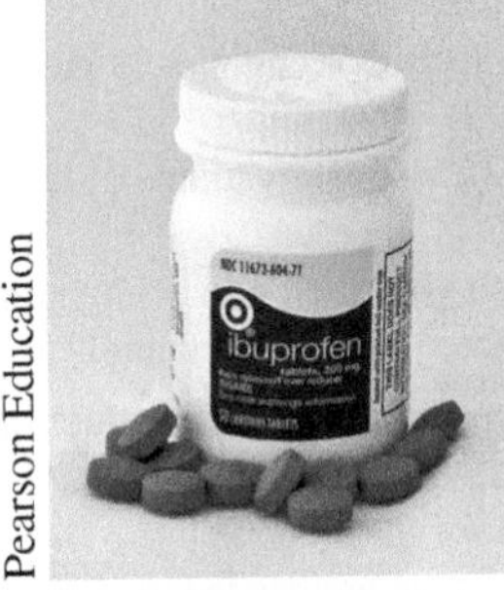

Pearson Education

Ibuprofen is an anti-inflammatory drug.

a. What is the molar mass of ibuprofen?
b. How many molecules are in 0.200 mole of ibuprofen?
c. How many atoms of H are in 0.100 mole of ibuprofen?
d. How many grams of ibuprofen contain 7.4×10^{25} atoms of C?

103 Calculate the molar mass of each of the following: (5)
a. $ZnSO_4$, zinc sulfate, zinc supplement
b. $Ca(IO_3)_2$, calcium iodate, iodine source in table salt
c. $C_5H_8NNaO_4$, monosodium glutamate, flavor enhancer

104 Calculate the molar mass of each of the following: (5)
a. $Mg(HCO_3)_2$, magnesium hydrogen carbonate
b. $Au(OH)_3$, gold(III) hydroxide, used in gold plating
c. $C_{18}H_{34}O_2$, oleic acid from olive oil

105 How many grams are in 0.150 mole of each of the following? (5)
a. K **b.** Cl_2 **c.** Na_2CO_3

106 How many grams are in 2.25 moles of each of the following? (5)
a. N_2 **b.** NaBr **c.** C_6H_{14}

107 How many moles are in 25.0 g of each of the following compounds? (5)
a. CO_2 **b.** $Al(OH)_3$ **c.** $MgCl_2$

108 How many moles are in 4.00 g of each of the following compounds? (5)
a. NH_3 **b.** $Ca(NO_3)_2$ **c.** SO_3

109 At a winery, glucose ($C_6H_{12}O_6$) in grapes undergoes fermentation to produce ethanol (C_2H_6O) and carbon dioxide. (6, 7)

$$\underset{\text{Glucose}}{C_6H_{12}O_6(aq)} \longrightarrow \underset{\text{Ethanol}}{2C_2H_6O(l)} + 2CO_2(g)$$

Moritz v.H./iStockphoto

Glucose in grapes ferments to produce ethanol.

a. How many grams of glucose are required to form 124 g of ethanol?
b. How many grams of ethanol would be formed from the reaction of 0.240 kg of glucose?

110 Gasohol is a fuel that contains ethanol (C_2H_6O), which burns in oxygen (O_2) to give carbon dioxide and water. (6, 7)

a. Write the balanced equation for the combustion of ethanol.
b. How many moles of O_2 are needed to completely react with 4.0 moles of C_2H_6O?
c. If a car produces 88 g of CO_2, how many grams of O_2 are used up in the reaction?
d. If you add 125 g of C_2H_6O to your fuel, how many grams of CO_2 and H_2O can be produced from the ethanol?

111 When ammonia (NH_3) reacts with fluorine, the products are dinitrogen tetrafluoride and hydrogen fluoride. (1, 6, 7)

a. Write the balanced equation for the reaction.
b. How many moles of each reactant are needed to produce 4.00 moles of HF?
c. How many grams of F_2 are required to react with 25.5 g of NH_3?
d. How many grams of N_2F_4 can be produced when 3.40 g of NH_3 reacts?

112 When peroxide (H_2O_2) is used in rocket fuels, it produces water and oxygen (O_2). (1, 6, 7)

a. Write the balanced equation for the reaction.
b. How many moles of peroxide are needed to produce 3.00 moles of water?
c. How many grams of peroxide are required to produce 36.5 g of O_2?
d. How many grams of water can be produced when 12.2 g of peroxide reacts?

113 Ethane gas, C_2H_6, reacts with chlorine gas, Cl_2, to form hexachloroethane gas, C_2Cl_6, and hydrogen chloride gas. (1, 6, 7)

a. Write the balanced equation for the reaction.
b. How many moles of chlorine gas must react to produce 1.60 moles of hexachloroethane?
c. How many grams of hydrogen chloride are produced when 50.0 g of ethane reacts?
d. How many grams of hexachloroethane are produced when 50.0 g of ethane reacts?

114 Propane gas, C_3H_8, a fuel for many barbecues, reacts with oxygen to produce water and carbon dioxide. Propane has a density of 2.02 g/L at room temperature. (1, 4, 6, 7)

Propane is converted to carbon dioxide and water when used as a fuel in a barbecue.

a. Write the balanced equation for the reaction.
b. How many grams of water form when 5.00 L of propane gas completely react?
c. How many grams of CO_2 are produced from 18.5 g of oxygen gas and excess propane?
d. How many grams of H_2O can be produced from the reaction of 8.50×10^{22} molecules of propane gas?

115 Acetylene gas, C_2H_2, burns in oxygen to produce carbon dioxide and water. If 62.0 g of CO_2 is produced when 22.5 g of C_2H_2 reacts with sufficient oxygen, what is the percent yield of CO_2 for the reaction? (1, 6, 7, 8)

116 When 50.0 g of iron(III) oxide reacts with carbon monoxide, 32.8 g of iron is produced. What is the percent yield of Fe for the reaction? (6, 7, 8)

$$Fe_2O_3(s) + 3CO(g) \longrightarrow 2Fe(s) + 3CO_2(g)$$

CHALLENGE QUESTIONS

117 Pentane gas, C_5H_{12}, reacts with oxygen to produce carbon dioxide and water. (6, 7, 8)

$$\underset{\text{Pentane}}{C_5H_{12}(g)} + 8O_2(g) \xrightarrow{\Delta} 5CO_2(g) + 6H_2O(g)$$

a. How many grams of pentane must react to produce 4.0 moles of water?
b. How many grams of CO_2 are produced from 32.0 g of oxygen and excess pentane?
c. How many grams of CO_2 are formed if 44.5 g of C_5H_{12} is reacted with 108 g of O_2?

118 When nitrogen dioxide (NO_2) from car exhaust combines with water in the air, it forms nitric acid (HNO_3), which causes acid rain, and nitrogen oxide. (6, 7, 8)

$$3NO_2(g) + H_2O(l) \longrightarrow 2HNO_3(aq) + NO(g)$$

a. How many molecules of NO_2 are needed to react with 0.250 mole of H_2O?
b. How many grams of HNO_3 are produced when 60.0 g of NO_2 completely reacts?
c. How many grams of HNO_3 can be produced if 225 g of NO_2 is reacted with 55.2 g of H_2O?

119 When a mixture of 12.8 g of Na and 10.2 g of Cl_2 reacts, what is the mass of NaCl that is produced? (6, 7, 8)

$$2Na(s) + Cl_2(g) \longrightarrow 2NaCl(s)$$

120 If a mixture of 35.8 g of CH_4 and 75.5 g of S reacts, how many grams of H_2S are produced? (6, 7, 8)

$$CH_4(g) + 4S(g) \longrightarrow CS_2(g) + 2H_2S(g)$$

121 The formation of nitrogen oxide, NO, from $N_2(g)$ and $O_2(g)$, requires 21.6 kcal of heat. (9)

$$N_2(g) + O_2(g) \longrightarrow 2NO(g) \quad \Delta H = +21.6 \text{ kcal}$$

a. How many kilocalories are required to form 3.00 g of NO?
b. What is the complete equation (including heat) for the decomposition of NO?
c. How many kilocalories are released when 5.00 g of NO decomposes to N_2 and O_2?

122 The formation of rust (Fe_2O_3) from solid iron and oxygen gas releases 1.7×10^3 kJ. (9)

$$4Fe(s) + 3O_2(g) \longrightarrow 2Fe_2O_3(s) \quad \Delta H = -1.7 \times 10^3 \text{ kJ}$$

a. How many kilojoules are released when 2.00 g of Fe reacts?
b. How many grams of rust form when 150 kcal are released?
c. What is the complete equation (including heat) for the formation of rust?

123 Write a balanced equation for each of the following reaction descriptions and identify each type of reaction: (1, 2)
a. An aqueous solution of lead(II) nitrate is mixed with aqueous sodium phosphate to produce solid lead(II) phosphate and aqueous sodium nitrate.
b. Gallium metal heated in oxygen gas forms solid gallium(III) oxide.
c. When solid sodium nitrate is heated, solid sodium nitrite and oxygen gas are produced.
d. Solid bismuth(III) oxide and solid carbon react to form bismuth metal and carbon monoxide gas.

124 A toothpaste contains 0.24% by mass sodium fluoride (NaF) used to prevent dental caries and 0.30% by mass triclosan, $C_{12}H_7Cl_3O_2$, a preservative and antigingivitis agent. One tube contains 119 g of toothpaste. (4, 5)

Components in toothpaste include triclosan and NaF.

Pearson Education

a. How many moles of NaF are in the tube of toothpaste?
b. How many fluoride ions (F^-) are in the tube of toothpaste?
c. How many grams of sodium ion (Na^+) are in 1.50 g of toothpaste?
d. How many molecules of triclosan are in the tube of toothpaste?

125 A gold bar is 2.31 cm long, 1.48 cm wide, and 0.0758 cm thick. (4, 5)
a. If gold has a density of 19.3 g/mL, what is the mass, in grams, of the gold bar?
b. How many atoms of gold are in the bar?
c. When the same mass of gold combines with oxygen, the oxide product has a mass of 5.61 g. How many moles of O are combined with the gold?

126 The gaseous hydrocarbon acetylene, C_2H_2, used in welders' torches, releases a large amount of heat when it burns according to the following equation: (6, 7, 8)

$$2C_2H_2(g) + 5O_2(g) \xrightarrow{\Delta} 4CO_2(g) + 2H_2O(g)$$

a. How many moles of water are produced from the complete reaction of 2.50 moles of oxygen?
b. How many grams of oxygen are needed to react completely with 2.25 g of acetylene?
c. How many grams of carbon dioxide are produced from the complete reaction of 78.0 g of acetylene?
d. If the reaction in part **c** produces 186 g of CO_2, what is the percent yield of CO_2 for the reaction?

127 Consider the following equation: (1, 2, 6, 7, 8)

$$Al(s) + O_2(g) \longrightarrow Al_2O_3(s)$$

a. Balance the equation.
b. Identify the type of reaction.
c. How many moles of oxygen are needed to react with 4.50 moles of Al?
d. How many grams of aluminum oxide are produced when 50.2 g of aluminum reacts?
e. When 13.5 g of aluminum is reacted with 8.00 g of oxygen, how many grams of aluminum oxide can form?
f. If 45.0 g of aluminum and 62.0 g of oxygen undergo a reaction that has a 70.0% yield, what mass of aluminum oxide forms?

128 Consider the equation for the reaction of sodium and nitrogen to form sodium nitride. (1, 2, 6, 7, 8)

$$Na(s) + N_2(g) \longrightarrow Na_3N(s)$$

a. Balance the equation.
b. If 80.0 g of sodium is reacted with 20.0 g of nitrogen gas, what mass of sodium nitride forms?
c. If the reaction in part **b** has a percent yield of 75.0%, how many grams of sodium nitride are actually produced?

ANSWERS

Answers to Study Checks

1 $2Al(s) + 3Cl_2(g) \longrightarrow 2AlCl_3(s)$

2 $Sb_2S_3(s) + 6HCl(aq) \longrightarrow 2SbCl_3(s) + 3H_2S(g)$

3 0.432 mole of H_2O

4 0.120 mole of aspirin

5 138.1 g/mole

6 80.9 g of Ag

7 0.945 mole of O_2

8 27.5 g of CO_2

9 84.7% yield

10 14.2 g of SO_2

11 **a.** endothermic **b.** 10.5 kJ

Answers to Selected Questions and Problems

1 **a.** not balanced **b.** balanced
c. not balanced **d.** balanced

3 **a.** $N_2(g) + O_2(g) \longrightarrow 2NO(g)$
b. $2HgO(s) \longrightarrow 2Hg(l) + O_2(g)$
c. $4Fe(s) + 3O_2(g) \longrightarrow 2Fe_2O_3(s)$
d. $2Na(s) + Cl_2(g) \longrightarrow 2NaCl(s)$
e. $2Cu_2O(s) + O_2(g) \longrightarrow 4CuO(s)$

5 **a.** $Mg(s) + 2AgNO_3(aq) \longrightarrow Mg(NO_3)_2(aq) + 2Ag(s)$
b. $CuCO_3(s) \longrightarrow CuO(s) + CO_2(g)$
c. $C_5H_{12}(g) + 8O_2(g) \xrightarrow{\Delta} 5CO_2(g) + 6H_2O(g)$
d. $Pb(NO_3)_2(aq) + 2NaCl(aq) \longrightarrow PbCl_2(s) + 2NaNO_3(aq)$
e. $2Al(s) + 6HCl(aq) \longrightarrow 2AlCl_3(aq) + 3H_2(g)$

7 a. decomposition reaction
b. single replacement reaction
c. combustion reaction
d. double replacement reaction

9 a. single replacement reaction
b. combination reaction
c. decomposition reaction
d. combustion reaction
e. double replacement reaction
f. double replacement reaction

11 a. $Mg(s) + Cl_2(g) \longrightarrow MgCl_2(s)$
b. $2HBr(g) \longrightarrow H_2(g) + Br_2(g)$
c. $Mg(s) + Zn(NO_3)_2(aq) \longrightarrow Zn(s) + Mg(NO_3)_2(aq)$
d. $K_2S(aq) + Pb(NO_3)_2(aq) \longrightarrow 2KNO_3(aq) + PbS(s)$
e. $2C_5H_{10}(l) + 15O_2(g) \xrightarrow{\Delta} 10CO_2(g) + 10H_2O(g)$

13 a. reduction **b.** oxidation
c. reduction **d.** reduction

15 a. Zn is oxidized; Cl_2 is reduced.
b. Br^- in NaBr is oxidized; Cl_2 is reduced.
c. The O^{2-} in PbO is oxidized; the Pb^{2+} is reduced.
d. Sn^{2+} is oxidized; Fe^{3+} is reduced.

17 a. reduction **b.** oxidation

19 Linoleic acid gains hydrogen atoms and is reduced.

21 a. 1.20×10^{23} atoms of Ag
b. 4.52×10^{23} molecules of C_3H_8O
c. 7.53×10^{23} atoms of Cr

23 a. 5.42 moles of Al **b.** 14.1 moles of C_2H_5OH
c. 0.478 mole of Au

25 a. 24 moles of H **b.** 1.0×10^2 moles of C
c. 0.040 mole of N

27 a. 3.01×10^{23} atoms of C
b. 7.71×10^{23} molecules of SO_2
c. 0.0867 mole of Fe

29 a. 6.00 moles of H **b.** 8.00 moles of O
c. 1.20×10^{24} atoms of P **d.** 4.82×10^{24} atoms of O

31 a. 188.2 g/mole **b.** 159.8 g/mole
c. 329.2 g/mole **d.** 342.3 g/mole
e. 58.3 g/mole **f.** 365.3 g/mole

33 a. 46.0 g **b.** 112 g
c. 14.8 g **d.** 112 g

35 a. 29.3 g **b.** 109 g
c. 4.05 g **d.** 194 g

37 a. 602 g **b.** 11 g

39 a. 0.463 mole of Ag **b.** 0.0167 mole of C
c. 0.882 mole of NH_3 **d.** 1.17 moles of SO_2

41 a. 0.78 mole of S **b.** 1.95 moles of S
c. 0.601 mole of S

43 a. 165 g of caffeine **b.** 0.144 mole of caffeine
c. 1.15 moles of C **d.** 8.08 g of N

45 a. $\frac{2 \text{ moles } SO_2}{1 \text{ mole } O_2}$ and $\frac{1 \text{ mole } O_2}{2 \text{ moles } SO_2}$
$\frac{2 \text{ moles } SO_2}{2 \text{ moles } SO_3}$ and $\frac{2 \text{ moles } SO_3}{2 \text{ moles } SO_2}$
$\frac{2 \text{ moles } SO_3}{1 \text{ mole } O_2}$ and $\frac{1 \text{ mole } O_2}{2 \text{ moles } SO_3}$
b. $\frac{4 \text{ moles P}}{5 \text{ moles } O_2}$ and $\frac{5 \text{ moles } O_2}{4 \text{ moles P}}$
$\frac{4 \text{ moles P}}{2 \text{ moles } P_2O_5}$ and $\frac{2 \text{ moles } P_2O_5}{4 \text{ moles P}}$
$\frac{5 \text{ moles } O_2}{2 \text{ moles } P_2O_5}$ and $\frac{2 \text{ moles } P_2O_5}{5 \text{ moles } O_2}$

47 a. 1.0 mole of O_2 **b.** 10. moles of H_2 **c.** 5.0 moles of H_2O

49 a. 1.25 moles of C **b.** 0.96 mole of CO
c. 1.0 mole of SO_2 **d.** 0.50 mole of CS_2

51 a. 77.5 g of Na_2O **b.** 6.26 g of O_2 **c.** 19.4 g of O_2

53 a. 19.2 g of O_2 **b.** 3.79 g of N_2 **c.** 54.0 g of H_2O

55 a. 3.65 g of H_2O **b.** 3.43 g of NO **c.** 7.53 g of HNO_3

57 a. $2PbS(s) + 3O_2(g) \longrightarrow 2PbO(s) + 2SO_2(g)$
b. 6.00 g of O_2
c. 17.4 g of SO_2
d. 137 g of PbS

59 a. 70.9% **b.** 63.2%

61 70.8 g of Al_2O_3

63 60.4%

65 a. Eight taxis can be used to pick up passengers.
b. Seven taxis can be driven.

67 a. 5.0 moles of H_2 **b.** 4.0 moles of H_2 **c.** 3.0 moles of N_2

69 a. limiting reactant SO_2; 2.00 moles of SO_3
b. limiting reactant H_2O; 0.500 mole of Fe_3O_4
c. limiting reactant O_2; 1.27 moles of CO_2

71 a. limiting reactant Cl_2; 25.1 g of $AlCl_3$
b. limiting reactant O_2; 13.5 g of H_2O
c. limiting reactant O_2; 26.7 g of SO_2

73 a. The activation energy is the energy required to break the bonds of the reacting molecules.
b. In exothermic reactions, the energy of the products is lower than that of the reactants.
c.

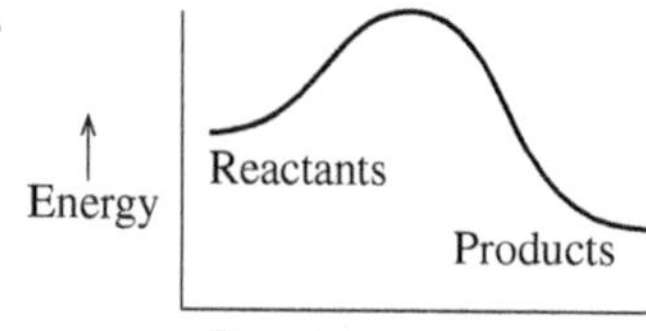

75 a. exothermic **b.** endothermic **c.** exothermic

77 a. exothermic; $\Delta H = -890$ kJ
b. endothermic; $\Delta H = +65.3$ kJ
c. exothermic; $\Delta H = -205$ kcal

79 578 kJ are released

81 a. 1, 1, 2 combination reaction
b. 2, 2, 1 decomposition reaction

83 a. reactants NO, O_2; product NO_2
b. $2NO(g) + O_2(g) \longrightarrow 2NO_2(g)$
c. combination reaction

85 a. reactant NI_3; products N_2, I_2
b. $2NI_3(s) \longrightarrow N_2(g) + 3I_2(g)$
c. decomposition reaction

87 a. reactants Cl_2, O_2; product OCl_2
b. $2Cl_2(g) + O_2(g) \longrightarrow 2OCl_2(g)$
c. combination reaction

89 1. a. S_2Cl_2 **b.** 135.2 g/mole **c.** 0.0740 mole
2. a. C_6H_6 **b.** 78.1 g/mole **c.** 0.128 mole

91 a. 252 g/mole **b.** 0.0991 mole **c.** 0.991 mole of C

93 a. 66.2 g of propane
b. 0.771 mole of propane
c. 27.8 g of C
d. 2.77×10^{22} atoms of H

95 a. $NH_3(g) + HCl(g) \longrightarrow NH_4Cl(s)$ Combination
b. $Fe_3O_4(s) + 4H_2(g) \longrightarrow 3Fe(s) + 4H_2O(g)$ Single replacement
c. $2Sb(s) + 3Cl_2(g) \longrightarrow 2SbCl_3(s)$ Combination
d. $C_5H_{12}(g) + 8O_2(g) \xrightarrow{\Delta} 5CO_2(g) + 6H_2O(g)$ Combustion
e. $2KBr(aq) + Cl_2(aq) \longrightarrow 2KCl(aq) + Br_2(l)$ Single replacement
f. $Al_2(SO_4)_3(aq) + 6NaOH(aq) \longrightarrow 3Na_2SO_4(aq) + 2Al(OH)_3(s)$ Double replacement

97 a. $Zn(s) + 2HCl(aq) \longrightarrow ZnCl_2(aq) + H_2(g)$
b. $BaCO_3(s) \xrightarrow{\Delta} BaO(s) + CO_2(g)$
c. $NaOH(aq) + HCl(aq) \longrightarrow NaCl(aq) + H_2O(l)$
d. $2Al(s) + 3F_2(g) \longrightarrow 2AlF_3(s)$

99 a. $Cu^0(s)$ is oxidized and $H^+(aq)$ is reduced.
b. $Fe^0(s)$ is oxidized and $Ni^{2+}(aq)$ is reduced.
c. $Ag^0(s)$ is oxidized and $Cu^{2+}(aq)$ is reduced.
d. $Cr^0(s)$ is oxidized and $Ni^{2+}(aq)$ is reduced.
e. $Zn^0(s)$ is oxidized and $Cu^{2+}(aq)$ is reduced.
f. $Zn^0(s)$ is oxidized and $Pb^{2+}(aq)$ is reduced.

101 a. 90.1 g/mole
b. 3.01×10^{23} molecules
c. 2.71×10^{24} atoms of C
d. 220 g of lactic acid

103 a. 161.5 g/mole **b.** 389.9 g/mole **c.** 169.1 g/mole

105 a. 5.87 g **b.** 10.7 g **c.** 15.9 g

107 a. 0.568 mole **b.** 0.321 mole **c.** 0.262 mole

109 a. 242 g of glucose
b. 123 g of ethanol

111 a. $2NH_3(g) + 5F_2(g) \longrightarrow N_2F_4(g) + 6HF(g)$
b. 1.33 moles of NH_3 and 3.33 moles of F_2
c. 143 g of F_2
d. 10.4 g of N_2F_4

113 a. $C_2H_6(g) + 6Cl_2(g) \longrightarrow C_2Cl_6(g) + 6HCl(g)$
b. 9.60 moles of chlorine
c. 364 g of HCl
d. 394 g of hexachloroethane

115 81.4%

117 a. 48 g of C_5H_{12} **b.** 27.5 g of CO_2 **c.** 92.8 g of CO_2

119 16.8 g of NaCl

121 a. 1.08 kcal are released
b. $2NO(g) \longrightarrow N_2(g) + O_2(g) + 21.6$ kcal
c. 1.80 kcal are required

123 a. $3Pb(NO_3)_2(aq) + 2Na_3PO_4(aq) \longrightarrow Pb_3(PO_4)_2(s) + 6NaNO_3(aq)$ Double replacement
b. $4Ga(s) + 3O_2(g) \xrightarrow{\Delta} 2Ga_2O_3(s)$ Combination
c. $2NaNO_3(s) \xrightarrow{\Delta} 2NaNO_2(s) + O_2(g)$ Decomposition
d. $Bi_2O_3(s) + 3C(s) \longrightarrow 2Bi(s) + 3CO(g)$ Single replacement

125 a. 5.00 g of gold
b. 1.53×10^{22} atoms of Au
c. 0.038 mole of oxygen

127 a. $4Al(s) + 3O_2(g) \longrightarrow 2Al_2O_3(s)$
b. combination reaction
c. 3.38 moles of oxygen
d. 94.8 g of aluminum oxide
e. 17.0 g of aluminum oxide
f. 59.5 g of aluminum oxide

Combining Ideas 2

CI.7 Some of the isotopes of silicon are listed in the following table:

Isotope	% Natural Abundance	Atomic Mass (amu)	Half-Life	Radiation Emitted
$^{27}_{14}Si$		26.99	4.2 s	Positron
$^{28}_{14}Si$	92.23	27.98	Stable	None
$^{29}_{14}Si$	4.67	28.98	Stable	None
$^{30}_{14}Si$	3.10	29.97	Stable	None
$^{31}_{14}Si$		30.98	2.6 h	Beta

a. In the following table, indicate the number of protons, neutrons, and electrons for each isotope listed:

Isotope	Number of Protons	Number of Neutrons	Number of Electrons
$^{27}_{14}Si$			
$^{28}_{14}Si$			
$^{29}_{14}Si$			
$^{30}_{14}Si$			
$^{31}_{14}Si$			

b. What is the electron configuration of silicon?

c. Calculate the atomic mass for silicon, using the isotopes that have a natural abundance.

d. Write the balanced nuclear equations for the decay of $^{27}_{14}Si$ and $^{31}_{14}Si$.

e. Draw the electron-dot formula and predict the shape of $SiCl_4$.

f. How many hours are needed for a sample of $^{31}_{14}Si$ with an activity of 16 μCi to decay to 2.0 μCi?

CI.8 K^+, an electrolyte required by the human body, is found in many foods, and in salt substitutes. One isotope of potassium is $^{40}_{19}K$, which has a natural abundance of 0.012% and a half-life of 1.30×10^9 y, and an activity of 7.0 μCi per gram. The isotope $^{40}_{19}K$ decays to $^{40}_{20}Ca$ or to $^{40}_{18}Ar$.

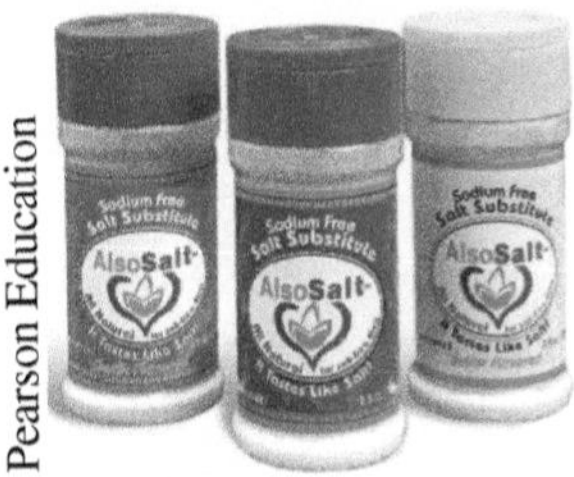

Potassium chloride is used as a salt substitute.

a. Write a balanced nuclear equation for each type of decay.

b. Identify the particle emitted for each type of decay.

c. How many K^+ ions are in 3.5 oz of KCl?

d. What is the activity of 25 g of KCl, in becquerels?

CI.9 Of much concern to environmentalists is the radioactive noble gas radon-222, which can seep from the ground into basements of homes and buildings. Radon-222 is a product of the decay of radium-226 that occurs naturally in rocks and soil in much of the United States. Radon-222, which has a half-life of 3.8 days, decays by emitting an alpha particle. Radon-222, which is a gas, can be inhaled into the lungs where it is strongly associated with lung cancer. Environmental agencies have set the maximum level of radon-222 in a home at 4 picocuries per liter (pCi/L) of air.

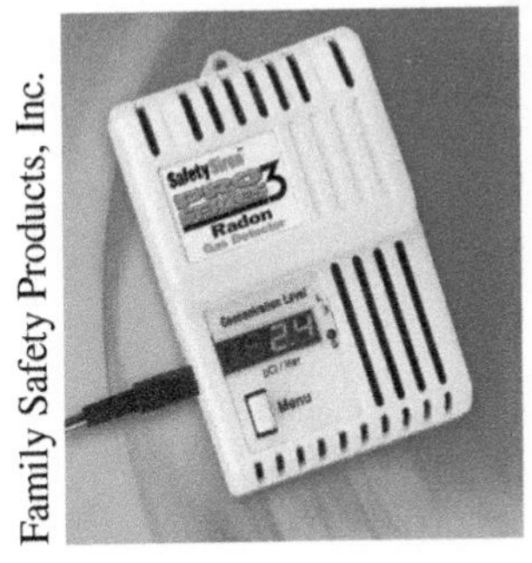

A home detection kit is used to measure the level of radon-222.

a. Write the balanced nuclear equation for the decay of Ra-226.

b. Write the balanced nuclear equation for the decay of Rn-222.

c. If a room contains 24 000 atoms of radon-222, how many atoms of radon-222 remain after 15.2 days?

d. Suppose a room in a home has a volume of 72 000 L (7.2×10^4 L). If the radon level is 2.5 pCi/L, how many alpha particles are emitted in one day?

CI.10 A sterling silver bracelet, which is 92.5% silver by mass, has a volume of 25.6 cm^3 and a density of 10.2 g/cm^3.

Sterling silver is 92.5% silver by mass.

a. What is the mass, in kilograms, of the bracelet?

b. How many atoms of silver are in the bracelet?

c. Determine the number of protons and neutrons in each of the two stable isotopes of silver: $^{107}_{47}Ag$ and $^{109}_{47}Ag$

CI.11 Consider the loss of electrons by atoms of element X in Group 2A (2), Period 3, and a gain of electrons by atoms of element Y in Group 7A (17), Period 3.

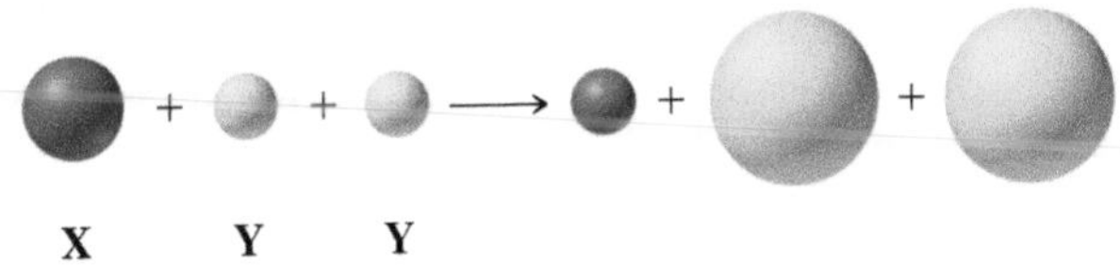

a. Which reactant has the higher electronegativity?
b. What are the ionic charges of X and Y in the product?
c. Write the electron configurations of the atoms X and Y.
d. Write the electron configurations of the ions of X and Y.
e. Write the formula and name for the ionic compound formed by the ions of X and Y.

CI.12 The active ingredient in Tums is calcium carbonate. One Tums tablet contains 500. mg of calcium carbonate.

Pearson Education

The active ingredient in Tums neutralizes excess stomach acid.

a. What is the formula for calcium carbonate?
b. What is the molar mass of calcium carbonate?
c. How many moles of calcium carbonate are in one roll of Tums that contains 12 tablets?
d. If a person takes two Tums tablets, how many grams of calcium are obtained?
e. If the daily recommended quantity of Ca^{2+} to maintain bone strength in older women is 1500 mg, how many tablets will supply the needed calcium?

CI.13 Acetone (propanone), a clear liquid solvent with an acrid odor, is used to remove nail polish, paints, and resins. It has a low boiling point and is highly flammable. The combustion of acetone has a ΔH of -28.5 kJ/g. Acetone has a density of 0.786 g/mL.

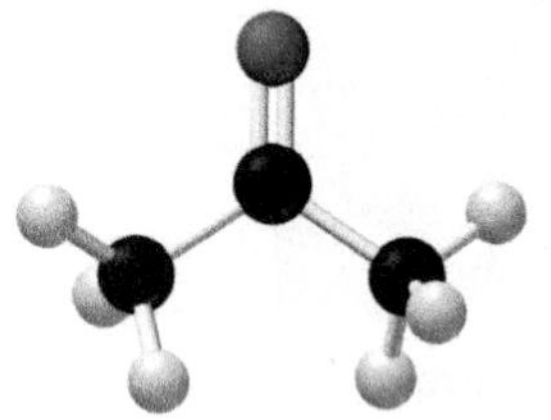

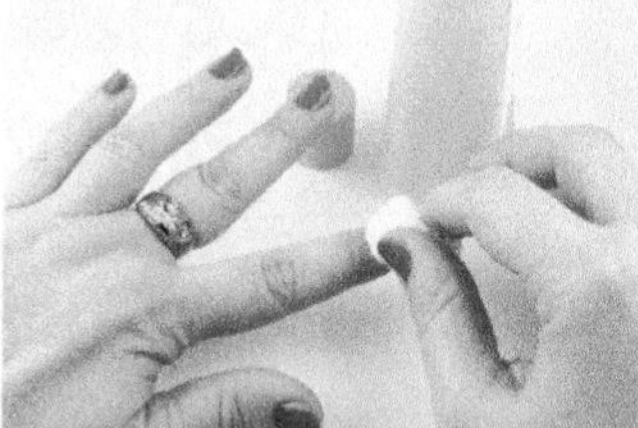

Victoria Visuals / iStockphoto

Acetone consists of carbon atoms (black), hydrogen atoms (white), and an oxygen atom (red).

a. What is the molecular formula of acetone?
b. What is the molar mass of acetone?
c. Identify the bonds C—C, C—H, and C—O in a molecule of acetone as polar covalent or nonpolar covalent.
d. Write the balanced equation for the combustion of acetone.
e. How many grams of oxygen gas are needed to react with 15.0 mL of acetone?
f. How much heat, in kilojoules, is given off for the reaction in part **e**?

CI.14 The compound butyric acid gives rancid butter its characteristic odor.

IS293 / Image Source / Alamy

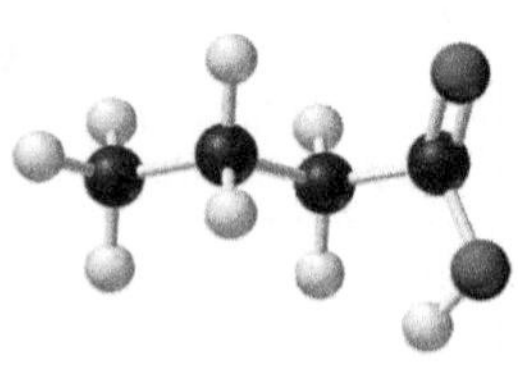

Butyric acid

Butyric acid produces the characteristic odor of rancid butter.

a. If black spheres are carbon atoms, white spheres are hydrogen atoms, and red spheres are oxygen atoms, what is the formula of butyric acid?
b. What is the molar mass of butyric acid?
c. How many grams of butyric acid contain 3.28×10^{23} atoms of O?
d. How many grams of carbon are in 5.28 g of butyric acid?
e. Butyric acid has a density of 0.959 g/mL at 20 °C. How many moles of butyric acid are contained in 1.56 mL of butyric acid?
f. Write a balanced equation for the combustion of butyric acid with oxygen gas to form carbon dioxide and water.
g. How many grams of oxygen are needed to completely react 1.58 g of butyric acid?
h. What mass of carbon dioxide is formed when 100. g of butyric acid and 100. g of oxygen react?

CI.15 Tamiflu®(Oseltamivir), $C_{16}H_{28}N_2O_4$, is an antiviral drug used to treat influenza. The preparation of Tamiflu begins with the extraction of shikimic acid from the seedpods of the Chinese spice, star anise (*Illicium verum*). From 2.6 g of star anise, 0.13 g of shikimic acid can be obtained and used to produce one capsule containing 75 mg of Tamiflu. The usual adult dosage for treatment of influenza is two capsules of Tamiflu daily for 5 days.

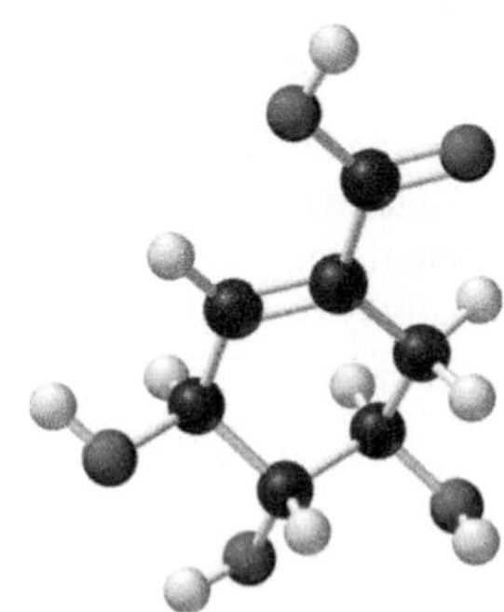

Shikimic acid

Shikimic acid is the basis for the antiviral drug in Tamiflu.

Photolibrary RF / Photolibrary

The spice called star anise is a plant source of shikimic acid.

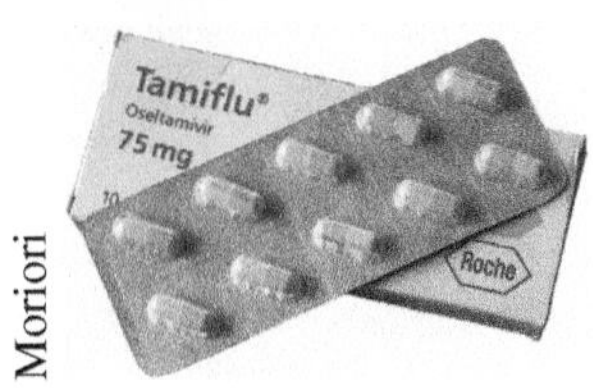

Moriori

a. What is the formula of shikimic acid? (Black spheres = C, white spheres = H, and red spheres = O)
b. What is the molar mass of shikimic acid?
c. How many moles of shikimic acid are contained in 130 g of shikimic acid?
d. How many capsules containing 75 mg of Tamiflu could be produced from 155 g of star anise?
e. What is the molar mass of Tamiflu?
f. How many kilograms of Tamiflu would be needed to treat all the people in a city with a population of 500 000 if each person takes two Tamiflu capsules a day for 5 days?

CI.16 When clothes have stains, bleach is often added to the wash to react with the soil and make the stains colorless. One brand of bleach contains 5.25% sodium hypochlorite by mass (active ingredient) with a density of 1.08 g/mL. The liquid bleach solution is prepared by bubbling chlorine gas into a solution of sodium hydroxide to produce sodium hypochlorite, sodium chloride, and water.

Pearson Education / Eric Schrader

The active component of bleach is sodium hypochlorite.

a. What is the chemical formula and molar mass of sodium hypochlorite?
b. How many hypochlorite ions are present in 1.00 gallon of bleach solution?
c. Write the balanced equation for the preparation of bleach.
d. How many grams of NaOH are required to produce the mass of sodium hypochlorite in 1.00 gallon of bleach?
e. If 165 g of Cl_2 is passed through a solution containing 275 g of NaOH and 162 g of sodium hypochlorite is produced, what is the percent yield of sodium hypochlorite for the reaction?

ANSWERS

CI.7 a.

Isotope	Number of Protons	Number of Neutrons	Number of Electrons
$^{27}_{14}Si$	14	13	14
$^{28}_{14}Si$	14	14	14
$^{29}_{14}Si$	14	15	14
$^{30}_{14}Si$	14	16	14
$^{31}_{14}Si$	14	17	14

b. $1s^22s^22p^63s^23p^2$
c. Atomic mass calculated from the three stable isotopes is 28.09 amu.
d. $^{27}_{14}Si \longrightarrow ^{27}_{13}Al + ^{0}_{+1}e$ and $^{31}_{14}Si \longrightarrow ^{31}_{15}P + ^{0}_{-1}e$
e.

```
      ..
     :Cl:
      |
 ..   |    ..
:Cl—Si—Cl:
 ..   |    ..
      |
     :Cl:
      ..
```

Tetrahedral

f. 7.8 h

CI.9 a. $^{226}_{88}Ra \longrightarrow ^{222}_{86}Rn + ^{4}_{2}He$
b. $^{222}_{86}Rn \longrightarrow ^{218}_{84}Po + ^{4}_{2}He$
c. 1500 atoms of radon-222 remain.
d. 5.8×10^8 alpha particles

CI.11 a. Y has the higher electronegativity.
b. X^{2+}, Y^-
c. $X = 1s^22s^22p^63s^2$ $Y = 1s^22s^22p^63s^23p^5$
d. $X^{2+} = 1s^22s^22p^6$ $Y^- = 1s^22s^22p^63s^23p^6$
e. $MgCl_2$, magnesium chloride

CI.13 a. C_3H_6O
b. 58.1 g/mole
c. nonpolar covalent bonds: C—C, C—H; polar covalent bond: C—O
d. $C_3H_6O(l) + 4O_2(g) \xrightarrow{\Delta} 3CO_2(g) + 3H_2O(g) + \text{energy}$
e. 26.0 g of O_2
f. 336 kJ

CI.15 a. $C_7H_{10}O_5$
b. 174.1 g/mole
c. 0.75 mole
d. 59 capsules
e. 312 g/mole
f. 400 kg

Gases

LOOKING AHEAD

Science Photo Library/Alamy

Visit **www.masteringchemistry.com** for self-study materials and instructor-assigned homework.

After soccer practice, Whitney complained that she was having difficulty breathing. Her father quickly took her to the emergency room where she was seen by a respiratory therapist. The respiratory therapist listened to Whitney's chest and then tested her breathing capacity using a spirometer. Based on her limited breathing capacity and the wheezing noise in her chest, Whitney was diagnosed as having asthma.

The therapist gave Whitney a nebulizer containing a bronchodilator that opens the airways and allows more air to go into the lungs. During the breathing treatment, the respiratory therapist measured the amount of oxygen (O_2) in her blood and explained to Whitney and her father that air is a mixture of gases containing 78% nitrogen (N_2) gas and 21% O_2 gas. Because Whitney had difficulty obtaining sufficient oxygen breathing air, the respiratory therapist gave her supplemental oxygen through an oxygen mask. Within a short period of time, Whitney's breathing returned to normal. The therapist then explained that the lungs work according to Boyle's Law: the volume of the lungs increases upon inhalation and the pressure decreases to make air flow in. However, during an asthma attack, the airways become restricted, and it becomes more difficult to expand the volume of the lungs.

Career: Respiratory Therapist

Respiratory therapists assess and treat a range of patients, including premature infants whose lungs have not developed and asthmatics or patients with emphysema or cystic fibrosis. In assessing patients, they perform a variety of diagnostic tests including breathing capacity, concentrations of oxygen and carbon dioxide in a patient's blood, as well as blood pH. In order to treat patients, therapists provide oxygen or aerosol medications to the patient, and chest physiotherapy to remove mucus from their lungs. Respiratory therapists also educate patients on how to correctly use their inhalers.

From Chapter 7 of *General, Organic, and Biological Chemistry: Structures of Life*, Fourth Edition. Karen C. Timberlake.

We all live at the bottom of a sea of gases called the atmosphere. The most important of these gases is oxygen, which constitutes about 21% of the atmosphere. Without oxygen, life on this planet would be impossible because oxygen is vital to all life processes of plants and animals. Ozone (O_3), formed in the upper atmosphere by the interaction of oxygen with ultraviolet light, absorbs some of the harmful radiation from space before it can strike Earth's surface. The other gases in the atmosphere include nitrogen (78%), argon, carbon dioxide (CO_2), and water vapor. Carbon dioxide gas, a product of combustion and metabolism, is used by plants in photosynthesis, a process that produces the oxygen that is essential for humans and animals.

The atmosphere has become a dumping ground for other gases, such as methane, chlorofluorocarbons (CFCs), and nitrogen oxides, as well as volatile organic compounds (VOCs), which are gases from paints, paint thinners, and cleaning supplies. The chemical reactions of these gases with sunlight and oxygen in the air are contributing to air pollution, ozone depletion, global warming, and acid rain. Such chemical changes can seriously affect our health and our lifestyle. An understanding of gases and the laws that govern gas behavior can help us understand the nature of matter and allow us to make decisions concerning important environmental and health issues.

LEARNING GOAL

Describe the kinetic molecular theory of gases and the properties of gases.

SELF-STUDY ACTIVITY
Properties of Gases

TUTORIAL
The Kinetic Molecular Theory of Gases

1 Properties of Gases

We are surrounded by gases, but not often aware of their presence. Of the elements on the periodic table, only a few exist as gases at room temperature: H_2, N_2, O_2, F_2, Cl_2, and the noble gases. Another group of gases includes the oxides of the nonmetals on the upper right corner of the periodic table, such as CO, CO_2, NO, NO_2, SO_2, and SO_3. Generally, molecules that are gases at room temperature have fewer than five atoms, which are from elements found in the first or second period.

The behavior of gases is quite different from that of liquids and solids. Gas particles are far apart, whereas particles of both liquids and solids are held close together. A gas has no definite shape or volume, and will completely fill any container. The attractive forces between gas particles are minimal. Thus, there are great distances between gas particles, which make a gas less dense than a solid or liquid, and easy to compress. A model for the behavior of a gas, called the **kinetic molecular theory of gases**, helps us understand gas behavior.

Kinetic Molecular Theory of Gases

1. **A gas consists of small particles (atoms or molecules) that move randomly with high velocities.** Gas molecules moving in random directions at high speeds cause a gas to fill the entire volume of a container.
2. **The attractive forces between the particles of a gas are usually very small.** Gas particles are far apart and fill a container of any size and shape.
3. **The actual volume of the gas molecules is extremely small compared to the volume that the gas occupies.** The volume of the gas is considered equal to the volume of the container. Most of the volume of a gas is empty space, which allows gases to be easily compressed.
4. **Gas particles are in constant motion, moving rapidly in straight paths.** When gas particles collide, they rebound and travel in new directions. Every time they hit the walls of a container, they exert pressure. An increase in the number or force of collisions against the walls of a container causes an increase in the pressure of the gas.

5. **The average kinetic energy of gas molecules is proportional to the Kelvin temperature.** Gas particles move faster as the temperature increases. At higher temperatures, gas particles hit the walls of the container with more force, producing higher pressures.

The kinetic molecular theory of gases helps explain some of the characteristics of gases. For example, we can quickly smell perfume when a bottle is opened on the opposite side of a room because its particles move rapidly in all directions. At room temperatures, the molecules of air are moving at about 450 m/s, which is 1000 mi/h. They move faster at higher temperatures and more slowly at lower temperatures. Sometimes tires and gas-filled containers explode when temperatures are too high. From the kinetic molecular theory of gases, we know that gas particles move faster when heated, hit the walls of a container with more force, and cause a buildup of pressure inside a container.

CONCEPT CHECK 1 **Properties of Gases**

Use the kinetic molecular theory of gases to explain each of the following:

a. You can smell the odor of cooking onions from far away.
b. The volume of a balloon filled with helium gas increases when left in the sun.

ANSWER

a. Molecules of gas, which carry the aroma of cooking food, move at high speeds in random directions and great distances to reach you in a different location.
b. Raising the temperature of a gas causes the gas particles to move faster, hitting the walls of the balloon more often and with more force, which increases its volume.

When we talk about a gas, we describe it in terms of four properties: pressure, volume, temperature, and the amount of gas.

Pressure (*P*)

Gas particles are extremely small and move rapidly. When they hit the walls of a container, they exert a **pressure** (see Figure 1). If we heat the container, the molecules move faster and smash into the walls more often and with increased force, thus increasing the pressure. The gas particles in the air, mostly oxygen and nitrogen, exert a pressure on us called **atmospheric pressure** (see Figure 2). As you go to higher altitudes, the atmospheric pressure decreases because the atmosphere thins out and there are fewer particles in the air. The most common units used for gas pressure measurement are *atmosphere* (atm) and *millimeters of mercury* (mmHg). On the TV weather report, you may hear or see the atmospheric pressure given in inches of mercury, or in countries other than the United States, kilopascals. In a hospital, the unit *torr* may be used.

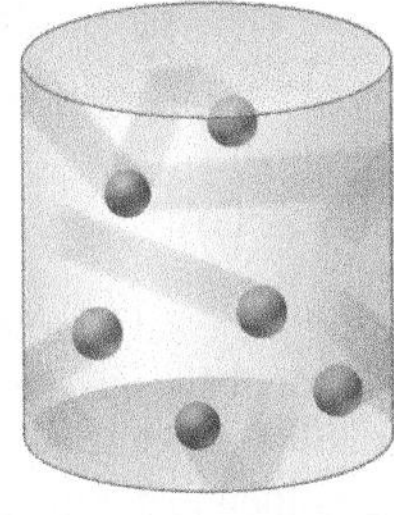

FIGURE 1 Gas particles move in straight lines within a container. The gas particles exert pressure when they collide with the walls of the container.

Q Why does heating the container increase the pressure of the gas within it?

Volume (*V*)

The volume of gas equals the size of the container in which the gas is placed. When you inflate a tire or a basketball, you are adding more gas particles. The increase in the number of particles hitting the walls of the tire or basketball increases the volume. Sometimes, on a cool morning, a tire looks flat. The volume of the tire has decreased because a lower temperature decreases the speed of the molecules, which in turn reduces the force of their impacts on the walls of the tire. The most common units for volume measurement are liters (L) and milliliters (mL).

Temperature (*T*)

The temperature of a gas is related to the kinetic energy of its particles. For example, if we have a gas at 200 K in a rigid container and heat it to a temperature of 400 K, the gas particles will have twice the kinetic energy that they did at 200 K. This also means that the gas at 400 K exerts twice the pressure of the gas at 200 K. Although you measure gas

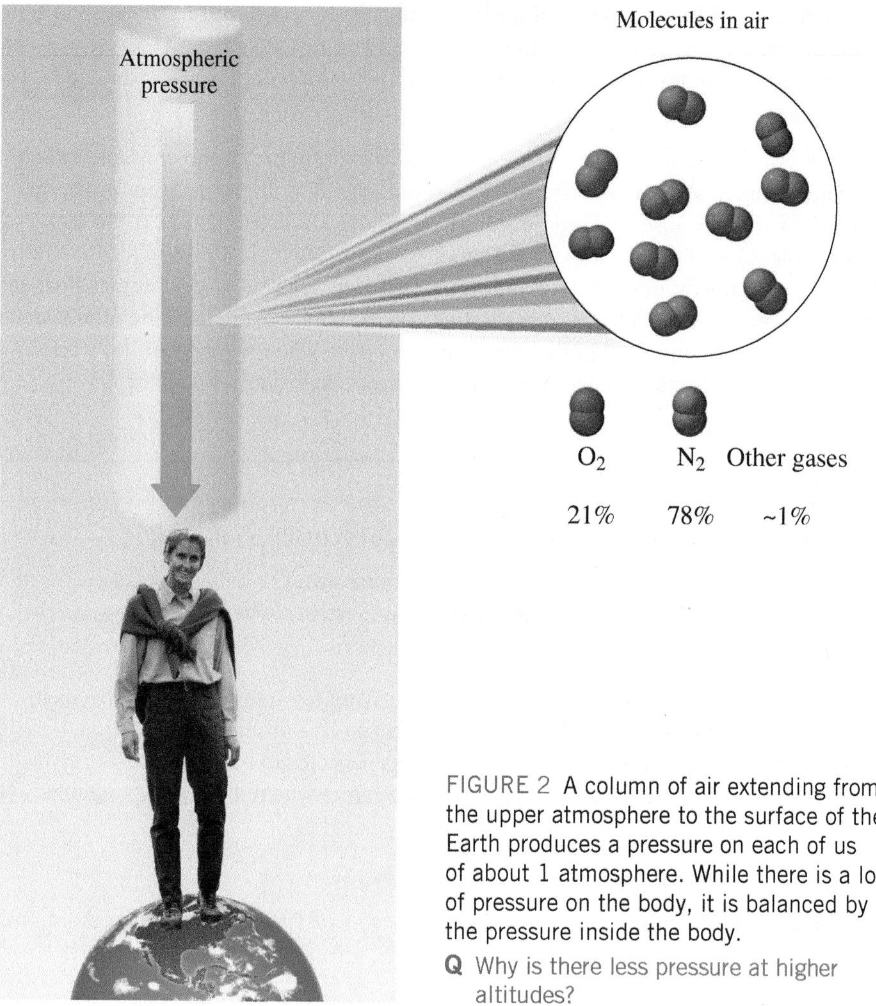

NASA

FIGURE 2 A column of air extending from the upper atmosphere to the surface of the Earth produces a pressure on each of us of about 1 atmosphere. While there is a lot of pressure on the body, it is balanced by the pressure inside the body.

Q Why is there less pressure at higher altitudes?

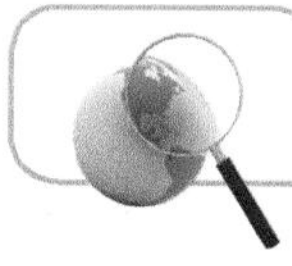

FORMING A GAS

Obtain baking soda and a jar or a plastic bottle. You will also need an elastic glove that will fit over the mouth of the jar or a balloon that will fit snugly over the top of the plastic bottle. Place a cup of vinegar in the jar or bottle. Sprinkle some baking soda into the fingertips of the glove or into the balloon. Carefully fit the glove or balloon over the top of the jar or bottle. Slowly lift the fingers of the glove or the balloon so that the baking soda falls into the vinegar. Watch what happens. Squeeze the glove or balloon.

QUESTIONS

1. Describe the properties of gas that you observe as the reaction takes place between vinegar and baking soda.
2. How do you know that a gas was formed?

temperature using a Celsius thermometer, all comparisons of gas behavior and all calculations related to temperature must use the Kelvin temperature scale. No one has yet achieved the conditions for absolute zero (0 K), but we predict that the particles will have zero kinetic energy and exert zero pressure at absolute zero.

Amount of Gas (n)

When you add air to a bicycle tire, you increase the amount of gas, which results in a higher pressure in the tire. Usually, we measure the amount of gas by its mass (grams). In gas law calculations, we need to change the grams of gas to moles.

A summary of the four properties of a gas is given in Table 1.

TABLE 1 Properties That Describe a Gas

Property	Description	Unit(s) of Measurement
Pressure (P)	The force exerted by gas against the walls of its container	atmosphere (atm); millimeters of mercury (mmHg); torr; pascal (Pa)
Volume (V)	The space occupied by a gas	liter (L); milliliter (mL); cubic meter (m^3)
Temperature (T)	The factor that determines the kinetic energy and rate of motion of gas particles	degree Celsius (°C); kelvin (K) *is required in calculations*
Amount (n)	The quantity of gas present in a container	grams (g); moles (n) *is required in calculations*

SAMPLE PROBLEM 1 **Properties of Gases**

Identify the property of a gas that is described by each of the following:

a. increases the kinetic energy of gas particles
b. the force of the gas particles hitting the walls of the container
c. the space that is occupied by a gas

SOLUTION

a. temperature **b.** pressure **c.** volume

STUDY CHECK 1

As more helium gas is added to a balloon, the number of grams of helium increases. What property of a gas is described?

QUESTIONS AND PROBLEMS

1 Properties of Gases

LEARNING GOAL: *Describe the kinetic molecular theory of gases and the properties of gases.*

1 Use the kinetic molecular theory of gases to explain each of the following:
a. Gas particles move faster at higher temperatures.
b. Gases can be compressed much more than liquids or solids.

2 Use the kinetic molecular theory of gases to explain each of the following:
a. A container of nonstick cooking spray explodes when thrown into a fire.
b. The air in a hot-air balloon is heated to make the balloon rise.

3 Identify the property of a gas that is measured in each of the following:
a. 350 K
b. 125 mL
c. 2.00 g of O_2
d. 755 mmHg

4 Identify the property of a gas that is measured in each of the following:
a. 425 K
b. 1.0 atm
c. 10.0 L
d. 0.50 mole of He

2 Gas Pressure

LEARNING GOAL

Describe the units of measurement used for pressure, and change from one unit to another.

When billions and billions of gas particles hit against the walls of a container, they exert **pressure**, which is defined as a force acting on a certain area.

$$\text{Pressure } (P) = \frac{\text{force}}{\text{area}}$$

The atmospheric pressure can be measured using a barometer (see Figure 3). At a pressure of exactly 1 atmosphere (atm), a mercury column in an inverted glass tube would be *exactly* 760 mm high. One **atmosphere (atm)** is defined as *exactly* 760 mmHg (millimeters of mercury). One atmosphere is also 760 torr, a pressure unit named to honor Evangelista Torricelli, the inventor of the barometer. Because the units of torr and mmHg are equal, they are used interchangeably.

$$1 \text{ atm} = 760 \text{ mmHg} = 760 \text{ torr (exact)}$$
$$1 \text{ mmHg} = 1 \text{ torr (exact)}$$

In SI units, pressure is measured in pascals (Pa); 1 atm is equal to 101 325 Pa. Because a pascal is a very small unit, pressures can be reported in kilopascals.

$$1 \text{ atm} = 101\,325 \text{ Pa} = 101.325 \text{ kPa}$$

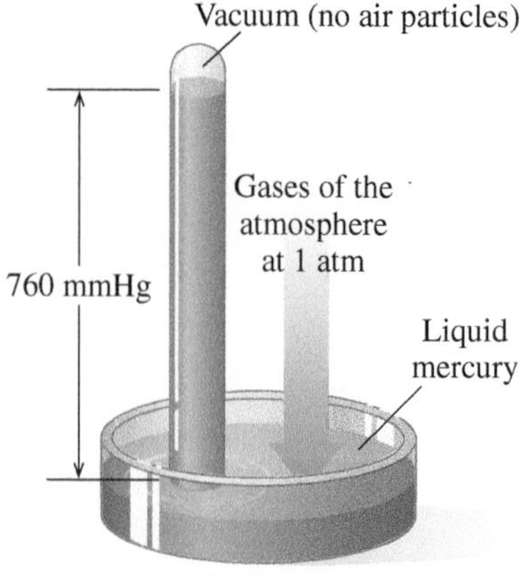

FIGURE 3 **A barometer:** The pressure exerted by the gases in the atmosphere is equal to the downward pressure of a mercury column in a closed glass tube. The height of the mercury column measured in mmHg is called atmospheric pressure.

Q Why does the height of the mercury column change from day to day?

TUTORIAL
Converting Between Units of Pressure

CASE STUDY
Scuba Diving and Blood Gases

The U.S. equivalent of 1 atm is 14.7 pounds per square inch (psi). When you use a pressure gauge to check the air pressure in the tires of a car, it may read 30–35 psi. This measurement is actually 30–35 psi above the pressure that the atmosphere exerts on the outside of the tire. Table 2 summarizes the various units used in the measurement of pressure.

TABLE 2 Units for Measuring Pressure

Unit	Abbreviation	Unit Equivalent to 1 atm
Atmosphere	atm	1 atm (exact)
Millimeters of Hg	mmHg	760 mmHg (exact)
Torr	torr	760 torr (exact)
Inches of Hg	in. Hg	29.9 in. Hg
Pounds per square inch	lb/in.^{2} (psi)	14.7 lb/in.^{2}
Pascal	Pa	101 325 Pa
Kilopascal	kPa	101.325 kPa

If you have a barometer in your home, it probably measures pressure in inches of mercury. Atmospheric pressure changes with variations in weather and altitude. On a hot, sunny day, a column of air has more particles, which increases the pressure on the surface of the mercury. The mercury column rises, indicating a higher atmospheric pressure. On a rainy day, the atmosphere exerts less pressure, which causes the mercury column to fall. In the weather report, this type of weather is called a *low-pressure system*. Above sea level, the density of the gases in the air decreases, which causes lower atmospheric pressures; the atmospheric pressure is greater than 760 mmHg at the Dead Sea because it is below sea level and the column of air above it is taller (see Table 3).

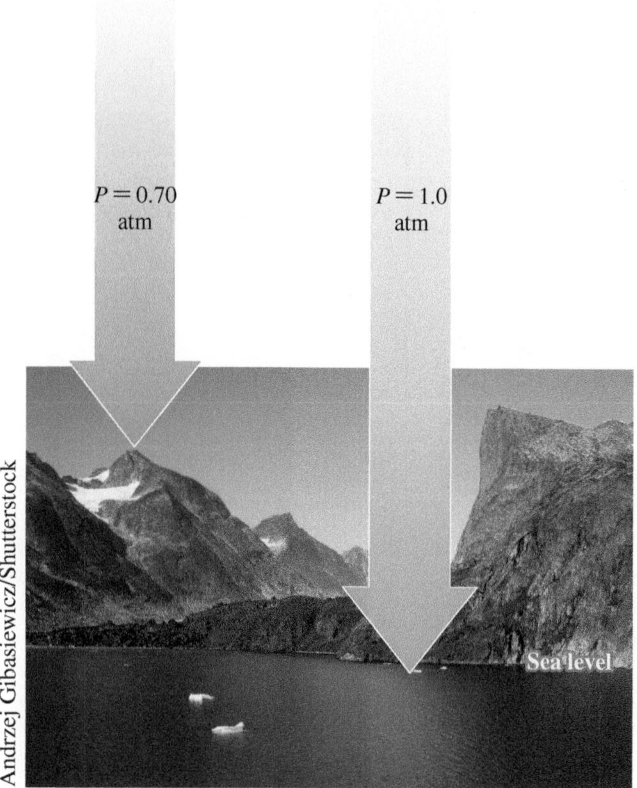

The atmospheric pressure decreases as the altitude increases.

TABLE 3 Altitude and Atmospheric Pressure

Location	Altitude (km)	Atmospheric Pressure (mmHg)
Dead Sea	−0.40	800
Sea level	0.00	760
Los Angeles	0.09	750
Las Vegas	0.70	700
Denver	1.60	630
Mount Whitney	4.50	440
Mount Everest	8.90	250

Divers must be concerned about increasing pressures on their ears and lungs when they dive below the surface of the ocean. Because water is more dense than air, the pressure on a diver increases rapidly as the diver descends. At a depth of 33 ft below the surface of the ocean, an additional 1 atm of pressure is exerted by the water on a diver, for a total of 2 atm. At 100 ft down, there is a total pressure of about 4 atm on a diver. The regulator that a diver carries continuously adjusts the pressure of the breathing mixture to match the increase in pressure.

CONCEPT CHECK 2 **Units of Pressure**

A sample of neon gas has a pressure of 0.50 atm. Calculate the pressure, in mmHg, of the neon.

ANSWER

The equality 1 atm = 760 mmHg can be written as two conversion factors:

$$\frac{760\ \text{mmHg}}{1\ \text{atm}} \quad \text{and} \quad \frac{1\ \text{atm}}{760\ \text{mmHg}}$$

Using the conversion factor that cancels atm and gives mmHg, we can set up the problem as:

$$0.50\ \cancel{\text{atm}} \times \frac{760\ \text{mmHg}}{1\ \cancel{\text{atm}}} = 380\ \text{mmHg}$$

Chemistry Link to Health

MEASURING BLOOD PRESSURE

Your blood pressure is one of the vital signs a doctor or nurse checks during a physical examination. It actually consists of two separate measurements. Acting as a pump, the heart contracts to create the pressure that pushes blood through the circulatory system. During contraction, the blood pressure is at its highest; this is your *systolic* pressure. When the heart muscles relax, the blood pressure falls; this is your *diastolic* pressure. The normal range for systolic pressure is 100–120 mmHg. For diastolic pressure, it is 60–80 mmHg. These two measurements are usually expressed as a ratio such as 100/80. These values are somewhat higher in older people. When blood pressures are elevated, say, 140/90, there is a greater risk of stroke, heart attack, or kidney damage. Low blood pressure prevents the brain from receiving adequate oxygen, causing dizziness and fainting.

The blood pressures are measured by a sphygmomanometer, an instrument consisting of a stethoscope and an inflatable cuff connected to a tube of mercury called a manometer. After the cuff is wrapped around the upper arm, it is pumped up with air until it cuts off the flow of blood through the arm. With the stethoscope over the artery, the air is slowly released from the cuff, decreasing the pressure on the artery. When blood flow first starts again in the artery, a noise can be heard through the stethoscope, signifying the systolic blood pressure as the pressure shown on the manometer. As air continues to be released, the cuff deflates until no sound is heard in the artery. A second pressure reading is taken at the moment of silence and denotes the diastolic pressure, the pressure when the heart is not contracting.

The use of digital blood pressure monitors is becoming more common. However, they have not been validated for use in all situations and can sometimes give inaccurate readings.

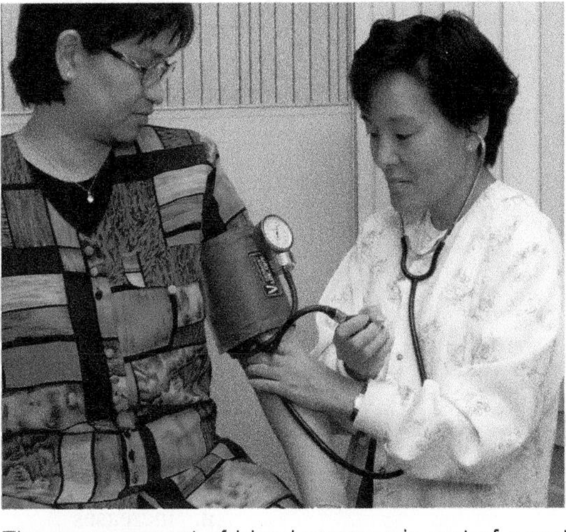

Pearson Education

The measurement of blood pressure is part of a routine physical examination.

QUESTIONS AND PROBLEMS

2 Gas Pressure

LEARNING GOAL: *Describe the units of measurement used for pressure, and change from one unit to another.*

5 What units are used to measure the pressure of a gas?

6 Which of the following statement(s) describes the pressure of a gas?
- **a.** the force of the gas particles on the walls of the container
- **b.** the number of gas particles in a container
- **c.** the volume of the container
- **d.** 3.00 atm
- **e.** 750 torr

7 An oxygen tank contains oxygen (O_2) at a pressure of 2.00 atm. What is the pressure in the tank in terms of the following units?
- **a.** torr
- **b.** mmHg

8 On a climb up Mt. Whitney, the atmospheric pressure is 467 mmHg. What is the pressure in terms of the following units?
- **a.** atm
- **b.** torr

LEARNING GOAL

Use the pressure–volume relationship (Boyle's law) to determine the new pressure or volume when the temperature and amount of gas are constant.

TUTORIAL
Pressure and Volume

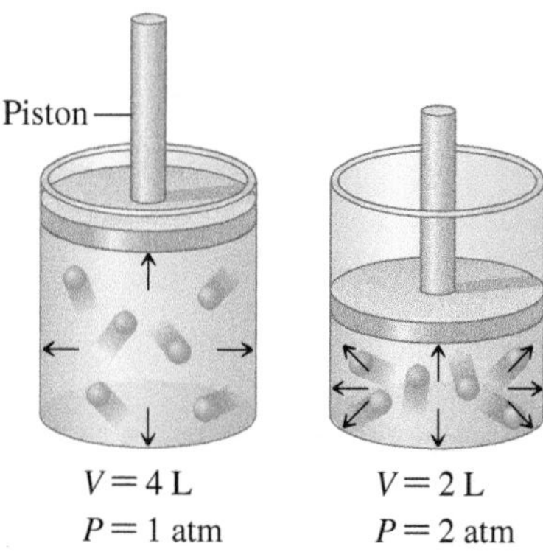

FIGURE 4 **Boyle's law**: As volume decreases, gas molecules become more crowded, which causes the pressure to increase. Pressure (P) and volume (V) are inversely related.

Q If the volume of a gas increases, what will happen to its pressure?

3 Pressure and Volume (Boyle's Law)

Imagine that you can see air particles hitting the walls inside a bicycle tire pump. What happens to the pressure inside the pump as you push down on the handle? As the volume decreases, there is a decrease in the surface area of the container. The air particles are crowded together, more collisions occur, and the pressure increases within the container.

When a change in one property (in this case, volume) causes a change in another property (in this case, pressure), the two properties are related. If the changes occur in opposite directions, the properties have an **inverse relationship**. The inverse relationship between the pressure and volume of a gas is known as **Boyle's law**. The law states that the volume (V) of a sample of gas changes inversely with the pressure (P) of the gas as long as there has been no change in the temperature (T) or amount of gas (n), as illustrated in Figure 4.

If the volume or pressure of a gas sample changes without any change in the temperature or in the amount of the gas, then the new pressure and volume will give the same PV product as the initial pressure and volume. Therefore, we can set the initial and final PV products equal to each other.

Boyle's Law

$P_1V_1 = P_2V_2$ No change in number of moles and temperature

CONCEPT CHECK 3 **Boyle's Law**

State and explain the reason for the change (*increases*, *decreases*) in the pressure of a gas that occurs in each of the following when n and T do not change:

	Pressure (P)	Volume (V)	Amount (n)	Temperature (T)
a.		decreases	constant	constant
b.		increases	constant	constant

ANSWER

a. When the volume of a gas decreases at constant n and T, the gas particles are closer together, which increases the number of collisions with the container walls. Therefore, pressure increases when volume decreases with no change in n and T.

b. When the volume of a gas increases at constant n and T, the gas particles move farther apart, which decreases the number of collisions with the container walls. Therefore, pressure decreases when the volume increases with no change in n and T.

	Pressure (P)	Volume (V)	Amount (n)	Temperature (T)
a.	increases	decreases	constant	constant
b.	decreases	increases	constant	constant

SAMPLE PROBLEM 2 **Calculating Pressure When Volume Changes**

A sample of hydrogen gas (H_2) has a volume of 5.0 L and a pressure of 1.0 atm. What is the new pressure, in atmospheres, if the volume is decreased to 2.0 L with no change in temperature and the amount of gas?

SOLUTION

Step 1 **Organize the data in a table of initial and final conditions.** In this problem, we want to know the final pressure (P_2) for the change in volume. We place the properties that change, which are the volume and pressure, in a table. The properties that do not change, which are temperature and amount of gas, are shown below the table. Because we are given the initial and final volume of the gas, we know that the volume decreases. We can predict that the pressure will increase. The properties that remain constant, in this case, are temperature (T) and the amount of gas (n).

Analyze the Problem

Conditions 1	Conditions 2	Know	Predict
$V_1 = 5.0$ L	$V_2 = 2.0$ L	V decreases	
$P_1 = 1.0$ atm	$P_2 = ?$ atm		P increases

Factors that remain constant: T and n

Step 2 **Rearrange the gas law equation to solve for the unknown quantity.** For a PV relationship, we use Boyle's law and solve for P_2 by dividing both sides by V_2.

$$P_1V_1 = P_2V_2$$

$$\frac{P_1V_1}{V_2} = \frac{P_2\cancel{V_2}}{\cancel{V_2}}$$

$$P_2 = P_1 \times \frac{V_1}{V_2}$$

Step 3 **Substitute values into the gas law equation and calculate.** When we substitute in the values, we see that the ratio of the volumes (volume factor) is greater than 1, which increases the pressure as we predicted in Step 1. Note that the units of volume (L) cancel to give the final pressure in atmospheres.

$$P_2 = 1.0 \text{ atm} \times \frac{5.0\,\cancel{\text{L}}}{2.0\,\cancel{\text{L}}} = 2.5 \text{ atm}$$

Volume factor increases pressure

STUDY CHECK 2

A sample of helium gas has a volume of 150 mL at 750 torr. If the volume expands to 450 mL at constant temperature, what is the new pressure in torr?

Guide to Using the Gas Laws

1. Organize the data in a table of initial and final conditions.
2. Rearrange the gas law equation to solve for the unknown quantity.
3. Substitute values into the gas law equation and calculate.

SAMPLE PROBLEM 3 Calculating Volume When Pressure Changes

The gauge on a 12-L tank of compressed oxygen reads 3800 mmHg. How many liters would this same gas occupy at a pressure of 0.75 atm at constant temperature and amount of gas?

SOLUTION

Step 1 **Organize the data in a table of initial and final conditions.** To match the units for initial and final pressures, we can either convert atm to mmHg, or mmHg to atm.

$$0.75\,\cancel{\text{atm}} \times \frac{760 \text{ mmHg}}{1\,\cancel{\text{atm}}} = 570 \text{ mmHg}$$

$$3800\,\cancel{\text{mmHg}} \times \frac{1 \text{ atm}}{760\,\cancel{\text{mmHg}}} = 5.0 \text{ atm}$$

We place the gas data using units of mmHg for pressure and liters for volume in a table. (We could have both pressures in units of atm as well.) We know that pressure decreases. We can predict that the volume increases.

Analyze the Problem

Conditions 1	Conditions 2	Know	Predict
$P_1 = 3800$ mmHg (5.0 atm)	$P_2 = 570$ mmHg (0.75 atm)	P decreases	
$V_1 = 12$ L	$V_2 = ?$ L		V increases

Factors that remain constant: T and n

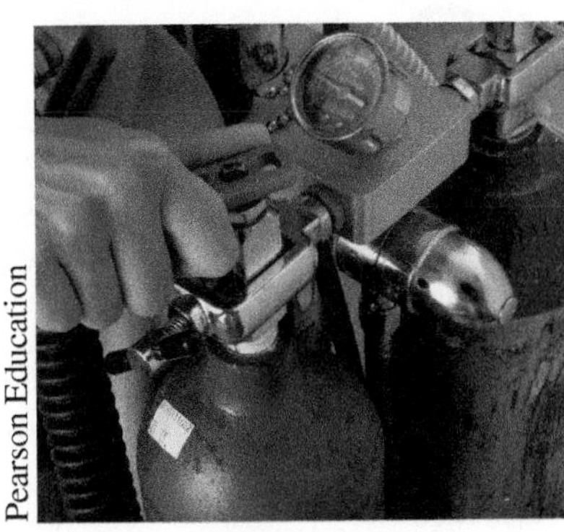
Pearson Education

A gauge indicates the pressure in a tank.

Step 2 **Rearrange the gas law equation to solve for the unknown quantity.** For a *PV* relationship, we use Boyle's law and solve for V_2 by dividing both sides by P_2. According to Boyle's law, a decrease in the pressure will cause an increase in the volume when *T* and *n* remain constant.

$$P_1V_1 = P_2V_2$$

$$\frac{P_1V_1}{P_2} = \frac{\cancel{P_2}V_2}{\cancel{P_2}}$$

$$V_2 = V_1 \times \frac{P_1}{P_2}$$

Step 3 **Substitute values into the gas law equation and calculate.** When we substitute in the values with pressures in units of mmHg or atm, the ratio of pressures (pressure factor) is greater than 1, which increases the volume as predicted in Step 1.

$$V_2 = 12\text{ L} \times \frac{3800\,\cancel{\text{mmHg}}}{570\,\cancel{\text{mmHg}}} = 80.\text{ L}$$

Pressure factor increases volume

or

$$V_2 = 12\text{ L} \times \frac{5.0\,\cancel{\text{atm}}}{0.75\,\cancel{\text{atm}}} = 80.\text{ L}$$

Pressure factor increases volume

STUDY CHECK 3

In an underground gas reserve, a bubble of methane gas (CH_4) has a volume of 45.0 mL at 1.60 atm. What volume, in milliliters, will it occupy when it reaches the surface where the atmospheric pressure is 745 mmHg, if there is no change in the temperature and amount of gas?

Chemistry Link to Health

PRESSURE–VOLUME RELATIONSHIP IN BREATHING

The importance of Boyle's law becomes more apparent when you consider the mechanics of breathing. Our lungs are elastic, balloon-like structures contained within an airtight chamber called the thoracic cavity. The diaphragm, a muscle, forms the flexible floor of the cavity.

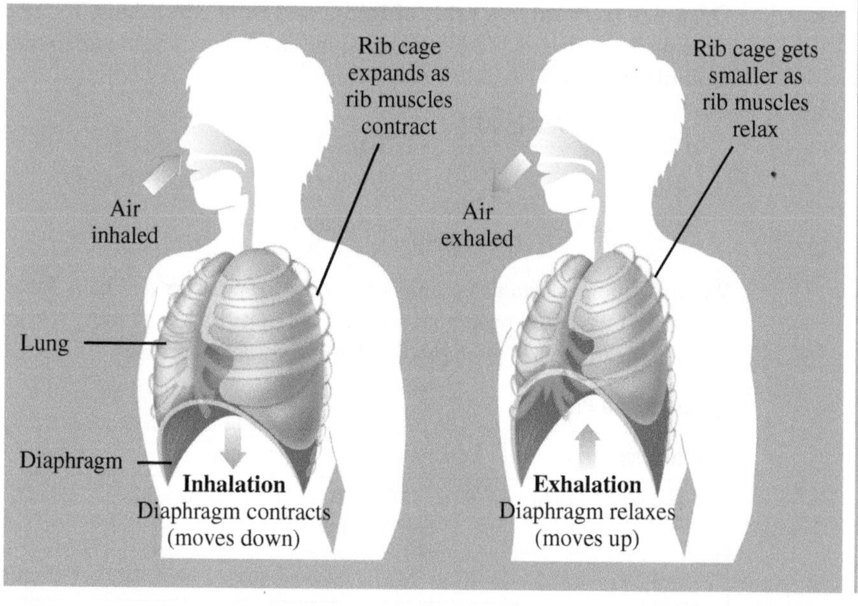

Inspiration

The process of taking a breath of air begins when the diaphragm contracts and the rib cage expands, causing an increase in the volume of the thoracic cavity. The elasticity of the lungs allows them to expand when the thoracic cavity expands. According to Boyle's law, the pressure inside the lungs decreases when their volume increases, causing the pressure inside the lungs to fall below the pressure of the atmosphere. This difference in pressures produces a *pressure gradient* between the lungs and the atmosphere. In a pressure gradient, molecules flow from an area of greater pressure to an area of lower pressure. Thus, we inhale as air flows into the lungs (*inspiration*), until the pressure within the lungs becomes equal to the pressure of the atmosphere.

Expiration

Expiration, or the exhalation phase of breathing, occurs when the diaphragm relaxes and moves back up into the thoracic cavity to its resting position. The volume of the thoracic cavity decreases, which squeezes the lungs and decreases their volume. Now the pressure in the lungs is greater than the pressure of the atmosphere, so air flows out of the lungs. Thus, breathing is a process in which pressure gradients are continuously created between the lungs and the environment because of the changes in the volume.

QUESTIONS AND PROBLEMS

3 Pressure and Volume (Boyle's Law)

LEARNING GOAL: *Use the pressure–volume relationship (Boyle's law) to determine the new pressure or volume when the temperature and amount of gas are constant.*

9 Why do scuba divers need to exhale air (and not hold their breath) when they ascend to the surface of the water?

10 Why does a sealed bag of chips expand when you take it to a higher altitude?

11 The air in a cylinder with a piston has a volume of 220 mL and a pressure of 650 mmHg.

a. To obtain a higher pressure inside the cylinder at constant temperature and amount of gas, should the cylinder change as shown in **A** or **B**? Explain your choice.

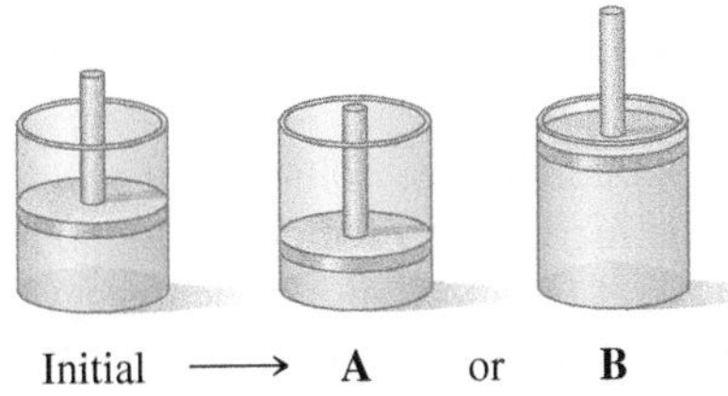

b. If the pressure inside the cylinder increases to 1.2 atm, what is the final volume, in milliliters, of the cylinder? Complete the following data table:

Property	Conditions 1	Conditions 2	Know	Predict
Pressure (*P*)				
Volume (*V*)				

12 A balloon is filled with helium gas. When the following changes are made at constant temperature, which of the diagrams (**A**, **B**, or **C**) shows the new volume of the balloon?

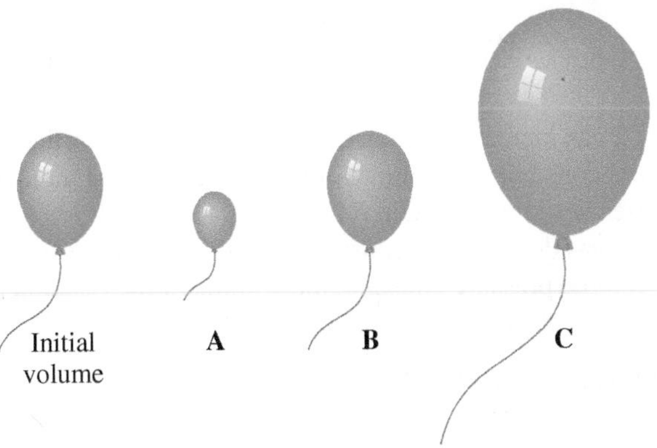

a. The balloon floats to a higher altitude where the outside pressure is lower.

b. The balloon is taken inside the house, but the atmospheric pressure remains the same.

c. The balloon is put in a hyperbaric chamber in which the pressure is increased.

13 A gas with a volume of 4.0 L is in a closed container. Indicate what changes (*increases*, *decreases*, *does not change*) in pressure must have occurred if the volume undergoes the following changes at constant temperature and amount of gas:

a. The volume is compressed to 2.0 L.
b. The volume expands to 12 L.
c. The volume is compressed to 0.40 mL.

14 A gas at a pressure of 2.0 atm is in a closed container. Indicate the changes (*increases*, *decreases*, *does not change*) in its volume when the pressure undergoes the following changes at constant temperature and amount of gas:

a. The pressure increases to 6.0 atm.
b. The pressure remains at 2.0 atm.
c. The pressure drops to 0.40 atm.

15 A 10.0-L balloon contains helium gas at a pressure of 655 mmHg. What is the new pressure, in mmHg, of the helium gas at each of the following volumes, if there is no change in temperature and amount of gas?

a. 20.0 L **b.** 2.50 L **c.** 1500. mL

16 The air in a 5.00-L tank has a pressure of 1.20 atm. What is the new pressure, in atm, of the air when the air is placed in tanks that have the following volumes, if there is no change in temperature and amount of gas?

a. 1.00 L **b.** 2500. mL **c.** 750. mL

17 A sample of nitrogen (N_2) has a volume of 50.0 L at a pressure of 760. mmHg. What is the volume, in liters, of the gas at each of the following pressures, if there is no change in temperature and amount of gas?

a. 1500 mmHg **b.** 4.00 atm **c.** 0.500 atm

18 A sample of methane (CH_4) has a volume of 25 mL at a pressure of 0.80 atm. What is the volume of the gas at each of the following pressures, if there is no change in temperature and amount of gas?

a. 0.40 atm **b.** 2.00 atm **c.** 2500 mmHg

19 Cyclopropane, C_3H_6, is a general anesthetic. A 5.0-L sample has a pressure of 5.0 atm. What is the volume of the anesthetic given to a patient at a pressure of 1.0 atm with no change in temperature and amount of gas?

20 The volume of air in a person's lungs is 615 mL at a pressure of 760. mmHg. Inhalation occurs as the pressure in the lungs drops to 752 mmHg with no change in temperature and amount of gas. To what volume, in milliliters, did the lungs expand?

21 Use the words *inspiration* or *expiration* to describe the part of the breathing cycle that occurs because of each of the following:
a. The diaphragm contracts (flattens out).
b. The volume of the lungs decreases.
c. The pressure within the lungs is less than that of the atmosphere.

22 Use the words *inspiration* or *expiration* to describe the part of the breathing cycle that occurs because of each of the following:
a. The diaphragm relaxes, moving up into the thoracic cavity.
b. The volume of the lungs expands.
c. The pressure within the lungs is greater than that of the atmosphere.

LEARNING GOAL

Use the temperature–volume relationship (Charles's law) to determine the new temperature or volume when the pressure and amount of gas are constant.

Larry Brownstein/Getty Images

As a gas in a hot-air balloon is heated, it expands.

4 Temperature and Volume (Charles's Law)

Suppose that you are going to take a ride in a hot-air balloon. The captain turns on a propane burner to heat the air inside the balloon. As the temperature rises, the air particles move faster and spread out, causing the volume of the balloon to increase. The hot air becomes less dense than the air outside, causing the balloon and its passengers to lift off. In 1787, Jacques Charles, a balloonist as well as a physicist, proposed that the volume of a gas is related to the temperature. This proposal became **Charles's law**, which states that the volume (V) of a gas is directly related to the temperature (T) when there is no change in the pressure (P) or amount (n) of gas (see Figure 5). A **direct relationship** is one in which the related properties increase or decrease together. For two conditions, we can write Charles's law as follows:

Charles's Law

$$\frac{V_1}{T_1} = \frac{V_2}{T_2} \quad \text{No change in number of moles and pressure}$$

All temperatures used in gas law calculations must be converted to their corresponding Kelvin (K) temperatures.

To determine the effect of changing temperature on the volume of a gas, the pressure and the amount of gas are kept constant. If we increase the temperature of a gas sample, we know from the kinetic molecular theory that the motion (kinetic energy) of the gas particles will also increase. To keep the pressure constant, the volume of the container must increase. If the temperature of the gas decreases, the volume of the container must decrease to maintain the same pressure when the amount of gas is constant.

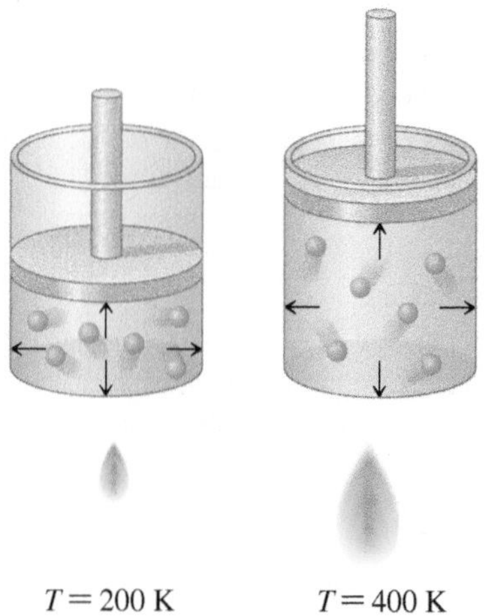

$T = 200$ K $\quad$ $T = 400$ K
$V = 1$ L $\quad$ $V = 2$ L

FIGURE 5 **Charles's law**: The Kelvin temperature of a gas is directly related to the volume of the gas when there is no change in the pressure and amount of gas. When the temperature increases, making the molecules move faster, the volume must increase to maintain constant pressure.

Q If the temperature of a gas decreases at constant pressure and amount of gas, how will the volume change?

CONCEPT CHECK 4 **Charles's Law**

State and explain the reason for the change (*increases, decreases*) in the volume of a gas that occurs for the following when P and n do not change:

Temperature (T)	Volume (V)	Pressure (P)	Amount (n)
a. increases		constant	constant
b. decreases		constant	constant

ANSWER

a. When the temperature of a gas increases at constant P and n, the gas particles move faster. To keep the pressure constant, the volume of the container must increase when temperature increases with no change in P and n.

b. When the temperature of a gas decreases at constant P and n, the gas particles move more slowly. To keep the pressure constant, the volume of the container must decrease when the temperature decreases with no change in P and n.

Temperature (T)	Volume (V)	Pressure (P)	Amount (n)
a. increases	increases	constant	constant
b. decreases	decreases	constant	constant

SAMPLE PROBLEM 4 Calculating Volume When Temperature Changes

MC™ TUTORIAL Temperature and Volume

A sample of argon gas has a volume of 5.40 L and a temperature of 15 °C. Find the new volume, in liters, of the gas after the temperature increases to 42 °C at constant pressure and amount of gas.

SOLUTION

Step 1 **Organize the data in a table of initial and final conditions.** The properties that change, which are the temperature and volume, are listed in the table. The properties that do not change, which are pressure and amount of gas, are shown below the table. When the temperature is given in degrees Celsius, it must be changed to kelvins. Because we know the initial and final temperatures of the gas, we know that the temperature increases. Thus, we can predict that the volume increases.

$$T_1 = 15\ ^\circ\text{C} + 273 = 288\ \text{K}$$

$$T_2 = 42\ ^\circ\text{C} + 273 = 315\ \text{K}$$

Analyze the Problem

Conditions 1	Conditions 2	Know	Predict
$T_1 = 288$ K	$T_2 = 315$ K	T increases	
$V_1 = 5.40$ L	$V_2 = ?$ L		V increases

Factors that remain constant: P and n

Step 2 **Rearrange the gas law equation to solve for the unknown quantity.** In this problem, we want to know the final volume (V_2) when the temperature increases. Using Charles's law, we solve for V_2 by multiplying both sides by T_2.

$$\frac{V_1}{T_1} = \frac{V_2}{T_2}$$

$$\frac{V_1}{T_1} \times T_2 = \frac{V_2}{\cancel{T_2}} \times \cancel{T_2}$$

$$V_2 = V_1 \times \frac{T_2}{T_1}$$

Step 3 **Substitute values into the gas law equation and calculate.** We see that the temperature has increased. Because temperature is directly related to volume, the volume must increase. When we substitute in the values, we see that the ratio of the temperatures (temperature factor) is greater than 1, which increases the volume, as predicted in Step 1.

$$V_2 = 5.40\ \text{L} \times \frac{315\ \cancel{\text{K}}}{288\ \cancel{\text{K}}} = 5.91\ \text{L}$$

Temperature factor increases volume

STUDY CHECK 4

A mountain climber with a body temperature of 37 °C inhales 486 mL of air at a temperature of −8 °C. What volume, in milliliters, will the air occupy in the lungs, if the pressure and amount of gas do not change?

Chemistry Link to the Environment

GREENHOUSE GASES

The term *greenhouse gases* was first used during the early 1800s for the gases in the atmosphere that trap heat. Among the greenhouse gases are carbon dioxide (CO_2), methane (CH_4), dinitrogen oxide (N_2O), and chlorofluorocarbons (CFCs). The molecules of greenhouse gases consist of more than two atoms that vibrate when heat is absorbed. By contrast, oxygen and nitrogen do not trap heat and are not greenhouse gases. Because the two atoms in their molecules are so tightly bonded, they do not absorb heat.

Greenhouse gases are beneficial in keeping the average surface temperature of the Earth at 15 °C. Without greenhouse gases, it is estimated that the average surface temperature of Earth would be −18 °C. Most scientists say that the concentration of greenhouse gases in the atmosphere and the surface temperature of Earth are increasing because of human activities. The increase in atmospheric carbon dioxide is mostly a result of the burning of fossil fuels and wood.

Methane (CH_4) is a colorless, odorless gas that is released by livestock, rice farming, the decomposition of organic plant material in landfills, and the mining, drilling, and transport of coal and oil. The contribution from livestock comes from the breakdown of organic material in the digestive tracts of cows, sheep, and camels. The level of methane in the atmosphere has increased about 150% since industrialization. In one year, as much as 5×10^{11} kg of methane are added to the atmosphere. Livestock produce about 20% of the greenhouse gases. In one day, one cow emits about 200 g of methane. For a global population of 1.5 billion livestock, a total of 3×10^{8} kg of methane is produced every day. In the past few years, methane levels have stabilized due to improvements in the recovery of methane. Methane remains in the atmosphere for about ten years, but its molecular structure causes it to trap 20 times more heat than does carbon dioxide.

Dinitrogen oxide (N_2O), commonly called nitrous oxide, is a colorless greenhouse gas that has a sweet odor. Most people recognize it as an anesthetic used in dentistry called "laughing gas." Although some dinitrogen oxide is released naturally from soil bacteria, its major sources are from agricultural and industrial processes. Atmospheric dinitrogen oxide has increased by about 15% since industrialization, caused by the extensive use of fertilizers, sewage treatment plants, and car exhaust. Each year, 1×10^{10} kg of dinitrogen oxide is added to the atmosphere. Dinitrogen oxide released today will remain in the atmosphere for about 150–180 years, where it has a greenhouse effect that is 300 times greater than that of carbon dioxide.

Chlorofluorinated gases (CFCs) are synthetic compounds containing chlorine, fluorine, and carbon. Chlorofluorocarbons were used as propellants in aerosol cans and as refrigerants in refrigerators and air conditioners. During the 1970s, scientists determined that CFCs in the atmosphere were destroying the protective ozone layer. Since then, many countries have banned the production and use of CFCs, and their levels in the atmosphere have declined slightly. Hydrofluorocarbons (HFCs), in which hydrogen atoms replace chlorine atoms, are now used as refrigerants. Although HFCs do not destroy the ozone layer, they are greenhouse gases because they trap heat in the atmosphere.

Based on current trends and climate models, scientists estimate that levels of atmospheric carbon dioxide will increase by about 2% each year up through 2025. As long as the greenhouse gases trap more heat than is reflected back into space, average surface temperatures on Earth will continue to rise. Efforts are taking place around the world to slow or decrease the emissions of greenhouse gases into the atmosphere. It is anticipated that temperatures will stabilize only when the amount of energy that reaches the surface of Earth is equal to the heat that is reflected back into space.

In 2007, former U.S. Vice President Al Gore and the United Nations Panel on Climate Change were awarded the Nobel Peace Prize for increasing global awareness of the relationship between human activities and global warming.

Percentages of Greenhouse Gases in the Atmosphere

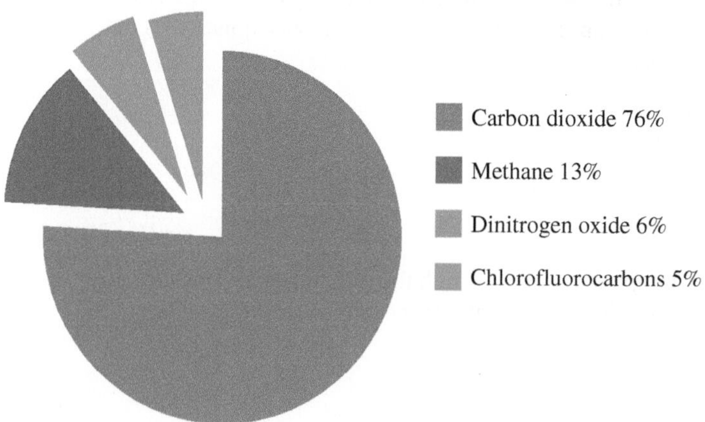

QUESTIONS AND PROBLEMS

4 Temperature and Volume (Charles's Law)

LEARNING GOAL: *Use the temperature–volume relationship (Charles's law) to determine the new temperature or volume when the pressure and amount of gas are constant.*

23 Select the diagram that shows the new volume of a balloon when the following changes are made at constant pressure:

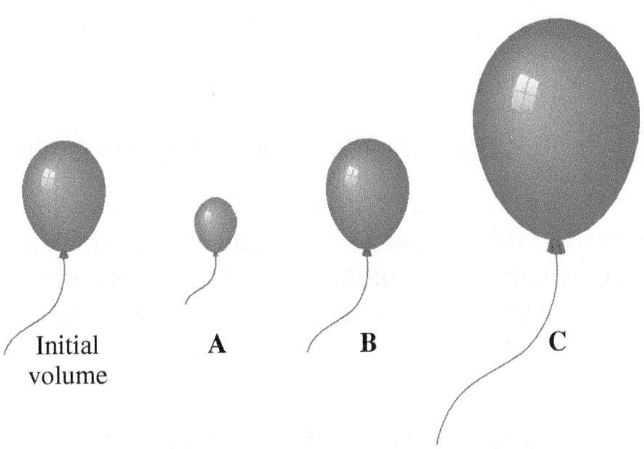

a. The temperature is changed from 100 K to 300 K.
b. The balloon is placed in a freezer.
c. The balloon is first warmed, and then returned to its starting temperature.

24 Indicate whether the final volume in each of the following is *the same*, *larger*, or *smaller* than the initial volume, if pressure and amount of gas do not change:
a. A volume of 505 mL of air on a cold winter day at −15 °C is breathed into the lungs, when body temperature is 37 °C.
b. The heater used to heat the air in a hot-air balloon is turned off.
c. A balloon filled with helium at the amusement park is left in a car on a hot day.

25 A sample of neon initially has a volume of 2.50 L at 15 °C. What final temperature, in degrees Celsius, is needed to change the volume of the gas to each of the following, if P and n do not change?
a. 5.00 L **b.** 1250 mL **c.** 7.50 L **d.** 3550 mL

26 A gas has a volume of 4.00 L at 0 °C. What final temperature, in degrees Celsius, is needed to change the volume of the gas to each of the following, if P and n do not change?
a. 1.50 L **b.** 1200 mL **c.** 250 L **d.** 50.0 mL

27 A balloon contains 2500 mL of helium gas at 75 °C. What is the final volume, in milliliters, of the gas when the temperature changes to each of the following, if P and n do not change?
a. 55 °C **b.** 680. K **c.** −25 °C **d.** 240. K

28 An air bubble has a volume of 0.500 L at 18 °C. What is the final volume, in liters, of the gas when the temperature changes to each of the following, if P and n do not change?
a. 0 °C **b.** 425 K **c.** −12 °C **d.** 575 K

5 Temperature and Pressure (Gay-Lussac's Law)

LEARNING GOAL

Use the temperature–pressure relationship (Gay-Lussac's law) to determine the new temperature or pressure when the volume and amount of gas are constant.

If we could observe the molecules of a gas as the temperature rises, we would notice that they move faster and hit the sides of the container more often and with greater force. If we maintain a constant volume and amount of gas, the pressure will increase. In the temperature–pressure relationship known as **Gay-Lussac's law**, the pressure of a gas is directly related to its Kelvin temperature. This means that an increase in temperature increases the pressure of a gas, and a decrease in temperature decreases the pressure of the gas as long as the volume and amount of gas do not change (see Figure 6).

Gay-Lussac's Law

$$\frac{P_1}{T_1} = \frac{P_2}{T_2} \quad \text{No change in number of moles and volume}$$

All temperatures used in gas law calculations must be converted to their corresponding Kelvin (K) temperatures.

FIGURE 6 **Gay-Lussac's law:** When the Kelvin temperature of a gas doubles at constant volume and amount of gas, the pressure also doubles.

Q How does a decrease in the temperature of a gas affect its pressure at constant volume and amount of gas?

CONCEPT CHECK 5 **Gay-Lussac's Law**

State and explain the reason for the change (*increases*, *decreases*) in the pressure of a gas that occurs for the following when V and n do not change:

	Temperature (T)	Pressure (P)	Volume (V)	Amount (n)
a.	increases		constant	constant
b.	decreases		constant	constant

TUTORIAL
Temperature and Pressure

ANSWER

a. When the temperature of a gas increases with no change in V and n, the particles of gas move faster. When the volume does not change, the gas particles collide more often with the container walls and with more force, increasing the pressure.

b. When the temperature of a gas decreases at constant V and n, the particles of gas move slower. When the volume does not change, the gas particles do not collide as often with the container walls and with less force, decreasing the pressure.

Temperature (T)	Pressure (P)	Volume (V)	Amount (n)
a. increases	increases	constant	constant
b. decreases	decreases	constant	constant

SAMPLE PROBLEM 5 Calculating Pressure When Temperature Changes

Aerosol containers can be dangerous if they are heated, because they can explode. Suppose a container of hair spray with a pressure of 4.0 atm at a room temperature of 25 °C is thrown into a fire. If the temperature of the gas inside the aerosol can reaches 402 °C, what will be its pressure in atmospheres? The aerosol container may explode if the pressure inside exceeds 8.0 atm. Would you expect it to explode?

SOLUTION

Step 1 **Organize the data in a table of initial and final conditions.** We list the properties that change, which are the pressure and temperature, in a table. The properties that do not change, which are volume and amount of gas, are shown below the table. The temperatures given in degrees Celsius must be changed to kelvins. Because we know the initial and final temperatures of the gas, we know that the temperature increases. Thus, we can predict that the pressure increases.

$$T_1 = 25\text{ °C} + 273 = 298\text{ K}$$
$$T_2 = 402\text{ °C} + 273 = 675\text{ K}$$

Analyze the Problem

Conditions 1	Conditions 2	Know	Predict
$P_1 = 4.0$ atm	$P_2 = ?$ atm		P increases
$T_1 = 298$ K	$T_2 = 675$ K	T increases	

Factors that remain constant: V and n

Step 2 **Rearrange the gas law equation to solve for the unknown quantity.** Using Gay-Lussac's law, we can solve for P_2 by multiplying both sides by T_2.

$$\frac{P_1}{T_1} = \frac{P_2}{T_2}$$

$$\frac{P_1}{T_1} \times T_2 = \frac{P_2}{\cancel{T_2}} \times \cancel{T_2}$$

$$P_2 = P_1 \times \frac{T_2}{T_1}$$

Step 3 **Substitute values into the gas law equation and calculate.** When we substitute in the values, we see that the ratio of the temperatures (temperature factor) is greater than 1, which increases pressure as predicted in Step 1.

$$P_2 = 4.0\text{ atm} \times \frac{675\text{ }\cancel{\text{K}}}{298\text{ }\cancel{\text{K}}} = 9.1\text{ atm}$$

Temperature factor increases pressure

Because the calculated pressure of 9.1 atm exceeds the limit of 8.0 atm for the can, we would expect the can to explode.

STUDY CHECK 5

In a storage area where the temperature has reached 55 °C, the pressure of oxygen gas in a 15.0-L steel cylinder is 965 torr. To what temperature, in degrees Celsius, would the gas have to be cooled to reduce the pressure to 850. torr?

Vapor Pressure and Boiling Point

We learned that liquid molecules with sufficient kinetic energy can break away from the surface of the liquid to become gas particles or vapor. In an open container, all the liquid will eventually evaporate. In a closed container, the vapor accumulates and creates pressure called **vapor pressure**. Each liquid exerts its own vapor pressure at a given temperature. As temperature increases, more vapor forms, and vapor pressure increases. Table 4 lists the vapor pressure of water at various temperatures.

A liquid reaches its boiling point when its vapor pressure becomes equal to the external pressure. As boiling occurs, bubbles of the gas form within the liquid and quickly rise to the surface. For example, at an atmospheric pressure of 760 mmHg, water will boil at 100 °C, the temperature at which its vapor pressure reaches 760 mmHg (see Table 5).

TABLE 4 Vapor Pressure of Water

Temperature (°C)	Vapor Pressure (mmHg)
0	5
10	9
20	18
30	32
37*	47
40	55
50	93
60	149
70	234
80	355
90	528
95	634
100	760

*At body temperature.

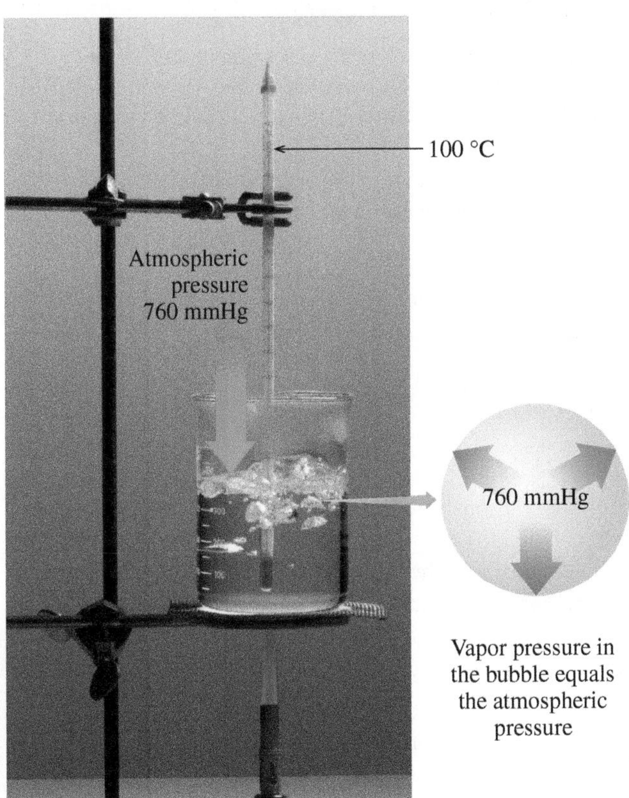

Water boils when its vapor pressure is equal to the pressure of the atmosphere.

TABLE 5 Pressure and the Boiling Point of Water

Pressure (mmHg)	Boiling Point (°C)
270	70
467	87
630	95
752	99
760	100
800	100.4
1075	110
1520 (2 atm)	120
3800 (5 atm)	160
7600 (10 atm)	180

TUTORIAL
Vapor Pressure and Boiling Point

At high altitudes, where atmospheric pressures are lower than 760 mmHg, the boiling point of water is lower than 100 °C. Earlier, we saw that the typical atmospheric pressure in Denver is 630 mmHg. This means that water in Denver needs a vapor pressure of 630 mmHg to boil. Because water has a vapor pressure of 630 mmHg at 95 °C, water boils at 95 °C in Denver.

In a closed container such as a pressure cooker, a pressure greater than 1 atm can be obtained, which means that water boils at a temperature higher than 100 °C. Laboratories and hospitals use closed containers called *autoclaves* to sterilize laboratory and surgical equipment.

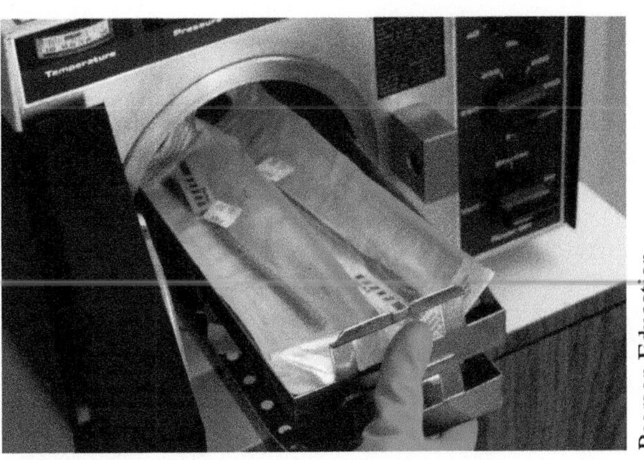

An autoclave used to sterilize equipment attains a temperature higher than 100 °C.

QUESTIONS AND PROBLEMS

5 Temperature and Pressure (Gay-Lussac's Law)

LEARNING GOAL: *Use the temperature–pressure relationship (Gay-Lussac's law) to determine the new temperature or pressure when the volume and amount of gas are constant.*

29 Why do aerosol cans explode if heated?

30 Why is there an increased danger of the tires on a car having a blowout when the car is driven on hot pavement in the desert?

31 For the following, calculate the final temperature of the gas, in degrees Celsius, when initial pressure is changed, with V and n constant:
- **a.** A sample of xenon at 25 °C and 745 mmHg is cooled to give a pressure of 625 mmHg.
- **b.** A tank of argon gas with a pressure of 0.950 atm at −18 °C is heated to give a pressure of 1250 torr.

32 For the following, calculate the final temperature of the gas, in degrees Celsius, when initial pressure is changed, with V and n constant:
- **a.** A tank of helium gas with a pressure of 250 torr at 0 °C is heated to give a pressure of 1500 torr.
- **b.** A sample of air at 40. °C and 745 mmHg is cooled to give a pressure of 685 mmHg.

33 Solve for the final pressure when each of the following temperature changes occurs, with V and n constant:
- **a.** A gas with an initial pressure of 1200 torr at 155 °C is cooled to 0 °C.
- **b.** A gas in an aerosol container at an initial pressure of 1.40 atm at 12 °C is heated to 35 °C.

34 Solve for the final pressure when each of the following temperature changes occurs, with V and n constant:
- **a.** A gas with an initial pressure of 1.20 atm at 75 °C is cooled to −22 °C.
- **b.** A sample of N_2 with an initial pressure of 780. mmHg at −75 °C is heated to 28 °C.

35 Match the terms *vapor pressure*, *atmospheric pressure*, and *boiling point* to the following descriptions:
- **a.** the temperature at which bubbles of vapor appear within the liquid
- **b.** the pressure exerted by a gas above the surface of its liquid

36 Match the terms *vapor pressure*, *atmospheric pressure*, and *boiling point* to the following descriptions:
- **a.** the pressure exerted on Earth by the particles in the air
- **b.** the temperature at which the vapor pressure of a liquid becomes equal to the external pressure

37 Explain each of the following observations:
- **a.** Water boils at 87 °C on the top of Mt. Whitney.
- **b.** Food cooks more quickly in a pressure cooker than in an open pan.

38 Explain each of the following observations:
- **a.** Boiling water at sea level is hotter than boiling water in the mountains.
- **b.** Water used to sterilize surgical equipment is heated to 120 °C at 2.0 atm in an autoclave.

6 The Combined Gas Law

LEARNING GOAL

Use the combined gas law to find the new pressure, volume, or temperature of a gas when changes in two of these properties are given and the amount of gas is constant.

All the pressure–volume–temperature relationships for gases that we have studied may be combined into a single relationship called the **combined gas law**. This expression is useful for studying the effect of changes in two of these variables on the third as long as the amount of gas (number of moles) remains constant.

Combined Gas Law

$$\frac{P_1V_1}{T_1} = \frac{P_2V_2}{T_2}$$ No change in moles of gas

By using the combined gas law, we can derive any of the gas laws by omitting those properties that do not change, as seen in Table 6.

TUTORIAL
The Combined Gas Law

TABLE 6 Summary of Gas Laws

Combined Gas Law	Properties Held Constant	Relationship	Name of Gas Law
$\frac{P_1V_1}{\cancel{T_1}} = \frac{P_2V_2}{\cancel{T_2}}$	T, n	$P_1V_1 = P_2V_2$	Boyle's
$\frac{\cancel{P_1}V_1}{T_1} = \frac{\cancel{P_2}V_2}{T_2}$	P, n	$\frac{V_1}{T_1} = \frac{V_2}{T_2}$	Charles's
$\frac{P_1\cancel{V_1}}{T_1} = \frac{P_2\cancel{V_2}}{T_2}$	V, n	$\frac{P_1}{T_1} = \frac{P_2}{T_2}$	Gay-Lussac's

CONCEPT CHECK 6 Combined Gas Law

State and explain the reason for the change (*increases*, *decreases*, *no change*) in a gas that occurs for the following when n does not change:

	Pressure (P)	Volume (V)	Temperature (K)	Amount (n)
a.		twice as large	half the Kelvin temperature	constant
b.	twice as large		twice as large	constant

ANSWER

a. Pressure decreases by one-half when the volume (at constant n) doubles. If the temperature in Kelvin is halved, the pressure is also halved. The changes in both V and T decrease the pressure to one-fourth its initial value.

b. No change. When the Kelvin temperature of a gas (at constant n) is doubled, the volume is doubled. But when the pressure is twice as much, the volume must decrease to one-half. The changes offset each other, and no change occurs in the volume.

	Pressure (P)	Volume (V)	Temperature (K)	Amount (n)
a.	one-fourth as large	twice as large	half the Kelvin temperature	constant
b.	twice as large	no change	twice as large	constant

SAMPLE PROBLEM 6 Using the Combined Gas Law

A 25.0-mL bubble is released from a diver's air tank at a pressure of 4.00 atm and a temperature of 11 °C. What is the volume, in milliliters, of the bubble when it reaches the ocean surface where the pressure is 1.00 atm and the temperature is 18 °C (assume the amount of gas in the bubble remains the same)?

T. O'Keefe/PhotoLink/Getty Images

Under water, the pressure on a diver is greater than the atmospheric pressure.

SOLUTION

Step 1 **Organize the data in a table of initial and final conditions.** We list the properties that change, which are the pressure, volume, and temperature, in a table. The property that remains constant, which is the amount of gas, is shown below the table. The temperatures in degrees Celsius must be changed to kelvins.

$$T_1 = 11\ °\text{C} + 273 = 284\ \text{K}$$
$$T_2 = 18\ °\text{C} + 273 = 291\ \text{K}$$

Analyze the Problem

Conditions 1	Conditions 2
$P_1 = 4.00$ atm	$P_2 = 1.00$ atm
$V_1 = 25.0$ mL	$V_2 = ?$ mL
$T_1 = 284$ K	$T_2 = 291$ K

Factor that remains constant: n

Step 2 **Rearrange the gas law equation to solve for the unknown quantity.** For changes in two conditions, we rearrange the combined gas law to solve for V_2.

$$\frac{P_1V_1}{T_1} = \frac{P_2V_2}{T_2}$$

$$\frac{P_1V_1}{T_1} \times \frac{T_2}{P_2} = \frac{\cancel{P_2}V_2 \times \cancel{T_2}}{\cancel{T_2} \times \cancel{P_2}}$$

$$V_2 = V_1 \times \frac{P_1}{P_2} \times \frac{T_2}{T_1}$$

Step 3 **Substitute values into the gas law equation and calculate.** From the data table, we determine that both the pressure decrease and the temperature increase will increase the volume.

$$V_2 = 25.0\text{ mL} \times \frac{4.00\text{ atm}}{1.00\text{ atm}} \times \frac{291\text{ K}}{284\text{ K}} = 102\text{ mL}$$

Pressure factor increases volume — Temperature factor increases volume

However, when the unknown value is decreased by one change but increased by the second change, it is not possible to predict the overall change.

STUDY CHECK 6

A weather balloon is filled with 15.0 L of helium at a temperature of 25 °C and a pressure of 685 mmHg. What is the pressure (mmHg) of the helium in the balloon in the upper atmosphere when the temperature is −35 °C and the volume becomes 34.0 L, if the amount of He does not change?

QUESTIONS AND PROBLEMS

6 The Combined Gas Law

LEARNING GOAL: *Use the combined gas law to find the new pressure, volume, or temperature of a gas when changes in two of these properties are given and the amount of gas is constant.*

39 A sample of helium gas has a volume of 6.50 L at a pressure of 845 mmHg and a temperature of 25 °C. What is the final pressure of the gas, in atmospheres, when the volume and temperature of the gas sample are changed to the following, if the amount of gas does not change?
a. 1850 mL and 325 K
b. 2.25 L and 12 °C
c. 12.8 L and 47 °C

40 A sample of argon gas has a volume of 735 mL at a pressure of 1.20 atm and a temperature of 112 °C. What is the final volume of the gas, in milliliters, when the pressure and temperature of the gas sample are changed to the following, if the amount of gas does not change?
a. 658 mmHg and 281 K
b. 0.55 atm and 75 °C
c. 15.4 atm and −15 °C

41 A 124-mL bubble of hot gas at 212 °C and 1.80 atm is emitted from an active volcano. What is the final temperature, in °C, of the gas in the bubble outside the volcano if the final volume of the bubble is 138 mL and the final pressure is 0.800 atm, if the amount of gas remains constant?

42 A scuba diver 60 ft below the ocean surface inhales 50.0 mL of compressed air from a scuba tank at an initial pressure of 3.00 atm and temperature of 8 °C. What is the final pressure of air, in atmospheres, in the lungs when the gas expands to 150.0 mL at a body temperature of 37 °C, and the amount of gas remains constant?

LEARNING GOAL

Use Avogadro's law to determine the amount or volume of a gas when the pressure and temperature are constant.

TUTORIAL
Volume and Moles

7 Volume and Moles (Avogadro's Law)

In our study of the gas laws, we have looked at changes in properties for a specified amount (n) of gas. Now we will consider how the properties of a gas change when there is a change in the number of moles or grams of the gas.

When you blow up a balloon, its volume increases because you are adding more air molecules. If the balloon has a hole in it, air leaks out, causing its volume to decrease. In 1811, Amedeo Avogadro formulated **Avogadro's law**, which states that the volume of a gas is directly related to the number of moles of a gas when pressure and temperature are not changed. For example, if the number of moles of a gas is doubled, then the volume will double as long as we do not change the pressure or the temperature (see Figure 7). At constant pressure and temperature, we can write Avogadro's law as follows:

Avogadro's Law

$$\frac{V_1}{n_1} = \frac{V_2}{n_2}$$ No change in pressure and temperature

SAMPLE PROBLEM 7 **Calculating Volume When There Is a Change in Moles**

A weather balloon with a volume of 44 L is filled with 2.0 moles of helium. To what volume, in liters, will the balloon expand if 3.0 moles of helium are added, to give a total of 5.0 moles of helium, if the pressure and temperature do not change?

SOLUTION

Step 1 **Organize the data in a table of initial and final conditions.** We list those properties that change, which are volume and amount (moles) of gas, in a table. The properties that do not change, which are pressure and temperature, are shown below the table. Because there is an increase in the number of moles of gas, we can predict that the volume increases.

Analyze the Problem

Conditions 1	Conditions 2	Know	Predict
$V_1 = 44$ L	$V_2 = ?$ L		V increases
$n_1 = 2.0$ moles	$n_2 = 5.0$ moles	n increases	

Factors that remain constant: P **and** T

Step 2 **Rearrange the gas law equation to solve for the unknown quantity.** Using Avogadro's law, we can solve for V_2.

$$\frac{V_1}{n_1} = \frac{V_2}{n_2}$$

$$n_2 \times \frac{V_1}{n_1} = \frac{V_2}{\cancel{n_2}} \times \cancel{n_2}$$

$$V_2 = V_1 \times \frac{n_2}{n_1}$$

Step 3 **Substitute values into the gas law equation and calculate.** When we substitute in the values, we see that the mole factor is greater than 1, which increases volume as predicted in Step 1.

$$V_2 = 44\text{ L} \times \frac{5.0\ \cancel{\text{moles}}}{2.0\ \cancel{\text{moles}}} = 110\text{ L}$$

Mole factor increases volume

STUDY CHECK 7

A sample containing 8.00 g of oxygen gas has a volume of 5.00 L. What is the volume, in liters, after 4.00 g of oxygen gas is added to the 8.00 g in the balloon, if temperature and pressure do not change?

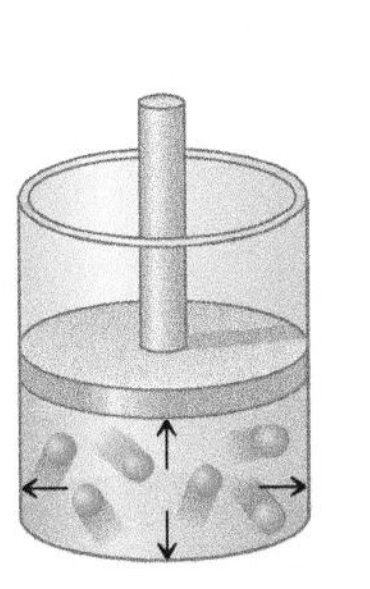
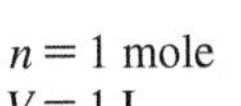

$n = 1$ mole
$V = 1$ L

$n = 2$ moles
$V = 2$ L

FIGURE 7 **Avogadro's law:** The volume of a gas is directly related to the number of moles of the gas. If the number of moles is doubled, the volume must double at constant pressure and temperature.

Q If a balloon has a leak, what happens to its volume?

iStockphoto

The molar volume of a gas at STP is about the same as the volume of three basketballs.

STP and Molar Volume

Using Avogadro's law, we can say that any two gases will have equal volumes if they contain the same number of moles of gas at the same temperature and pressure. To help us make comparisons between different gases, arbitrary conditions called *standard temperature* (273 K) and *standard pressure* (1 atm), together abbreviated **STP**, were selected by scientists.

STP Conditions

Standard temperature is *exactly* 0 °C (273 K).

Standard pressure is *exactly* 1 atm (760 mmHg).

At STP, one mole of any gas occupies a volume of 22.4 L, which is about the same as the volume of three basketballs. This volume of 22.4 L of any gas at STP is called the **molar volume** (see Figure 8).

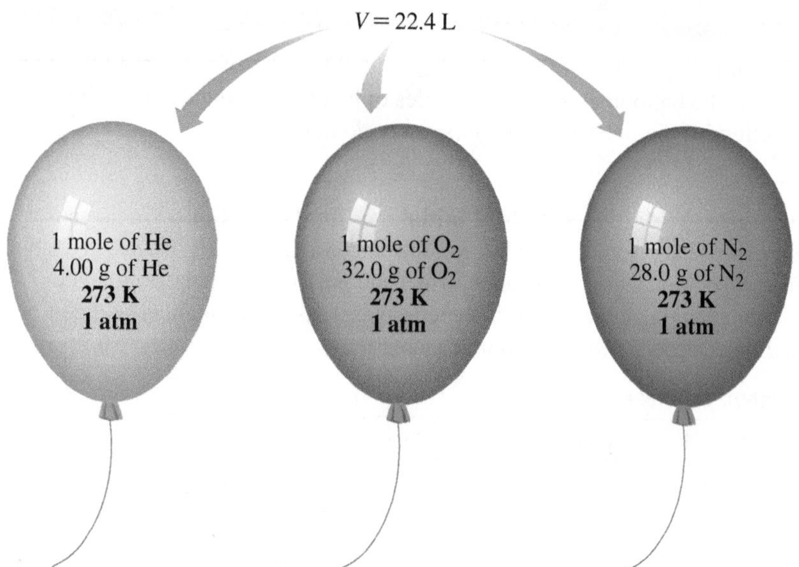

FIGURE 8 Avogadro's law indicates that 1 mole of any gas at STP has a volume of 22.4 L.

Q What volume of gas, in liters, is occupied by 16.0 g of methane gas, CH_4, at STP?

When a gas is at STP conditions (0 °C and 1 atm), its molar volume can be written as a conversion factor and used to convert between the number of moles of gas and its volume, in liters.

1 mole of gas at STP = 22.4 L

Molar Volume Conversion Factors

$$\frac{1 \text{ mole gas}}{22.4 \text{ L (STP)}} \quad \text{and} \quad \frac{22.4 \text{ L (STP)}}{1 \text{ mole gas}}$$

CONCEPT CHECK 7 **Molar Volume**

Write the equality and conversion factors for the molar volume of helium at STP.

ANSWER

The equality for the molar volume of helium at STP is:

1 mole of He = 22.4 L of He

Because an equality has two conversion factors, we write the factors for the molar volume for helium as:

$$\frac{22.4 \text{ L He (STP)}}{1 \text{ mole He}} \quad \text{and} \quad \frac{1 \text{ mole He}}{22.4 \text{ L He (STP)}}$$

Guide to Using Molar Volume

1. State the given and needed quantities.
2. Write a plan to calculate the needed quantity.
3. Write the equalities and conversion factors including 22.4 L/mole at STP.
4. Set up the problem with factors to cancel units.

SAMPLE PROBLEM 8 **Using Molar Volume to Find Volume at STP**

What is the volume, in liters, of 64.0 g of O_2 gas at STP?

SOLUTION

Step 1 **State the given and needed quantities.**

Analyze the Problem

Given	Need
64.0 g of O_2 gas at STP	liters of O_2 gas at STP

Step 2 **Write a plan to calculate the needed quantity.**

grams of O_2 → Molar mass → moles of O_2 → Molar volume → liters of O_2

Step 3 **Write the equalities and conversion factors including 22.4 L/mole at STP.**

1 mole of O_2 = 32.0 g of O_2

$$\frac{32.0\ g\ O_2}{1\ mole\ O_2} \text{ and } \frac{1\ mole\ O_2}{32.0\ g\ O_2}$$

1 mole of O_2 = 22.4 L of O_2 (STP)

$$\frac{22.4\ L\ O_2\ (STP)}{1\ mole\ O_2} \text{ and } \frac{1\ mole\ O_2}{22.4\ L\ O_2\ (STP)}$$

Step 4 **Set up the problem with factors to cancel units.**

$$64.0\ \cancel{g\ O_2} \times \frac{1\ \cancel{mole\ O_2}}{32.0\ \cancel{g\ O_2}} \times \frac{22.4\ L\ O_2\ (STP)}{1\ \cancel{mole\ O_2}} = 44.8\ L \text{ of } O_2 \text{ at STP}$$

STUDY CHECK 8

How many grams of $N_2(g)$ are in 5.6 L of $N_2(g)$ at STP?

Gases in Reactions at STP

We can use the molar volume at STP to determine the moles of a gas in a reaction. Once we know the moles of gas in a reaction, we can use a mole–mole factor to determine the moles of any other substance as we have done before.

SAMPLE PROBLEM 9 Gases in Chemical Reactions at STP

When potassium metal reacts with chlorine gas, the product is solid potassium chloride.

$$2K(s) + Cl_2(g) \longrightarrow 2KCl(s)$$

How many grams of potassium chloride are produced when 7.25 L of chlorine gas at STP reacts with potassium?

SOLUTION

Step 1 **State the given and needed quantities.**

Analyze the Problem

Given	Need
7.25 L of Cl_2 at STP	grams of KCl
Equation	
$2K(s) + Cl_2(g) \longrightarrow 2KCl(s)$	

Step 2 **Write a plan to calculate the needed quantity.**

liters of Cl_2 → Molar volume → moles of Cl_2 → Mole–mole factor → moles of KCl → Molar mass → grams of KCl

Step 3 **Write the equalities and conversion factors including the molar volume.**

1 mole of Cl_2 = 22.4 L of Cl_2 (STP)

$$\frac{22.4\ L\ Cl_2\ (STP)}{1\ mole\ Cl_2} \text{ and } \frac{1\ mole\ Cl_2}{22.4\ L\ Cl_2\ (STP)}$$

1 mole of Cl_2 = 2 moles of KCl

$$\frac{2\ moles\ KCl}{1\ mole\ Cl_2} \text{ and } \frac{1\ mole\ Cl_2}{2\ moles\ KCl}$$

1 mole of KCl = 74.6 g of KCl

$$\frac{1\ mole\ KCl}{74.6\ g\ KCl} \text{ and } \frac{74.6\ g\ KCl}{1\ mole\ KCl}$$

Guide to Reactions Involving Gases

1. State the given and needed quantities.
2. Write a plan to calculate the needed quantity.
3. Write the equalities and conversion factors including the molar volume.
4. Set up the problem and calculate.

Step 4 Set up the problem and calculate.

$$7.25\ \cancel{\text{L Cl}_2\text{ (STP)}} \times \frac{1\ \cancel{\text{mole Cl}_2}}{22.4\ \cancel{\text{L Cl}_2\text{ (STP)}}} \times \frac{2\ \cancel{\text{moles KCl}}}{1\ \cancel{\text{mole Cl}_2}} \times \frac{74.6\text{ g KCl}}{1\ \cancel{\text{mole KCl}}} = 48.3\text{ g of KCl}$$

STUDY CHECK 9

H_2 gas forms when zinc metal reacts with aqueous HCl according to the following equation:

$$Zn(s) + 2HCl(aq) \longrightarrow ZnCl_2(aq) + H_2(g)$$

How many liters of H_2 gas at STP are produced when 15.8 g of zinc reacts?

QUESTIONS AND PROBLEMS

7 Volume and Moles (Avogadro's Law)

LEARNING GOAL: *Use Avogadro's law to determine the amount or volume of a gas when the pressure and temperature are constant.*

43 What happens to the volume of a bicycle tire or a basketball when you use an air pump to add air?

44 Sometimes when you blow up a balloon and release it, it flies around the room. What is happening to the air that was in the balloon and its volume?

45 A sample containing 1.50 moles of neon gas has an initial volume of 8.00 L. What is the final volume of gas, in liters, when the following changes occur in the quantity of the gas at constant pressure and temperature?

a. A leak allows one-half of the neon atoms to escape.
b. A sample of 25.0 g of neon is added to the 1.50 moles of neon gas in the container.
c. A sample of 3.50 moles of O_2 is added to the 1.50 moles of neon gas in the container.

46 A sample containing 4.80 g of O_2 gas has an initial volume of 15.0 L. Pressure and temperature remain constant.

a. What is the final volume if 0.500 mole of O_2 gas is added?
b. Oxygen is released until the volume is 10.0 L. How many moles of O_2 remain?
c. What is the final volume after 4.00 g of He is added to the 4.80 g of O_2 gas in the container?

47 Use the molar volume of a gas to solve the following at STP:

a. the number of moles of O_2 in 44.8 L of O_2 gas
b. the number of moles of CO_2 in 4.00 L of CO_2 gas
c. the volume (L) of 6.40 g of O_2
d. the volume (mL) occupied by 50.0 g of neon

48 Use the molar volume of a gas to solve the following at STP:

a. the volume (L) occupied by 2.50 moles of N_2
b. the volume (mL) occupied by 0.420 mole of He
c. the number of grams of neon contained in 11.2 L of Ne gas
d. the number of grams of H_2 in 1620 mL of H_2 gas

49 Mg metal reacts with HCl to produce hydrogen gas.

$$Mg(s) + 2HCl(aq) \longrightarrow MgCl_2(aq) + H_2(g)$$

What volume, in liters, of H_2 at STP is released when 8.25 g of Mg reacts?

50 Aluminum oxide can be formed from its elements.

$$4Al(s) + 3O_2(g) \xrightarrow{\Delta} 2Al_2O_3(s)$$

How many grams of Al will react with 12.0 L of O_2 at STP?

LEARNING GOAL

Use the ideal gas law equation to solve for P, V, T, or n of a gas when given three of the four values in the ideal gas law.

TUTORIAL
Introduction to the Ideal Gas Law

8 The Ideal Gas Law

The **ideal gas law** is the combination of the four properties used in the measurement of a gas—pressure (P), volume (V), temperature (T), and amount (n)—to give a single expression, which is written as follows:

Ideal Gas Law

$$PV = nRT$$

Rearranging the ideal gas law equation shows that the four gas properties equal a constant, R.

$$\frac{PV}{nT} = R$$

To calculate the value of R, we substitute the STP conditions for molar volume into the expression: 1 mole of any gas occupies 22.4 L at STP (273 K and 1 atm).

$$R = \frac{(1.00\text{ atm})(22.4\text{ L})}{(1.00\text{ mole})(273\text{ K})} = \frac{0.0821\text{ L}\cdot\text{atm}}{\text{mole}\cdot\text{K}}$$

The value for R, the **ideal gas constant**, is 0.0821 L · atm per mole · K. If we use 760. mmHg for the pressure, we obtain another useful value for R: 62.4 L · mmHg per mole · K.

$$R = \frac{(760.\ \text{mmHg})(22.4\ \text{L})}{(1.00\ \text{mole})(273\ \text{K})} = \frac{62.4\ \text{L} \cdot \text{mmHg}}{\text{mole} \cdot \text{K}}$$

SELF-STUDY ACTIVITY
The Ideal Gas Law

The ideal gas law is a useful expression when you are given the values for any three of the four properties of a gas. In working problems using the ideal gas law, the units of each variable must match the units in the R you select.

Ideal Gas Constant (*R*)	$\frac{0.0821\ \text{L} \cdot \text{atm}}{\text{mole} \cdot \text{K}}$	$\frac{62.4\ \text{L} \cdot \text{mmHg}}{\text{mole} \cdot \text{K}}$
Pressure (*P*)	atm	mmHg
Volume (*V*)	L	L
Amount (*n*)	moles	moles
Temperature (*T*)	K	K

SAMPLE PROBLEM 10 Using the Ideal Gas Law

Dinitrogen oxide, N_2O, which is used in dentistry, is an anesthetic also called "laughing gas." What is the pressure, in atmospheres, of 0.350 mole of N_2O at 22 °C in a 5.00 L container?

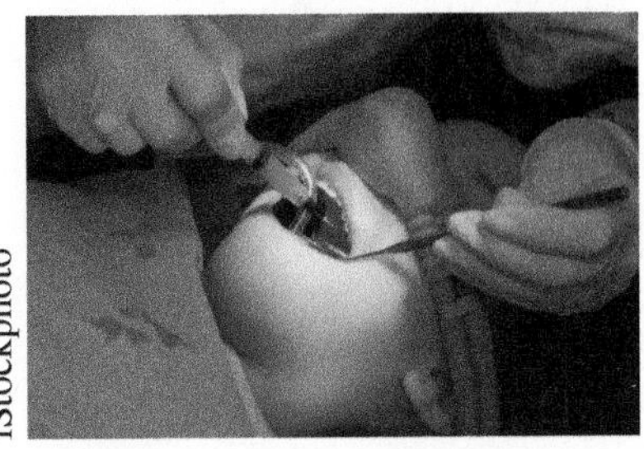

iStockphoto

Dinitrogen oxide is used as an anesthetic in dentistry.

SOLUTION

Step 1 **State the given and needed quantities.** When three of the four quantities (P, V, n, and T) are known, we use the ideal gas law equation to solve for the unknown quantity. It is helpful to organize the data in a table. The temperature is converted from degrees Celsius to kelvins so that the units of V, n, and T match the units of the gas constant R.

Analyze the Problem

Property	*P*	*V*	*n*	*R*	*T*
Given		5.00 L	0.350 mole	$\frac{0.0821\ \text{L} \cdot \text{atm}}{\text{mole} \cdot \text{K}}$	22 °C 22 °C + 273 = 295 K
Need	? atm				

Step 2 **Rearrange the ideal gas law equation to solve for the needed quantity.** By dividing both sides of the ideal gas law equation by V, we solve for pressure, P.

$$PV = nRT \quad \text{Ideal gas law equation}$$

$$P\frac{\cancel{V}}{\cancel{V}} = \frac{nRT}{V}$$

$$P = \frac{nRT}{V}$$

Step 3 **Substitute the gas data into the equation and calculate the needed quantity.**

$$P = \frac{0.350\ \cancel{\text{mole}} \times \frac{0.0821\ \cancel{\text{L}} \cdot \text{atm}}{\cancel{\text{mole}} \cdot \cancel{\text{K}}} \times 295\ \cancel{\text{K}}}{5.00\ \cancel{\text{L}}} = 1.70\ \text{atm}$$

STUDY CHECK 10

Chlorine gas, Cl_2, is used to purify water. How many moles of chlorine gas are in a 7.00 L tank if the gas has a pressure of 865 mmHg and a temperature of 24 °C?

Guide to Using the Ideal Gas Law

1. State the given and needed quantities.
2. Rearrange the ideal gas law equation to solve for the needed quantity.
3. Substitute the gas data into the equation and calculate the needed quantity.

SAMPLE PROBLEM 11 Calculating Mass Using the Ideal Gas Law Equation

Butane, C_4H_{10}, is used as a fuel for barbecues and as an aerosol propellant. If you have 108 mL of butane at 715 mmHg and 25 °C, what is the mass, in grams, of the butane?

SOLUTION

Step 1 **State the given and needed quantities.** When three of the four quantities (P, V, n, and T) are known, we use the ideal gas law equation to solve for the unknown quantity. It is helpful to organize the data in a table. Because the pressure is given in mmHg, we will use R in mmHg. The volume given in milliliters (mL) is converted to a volume in liters (L). The temperature is converted from degrees Celsius to kelvins.

Analyze the Problem

Property	P	V	n	R	T
Given	715 mmHg	108 mL (0.108 L)		$\frac{62.4\ \text{L} \cdot \text{mmHg}}{\text{mole} \cdot \text{K}}$	25 °C 25 °C + 273 = 298 K
Need			? mole (? g)		

Step 2 **Rearrange the ideal gas law equation to solve for the needed quantity.** By dividing both sides of the ideal gas law equation by RT, we solve for moles, n.

$$PV = n\,RT \quad \text{Ideal gas law equation}$$

$$\frac{PV}{RT} = n\,\frac{\cancel{RT}}{\cancel{RT}}$$

$$n = \frac{PV}{RT}$$

Step 3 **Substitute the gas data into the equation and calculate the needed quantity.**

$$n = \frac{715\ \cancel{\text{mmHg}} \times 0.108\ \cancel{\text{L}}}{\dfrac{62.4\ \cancel{\text{L}} \cdot \cancel{\text{mmHg}}}{\text{mole} \cdot \cancel{\text{K}}} \times 298\ \cancel{\text{K}}} = 0.00415\ \text{mole}\ (4.15 \times 10^{-3}\ \text{mole})$$

Now we convert the moles of butane to grams using its molar mass of 58.1 g/mole.

$$0.00415\ \cancel{\text{mole } C_4H_{10}} \times \frac{58.1\ \text{g } C_4H_{10}}{1\ \cancel{\text{mole } C_4H_{10}}} = 0.241\ \text{g of } C_4H_{10}$$

STUDY CHECK 11

What is the volume of 1.20 g of carbon monoxide at 8 °C if it has a pressure of 724 mmHg?

SAMPLE PROBLEM 12 Molar Mass of a Gas Using the Ideal Gas Law

What is the molar mass of a gas if a 3.16-g sample at 0.750 atm and 45 °C occupies a volume of 2.05 L?

SOLUTION

Step 1 **State the given and needed quantities.** It is helpful to organize the data in a table.

Analyze the Problem

Property	P	V	n	R	T	Mass
Given	0.750 atm	2.05 L		$\frac{0.0821\ \text{L} \cdot \text{atm}}{\text{mole} \cdot \text{K}}$	45 °C 45 °C + 273 = 318 K	3.16 g
Need			? mole (? molar mass)			

Step 2 Rearrange the ideal gas law equation to solve for the number of moles.

$PV = nRT$ Ideal gas law equation

To solve the ideal gas law equation for n, we divide both sides by RT.

$$\frac{PV}{RT} = \frac{n\cancel{RT}}{\cancel{RT}}$$

$$n = \frac{PV}{RT}$$

$$n = \frac{0.750\ \cancel{\text{atm}} \times 2.05\ \cancel{\text{L}}}{\frac{0.0821\ \cancel{\text{L}} \cdot \cancel{\text{atm}}}{\text{mole} \cdot \cancel{\text{K}}} \times 318\ \cancel{\text{K}}} = 0.0589\ \text{mole}$$

Step 3 Obtain the molar mass by dividing the given number of grams by the number of moles.

$$\text{Molar mass} = \frac{\text{mass}}{\text{moles}} = \frac{3.16\ \text{g}}{0.0589\ \text{mole}} = 53.7\ \text{g/mole}$$

STUDY CHECK 12

What is the molar mass of an unknown gas in a 1.50-L container if 0.488 g of the gas has a pressure of 0.0750 atm at 19 °C?

Guide to Calculating the Molar Mass of a Gas

1. State the given and needed quantities.
2. Rearrange the ideal gas law equation to solve for the number of moles.
3. Obtain the molar mass by dividing the given number of grams by the number of moles.

Chemical Reactions and the Ideal Gas Law

If a gas is not at STP, we use its pressure (P), volume (V), and temperature (T) to determine the moles of that gas involved in a reaction. Then we can determine the moles of any other substance by using the mole–mole factors.

SAMPLE PROBLEM 13 Chemical Equations Using the Ideal Gas Law

Limestone ($CaCO_3$) reacts with HCl to produce aqueous calcium chloride and carbon dioxide gas.

$$CaCO_3(s) + 2HCl(aq) \longrightarrow CaCl_2(aq) + CO_2(g) + H_2O(l)$$

How many liters of CO_2 are produced at 752 mmHg and 24 °C from a 25.0-g sample of limestone?

SOLUTION

Step 1 State the given and needed quantities.

Analyze the Problem

Given		Need
Reactant:	25.0 g of $CaCO_3$	liters of $CO_2(g)$
Product:	$CO_2(g)$ at 752 mmHg, 24 °C (24 °C + 273 = 297 K)	
Equation		
$CaCO_3(s) + 2HCl(aq) \longrightarrow CaCl_2(aq) + CO_2(g) + H_2O(l)$		

Step 2 Write a plan to convert the given quantity to the needed moles.

grams of $CaCO_3$ → Molar mass → moles of $CaCO_3$ → Mole–mole factor → moles of CO_2

Guide to Reactions Involving the Ideal Gas Law

1. State the given and needed quantities.
2. Write a plan to convert the given quantity to the needed moles.
3. Write the equalities for molar mass and mole–mole factors.
4. Set up the problem to calculate moles of needed quantity.
5. Convert the moles of needed to mass or volume using the molar mass or the ideal gas law equation.

Step 3 Write the equalities for molar mass and mole–mole factors.

$$1 \text{ mole of } CaCO_3 = 100.1 \text{ g of } CaCO_3 \qquad \frac{100.1 \text{ g } CaCO_3}{1 \text{ mole } CaCO_3} \text{ and } \frac{1 \text{ mole } CaCO_3}{100.1 \text{ g } CaCO_3}$$

$$1 \text{ mole of } CaCO_3 = 1 \text{ mole of } CO_2 \qquad \frac{1 \text{ mole } CaCO_3}{1 \text{ mole } CO_2} \text{ and } \frac{1 \text{ mole } CO_2}{1 \text{ mole } CaCO_3}$$

Step 4 Set up the problem to calculate moles of needed quantity.

$$25.0 \text{ g } \cancel{CaCO_3} \times \frac{1 \text{ mole } \cancel{CaCO_3}}{100.1 \text{ g } \cancel{CaCO_3}} \times \frac{1 \text{ mole } CO_2}{1 \text{ mole } \cancel{CaCO_3}} = 0.250 \text{ mole of } CO_2$$

Step 5 Convert the moles of needed to volume using the ideal gas law equation. Now the ideal gas law equation is rearranged to solve for volume (L) of gas. Then substitute in the given quantities and calculate V.

$$V = \frac{nRT}{P}$$

$$V = \frac{0.250 \text{ } \cancel{\text{mole}} \times \frac{62.4 \text{ L} \cdot \cancel{\text{mmHg}}}{\cancel{\text{mole}} \cdot \cancel{\text{K}}} \times 297 \text{ } \cancel{\text{K}}}{752 \text{ } \cancel{\text{mmHg}}} = 6.16 \text{ L of } CO_2$$

STUDY CHECK 13

If 12.8 g of aluminum reacts with HCl, how many liters of H_2 would be formed at 715 mmHg and 19 °C?

$$2Al(s) + 6HCl(aq) \longrightarrow 2AlCl_3(aq) + 3H_2(g)$$

QUESTIONS AND PROBLEMS

8 The Ideal Gas Law

LEARNING GOAL: *Use the ideal gas law equation to solve for P, V, T, or n of a gas when given three of the four values in the ideal gas law.*

51 Calculate the pressure, in atmospheres, of 2.00 moles of helium gas in a 10.0-L container at 27 °C.

52 What is the volume, in liters, of 4.0 moles of methane gas, CH_4, at 18 °C and 1.40 atm?

53 An oxygen gas container has a volume of 20.0 L. How many grams of oxygen are in the container if the gas has a pressure of 845 mmHg at 22 °C?

54 A 10.0-g sample of krypton gas has a temperature of 25 °C at 575 mmHg. What is the volume, in milliliters, of the krypton gas?

55 A 25.0-g sample of nitrogen, N_2, has a volume of 50.0 L and a pressure of 630. mmHg. What is the temperature, in kelvins and degrees Celsius, of the gas?

56 A 0.226-g sample of carbon dioxide, CO_2, has a volume of 525 mL and a pressure of 455 mmHg. What is the temperature, in kelvins and degrees Celsius, of the gas?

57 Using molar volume (STP) or the ideal gas law equation, determine the molar mass, g/mole, of each of the following:
- **a.** 0.84 g of a gas that has a volume of 450 mL at STP
- **b.** 1.48 g of a gas that has a volume of 1.00 L at 685 mmHg and 22 °C
- **c.** 2.96 g of a gas that has a volume of 2.30 L at 0.95 atm and 24 °C

58 Using molar volume (STP) or the ideal gas law equation, determine the molar mass, g/mole, of each of the following:
- **a.** 11.6 g of a gas that has a volume of 2.00 L at STP
- **b.** 0.726 g of a gas that has a volume of 855 mL at 1.20 atm and 18 °C
- **c.** 2.32 g of a gas that has a volume of 1.23 L at 685 mmHg and 25 °C

59 Butane undergoes combustion when it reacts with oxygen to produce carbon dioxide and water. Using the ideal gas law equation, calculate the volume, in liters, of oxygen needed to burn all the butane at 0.850 atm and 25 °C if a tank contains 55.2 g of butane.

$$2C_4H_{10}(g) + 13O_2(g) \xrightarrow{\Delta} 8CO_2(g) + 10H_2O(g)$$

60 When heated to 350. °C at 0.950 atm, ammonium nitrate decomposes to produce nitrogen, water, and oxygen gases. Using the ideal gas law equation, calculate the volume, in liters, of water vapor produced when 25.8 g of NH_4NO_3 decomposes.

$$2NH_4NO_3(s) \xrightarrow{\Delta} 2N_2(g) + 4H_2O(g) + O_2(g)$$

61 Potassium nitrate decomposes to potassium nitrite and oxygen. Using the ideal gas law equation, calculate the volume, in liters, of the O_2 produced if the decomposition of 50.0 g of KNO_3 takes place at 35 °C and 1.19 atm.

$$2KNO_3(s) \xrightarrow{\Delta} 2KNO_2(s) + O_2(g)$$

62 Nitrogen dioxide reacts with water to produce oxygen and ammonia. Using the ideal gas law equation, calculate the grams of NH_3 that can be produced when 4.00 L of NO_2 react at a temperature of 415 °C and a pressure of 725 mmHg.

$$4NO_2(g) + 6H_2O(g) \xrightarrow{\Delta} 7O_2(g) + 4NH_3(g)$$

9 Partial Pressures (Dalton's Law)

LEARNING GOAL

Use Dalton's law of partial pressures to calculate the total pressure of a mixture of gases.

TUTORIAL
Mixture of Gases

Many gas samples are a mixture of gases. For example, the air you breathe is a mixture of mostly oxygen and nitrogen gases. Scientists have observed that all gas particles in ideal gas mixtures behave in the same way. Therefore, the total pressure of the gases in a mixture is a result of the collisions of the gas particles, regardless of what type of gas they are.

In a gas mixture, each gas exerts its **partial pressure**, which is the pressure it would exert if it were the only gas in the container. **Dalton's law** states that the total pressure of a gas mixture is the sum of the partial pressures of the gases in the mixture.

Dalton's Law

$$P_{total} = P_1 + P_2 + P_3 + \cdots$$

Total pressure of a gas mixture = Sum of the partial pressures of the gases in the mixture

Suppose we have two separate tanks, one filled with helium at 2.0 atm and the other filled with argon at 4.0 atm. When the gases are combined in a single tank with the same volume and temperature, the number of gas molecules, not the type of gas, determines the pressure in a container. The pressure of the gases in the gas mixture would be 6.0 atm, which is the sum of their individual or partial pressures.

$$P_{total} = P_{He} + P_{Ar} = 2.0\text{ atm} + 4.0\text{ atm} = 6.0\text{ atm}$$

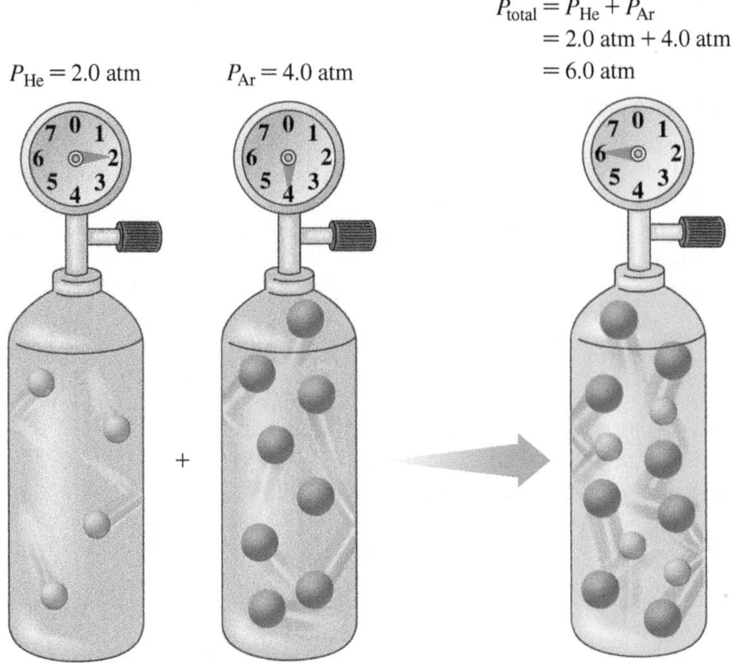

The total pressure of two gases is the sum of their partial pressures.

CONCEPT CHECK 8 **Pressure of a Gas Mixture**

A scuba tank is filled with Trimix, a breathing gas mixture for deep scuba diving. The tank contains oxygen with a partial pressure of 20. atm, nitrogen with a partial pressure of 40. atm, and helium with a partial pressure of 140. atm. What is the total pressure of the breathing mixture, in atmospheres?

ANSWER

Using Dalton's law of partial pressures, we add together the partial pressures of oxygen, nitrogen, and helium present in the mixture.

$$P_{total} = P_{oxygen} + P_{nitrogen} + P_{helium}$$

$$P_{total} = 20.\text{ atm} + 40.\text{ atm} + 140.\text{ atm} = 200.\text{ atm}$$

Therefore, when oxygen, nitrogen, and helium are placed in the same container, the sum of their partial pressures is the total pressure of the mixture, which is 200. atm.

TABLE 7 Typical Composition of Air

Gas	Partial Pressure (mmHg)	Percentage (%)
Nitrogen, N_2	594	78.2
Oxygen, O_2	160.	21.0
Carbon dioxide, CO_2; Argon, Ar; Water vapor, H_2O	6	0.8
Total air	760.	100

Guide to Solving for Partial Pressure

1. Write the equation for the sum of the partial pressures.
2. Rearrange the equation to solve for the unknown pressure.
3. Substitute known pressures into the equation and calculate the unknown partial pressure.

Air Is a Gas Mixture

The air you breathe is a mixture of gases. What we call the *atmospheric pressure* is actually the sum of the partial pressures of all the gases in the air. Table 7 lists partial pressures for the gases in air on a typical day.

SAMPLE PROBLEM 14 Partial Pressure of a Gas in a Mixture

A Heliox breathing mixture of oxygen and helium is prepared for a scuba diver who is going to descend 200 ft below the ocean surface. At that depth, the diver breathes a gas mixture that has a total pressure of 7.00 atm. If the partial pressure of the oxygen in the tank at that depth is 1140 mmHg, what is the partial pressure of the helium in the breathing mixture?

SOLUTION

Step 1 **Write the equation for the sum of the partial pressures.** From Dalton's law of partial pressures, we know that the total pressure is equal to the sum of the partial pressures.

$$P_{\text{total}} = P_{O_2} + P_{He}$$

Step 2 **Rearrange the equation to solve for the unknown pressure.** To solve for the partial pressure of helium (P_{He}), we rearrange the expression to give the following:

$$P_{He} = P_{\text{total}} - P_{O_2}$$

Convert units to match.

$$P_{O_2} = 1140 \, \cancel{\text{mmHg}} \times \frac{1 \text{ atm}}{760 \, \cancel{\text{mmHg}}} = 1.50 \text{ atm}$$

Step 3 **Substitute known pressures into the equation and calculate the unknown partial pressure.**

$$P_{He} = P_{\text{total}} - P_{O_2}$$

$$P_{He} = 7.00 \text{ atm} - 1.50 \text{ atm} = 5.50 \text{ atm}$$

STUDY CHECK 14

An anesthetic consists of a mixture of cyclopropane gas, C_3H_6, and oxygen gas, O_2. If the mixture has a total pressure of 1.09 atm, and the partial pressure of the cyclopropane is 73 torr, what is the partial pressure (torr) of the oxygen in the anesthetic?

Chemistry Link to Health

BLOOD GASES

Our cells continuously use oxygen and produce carbon dioxide. Both gases move in and out of the lungs through the membranes of the alveoli, the tiny air sacs at the ends of the airways in the lungs. An exchange of gases occurs in which oxygen from the air diffuses into the lungs and into the blood, while carbon dioxide produced in the cells is carried to the lungs to be exhaled. In Table 8, partial pressures are given for the gases in the air that we inhale (inspired air), the air in the alveoli, and the air that we exhale (expired air).

At sea level, oxygen normally has a partial pressure of 100 mmHg in the alveoli of the lungs. Because the partial pressure of oxygen in venous blood is 40 mmHg, oxygen diffuses from the alveoli into the bloodstream. The oxygen combines with hemoglobin, which carries it to the tissues of the body, where the partial pressure of oxygen can be very low, less than 30 mmHg. Oxygen diffuses from the blood where the partial pressure of O_2 is high into the tissues, where O_2 pressure is low.

TABLE 8 Partial Pressures of Gases During Breathing

	Partial Pressure (mmHg)		
Gas	Inspired Air	Alveolar Air	Expired Air
Nitrogen, N_2	594	573	569
Oxygen, O_2	160	100	116
Carbon dioxide, CO_2	0.3	40	28
Water vapor, H_2O	5.7	47	47
Total	760.	760.	760.

As oxygen is used in the cells of the body during metabolic processes, carbon dioxide is produced, so the partial pressure of CO_2 may be as high as 50 mmHg or more. Carbon dioxide diffuses from the tissues into the bloodstream and is carried to the lungs. There it diffuses out of the blood, where CO_2 has a partial pressure of 46 mmHg, into the alveoli, where the CO_2 is at 40 mmHg, and is exhaled. Table 9 gives the partial pressures of blood gases in the tissues, and in oxygenated and deoxygenated blood.

TABLE 9 Partial Pressures of Oxygen and Carbon Dioxide in Blood and Tissues

	Partial Pressure (mmHg)		
Gas	**Oxygenated Blood**	**Deoxygenated Blood**	**Tissues**
O_2	100	40	30 or less
CO_2	40	46	50 or greater

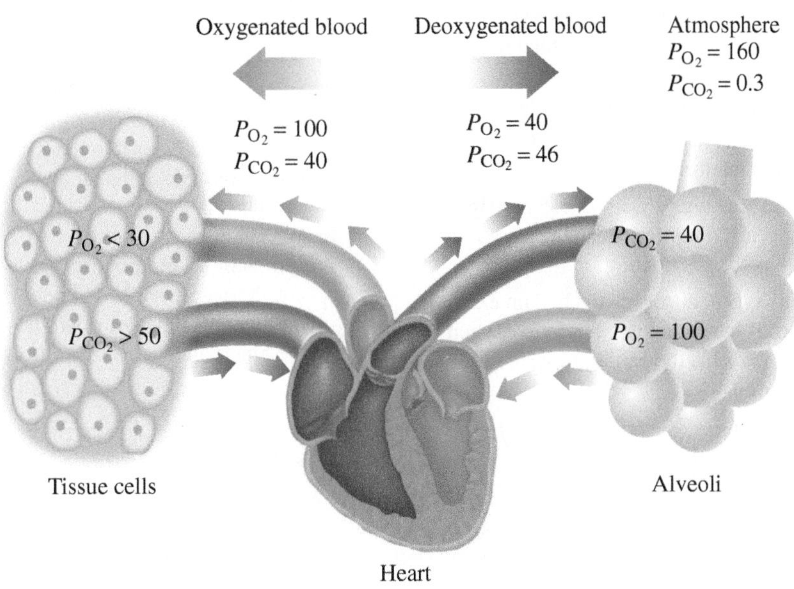

Chemistry Link to Health

HYPERBARIC CHAMBERS

A burn patient may undergo treatment for burns and infections in a hyperbaric chamber, a device in which pressures can be obtained that are two to three times greater than atmospheric pressure. A greater oxygen pressure increases the level of dissolved oxygen in the blood and tissues. Because high levels of oxygen are toxic to many strains of bacteria, this helps fight bacterial infections. The hyperbaric chamber may also be used to counteract carbon monoxide (CO) poisoning and to treat some cancers. In carbon monoxide poisoning, CO has a much stronger affinity for hemoglobin than oxygen does.

The blood is normally capable of dissolving up to 95% of the oxygen available to it. Thus, if the partial pressure of the oxygen in the hyperbaric chamber is 2280 mmHg (3 atm), about 2170 mmHg of oxygen can dissolve in the blood, saturating the tissues. In the treatment for carbon monoxide poisoning, oxygen at high pressure is used to displace the CO from the hemoglobin faster than breathing pure oxygen at 1 atm.

A patient undergoing treatment in a hyperbaric chamber must also undergo decompression (reduction of pressure) at a rate that slowly reduces the concentration of dissolved oxygen in the blood. If decompression is too rapid, the oxygen dissolved in the blood may form gas bubbles in the circulatory system.

Similarly, if a scuba diver does not decompress slowly, a condition called the "bends" may occur. While below the surface of the ocean, a diver uses a breathing mixture with higher pressures. If there is nitrogen in the mixture, higher quantities of nitrogen gas will dissolve in the blood. If the diver ascends to the surface too quickly, the dissolved nitrogen forms gas bubbles that can block a blood vessel and cut off the flow of blood in the joints and tissues of the body and be quite painful. A diver suffering from the bends is placed immediately into a hyperbaric chamber, where pressure is first increased and then slowly decreased. The dissolved nitrogen can then diffuse through the lungs as the pressure is decreasing until atmospheric pressure is reached.

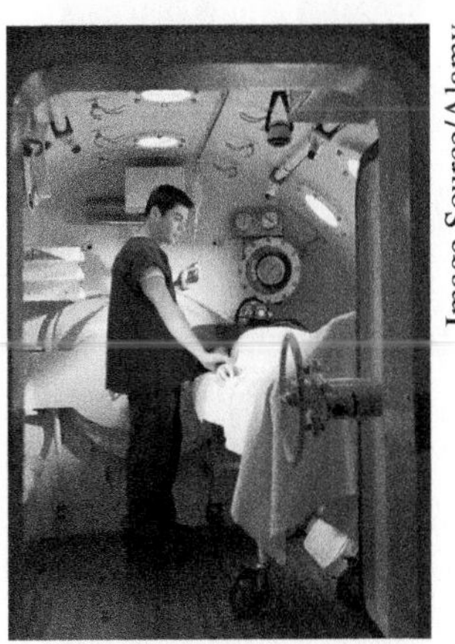

Image Source/Alamy

A hyperbaric chamber is used in the treatment of certain diseases.

QUESTIONS AND PROBLEMS

9 Partial Pressures (Dalton's Law)

LEARNING GOAL: *Use Dalton's law of partial pressures to calculate the total pressure of a mixture of gases.*

63 A typical air sample in the lungs contains oxygen at 98 mmHg, nitrogen at 573 mmHg, carbon dioxide at 40. mmHg, and water vapor at 47 mmHg. What is the total pressure, in mmHg, of the gas sample?

64 A Nitrox II gas mixture for scuba diving contains oxygen gas at 53 atm and nitrogen gas at 94 atm. What is the total pressure, in atm, of the scuba gas mixture?

65 In a gas mixture, the partial pressures are nitrogen 425 torr, oxygen 115 torr, and helium 225 torr. What is the total pressure (torr) exerted by the gas mixture?

66 In a gas mixture, the partial pressures are argon 415 mmHg, neon 75 mmHg, and nitrogen 125 mmHg. What is the total pressure (mmHg) exerted by the gas mixture?

67 A gas mixture containing oxygen, nitrogen, and helium exerts a total pressure of 925 torr. If the partial pressures are oxygen 425 torr and helium 75 torr, what is the partial pressure (atm) of the nitrogen in the mixture?

68 A gas mixture containing oxygen, nitrogen, and neon exerts a total pressure of 1.20 atm. If helium added to the mixture increases the pressure to 1.50 atm, what is the partial pressure (mmHg) of the helium?

69 In certain lung ailments such as emphysema, there is a decrease in the ability of oxygen to diffuse into the blood.

a. How would the partial pressure of oxygen in the blood change?

b. Why does a person with severe emphysema sometimes use a portable oxygen tank?

70 An injury to the head can affect the ability of a person to ventilate (breathe in and out), and so can certain drugs.

a. What would happen to the partial pressures of oxygen and carbon dioxide in the blood if a person cannot properly ventilate?

b. When a person with hypoventilation is placed on a ventilator, an air mixture is delivered at pressures that are alternately above and below the air pressure in the person's lung. How will this move oxygen gas into the lungs, and carbon dioxide out?

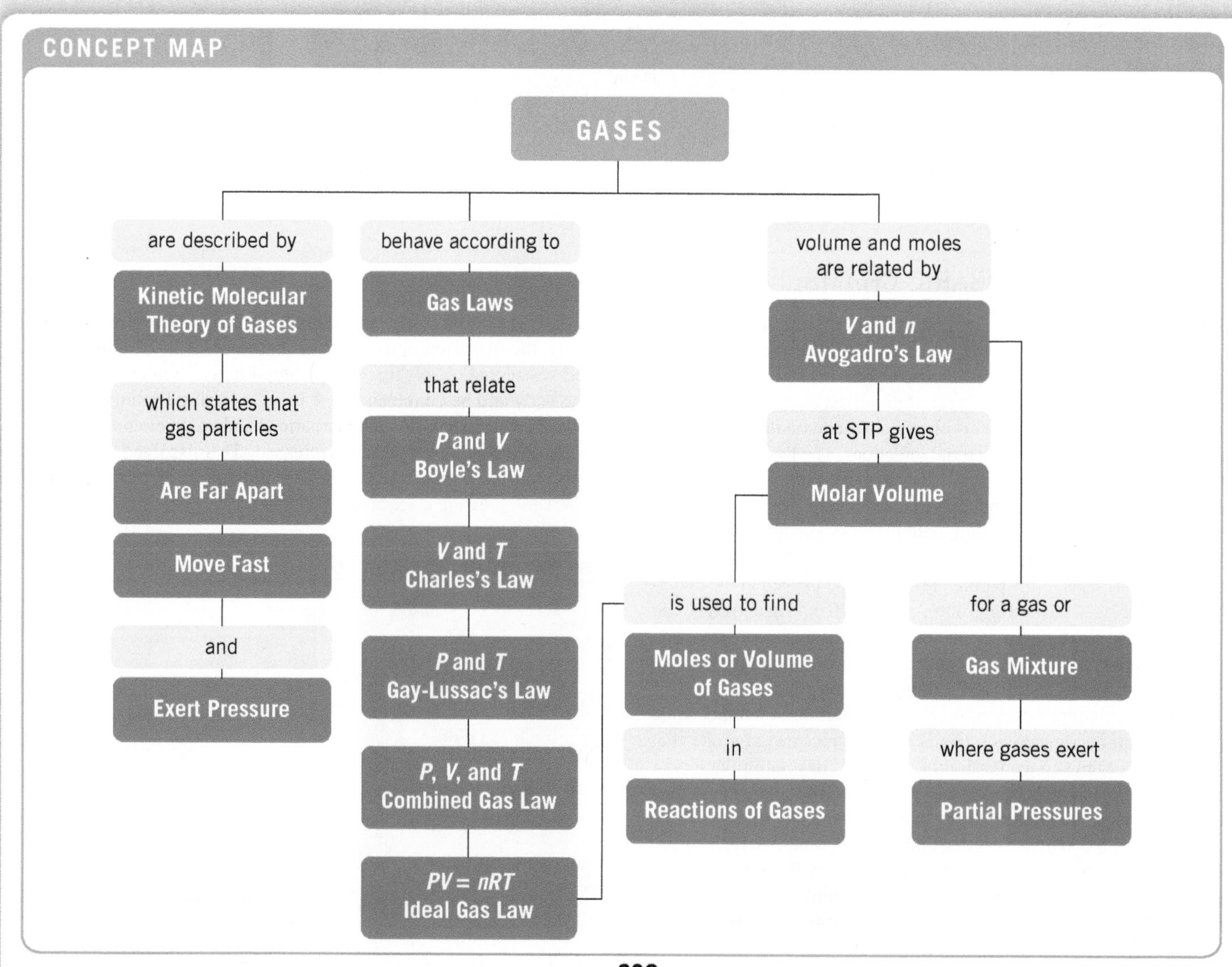

CHAPTER REVIEW

1 Properties of Gases

LEARNING GOAL: *Describe the kinetic molecular theory of gases and the properties of gases.*

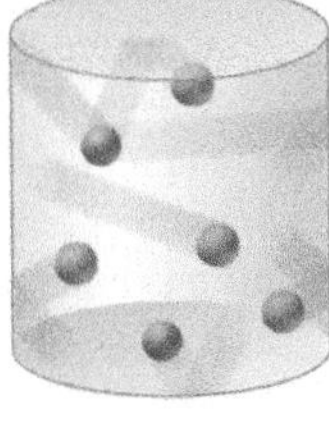

- In a gas, particles are so far apart and moving so fast that their attractions are negligible.
- A gas is described by the physical properties of pressure (P), volume (V), temperature (T), and amount in moles (n).

2 Gas Pressure

LEARNING GOAL: *Describe the units of measurement used for pressure, and change from one unit to another.*

Vacuum (no air particles)
Gases of the atmosphere at 1 atm
760 mmHg
Liquid mercury

- A gas exerts pressure, the force of the gas particles striking the walls of a container.
- Gas pressure is measured in units such as torr, mmHg, atm, and Pa.

3 Pressure and Volume (Boyle's Law)

LEARNING GOAL: *Use the pressure–volume relationship (Boyle's law) to determine the new pressure or volume when the temperature and amount of gas are constant.*

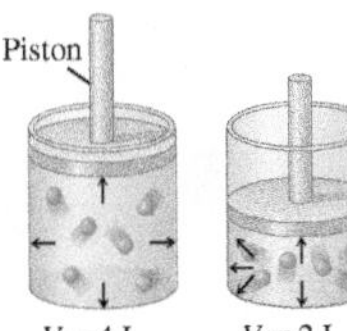

- The volume (V) of a gas changes inversely with the pressure (P) of the gas if there is no change in the temperature and the amount of gas.

$$P_1V_1 = P_2V_2$$

- This means that the pressure increases if volume decreases; pressure decreases if volume increases.

4 Temperature and Volume (Charles's Law)

LEARNING GOAL: *Use the temperature–volume relationship (Charles's law) to determine the new temperature or volume when the pressure and amount of gas are constant.*

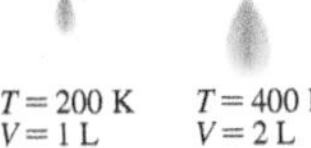

- The volume (V) of a gas is directly related to its Kelvin temperature (T) when there is no change in the pressure and amount of the gas.

$$\frac{V_1}{T_1} = \frac{V_2}{T_2}$$

- Therefore, if temperature increases, the volume of the gas increases; if temperature decreases, volume decreases.

5 Temperature and Pressure (Gay-Lussac's Law)

LEARNING GOAL: *Use the temperature–pressure relationship (Gay-Lussac's law) to determine the new temperature or pressure when the volume and amount of gas are constant.*

- The pressure (P) of a gas is directly related to its Kelvin temperature (T).

$$\frac{P_1}{T_1} = \frac{P_2}{T_2}$$

- This relationship means that an increase in temperature increases the pressure of a gas, and a decrease in temperature decreases the pressure, as long as the volume and amount of gas remain constant.

- Vapor pressure is the pressure of the gas that forms when a liquid evaporates.
- At the boiling point of a liquid, the vapor pressure equals the external pressure.

6 The Combined Gas Law

LEARNING GOAL: *Use the combined gas law to find the new pressure, volume, or temperature of a gas when changes in two of these properties are given and the amount of gas is constant.*

T. O'Keefe/PhotoLink/Getty Images

- The combined gas law is the relationship of pressure (P), volume (V), and temperature (T) for a constant amount of gas.
- This expression is used to determine the effect of changes in two of the variables on the third.

$$\frac{P_1V_1}{T_1} = \frac{P_2V_2}{T_2}$$

7 Volume and Moles (Avogadro's Law)

LEARNING GOAL: *Use Avogadro's law to determine the amount or volume of a gas when the pressure and temperature are constant.*

$V = 22.4$ L
1 mole of O_2
32.0 g of O_2
273 K
1 atm

- The volume (V) of a gas is directly related to the number of moles (n) of the gas when the pressure and temperature of the gas do not change.

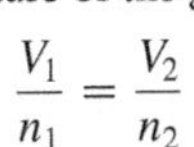

$$\frac{V_1}{n_1} = \frac{V_2}{n_2}$$

- If the moles of gas increase, the volume must increase; if the moles of gas decrease, the volume must decrease.
- At standard temperature (273 K) and standard pressure (1 atm), abbreviated STP, one mole of any gas has a volume of 22.4 L.

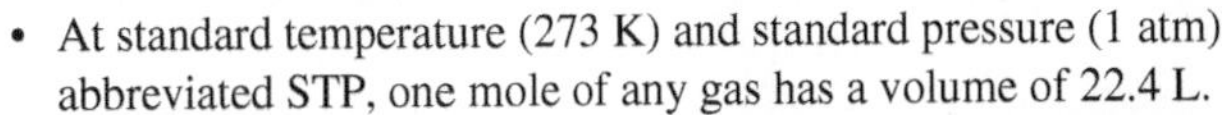

8 The Ideal Gas Law

LEARNING GOAL: *Use the ideal gas law equation to solve for P, V, T, or n of a gas when given three of the four values in the ideal gas law.*

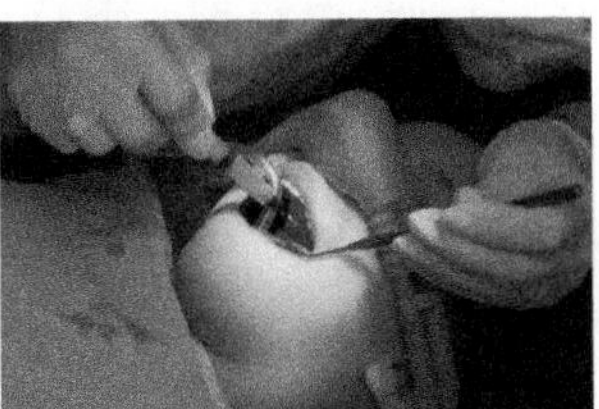
Yuri Bathan/iStockphoto

- The ideal gas law equation gives the relationship of all the quantities P, V, n, and T that describe and measure a gas: $$PV = nRT.$$
- Any of the four variables can be calculated if the other three are known.

9 Partial Pressures (Dalton's Law)

LEARNING GOAL: *Use Dalton's law of partial pressures to calculate the total pressure of a mixture of gases.*

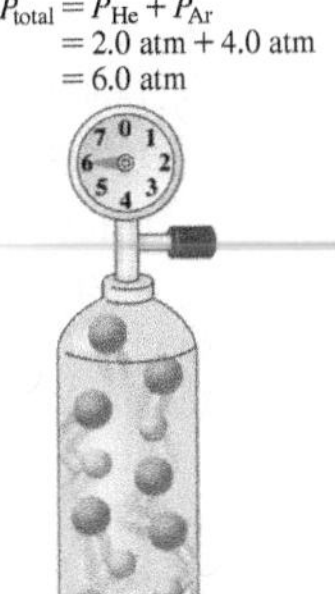

- In a mixture of two or more gases, the total pressure is the sum of the partial pressures of the individual gases.

$$P_{total} = P_1 + P_2 + P_3 + \cdots$$

- The partial pressure of a gas in a mixture is the pressure it would exert if it were the only gas in the container.

KEY TERMS

atmosphere (atm) The pressure exerted by a column of mercury 760 mm high.

atmospheric pressure The pressure exerted by the atmosphere.

Avogadro's law A gas law stating that the volume of a gas is directly related to the number of moles of the gas when pressure and temperature do not change.

Boyle's law A gas law stating that the pressure of a gas is inversely related to the volume when temperature (K) and amount (moles) of the gas do not change.

Charles's law A gas law stating that the volume of a gas changes directly with a change in Kelvin temperature when pressure and amount (moles) of the gas do not change.

combined gas law A relationship that combines several gas laws relating pressure, volume, and temperature, when the amount of gas does not change.

$$\frac{P_1 V_1}{T_1} = \frac{P_2 V_2}{T_2}$$

Dalton's law A gas law stating that the total pressure exerted by a mixture of gases in a container is the sum of the partial pressures that each gas would exert alone.

direct relationship A relationship in which two properties increase or decrease together.

Gay-Lussac's law A gas law stating that the pressure of a gas changes directly with a change in Kelvin temperature when the number of moles of the gas and its volume do not change.

ideal gas constant, *R* A numerical value that relates the quantities P, V, n, and T in the ideal gas law equation, $PV = nRT$.

ideal gas law A law that combines the four measured properties of a gas in the equation $PV = nRT$.

inverse relationship A relationship in which two properties change in opposite directions.

kinetic molecular theory of gases A model used to explain the behavior of gases.

molar volume A volume of 22.4 L occupied by 1 mole of a gas at STP conditions of 0 °C (273 K) and 1 atm.

partial pressure The pressure exerted by a single gas in a gas mixture.

pressure The force exerted by gas particles that hit the walls of a container.

STP Standard conditions of exactly 0 °C (273 K) temperature and 1 atm pressure used for the comparison of gases.

vapor pressure The pressure exerted by the particles of vapor above a liquid.

UNDERSTANDING THE CONCEPTS

The chapter sections to review are shown in parentheses at the end of each question.

71 At 100 °C, which of the following diagrams (**1**, **2**, or **3**) represents a gas sample that exerts the: (7)

a. lowest pressure? **b.** highest pressure?

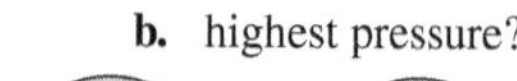

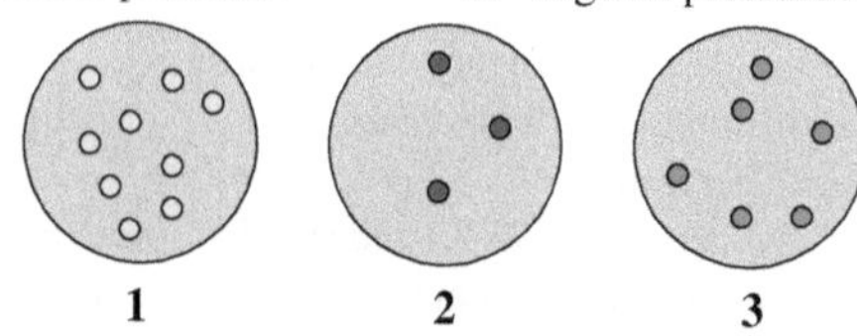

72 Indicate which diagram (**1**, **2**, or **3**) represents the volume of a gas sample in a flexible container when each of the following changes (**a–e**) takes place: (3, 4)

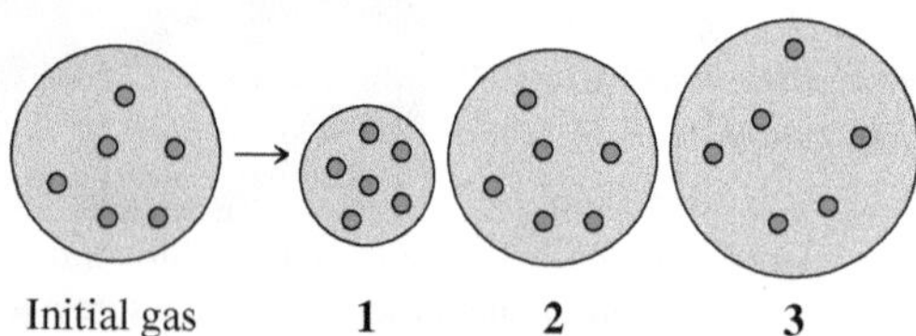

a. Temperature increases at constant pressure.

b. Temperature decreases at constant pressure.

c. Atmospheric pressure increases at constant temperature.

d. Atmospheric pressure decreases at constant temperature.

e. Doubling the atmospheric pressure and doubling the Kelvin temperature.

73 A balloon is filled with helium gas with a partial pressure of 1.00 atm, and neon gas with a partial pressure of 0.50 atm. For each of the following changes of the initial balloon, select the diagram (**A**, **B**, or **C**) that shows the final volume of the balloon: (3, 4, 7)

a. The balloon is put in a cold storage unit (P and n constant).

b. The balloon floats to a higher altitude where the pressure is less (n and T are constant).

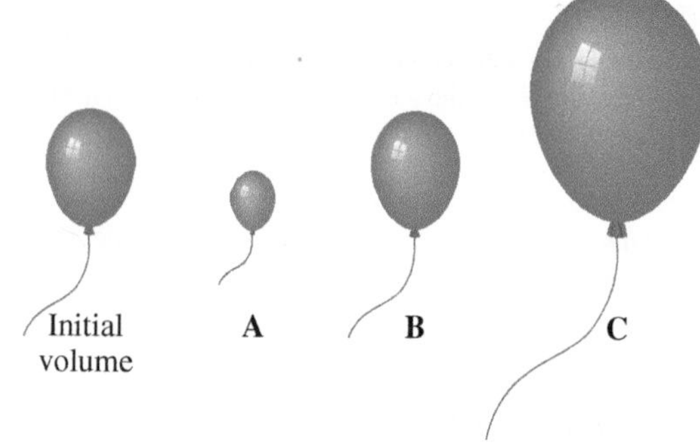

c. All of the neon gas is removed (T and P constant).

d. The Kelvin temperature doubles and one-half of the gas atoms leak out (P is constant).

e. 2.0 moles of O_2 gas is added at constant T and P.

74 Indicate if pressure *increases*, *decreases*, or *does not change* in each of the following: (3, 5, 7)

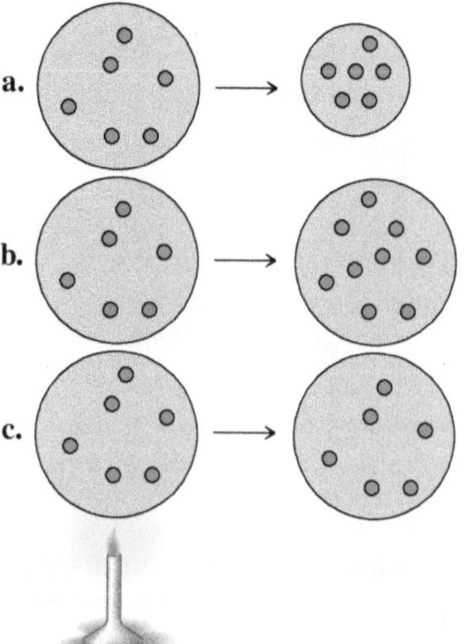

ADDITIONAL QUESTIONS AND PROBLEMS

For instructor-assigned homework, go to www.masteringchemistry.com.

75 At a restaurant, a customer chokes on a piece of food. You put your arms around the person's waist and use your fists to push up on the person's abdomen, an action called the *Heimlich maneuver*. (3)

   a. How would this action change the volume of the chest and lungs?

   b. Why does it cause the person to expel the food item from the airway?

76 An airplane is pressurized to 650. mmHg. (9)

   a. If air is 21% oxygen, what is the partial pressure of oxygen on the plane?

   b. If the partial pressure of oxygen drops below 100. mmHg, passengers become drowsy. If this happens, oxygen masks are released. What is the total cabin pressure at which oxygen masks are dropped?

77 In 1783, Jacques Charles launched his first balloon filled with hydrogen gas, which he chose because it was lighter than air. The balloon had a volume of 31 000 L when it reached an altitude of 1000 m, where the pressure was 658 mmHg and the temperature was −8 °C. How many kilograms of hydrogen were used to fill the balloon at STP? (7)

Library of Congress

Jacques Charles used hydrogen to launch his balloon in 1783.

78 Your spaceship has docked at a space station above Mars. The temperature inside the space station is a carefully controlled 24 °C at a pressure of 745 mmHg. A balloon with a volume of 425 mL drifts into the airlock where the temperature is −95 °C and the pressure is 0.115 atm. What is the new volume, in milliliters, of the balloon if *n* remains constant and the balloon is very elastic? (6)

79 A fire extinguisher has a pressure of 10. atm at 25 °C. What is the pressure, in atmospheres, if the fire extinguisher is used at a temperature of 75 °C and *V* and *n* remain constant? (5)

80 A weather balloon has a volume of 750 L when filled with helium at 8 °C at a pressure of 380 torr. What is the new volume of the balloon when the pressure is 0.20 atm, the temperature is −45 °C, and *n* remains constant? (6)

81 A sample of hydrogen (H_2) gas at 127 °C has a pressure of 2.00 atm. At what temperature (°C) will the pressure of the H_2 decrease to 0.25 atm, if *V* and *n* remain constant? (5)

82 A sample of nitrogen (N_2) gas has a pressure of 745 mmHg at 30. °C. What is the pressure when the temperature rises to 125 °C? (5)

83 How many moles of CO_2 are in 35.0 L of $CO_2(g)$ at 1.2 atm and 5 °C? (8)

84 A container is filled with 0.67 mole of O_2 at 5 °C and 845 mmHg. What is the volume, in milliliters, of the container? (8)

85 A 2.00-L container is filled with methane gas (CH_4) at a pressure of 2500. mmHg and a temperature of 18 °C. How many grams of methane are in the container? (8)

86 A steel cylinder with a volume of 15.0 L is filled with 50.0 g of nitrogen gas at 25 °C. What is the pressure, in atmospheres, of the N_2 gas in the cylinder? (8)

87 When heated, calcium carbonate decomposes to give calcium oxide and carbon dioxide gas. If 56.0 g of $CaCO_3$ react, how many liters of CO_2 gas are produced at STP? (7)

$$CaCO_3(s) \xrightarrow{\Delta} CaO(s) + CO_2(g)$$

88 Magnesium reacts with oxygen to form magnesium oxide. How many liters of oxygen gas at STP are needed to react completely with 8.0 g of magnesium? (7)

$$2Mg(s) + O_2(g) \xrightarrow{\Delta} 2MgO(s)$$

89 In the Haber process, H_2 and N_2 react to produce ammonia (NH_3). How many grams of N_2 are needed to produce 150 L of ammonia at STP? (6)

$$3H_2(g) + N_2(g) \longrightarrow 2NH_3(g)$$

90 How many liters of H_2 gas at STP can be produced from the reaction of 2.45 g of Al with excess HCl? (6)

$$2Al(s) + 6HCl(aq) \longrightarrow 2AlCl_3(aq) + 3H_2(g)$$

91 Aluminum oxide can be formed from its elements. What volume, in liters, of oxygen at STP is needed to completely react 5.4 g of Al? (6)

$$4Al(s) + 3O_2(g) \xrightarrow{\Delta} 2Al_2O_3(s)$$

92 Glucose, $C_6H_{12}O_6$, is metabolized in living systems to CO_2 and H_2O. How many grams of water can be produced from 12.5 L of O_2 at STP? (6)

$$C_6H_{12}O_6(s) + 6O_2(g) \longrightarrow 6CO_2(g) + 6H_2O(l)$$

93 A sample of gas with a mass of 1.62 g has a volume of 941 mL at a pressure of 748 torr and a temperature of 20 °C. What is the molar mass, g/mole, of the gas? (8)

94 What is the molar mass, g/mole, of a gas if 1.15 g of the gas has a volume of 225 mL at STP? (7, 8)

95 Nitrogen dioxide reacts with water to produce oxygen and ammonia. How many liters of O_2 are produced when 0.42 mole of NO_2 reacts at STP? (7, 8)

$$4NO_2(g) + 6H_2O(g) \xrightarrow{\Delta} 7O_2(g) + 4NH_3(g)$$

96 What is the volume, in liters, of H_2 gas produced at STP from the reaction of 25.0 g of Al? (7)

$$2Al(s) + 3H_2SO_4(aq) \longrightarrow Al_2(SO_4)_3(aq) + 3H_2(g)$$

97 A weather balloon is partially filled with helium to allow for expansion at high altitudes. At STP, a weather balloon is filled with enough helium to give a volume of 25.0 L. How many grams of helium were added to the balloon? (6, 7)

98 At an altitude of 30.0 km, where the temperature is −35 °C, a weather balloon containing 1.75 moles of helium has a volume of 2460 L. What is the pressure, in mmHg, of the helium inside the balloon? (8)

99 A gas mixture contains oxygen and argon at partial pressures of 0.60 atm and 425 mmHg. If nitrogen gas added to the sample increases the total pressure to 1250 torr, what is the partial pressure, in torr, of the nitrogen added? (9)

100 A gas mixture contains helium and oxygen at partial pressures of 255 torr and 0.450 atm. What is the total pressure, in mmHg, of the mixture after it is placed in a container one-half the volume of the original container? (9)

CHALLENGE QUESTIONS

101 A gas sample has a volume of 4250 mL at 15 °C and 745 mmHg. What is the new temperature (°C) after the sample is transferred to a new container with a volume of 2.50 L and a pressure of 1.20 atm? (6)

102 In the fermentation of glucose (wine making), a volume of 780 mL of CO_2 gas was produced at 37 °C and 1.00 atm. What is the volume (L) of the gas when measured at 22 °C and 675 mmHg? (6)

103 When a car is involved in a collision, sodium azide, NaN_3, in the airbags reacts to produce nitrogen gas, which fills the airbags within 0.03 s. How many liters of N_2 are produced at STP if one airbag contains 132 g of NaN_3? (7)

$$2NaN_3(s) \longrightarrow 2Na(s) + 3N_2(g)$$

104 Ammonia reacts with oxygen to produce nitrogen oxide and water. How many liters of nitrogen oxide at STP are produced from the reaction of 50. g of NH_3? (7, 8)

$$4NH_3(g) + 5O_2(g) \longrightarrow 4NO(g) + 6H_2O(g)$$

105 A 1.00-g sample of dry ice (CO_2) is placed in a container that has a volume of 4.60 L and a temperature of 24 °C. What is the pressure of CO_2, in mmHg, inside the container after all the dry ice changes to a gas? (8)

$$CO_2(s) \longrightarrow CO_2(g)$$

106 A 250-mL sample of nitrogen (N_2) has a pressure of 745 mmHg at 30. °C. What is the mass, in grams, of the nitrogen gas? (8)

107 Hydrogen gas can be produced in the laboratory through the reaction of magnesium metal with hydrochloric acid. What is the volume, in liters, of H_2 gas produced at 24 °C and 835 mmHg, from the reaction of 12.0 g of Mg? (8)

$$Mg(s) + 2HCl(aq) \longrightarrow MgCl_2(aq) + H_2(g)$$

108 In the formation of smog, nitrogen and oxygen gas react to form nitrogen dioxide. How many grams of nitrogen dioxide will be produced when 2.0 L of nitrogen at 840 mmHg and 24 °C are completely reacted? (8)

$$N_2(g) + 2O_2(g) \longrightarrow 2NO_2(g)$$

109 Solid aluminum reacts with H_2SO_4 to form H_2 gas and aluminum sulfate. How many grams of Al can react when 415 mL of H_2 gas is produced at 23 °C at a pressure of 734 mmHg? (8)

$$2Al(s) + 3H_2SO_4(aq) \longrightarrow 3H_2(g) + Al_2(SO_4)_3(aq)$$

110 When heated, solid $KClO_3$ forms solid KCl and O_2 gas. When a sample of $KClO_3$ is heated, 226 mL of O_2 gas is produced with a pressure of 719 mmHg and a temperature of 26 °C. How many grams of $KClO_3$ reacted? (8)

$$2KClO_3(s) \xrightarrow{\Delta} 2KCl(s) + 3O_2(g)$$

ANSWERS

Answers to Study Checks

1 The mass, in grams, gives the amount of gas.

2 250 torr

3 73.5 mL

4 569 mL

5 16 °C

6 241 mmHg

7 7.50 L

8 7.0 g of N_2

9 5.41 L of H_2

10 0.327 mole of Cl_2

11 1.04 L

12 104 g/mole

13 18.1 L of H_2

14 755 torr

Answers to Selected Questions and Problems

1 **a.** At a higher temperature, gas particles have greater kinetic energy, which makes them move faster.
b. Because there are great distances between the particles of a gas, they can be pushed closer together and still remain a gas.

3 **a.** temperature
b. volume
c. amount
d. pressure

5 atmospheres (atm), mmHg, torr, lb/in.^{2}, kPa

7 **a.** 1520 torr
b. 1520 mmHg

9 As the scuba diver ascends to the surface, external pressure decreases. If the air in the lungs, which is at a higher pressure, were not exhaled, its volume would expand and severely damage the lungs. The pressure of the gas in the lungs must adjust to changes in the external pressure.

11 a. The pressure is greater in cylinder **A**. According to Boyle's law, a decrease in volume pushes the gas particles closer together, which will cause an increase in the pressure.

b.

Property	Conditions 1	Conditions 2	Know	Predict
Pressure (*P*)	650 mmHg	1.2 atm (910 mmHg)	*P* increases	
Volume (*V*)	220 mL	160 mL		*V* decreases

13 a. increases **b.** decreases **c.** increases

15 a. 328 mmHg **b.** 2620 mmHg **c.** 4370 mmHg

17 a. 25 L **b.** 12.5 L **c.** 100. L

19 25 L

21 a. inspiration **b.** expiration **c.** inspiration

23 a. C **b.** A **c.** B

25 a. 303 °C **b.** −129 °C
c. 591 °C **d.** 136 °C

27 a. 2400 mL **b.** 4900 mL
c. 1800 mL **d.** 1700 mL

29 An increase in temperature increases the pressure inside the can. When the pressure exceeds the pressure limit of the can, it explodes.

31 a. −23 °C **b.** 168 °C

33 a. 770 torr **b.** 1.51 atm

35 a. boiling point **b.** vapor pressure

37 a. On top of a mountain, water boils below 100 °C because the atmospheric (external) pressure is less than 1 atm.
b. Because the pressure inside a pressure cooker is greater than 1 atm, water boils above 100 °C. At a higher temperature, food cooks faster.

39 a. 4.26 atm **b.** 3.07 atm **c.** 0.606 atm

41 −33 °C

43 The volume increases because the number of gas particles is increased.

45 a. 4.00 L **b.** 14.6 L **c.** 26.7 L

47 a. 2.00 moles of O_2
b. 0.179 mole of CO_2
c. 4.48 L
d. 55 400 mL

49 7.60 L of H_2

51 4.93 atm

53 29.4 g of O_2

55 565 K (292 °C)

57 a. 42 g/mole **b.** 39.8 g/mole **c.** 33 g/mole

59 178 L of O_2

61 5.25 L of O_2

63 758 mmHg

65 765 torr

67 0.559 atm

69 a. The partial pressure of oxygen will be lower than normal.
b. Breathing a higher concentration of oxygen will help to increase the supply of oxygen in the lungs and blood and raise the partial pressure of oxygen in the blood.

71 a. 2 **b.** 1

73 a. A **b.** C
c. A **d.** B
e. C

75 a. The volume of the chest and lungs is decreased.
b. The decrease in volume increases the pressure, which can dislodge the food in the trachea.

77 2.5 kg of H_2

79 12 atm

81 −223 °C

83 1.8 moles of CO_2

85 4.40 g

87 12.5 L of CO_2

89 94 g of N_2

91 3.4 L of O_2

93 42.1 g/mole

95 16 L of O_2

97 4.46 g of helium

99 370 torr

101 −66 °C

103 68.2 L of N_2

105 91.5 mmHg

107 11.0 L of H_2

109 0.297 g of Al

Solutions

From Chapter 8 of *General, Organic, and Biological Chemistry: Structures of Life*, Fourth Edition. Karen C. Timberlake.

Solutions

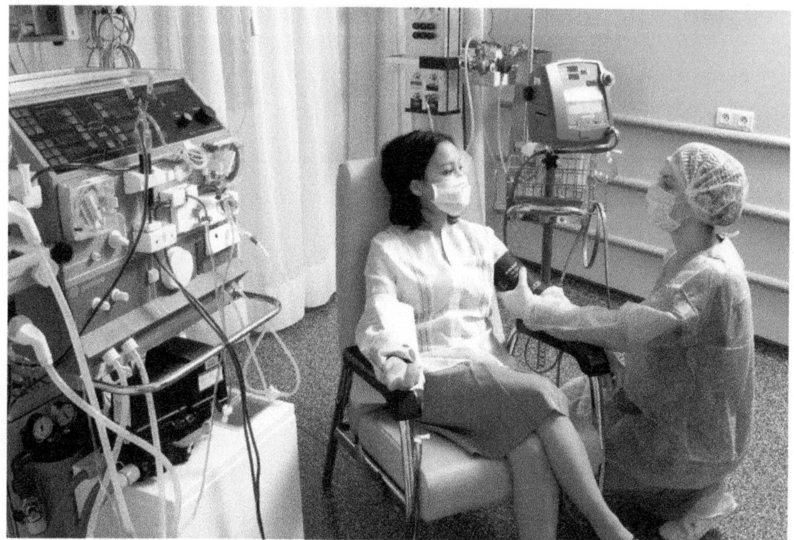

AJPhoto/Photo Researchers, Inc.

LOOKING AHEAD

Visit **www.masteringchemistry.com** for self-study materials and instructor-assigned homework.

When Michelle's kidneys stopped functioning, she was placed on dialysis three times a week. As she enters the dialysis unit, her dialysis nurse, Amanda, asks Michelle how she is feeling. Michelle indicates that she feels tired today and has considerable swelling around her ankles.

The dialysis nurse informs Michelle that her side effects are due to her body's inability to regulate the amount of water in her cells. She explains that the amount of water is regulated by the concentration of electrolytes in her body fluids and the rate at which waste products are removed from her body. Amanda explains that although water is essential for the many chemical reactions that occur in the body, the amount of water can become too high or too low, due to various diseases and conditions.

Because Michelle's kidneys no longer perform dialysis, she cannot regulate the amount of electrolytes or waste products in her body fluids. As a result, she has an electrolyte imbalance and a build-up of waste products, so her body is retaining water. Amanda then explains that the dialysis machine does the work of her kidneys to reduce the high levels of electrolytes and waste products.

Career: Dialysis Nurse

A dialysis nurse specializes in assisting patients with kidney disease undergoing dialysis. This requires monitoring the patient before, during, and after dialysis for any complications such as a drop in blood pressure or cramping. The dialysis nurse connects the patient to the dialysis unit via a dialysis catheter that is inserted into the neck or chest, which must be kept clean to prevent infection. A dialysis nurse must have considerable knowledge about how the dialysis machine functions to ensure that it is operating correctly at all times.

Solutions are everywhere around us. Most consist of one substance dissolved in another. The air we breathe is a solution of primarily oxygen and nitrogen gases. Carbon dioxide gas dissolved in water makes carbonated drinks. When we make solutions of coffee or tea, we use hot water to dissolve substances from coffee beans or tea leaves. The ocean is also a solution, consisting of many salts, such as sodium chloride, dissolved in water. In a hospital, antiseptic tincture of iodine is a solution of iodine dissolved in ethanol.

Our body fluids contain water and dissolved substances, such as glucose and urea, and ions called electrolytes, such as K^+, Na^+, Cl^-, Mg^{2+}, HCO_3^-, and HPO_4^{2-}. Proper amounts of each of these dissolved substances and water must be maintained in the body fluids. Small changes in electrolyte levels can seriously disrupt cellular processes, endangering our health. Therefore, the measurement of their concentrations is a valuable diagnostic tool.

Through the processes of osmosis and dialysis, water, essential nutrients, and waste products enter and leave the cells of the body. In osmosis, water flows in and out of the cells of the body. In dialysis, small particles in solution as well as water diffuse through semipermeable membranes. The kidneys utilize osmosis and dialysis to regulate the amount of water and electrolytes that are excreted.

1 Solutions

LEARNING GOAL

Identify the solute and solvent in a solution; describe the formation of a solution.

A **solution** is a homogeneous mixture in which one substance called the **solute** is uniformly dispersed in another substance called the **solvent** (see Figure 1). When a small amount of salt is dissolved in water, the salt-water solution tastes slightly salty. When more salt is dissolved, the salt-water solution tastes very salty. Usually, the solute (in this case, salt) is the substance present in the smaller amount, whereas the solvent (in this case, water) is present in the larger amount. For example, when a solution is composed of 5.0 g of salt and 50. g of water, salt is the solute, and water is the solvent.

A solution consists of at least one solute dispersed in a solvent.

CONCEPT CHECK 1 **Identifying a Solute and a Solvent**

Identify the solute and the solvent in each of the following solutions:

a. 15 g of sugar dissolved in 500 g of water
b. 75 mL of water mixed with 25 mL of isopropyl alcohol
c. a tincture of iodine prepared with 0.10 g of I_2 and 10.0 g of ethanol

ANSWER

a. Sugar, the smaller quantity, is the solute; water is the solvent.
b. Isopropyl alcohol, which has the smaller volume, is the solute; water is the solvent.
c. Iodine, the smaller quantity, is the solute; ethanol is the solvent.

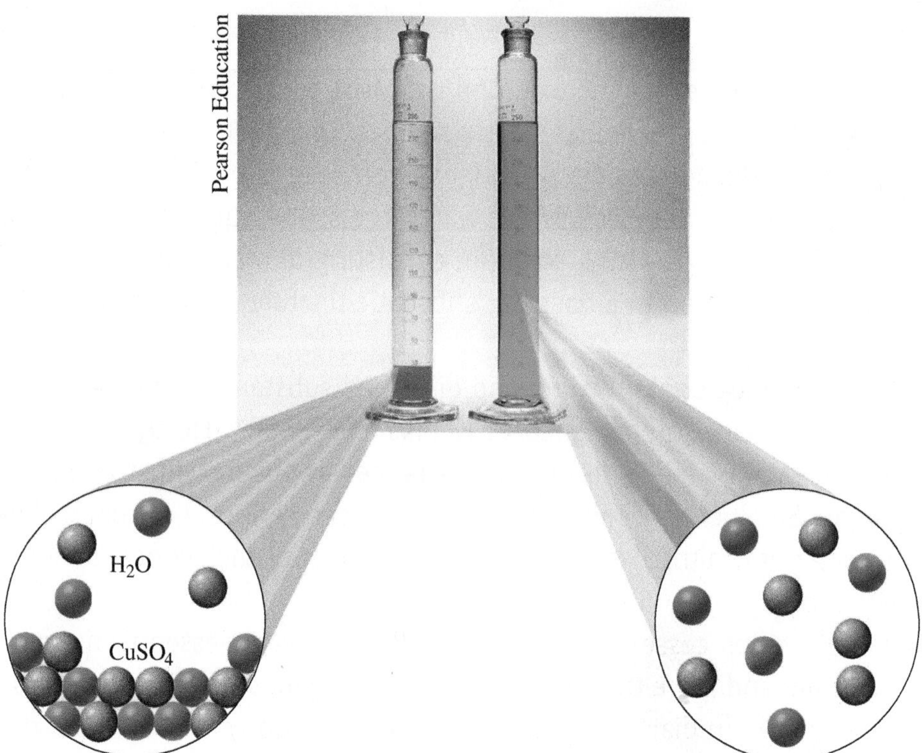

FIGURE 1 A solution of copper(II) sulfate ($CuSO_4$) forms as particles of solute dissolve, move away from the crystals, and become evenly dispersed among the solvent (water) molecules.

Q What does the uniform blue color in the graduated cylinder on the right indicate about the $CuSO_4$ solution?

Types of Solutes and Solvents

Solutes and solvents may be solids, liquids, or gases. The solution that forms has the same physical state as the solvent. When sugar crystals are dissolved in water, the resulting sugar solution is liquid. Sugar is the solute, and water is the solvent. Soda water and soft drinks are prepared by dissolving carbon dioxide gas in water. The carbon dioxide gas is the solute, and water is the solvent. Table 1 lists some solutes and solvents and their solutions.

TABLE 1 Some Examples of Solutions

Type	Example	Primary Solute	Solvent
Gas Solutions			
Gas in a gas	Air	Oxygen (gas)	Nitrogen (gas)
Liquid Solutions			
Gas in a liquid	Soda water	Carbon dioxide (gas)	Water (liquid)
	Household ammonia	Ammonia (gas)	Water (liquid)
Liquid in a liquid	Vinegar	Acetic acid (liquid)	Water (liquid)
Solid in a liquid	Seawater	Sodium chloride (solid)	Water (liquid)
	Tincture of iodine	Iodine (solid)	Ethanol (liquid)
Solid Solutions			
Solid in a solid	Brass	Zinc (solid)	Copper (solid)
	Steel	Carbon (solid)	Iron (solid)

SELF-STUDY ACTIVITY
Hydrogen Bonding

Water as a Solvent

Water is one of the most common solvents in nature. In the H_2O molecule, an oxygen atom shares electrons with two hydrogen atoms. Because oxygen is much more electronegative than hydrogen, the O—H bonds are polar. In each polar bond, the oxygen atom has a partial negative (δ^-) charge, and the hydrogen atom has a partial positive (δ^+) charge. Because the water molecule has a bent shape, water is a *polar solvent*.

We learned that *hydrogen bonds* are interactions between molecules where partially positive hydrogen atoms are attracted to the partially negative atoms of O, N, or F. In the diagram to the right, hydrogen bonds are shown as dotted lines. Although hydrogen bonds are much weaker than covalent or ionic bonds, there are many of them linking water molecules together. Hydrogen bonds also are important in the properties of biological compounds such as proteins, carbohydrates, and DNA.

Pearson Education

Partial negative charge

Partial positive charge

δ^-

δ^+

Hydrogen bonds

In water, hydrogen bonds form between a partially positive hydrogen atom in one water molecule and a partially negative oxygen atom in another.

Chemistry Link to Health

WATER IN THE BODY

The average adult body contains about 60% water by mass, and the average infant about 75%. About 60% of the body's water is contained within the cells as intracellular fluids; the other 40% makes up extracellular fluids, which include the interstitial fluid in tissue and the plasma in the blood. These external fluids carry nutrients and waste materials between the cells and the circulatory system.

Every day you lose between 1500 and 3000 mL of water from the kidneys as urine, from the skin as perspiration, from the lungs as you exhale, and from the gastrointestinal tract. Serious dehydration can occur in an adult if there is a 10% loss in total body fluid. A 20% loss of fluid can be fatal. An infant suffers severe dehydration with a 5–10% loss in body fluid.

24 Hours

Water gain	
Liquid	1000 mL
Food	1200 mL
Metabolism	300 mL
Total	2500 mL

Water loss	
Urine	1500 mL
Perspiration	300 mL
Breath	600 mL
Feces	100 mL
Total	2500 mL

Water loss is continually replaced by the liquids and foods in the diet, and from metabolic processes that produce water in the cells of the body. Table 2 lists the percentage by mass of water contained in some foods.

Thinkstock Images/Getty Images

The water lost from the body is replaced by the intake of fluids.

TABLE 2 Percentage of Water in Some Foods

Food	Water (% by mass)	Food	Water (% by mass)
Vegetables		**Meats/Fish**	
Carrot	88	Chicken, cooked	71
Celery	94	Hamburger, broiled	60
Cucumber	96	Salmon	71
Tomato	94		
Fruits		**Milk Products**	
Apple	85	Cottage cheese	78
Cantaloupe	91	Milk, whole	87
Orange	86	Yogurt	88
Strawberry	90		
Watermelon	93		

Formation of Solutions

The interactions between solute and solvent will determine whether a solution will form. Initially, energy is needed to separate the particles in the solute and to move the solvent particles apart. Then, energy is released as solute particles move between the solvent particles to form a solution. However, attractive forces between the solute and the solvent particles must be strong enough to provide the energy for the initial separation. These attractive forces only occur when the solute and the solvent have similar polarities. If there is no attraction between a solute and a solvent, there is not sufficient energy to form a solution (see Table 3).

TABLE 3 Possible Combinations of Solutes and Solvents

Solutions Will Form		Solutions Will Not Form	
Solute	**Solvent**	**Solute**	**Solvent**
Polar	Polar	Polar	Nonpolar
Nonpolar	Nonpolar	Nonpolar	Polar

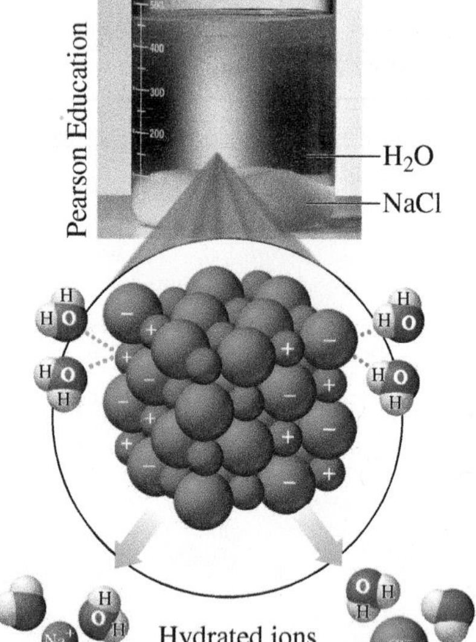

FIGURE 2 Ions on the surface of a crystal of NaCl dissolve in water as they are attracted to the polar water molecules that pull the ions into solution and surround them.

Q What helps keep the Na^+ and Cl^- ions in solution?

Solutions with Ionic and Polar Solutes

In ionic solutes such as sodium chloride, NaCl, there are strong solute–solute attractions between positively charged Na^+ ions and negatively charged Cl^- ions. When NaCl crystals are placed in water, the process of dissolution begins as the partially negatively charged oxygen atoms in water molecules attract positive Na^+ ions, and the partially positive hydrogen atoms in other water molecules attract negative Cl^- ions (see Figure 2). This process called **hydration** diminishes the attractions between the Na^+ and Cl^- ions and keeps them in solution. The strong solute–solvent attractions between the Na^+ and Cl^- ions and the polar water molecules provide the energy to form the solution.

In the equation for the formation of the NaCl solution, the solid and aqueous NaCl are shown with the formula H_2O over the arrow, which indicates that water is needed for the dissociation process but is not a reactant.

$$\text{NaCl}(s) \xrightarrow{\text{H}_2\text{O}} \text{Na}^+(aq) + \text{Cl}^-(aq)$$

In another example, we find that a polar covalent compound such as methanol, $CH_3—OH$, is soluble in water because methanol has a polar —OH group that forms hydrogen bonds with water.

Molecules of polar covalent compound methanol, $CH_3—OH$, form hydrogen bonds with polar water molecules to form a methanol–water solution.

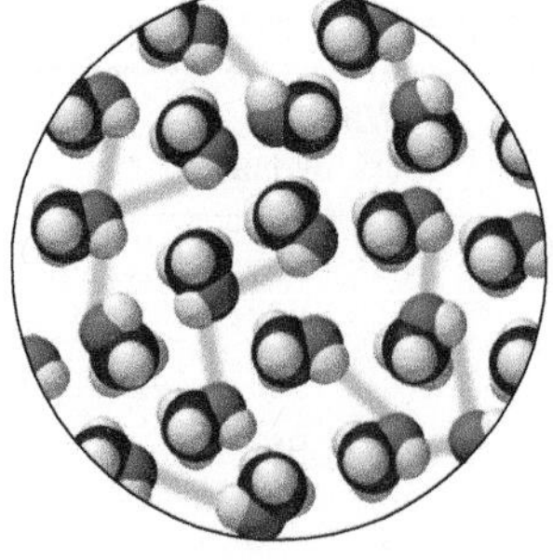

Methanol (CH_3 — OH) solute

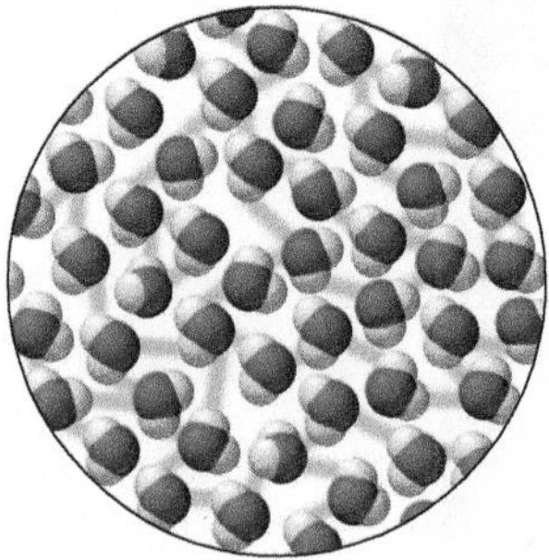

Water solvent

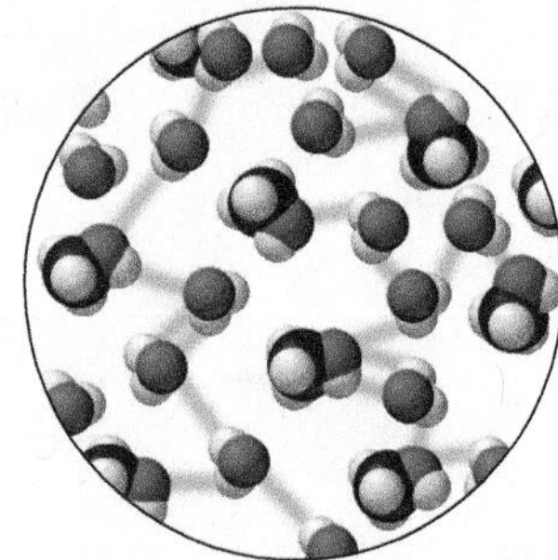

Methanol–water solution with hydrogen bonding

Solutions with Nonpolar Solutes

Compounds containing nonpolar molecules such as iodine (I_2), oil, or grease do not dissolve in water, because there is little or no interaction between the particles of a nonpolar solute and a polar solvent. Nonpolar solutes require nonpolar solvents for a solution to form. The expression "*like dissolves like*" is a way of saying that the polarities of a solute and a solvent must be similar to form a solution. Figure 3 illustrates the formation of some polar and nonpolar solutions.

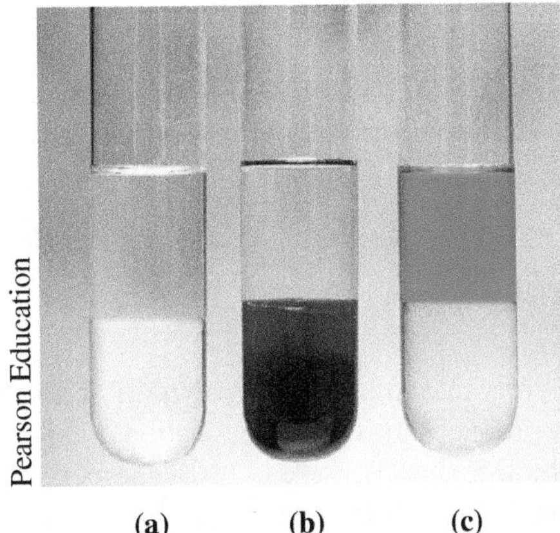

Pearson Education

(a) (b) (c)

FIGURE 3 Like dissolves like. In each test tube, the lower layer is CH_2Cl_2 (more dense), and the upper layer is water (less dense). **(a)** CH_2Cl_2 is nonpolar and water is polar; the two layers do not mix. **(b)** The nonpolar solute I_2 (purple) is soluble in the nonpolar CH_2Cl_2 layer. **(c)** The ionic solute $Ni(NO_3)_2$ (green) is soluble in the polar water layer.

Q In which layer would polar molecules of sugar be soluble?

CONCEPT CHECK 2 Polar and Nonpolar Solutes

Indicate whether each of the following substances will form solutions with water. Explain.

a. KCl
b. octane, C_8H_{18}, a compound in gasoline
c. ethanol, C_2H_5OH, in mouthwash

ANSWER

a. Yes. KCl is an ionic compound. The solute–solvent attractions between the ions K^+ and Cl^- and polar water molecules provide the energy to break solute–solute and solvent–solvent bonds. Thus, a KCl solution will form.

b. No. Octane, C_8H_{18}, is a nonpolar compound of carbon and hydrogen, which means it does not form a solution with the polar water molecules. There are no attractions between a nonpolar solute and a polar solvent. Thus, no solution forms.

c. C_2H_5OH is a polar solute. Because attractions between a polar solute and the polar solvent water release energy to break solute–solute and solvent–solvent bonds, a C_2H_5OH solution will form.

LIKE DISSOLVES LIKE

Mix together small amounts of the following substances:

a. oil and water
b. water and vinegar
c. salt and water
d. sugar and water
e. salt and oil

QUESTIONS

1. Which of the mixtures formed a solution? Which did not?
2. Why do some mixtures form solutions, but others do not?

QUESTIONS AND PROBLEMS

1 Solutions

LEARNING GOAL: *Identify the solute and solvent in a solution; describe the formation of a solution.*

1 Identify the solute and the solvent in each solution composed of the following:
a. 10.0 g of NaCl and 100.0 g of H_2O
b. 50.0 mL of ethanol, C_2H_5OH, and 10.0 mL of H_2O
c. 0.20 L of O_2 and 0.80 L of N_2 at STP

2 Identify the solute and the solvent in each solution composed of the following:
a. 10 mL of acetic acid and 200 mL of water
b. 100.0 g of water and 5.0 g of sugar
c. 1.0 mL of Br_2 and 50.0 mL of methylene chloride

3 Describe the formation of an aqueous KI solution when KI dissolves in water.

4 Describe the formation of an aqueous LiBr solution when LiBr dissolves in water.

5 Water is a polar solvent and carbon tetrachloride, CCl_4, is a nonpolar solvent. In which solvent is each of the following more likely to be soluble?
a. $NaNO_3$, ionic
b. I_2, nonpolar
c. sucrose (table sugar), polar
d. gasoline, nonpolar

6 Water is a polar solvent; hexane is a nonpolar solvent. In which solvent is each of the following more likely to be soluble?
a. vegetable oil, nonpolar
b. benzene, nonpolar
c. LiCl, ionic
d. Na_2SO_4, ionic

LEARNING GOAL

Identify solutes as electrolytes or nonelectrolytes.

2 Electrolytes and Nonelectrolytes

Solutes can be classified by their ability to conduct an electrical current. When **electrolytes** dissolve in water, they separate into ions that conduct electricity. When **nonelectrolytes** dissolve in water, they dissolve as molecules, not as ions. The solutions of nonelectrolytes do not conduct electricity.

To test solutions for the presence of ions, we can use an apparatus that consists of a battery and a pair of electrodes connected by wires to a light bulb. The light bulb glows when electricity flows, which can only happen when the electrolytes provide ions that move between the electrodes to complete the circuit.

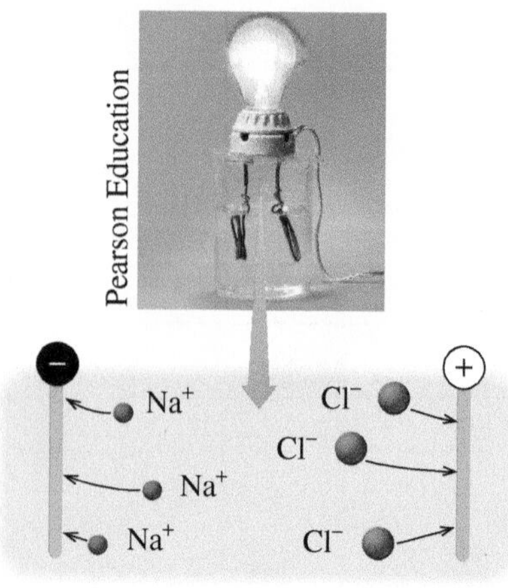

Strong electrolyte

A strong electrolyte completely dissociates into ions in an aqueous solution.

Electrolytes

Electrolytes can be further classified as *strong electrolytes* and *weak electrolytes.* For all electrolytes, some or all of the solute that dissolves produces ions, a process called *dissociation.* For a **strong electrolyte**, such as sodium chloride (NaCl), there is 100% dissociation of the solute into ions. When the electrodes from the light bulb apparatus are placed in a NaCl solution, the light bulb is very bright.

In an equation for dissociation, the charges must balance. For example, magnesium nitrate dissociates to give one magnesium ion for every two nitrate ions. Only the ionic bonds between Mg^{2+} and NO_3^- are broken; the covalent bonds within the polyatomic ion are retained. The dissociation for $Mg(NO_3)_2$ is written as follows:

$$Mg(NO_3)_2(s) \xrightarrow{H_2O} Mg^{2+}(aq) + 2NO_3^-(aq)$$

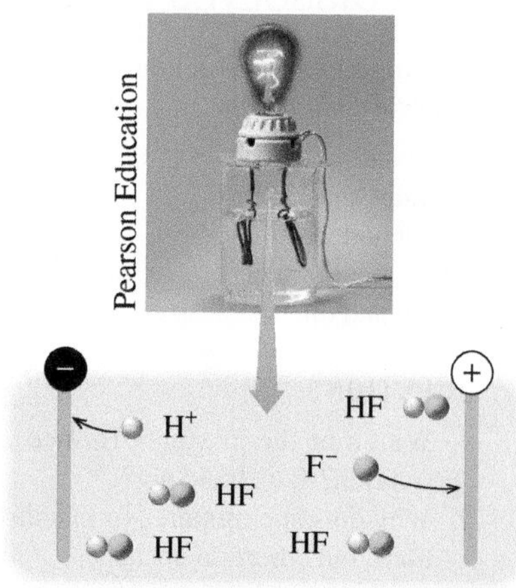

Weak electrolyte

A weak electrolyte forms mostly molecules and a few ions in an aqueous solution.

Weak Electrolytes

A **weak electrolyte** is a compound that dissolves in water mostly as molecules. Only a few of the dissolved solute molecules separate, producing a small number of ions in solution. Thus, solutions of weak electrolytes do not conduct electrical current as well as solutions of strong electrolytes. For example, an aqueous solution of the weak electrolyte HF contains mostly HF molecules and only a few H^+ and F^- ions. When the electrodes of the light bulb apparatus are placed in a solution of a weak electrolyte, the glow of the light bulb is very dim. As more H^+ and F^- ions form, some recombine to give HF molecules. These forward and reverse reactions of molecules to ions and back again are indicated by two arrows between reactant and products that point in opposite directions.

$$HF(aq) \underset{\text{Recombination}}{\overset{\text{Dissociation}}{\rightleftarrows}} H^+(aq) + F^-(aq)$$

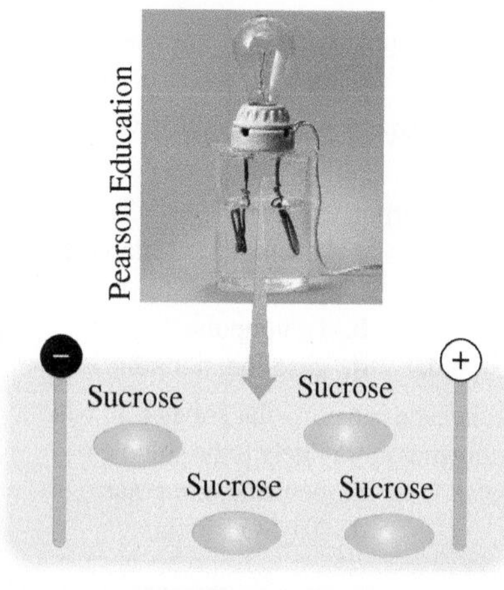

Nonelectrolyte

A nonelectrolyte dissolves as molecules in an aqueous solution.

Nonelectrolytes

A nonelectrolyte such as sucrose (sugar) dissolves in water as molecules, which do not dissociate into ions. When electrodes of the light bulb apparatus are placed in a solution of a nonelectrolyte, the light bulb does not glow, because the solution does not contain ions and cannot conduct electricity.

$$\underset{\text{Sucrose}}{C_{12}H_{22}O_{11}(s)} \xrightarrow{H_2O} \underset{\text{Solution of sucrose molecules}}{C_{12}H_{22}O_{11}(aq)}$$

Table 4 summarizes the classification of solutes in aqueous solutions.

TABLE 4 Classification of Solutes in Aqueous Solutions

Type of Solute	Dissociates	Types of Particles in Solution	Conducts Electricity?	Examples
Strong electrolyte	Completely	Ions only	Yes	Ionic compounds such as $NaCl$, KBr, $MgCl_2$, $NaNO_3$, $NaOH$, KOH, HCl, HBr, HI, HNO_3, $HClO_4$, H_2SO_4
Weak electrolyte	Partially	Mostly molecules and a few ions	Weakly	HF, H_2O, NH_3, $HC_2H_3O_2$ (acetic acid)
Nonelectrolyte	None	Molecules only	No	Carbon compounds such as CH_3OH (methanol), C_2H_5OH (ethanol), $C_{12}H_{22}O_{11}$ (sucrose), CH_4N_2O (urea)

CONCEPT CHECK 3 Solutions of Electrolytes and Nonelectrolytes

Indicate whether solutions of each of the following contain only ions, only molecules, or mostly molecules and a few ions:

a. Na_2SO_4, a strong electrolyte **b.** CH_3OH, a nonelectrolyte
c. hypochlorous acid, $HClO$, a weak electrolyte

ANSWER

a. An aqueous solution of Na_2SO_4 contains only the ions Na^+ and SO_4^{2-}.
b. A nonelectrolyte such as CH_3OH produces only molecules when it dissolves in water.
c. A solution of $HClO$ contains mostly $HClO$ molecules and a few ions of H^+ and ClO^-.

TUTORIAL
Electrolytes and Ionization

Equivalents

Body fluids contain a mixture of several electrolytes, such as Na^+, Cl^-, K^+, and Ca^{2+}. We measure each individual ion in terms of an **equivalent (Eq)**, which is the amount of that ion equal to 1 mole of positive or negative electrical charge. For example, 1 mole of Na^+ ions and 1 mole of Cl^- ions are each 1 equivalent or 1000 milliequivalents (mEq) because they each contain 1 mole of charge. For an ion with a charge of 2+ or 2−, there are 2 equivalents for each mole. Some examples of ions and equivalents are shown in Table 5.

TABLE 5 Equivalents of Electrolytes

Ion	Electrical Charge	Number of Equivalents in 1 Mole
Na^+	1+	1 Eq
Ca^{2+}	2+	2 Eq
Fe^{3+}	3+	3 Eq
Cl^-	1−	1 Eq
SO_4^{2-}	2−	2 Eq

In any solution, the charge of the positive ions is always balanced by the charge of the negative ions. For example, a solution containing 25 mEq/L of Na^+ and 4 mEq/L of K^+ has a total positive charge of 29 mEq/L. If Cl^- is the only anion in the solution, its concentration must be 29 mEq/L.

SAMPLE PROBLEM 1 **Electrolyte Concentration**

The laboratory tests for a patient indicate a blood calcium (Ca^{2+}) level of 8.8 mEq/L.

a. How many moles of calcium ion are in 0.50 L of blood?
b. If chloride ion is the only other ion present, what is its concentration in mEq/L?

SOLUTION

a. Using the volume and the electrolyte concentration (in mEq/L), we can find the number of equivalents in 0.50 L of blood.

$$0.50\ \cancel{L} \times \frac{8.8\ \cancel{mEq\ Ca^{2+}}}{1\ \cancel{L}} \times \frac{1\ Eq\ Ca^{2+}}{1000\ \cancel{mEq\ Ca^{2+}}} = 0.0044\ Eq\ of\ Ca^{2+}$$

We can then convert equivalents to moles (for Ca^{2+}, there are 2 Eq/mole).

$$0.0044\ \cancel{Eq\ Ca^{2+}} \times \frac{1\ mole\ Ca^{2+}}{2\ \cancel{Eq\ Ca^{2+}}} = 0.0022\ mole\ of\ Ca^{2+}$$

b. If the concentration of Ca^{2+} is 8.8 mEq/L, then the concentration of Cl^- must be 8.8 mEq/L to balance the charge.

STUDY CHECK 1

A Ringer's solution for intravenous fluid replacement contains 155 mEq of Cl^- per liter of solution. If a patient receives 1250 mL of Ringer's solution, how many moles of chloride ion were given?

QUESTIONS AND PROBLEMS

2 Electrolytes and Nonelectrolytes

LEARNING GOAL: *Identify solutes as electrolytes or nonelectrolytes.*

7 KF is a strong electrolyte, and HF is a weak electrolyte. How is the solution of KF different from that of HF?

8 NaOH is a strong electrolyte, and CH_3OH is a nonelectrolyte. How is the solution of NaOH different from that of CH_3OH?

9 Write a balanced equation for the dissociation of each of the following strong electrolytes in water:
a. KCl **b.** $CaCl_2$
c. K_3PO_4 **d.** $Fe(NO_3)_3$

10 Write a balanced equation for the dissociation of each of the following strong electrolytes in water:
a. LiBr **b.** $NaNO_3$
c. $CuCl_2$ **d.** K_2CO_3

11 Indicate whether aqueous solutions of each of the following contain only ions, only molecules, or mostly molecules and a few ions:
a. acetic acid ($HC_2H_3O_2$), a weak electrolyte
b. NaBr, a strong electrolyte
c. fructose ($C_6H_{12}O_6$), a nonelectrolyte

12 Indicate whether aqueous solutions of each of the following contain only ions, only molecules, or mostly molecules and a few ions:
a. NH_4Cl, a strong electrolyte
b. ethanol (C_2H_5OH), a nonelectrolyte
c. hydrocyanic acid (HCN), a weak electrolyte

13 Classify each solute represented in the following equations as a strong, weak, or nonelectrolyte:

a. $K_2SO_4(s) \xrightarrow{H_2O} 2K^+(aq) + SO_4^{2-}(aq)$

b. $NH_4OH(aq) \underset{}{\overset{H_2O}{\rightleftarrows}} NH_4^+(aq) + OH^-(aq)$

c. $C_6H_{12}O_6(s) \xrightarrow{H_2O} C_6H_{12}O_6(aq)$

14 Classify each solute represented in the following equations as a strong, weak, or nonelectrolyte:

a. $CH_3OH(l) \xrightarrow{H_2O} CH_3OH(aq)$

b. $MgCl_2(s) \xrightarrow{H_2O} Mg^{2+}(aq) + 2Cl^-(aq)$

c. $HClO(aq) \overset{H_2O}{\rightleftarrows} H^+(aq) + ClO^-(aq)$

15 Indicate the number of equivalents in each of the following:
a. 1 mole of K^+ **b.** 2 moles of OH^-
c. 1 mole of Ca^{2+} **d.** 3 moles of CO_3^{2-}

16 Indicate the number of equivalents in each of the following:
a. 1 mole of Mg^{2+} **b.** 0.5 mole of H^+
c. 4 moles of Cl^- **d.** 2 moles of Fe^{3+}

17 A physiological saline solution contains 154 mEq/L, each of Na^+ and Cl^-. How many moles each of Na^+ and Cl^- are in 1.00 L of the saline solution?

18 A solution to replace potassium loss contains 40. mEq/L, each of K^+ and Cl^-. How many moles each of K^+ and Cl^- are in 1.5 L of the solution?

19 A solution contains 40. mEq/L of Cl^- and 15 mEq/L of HPO_4^{2-}. If Na^+ is the only cation in the solution, what is the Na^+ concentration, in milliequivalents per liter?

20 A sample of Ringer's solution contains the following concentrations (mEq/L) of cations: Na^+ 147, K^+ 4, and Ca^{2+} 4. If Cl^- is the only anion in the solution, what is the Cl^- concentration, in milliequivalents per liter?

Chemistry Link to Health

ELECTROLYTES IN BODY FLUIDS

Electrolytes in the body play an important role in maintaining the proper function of the cells and organs in the body. Typically, the electrolytes sodium, potassium, chloride, and bicarbonate are measured in a blood test. Sodium ions regulate the water content in the body and are important in carrying electrical impulses through the nervous system. Potassium ions are also involved in the transmission of electrical impulses and play a role in the maintenance of a regular heartbeat. Chloride ions balance the charges of the positive ions and also control the balance of fluids in the body. Bicarbonate is important in maintaining the proper pH of the blood. Sometimes when vomiting, diarrhea, or sweating is excessive, the concentrations of certain electrolytes may decrease. Then fluids such as Pedialyte may be given to return electrolyte levels to normal.

The concentrations of electrolytes present in body fluids and in intravenous fluids given to a patient are often expressed in milliequivalents per liter (mEq/L) of solution: 1 Eq = 1000 mEq. For example, one liter of Pedialyte contains the following electrolytes: Na^+ 45 mEq, K^+ 20 mEq, Cl^- 35 mEq, and $citrate^{3-}$ 30 mEq.

Table 6 gives the concentrations of some typical electrolytes in blood plasma. There is a charge balance because the total number of positive charges is equal to the total number of negative charges. The use of a specific intravenous solution depends on the nutritional, electrolyte, and fluid needs of the individual patient. Examples of various types of solutions are given in Table 7.

TABLE 6 Some Typical Concentrations of Electrolytes in Blood Plasma

Electrolyte	Concentration (mEq/L)
Cations	
Na^+	138
K^+	5
Mg^{2+}	3
Ca^{2+}	4
Total	150
Anions	
Cl^-	110
HCO_3^-	30
HPO_4^{2-}	4
Proteins	6
Total	150

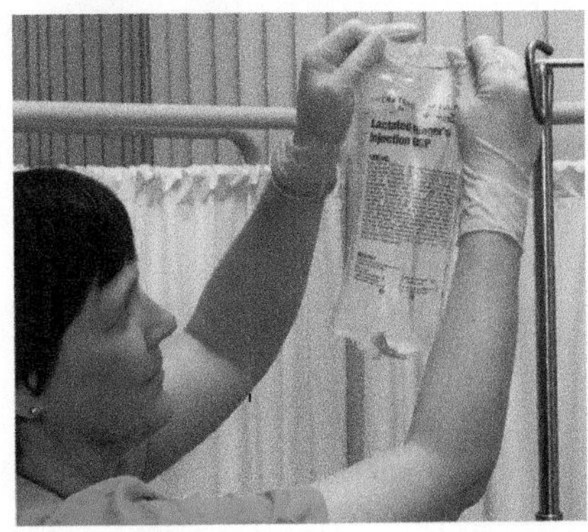

Pearson Education

An intravenous solution is used to replace electrolytes in the body.

TABLE 7 Electrolyte Concentrations in Intravenous Replacement Solutions

Solution	Electrolytes (mEq/L)	Use
Sodium chloride (0.9%)	Na^+ 154, Cl^- 154	Replacement of fluid loss
Potassium chloride with 5% dextrose	K^+ 40, Cl^- 40	Treatment of malnutrition (low potassium levels)
Ringer's solution	Na^+ 147, K^+ 4, Ca^{2+} 4, Cl^- 155	Replacement of fluids and electrolytes lost through dehydration
Maintenance solution with 5% dextrose	Na^+ 40, K^+ 35, Cl^- 40, $lactate^-$ 20, HPO_4^{2-} 15	Maintenance of fluid and electrolyte levels
Replacement solution (extracellular)	Na^+ 140, K^+ 10, Ca^{2+} 5, Mg^{2+} 3, Cl^- 103, $acetate^-$ 47, $citrate^{3-}$ 8	Replacement of electrolytes in extracellular fluids

3 Solubility

LEARNING GOAL

Define solubility. Distinguish between an unsaturated and a saturated solution; identify a salt as soluble or insoluble.

The term *solubility* is used to describe the amount of a solute that can dissolve in a given amount of solvent. Many factors, such as the type of solute, the type of solvent, and the temperature, affect the solubility of a solute. **Solubility**, usually expressed in grams of solute in 100 grams of solvent, is the maximum amount of solute that can be dissolved at a certain temperature. If a solute readily dissolves when added to the solvent, the solution does not contain the maximum amount of solute. We call this solution an **unsaturated solution**.

SELF-STUDY ACTIVITY
Solubility

TUTORIAL
Introduction to Solubility and Solution Formation

A solution that contains all the solute that can dissolve is a **saturated solution**. When a solution is saturated, the rate at which solute dissolves becomes equal to the rate at which solid forms, a process known as recrystallization. Then there is no further change in the amount of dissolved solute in solution.

$$\text{Solute} + \text{solvent} \underset{\text{Solute recrystallizes}}{\overset{\text{Solute dissolves}}{\rightleftarrows}} \text{Saturated solution}$$

We can prepare a saturated solution by adding an amount of solute greater than that needed to reach maximum solubility (saturation). Stirring the solution will dissolve the maximum amount of solute and leave the excess on the bottom of the container. Once we have a saturated solution, the addition of more solute will increase only the amount of undissolved solute.

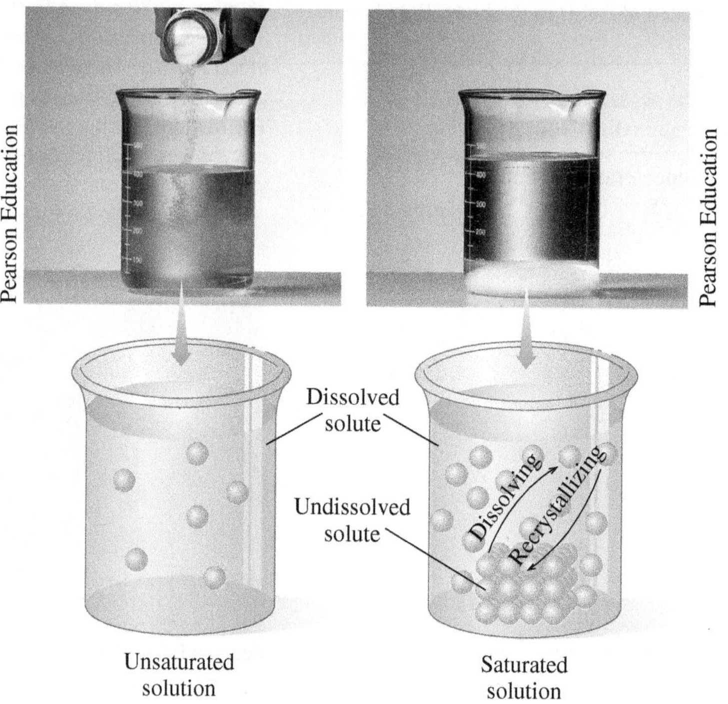

More solute can dissolve in an unsaturated solution, but not in a saturated solution.

SAMPLE PROBLEM 2 Saturated Solutions

At 20 °C, the solubility of KCl is 34 g/100 g of water. In the laboratory, a student mixes 75 g of KCl with 200. g of water at a temperature of 20 °C.

a. How much of the KCl can dissolve?
b. Is the solution saturated or unsaturated?
c. What is the mass, in grams, of any solid KCl on the bottom of the container?

SOLUTION

a. KCl has a solubility of 34 g of KCl in 100 g of water. Using its solubility as a conversion factor, we can calculate the maximum amount of KCl that can dissolve in 200. g of water as follows:

$$200.\ \text{g}\ \cancel{\text{H}_2\text{O}} \times \frac{34\ \text{g KCl}}{100\ \text{g}\ \cancel{\text{H}_2\text{O}}} = 68\ \text{g of KCl}$$

b. Because 75 g of KCl exceeds the maximum amount (68 g) that can dissolve in 200. g of water, the KCl solution is saturated.

c. If we add 75 g of KCl to 200. g of water and only 68 g of KCl can dissolve, there is 7 g (75 g − 68 g) of solid (undissolved) KCl on the bottom of the container.

STUDY CHECK 2

At 40 °C, the solubility of KNO_3 is 65 g/100 g of water. How many grams of KNO_3 will dissolve in 120 g of water at 40 °C?

Chemistry Link to Health

GOUT AND KIDNEY STONES: A PROBLEM OF SATURATION IN BODY FLUIDS

The conditions of gout and kidney stones involve compounds in the body that exceed their solubility levels and form solid products. Gout affects adults, primarily men, over the age of 40. Attacks of gout may occur when the concentration of uric acid in blood plasma exceeds its solubility, which is 7 mg/100 mL of plasma at 37 °C. Insoluble deposits of needle-like crystals of uric acid can form in the cartilage, tendons, and soft tissues, where they cause painful gout attacks. They may also form in the tissues of the kidneys, where they can cause renal damage. High levels of uric acid in the body can be caused by an increase in uric acid production, failure of the kidneys to remove uric acid, or by a diet with an overabundance of foods containing purines, which are metabolized to uric acid in the body. Foods in the diet that contribute to high levels of uric acid include certain meats, sardines, mushrooms, asparagus, and beans. Drinking alcoholic beverages such as beer may significantly increase uric acid levels and bring about gout attacks.

Treatment for gout involves dietary changes and drugs. Depending on the levels of uric acid, a medication such as probenecid can be used to help the kidneys eliminate uric acid, or allopurinol can be administered to block the production of uric acid by the body.

Kidney stones are solid materials that form in the urinary tract. Most kidney stones are composed of calcium phosphate and calcium oxalate, although they can be solid uric acid. The excessive ingestion of minerals and insufficient water intake can cause the concentration of mineral salts to exceed their solubility and lead to the formation of kidney stones. When a kidney stone passes through the urinary tract, it causes considerable pain and discomfort, necessitating the use of painkillers and possibly surgery. Sometimes ultrasound is used to break up kidney stones. Persons prone to kidney stones are advised to drink six to eight glasses of water every day to prevent saturation levels of minerals in the urine.

Custom Medical Stock Photo

Gout occurs when uric acid exceeds its solubility.

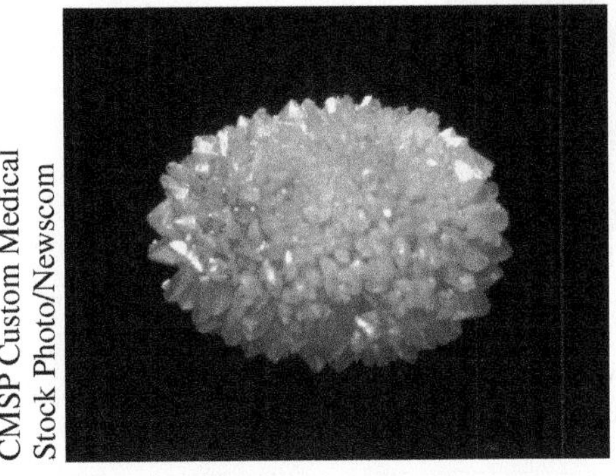

CMSP Custom Medical Stock Photo/Newscom

Kidney stones form when calcium phosphate exceeds its solubility.

Effect of Temperature on Solubility

MC TUTORIAL Solubility

The solubility of most solids becomes greater as temperature increases, which means that solutions usually can contain more dissolved solute at higher temperatures. A few substances show little change in solubility at higher temperatures, and a few are less soluble (see Figure 4). For example, when you add sugar to iced tea, some undissolved sugar may quickly collect on the bottom of the glass. But if you add sugar to hot tea, many teaspoons of sugar are needed before solid sugar appears. Hot tea dissolves more sugar than does cold tea because the solubility of sugar is much greater at a higher temperature.

When a saturated solution is carefully cooled, it becomes a *supersaturated solution* because it contains more solute than the solubility allows, although it is still completely liquid. Such a solution is unstable, and if the solution is agitated or if a solute crystal is added, the excess solute will recrystallize to give a saturated solution again.

Conversely, the solubility of a gas in water decreases as the temperature increases. At higher temperatures, more gas molecules have the energy to escape from the solution. Perhaps you have observed the bubbles

FIGURE 4 In water, most common solids are more soluble as the temperature increases.

Q Compare the solubility of $NaNO_3$ at 20 °C and 60 °C.

TUTORIAL
Solubility of Gases and Solids in Water

escaping from a cold carbonated soft drink as it warms. At high temperatures, bottles containing carbonated solutions may burst as more gas molecules leave the solution and increase the gas pressure inside the bottle. Biologists have found that increased temperatures in rivers and lakes cause the amount of dissolved oxygen to decrease until the warm water can no longer support a biological community. In the early morning, the surface of a lake or pond contains cooler water, which has more dissolved oxygen and therefore more fish. Electricity-generating plants are required to have their own ponds to use with their cooling towers to lessen the threat of thermal pollution to surrounding waterways.

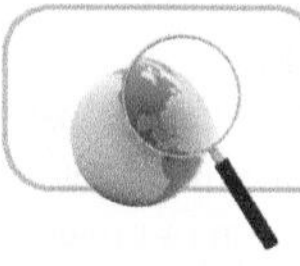

Explore Your World

PREPARING ROCK CANDY

Need: 1 cup of water, 3 cups of granulated sugar, clean narrow glass or jar, wooden stick (skewer) or thick string that is the height of the glass, pencil, and food coloring (optional)

Pearson Education/Eric Schrader

Rock candy can be made from a saturated solution of sugar (sucrose).

Process:

1. Place the water and two cups of sugar in a pan and begin heating and stirring. The sugar should all dissolve. Continue heating, but not boiling, adding small amounts of the remaining sugar and stirring thoroughly each time, until some of the sugar no longer dissolves. There may be some sugar crystals on the bottom of the pan. Carefully pour the sugar solution into the glass or jar. Add 2–3 drops of food coloring, if desired.
2. Wet the wooden stick and roll it in granulated sugar to provide crystals for the sugar solution to attach to. Place the stick in the sugar solution. If using string, tape it to a pencil so it will hang slightly above the bottom of the glass. Wet the lower half of the string, roll it in the granulated sugar, and place the pencil across the top of the glass with the string in the sugar solution. Place the glass and wooden stick or string in a place where it will not be disturbed. You should see sugar crystals grow over the next several days.

QUESTIONS

1. Why did more sugar dissolve as the solution was heated?
2. How did you know when you obtained a saturated solution?
3. Why did you see crystals forming on the stick or string over time?

Henry's Law

Henry's law states that the solubility of gas in a liquid is directly related to the pressure of that gas above the liquid. At higher pressures, there are more gas molecules available to enter and dissolve in the liquid. A can of soda is carbonated by using CO_2 gas at high pressure to increase the solubility of the CO_2 in the beverage. When you open the soda can at atmospheric pressure, the pressure on the CO_2 drops, which decreases the solubility of CO_2. As a result, bubbles of CO_2 rapidly escape from the solution. The burst of bubbles is even more noticeable when you open a warm can of soda.

CONCEPT CHECK 4 **Factors Affecting Solubility**

Indicate whether there is an increase or decrease in each of the following:

a. the solubility of sugar in water at 45 °C compared to its solubility in water at 25 °C
b. the solubility of O_2 in a lake as the water warms

ANSWER

a. A decrease in the temperature of the water from 45 °C to 25 °C decreases the solubility of the sugar.
b. An increase in the temperature of the water decreases the solubility of O_2 gas.

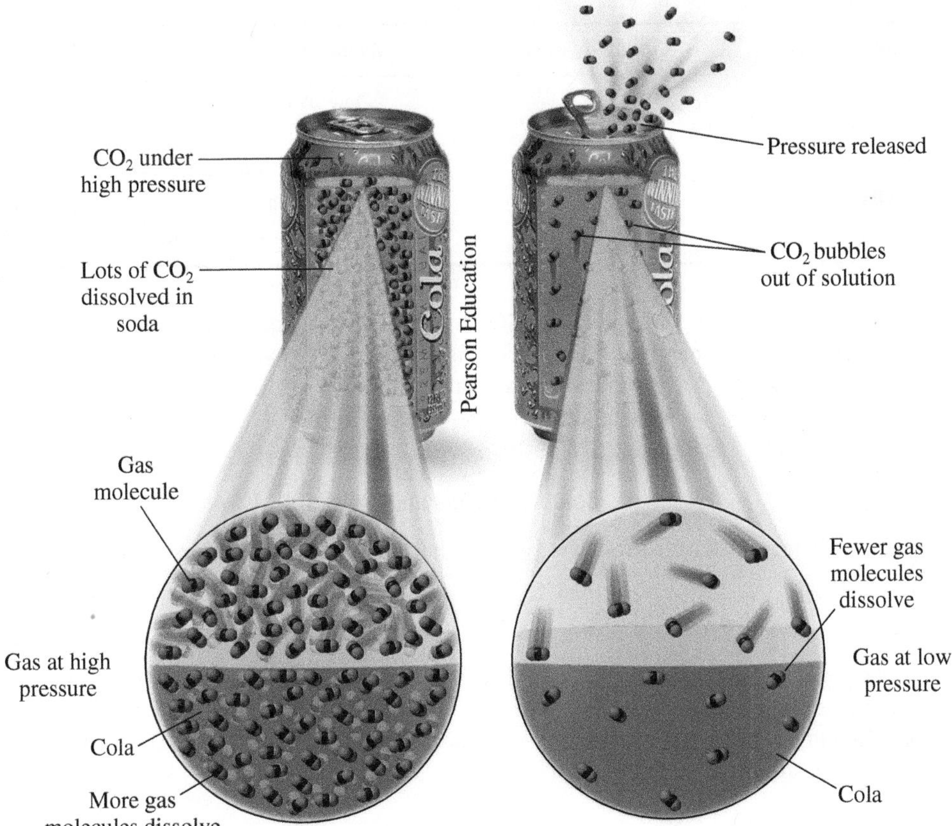

When the pressure of a gas above a solution decreases, the solubility of that gas in the solution also decreases.

Soluble and Insoluble Salts

Up to now, we have considered ionic compounds that dissolve in water: They are **soluble salts**. However, some ionic compounds do not separate into ions in water. They are **insoluble salts** that remain as solids even in contact with water.

Salts that are soluble in water typically contain at least one of the following ions: Li^+, Na^+, K^+, NH_4^+, NO_3^-, or $C_2H_3O_2^-$. *Only a salt containing a soluble cation or anion will dissolve in water.* Salts containing Cl^-, Br^-, or I^- are soluble unless combined with Ag^+, Pb^{2+}, or Hg_2^{2+}; then they are insoluble. Similarly, most salts containing SO_4^{2-} are soluble, but a few are insoluble as shown in Table 8. Most other salts including those containing the anions CO_3^{2-}, S^{2-}, PO_4^{3-}, or OH^- are insoluble (see Figure 5). In an insoluble salt, attractions between its positive and negative ions are too strong for the polar water molecules to break. We can use the solubility rules to predict whether a salt (a solid ionic compound) would be expected to dissolve in water. Table 9 illustrates the use of these rules.

TABLE 8 Solubility Rules for Ionic Solids in Water

An ionic solid is:	
Soluble if it contains:	**Insoluble if it contains:**
Li^+, Na^+, K^+	None
NH_4^+	None
NO_3^-, $C_2H_3O_2^-$	None
Cl^-, Br^-, I^-	Ag^+, Pb^{2+}, or Hg_2^{2+}
SO_4^{2-}	Ba^{2+}, Pb^{2+}, Ca^{2+}, Sr^{2+},
	CO_3^{2-}, S^{2-}, PO_4^{3-}, OH^-

Pearson Education

CdS

Pearson Education

FeS

Pearson Education

PbI_2

Pearson Education

$Ni(OH)_2$

FIGURE 5 If a salt contains a cation and anion that are not soluble, that salt is insoluble. For example, combinations of cadmium and sulfide, iron and sulfide, lead and iodide, and nickel and hydroxide do not contain any soluble ions. Thus, they form insoluble salts.

Q What makes each of these salts insoluble in water?

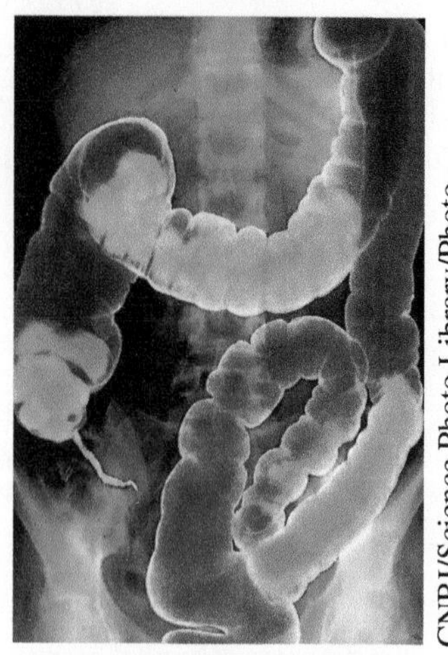
CNRI/Science Photo Library/Photo Researchers, Inc.

FIGURE 6 A barium sulfate-enhanced X-ray of the abdomen shows the large intestine.

Q Is $BaSO_4$ a soluble or an insoluble substance?

TABLE 9 Using Solubility Rules

Ionic Compound	Solubility in Water	Reasoning
K_2S	Soluble	Contains K^+
$Ca(NO_3)_2$	Soluble	Contains NO_3^-
$PbCl_2$	Insoluble	Forms an insoluble chloride with Pb^{2+}
NaOH	Soluble	Contains Na^+
$AlPO_4$	Insoluble	Contains no soluble ions

In medicine, the insoluble salt $BaSO_4$ is used as an opaque substance to enhance X-rays of the gastrointestinal tract. $BaSO_4$ is so insoluble that it does not dissolve in gastric fluids (see Figure 6). Other barium salts cannot be used; they would dissolve in water, releasing Ba^{2+}, which is poisonous.

CONCEPT CHECK 5 **Soluble and Insoluble Salts**

Predict whether each of the following salts is soluble in water and explain why:

a. Na_3PO_4 **b.** $CaCO_3$

ANSWER

a. The salt Na_3PO_4 is soluble in water because any compound that contains Na^+ is soluble.

b. The salt $CaCO_3$ is insoluble in water because it does not contain a soluble positive ion or a soluble negative ion.

TUTORIAL
Writing Net Ionic Equations

Formation of a Solid

We can use solubility rules to predict whether a solid, called a *precipitate*, forms when two solutions of ionic compounds are mixed as shown in Sample Problem 3.

Guide to Writing the Formation of Equations for an Insoluble Salt

1. Write the ions of the reactants.
2. Write the combinations of ions and determine if any are insoluble.
3. Write the ionic equation including any solid.
4. Write the net ionic equation.

SAMPLE PROBLEM 3 **Writing Equations for the Formation of an Insoluble Salt**

When solutions of NaCl and $AgNO_3$ are mixed, a white solid forms. Write the ionic and net ionic equations for the reaction.

SOLUTION

Step 1 **Write the ions of the reactants.**

Reactants
(initial combinations)

$Ag^+(aq) + NO_3^-(aq)$

$Na^+(aq) + Cl^-(aq)$

Step 2 **Write the combinations of ions and determine if any are insoluble.** When we look at the ions of each solution, we see that the combination of Ag^+ and Cl^- forms an insoluble salt.

Mixture (new combinations)	Product	Soluble
$Ag^+(aq) + Cl^-(aq)$	$AgCl(s)$	No
$Na^+(aq) + NO_3^-(aq)$	$NaNO_3$	Yes

Step 3 **Write the ionic equation including any solid.** In the **ionic equation**, we show all the ions of the reactants. The products include the solid AgCl that forms along with the remaining ions Na^+ and NO_3^-.

$$Ag^+(aq) + NO_3^-(aq) + Na^+(aq) + Cl^-(aq) \longrightarrow AgCl(s) + Na^+(aq) + NO_3^-(aq)$$

Step 4 **Write the net ionic equation.** To write a **net ionic equation**, we remove the Na^+ and NO_3^- ions, known as *spectator ions*, which are unchanged. This leaves only the ions and solid of the chemical reaction.

$$Ag^+(aq) + \underbrace{\cancel{NO_3^-(aq)} + \cancel{Na^+(aq)}}_{\text{Spectator ions}} + Cl^-(aq) \longrightarrow AgCl(s) + \underbrace{\cancel{Na^+(aq)} + \cancel{NO_3^-(aq)}}_{\text{Spectator ions}}$$

$$Ag^+(aq) + Cl^-(aq) \longrightarrow AgCl(s) \quad \text{Net ionic equation}$$

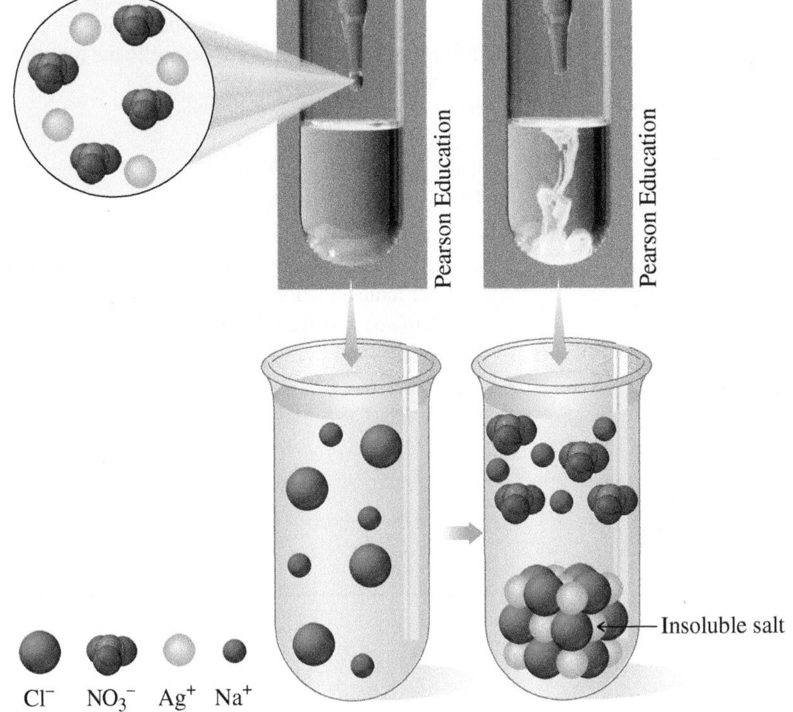

Type of Equation			
Chemical	$AgNO_3(aq)$	$+ NaCl(aq) \longrightarrow$	$AgCl(s) + NaNO_3(aq)$
Ionic	$Ag^+(aq) + NO_3^-(aq)$	$+ Na^+(aq) + Cl^-(aq) \longrightarrow$	$AgCl(s) + Na^+(aq) + NO_3^-(aq)$
Net ionic	$Ag^+(aq)$	$+ Cl^-(aq) \longrightarrow$	$AgCl(s)$

STUDY CHECK 3

Predict whether a solid might form in each of the following mixtures of solutions. If so, write the net ionic equation for the reaction.

a. $NH_4Cl(aq) + Ca(NO_3)_2(aq)$

b. $Pb(NO_3)_2(aq) + KCl(aq)$

QUESTIONS AND PROBLEMS

3 Solubility

LEARNING GOAL: *Define solubility. Distinguish between an unsaturated and a saturated solution; identify a salt as soluble or insoluble.*

21 State whether each of the following refers to a saturated or unsaturated solution:

a. A crystal added to a solution does not change in size.

b. A sugar cube completely dissolves when added to a cup of coffee.

22 State whether each of the following refers to a saturated or unsaturated solution:

a. A spoonful of salt added to boiling water dissolves.

b. A layer of sugar forms on the bottom of a glass of tea as ice is added.

Use the following table for Problems 23–26.

Substance	Solubility (g/100 g H_2O)	
	20 °C	50 °C
KCl	34	43
$NaNO_3$	88	110
$C_{12}H_{22}O_{11}$ (sugar)	204	260

23 Use the previous table to determine whether each of the following solutions will be saturated or unsaturated at 20 °C:
  a. adding 25 g of KCl to 100. g of H_2O
  b. adding 11 g of $NaNO_3$ to 25 g of H_2O
  c. adding 400. g of sugar to 125 g of H_2O

24 Use the previous table to determine whether each of the following solutions will be saturated or unsaturated at 50 °C:
  a. adding 25 g of KCl to 50. g of H_2O
  b. adding 150. g of $NaNO_3$ to 75 g of H_2O
  c. adding 80. g of sugar to 25 g of H_2O

25 A solution containing 80. g of KCl in 200. g of H_2O at 50 °C is cooled to 20 °C.
  a. How many grams of KCl remain in solution at 20 °C?
  b. How many grams of solid KCl crystallized after cooling?

26 A solution containing 80. g of $NaNO_3$ in 75 g of H_2O at 50 °C is cooled to 20 °C.
  a. How many grams of $NaNO_3$ remain in solution at 20 °C?
  b. How many grams of solid $NaNO_3$ crystallized after cooling?

27 Explain the following observations:
  a. More sugar dissolves in hot tea than in iced tea.
  b. Champagne in a warm room goes flat.
  c. A warm can of soda has more spray when opened than a cold one.

28 Explain the following observations:
  a. An open can of soda loses its "fizz" quicker at room temperature than in the refrigerator.
  b. Chlorine gas in tap water escapes as the water warms to room temperature.
  c. Less sugar dissolves in iced coffee than in hot coffee.

29 Predict whether each of the following ionic compounds is soluble in water:
  a. LiCl **b.** AgCl **c.** $BaCO_3$
  d. K_2O **e.** $Fe(NO_3)_3$

30 Predict whether each of the following ionic compounds is soluble in water:
  a. PbS **b.** KI **c.** Na_2S
  d. Ag_2O **e.** $CaSO_4$

31 Determine whether a solid forms when solutions containing the following salts are mixed. If so, write the ionic equation and the net ionic equation.
  a. $KCl(aq)$ and $Na_2S(aq)$
  b. $AgNO_3(aq)$ and $K_2S(aq)$
  c. $CaCl_2(aq)$ and $Na_2SO_4(aq)$
  d. $CuCl_2(aq)$ and $Li_3PO_4(aq)$

32 Determine whether a solid forms when solutions containing the following salts are mixed. If so, write the ionic equation and the net ionic equation.
  a. $Na_3PO_4(aq)$ and $AgNO_3(aq)$
  b. $K_2SO_4(aq)$ and $Na_2CO_3(aq)$
  c. $Pb(NO_3)_2(aq)$ and $Na_2CO_3(aq)$
  d. $BaCl_2(aq)$ and $KOH(aq)$

LEARNING GOAL

Calculate the concentration of a solute in a solution; use concentration to calculate the amount of solute or solution.

4 Solution Concentration

The amount of solute dissolved in a certain amount of solution is called the **concentration** of the solution. We will look at the concentrations that are a ratio of a certain amount of solute in a given amount of solution:

$$\text{Concentration of a solution} = \frac{\text{amount of solute}}{\text{amount of solution}}$$

TUTORIAL
Calculating Percent Concentration

Mass Percent (m/m) Concentration

Mass percent (m/m) describes the mass of the solute in grams for exactly 100 g of solution. In the calculation of mass percent (m/m), the units of mass of the solute and solution must be the same. If the mass of the solute is given as grams, then the mass of the solution must also be grams. The mass of the solution is the sum of the mass of the solute and the mass of the solvent.

$$\text{Mass percent (m/m)} = \frac{\text{mass of solute (g)}}{\text{mass of solute (g)} + \text{mass of solvent (g)}} \times 100\%$$

$$= \frac{\text{mass of solute (g)}}{\text{mass of solution (g)}} \times 100\%$$

Suppose we prepared a solution by mixing 8.00 g of KCl (solute) with 42.00 g of water (solvent). Together, the mass of the solute and mass of solvent give the mass of the solution (8.00 g + 42.00 g = 50.00 g). Mass percent is calculated by substituting the mass of the solute and the mass of the solution into the mass percent expression.

$$\frac{8.00 \text{ g KCl}}{\underbrace{50.00 \text{ g solution}}_{\substack{8.00 \text{ g KCl} + 42.00 \text{ g H}_2\text{O} \\ (\text{Solute} + \text{Solvent})}}} \times 100\% = 16.0\% \text{ (m/m) KCl solution}$$

Pearson Education

Add 8.00 g of KCl

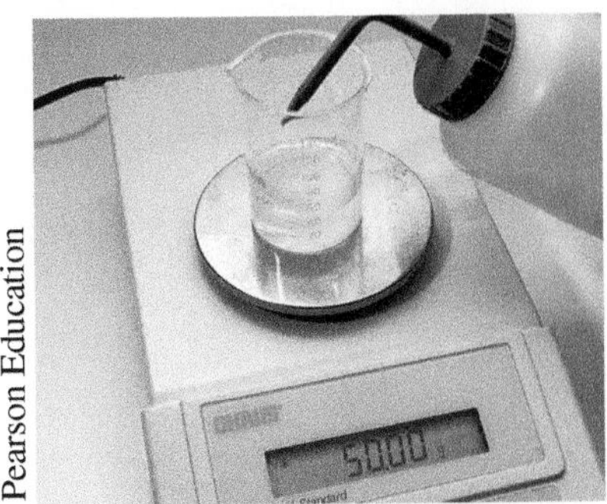

Pearson Education

Add water until the solution weighs 50.00 g

When water is added to 8.00 g of KCl to form 50.00 g of KCl solution, the mass percent concentration is 16.0% (m/m).

CONCEPT CHECK 6 Mass Percent Concentration

A NaBr solution is prepared by adding 4.0 g of NaBr to 50.0 g of H_2O.

a. What is the mass of the solution?

b. Is the final concentration of the NaBr solution equal to 7.4% (m/m), 8.0% (m/m), or 80.% (m/m)?

ANSWER

a. The mass of the NaBr solution is the sum of 4.0 g of NaBr solute and 50.0 g of H_2O solvent, which is 54.0 g (4.0 g NaBr + 50.0 g H_2O).

b. The mass percent of the NaBr solution is equal to 7.4% (m/m).

$$\frac{4.0 \text{ g NaBr}}{54.0 \text{ g solution}} \times 100\% = 7.4\% \text{ (m/m) NaBr solution}$$

SAMPLE PROBLEM 4 Calculating Mass Percent (m/m) Concentration

What is the mass percent (m/m) of NaOH in a solution prepared by dissolving 30.0 g of NaOH in 120.0 g of H_2O?

SOLUTION

Step 1 State the given and needed quantities. Using the following table, we can organize the information in the problem:

Analyze the Problem

Given	Need
30.0 g of NaOH solute	Mass percent (m/m)
30.0 g NaOH + 120.0 g H_2O = 150.0 g of NaOH solution	

Step 2 Write the concentration expression.

$$\text{Mass percent (m/m)} = \frac{\text{grams of solute}}{\text{grams of solution}} \times 100\%$$

Step 3 Substitute solute and solution quantities into the expression and calculate.

$$\text{Mass percent (m/m)} = \frac{\overset{\text{mass of solute}}{30.0 \text{ g NaOH}}}{\underset{\text{mass of solution}}{150.0 \text{ g NaOH solution}}} \times 100\%$$

$$= 20.0\% \text{ (m/m) NaOH solution}$$

STUDY CHECK 4

What is the mass percent (m/m) of NaCl in a solution made by dissolving 2.0 g of NaCl in 56.0 g of H_2O?

Guide to Calculating Solution Concentration

1. State the given and needed quantities.
2. Write the concentration expression.
3. Substitute solute and solution quantities into the expression and calculate.

Pearson Education/Eric Schrader

The label indicates that vanilla extract contains 35% (v/v) alcohol.

Volume Percent (v/v) Concentation

Because the volumes of liquids or gases are easily measured, the concentrations of their solutions are often expressed as **volume percent (v/v)**. The units of volume used in the ratio must be the same; for example, both in milliliters or both in liters.

$$\text{Volume percent (v/v)} = \frac{\text{volume of solute}}{\text{volume of solution}} \times 100\%$$

We interpret a volume percent (v/v) as the volume of solute in exactly 100 mL of solution. On a bottle of extract of vanilla, a label that reads alcohol 35% (v/v) means 35 mL of ethanol solute in exactly 100 mL of vanilla solution.

SAMPLE PROBLEM 5 **Calculating Volume Percent (v/v) Concentration**

A bottle contains 59 mL of lemon extract. If the extract solution contains 49 mL of alcohol, what is the volume percent (v/v) of the alcohol in the extract solution?

SOLUTION

Step 1 **State the given and needed quantities.**

Analyze the Problem

Given	Need
49 mL of alcohol solute	Volume percent (v/v)
59 mL of lemon extract solution	

Step 2 **Write the concentration expression.**

$$\text{Volume percent (v/v)} = \frac{\text{volume of solute}}{\text{volume of solution}} \times 100\%$$

Step 3 **Substitute solute and solution quantities into the expression and calculate.**

$$\text{Volume percent (v/v)} = \frac{\overset{\text{volume of solute}}{49 \text{ mL alcohol}}}{\underset{\text{volume of solution}}{59 \text{ mL solution}}} \times 100\%$$

$$= 83\% \text{ (v/v) alcohol solution}$$

Pearson Education/Eric Schrader

Lemon extract is a mixture of lemon flavor and alcohol.

STUDY CHECK 5

What is the volume percent (v/v) of bromine in a solution prepared by dissolving 12 mL of bromine in the solvent carbon tetrachloride to make 250 mL of solution?

TUTORIAL
Calculating Percent Concentration

Mass/Volume Percent (m/v) Concentration

Mass/volume percent (m/v) describes the mass of the solute in grams for exactly 100 mL of solution. In the calculation of mass/volume percent, the unit of mass of the solute is grams and the unit of volume is milliliters.

$$\text{Mass/volume percent (m/v)} = \frac{\text{grams of solute}}{\text{milliliters of solution}} \times 100\%$$

The mass/volume percent is widely used in hospitals and pharmacies for the preparation of intravenous solutions and medicines. For example, a 5% (m/v) glucose solution contains 5 g of glucose in exactly 100 mL of solution. The volume of solution represents the combined volumes of the glucose and H_2O.

SAMPLE PROBLEM 6 **Calculating Mass/Volume Percent (m/v) Concentration**

A student prepared a solution by dissolving 5.0 g of KI in enough water to give a final volume of 250 mL. What is the mass/volume percent (m/v) of the KI in the solution?

SOLUTION

Step 1 **State the given and needed quantities.**

Analyze the Problem

Given	Need
5.0 g of KI solute	Mass/volume percent (m/v)
250 mL of KI solution	

Step 2 **Write the concentration expression.**

$$\text{Mass/volume percent (m/v)} = \frac{\text{grams of solute}}{\text{milliliters of solution}} \times 100\%$$

Step 3 **Substitute solute and solution quantities into the expression and calculate.**

$$\text{Mass/volume percent (m/v)} = \frac{\overset{\text{Mass of solute}}{5.0\ \text{g KI}}}{\underset{\text{Volume of solution}}{250\ \text{mL solution}}} \times 100\%$$

$$= 2.0\%\ \text{(m/v) KI solution}$$

STUDY CHECK 6

What is the mass/volume percent (m/v) of NaOH in a solution prepared by dissolving 12 g of NaOH in enough water to make 220 mL of solution?

Water is added to 5.0 g of KI to make 250 mL of KI solution.

Molarity (M) Concentration

When chemists work with solutions, they often use **molarity (M)**, a concentration that states the number of moles of solute in exactly 1 liter of solution.

$$\text{Molarity (M)} = \frac{\text{moles of solute}}{\text{liters of solution}}$$

For example, if 2.0 moles of NaCl is dissolved in enough water to prepare 1.0 L of solution, the resulting NaCl solution has a molarity of 2.0 M. The abbreviation M indicates the units of moles per liter (moles/L).

$$\text{M} = \frac{\text{moles of solute}}{\text{liters of solution}} = \frac{2.0\ \text{moles NaCl}}{1.0\ \text{L solution}} = 2.0\ \text{M NaCl solution}$$

The molarity of a solution can be calculated knowing the moles of solute and the volume of solution in liters as shown in Sample Problem 7.

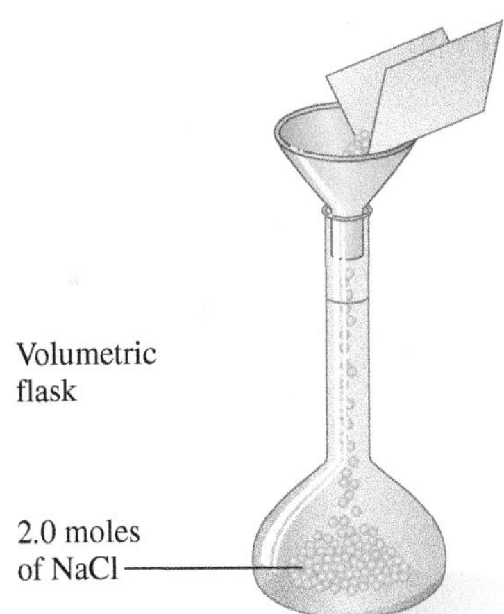

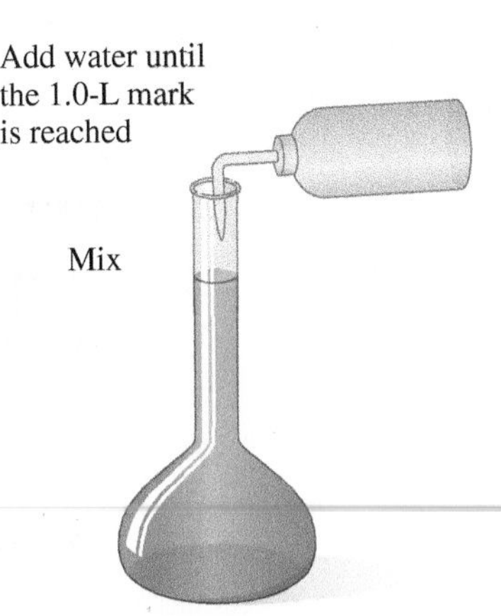

A 2.0 M NaCl solution

A solution of 2.0 moles of NaCl and water added to the 1-L mark is a 2.0 M NaCl solution.

SAMPLE PROBLEM 7 **Calculating Molarity**

What is the molarity (M) of 60.0 g of NaOH in 0.250 L of solution?

SOLUTION

Step 1 **State the given and needed quantities.** For molarity, we need the quantity, in moles, and the volume of the solution in liters.

Analyze the Problem

Given	Need
60.0 g of NaOH solute	Molarity
0.250 L of NaOH solution	

To calculate the moles of NaOH, we need to write the equality and conversion factors for the molar mass of NaOH. Then the moles in 60.0 g of NaOH can be determined.

$$1 \text{ mole of NaOH} = 40.0 \text{ g of NaOH}$$
$$\frac{1 \text{ mole NaOH}}{40.0 \text{ g NaOH}} \quad \text{and} \quad \frac{40.0 \text{ g NaOH}}{1 \text{ mole NaOH}}$$

$$\text{moles of NaOH} = 60.0 \cancel{\text{g NaOH}} \times \frac{1 \text{ mole NaOH}}{40.0 \cancel{\text{g NaOH}}}$$
$$= 1.50 \text{ moles of NaOH}$$

Step 2 **Write the concentration expression.**

$$\text{Molarity (M)} = \frac{\text{moles of solute}}{\text{liters of solution}}$$

Step 3 **Substitute solute and solution quantities into the expression and calculate.**

$$\text{M} = \frac{1.50 \text{ moles NaOH}}{0.250 \text{ L solution}} = \frac{6.00 \text{ moles NaOH}}{1 \text{ L solution}} = 6.00 \text{ M NaOH solution}$$

STUDY CHECK 7

What is the molarity of a solution that contains 75.0 g of KNO_3 dissolved in 0.350 L of solution?

Table 10 summarizes the types of units used in the various types of concentration expressions for solutions.

TABLE 10 Summary of Types of Concentration Expressions and Their Units

Concentration Units	Mass Percent (m/m)	Volume Percent (v/v)	Mass/Volume Percent (m/v)	Molarity (M)
Solute	g	mL	g	mole
Solution	g	mL	mL	L

Using Concentrations as Conversion Factors

TUTORIAL
Percent Concentration as a Conversion Factor

In the preparation of solutions, we often need to calculate the amount of solute or volume of solution. Then the concentration of that solution is useful as a conversion factor. The value of 100 in the denominator of a percent expression is an *exact* number. Some examples of percent concentrations and molarity, their meanings, and possible conversion factors are given in Table 11. Some examples of using percent concentration or molarity as conversion factors are given in Sample Problems 8 and 9.

TABLE 11 Conversion Factors from Percent Concentrations

Percent Concentration	Meaning	Conversion Factors		
15% (m/m) KCl solution	15 g of KCl in 100 g of KCl solution	$\frac{15 \text{ g KCl}}{100 \text{ g solution}}$	and	$\frac{100 \text{ g solution}}{15 \text{ g KCl}}$
12% (v/v) ethanol solution	12 mL of ethanol in 100 mL of ethanol solution	$\frac{12 \text{ mL ethanol}}{100 \text{ mL solution}}$	and	$\frac{100 \text{ mL solution}}{12 \text{ mL ethanol}}$
5% (m/v) glucose solution	5 g of glucose in 100 mL of glucose solution	$\frac{5 \text{ g glucose}}{100 \text{ mL solution}}$	and	$\frac{100 \text{ mL solution}}{5 \text{ g glucose}}$
Molarity				
6.0 M HCl solution	6.0 moles of HCl in 1 liter of HCl solution	$\frac{6.0 \text{ moles HCl}}{1 \text{ L solution}}$	and	$\frac{1 \text{ L solution}}{6.0 \text{ moles HCl}}$

SAMPLE PROBLEM 8 **Using Mass/Volume Percent to Find Mass of Solute**

A topical antibiotic is 1.0% (m/v) clindamycin. How many grams of clindamycin are in 60. mL of the 1.0% (m/v) solution?

SOLUTION

Step 1 **State the given and needed quantities.**

Analyze the Problem

Given	Need
60. mL of 1.0% (m/v) clindamycin solution	grams of clindamycin

Step 2 **Write a plan to calculate the mass or volume.**

milliliters of solution → % (m/v) factor → grams of clindamycin

Step 3 **Write equalities and conversion factors.** The mass/volume percent (m/v) indicates the grams of a solute in every 100 mL of a solution. The 1.0% (m/v) can be written as two conversion factors.

$$1.0 \text{ g of clindamycin} = 100 \text{ mL of solution}$$
$$\frac{1.0 \text{ g clindamycin}}{100 \text{ mL solution}} \quad \text{and} \quad \frac{100 \text{ mL solution}}{1.0 \text{ g clindamycin}}$$

Step 4 **Set up the problem to calculate the mass or volume.** The volume of the solution is converted to mass of solute using the conversion factor that cancels mL.

$$60.\ \cancel{\text{mL solution}} \times \frac{1.0 \text{ g clindamycin}}{100\ \cancel{\text{mL solution}}} = 0.60 \text{ g of clindamycin}$$

STUDY CHECK 8

Calculate the grams of KCl in 225 g of an 8.00% (m/m) KCl solution.

Guide to Using Concentration to Calculate Mass or Volume

1. State the given and needed quantities.
2. Write a plan to calculate the mass or volume.
3. Write equalities and conversion factors.
4. Set up the problem to calculate the mass or volume.

SAMPLE PROBLEM 9 **Using Molarity to Find Volume**

How many liters of a 2.00 M NaCl solution are needed to provide 67.3 g of NaCl?

SOLUTION

Step 1 **State the given and needed quantities.**

Analyze the Problem

Given	Need
67.3 g of NaCl	liters of NaCl solution
2.00 M NaCl solution	

Step 2 **Write a plan to calculate the mass or volume.**

grams of NaCl → Molar mass → moles of NaCl → Molarity → liters of NaCl solution

Step 3 **Write equalities and conversion factors.**

$$1 \text{ mole of NaCl} = 58.5 \text{ g of NaCl}$$
$$\frac{1 \text{ mole NaCl}}{58.5 \text{ g NaCl}} \quad \text{and} \quad \frac{58.5 \text{ g NaCl}}{1 \text{ mole NaCl}}$$

The molarity of any solution can be written as two conversion factors.

$$1 \text{ L of NaCl solution} = 2.00 \text{ moles of NaCl}$$

$$\frac{1 \text{ L NaCl solution}}{2.00 \text{ moles NaCl}} \quad \text{and} \quad \frac{2.00 \text{ moles NaCl}}{1 \text{ L NaCl solution}}$$

Step 4 **Set up the problem to calculate the mass or volume.**

$$\text{liters of NaCl solution} = 67.3 \cancel{\text{g NaCl}} \times \frac{1 \cancel{\text{mole NaCl}}}{58.5 \cancel{\text{g NaCl}}} \times \frac{1 \text{ L NaCl solution}}{2.00 \cancel{\text{moles NaCl}}}$$

$$= 0.575 \text{ L of NaCl solution}$$

STUDY CHECK 9

How many milliliters of a 6.00 M HCl solution will provide 10.4 g of HCl?

QUESTIONS AND PROBLEMS

4 Solution Concentration

LEARNING GOAL: *Calculate the concentration of a solute in a solution; use concentration to calculate the amount of solute or solution.*

33 Calculate the mass percent (m/m) for the solute in each of the following solutions:
- **a.** 25 g of KCl and 125 g of H_2O
- **b.** 12 g of sugar in 225 g of tea solution with sugar
- **c.** 8.0 g of $CaCl_2$ in 80.0 g of $CaCl_2$ solution

34 Calculate the mass percent (m/m) for the solute in each of the following solutions:
- **a.** 75 g of NaOH in 325 g of NaOH solution
- **b.** 2.0 g of KOH and 20.0 g of H_2O
- **c.** 48.5 g of Na_2CO_3 in 250.0 g of Na_2CO_3 solution

35 Calculate the mass/volume percent (m/v) for the solute in each of the following solutions:
- **a.** 75 g of Na_2SO_4 in 250 mL of Na_2SO_4 solution
- **b.** 39 g of sucrose in 355 mL of a carbonated drink

36 Calculate the mass/volume percent (m/v) for the solute in each of the following solutions:
- **a.** 2.50 g of LiCl in 50.0 mL of LiCl solution
- **b.** 7.5 g of casein in 120 mL of low-fat milk

37 Calculate the molarity (M) of the following solutions:
- **a.** 2.00 moles of glucose in 4.00 L of glucose solution
- **b.** 4.00 g of KOH in 2.00 L of KOH solution
- **c.** 5.85 g of NaCl in 400. mL of NaCl solution

38 Calculate the molarity (M) of the following solutions:
- **a.** 0.500 mole of glucose in 0.200 L of glucose solution
- **b.** 36.5 g of HCl in 1.00 L of HCl solution
- **c.** 30.0 g of NaOH in 350. mL of NaOH solution

39 Calculate the amount of solute, in grams or milliliters, needed to prepare the following solutions:
- **a.** 50.0 mL of a 5.0% (m/v) KCl solution
- **b.** 1250 mL of a 4.0% (m/v) NH_4Cl solution
- **c.** 250. mL of a 10.0% (v/v) acetic acid solution

40 Calculate the amount of solute, in grams or milliliters, needed to prepare the following solutions:
- **a.** 150 mL of a 40.0% (m/v) $LiNO_3$ solution
- **b.** 450 mL of a 2.0% (m/v) KOH solution
- **c.** 225 mL of a 15% (v/v) isopropyl alcohol solution

41 A mouthwash contains 22.5% (v/v) alcohol. If the bottle of mouthwash contains 355 mL, what is the volume, in milliliters, of the alcohol?

42 Champagne is an 11% (v/v) alcohol solution. If there are 750 mL of champagne in a bottle, how many milliliters of alcohol are present?

43 A patient receives 100. mL of a 20.% (m/v) mannitol solution every hour.
- **a.** How many grams of mannitol are given in 1 h?
- **b.** How many grams of mannitol does the patient receive in 12 h?

44 A patient receives 250 mL of a 4.0% (m/v) amino acid solution twice a day.
- **a.** How many grams of amino acids are in 250 mL of solution?
- **b.** How many grams of amino acids does the patient receive in 1 day?

45 A patient needs 100. g of glucose in the next 12 h. How many liters of a 5% (m/v) glucose solution must be given?

46 A patient received 2.0 g of NaCl in 8 h. How many milliliters of a 0.9% (m/v) NaCl (saline) solution were delivered?

47 Calculate the amount of solution (g or mL) that contains each of the following amounts of solute:
- **a.** 5.0 g of $LiNO_3$ from a 25% (m/m) $LiNO_3$ solution
- **b.** 40.0 g of KOH from a 10.0% (m/v) KOH solution
- **c.** 2.0 mL of formic acid from a 10.0% (v/v) formic acid solution

48 Calculate the amount of solution (g or mL) that contains each of the following amounts of solute:
- **a.** 7.50 g of NaCl from a 2.0% (m/m) NaCl solution
- **b.** 4.0 g of NaF from a 25% (m/v) NaF solution
- **c.** 20.0 g of KBr from an 8.0% (m/m) KBr solution

49 Calculate the moles of solute needed to prepare each of the following:
a. 1.00 L of a 3.00 M NaCl solution
b. 0.400 L of a 1.00 M KBr solution
c. 125 mL of a 2.00 M $MgCl_2$ solution

50 Calculate the moles of solute needed to prepare each of the following:
a. 5.00 L of a 2.00 M $CaCl_2$ solution
b. 4.00 L of a 0.100 M NaOH solution
c. 215 mL of a 4.00 M HNO_3 solution

51 Calculate the grams of solute needed to prepare each of the following:
a. 2.00 L of a 1.50 M NaOH solution
b. 4.00 L of a 0.200 M KCl solution
c. 25.0 mL of a 6.00 M HCl solution

52 Calculate the grams of solute needed to prepare each of the following:
a. 2.00 L of a 6.00 M NaOH solution
b. 5.00 L of a 0.100 M $CaCl_2$ solution
c. 175 mL of a 3.00 M $NaNO_3$ solution

53 Calculate the volume indicated for each of the following:
a. liters of a 2.00 M KBr solution to obtain 3.00 moles of KBr
b. milliliters of a 1.50 M NaCl solution to obtain 4.78 g of NaCl
c. milliliters of a 0.800 M $Ca(NO_3)_2$ solution to obtain 0.0500 mole of $Ca(NO_3)_2$

54 Calculate the volume indicated for each of the following:
a. liters of a 4.00 M KCl solution to obtain 0.100 mole of KCl
b. milliliters of a 6.00 M HCl solution to obtain 18.3 g of HCl
c. milliliters of a 2.50 M K_2SO_4 solution to obtain 1.20 moles of K_2SO_4

5 Dilution of Solutions and Solution Reactions

LEARNING GOAL

Calculate the new concentration or volume of a diluted solution. Given the volume and concentration of a solution, calculate the amount of another reactant or product in a reaction.

In chemistry and biology, we often prepare diluted solutions from more concentrated (stock) solutions. In a process called **dilution**, a solvent, usually water, is added to a solution, which increases the volume. As a result, the concentration of the solution decreases. In an everyday example, you are making a dilution when you add three cans of water to a can of concentrated orange juice.

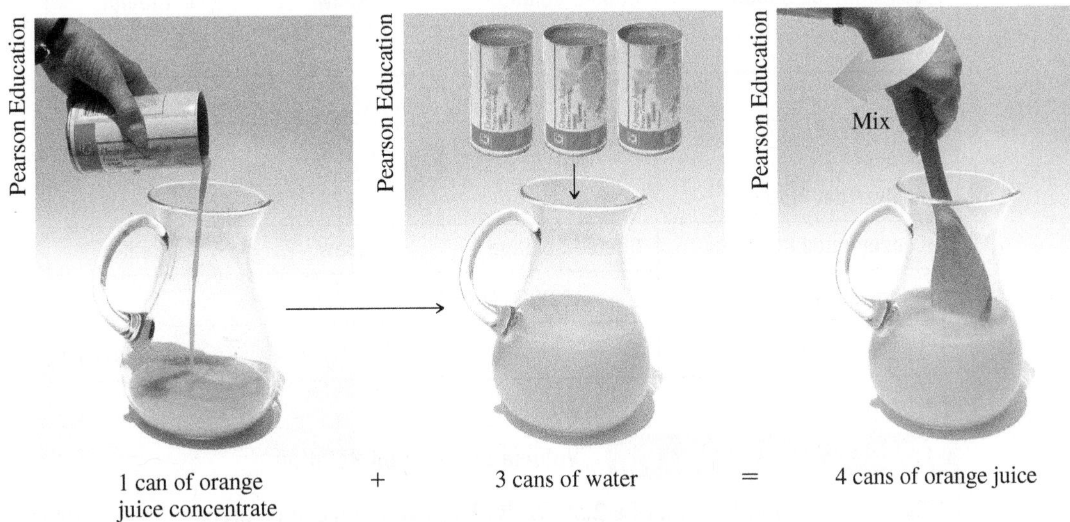

One can of orange juice concentrate will make four cans of orange juice.

Although the addition of solvent increases the volume, the amount of solute doesn't change; it is the same in the concentrated solution and the diluted solution (see Figure 7).

MC™ TUTORIAL Dilution

Grams or moles of solute = grams or moles of solute
Concentrated solution — Diluted solution

We can write this equality in terms of the concentration, C, and the volume, *V*. The concentration, C, may be percent concentration or molarity.

$$C_1V_1 = C_2V_2$$

Concentrated solution — Diluted solution

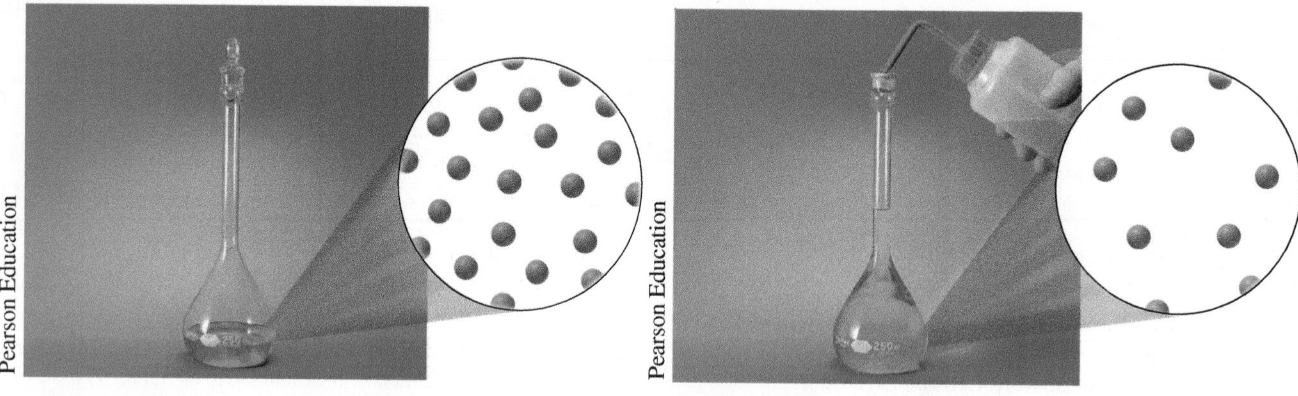

FIGURE 7 When water is added to a concentrated solution, there is no change in the number of particles, but the solute particles spread out as the volume of the diluted solution increases.

Q What is the concentration of the diluted solution after an equal volume of water is added to a sample of a 6 M HCl solution?

If we are given any three of the four variables, we can rearrange the dilution expression to solve for the unknown quantity as seen in Concept Check 7 and Sample Problem 10.

CONCEPT CHECK 7 **Volume of a Diluted Solution**

A 50.0-mL sample of a 20.0% (m/v) $SrCl_2$ solution is diluted with water to give a 5.00% (m/v) $SrCl_2$ solution. Use this data to complete the following table with the given concentrations and volumes of the solutions. Indicate what we know as *increases* or *decreases*, and predict the change in the unknown as *increases* or *decreases*.

Analyze the Problem

Concentrated Solution	Diluted Solution	Know	Predict
$C_1 =$	$C_2 =$		
$V_1 =$	$V_2 =$		

ANSWER

Analyze the Problem

Concentrated Solution	Diluted Solution	Know	Predict
$C_1 = 20.0\%$ (m/v)	$C_2 = 5.00\%$ (m/v)	C decreases	
$V_1 = 50.0$ mL	$V_2 = ?$ mL		*V* increases

SAMPLE PROBLEM 10 **Volume of a Diluted Solution**

What volume, in milliliters, of a 2.5% (m/v) KOH solution can be prepared by diluting 50.0 mL of a 12% (m/v) KOH solution?

Guide to Calculating Dilution Quantities

1. Prepare a table of the concentrations and volumes of the solutions.
2. Rearrange the dilution expression to solve for the unknown quantity.
3. Substitute the known quantities into the dilution expression and calculate.

SOLUTION

Step 1 **Prepare a table of the concentrations and volumes of the solutions.** For our problem analysis, we organize the solution data in a table, making sure that the units of concentration and volume are the same.

Analyze the Problem

Concentrated Solution	Diluted Solution	Know	Predict
$C_1 = 12\%$ (m/v)	$C_2 = 2.5\%$ (m/v)	C decreases	
$V_1 = 50.0$ mL	$V_2 = ?$ mL		*V* increases

Step 2 **Rearrange the dilution expression to solve for the unknown quantity.**

$$C_1V_1 = C_2V_2$$

Divide both sides by C_2.
$$\frac{C_1V_1}{C_2} = \frac{\cancel{C_2}V_2}{\cancel{C_2}}$$

$$V_2 = V_1 \times \frac{C_1}{C_2}$$

Step 3 **Substitute the known quantities into the dilution expression and calculate.**

$$V_2 = 50.0 \text{ mL} \times \frac{12\%}{2.5\%} = 240 \text{ mL of diluted KOH solution}$$

Concentration factor increases volume

When the initial volume (V_1) is multiplied by a ratio of the percent concentrations (concentration factor) that is greater than 1, the volume of the solution increases as predicted in Step 1.

STUDY CHECK 10

What is the final volume, in milliliters, when 25.0 mL of a 15% (m/v) KCl solution is diluted to a 3.0% (m/v) KCl solution?

SAMPLE PROBLEM 11 **Molarity of a Diluted Solution**

What is the molarity of a solution that is prepared by diluting 75.0 mL of a 4.00 M KCl solution to a volume of 500. mL?

SOLUTION

Step 1 **Prepare a table of the concentrations and volumes of the solutions.** We organize the solution data in a table, making sure that the units of concentration and volume are the same.

Analyze the Problem

Concentrated Solution	Diluted Solution	Know	Predict
$C_1 = 4.00$ M	$C_2 = ?$ M		C (molarity) decreases
$V_1 = 75.0$ mL	$V_2 = 500.$ mL	V increases	

Step 2 **Rearrange the dilution expression to solve for the unknown quantity.**

$$C_1V_1 = C_2\,V_2$$

Divide both sides by V_2.
$$\frac{C_1V_1}{V_2} = C_2\,\frac{\cancel{V_2}}{\cancel{V_2}}$$

$$C_2 = C_1 \times \frac{V_1}{V_2}$$

Step 3 **Substitute the known quantities into the dilution expression and calculate.**

$$C_2 = 4.00 \text{ M} \times \frac{75 \cancel{\text{mL}}}{500. \cancel{\text{mL}}} = 0.600 \text{ M (diluted KCl solution)}$$

Volume factor decreases concentration

When the initial molarity is multiplied by a ratio of the volumes (volume factor) that is less than 1, the molarity of the solution decreases as predicted in Step 1.

STUDY CHECK 11

What is the molarity of a solution prepared when 75.0 mL of a 10.0 M $NaNO_3$ solution is diluted to a volume of 600. mL?

TUTORIAL
Solution Stoichiometry

Solutions and Chemical Reactions

When chemical reactions involve aqueous solutions, we use molarity and volume to determine the moles or grams of the substances required or produced. Using the balanced chemical equation, we can determine the volume of a solution from the molarity and moles or grams of a solute as seen in Sample Problem 12. This is the same type of calculation, when we calculated moles or grams of product from the given amount of reactant.

Pearson Education

$Zn(s)$ in HCl produces bubbles of hydrogen gas and $ZnCl_2$.

SAMPLE PROBLEM 12 Volume of a Solution in a Reaction

Zinc reacts with HCl to produce $ZnCl_2$ and hydrogen gas H_2.

$$Zn(s) + 2HCl(aq) \longrightarrow ZnCl_2(aq) + H_2(g)$$

How many liters of a 1.50 M HCl solution completely react with 5.32 g of zinc?

SOLUTION

Step 1 **State the given and needed quantities.**

Analyze the Proble

Given	Need
5.32 g of Zn	
1.50 M HCl solution	liters of HCl solution
Equation	
$Zn(s) + 2HCl(aq) \longrightarrow ZnCl_2(aq) + H_2(g)$	

Step 2 **Write a plan to calculate the needed quantity or concentration.**

grams of Zn → Molar mass → moles of Zn → Mole–mole factor → moles of HCl → Molarity → liters of HCl solution

Guide to Calculations Involving Solutions in Chemical Reactions

1. State the given and needed quantities.
2. Write a plan to calculate the needed quantity or concentration.
3. Write equalities and conversion factors including mole–mole and concentration factors.
4. Set up the problem to calculate the needed quantity or concentration.

Step 3 **Write equalities and conversion factors including mole–mole and concentration factors.**

1 mole of Zn = 65.4 g of Zn

$$\frac{1 \text{ mole Zn}}{65.4 \text{ g Zn}} \quad \text{and} \quad \frac{65.4 \text{ g Zn}}{1 \text{ mole Zn}}$$

1 mole of Zn = 2 moles of HCl

$$\frac{1 \text{ mole Zn}}{2 \text{ moles HCl}} \quad \text{and} \quad \frac{2 \text{ moles HCl}}{1 \text{ mole Zn}}$$

1 L of HCl solution = 1.50 moles of HCl

$$\frac{1 \text{ L HCl solution}}{1.50 \text{ moles HCl}} \quad \text{and} \quad \frac{1.50 \text{ moles HCl}}{1 \text{ L HCl solution}}$$

Step 4 **Set up the problem to calculate the needed quantity or concentration.**

We can write the problem setup as seen in our plan:

$$5.32 \cancel{\text{g Zn}} \times \frac{1 \cancel{\text{mole Zn}}}{65.4 \cancel{\text{g Zn}}} \times \frac{2 \cancel{\text{moles HCl}}}{1 \cancel{\text{mole Zn}}} \times \frac{1 \text{ L HCl solution}}{1.50 \cancel{\text{moles HCl}}} = 0.108 \text{ L of HCl solution}$$

STUDY CHECK 12

Using the reaction in Sample Problem 12, how many grams of zinc can react with 225 mL of a 0.200 M HCl solution?

SAMPLE PROBLEM 13 Volume of a Reactant in a Solution

How many liters of a 0.250 M $BaCl_2$ solution are needed to react with 0.0325 L of a 0.160 M Na_2SO_4 solution?

$$Na_2SO_4(aq) + BaCl_2(aq) \longrightarrow BaSO_4(s) + 2NaCl(aq)$$

SOLUTION

Step 1 State the given and needed quantities.

Analyze the Problem

Given	Need
0.0325 L of 0.160 M Na_2SO_4 solution	
0.250 M $BaCl_2$ solution	liters of $BaCl_2$ solution
Equation	
$Na_2SO_4(aq) + BaCl_2(aq) \longrightarrow BaSO_4(s) + 2NaCl(aq)$	

Step 2 Write a plan to calculate the needed quantity or concentration.

liters of Na_2SO_4 solution → Molarity → moles of Na_2SO_4 → Mole–mole factor → moles of $BaCl_2$ → Molarity → liters of $BaCl_2$ solution

Step 3 Write equalities and conversion factors including mole–mole and concentration factors.

1 L of Na_2SO_4 solution = 0.160 mole of Na_2SO_4

$$\frac{1\text{ L }Na_2SO_4\text{ solution}}{0.160\text{ mole }Na_2SO_4} \text{ and } \frac{0.160\text{ mole }Na_2SO_4}{1\text{ L }Na_2SO_4\text{ solution}}$$

1 mole of Na_2SO_4 = 1 mole of $BaCl_2$

$$\frac{1\text{ mole }Na_2SO_4}{1\text{ mole }BaCl_2} \text{ and } \frac{1\text{ mole }BaCl_2}{1\text{ mole }Na_2SO_4}$$

1 L $BaCl_2$ solution = 0.250 mole of $BaCl_2$

$$\frac{1\text{ L }BaCl_2\text{ solution}}{0.250\text{ mole }BaCl_2} \text{ and } \frac{0.250\text{ mole }BaCl_2}{1\text{ L }BaCl_2\text{ solution}}$$

Step 4 Set up the problem to calculate the needed quantity or concentration.

$$0.0325\ \cancel{\text{L }Na_2SO_4\text{ solution}} \times \frac{0.160\ \cancel{\text{mole }Na_2SO_4}}{1\ \cancel{\text{L }Na_2SO_4\text{ solution}}} \times \frac{1\ \cancel{\text{mole }BaCl_2}}{1\ \cancel{\text{mole }Na_2SO_4}} \times \frac{1\text{ L }BaCl_2\text{ solution}}{0.250\ \cancel{\text{mole }BaCl_2}} = 0.0208\text{ L of }BaCl_2\text{ solution}$$

STUDY CHECK 13

For the reaction in Sample Problem 13, how many liters of a 0.330 M Na_2SO_4 solution are needed to react with 0.0268 L of a 0.216 M $BaCl_2$ solution?

Figure 8 gives a summary of the pathways and conversion factors needed for substances, including solutions, involved in chemical reactions.

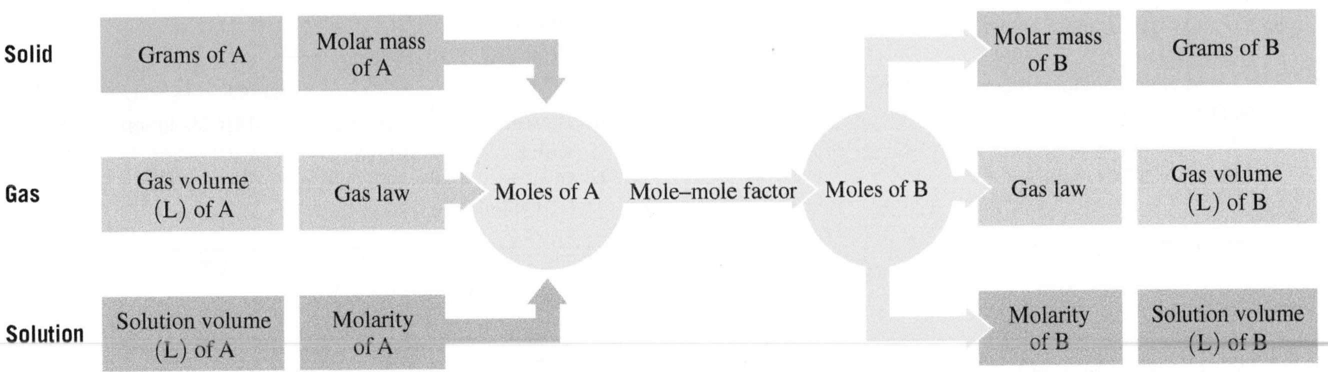

FIGURE 8 In calculations involving chemical reactions, substance A is converted to moles of A using molar mass (if solid), gas laws (if gas), or molarity (if solution). Then moles of A are converted to moles of substance B, which are converted to grams of solid, liters of gas, or liters of solution, as needed.

Q What sequence of conversion factors would you use to calculate the number of grams of $CaCO_3$ needed to react with 1.50 L of a 2.00 M HCl solution in the reaction: $2HCl(aq) + CaCO_3(s) \longrightarrow CaCl_2(aq) + CO_2(g) + H_2O(l)$?

QUESTIONS AND PROBLEMS

5 Dilution of Solutions and Solution Reactions

***LEARNING GOAL:** Calculate the new concentration or volume of a diluted solution. Given the volume and concentration of a solution, calculate the amount of another reactant or product in a reaction.*

55 Calculate the final concentration of each of the following diluted solutions:

a. 2.0 L of a 6.0 M HCl solution is added to water so that the final volume is 6.0 L.

b. Water is added to 0.50 L of a 12 M NaOH solution to make 3.0 L of a diluted NaOH solution.

c. A 10.0-mL sample of a 25% (m/v) KOH solution is diluted with water so that the final volume is 100.0 mL.

d. A 50.0-mL sample of a 15% (m/v) H_2SO_4 solution is added to water to give a final volume of 250 mL.

56 Calculate the final concentration of each of the following diluted solutions:

a. 1.0 L of a 4.0 M HNO_3 solution is added to water so that the final volume is 8.0 L.

b. Water is added to 0.25 L of a 6.0 M NaF solution to make 2.0 L of a diluted NaF solution.

c. A 50.0-mL sample of an 8.0% (m/v) KBr solution is diluted with water so that the final volume is 200.0 mL.

d. A 5.0-mL sample of a 50.0% (m/v) acetic acid ($HC_2H_3O_2$) solution is added to water to give a final volume of 25 mL.

57 What is the volume, in milliliters, of each of the following diluted solutions?

a. a 1.50 M HCl solution prepared from 20.0 mL of a 6.00 M HCl solution

b. a 2.0% (m/v) LiCl solution prepared from 50.0 mL of a 10.0% (m/v) LiCl solution

c. a 0.500 M H_3PO_4 solution prepared from 50.0 mL of a 6.00 M H_3PO_4 solution

d. a 5.0% (m/v) glucose solution prepared from 75 mL of a 12% (m/v) glucose solution

58 What is the volume, in milliliters, of each of the following diluted solutions?

a. a 1.00% (m/v) H_2SO_4 solution prepared from 10.0 mL of a 20.0% H_2SO_4 solution

b. a 0.10 M HCl solution prepared from 25 mL of a 6.0 M HCl solution

c. a 1.0 M NaOH solution prepared from 50.0 mL of a 12 M NaOH solution

d. a 1.0% (m/v) $CaCl_2$ solution prepared from 18 mL of a 4.0% (m/v) $CaCl_2$ solution

59 Determine the volume, in milliliters, required to prepare each of the following diluted solutions:

a. 255 mL of a 0.200 M HNO_3 solution using a 4.00 M HNO_3 solution

b. 715 mL of a 0.100 M $MgCl_2$ solution using a 6.00 M $MgCl_2$ solution

c. 0.100 L of a 0.150 M KCl solution using an 8.00 M KCl solution

60 Determine the volume, in milliliters, required to prepare each of the following diluted solutions:

a. 20.0 mL of a 0.250 M KNO_3 solution using a 6.00 M KNO_3 solution

b. 25.0 mL of a 2.50 M H_2SO_4 solution using a 12.0 M H_2SO_4 solution

c. 0.500 L of a 1.50 M NH_4Cl solution using a 10.0 M NH_4Cl solution

61 Answer the following for the reaction:

$$Pb(NO_3)_2(aq) + 2KCl(aq) \longrightarrow PbCl_2(s) + 2KNO_3(aq)$$

a. How many grams of $PbCl_2$ will be formed from 50.0 mL of a 1.50 M KCl solution?

b. How many milliliters of a 2.00 M $Pb(NO_3)_2$ solution will react with 50.0 mL of a 1.50 M KCl solution?

62 Answer the following for the reaction:

$$NiCl_2(aq) + 2NaOH(aq) \longrightarrow Ni(OH)_2(s) + 2NaCl(aq)$$

a. How many milliliters of a 0.200 M NaOH solution are needed to react with 18.0 mL of a 0.500 M $NiCl_2$ solution?

b. How many grams of $Ni(OH)_2$ are produced from the reaction of 35.0 mL of a 0.200 M NaOH solution?

63 Answer the following for the reaction:

$$Mg(s) + 2HCl(aq) \longrightarrow MgCl_2(aq) + H_2(g)$$

a. How many milliliters of a 6.00 M HCl solution are required to react with 15.0 g of magnesium?

b. How many moles of hydrogen gas form when 0.500 L of a 2.00 M HCl solution reacts?

64 The calcium carbonate in limestone reacts with HCl to produce a calcium chloride solution, liquid water, and carbon dioxide gas.

$$CaCO_3(s) + 2HCl(aq) \longrightarrow CaCl_2(aq) + H_2O(l) + CO_2(g)$$

a. How many milliliters of a 0.200 M HCl solution can react with 8.25 g of $CaCO_3$?

b. How many moles of CO_2 form when 15.5 mL of a 3.00 M HCl solution react?

LEARNING GOAL

Identify a mixture as a solution, a colloid, or a suspension. Describe how the number of particles in a solution affects the freezing point, boiling point, and osmotic pressure of a solution.

6 Properties of Solutions

The solute particles in a solution play an important role in determining the properties of that solution. In most of the solutions discussed so far, the solute is dissolved as small particles that are uniformly dispersed throughout the solvent to give a homogeneous solution. When you observe a solution, such as salt water, you cannot visually distinguish the solute from the solvent. The solution appears transparent, although it may have a color. The particles are so small that they go through filters and through semipermeable membranes. A **semipermeable membrane** allows solvent molecules such as water and very small solute particles to pass through, but does not allow the passage of large solute molecules.

Colloids

The particles in a colloidal dispersion, or **colloid**, are much larger than solute particles in a solution. Colloidal particles are large molecules, such as proteins, or groups of molecules or ions. Colloids are homogeneous mixtures that do not separate or settle out. Colloidal particles are small enough to pass through filters but too large to pass through semipermeable membranes. Table 12 lists several examples of colloids.

TABLE 12 Examples of Colloids

	Substance Dispersed	Dispersing Medium
Fog, clouds, sprays	Liquid	Gas
Dust, smoke	Solid	Gas
Shaving cream, whipped cream, soapsuds	Gas	Liquid
Styrofoam, marshmallows	Gas	Solid
Mayonnaise, homogenized milk, hand lotions	Liquid	Liquid
Cheese, butter	Liquid	Solid
Blood plasma, paints (latex), gelatin	Solid	Liquid

Chemistry Link to Health

COLLOIDS AND SOLUTIONS IN THE BODY

In the body, colloids are retained by semipermeable membranes. For example, the intestinal lining allows solution particles to pass into the blood and lymph circulatory systems. However, the colloids from foods are too large to pass through the membrane, and they remain in the intestinal tract. Digestion breaks down large colloidal particles, such as starch and protein, into smaller particles, such as glucose and amino acids, that can pass through the intestinal membrane and enter the circulatory system. However, human digestive processes cannot break down certain foods, such as bran, a form of fiber, and they move through the intestine intact.

Because large proteins, such as enzymes, are colloids, they remain inside cells. However, many of the substances that must be obtained by cells, such as oxygen, amino acids, electrolytes, glucose, and minerals, can pass through cellular membranes. Waste products, such as urea and carbon dioxide, pass out of the cell to be excreted.

Suspensions

Suspensions are heterogeneous, nonuniform mixtures that are very different from solutions or colloids. The particles of a suspension are so large that they can often be seen with the naked eye. These particles are trapped by filters and semipermeable membranes.

The weight of the suspended solute particles causes them to settle out soon after mixing. If you stir muddy water, it mixes but then quickly separates as the suspended particles settle to the bottom and leave clear liquid at the top. You can find suspensions among the medications in a hospital or in your medicine cabinet. These include Kaopectate, calamine lotion, antacid mixtures, and liquid penicillin. It is important to "shake well before using" to suspend all the particles before giving a medication that is a suspension.

Water-treatment plants make use of the properties of suspensions to purify water. When flocculants such as aluminum sulfate or iron(III) sulfate are added to untreated water, they react with small particles of impurities to form large suspended particles called *floc*. In the water-treatment plant, a system of filters traps the suspended particles but allows clean water to pass through.

Table 13 compares the different types of mixtures, and Figure 9 illustrates some properties of solutions, colloids, and suspensions.

TABLE 13 Comparison of Solutions, Colloids, and Suspensions

Type of Mixture	Type of Particle	Settling	Separation
Solution	Small particles such as atoms, ions, or small molecules	Particles do not settle	Particles cannot be separated by filters or semipermeable membranes
Colloid	Larger molecules or groups of molecules or ions	Particles do not settle	Particles can be separated by semipermeable membranes but not by filters
Suspension	Very large particles that may be visible	Particles settle rapidly	Particles can be separated by filters

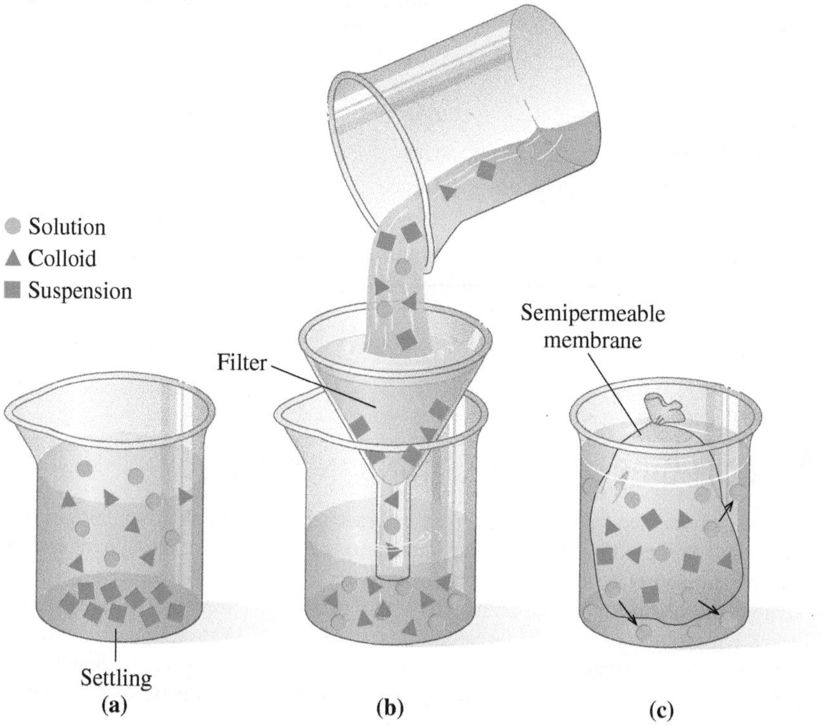

FIGURE 9 Properties of different types of mixtures: **(a)** Suspensions settle out; **(b)** suspensions are separated by a filter; **(c)** solution particles go through a semipermeable membrane, but colloids and suspensions do not.

Q A filter can be used to separate suspension particles from a solution, but a semipermeable membrane is needed to separate colloids from a solution. Explain.

CONCEPT CHECK 8 **Classifying Types of Mixtures**

Classify each of the following as a solution, a colloid, or a suspension:

a. a mixture that has particles that settle upon standing
b. a mixture whose solute particles pass through both filters and membranes
c. an enzyme, which is a large protein molecule, that cannot pass through cellular membranes, but does pass through a filter

ANSWER

a. A suspension has very large particles that settle upon standing.
b. A solution contains particles small enough to pass through both filters and membranes.
c. A colloid contains particles that are small enough to pass through a filter, but too large to pass through a membrane.

Freezing Point Lowering and Boiling Point Elevation

When a solute is added to water, the physical properties such as freezing point and boiling point change. The freezing point is lowered and boiling point is raised. These types of changes, known as *colligative properties*, depend only upon the number of molecules or solute particles in a given volume of solvent and not on the kind of particles.

Probably one familiar example of lowering the freezing point is the process of spreading salt on icy sidewalks and roads when temperatures drop below freezing. The particles from the salt combine with water to lower the freezing point, which causes the ice to melt. Another example is the addition of antifreeze, such as ethylene glycol, $C_2H_6O_2$, to the water in a car radiator. If the ethylene glycol and water mixture is about 50% water by mass, it does not freeze until the temperature drops to about −37 °C (−34 °F) and does not boil unless the temperature goes above 124 °C (255 °F). The solution in the radiator prevents the water from forming ice in cold weather and boiling over on a hot desert highway.

Florida Images/Alamy

A truck spreads calcium chloride on the road to melt ice and snow.

Insects and fish in climates with subfreezing temperatures control ice formation by producing biological antifreezes made of glycerol, proteins, and sugars such as glucose, within their bodies. Some insects can survive temperatures below −60 °C. These forms of biological antifreezes may one day be applied to the long-term preservation of human organs.

The lowering of the freezing point is due to solute particles, which disrupt the formation of the solid ice structure. When a solute is added to a solvent, the solvent molecules are prevented from forming a solid. In order to freeze the solution, the temperature must be lower than the freezing point of the solvent. The greater the solute concentration, the lower the freezing point will be. A similar effect happens to the boiling point of a solvent. When a solute is added to a solvent, the vapor pressure of the solvent is decreased. In order to boil the solution, the temperature must be higher than that of the solvent to attain the vapor pressure necessary to boil.

Argonaut/Shutterstock

The Alaskan Upis beetle produces biological antifreeze to survive subfreezing temperatures.

One mole of particles in 1000 g of water lowers the freezing point from 0 °C to −1.86 °C. If there are 2 moles of particles in 1000 g of water, the freezing point drops to −3.72 °C. A similar change occurs with the boiling point of water. One mole of particles in 1000 g of water raises the boiling point by 0.52 °C, from 100. °C to 100.52 °C.

As we discussed in Section 2, a solute that is a nonelectrolyte dissolves as molecules, whereas a solute that is a strong electrolyte dissolves entirely as ions. The solute in antifreeze, which is ethylene glycol, $C_2H_6O_2$, dissolves as molecules. The salt $CaCl_2$ used to melt ice on roads and sidewalks produces 3 moles of particles, 1 mole of Ca^{2+} and 2 moles of Cl^-, from 1 mole of $CaCl_2$, which will lower the freezing point of water three times more than one mole of ethylene glycol. The effect of solute particles on the freezing point and the boiling point is summarized in Table 14.

Nonelectrolyte:

$$1 \text{ mole of } C_2H_6O_2(l) = 1 \text{ mole of } C_2H_6O_2(aq)$$

Strong electrolytes:

$$1 \text{ mole of NaCl}(s) = \underbrace{1 \text{ mole of } Na^+(aq) + 1 \text{ mole of } Cl^-(aq)}_{2 \text{ moles of particles } (aq)}$$

$$1 \text{ mole of } CaCl_2(s) = \underbrace{1 \text{ mole of } Ca^{2+}(aq) + 2 \text{ moles of } Cl^-(aq)}_{3 \text{ moles of particles } (aq)}$$

TABLE 14 Effect of Solute Concentration on Freezing and Boiling Points of 1000 g of Water

Substance	Type of Solute	Moles of Solute Particles	Freezing Point	Boiling Point
Pure water	None	0	0 °C	100 °C
1 mole of ethylene glycol	Nonelectrolyte	1 mole	−1.86 °C	100.52 °C
1 mole of NaCl	Strong electrolyte	2 moles	−3.72 °C	101.04 °C
1 mole of $CaCl_2$	Strong electrolyte	3 moles	−5.58 °C	101.56 °C

iStockphoto

Ethylene glycol is added to a car radiator to form a solution that has a lower freezing point and a higher boiling point than water.

CONCEPT CHECK 9 **Freezing Point Changes**

In each pair, identify the solution that will have a lower freezing point. Explain.

a. 1.0 mole of NaOH (strong electrolyte) and 1.0 mole of ethylene glycol (nonelectrolyte) each in 1.0 L of water.

b. 0.20 mole of KNO_3 (strong electrolyte) and 0.20 mole of $Ca(NO_3)_2$ (strong electrolyte) each in 1.0 L of water.

ANSWER

a. When 1.0 mole of NaOH dissolves in water, it will produce 2.0 moles of particles because each NaOH dissociates to give two particles, Na^+ and OH^-. However, 1.0 mole of ethylene glycol dissolves as molecules to produce only 1.0 mole of particles. Thus, 1.0 mole of NaOH in 1.0 L of water will have the lower freezing point.

b. When 0.20 mole of KNO_3 dissolves in water, it will produce 0.40 mole of particles because each KNO_3 dissociates to give two particles, K^+ and NO_3^-. When 0.20 mole of $Ca(NO_3)_2$ dissolves in water, it will produce 0.60 mole of particles because each $Ca(NO_3)_2$ dissociates to give three particles, Ca^{2+} and $2NO_3^-$. Thus, 0.20 mole of $Ca(NO_3)_2$ in 1.0 L of water will have the lower freezing point.

Osmotic Pressure

SELF-STUDY ACTIVITY
Diffusion

TUTORIAL
Osmosis

In **osmosis**, a semipermeable membrane allows molecules of the solvent, water, to move through but retains the solute molecules. In this process of diffusion, water moves from the compartment where its concentration is higher to the side where it has a lower concentration. In terms of solute concentration, water flows through the membrane in the direction that will equalize or attempt to equalize the concentrations of solute on both sides. Although water can flow in both directions through the semipermeable membrane, the net flow of water is from the side with the lower solute concentration into the side with the higher solute concentration.

If an osmosis apparatus contains water on one side and a sucrose solution on the other side, the net flow of water will be from the pure water into the sucrose solution, which increases its volume and lowers its sucrose concentration. In the case where two sucrose solutions with different concentrations are placed on each side of the semipermeable membrane, water will flow from the side containing the lower sucrose concentration into the side containing the higher sucrose concentration.

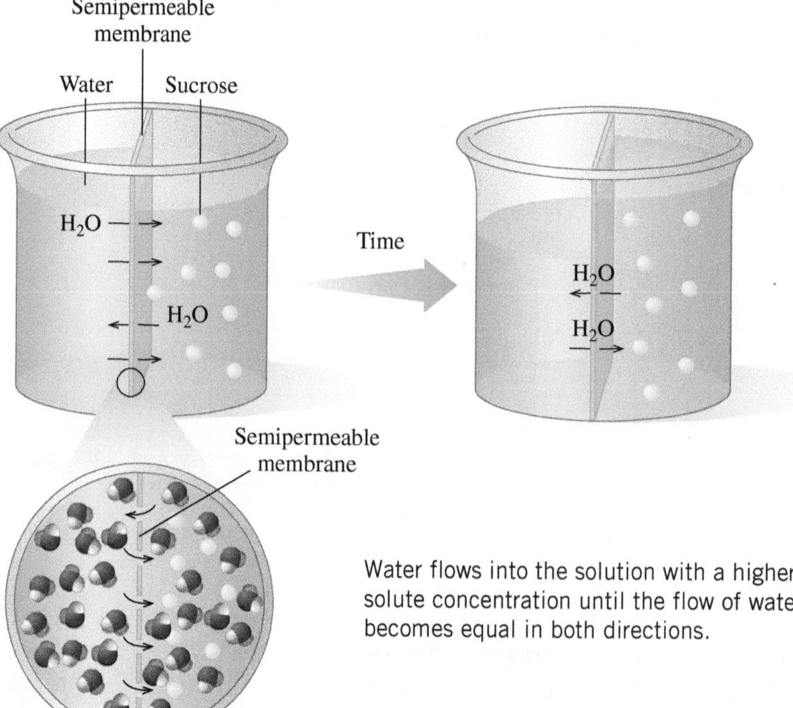

Water flows into the solution with a higher solute concentration until the flow of water becomes equal in both directions.

Eventually, the height of the sucrose solution creates sufficient pressure to equalize the flow of water between the two compartments. This pressure, called **osmotic pressure**, prevents the flow of additional water into the more concentrated solution. Then there is no further change in the volumes of the two solutions. The osmotic pressure depends on the concentration of solute particles in the solution. The greater the number of particles dissolved, the higher its osmotic pressure. In this example, the sucrose solution has a higher osmotic pressure than pure water, which has an osmotic pressure of zero.

In a process called *reverse osmosis*, a pressure greater than the osmotic pressure is applied to a solution so that it is forced through a purification membrane. The flow of water is reversed because water flows from an area of lower water concentration to an area of higher water concentration. The molecules and ions in solution stay behind, trapped by the membrane, while water passes through the membrane. This process of reverse osmosis is used in a few desalination plants to obtain pure water from sea (salt) water. However, the pressure that must be applied requires so much energy that reverse osmosis is not yet an economical method for obtaining pure water in most parts of the world.

CONCEPT CHECK 10 **Osmotic Pressure**

A 2% (m/v) sucrose solution and an 8% (m/v) sucrose solution are separated by a semipermeable membrane.

a. Which sucrose solution exerts the greater osmotic pressure?
b. In what direction does water flow initially?
c. Which solution will have the higher level of liquid at equilibrium?

ANSWER

a. The 8% (m/v) sucrose solution has the higher solute concentration, more solute particles, and the greater osmotic pressure.
b. Initially, water will flow out of the 2% (m/v) solution into the more concentrated 8% (m/v) solution.
c. The level of the 8% (m/v) solution will be higher.

EVERYDAY OSMOSIS

1. Place a few pieces of dried fruit such as raisins, prunes, or banana chips in water. Observe them after 1 hour or more. Look at them again the next day.
2. Place some grapes in a concentrated salt-water solution. Observe them after 1 h or more. Look at them again the next day.
3. Place one potato slice in water and another slice in a concentrated salt-water solution. After 1 or 2 h, observe the shapes and sizes of the slices. Look at them again the next day.

QUESTIONS

1. How did the shape of the dried fruit change after being in water? Explain.
2. How did the appearance of the grapes change after being in a concentrated salt-water solution? Explain.
3. How does the appearance of the potato slice that was placed in water compare to the appearance of the potato slice placed in salt water? Explain.
4. At the grocery store, why are sprinklers used to spray water on fresh produce such as lettuce, carrots, and cucumbers?

Isotonic Solutions

Because the cell membranes in biological systems are semipermeable, osmosis is an ongoing process. The solutes in body solutions such as blood, tissue fluids, lymph, and plasma all exert osmotic pressure. Most intravenous solutions are **isotonic solutions**, which exert the same osmotic pressure as body fluids, such as blood. *Iso* means "equal to," and *tonic* refers to the osmotic pressure of the solution in the cell. Isotonic solutions include 0.9% (m/v) NaCl solution and 5% (m/v) glucose solution. Although they do not contain the same particles, a 0.9% (m/v) NaCl solution as well as a 5% (m/v) glucose solution are both 0.3 M (Na^+ and Cl^- ions or glucose molecules). A red blood cell placed in an isotonic solution retains its volume because there is an equal flow of water into and out of the cell (see Figure 10a).

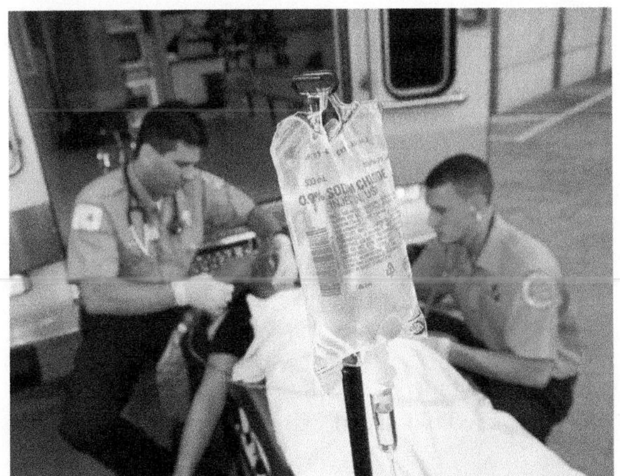

Thinkstock Images/Getty Images

A 0.9% NaCl solution is isotonic with the solute concentration of the blood cells of the body.

Hypotonic and Hypertonic Solutions

If a red blood cell is placed in a solution that is not isotonic, the differences in osmotic pressure inside and outside the cell can drastically alter the volume of the cell. When a red blood cell is placed in a **hypotonic solution**, which has a lower solute concentration (*hypo* means "lower than"), water flows into the cell by osmosis in order to dilute the solutes within the cell (see Figure 10b). The increase in fluid causes the cell to swell, and possibly burst—a process called **hemolysis**. A similar process occurs when you place dehydrated food, such as raisins or dried fruit, in water. The water enters the cells, and the food becomes plump and smooth.

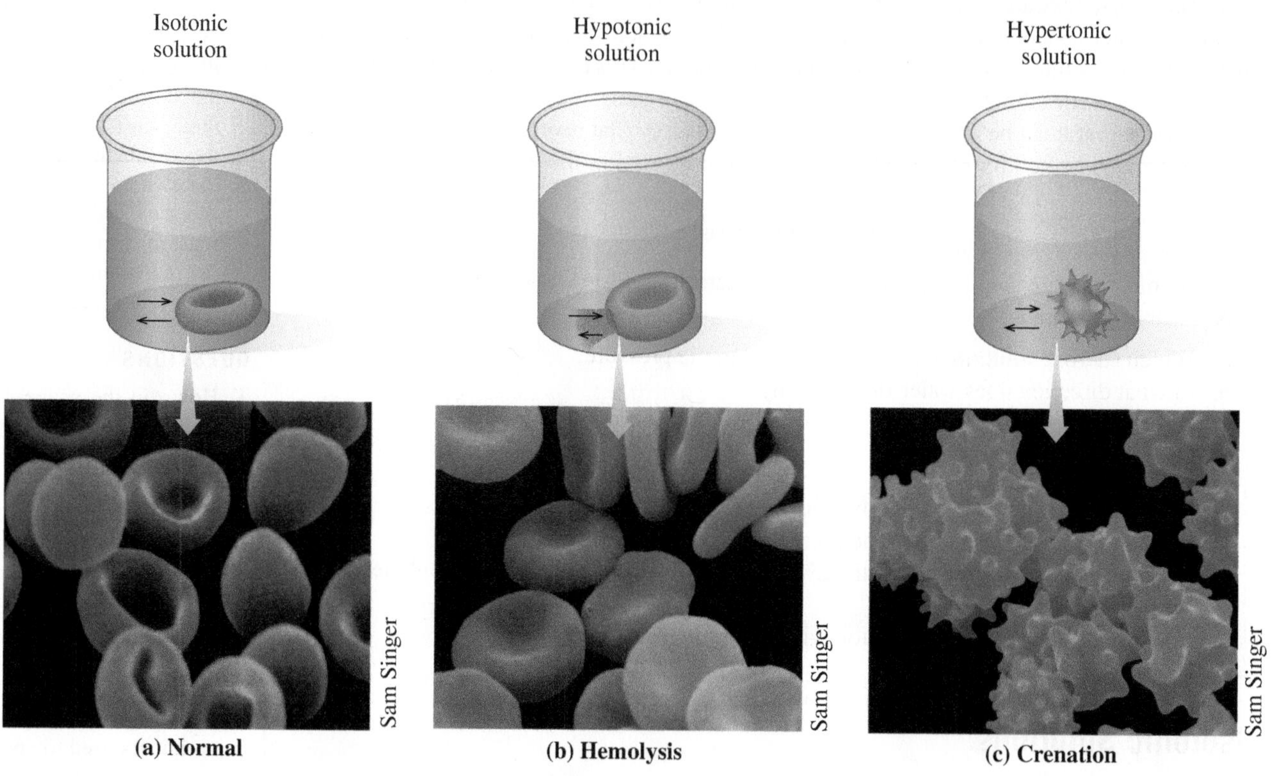

FIGURE 10 **(a)** In an isotonic solution, a red blood cell retains its normal volume. **(b)** Hemolysis: In a hypotonic solution, water flows into a red blood cell, causing it to swell and burst. **(c)** Crenation: In a hypertonic solution, water leaves the red blood cell, causing it to shrink.

Q What happens to a red blood cell placed in a 4% (m/v) NaCl solution?

If a red blood cell is placed in a **hypertonic solution**, which has a higher solute concentration than that inside the red blood cell (*hyper* means "greater than"), water molecules flow out of the cell by osmosis to dilute the solutes outside the cell. Suppose a red blood cell is placed in a 10% (m/v) NaCl solution. Because the osmotic pressure in the red blood cell is equal to that of a 0.9% (m/v) NaCl solution, the 10% (m/v) NaCl solution has a much greater osmotic pressure. As water is lost, the cell shrinks—a process called **crenation** (see Figure 10c). A similar process occurs when making pickles, which uses a hypertonic salt solution that causes the cucumbers to shrivel as they lose water.

SAMPLE PROBLEM 14 **Isotonic, Hypotonic, and Hypertonic Solutions**

Describe each of the following solutions as isotonic, hypotonic, or hypertonic. Indicate whether a red blood cell placed in each solution will undergo hemolysis, crenation, or no change.

a. a 5% (m/v) glucose solution **b.** a 0.2% (m/v) NaCl solution

SOLUTION

a. A 5% (m/v) glucose solution is isotonic. A red blood cell will not undergo any change.
b. A 0.2% (m/v) NaCl solution is hypotonic. A red blood cell will undergo hemolysis.

STUDY CHECK 14

What will happen to a red blood cell placed in a 10% (m/v) glucose solution?

Dialysis

TUTORIAL
Dialysis

Dialysis is a process that is similar to osmosis. In dialysis, a semipermeable membrane, called a *dialyzing membrane*, has small holes that permit small solute molecules and ions as well as solvent water molecules to pass through, but still retain large particles, such as colloids. Dialysis is a way to separate solution particles from colloids.

Suppose we fill a cellophane bag with a solution containing NaCl, glucose, starch, and protein and place it in pure water. Cellophane is a dialyzing membrane, and the sodium ions, chloride ions, and glucose molecules will pass through it into the surrounding water. However, starch and protein remain inside because they are colloids. Water molecules will flow by osmosis into the cellophane bag. Eventually the concentrations of sodium ions, chloride ions, and glucose molecules inside and outside the dialysis bag become equal. To remove more NaCl or glucose, the cellophane bag must be placed in a fresh sample of pure water.

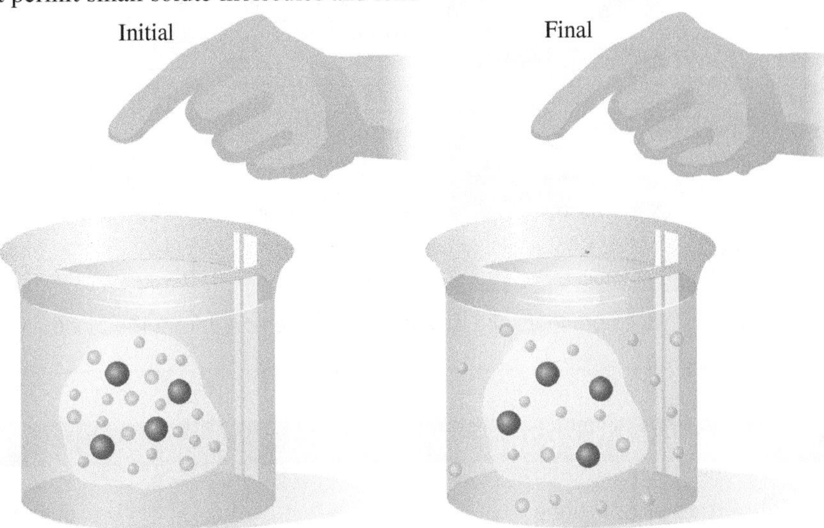

Chemistry Link to Health

DIALYSIS BY THE KIDNEYS AND THE ARTIFICIAL KIDNEY

The fluids of the body undergo dialysis by the membranes of the kidneys, which remove waste materials, excess salts, and water. In an adult, each kidney contains about 2 million nephrons, the functional unit of the kidney. At the top of each nephron, there is a network of arterial capillaries called the *glomerulus*.

As blood flows into the nephron, small particles, such as amino acids, glucose, urea, water, and certain ions, will move through the capillary membranes of the glomerulus. As this solution moves through the membrane of the glomerulus, substances still of value to the body (such as amino acids, glucose, certain ions, and 99% of the water) are reabsorbed. The major waste product, urea, is excreted in the urine.

Hemodialysis

If the kidneys fail to dialyze waste products, increased levels of urea can become life-threatening in a relatively short time. A person with kidney failure must use an artificial kidney, which cleanses the blood by **hemodialysis**.

A typical artificial kidney machine contains a large tank filled with water containing selected electrolytes. In the center of this dialyzing bath (dialysate), there is a dialyzing coil or membrane made of cellulose tubing. As the patient's blood flows through the dialyzing coil, the highly concentrated waste products dialyze out of the blood. No blood is lost, because the membrane is not permeable to large particles such as red blood cells.

Dialysis patients do not produce much urine. As a result, they retain large amounts of water between dialysis treatments, which produces a strain on the heart. The intake of fluids for a dialysis patient may be restricted to as little as a few teaspoons of water a day. In the dialysis procedure, the pressure of the blood is increased as it circulates through the dialyzing coil so water can be squeezed out of the blood. For some dialysis patients, 2–10 L of water may be removed during one treatment. Dialysis patients typically have from two to three treatments a week, each treatment requiring about 5–7 h. Some of the newer treatments require less time. For many patients, dialysis is done at home with a home dialysis unit.

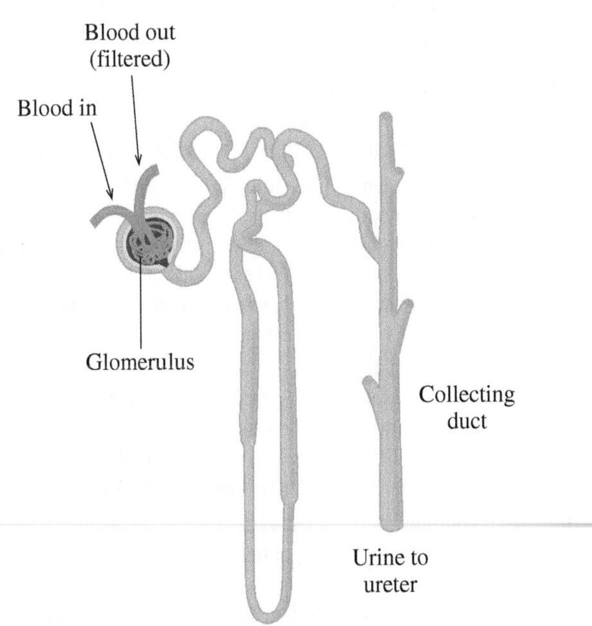

In the kidneys, the nephrons each contain a glomerulus where urea and waste products are removed from the blood to form urine.

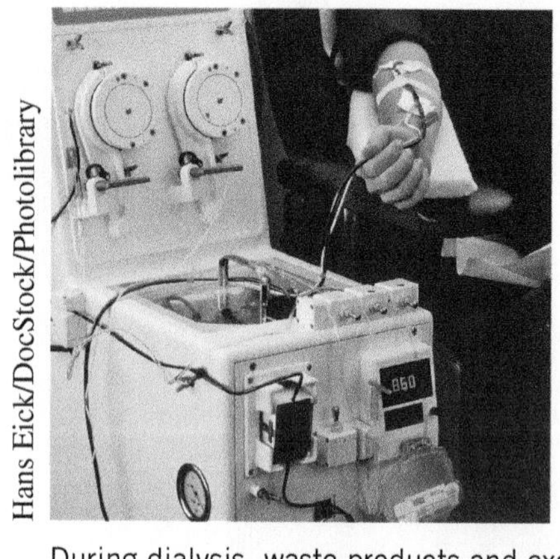

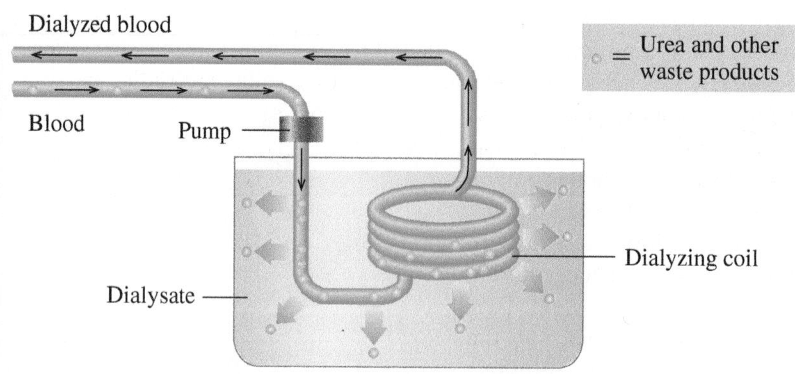

During dialysis, waste products and excess water are removed from the blood.

QUESTIONS AND PROBLEMS

6 Properties of Solutions

LEARNING GOAL: *Identify a mixture as a solution, a colloid, or a suspension. Describe how the number of particles in a solution affects the freezing point, boiling point, and osmotic pressure of a solution.*

65 Identify the following as characteristic of a solution, a colloid, or a suspension:
- **a.** a mixture that cannot be separated by a semipermeable membrane
- **b.** a mixture that settles out upon standing

66 Identify the following as characteristic of a solution, a colloid, or a suspension:
- **a.** Particles of this mixture remain inside a semipermeable membrane but pass through filters.
- **b.** The particles of solute in this mixture are very large and visible.

67 In each pair, identify the solution that will have a lower freezing point. Explain.
- **a.** 1.0 mole of glycerol (nonelectrolyte) and 2.0 moles of ethylene glycol (nonelectrolyte) each in 1.0 L of water
- **b.** 0.50 mole of KCl (strong electrolyte) and 0.50 mole of $MgCl_2$ (strong electrolyte) each in 2.0 L of water

68 In each pair, identify the solution that will have a higher boiling point. Explain.
- **a.** 1.50 moles of LiOH (strong electrolyte) and 3.00 moles of KOH (strong electrolyte) each in 0.50 L of water
- **b.** 0.40 mole of $Al(NO_3)_3$ (strong electrolyte) and 0.40 mole of CsCl (strong electrolyte) each in 0.50 L of water

69 A 10% (m/v) starch solution is separated from a 1% (m/v) starch solution by a semipermeable membrane. (Starch is a colloid.)
- **a.** Which compartment has the higher osmotic pressure?
- **b.** In which direction will water flow initially?
- **c.** In which compartment will the volume level rise?

70 Two solutions, a 0.1% (m/v) albumin solution and a 2% (m/v) albumin solution, are separated by a semipermeable membrane. (Albumin is a colloid.)
- **a.** Which compartment has the higher osmotic pressure?
- **b.** In which direction will water flow initially?
- **c.** In which compartment will the volume level rise?

71 Indicate the compartment (A or B) that will increase in volume for each of the following pairs of solutions separated by semipermeable membranes:

Solution in A	Solution in B
a. 5% (m/v) starch	10% (m/v) starch
b. 8% (m/v) albumin	4% (m/v) albumin
c. 0.1% (m/v) sucrose	10% (m/v) sucrose

72 Indicate the compartment (A or B) that will increase in volume for each of the following pairs of solutions separated by semipermeable membranes:

Solution in A	Solution in B
a. 20% (m/v) starch	10% (m/v) starch
b. 10% (m/v) albumin	2% (m/v) albumin
c. 0.5% (m/v) sucrose	5% (m/v) sucrose

73 Are the following solutions isotonic, hypotonic, or hypertonic compared with a red blood cell?
- **a.** distilled H_2O
- **b.** 1% (m/v) glucose
- **c.** 0.9% (m/v) NaCl
- **d.** 15% (m/v) glucose

74 Will a red blood cell undergo crenation, hemolysis, or no change in each of the following solutions?
- **a.** 1% (m/v) glucose
- **b.** 2% (m/v) NaCl
- **c.** 5% (m/v) glucose
- **d.** 0.1% (m/v) NaCl

75 Each of the following mixtures is placed in a dialyzing bag and immersed in distilled water. Which substances will be found outside the bag in the distilled water?
- **a.** NaCl solution
- **b.** starch solution (colloid) and alanine, an amino acid, solution
- **c.** NaCl solution and starch solution (colloid)
- **d.** urea solution

76 Each of the following mixtures is placed in a dialyzing bag and immersed in distilled water. Which substances will be found outside the bag in the distilled water?
- **a.** KCl solution and glucose solution
- **b.** an albumin solution (colloid)
- **c.** an albumin solution (colloid), KCl solution, and glucose solution
- **d.** urea solution and NaCl solution

CONCEPT MAP

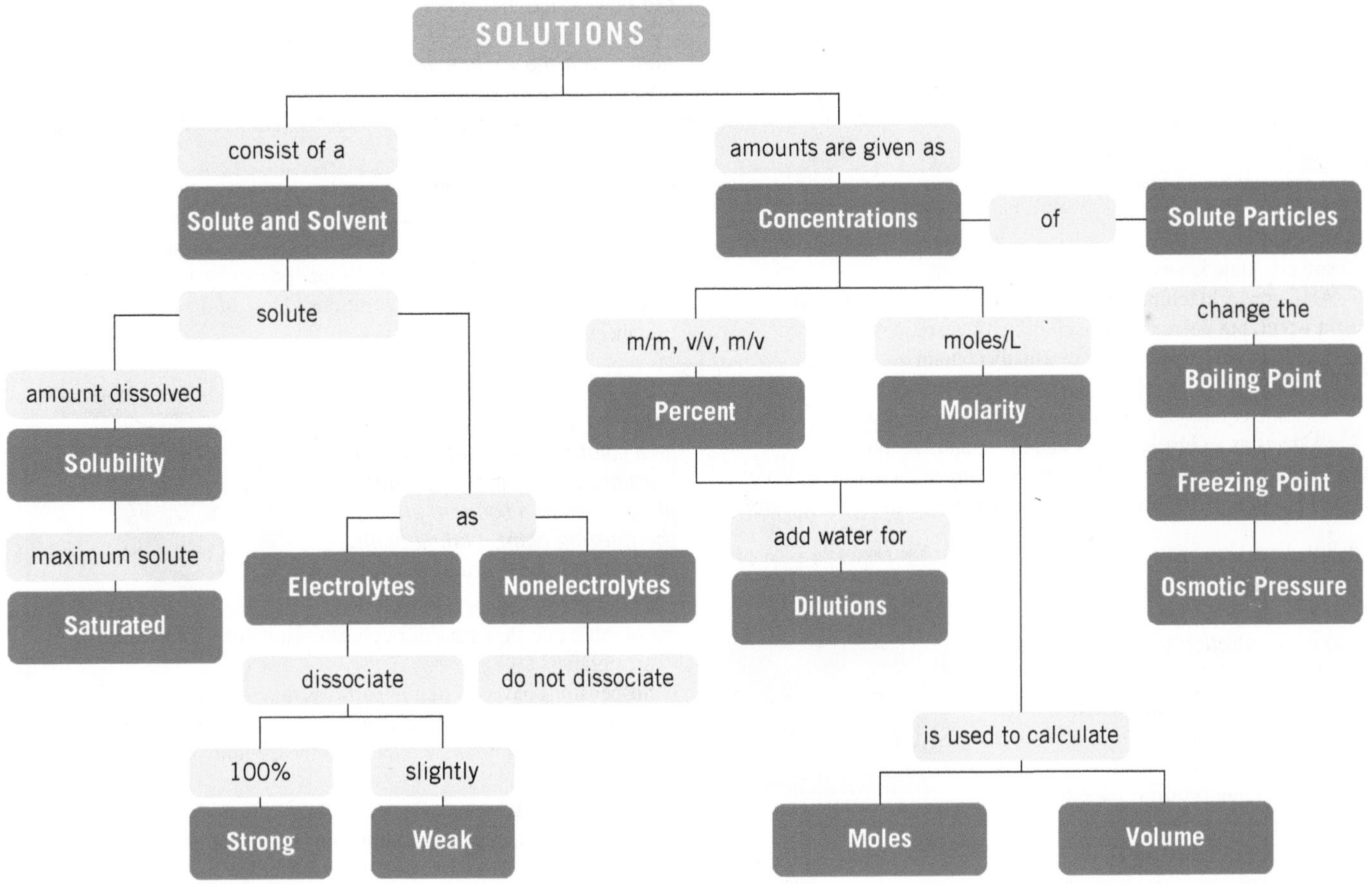

SOLUTIONS

- consist of a **Solute and Solvent**
  - solute
    - amount dissolved **Solubility**
      - maximum solute **Saturated**
    - as **Electrolytes**
      - dissociate
        - 100% **Strong**
        - slightly **Weak**
    - as **Nonelectrolytes**
      - do not dissociate
- amounts are given as **Concentrations** of **Solute Particles**
  - m/m, v/v, m/v **Percent**
  - moles/L **Molarity**
    - is used to calculate **Moles**, **Volume**
  - **Percent** and **Molarity**: add water for **Dilutions**
  - **Solute Particles** change the **Boiling Point**, **Freezing Point**, **Osmotic Pressure**

CHAPTER REVIEW

1 Solutions

LEARNING GOAL: *Identify the solute and solvent in a solution; describe the formation of a solution.*

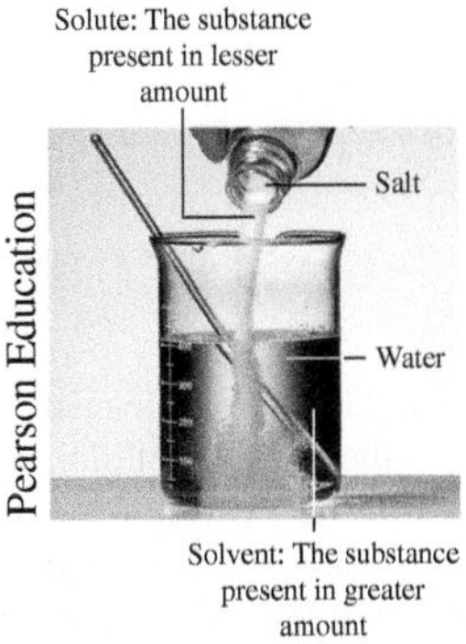

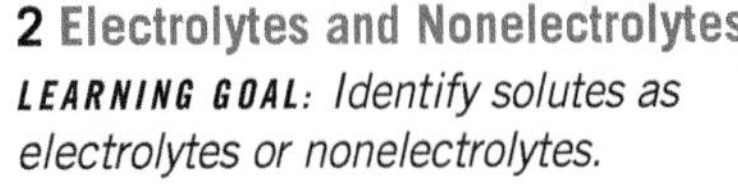

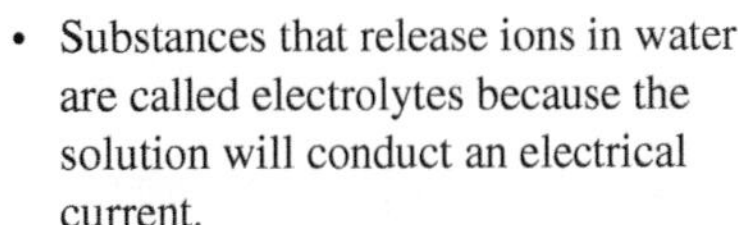

- A solution forms when a solute, usually the smaller quantity, dissolves in a solvent.
- In a solution, the particles of solute are evenly dispersed in the solvent.
- The solute and solvent may be solid, liquid, or gas.
- The polar O—H groups form hydrogen bonds between water molecules.
- An ionic solute dissolves in water—a polar solvent—because the polar water molecules attract and pull the ions into solution, where they become hydrated.
- The expression "like dissolves like" means that a polar or ionic solute dissolves in a polar solvent while a nonpolar solute requires a nonpolar solvent.

2 Electrolytes and Nonelectrolytes

LEARNING GOAL: *Identify solutes as electrolytes or nonelectrolytes.*

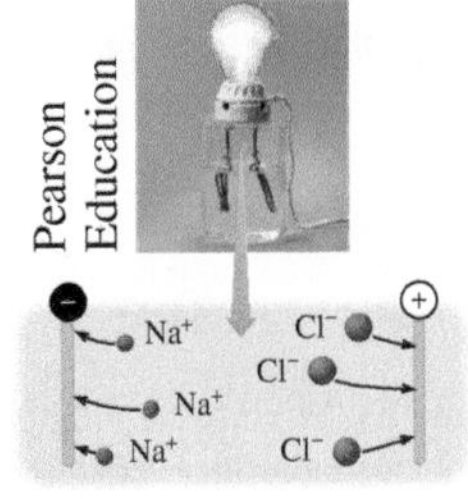

Strong electrolyte

- Substances that release ions in water are called electrolytes because the solution will conduct an electrical current.
- Strong electrolytes are completely ionized, whereas weak electrolytes are only partially ionized.
- Nonelectrolytes are substances that dissolve in water to produce molecules and cannot conduct electrical currents.
- An equivalent (Eq) is the amount of an electrolyte that carries 1 mole of positive or negative charge.
- In fluid replacement solutions, the concentrations of electrolytes are expressed as mEq/L of solution.

3 Solubility

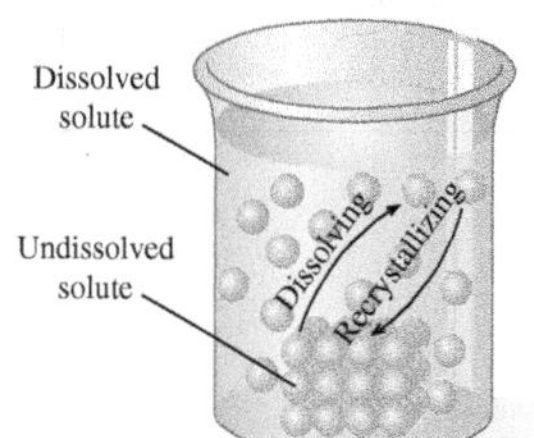

Saturated solution

LEARNING GOAL: *Define solubility. Distinguish between an unsaturated and a saturated solution; identify a salt as soluble or insoluble.*

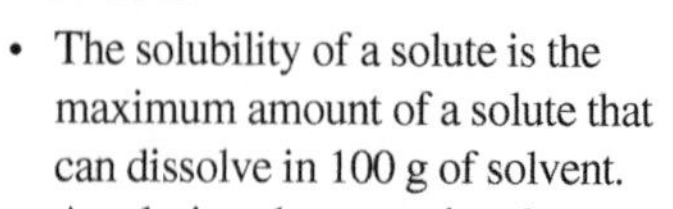

- The solubility of a solute is the maximum amount of a solute that can dissolve in 100 g of solvent.
- A solution that contains the maximum amount of dissolved solute is a saturated solution.
- A solution containing less than the maximum amount of dissolved solute is unsaturated.

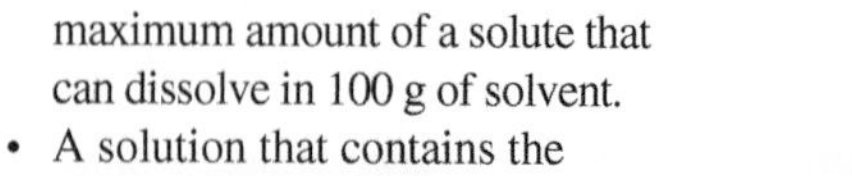

- An increase in temperature increases the solubility of most solids in water, but decreases the solubility of gases in water.

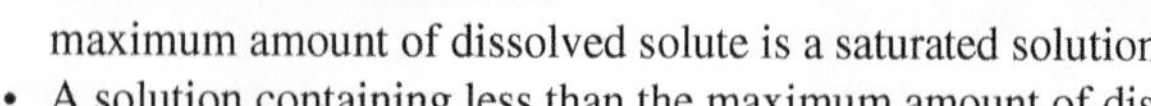

- Salts that are soluble in water usually contain Li^+, Na^+, K^+, NH_4^+, NO_3^-, or acetate $C_2H_3O_2^-$.
- An ionic equation consists of writing the reactants as ions and the products as an insoluble salt and the remaining ions.
- A net ionic equation is written by removing all the ions that do not change during the reaction (spectator ions) from the ionic equation.

4 Solution Concentration

LEARNING GOAL: *Calculate the concentration of a solute in a solution; use concentration to calculate the amount of solute or solution.*

Water added to make a solution — 250 mL — 5.0 g of KI — Pearson Education

- The concentration of a solution is the amount of solute dissolved in a certain amount of solution.
- Mass percent (m/m) is the ratio of the mass of the solute to the mass of the solution multiplied by 100%.
- Volume percent (v/v) is the ratio of the volume of the solute to the volume of the solution multiplied by 100%.
- Mass/volume percent (m/v) is the ratio of the mass of the solute to the volume of the solution multiplied by 100%.
- Molarity (M) is the ratio of the moles of the solute to the volume in liters of the solution.
- In calculations of grams or milliliters of solute or solution, the percent concentration is used as a conversion factor.
- In calculations with moles of solute and liters of solution, the molarity is used as a conversion factor.

5 Dilution of Solutions and Solution Reactions

LEARNING GOAL: *Calculate the new concentration or volume of a diluted solution. Given the volume and concentration of a solution, calculate the amount of another reactant or product in a reaction.*

- In a dilution, a solvent such as water is added to a solution, which increases its volume and decreases its concentration.
- If the mass or solution volume and molarity of substances in a reaction are given, the balanced equation can be used to determine the quantities or concentrations of any of the other substances in the reaction.

6 Properties of Solutions

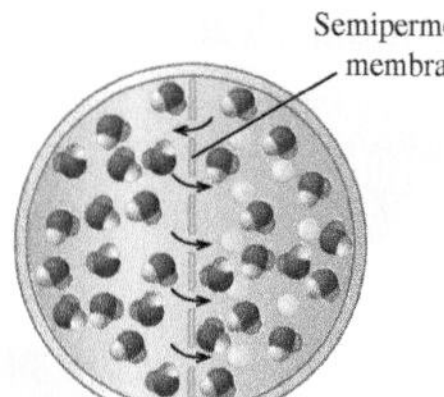

LEARNING GOAL: *Identify a mixture as a solution, a colloid, or a suspension. Describe how the number of particles in a solution affects the freezing point, boiling point, and osmotic pressure of a solution.*

- Colloids contain particles that do not settle out; they pass through filters but not semipermeable membranes.
- Suspensions have very large particles that settle out of solution.
- The particles of solute in a solution lower the freezing point, raise the boiling point, and increase the osmotic pressure of the solution.
- In osmosis, solvent (water) passes through a semipermeable membrane from a solution with a lower osmotic pressure (lower solute concentration) to a solution with a higher osmotic pressure (higher solute concentration).
- Isotonic solutions have osmotic pressures equal to that of body fluids.
- A red blood cell maintains its volume in an isotonic solution, but swells and may burst (hemolyze) in a hypotonic solution and shrinks (crenates) in a hypertonic solution.
- In dialysis, water and small solute particles pass through a dialyzing membrane, while larger solute particles are retained.

KEY TERMS

colloids Mixtures having particles that are moderately large. Colloids pass through filters but cannot pass through semipermeable membranes.

concentration A measure of the amount of solute that is dissolved in a specified amount of solution.

crenation The shriveling of a cell due to water leaving the cell when the cell is placed in a hypertonic solution.

dialysis A process in which water and small solute particles pass through a semipermeable membrane.

dilution A process by which water (solvent) is added to a solution to increase the volume and decrease (dilute) the concentration of the solute.

electrolyte A substance that produces ions when dissolved in water; its solution conducts electricity.

equivalent (Eq) The amount of a positive or negative ion that supplies 1 mole of electrical charge.

hemodialysis A cleansing of the blood by an artificial kidney using the principle of dialysis.

hemolysis A swelling and bursting of red blood cells in a hypotonic solution due to an increase in fluid volume.

Henry's law The solubility of a gas in a liquid is directly related to the pressure of that gas above the liquid.

hydration The process of surrounding dissolved ions by water molecules.

hypertonic solution A solution that has a higher osmotic pressure than the red blood cells of the body.

hypotonic solution A solution that has a lower osmotic pressure than the red blood cells of the body.

insoluble salt An ionic compound that does not dissolve in water.

ionic equation An equation for a reaction in solution that gives all the individual ions, both reacting ions and spectator ions.

isotonic solution A solution that has the same osmotic pressure as that of the red blood cells of the body.

mass percent (m/m) The grams of solute in exactly 100 g of solution.

mass/volume percent (m/v) The grams of solute in exactly 100 mL of solution.

molarity (M) The number of moles of solute in exactly 1 L of solution.

net ionic equation An equation for a reaction in solution that gives only the reactants and products involved in a chemical change.

nonelectrolyte A substance that dissolves in water as molecules; its solution does not conduct an electrical current.

osmosis The flow of a solvent, usually water, through a semipermeable membrane into a solution of higher solute concentration.

osmotic pressure The pressure that prevents the flow of water into the more concentrated solution.

saturated solution A solution containing the maximum amount of solute that can dissolve at a given temperature. Any additional solute will remain undissolved in the container.

semipermeable membrane A membrane that permits the passage of certain substances while blocking or retaining others.

solubility The maximum amount of solute that can dissolve in exactly 100 g of solvent, usually water, at a given temperature.

soluble salt An ionic compound that dissolves in water.

solute The component in a solution that is present in the smaller quantity.

solution A homogeneous mixture in which the solute is made up of small particles (ions or molecules) that can pass through filters and semipermeable membranes.

solvent The substance in which the solute dissolves; usually the component present in the greatest amount.

strong electrolyte A polar or ionic compound that ionizes completely when it dissolves in water. Its solution is a good conductor of electricity.

suspension A mixture in which the solute particles are large enough and heavy enough to settle out and be retained by both filters and semipermeable membranes.

unsaturated solution A solution that contains less solute than can be dissolved.

volume percent (v/v) A percent concentration that relates the volume of the solute to the volume of the solution.

weak electrolyte A substance that produces only a few ions along with many molecules when it dissolves in water. Its solution is a weak conductor of electricity.

UNDERSTANDING THE CONCEPTS

The chapter sections to review are shown in parentheses at the end of each question.

77 Select the diagram that represents the solution formed by a solute ⚫⚫ that is a: (2)

a. nonelectrolyte **b.** weak electrolyte
c. strong electrolyte

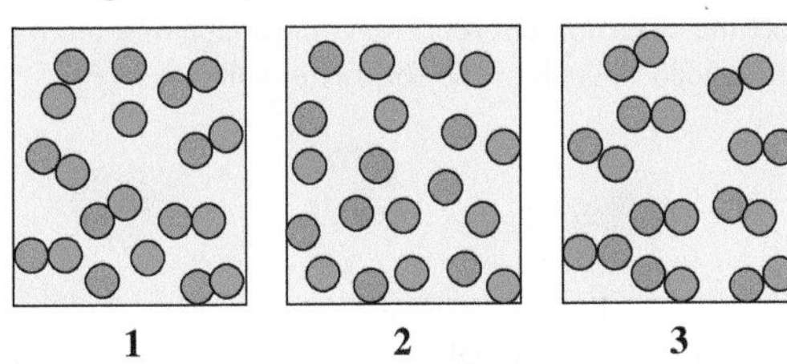

78 Match the diagrams with each of the following: (1)

a. a polar solute and a polar solvent
b. a nonpolar solute and a polar solvent
c. a nonpolar solute and a nonpolar solvent

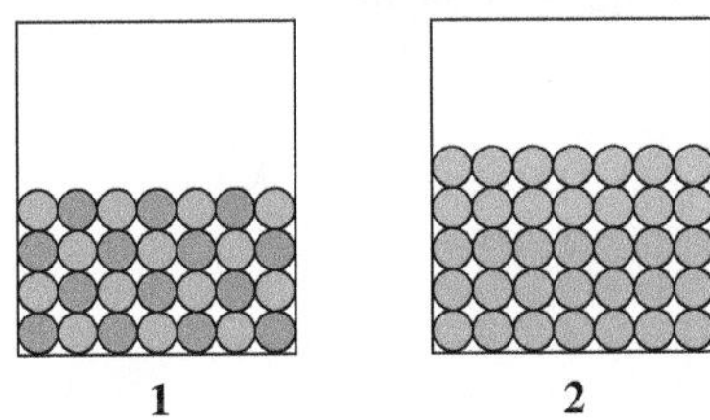

79 Select the container that represents the dilution of a 4% (m/v) NaCl solution to each of the following: (5)

a. a 2% (m/v) NaCl solution
b. a 1% (m/v) NaCl solution

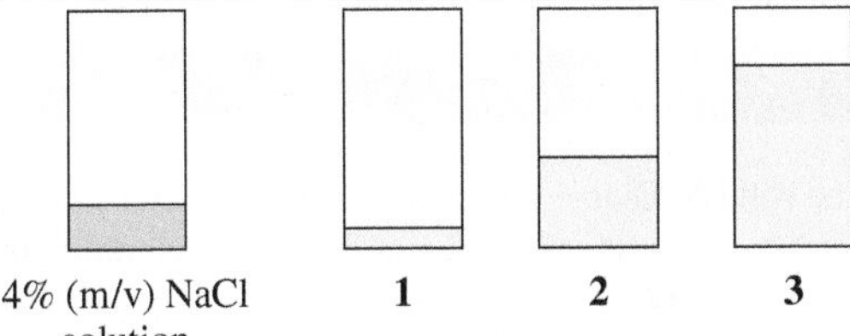

80 If all the solute is dissolved in Figure 1, how would heating or cooling the solution cause each of the following changes? (3)

a. 2 to 3
b. 2 to 1

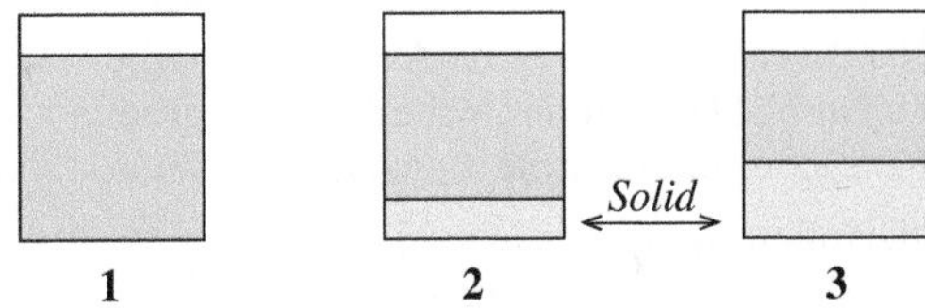

81 A pickle is made by soaking a cucumber in brine, a salt-water solution. What makes the smooth cucumber become wrinkled like a prune? (6)

Simon Watson/Jupiter Images

82 Why do the lettuce leaves in a salad wilt after a vinaigrette dressing containing salt is added? (6)

Ocean/Corbis

Use the following beakers and solutions for Questions 83 and 84:

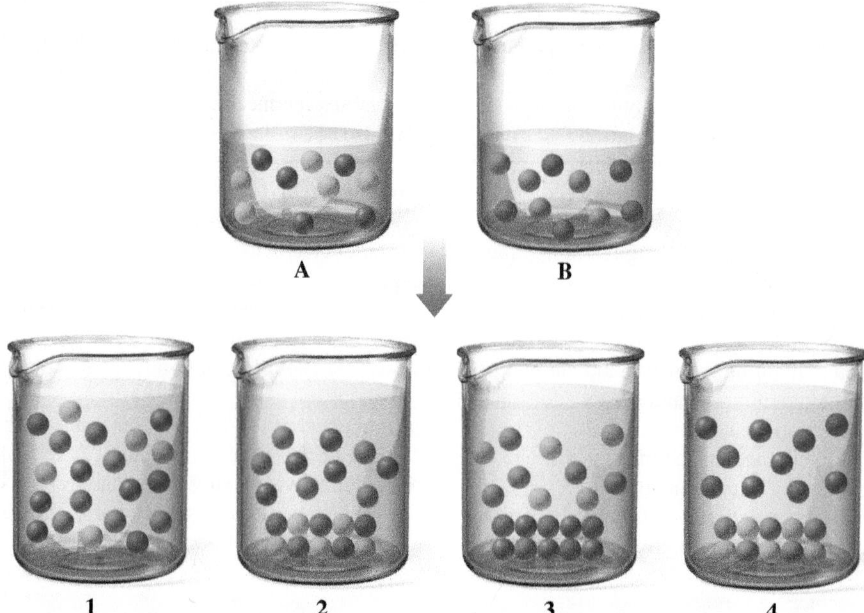

83 Use the following types of ions: (3)

Na^+ Cl^- Ag^+ NO_3^-

a. Select the beaker (1, 2, 3, or 4) that contains the products after the solutions in beakers A and B are mixed.
b. If an insoluble salt forms, write the ionic equation.
c. If a reaction occurs, write the net ionic equation.

84 Use the following types of ions: (3)

K^+ NO_3^- NH_4^+ Br^-

a. Select the beaker (1, 2, 3, or 4) that contains the products after the solutions in beakers A and B are mixed.
b. If an insoluble salt forms, write the ionic equation.
c. If a reaction occurs, write the net ionic equation.

85 A semipermeable membrane separates two compartments, A and B. If the levels of solutions in A and B are equal initially, select the diagram that illustrates the final levels for each of the following: (6)

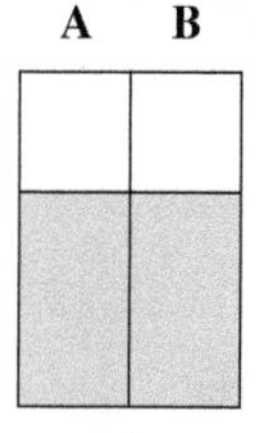

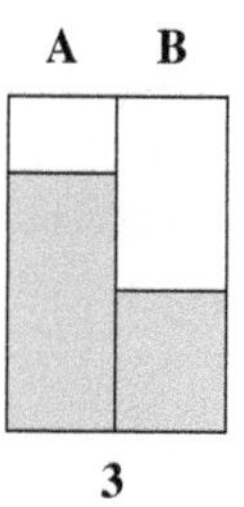

A B

3

Solution in A	Solution in B
a. 2% (m/v) starch	8% (m/v) starch
b. 1% (m/v) starch	1% (m/v) starch
c. 5% (m/v) sucrose	1% (m/v) sucrose
d. 0.1% (m/v) sucrose	1% (m/v) sucrose

86 Select the diagram that represents the shape of a red blood cell when placed in each of the following solutions: (6)

1
Normal red blood cell

2

3

a. 0.9% (m/v) NaCl solution
b. 10% (m/v) glucose solution
c. 0.01% (m/v) NaCl solution
d. 5% (m/v) glucose solution
e. 1% (m/v) glucose solution

ADDITIONAL QUESTIONS AND PROBLEMS

For instructor-assigned homework, go to www.masteringchemistry.com.

87 If sodium chloride has a solubility of 36.0 g of NaCl in 100 g of H_2O at 20 °C, how many grams of water are needed to prepare a saturated solution containing 80.0 g of NaCl? (3)

88 If the solid NaCl in a saturated solution of NaCl continues to dissolve, why is there no change in the concentration of the NaCl solution? (3)

89 Potassium nitrate has a solubility of 32 g of KNO_3 in 100 g of H_2O at 20 °C. State if each of the following forms an unsaturated or saturated solution at 20 °C: (3)
a. 32 g of KNO_3 and 200. g of H_2O
b. 19 g of KNO_3 and 50. g of H_2O
c. 68 g of KNO_3 and 150. g of H_2O

90 Potassium fluoride has a solubility of 92 g of KF in 100 g of H_2O at 18 °C. State if each of the following forms an unsaturated or saturated solution at 18 °C: (3)
a. 46 g of KF and 100. g of H_2O
b. 46 g of KF and 50. g of H_2O
c. 184 g of KF and 150. g of H_2O

91 Indicate whether each of the following ionic compounds is soluble or insoluble in water: (3)
a. $CuCO_3$
b. $NaHCO_3$
c. $Mg_3(PO_4)_2$
d. $(NH_4)_2SO_4$
e. FeO
f. $Ca(OH)_2$

92 Indicate whether each of the following ionic compounds is soluble or insoluble in water: (3)
a. Na_3PO_4
b. $PbBr_2$
c. KCl
d. $(NH_4)_2S$
e. $MgCO_3$
f. $FePO_4$

93 Write the net ionic equation to show the formation of a solid (insoluble salt) when the following solutions are mixed. Write *none* if there is no precipitate. (3)
a. $AgNO_3(aq)$ and $LiCl(aq)$
b. $NaCl(aq)$ and $KNO_3(aq)$
c. $Na_2SO_4(aq)$ and $BaCl_2(aq)$

94 Write the net ionic equation to show the formation of a solid (insoluble salt) when the following solutions are mixed. Write *none* if there is no precipitate. (3)
a. $Ca(NO_3)_2(aq)$ and $Na_2S(aq)$
b. $Na_3PO_4(aq)$ and $Pb(NO_3)_2(aq)$
c. $FeCl_3(aq)$ and $NH_4NO_3(aq)$

95 Calculate the mass percent (m/m) of a solution containing 15.5 g of Na_2SO_4 and 75.5 g of H_2O. (4)

96 Calculate the mass percent (m/m) of a solution containing 26 g of K_2CO_3 and 724 g of H_2O. (4)

97 What is the molarity of a solution containing 0 g of NaOH in 400. mL of NaOH solution? (5)

98 What is the molarity of a solution containing 15.6 g of KCl in 274 mL of KCl solution? (5)

99 How many grams of solute are in each of the following solutions? (5)
a. 2.20 L of a 3.00 M $Al(NO_3)_3$ solution
b. 75.0 mL of a 0.500 M $C_6H_{12}O_6$ solution
c. 0.150 L of a 0.320 M NH_4Cl solution

100 How many grams of solute are in each of the following solutions? (5)
a. 428 mL of a 0.450 M Na_2SO_4 solution
b. 10.5 mL of a 2.50 M $AgNO_3$ solution
c. 28.4 mL of a 6.00 M H_3PO_4 solution

101 A patient receives all her nutrition from fluids given through the vena cava. Every 12 h, 750 mL of a solution that is 4% (m/v) amino acids (protein) and 25% (m/v) glucose (carbohydrate) is given along with 500 mL of a 10% (m/v) lipid (fat) solution. (4)
a. In 1 day, how many grams of amino acids, glucose, and lipid are given to the patient?
b. How many kilocalories does she obtain in 1 day?

102 A patient receives an intravenous solution of a 5.0% (m/v) glucose solution. How many liters of the glucose solution would the patient be given to obtain 75 g of glucose? (4)

103 How many milliliters of a 12% (v/v) propyl alcohol solution would you need to obtain 4.5 mL of propyl alcohol? (4)

104 An 80-proof brandy is 40.0% (v/v) ethyl alcohol. The "proof" is twice the percent concentration of alcohol in the beverage. How many milliliters of alcohol are present in 750 mL of brandy? (4)

105 Calculate the concentration, percent or molarity, of the solution when water is added to prepare each of the following solutions: (5)
a. 25.0 mL of a 0.200 M NaBr solution diluted to 50.0 mL
b. 15.0 mL of a 12.0% (m/v) K_2SO_4 solution diluted to 40.0 mL
c. 75.0 mL of a 6.00 M NaOH solution diluted to 255 mL

106 Calculate the concentration, percent or molarity, of the solution when water is added to prepare each of the following solutions: (5)
a. 25.0 mL of an 18.0 M HCl solution diluted to 500. mL
b. 50.0 mL of a 15.0% (m/v) NH_4Cl solution diluted to 125 mL
c. 4.50 mL of an 8.50 M KOH solution diluted to 75.0 mL

107 What is the final volume, in milliliters, when 25.0 mL of each of the following solutions is diluted to provide the given concentration? (5)
a. 10.0% (m/v) HCl solution to give a 2.50% (m/v) HCl solution
b. 5.00 M HCl solution to give a 1.00 M HCl solution
c. 6.00 M HCl solution to give a 0.500 M HCl solution

108 What is the final volume, in milliliters, when 5.00 mL of each of the following solutions is diluted to provide the given concentration? (5)
a. 20.0% (m/v) NaOH solution to give a 4.00% (m/v) NaOH solution
b. 0.600 M NaOH solution to give a 0.100 M NaOH solution
c. 16.0% (m/v) NaOH solution to give a 2.00% (m/v) NaOH solution

CHALLENGE QUESTIONS

109 A solution is prepared with 70.0 g of HNO_3 and 130.0 g of H_2O. The HNO_3 solution has a density of 1.21 g/mL. (4, 5)
a. What is the mass percent (m/m) of the HNO_3 solution?
b. What is the total volume of the solution?
c. What is the mass/volume percent (m/v)?
d. What is its molarity (M)?

110 A solution is prepared by dissolving 22.0 g of NaOH in 118.0 g of water. The NaOH solution has a density of 1.15 g/mL. (4, 5)
a. What is the mass percent (m/m) of the NaOH solution?
b. What is the total volume of the solution?
c. What is the mass/volume percent (m/v)?
d. What is its molarity (M)?

111 The antacid Amphogel contains aluminum hydroxide $Al(OH)_3$. How many milliliters of a 6.00 M HCl solution are required to react with 60.0 mL of a 1.00 M $Al(OH)_3$ solution? (5)

$$Al(OH)_3(s) + 3HCl(aq) \longrightarrow AlCl_3(aq) + 3H_2O(l)$$

112 Calcium carbonate, $CaCO_3$, reacts with stomach acid (HCl, hydrochloric acid) according to the following equation: (5)

$$CaCO_3(s) + 2HCl(aq) \longrightarrow CaCl_2(aq) + H_2O(l) + CO_2(g)$$

Tums, an antacid, contains $CaCO_3$. If Tums is added to 20.0 mL of a 0.400 M HCl solution, how many grams of CO_2 gas are produced?

113 How many grams of NO gas can be produced from 80.0 mL of a 4.00 M HNO_3 solution and excess Cu? (5)

$$3Cu(s) + 8HNO_3(aq) \longrightarrow 3Cu(NO_3)_2(aq) + 4H_2O(l) + 2NO(g)$$

114 A 355-mL sample of a HCl solution reacts with excess Mg to produce 4.20 L of H_2 gas measured at 745 mmHg and 35 °C. What is the molarity of the HCl solution? (5)

$$Mg(s) + 2HCl(aq) \longrightarrow MgCl_2(aq) + H_2(g)$$

115 Write the net ionic equation to show the formation of a solid (insoluble salt) when the following solutions are mixed. Write *none* if there is no precipitate. (3)

a. $AgNO_3(aq) + Na_2SO_4(aq)$
b. $KCl(aq) + Pb(NO_3)_2(aq)$
c. $CaCl_2(aq) + (NH_4)_3PO_4(aq)$
d. $K_2SO_4(aq) + BaCl_2(aq)$

116 Write the net ionic equation to show the formation of a solid (insoluble salt) when the following solutions are mixed. Write *none* if there is no precipitate. (3)

a. $Pb(NO_3)_2(aq) + NaBr(aq)$
b. $AgNO_3(aq) + (NH_4)_2CO_3(aq)$
c. $Na_3PO_4(aq) + Al(NO_3)_3(aq)$
d. $NaOH(aq) + CuCl_2(aq)$

117 In a laboratory experiment, a 10.0-mL sample of NaCl solution is poured into an evaporating dish with a mass of 24.10 g. The combined mass of the evaporating dish and NaCl solution is 36.15 g. After heating, the evaporating dish and dry NaCl have a combined mass of 25.50 g. (4, 5)

a. What is the mass percent (m/m) of the NaCl solution?
b. What is the molarity (M) of the NaCl solution?
c. If water is added to 10.0 mL of the initial NaCl solution to give a final volume of 60.0 mL, what is the molarity (M) of the diluted NaCl solution?

118 In a laboratory experiment, a 15.0-mL sample of KCl solution is poured into an evaporating dish with a mass of 24.10 g. The combined mass of the evaporating dish and KCl solution is 41.50 g. After heating, the evaporating dish and dry KCl have a combined mass of 28.28 g. (4, 5)

a. What is the mass percent (m/m) of the KCl solution?
b. What is the molarity (M) of the KCl solution?
c. If water is added to 10.0 mL of the initial KCl solution to give a final volume of 60.0 mL, what is the molarity of the diluted KCl solution?

ANSWERS

Answers to Study Checks

1 0.194 mole of Cl^-

2 78 g of KNO_3

3 a. No solid forms.
b. $Pb^{2+}(aq) + 2Cl^-(aq) \longrightarrow PbCl_2(s)$

4 3.4% (m/m) NaCl solution

5 4.8% (m/v) Br_2 in CCl_4

6 5.5% (m/v) NaOH solution

7 2.12 M KNO_3 solution

8 18.0 g of KCl

9 47.5 mL of HCl solution

10 125 mL of KCl solution

11 1.25 M $NaNO_3$ solution

12 1.47 g of Zn

13 0.0175 L of Na_2SO_4 solution

14 The red blood cell will shrink (crenate).

Answers to Selected Questions and Problems

1 a. NaCl, solute; water, solvent
b. water, solute; ethanol, solvent
c. oxygen, solute; nitrogen, solvent

3 The polar water molecules pull the K^+ and I^- ions away from the solid and into solution, where they are hydrated.

5 a. water **b.** CCl_4 **c.** water **d.** CCl_4

7 In a solution of KF, only the ions of K^+ and F^- are present in the solvent. In an HF solution, there are a few ions of H^+ and F^- present, but mostly dissolved HF molecules.

9 a. $KCl(s) \xrightarrow{H_2O} K^+(aq) + Cl^-(aq)$
b. $CaCl_2(s) \xrightarrow{H_2O} Ca^{2+}(aq) + 2Cl^-(aq)$
c. $K_3PO_4(s) \xrightarrow{H_2O} 3K^+(aq) + PO_4^{3-}(aq)$
d. $Fe(NO_3)_3(s) \xrightarrow{H_2O} Fe^{3+}(aq) + 3NO_3^-(aq)$

11 a. mostly molecules and a few ions
b. ions only **c.** molecules only

13 a. strong electrolyte
b. weak electrolyte **c.** nonelectrolyte

15 a. 1 Eq **b.** 2 Eq **c.** 2 Eq **d.** 6 Eq

17 0.154 mole of Na^+, 0.154 mole of Cl^-

19 55 mEq/L

21 a. saturated **b.** unsaturated

23 a. unsaturated **b.** unsaturated
c. saturated

25 a. 68 g of KCl **b.** 12 g of KCl

27 a. The solubility of solid solutes typically increases as temperature increases.
b. The solubility of a gas is less at a higher temperature.
c. Gas solubility is less at a higher temperature and the CO_2 pressure in the can is increased.

29 a. soluble **b.** insoluble **c.** insoluble
d. soluble **e.** soluble

31 a. No solid forms.
b. $2Ag^+(aq) + 2NO_3^-(aq) + 2K^+(aq) + S^{2-}(aq) \longrightarrow Ag_2S(s) + 2K^+(aq) + 2NO_3^-(aq)$
$2Ag^+(aq) + S^{2-}(aq) \longrightarrow Ag_2S(s)$
c. $Ca^{2+}(aq) + 2Cl^-(aq) + 2Na^+(aq) + SO_4^{2-}(aq) \longrightarrow CaSO_4(s) + 2Na^+(aq) + 2Cl^-(aq)$
$Ca^{2+}(aq) + SO_4^{2-}(aq) \longrightarrow CaSO_4(s)$
d. $3Cu^{2+}(aq) + 6Cl^-(aq) + 6Li^+(aq) + 2PO_4^{3-}(aq) \longrightarrow Cu_3(PO_4)_2(s) + 6Li^+(aq) + 6Cl^-(aq)$
$3Cu^{2+}(aq) + 2PO_4^{3-}(aq) \longrightarrow Cu_3(PO_4)_2(s)$

33 a. 17% (m/m) KCl solution **b.** 5.3% (m/m) sugar solution
c. 10.% (m/m) $CaCl_2$ solution

35 a. 30.% (m/v) Na_2SO_4 solution
b. 11% (m/v) sucrose solution

37 a. 0.500 M glucose solution **b.** 0.0357 M KOH solution
c. 0.250 M NaCl solution

39 a. 2.5 g of KCl **b.** 50. g of NH_4Cl
c. 25.0 mL of acetic acid

41 79.9 mL of alcohol

43 a. 20. g of mannitol **b.** 240 g of mannitol

45 2 L of glucose solution

47 a. 20. g of $LiNO_3$ solution **b.** 400. mL of KOH solution
c. 20. mL of formic acid solution

49 a. 3.00 moles of NaCl **b.** 0.400 mole of KBr
c. 0.250 mole of $MgCl_2$

51 a. 120. g of NaOH **b.** 59.7 g of KCl
c. 5.48 g of HCl

53 a. 1.50 L **b.** 54.5 mL **c.** 62.5 mL

55 a. 2.0 M HCl solution **b.** 2.0 M NaOH solution
c. 2.5% (m/v) KOH solution
d. 3.0% (m/v) H_2SO_4 solution

57 a. 80.0 mL of HCl solution **b.** 250 mL of LiCl solution
c. 600. mL of H_3PO_4 solution
d. 180 mL of glucose solution

59 a. 12.8 mL of HNO_3 solution **b.** 11.9 mL of $MgCl_2$ solution
c. 1.88 mL of KCl solution

61 a. 10.4 g of $PbCl_2$
b. 18.8 mL of $Pb(NO_3)_2$ solution

63 a. 206 mL of HCl solution **b.** 0.500 mole of H_2 gas

65 a. solution **b.** suspension

67 a. 2.0 moles of ethylene glycol in 1.0 L of water will have a lower freezing point because it has more particles in solution.
b. 0.50 mole of $MgCl_2$ in 2.0 L of water has a lower freezing point because each formula unit of $MgCl_2$ dissociates in water to give three particles, whereas each formula unit of KCl dissociates to give only two particles.

69 a. 10% (m/v) starch solution
b. from the 1% (m/v) starch solution into the 10% (m/v) starch solution
c. 10% (m/v) starch solution

71 a. **B** 10% (m/v) starch solution
b. **A** 8% (m/v) albumin solution
c. **B** 10% (m/v) sucrose solution

73 a. hypotonic **b.** hypotonic
c. isotonic **d.** hypertonic

75 a. NaCl **b.** alanine
c. NaCl **d.** urea

77 a. 3 **b.** 1 **c.** 2

79 a. 2 **b.** 3

81 The skin of the cucumber acts like a semipermeable membrane through which the pickle loses water to the hypertonic brine solution.

83 a. beaker 3
b. $Na^+(aq) + Cl^-(aq) + Ag^+(aq) + NO_3^-(aq) \longrightarrow AgCl(s) + Na^+(aq) + NO_3^-(aq)$
c. $Ag^+(aq) + Cl^-(aq) \longrightarrow AgCl(s)$

85 a. 2 **b.** 1 **c.** 3 **d.** 2

87 222 g of water

89 a. unsaturated **b.** saturated **c.** saturated

91 a. insoluble **b.** soluble **c.** insoluble
d. soluble **e.** insoluble **f.** insoluble

93 a. $Ag^+(aq) + Cl^-(aq) \longrightarrow AgCl(s)$ **b.** none
c. $Ba^{2+}(aq) + SO_4^{2-}(aq) \longrightarrow BaSO_4(s)$

95 17.0% (m/m) Na_2SO_4 solution

97 0.50 M NaOH solution

99 a. 1410 g of $Al(NO_3)_3$ **b.** 6.75 g of $C_6H_{12}O_6$
c. 2.57 g of NH_4Cl

101 a. 60 g of amino acids, 380 g of glucose, and 100 g of lipids
b. 2700 kcal

103 38 mL of propyl alcohol solution

105 a. 0.100 M NaBr solution **b.** 4.50% (m/v) K_2SO_4 solution
c. 1.76 M NaOH solution

107 a. 100. mL **b.** 125 mL **c.** 300. mL

109 a. 35.0% (m/m) HNO_3 solution
b. 165 mL
c. 42.4% (m/v) HNO_3 solution
d. 6.73 M HNO_3 solution

111 30.0 mL of HCl solution

113 2.40 g of NO

115 a. $2Ag^+(aq) + SO_4^{2-}(aq) \longrightarrow Ag_2SO_4(s)$
b. $Pb^{2+}(aq) + 2Cl^-(aq) \longrightarrow PbCl_2(s)$
c. $3Ca^{2+}(aq) + 2PO_4^{3-}(aq) \longrightarrow Ca_3(PO_4)_2(s)$
d. $Ba^{2+}(aq) + SO_4^{2-}(aq) \longrightarrow BaSO_4(s)$

117 a. 11.6% (m/m) NaCl solution
b. 2.39 M NaCl solution
c. 0.398 M NaCl solution

Reaction Rates and Chemical Equilibrium

Reaction Rates and Chemical Equilibrium

PhotoStock-Israel/Photo Researchers, Inc.

LOOKING AHEAD

Visit **www.masteringchemistry.com** for self-study materials and instructor-assigned homework.

Peter, a chemical oceanographer, is collecting data concerning the amount of dissolved gases, specifically carbon dioxide (CO_2), in the Atlantic Ocean. Studies indicate that CO_2 in the atmosphere has increased as much as 25% since the 18th century, which has resulted in a scientific debate regarding its effects. The exact role of the oceans in this debate is currently unknown. Peter's research involves measuring the amount of dissolved CO_2 in the oceans and determining its impact on global conditions such as temperature.

The oceans are a complex mixture of many different chemicals including gases, elements and minerals, organic and particulate matter. Due to this, the oceans have been called a "chemical soup" which can complicate a study like Peter's. Peter understands that CO_2 is absorbed in the ocean via a series of equilibrium reactions. An equilibrium reaction is a reversible reaction in which both the products and the reactants are present. If the equilibrium reactions shift according to Le Châtelier's principle, an increase in the CO_2 concentration could eventually increase the amount of dissolved calcium carbonate, $CaCO_3$, which makes up coral reefs and shells. However, Peter must first determine the rate at which CO_2 is absorbed into the seawater and how it affects the amount of $CaCO_3$ in the water to determine if this is occurring.

Career: Chemical Oceanographer

A chemical oceanographer, also called a marine chemist, studies the chemistry of the ocean. One area of study includes how chemicals or pollutants enter into and affect the ocean. This can range from sewage and oil or fuels, to chemical fertilizers and storm drain overflows. Oceanographers analyze how these chemicals interact with seawater, marine life and sediments, as they can behave differently due to the ocean's varied environmental conditions. Chemical oceanographers also study how the various elements are cycled within the ocean. For instance, oceanographers quantify the amount and rate at which carbon dioxide is absorbed from the ocean's surface and eventually transferred to deep waters. Chemical oceanographers also aid ocean engineers in the development of instruments and vessels that enable researchers to collect data and discover previously unknown marine life.

Earlier, we looked at chemical reactions and determined the amounts of substances that react and the products that form. Now we are interested in how fast a reaction goes. If we know how fast a medication acts on the body, we can adjust the time over which the medication is taken. In construction, substances are added to cement to make it dry faster so work can continue. Some reactions, such as explosions or the formation of precipitates in a solution, are very fast. We know that when we roast a turkey or bake a cake, the reaction is slower. Some reactions, such as the tarnishing of silver or the aging of the body, are even slower (see Figure 1). We will see that some reactions need energy to keep running, whereas other reactions produce energy. We burn gasoline in our automobile engines to produce energy to make our cars move. In a similar way, we metabolize components from the foods in our diet to obtain the energy we need to make our bodies move. We will also look at the effect of changing the concentrations of reactants or products on the rate of reaction.

Up to now, we have considered a reaction as proceeding in a forward direction from reactants to products. However, in many reactions a reverse reaction also takes place as products collide to reform reactants. When the forward and reverse reactions take place at the same rates, the amounts of reactants and products stay the same. When this balance in the forward and reverse rate is reached, we say that the reaction has reached *equilibrium*. At equilibrium, both reactants and products are present, though some reaction mixtures contain mostly reactants and form only a few products, while others contain mostly products and few reactants.

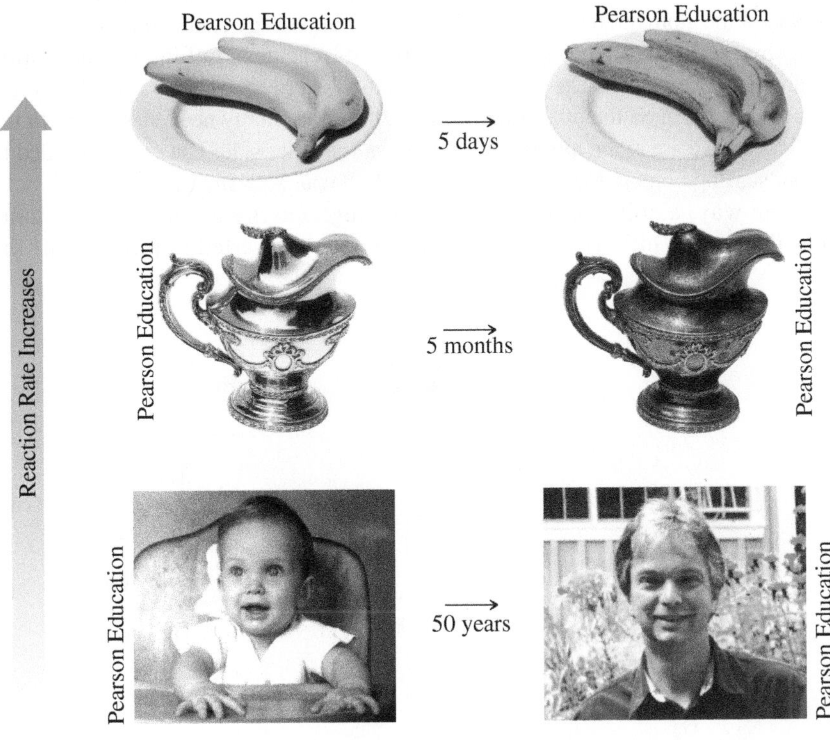

FIGURE 1 Reaction rates vary greatly for everyday processes. A banana ripens in a few days, silver tarnishes in a few months, while the aging process of humans takes many years.

Q How would you compare the rates of the reaction that forms sugars in plants by photosynthesis with the reactions that digest sugars in the body?

1 Rates of Reactions

LEARNING GOAL

Describe how temperature, concentration, and catalysts affect the rate of a reaction.

For a chemical reaction to take place, the molecules of the reactants must come in contact with each other. The **collision theory** indicates that a reaction takes place only when molecules collide with the proper orientation and with sufficient energy. Many collisions can occur, but only a few actually lead to the formation of product. For example, consider the reaction of

Collision that forms products

Collisions that do not form products

Insufficient energy

Wrong orientation

FIGURE 2 Reacting molecules must collide, have a minimum amount of energy, and have the proper orientation to form products.

Q What happens when reacting molecules collide with the minimum energy but do not have the proper orientation?

nitrogen (N_2) and oxygen (O_2) molecules (see Figure 2). To form the nitrogen oxide (NO) product, the collisions between the N_2 and the O_2 molecules must place the atoms in the proper orientation. If the molecules are not aligned properly, no reaction takes place.

Activation Energy

Even when a collision has the proper orientation, there still must be sufficient energy to break the bonds between the atoms of the reactants. The **activation energy** is the minimum amount of energy required to break the bonds between atoms of reactants. In Figure 3, activation energy appears as an energy hill. The concept of activation energy is analogous to climbing a hill. To reach a destination on the other side, we must have the energy needed to climb to the top of the hill. Once we are at the top, we can run down the other side. The energy needed to get us from our starting point to the top of the hill would be our activation energy.

In the same way, a collision must provide enough energy to push the reactants to the top of the energy hill. Then the reactants may be converted to products. If the

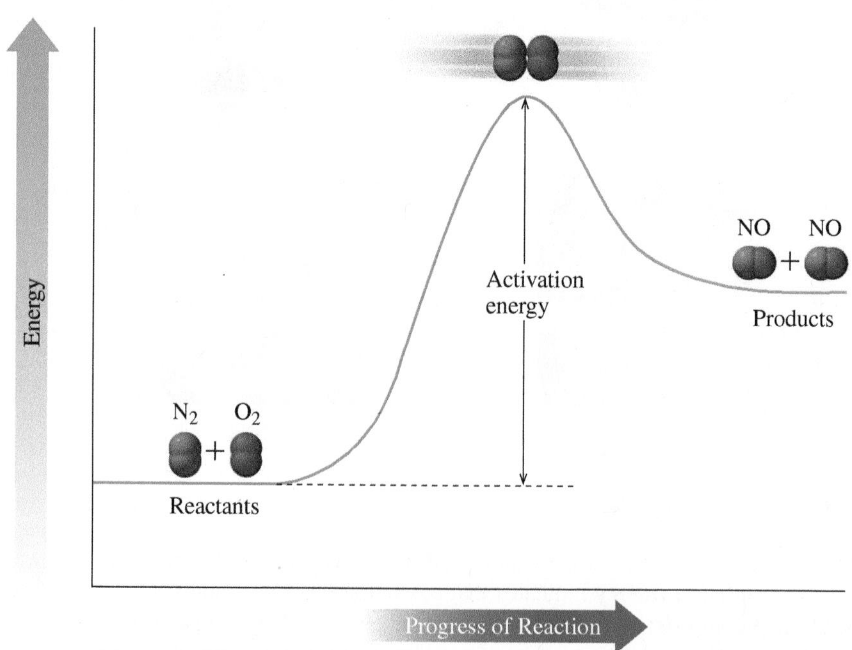

FIGURE 3 The activation energy is the minimum energy needed to convert the colliding molecules into product.

Q What happens in a collision of reacting molecules that have the proper orientation but not the energy of activation?

energy provided by the collision is less than the activation energy, the molecules simply bounce apart, and no reaction occurs. The features that lead to a successful reaction are summarized as follows:

Three Conditions Required for a Reaction to Occur

1. Collision	The reactants must collide.
2. Orientation	The reactants must align properly to break and form bonds.
3. Energy	The collision must provide the energy of activation.

Reaction Rates

The **rate** (or speed) **of reaction** is determined by measuring the amount of a reactant used up, or the amount of a product formed, in a certain period of time.

$$\text{Rate of reaction} = \frac{\text{change in concentration of reactant or product}}{\text{change in time}}$$

Perhaps we can describe the rate of reaction by the analogy of eating a pizza. When we start to eat, we have a whole pizza. As time goes by, there are fewer slices of pizza left. If we know how long it took to eat the pizza, we could determine the rate at which the pizza was consumed. Let's assume 4 slices are eaten every 8 minutes. That gives a rate of $\frac{1}{2}$ slice per minute. After 16 minutes, all 8 slices are gone.

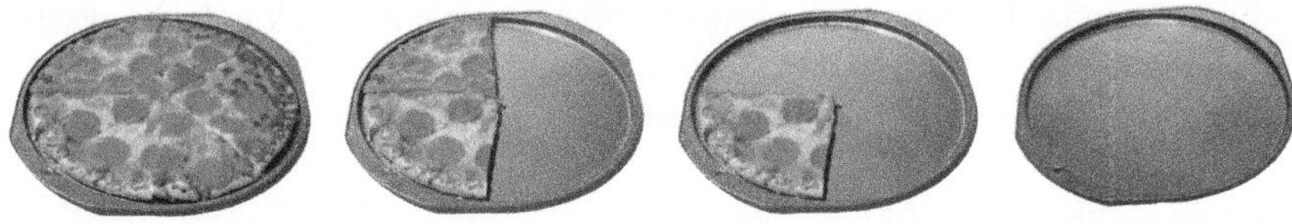

Pearson Education

Rate at Which Pizza Slices Are Eaten

Slices Eaten	0	4 slices	6 slices	8 slices
Time (min)	0	8 min	12 min	16 min

$$\text{Rate} = \frac{4\text{ slices}}{8\text{ min}} = \frac{1\text{ slice}}{2\text{ min}} = \frac{\frac{1}{2}\text{ slice}}{1\text{ min}}$$

TUTORIAL
Factors That Affect Rate

Factors That Affect the Rate of a Reaction

Some reactions go very fast, while others are very slow. For any reaction, the rate is affected by changes in temperature, changes in the concentrations of the reactants, and the addition of catalysts.

Temperature At higher temperatures, the increase in kinetic energy makes the reacting molecules move faster. As a result, more collisions occur, and more colliding molecules have sufficient energy to react and form products. If we want food to cook faster, we use more heat to raise the temperature. When body temperature rises, there is an increase in the pulse rate, rate of breathing, and metabolic rate. On the other hand, we slow down reactions by lowering the temperature. We refrigerate perishable foods to retard spoilage and make them last longer. For some injuries, we apply ice to lessen the bruising process.

Concentrations of Reactants For virtually all reactions, the rate of a reaction increases when the concentrations of the reactants increase. When there are more reacting molecules, more collisions that form products can occur, and the reaction goes faster (see Figure 4). For example, a person having difficulty breathing may be given oxygen. The increase in the number of oxygen molecules in the lungs increases the rate at which oxygen combines with hemoglobin and helps the patient breathe more easily.

Catalysts Another way to speed up a reaction is to lower the activation energy. We saw that the activation energy is the minimum energy needed to break apart the bonds of the reacting molecules. If a collision provides less energy than the activation energy, the

Reaction:

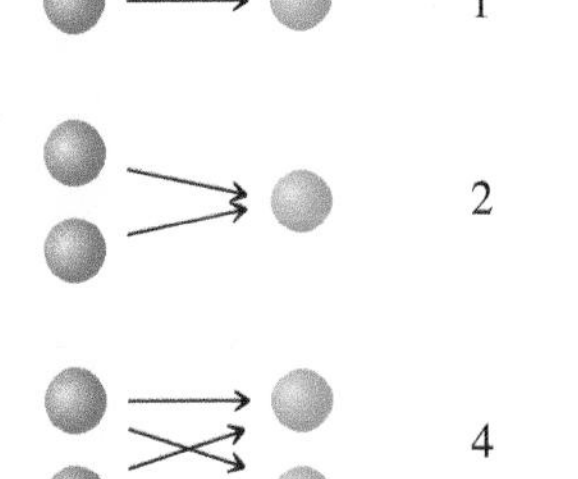

FIGURE 4 Increasing the concentration of the reactants increases the number of collisions that are possible.

Q Why does doubling the number of reactants increase the rate of reaction?

TUTORIAL
Activation Energy and Catalysis

TUTORIAL
Factors That Affect the Rate of a Chemical Reaction

bonds do not break apart and the molecules bounce apart. A **catalyst** speeds up a reaction by lowering the activation energy, which allows more collisions of the reactants to have sufficient energy to form products. During any catalyzed reaction, the catalyst is not changed or consumed.

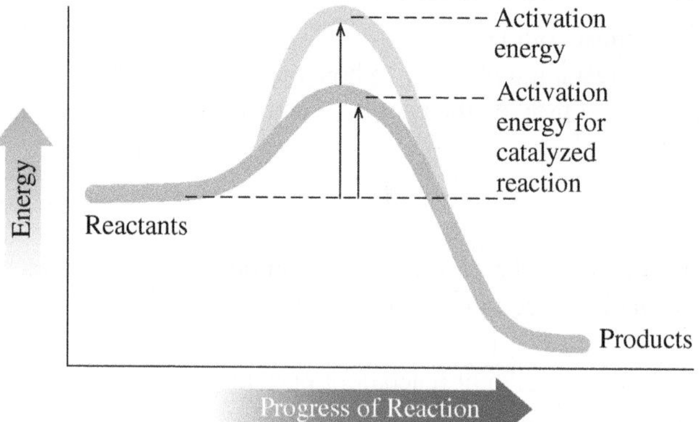

Pearson Education/Eric Schrader

Enzymes in laundry detergent catalyze the removal of stains at low temperatures.

Catalysts have many uses in industry. In the manufacturing of margarine, hydrogen (H_2) is added to vegetable oils. Normally, the reaction is very slow because it has a high activation energy. However, when platinum (Pt) is used as a catalyst, the reaction occurs rapidly. In the body, biocatalysts called enzymes make most metabolic reactions proceed at rates necessary for proper cellular activity. Enzymes are added to laundry detergents to break down proteins (proteases), starches (amylases), or greases (lipases) that have stained clothes. Such enzymes function at the low temperatures that are used in home washing machines, and are reusable and biodegradable as well.

A summary of the factors affecting reaction rates is given in Table 1.

TABLE 1 Factors That Increase Reaction Rate

Factor	Reason
Higher temperature	More collisions, more collisions with energy of activation
More reactants	More collisions
Adding a catalyst	Lowers energy of activation

CONCEPT CHECK 1 **Rate of Reactions**

Describe how decreasing the concentration of a reactant would change the rate of a reaction.

ANSWER

If the concentration of a reactant is decreased, there will be fewer collisions of the reactant molecules, which would slow the rate of reaction.

SAMPLE PROBLEM 1 **Factors That Affect the Rate of Reaction**

Indicate whether the following changes will increase, decrease, or have no effect upon the rate of reaction:

a. increase in temperature
b. increase in the number of reactant molecules
c. adding a catalyst

SOLUTION

a. increase **b.** increase **c.** increase

STUDY CHECK 1

How does the lowering of temperature affect the rate of reaction?

Chemistry Link to the Environment

CATALYTIC CONVERTERS

For over 30 years, manufacturers have been required to include catalytic converters on the exhaust systems of gasoline automobile engines. When gasoline burns, the products found in the exhaust of a car contain high levels of pollutants. These include carbon monoxide (CO) from incomplete combustion, hydrocarbons such as C_8H_{18} (octane) from unburned fuel, and nitrogen oxide (NO) from the reaction of N_2 and O_2 at the high temperatures reached within the engine. Carbon monoxide is toxic, and unburned hydrocarbons and nitrogen oxide are involved in the formation of smog and acid rain.

The purpose of a catalytic converter is to lower the activation energy for reactions that convert each of these pollutants into substances such as CO_2, N_2, O_2, and H_2O, which are already present in the atmosphere.

$$2CO(g) + O_2(g) \longrightarrow 2CO_2(g)$$

$$2C_8H_{18}(g) + 25O_2(g) \longrightarrow 16CO_2(g) + 18H_2O(g)$$

$$2NO(g) \longrightarrow N_2(g) + O_2(g)$$

A catalytic converter consists of solid-particle catalysts, such as platinum (Pt) and palladium (Pd), on a ceramic honeycomb that provides a large surface area and facilitates contact with pollutants. As the pollutants pass through the converter, they react with the catalysts. Today, we all use unleaded gasoline because lead interferes with the ability of the Pt and Pd catalysts in the converter to react with the pollutants.

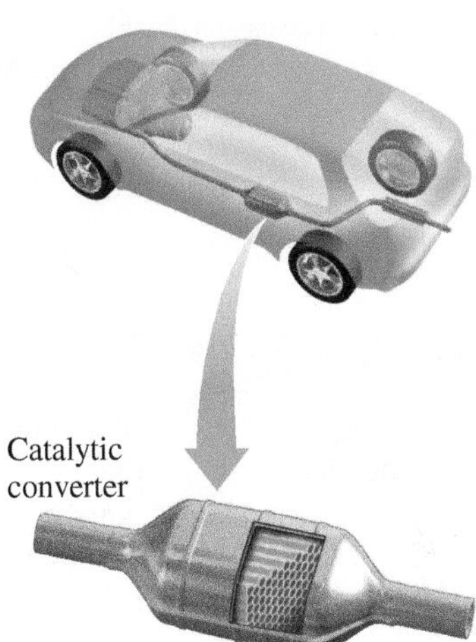

$$2NO(g) \longrightarrow N_2(g) + O_2(g)$$

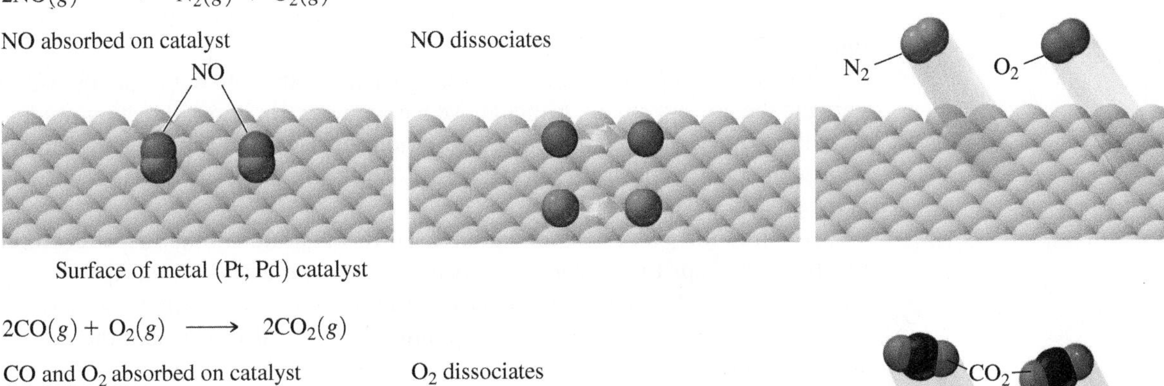

Surface of metal (Pt, Pd) catalyst

$$2CO(g) + O_2(g) \longrightarrow 2CO_2(g)$$

CO and O_2 absorbed on catalyst

O_2 dissociates

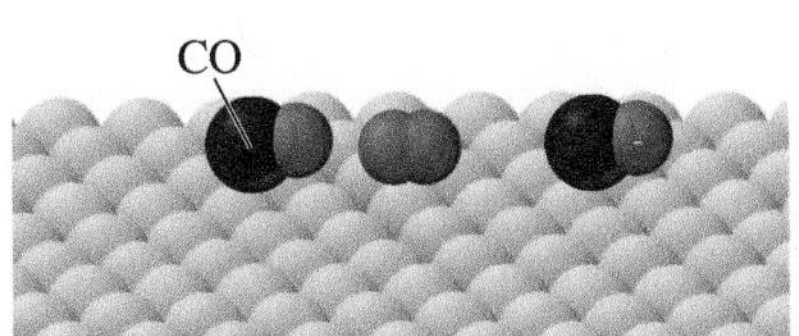

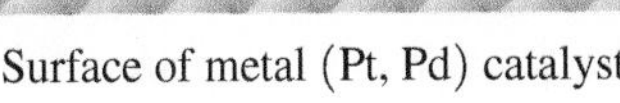

Surface of metal (Pt, Pd) catalyst

QUESTIONS AND PROBLEMS

1 Rates of Reactions

LEARNING GOAL: *Describe how temperature, concentration, and catalysts affect the rate of a reaction.*

1 Why does bread grow mold more quickly at room temperature than in the refrigerator?

2 Why is pure oxygen used in cases of respiratory distress?

3 In the following reaction, what happens to the number of collisions between the reactants when more Br_2 molecules are added?

$$H_2(g) + Br_2(g) \longrightarrow 2HBr(g)$$

4 In the following reaction, what happens to the number of collisions between the reactants when the volume of the reaction container is increased?

$$H_2(g) + Br_2(g) \longrightarrow 2HBr(g)$$

5 In the following reaction, what happens to the number of collisions between the reactants when the temperature of the reaction is increased?

$$N_2(g) + O_2(g) \longrightarrow 2NO(g)$$

6 In the following reaction, what happens to the number of collisions between the reactants when the volume of the reaction container is decreased?

$$N_2(g) + O_2(g) \longrightarrow 2NO(g)$$

7 A catalytic converter accelerates the reaction of carbon monoxide with oxygen to produce carbon dioxide. How would each of the following changes affect the rate of the reaction shown here?

$$2CO(g) + O_2(g) \longrightarrow 2CO_2(g)$$

a. adding more $CO(g)$
b. raising the temperature
c. removing the catalyst
d. removing some $O_2(g)$

8 How would each of the following changes affect the rate of the reaction shown here?

$$2NO(g) + 2H_2(g) \longrightarrow N_2(g) + 2H_2O(g)$$

a. adding more $NO(g)$
b. lowering the temperature
c. removing some $H_2(g)$
d. adding a catalyst

LEARNING GOAL

Use the concept of reversible reactions to explain chemical equilibrium.

2 Chemical Equilibrium

In earlier chapters, we considered only the *forward reaction* in an equation and assumed that all of the reactants were converted to products. However, most of the time, reactants are not completely converted to products because a *reverse reaction* takes place in which products come together and form the reactants. When a reaction proceeds in both a forward and reverse direction, it is said to be reversible. We have looked at other reversible processes. For example, the melting of solids to form liquids and the freezing of liquids into solids is a reversible physical change. Even in our daily life, we have reversible events. We go from home to school, and we return from school to home. We go up an escalator and come back down. We put money in our bank account and take money out.

An analogy for a forward and reverse reaction can be found in the phrase "We are going to the grocery store." Although we mention our trip in one direction, we know that we will also return home from the grocery store. Because our trip has both a forward and reverse direction, we can say the trip is reversible. It is not very likely that we would stay at the grocery store forever.

A trip to the grocery store can be used to illustrate another aspect of reversible reactions. Perhaps the grocery store is nearby and we usually walk. However, we can change our rate. Suppose that one day we drive to the store, which increases our rate and gets us to the store faster. Correspondingly, a car also increases the rate at which we return home.

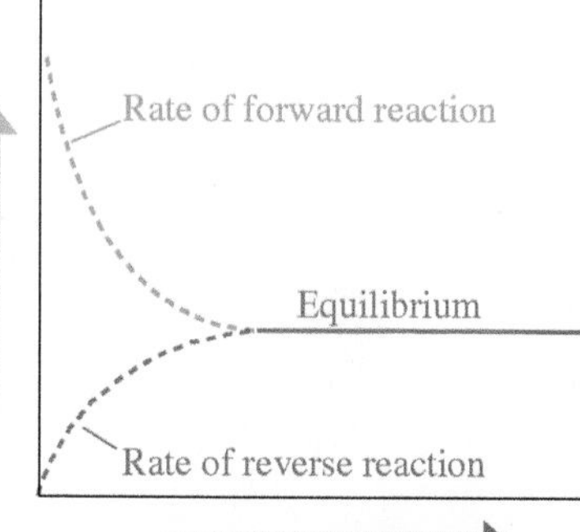

Reversible Reactions

A **reversible reaction** proceeds in both the forward and reverse directions. That means there are two reaction rates: the rate of the forward reaction and the rate of the reverse reaction. When molecules begin to react, the rate of the forward reaction is faster than the rate of the reverse reaction. As reactants are consumed and products accumulate, the rate of the forward reaction decreases, whereas the rate of the reverse reaction increases.

SAMPLE PROBLEM 2 Reversible Reactions

Write the forward and reverse reactions for each of the following:

a. $N_2(g) + 3H_2(g) \rightleftarrows 2NH_3(g)$
b. $2CO(g) + O_2 \rightleftarrows 2CO_2(g)$

SOLUTION

The equations are separated into forward and reverse reactions.

a. Forward reaction: $N_2(g) + 3H_2(g) \longrightarrow 2NH_3(g)$
Reverse reaction: $N_2(g) + 3H_2(g) \longleftarrow 2NH_3(g)$

b. Forward reaction: $2CO(g) + O_2(g) \longrightarrow 2CO_2(g)$
Reverse reaction: $2CO(g) + O_2(g) \longleftarrow 2CO_2(g)$

STUDY CHECK 2

Write the equation for the equilibrium reaction that contains the following reverse reaction:

$$H_2(g) + Br_2(g) \longleftarrow 2HBr(g)$$

MC™

SELF-STUDY ACTIVITY
Equilibrium

TUTORIAL
Chemical Equilibrium

Chemical Equilibrium

Eventually, the rates of the forward and reverse reactions are equal; the reactants form products as often as products form reactants. A reaction reaches **chemical equilibrium** when there is no further change in the concentrations of the reactants or products even though the two reactions continue at equal but opposite rates.

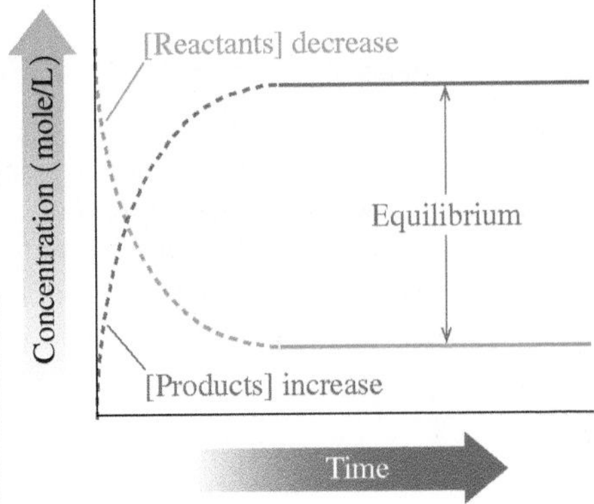

At equilibrium:

The rate of the forward reaction is equal to the rate of the reverse reaction.

No further changes occur in the concentrations of the reactants or products; the forward and reverse reactions continue at equal rates.

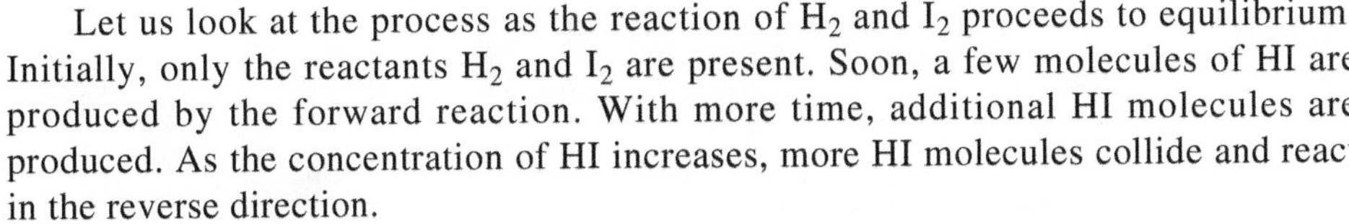

Let us look at the process as the reaction of H_2 and I_2 proceeds to equilibrium. Initially, only the reactants H_2 and I_2 are present. Soon, a few molecules of HI are produced by the forward reaction. With more time, additional HI molecules are produced. As the concentration of HI increases, more HI molecules collide and react in the reverse direction.

Forward reaction: $H_2(g) + I_2(g) \longrightarrow 2HI(g)$

Reverse reaction: $H_2(g) + I_2(g) \longleftarrow 2HI(g)$

As HI product builds up, the rate of the reverse reaction increases, while the rate of the forward reaction decreases. Eventually the rates become equal, which means the reaction has reached equilibrium. Even though the concentrations remain constant at equilibrium, the forward and reverse reactions continue to occur. The forward and reverse reactions are usually shown together in a single equation by using a double arrow. A reversible reaction is two opposing reactions that occur at the same time (see Figure 5).

$$H_2(g) + I_2(g) \underset{\text{Reverse reaction}}{\overset{\text{Forward reaction}}{\rightleftarrows}} 2HI(g)$$

We might also set up a reaction starting with only reactants or starting with only products. Let's look at the initial reactions in each, the forward and reverse reactions, and the equilibrium mixture from each for the following reaction:

$$2SO_2(g) + O_2(g) \rightleftarrows 2SO_3(g)$$

In the container with only the reactants SO_2 and O_2, the forward reaction takes place initially. As product SO_3 is formed, the rate of the reverse reaction increases. In the container with only the product SO_3, the reverse reaction takes place initially. As reactants are formed, the rate of the forward reaction increases. Eventually, the rates of both the forward and reverse reactions become equal. Then the equilibrium mixtures contain the same amounts of SO_2, O_2, and SO_3 in each.

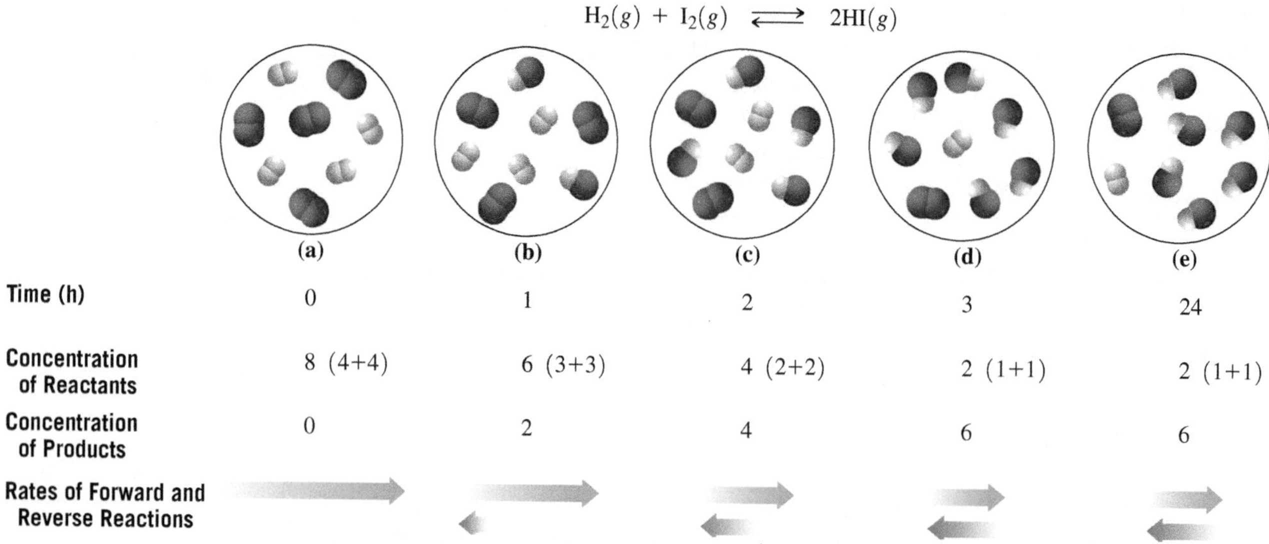

FIGURE 5 **(a)** Initially, the reaction flask contains only the reactants H_2 and I_2. **(b)** The forward reaction between H_2 and I_2 begins to produce HI. **(c)** As the reaction proceeds, there are fewer molecules of H_2 and I_2 and more molecules of HI, which increases the rate of the reverse reaction. **(d)** At equilibrium, the concentrations of reactants H_2 and I_2 and product HI are constant. **(e)** The reaction continues, with the rate of the forward reaction equal to the rate of the reverse reaction.

Q How do the rates of the forward and reverse reactions compare once a chemical reaction reaches equilibrium?

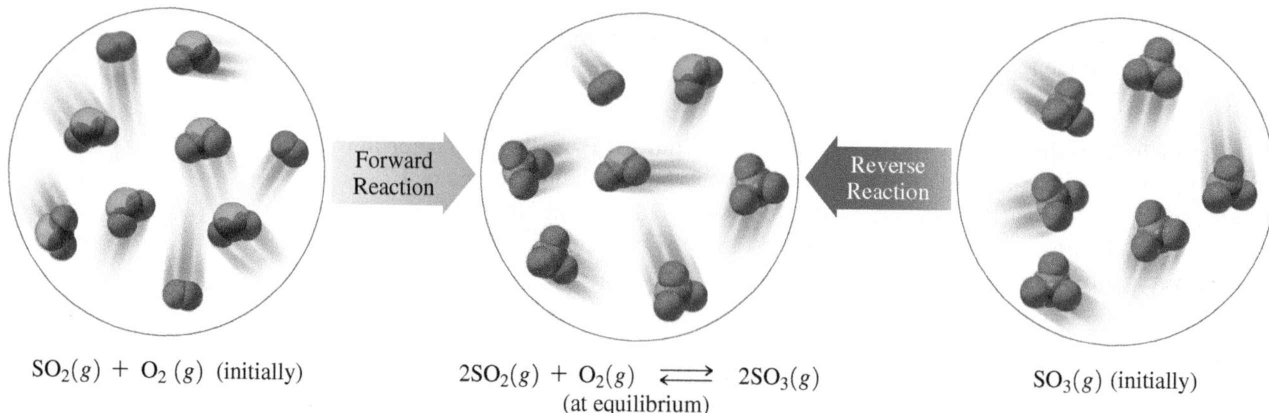

One sample initially contains SO_2 and O_2. Another sample contains only SO_3. At equilibrium, both mixtures contain small amounts of reactants SO_2 and O_2 and a large amount of product SO_3.

CONCEPT CHECK 2 Reaction Rates and Equilibrium

Complete each of the following with equal or not equal, faster or slower, change or do not change:

a. Before equilibrium is reached, the concentrations of the reactants and products ________.
b. Initially, reactants placed in a container have a ________ rate of reaction than the rate of reaction of the products.
c. At equilibrium, the rate of the forward reaction is ________ to the rate of the reverse reaction.
d. At equilibrium, the concentrations of the reactants and products ________.

ANSWER

a. Before equilibrium is reached, the concentrations of the reactants and products *change*.
b. Initially, reactants placed in a container have a *faster* rate of reaction than the rate of reaction of the products.
c. At equilibrium, the rate of the forward reaction is *equal* to the rate of the reverse reaction.
d. At equilibrium, the concentrations of the reactants and products *do not change*.

QUESTIONS AND PROBLEMS

2 Chemical Equilibrium

LEARNING GOAL: *Use the concept of reversible reactions to explain chemical equilibrium.*

9 What is meant by the term “reversible reaction”?

10 When does a reversible reaction reach equilibrium?

11 Which of the following processes are reversible?
- **a.** breaking a glass
- **b.** melting snow
- **c.** heating a pan

12 Which of the following processes are not reversible?
- **a.** boiling water
- **b.** eating a pizza
- **c.** walking up a hill

13 Which of the following are at equilibrium?
- **a.** The rate of the forward reaction is twice as fast as the rate of the reverse reaction.
- **b.** The concentrations of the reactants and the products do not change.
- **c.** The rate of the reverse reaction does not change.

14 Which of the following are not at equilibrium?
- **a.** The rates of the forward and reverse reactions are equal.
- **b.** The rate of the forward reaction does not change.
- **c.** The concentrations of reactants and the products are not constant.

3 Equilibrium Constants

LEARNING GOAL

Calculate the equilibrium constant for a reversible reaction given the concentrations of reactants and products at equilibrium.

At equilibrium, reactions occur in opposite directions at the same rate, which means the concentrations of the reactants and products remain constant. We can use a ski lift as an analogy. Early in the morning, skiers at the bottom of the mountain begin to ride the ski lift up to the slopes. As skiers reach the top of the mountain, they ski down. Eventually, the number of people riding up the ski lift becomes equal to the number of people skiing down the mountain. When there is no further change in the number of skiers on the slopes; the system is at equilibrium.

Steve Mason/Getty Images

At equilibrium, the number of people riding the lift and the number of people skiing on the slope are constant.

Equilibrium Constant Expression

Because the concentrations in a reaction at equilibrium no longer change, they can be used to set up a relationship between the products and the reactants. Suppose we write a general equation for reactants A and B that form products C and D. The small italic letters are the coefficients in the balanced equation.

$$aA + bB \rightleftharpoons cC + dD$$

An **equilibrium constant expression** can be written that multiplies the concentrations of the products and divides by the concentrations of the reactants. Each concentration is raised to a power that is its coefficient in the balanced chemical equation. The square bracket around each substance indicates that the concentration is expressed in moles per liter (M). The **equilibrium constant, K_c**, is the numerical value obtained by substituting molar concentrations at equilibrium into the expression. For our general reaction, the equilibrium constant expression is:

$$K_c = \frac{[\text{Products}]}{[\text{Reactants}]} = \frac{[C]^c[D]^d}{[A]^a[B]^b}$$

Equilibrium constant (for K_c); Equilibrium constant expression; Coefficients (pointing to the exponents)

TUTORIAL
Equilibrium Constant

We can now describe how to write the equilibrium constant expression for the reaction of H_2 and I_2 that forms HI. First, we need to write the balanced chemical equation with a double arrow between the reactants and the products.

$$H_2(g) + I_2(g) \rightleftharpoons 2HI(g)$$

Second, we show the concentration of the products using brackets in the numerator and the concentrations of the reactants in brackets in the denominator.

$$\frac{[\text{Products}]}{[\text{Reactants}]} \longrightarrow \frac{[HI]}{[H_2][I_2]}$$

Finally, we write any coefficient in the balanced chemical equation as an exponent of its concentration (the coefficient 1 is understood) and set it equal to K_c.

$$K_c = \frac{[\text{Products}]}{[\text{Reactants}]} = \frac{[HI]^2}{[H_2][I_2]}$$

CONCEPT CHECK 3 **Equilibrium Constant Expression**

Select the correctly written equilibrium constant expression for the following reaction, and explain your choice:

$$CH_4(g) + H_2O(g) \rightleftharpoons CO(g) + 3H_2(g)$$

a. $K_c = \frac{[CO][3H_2]}{[CH_4][H_2O]}$ **b.** $K_c = \frac{[CO][H_2]^3}{[CH_4][H_2O]}$

c. $K_c = \frac{[CH_4][H_2O]}{[CO][H_2]^3}$ **d.** $K_c = \frac{[CO][H_2]}{[CH_4][H_2O]}$

ANSWER

The correct equilibrium constant expression is **b**. The products are written in the numerator and the reactants are in the denominator. Because H_2 has a coefficient of 3 in the balanced equation, an exponent of 3 is used with the concentration of H_2.

SAMPLE PROBLEM 3 **Writing an Equilibrium Constant Expression**

Write the equilibrium constant expression for the following:

$$2SO_2(g) + O_2(g) \rightleftharpoons 2SO_3(g)$$

SOLUTION

Guide to Writing the K_c Expression

1. Write the balanced chemical equation.
2. Write the concentrations of the products as the numerator and the reactants as the denominator.
3. Write any coefficient in the equation as an exponent.

Step 1 **Write the balanced chemical equation.**

$$2SO_2(g) + O_2(g) \rightleftharpoons 2SO_3(g)$$

Step 2 **Write the concentrations of the products as the numerator and the reactants as the denominator.** Write the concentration of the product SO_3 in the numerator and the concentrations of the reactants SO_2 and O_2 each in the denominator.

$$\frac{[\text{Products}]}{[\text{Reactants}]} \longrightarrow \frac{[SO_3]}{[SO_2][O_2]}$$

Step 3 **Write any coefficient in the equation as an exponent.** Write the coefficient 2 as an exponent of the concentration of SO_2 and the coefficient 2 as an exponent of the concentration of SO_3.

$$K_c = \frac{[SO_3]^2}{[SO_2]^2[O_2]}$$

STUDY CHECK 3

Write the balanced chemical equation that would give the following equilibrium constant expression:

$$K_c = \frac{[NO_2]^2}{[NO]^2[O_2]}$$

Heterogeneous Equilibrium

Up to now, our examples have been reactions that involve only gases. A reaction in which all the reactants and products are gases is a **homogeneous equilibrium**. When the reactants and products are in two or more physical states, the equilibrium is termed a **heterogeneous equilibrium**. In the following example, solid calcium carbonate reaches equilibrium with solid calcium oxide and carbon dioxide gas; this is a heterogeneous equilibrium (see Figure 6).

$$CaCO_3(s) \rightleftharpoons CaO(s) + CO_2(g)$$

In contrast to gases, the concentrations of pure solids and pure liquids in a heterogeneous equilibrium are constant; they do not change. Therefore, pure solids and liquids are not included in the equilibrium constant expression. For this heterogeneous equilibrium, the K_c expression does not include the concentration of $CaCO_3(s)$ or $CaO(s)$. It is written as $K_c = [CO_2]$.

FIGURE 6 At equilibrium at constant temperature, the concentration of CO_2 is the same regardless of the amounts of $CaCO_3(s)$ and $CaO(s)$ in the container.

Q Why are the concentrations of $CaO(s)$ and $CaCO_3(s)$ not included in K_c for the decomposition of $CaCO_3$?

SAMPLE PROBLEM 4 **Heterogeneous Equilibrium Constant Expression**

Write the equilibrium constant expression for the following reaction at equilibrium:

$$4HCl(g) + O_2(g) \rightleftharpoons 2H_2O(l) + 2Cl_2(g)$$

SOLUTION

Step 1 **Write the balanced chemical equation.**

$$4HCl(g) + O_2(g) \rightleftharpoons 2H_2O(l) + 2Cl_2(g)$$

Step 2 **Write the concentrations of the products as the numerator and the reactants as the denominator.** In this heterogeneous reaction, the concentration of the liquid H_2O is not included in the equilibrium constant expression.

$$\frac{[\text{Products}]}{[\text{Reactants}]} \begin{matrix} \longrightarrow \\ \longrightarrow \end{matrix} \frac{[Cl_2]}{[HCl][O_2]}$$

Step 3 **Write any coefficient in the equation as an exponent.**

$$K_c = \frac{[Cl_2]^2}{[HCl]^4[O_2]}$$

STUDY CHECK 4

Solid iron(II) oxide and carbon monoxide gas react to produce solid iron and carbon dioxide gas. Write the balanced chemical equation and the equilibrium constant expression for this reaction at equilibrium.

Calculating Equilibrium Constants

The numerical value of the equilibrium constant is calculated from the equilibrium constant expression by substituting experimentally measured concentrations of the reactants and products at equilibrium into the expression. For example, the equilibrium constant expression for the reaction of H_2 and I_2 is written:

$$H_2(g) + I_2(g) \rightleftharpoons 2HI(g) \qquad K_c = \frac{[HI]^2}{[H_2][I_2]}$$

In the first experiment, the molar concentrations for the reactants and products at equilibrium are found to be $[H_2] = 0.10$ M, $[I_2] = 0.20$ M, and $[HI] = 1.04$ M. When we substitute these values into the equilibrium constant expression, we obtain its numerical value.

In additional experiments 2 and 3, the mixtures have different equilibrium concentrations. However, when these concentrations are used to calculate the equilibrium constant, we obtain the same value of K_c for each (see Table 2). *Thus, a reaction at a specific temperature has only one value for the equilibrium constant.*

The units of K_c depend on the specific equation. In this example, the units of $[M]^2/[M]^2$ cancel out to give a value of 54. In other equations, the concentration units do not cancel. However, in this text, the numerical value will be given without any units as shown in Sample Problem 5.

TABLE 2 Equilibrium Constant for $H_2(g) + I_2(g) \rightleftharpoons 2HI(g)$ at 427 °C

Experiment	Concentrations at Equilibrium			Equilibrium Constant
	$[H_2]$	$[I_2]$	$[HI]$	$K_c = \frac{[HI]^2}{[H_2][I_2]}$
1	0.10 M	0.20 M	1.04 M	$K_c = \frac{[1.04]^2}{[0.10][0.20]} = 54$
2	0.20 M	0.20 M	1.47 M	$K_c = \frac{[1.47]^2}{[0.20][0.20]} = 54$
3	0.30 M	0.17 M	1.66 M	$K_c = \frac{[1.66]^2}{[0.30][0.17]} = 54$

SAMPLE PROBLEM 5 Calculating an Equilibrium Constant

The decomposition of dinitrogen tetroxide forms nitrogen dioxide.

$N_2O_4(g) \rightleftharpoons 2NO_2(g)$

What is the value of K_c at 100 °C if a reaction mixture at equilibrium contains $[N_2O_4] =$ 0.45 M and $[NO_2] = 0.31$ M?

SOLUTION

Analyze the Problem

	Reactant	Product	Equilibrium Constant
Chemical Reaction	$N_2O_4(g) \rightleftharpoons 2NO_2(g)$		
Equilibrium	0.45 M N_2O_4	0.31 M NO_2	K_c

Guide to Calculating the K_c Value

1 Write the K_c expression for the equilibrium.

2 Substitute equilibrium (molar) concentrations and calculate K_c.

Step 1 Write the K_c expression for the equilibrium.

$$K_c = \frac{[\text{Products}]}{[\text{Reactants}]} = \frac{[NO_2]^2}{[N_2O_4]}$$

Step 2 Substitute equilibrium (molar) concentrations and calculate K_c. Note that the numerical value of K_c is given without any units.

$$K_c = \frac{[0.31]^2}{[0.45]} = 0.21$$

STUDY CHECK 5

Ammonia decomposes when heated to give nitrogen and hydrogen.

$2NH_3(g) \rightleftharpoons 3H_2(g) + N_2(g)$

Calculate the equilibrium constant if an equilibrium mixture contains $[NH_3] = 0.040$ M, $[H_2] = 0.60$ M, and $[N_2] = 0.20$ M.

QUESTIONS AND PROBLEMS

3 Equilibrium Constants

LEARNING GOAL: *Calculate the equilibrium constant for a reversible reaction given the concentrations of reactants and products at equilibrium.*

15 Write the equilibrium constant expression for each of the following reactions:

a. $CH_4(g) + 2H_2S(g) \rightleftharpoons CS_2(g) + 4H_2(g)$

b. $2NO(g) \rightleftharpoons N_2(g) + O_2(g)$

c. $2SO_3(g) + CO_2(g) \rightleftharpoons CS_2(g) + 4O_2(g)$

16 Write the equilibrium constant expression for each of the following reactions:

a. $2HBr(g) \rightleftharpoons H_2(g) + Br_2(g)$

b. $CO(g) + 2H_2(g) \rightleftharpoons CH_3OH(g)$

c. $CH_4(g) + Cl_2(g) \rightleftharpoons CH_3Cl(g) + HCl(g)$

17 Identify each of the following as a homogeneous or heterogeneous equilibrium:
a. $2O_3(g) \rightleftharpoons 3O_2(g)$
b. $2NaHCO_3(s) \rightleftharpoons Na_2CO_3(s) + CO_2(g) + H_2O(g)$
c. $CH_4(g) + H_2O(g) \rightleftharpoons 3H_2(g) + CO(g)$
d. $4HCl(g) + Si(s) \rightleftharpoons SiCl_4(g) + 2H_2(g)$

18 Identify each of the following as a homogeneous or heterogeneous equilibrium:
a. $CO(g) + H_2(g) \rightleftharpoons C(s) + H_2O(g)$
b. $CO(g) + 2H_2(g) \rightleftharpoons CH_3OH(l)$
c. $CS_2(g) + 4H_2(g) \rightleftharpoons CH_4(g) + 2H_2S(g)$
d. $Br_2(g) + Cl_2(g) \rightleftharpoons 2BrCl(g)$

19 Write the equilibrium constant expression for each of the reactions in Problem 17.

20 Write the equilibrium constant expression for each of the reactions in Problem 18.

21 What is the K_c for the following reaction at equilibrium if $[N_2O_4] = 0.030$ M and $[NO_2] = 0.21$ M?

$$N_2O_4(g) \rightleftharpoons 2NO_2(g)$$

22 What is the K_c for the following reaction at equilibrium if $[CO_2] = 0.30$ M, $[H_2] = 0.033$ M, $[CO] = 0.20$ M, and $[H_2O] = 0.30$ M?

$$CO_2(g) + H_2(g) \rightleftharpoons CO(g) + H_2O(g)$$

23 What is the K_c for the following reaction at equilibrium at 1000 °C if $[CO] = 0.50$ M, $[H_2] = 0.30$ M, $[CH_4] = 1.8$ M, and $[H_2O] = 2.0$ M?

$$CO(g) + 3H_2(g) \rightleftharpoons CH_4(g) + H_2O(g)$$

24 What is the K_c for the following reaction at equilibrium at 500 °C if $[N_2] = 0.44$ M, $[H_2] = 0.40$ M, and $[NH_3] = 2.2$ M?

$$N_2(g) + 3H_2(g) \rightleftharpoons 2NH_3(g)$$

25 What is the K_c for the following reaction at equilibrium at 750 °C if $[CO] = 0.20$ M and $[CO_2] = 0.052$ M?

$$FeO(s) + CO(g) \rightleftharpoons Fe(s) + CO_2(g)$$

26 What is the K_c for the following reaction at equilibrium at 800 °C if $[CO_2] = 0.030$ M?

$$CaCO_3(s) \rightleftharpoons CaO(s) + CO_2(g)$$

4 Using Equilibrium Constants

LEARNING GOAL

Use an equilibrium constant to predict the extent of reaction and to calculate equilibrium concentrations.

The values of equilibrium constants can be large or small. The size of the constant depends on whether equilibrium is reached with more products than reactants, or more reactants than products. *However, the size of an equilibrium constant does not effect how fast equilibrium is reached.*

Equilibrium with a Large K_c

When a reaction has a large equilibrium constant, it means that the forward reaction produced a large amount of products when equilibrium was reached. Then the equilibrium mixture contains mostly products, which makes the concentrations of the products in the numerator larger than the concentrations of the reactants in the denominator. Thus at equilibrium, this reaction has a large K_c.

$$2SO_2(g) + O_2(g) \rightleftharpoons 2SO_3(g)$$

$$K_c = \frac{[SO_3]^2}{[SO_2]^2[O_2]} \quad \frac{\text{Mostly products}}{\text{Few reactants}} = 3.4 \times 10^2$$

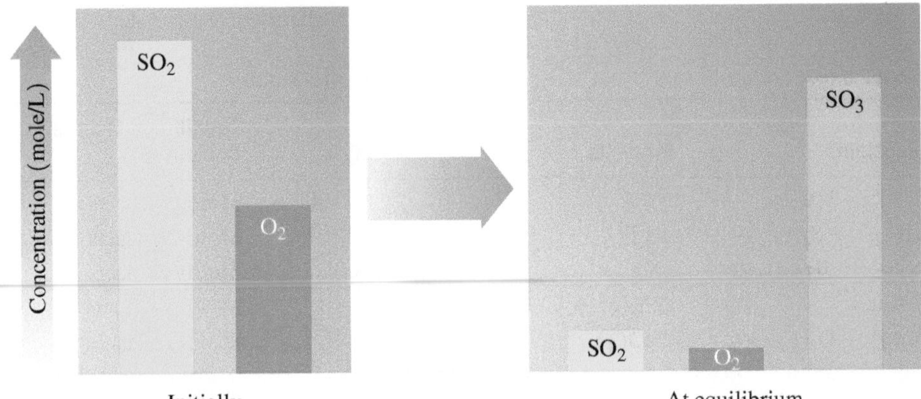

The equilibrium mixture contains a large amount of the product SO_3 and only a small amount of the reactants SO_2 and O_2, which results in a large K_c.

Equilibrium with a Small K_c

When a reaction has a small equilibrium constant, it means that the reverse reaction converted most of the products back to reactants when equilibrium was reached. Thus, the equilibrium mixture contains mostly reactants, which makes the concentrations of the products in the numerator much smaller than the concentrations of the reactants in the denominator. For example, the reaction of N_2 and O_2 to form NO has a small K_c. When equilibrium is reached for this reaction, the equilibrium mixture contains mostly reactants, N_2 and O_2, and only a few molecules of the product NO. Reactions with very small K_c produce essentially no products.

$$N_2(g) + O_2(g) \rightleftharpoons 2NO(g)$$

$$K_c = \frac{[NO]^2}{[N_2][O_2]} \quad \frac{\text{Few products}}{\text{Mostly reactants}} = 2 \times 10^{-9}$$

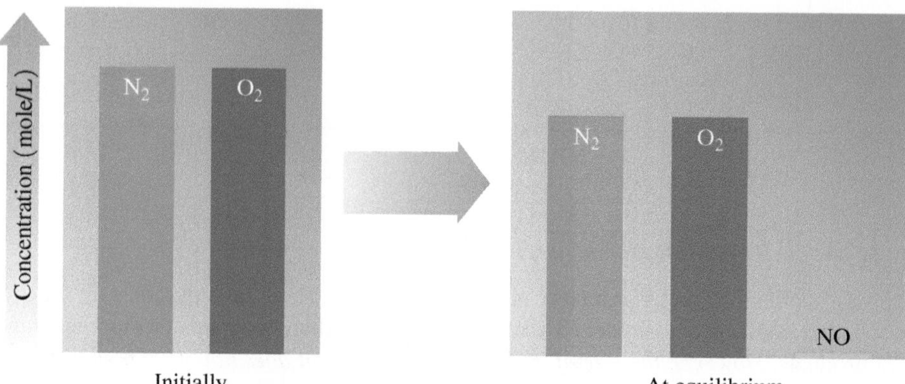

The equilibrium mixture contains a very small amount of the product NO and a large amount of the reactants N_2 and O_2, which results in a small K_c.

Only a few reactions have equilibrium constants close to 1, which means they have about equal concentrations of reactants and products. Moderate amounts of reactants have been converted to products when equilibrium was reached (see Figure 7). Table 3 lists some equilibrium constants and the extent of their reaction.

Small K_c	$K_c \approx 1$	Large K_c
Favors Reactants		Favors Products
Reactants >> Products Little reaction takes place	Reactants ≈ Products Moderate reaction	Reactants << Products Reaction almost complete

FIGURE 7 At equilibrium, a reaction with a large K_c contains mostly products, whereas a reaction with a small K_c contains mostly reactants.

Q Does a reaction with a $K_c = 1.2 \times 10^{15}$ contain mostly reactants or products at equilibrium?

TABLE 3 Examples of Reactions with Large and Small K_c Values

Reactants		Products	K_c	Equilibrium Mixture Contains
$2CO(g) + O_2(g)$	$\rightleftharpoons$	$2CO_2(g)$	2×10^{11}	Mostly products
$2H_2(g) + S_2(g)$	$\rightleftharpoons$	$2H_2S(g)$	1.1×10^{7}	Mostly products
$N_2(g) + 3H_2(g)$	$\rightleftharpoons$	$2NH_3(g)$	1.6×10^{2}	Mostly products
$PCl_5(g)$	$\rightleftharpoons$	$PCl_3(g) + Cl_2(g)$	1.2×10^{-2}	Mostly reactants
$N_2(g) + O_2(g)$	$\rightleftharpoons$	$2NO(g)$	2×10^{-9}	Mostly reactants

Calculating Concentrations at Equilibrium

We have seen that reactions can reach equilibrium without using up all the reactants. Then we need to use the equilibrium constant to calculate the amount of a reactant or product that would be found in the equilibrium mixture. In this type of problem, we are given the value of the equilibrium constant for a specific reaction and all the concentrations except one, as shown in Sample Problem 6.

TUTORIAL
Calculations Using the Equilibrium Constant

SAMPLE PROBLEM 6 Calculating Concentration Using an Equilibrium Constant

Phosgene ($COCl_2$) is a toxic substance that is produced by the reaction of carbon monoxide and chlorine; the K_c for the reaction is 5.0.

$$CO(g) + Cl_2(g) \rightleftharpoons COCl_2(g)$$

If the concentrations for the reaction at equilibrium are $[CO] = 0.64$ M and $[Cl_2] = 0.25$ M, what is the concentration of $COCl_2(g)$?

SOLUTION

Analyze the Problem

	Reactants		Product	Equilibrium Constant
Reaction	$CO(g) + Cl_2(g) \rightleftharpoons COCl_2(g)$			
Equilibrium	0.64 M	0.25 M	M $COCl_2$	$K_c = 5.0$

Step 1 **Write the K_c expression for the equilibrium equation.** Using the balanced chemical equation, the equilibrium constant expression is written as:

$$K_c = \frac{[\text{Products}]}{[\text{Reactants}]} = \frac{[COCl_2]}{[CO][Cl_2]}$$

Step 2 **Solve the K_c expression for the unknown concentration.** To rearrange the expression for $[COCl_2]$, we multiply both sides by $[CO][Cl_2]$, which cancels $[CO][Cl_2]$ on the right side.

$$K_c[CO][Cl_2] = \frac{[COCl_2]\cancel{[CO]}\cancel{[Cl_2]}}{\cancel{[CO]}\cancel{[Cl_2]}} = [COCl_2]$$

Step 3 **Substitute the known values into the rearranged K_c expression and calculate.** Substituting the molar concentrations for the equilibrium mixture and the K_c value into the equilibrium constant expression gives the $COCl_2$ concentration.

$$[COCl_2] = K_c[CO][Cl_2] = 5.0[0.64][0.25] = 0.80\text{ M}$$

STUDY CHECK 6

Ethanol can be produced by reacting ethylene (C_2H_4) with water vapor. At 327 °C, the reaction has a K_c of 9.0×10^3.

$$C_2H_4(g) + H_2O(g) \rightleftharpoons C_2H_5OH(g)$$

If the concentrations at equilibrium are $[C_2H_4] = 0.020$ M and $[H_2O] = 0.015$ M, what is the concentration of C_2H_5OH?

Guide to Using the K_c Value

1. Write the K_c expression for the equilibrium equation.
2. Solve the K_c expression for the unknown concentration.
3. Substitute the known values into the rearranged K_c expression and calculate.

QUESTIONS AND PROBLEMS

4 Using Equilibrium Constants

LEARNING GOAL: *Use an equilibrium constant to predict the extent of reaction and to calculate equilibrium concentrations.*

27 Indicate whether each of the following reactions contains mostly products, mostly reactants, or both reactants and products at equilibrium:

a. $Cl_2(g) + 2NO(g) \rightleftharpoons 2NOCl(g)$ $K_c = 3.7 \times 10^8$

b. $H_2O(g) + CH_4(g) \rightleftharpoons CO(g) + 3H_2(g)$ $K_c = 4.7$

c. $3O_2(g) \rightleftharpoons 2O_3(g)$ $K_c = 1.7 \times 10^{-56}$

28 Indicate whether each of the following reactions contains mostly products, mostly reactants, or both reactants and products at equilibrium:

a. $CO(g) + Cl_2(g) \rightleftharpoons COCl_2(g)$ $K_c = 5.0$

b. $2HF(g) \rightleftharpoons H_2(g) + F_2(g)$ $K_c = 1.0 \times 10^{-95}$

c. $2NO(g) + O_2(g) \rightleftharpoons 2NO_2(g)$ $K_c = 6.0 \times 10^{13}$

29 The equilibrium constant, K_c, for the reaction of H_2 and I_2 is 54 at 425 °C. If the equilibrium mixture contains 0.015 M I_2 and 0.030 M HI, what is the concentration of H_2?

$$H_2(g) + I_2(g) \rightleftharpoons 2HI(g)$$

30 The equilibrium constant, K_c, for the decomposition of N_2O_4 is 4.6×10^{-3}. If the equilibrium mixture contains 0.050 M NO_2, what is the concentration of N_2O_4?

$$N_2O_4(g) \rightleftharpoons 2NO_2(g)$$

31 The equilibrium constant, K_c, for the decomposition of NOBr is 2.0 at 100 °C. If the system at equilibrium contains 2.0 M NO and 1.0 M Br_2, what is the concentration of NOBr?

$$2NOBr(g) \rightleftharpoons 2NO(g) + Br_2(g)$$

32 The equilibrium constant, K_c, for the reaction of H_2 and N_2 is 1.7×10^2 at 225 °C. If the system at equilibrium contains 0.18 M H_2 and 0.020 M N_2, what is the concentration of NH_3?

$$3H_2(g) + N_2(g) \rightleftharpoons 2NH_3(g)$$

LEARNING GOAL

Use Le Châtelier's principle to describe the changes made in equilibrium concentrations when reaction conditions change.

5 Changing Equilibrium Conditions: Le Châtelier's Principle

We have seen that when a reaction reaches equilibrium, the rates of the forward and reverse reactions are equal, and the concentrations remain constant. Now we will look at how a system at equilibrium responds to changes in concentration, pressure, and temperature. There are several ways to disturb the equilibrium, including removing or adding one of the reactants or products, or decreasing or increasing the volume or temperature.

TUTORIAL
Le Châtelier's Principle

Le Châtelier's Principle

When we alter any of the conditions of a system at equilibrium, the rates of the forward and reverse reactions will no longer be equal. We say that a *stress* is placed on the equilibrium. Then the system responds by changing the rate of the forward or reverse reaction in the direction that relieves that stress to reestablish equilibrium. We can use **Le Châtelier's principle**, which states that when a system at equilibrium is disturbed, the system will shift in the direction that will reduce that stress.

Water at equilibrium

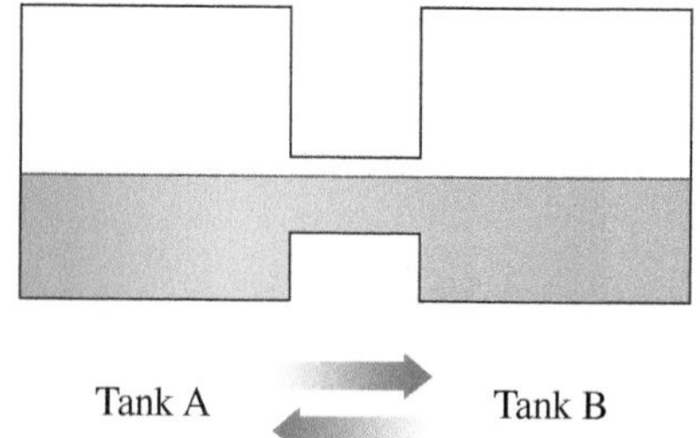

Tank A Tank B

Stress as water is added to first tank
Increasing rate of forward direction

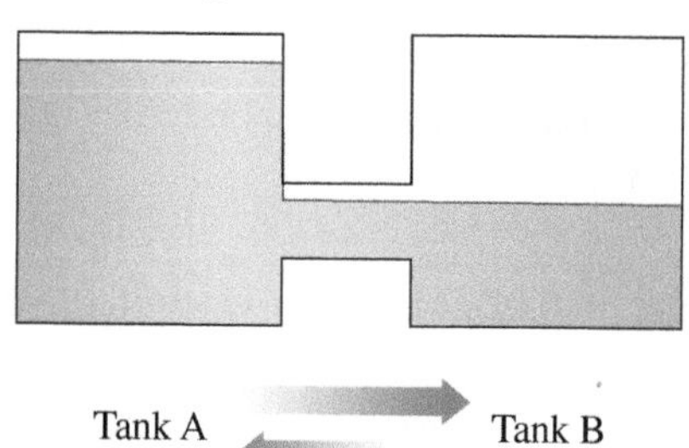

Tank A Tank B

New equilibrium established

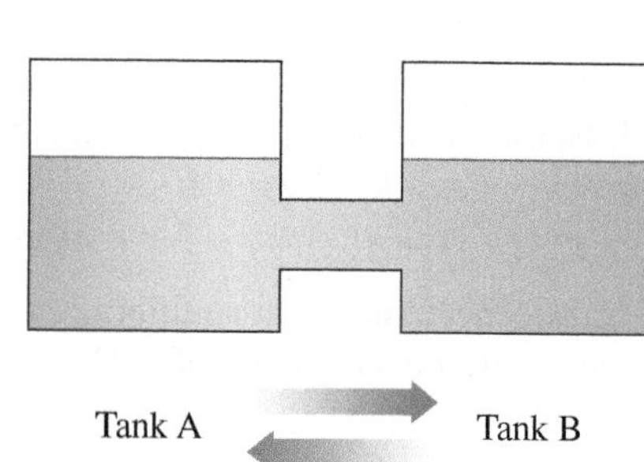

Tank A Tank B

When water is added to one tank, the levels readjust to equalize.

Suppose we have two water tanks connected by a pipe. When the water levels are equal, water moves equally in the forward direction (Tank A to Tank B) and in the reverse direction (Tank B to Tank A). Suppose we add more water to Tank A. With a higher level of water in Tank A, more water moves in the forward direction from Tank A to Tank B than in the reverse direction from Tank B to Tank A, which is shown with a longer arrow. Eventually, equilibrium is reached as the levels in both tanks again become equal, but higher than before.

Effect of Concentration Changes on Equilibrium

We will now use the reaction of H_2 and I_2 to illustrate how a change in concentration disturbs the equilibrium, and how the system responds to that stress.

$$H_2(g) + I_2(g) \rightleftharpoons 2HI(g)$$

Suppose that more of the reactant H_2 is added to the equilibrium mixture, which increases the concentration of H_2. Because a K_c cannot change for a reaction at a given temperature, adding more H_2 places a stress on the system (see Figure 8). Then the system relieves this stress by increasing the rate of the forward reaction. Thus, more products are formed until the system is again at equilibrium. According to Le Châtelier's principle, adding more reactant causes the system to *shift* in the direction of the products until equilibrium is reestablished.

Add H_2

$$H_2(g) + I_2(g) \rightleftharpoons 2HI(g)$$

Suppose now that some H_2 is removed from the reaction mixture at equilibrium, which lowers the concentration of H_2. To relieve this stress, the rate of the forward reaction is slowed. From using Le Châtelier's principle, we know that when some of the reactants are removed, the system will *shift* in the direction of the reactants until equilibrium is reestablished.

Remove H_2

$$H_2(g) + I_2(g) \rightleftharpoons 2HI(g)$$

There can also be an increase or decrease in the concentrations of the products of an equilibrium mixture. For example, if more HI is added, there is an increase in the rate of the reaction in the reverse direction, which converts some of the products to reactants. The concentration of the products decreases and the concentration of the reactants increases until equilibrium is reestablished. Using Le Châtelier's principle, we see that the addition of a product causes the system to *shift* in the direction of the reactants.

Add HI

$$H_2(g) + I_2(g) \rightleftharpoons 2HI(g)$$

In another example, some HI is removed from an equilibrium mixture, which decreases the concentration of the products. Then there is a *shift* in the direction of the products to reestablish equilibrium.

Remove HI

$$H_2(g) + I_2(g) \rightleftharpoons 2HI(g)$$

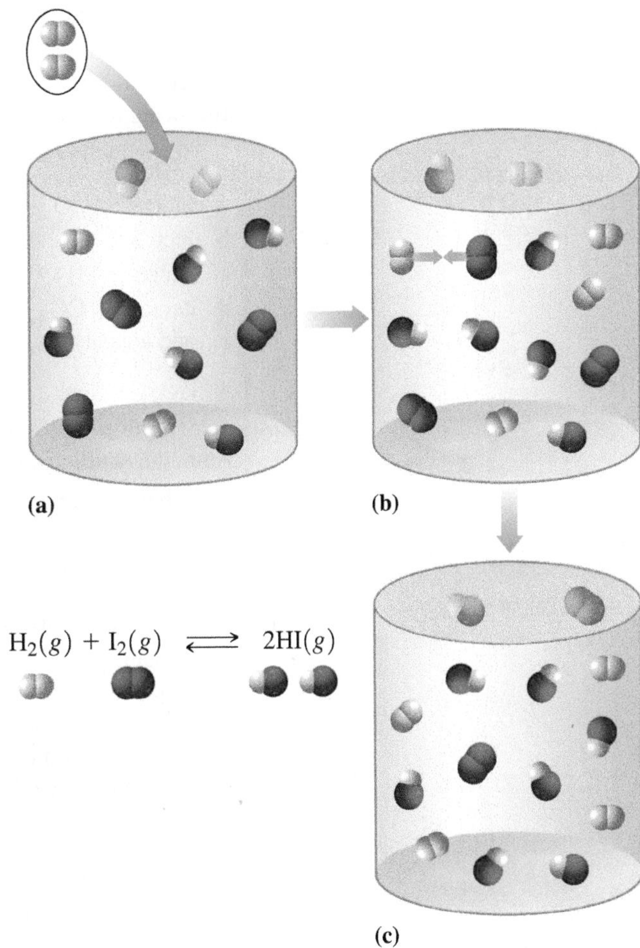

FIGURE 8 **(a)** The addition of H_2 places stress on the equilibrium system of $H_2(g) + I_2(g) \rightleftharpoons 2HI(g)$. **(b)** To relieve the stress, the forward reaction converts some reactants H_2 and I_2 to product HI. **(c)** A new equilibrium is established when the rates of the forward reaction and the reverse reaction become equal.

Q If more product HI is added, will the equilibrium shift in the direction of the products or reactants? Why?

TUTORIAL
Predicting Equilibrium Shifts

In summary, Le Châtelier's principle indicates that a stress caused by adding a substance at equilibrium is relieved when the equilibrium system shifts the reaction away from that substance. Adding more reactant causes an increase in the forward reaction to products. Adding more product causes an increase in the reverse reaction to reactants. When some of a substance is removed, the equilibrium system shifts in the direction of that substance. These features of Le Châtelier's principle are summarized in Table 4.

TABLE 4 Effect of Concentration Change on Equilibrium
$H_2(g) + I_2(g) \rightleftharpoons 2HI(g)$

Stress	Shift in the Direction of
Increase $[H_2]$	Products
Decrease $[H_2]$	Reactants
Increase $[I_2]$	Products
Decrease $[I_2]$	Reactants
Increase $[HI]$	Reactants
Decrease $[HI]$	Products

Effect of a Catalyst on Equilibrium

Sometimes a catalyst is added to a reaction. We showed that a catalyst speeds up a reaction by lowering the activation energy. As a result, the rates of the forward and reverse reactions both increase. The time required to reach equilibrium is shorter, but the same ratios of products and reactants are attained. Therefore, a catalyst speeds up the forward and reverse reactions, but it has no effect on the concentrations of the reactants and products in the equilibrium mixture.

CONCEPT CHECK 4 **Effect of Changes in Concentrations on Equilibrium**

Describe the effect of each of the following changes on the equilibrium mixture of the following reaction:

$$CO(g) + H_2O(g) \rightleftharpoons CO_2(g) + H_2(g)$$

a. increase $[CO]$
b. increase $[H_2]$
c. decrease $[H_2O]$
d. decrease $[CO_2]$
e. add a catalyst

ANSWER

According to Le Châtelier's principle, when stress is applied to a reaction at equilibrium, the equilibrium will shift to relieve the stress.

a. When the concentration of the reactant CO increases, the rate of the forward reaction increases to shift the equilibrium in the direction of the products until equilibrium is reestablished.
b. When the concentration of the product H_2 increases, the rate of the reverse reaction increases to shift the equilibrium in the direction of the reactants until equilibrium is reestablished.
c. When the concentration of the reactant H_2O decreases, the rate of the reverse reaction increases to shift the equilibrium in the direction of the reactants until equilibrium is reestablished.
d. When the concentration of the product CO_2 decreases, the rate of the forward reaction increases to shift the equilibrium in the direction of the products until equilibrium is reestablished.
e. When a catalyst is added, it changes the rates of the forward and reverse reactions equally, which does not cause any shift in the equilibrium system.

Effect of Volume Change on Equilibrium

If there is a change in the volume of a gas mixture at equilibrium, there will also be a change in the concentrations of those gases. Decreasing the volume will increase the concentration of gases, whereas increasing the volume will decrease their concentration. Then the system responds to reestablish equilibrium.

Let's look at the effect of decreasing the volume of the equilibrium mixture of the following reaction:

$$2CO(g) + O_2(g) \rightleftharpoons 2CO_2(g)$$

If we decrease the volume, there is an increase in all the concentrations. According to Le Châtelier's principle, the increase in concentration is relieved when the system shifts in the direction of the fewer number of moles.

Decrease *V* →

$$\underset{3\text{ moles}}{2CO(g) + O_2(g)} \rightleftharpoons \underset{2\text{ moles}}{2CO_2(g)}$$

On the other hand, when the volume of the equilibrium gas mixture increases, the concentrations of all the gases decrease. Then the system shifts in the direction of the greater number of moles to reestablish equilibrium (see Figure 9).

← Increase *V*

$$\underset{3\text{ moles}}{2CO(g) + O_2(g)} \rightleftharpoons \underset{2\text{ moles}}{2CO_2(g)}$$

When a reaction has the same number of moles of reactants as products, a volume change does not affect the equilibrium mixture because the concentrations of the reactants and products change in the same way.

$$\underset{2\text{ moles}}{H_2(g) + I_2(g)} \rightleftharpoons \underset{2\text{ moles}}{2HI(g)}$$

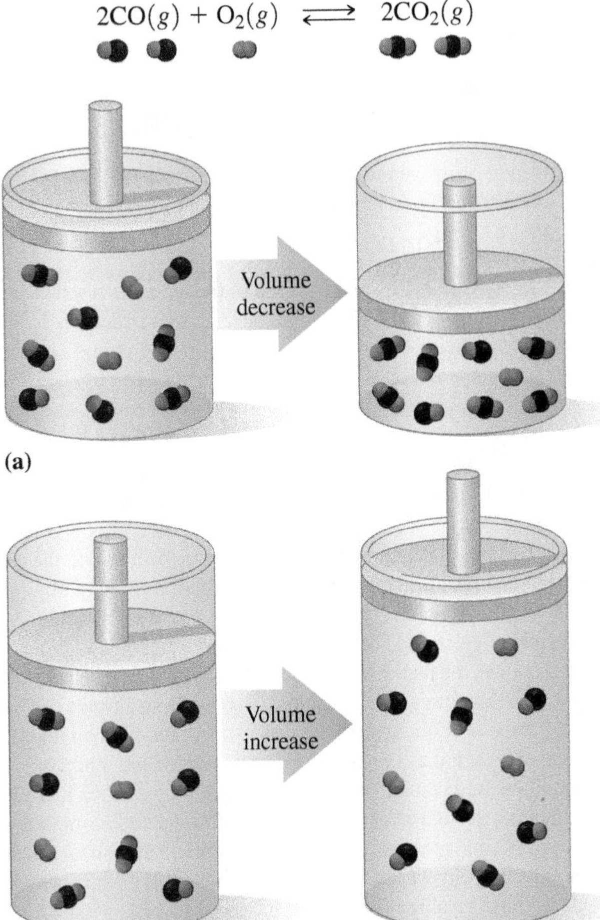

FIGURE 9 **(a)** A decrease in the volume of the container causes the system to shift in the direction of fewer moles of gas. **(b)** An increase in the volume of the container causes the system to shift in the direction of more moles of gas.

Q If you want to increase the products, would you increase or decrease the volume of the reaction container?

SAMPLE PROBLEM 7 Effect of Changes in Volume on Equilibrium

Indicate the effect of decreasing the volume of the container for each of the following at equilibrium:

a. $C_2H_2(g) + 2H_2(g) \rightleftharpoons C_2H_6(g)$
b. $2NO_2(g) \rightleftharpoons 2NO(g) + O_2(g)$
c. $CO(g) + H_2O(g) \rightleftharpoons CO_2(g) + H_2(g)$

SOLUTION

a. The system shifts in the direction of the product, which has fewer moles of gas.

$$\underset{3\text{ moles}}{C_2H_2(g) + 2H_2(g)} \longrightarrow \underset{1\text{ mole}}{C_2H_6(g)}$$

b. The system shifts in the direction of the reactant, which has fewer moles of gas.

$$\underset{2\text{ moles}}{2NO_2(g)} \longleftarrow \underset{3\text{ moles}}{2NO(g) + O_2(g)}$$

c. There is no shift in the system because the moles of reactant are equal to the moles of product.

$$\underset{2\text{ moles}}{CO(g) + H_2O(g)} \rightleftharpoons \underset{2\text{ moles}}{CO_2(g) + H_2(g)}$$

STUDY CHECK 7

Suppose you want to increase the yield of product in the following reaction. Would you increase or decrease the volume of the reaction container?

$$CO(g) + 2H_2(g) \rightleftharpoons CH_3OH(g)$$

Chemistry Link to Health

OXYGEN–HEMOGLOBIN EQUILIBRIUM AND HYPOXIA

The transport of oxygen involves an equilibrium between hemoglobin (Hb), oxygen, and oxyhemoglobin (HbO_2).

$$Hb + O_2 \rightleftharpoons HbO_2$$

When the O_2 level is high in the alveoli of the lung, the reaction favors the product HbO_2. In the tissues where O_2 concentration is low, the reverse reaction releases the oxygen from the hemoglobin. The equilibrium constant expression is written:

$$K_c = \frac{[HbO_2]}{[Hb][O_2]}$$

At normal atmospheric pressure, oxygen diffuses into the blood because the partial pressure of oxygen in the alveoli is higher than that in the blood. At an altitude above 8000 ft, a decrease in the atmospheric pressure results in a significant reduction in the partial pressure of oxygen, which means that there is less oxygen available for the blood and body tissues. The fall in atmospheric pressure at higher altitudes decreases the partial pressure of inhaled oxygen, and there is less driving pressure for gas exchange in the lungs. At an altitude of 18 000 feet, a person will obtain 29% less oxygen. When oxygen levels are lowered, a person may experience *hypoxia*, which has symptoms that include increased respiratory rate, headache, decreased mental acuteness, fatigue, decreased physical coordination, nausea, vomiting, and cyanosis. A similar problem occurs in persons with a history of lung disease that impairs gas diffusion in the alveoli or in persons who have a reduced number of red blood cells, such as smokers.

According to Le Châtelier's principle, we see that a decrease in oxygen will shift the equilibrium in the direction of the reactants. Such a shift depletes the concentration of HbO_2 and causes the hypoxia condition.

$$Hb + O_2 \longleftarrow HbO_2$$

Immediate treatment of altitude sickness includes hydration, rest, and if necessary, descending to a lower altitude. The adaptation to lowered oxygen levels requires about 10 days. During this time, the bone marrow increases red blood cell production, providing more hemoglobin. A person living at a high altitude can have 50% more red blood cells than someone at sea level. This increase in hemoglobin causes a shift in the equilibrium in the direction of the HbO_2 product. Eventually, the higher concentration of HbO_2 will provide more oxygen to the tissues and the symptoms of hypoxia will lessen.

$$Hb + O_2 \longrightarrow HbO_2$$

For some who climb high mountains, it is important to stop and acclimatize for several days at increasing altitudes. At very high altitudes, it may be necessary to use an oxygen tank.

Peter Giovannini/Photolibrary

Hypoxia may occur at high altitudes where the oxygen concentration is lower.

Effect of Temperature Change on Equilibrium

We can think of heat as a reactant or a product in a reaction. For example, in the equation for an endothermic reaction, heat is written on the reactant side. When the temperature of an endothermic reaction increases, the system responds by shifting in the direction of the products to remove heat.

Increase T

$$N_2(g) + O_2(g) + \text{heat} \rightleftharpoons 2NO(g)$$

If the temperature is lowered for an endothermic reaction, there is a decrease in heat. Then the system shifts in the direction of the reactants to add heat.

Decrease T

$$N_2(g) + O_2(g) + \text{heat} \rightleftharpoons 2NO(g)$$

In the equation for an exothermic reaction, heat is written on the product side. When the temperature of an exothermic reaction increases, the system responds by shifting in the direction of the reactants to remove heat.

Increase T

$$2SO_2(g) + O_2(g) \rightleftharpoons 2SO_3(g) + \text{heat}$$

If the temperature is lowered for an exothermic reaction, there is a decrease in heat. Then the system shifts in the direction of the products to add heat.

Decrease T

$$2SO_2(g) + O_2(g) \rightleftharpoons 2SO_3(g) + \text{heat}$$

SAMPLE PROBLEM 8 Effect of Temperature Change on Equilibrium

Indicate the change that takes place when the temperature is increased for each of the following systems at equilibrium:

a. $N_2(g) + 3H_2(g) \rightleftharpoons 2NH_3(g) + 92\ \text{kJ}$
b. $N_2(g) + O_2(g) + 180\ \text{kJ} \rightleftharpoons 2NO(g)$

SOLUTION

a. When the temperature is increased for an exothermic reaction, the system shifts in the direction of the reactants to remove heat.
b. When the temperature is increased for an endothermic reaction, the system shifts in the direction of the products to remove heat.

STUDY CHECK 8

Indicate the change that takes place when the temperature is decreased for each of the reactions at equilibrium in Sample Problem 8.

Table 5 summarizes the ways we can use Le Châtelier's principle to determine the shift in equilibrium that relieves stress caused by the change in a condition.

TABLE 5 Effects of Condition Changes on Equilibrium

Condition	Change (stress)	Remove Stress in the Direction of
Concentration	Add a reactant	Products (forward reaction)
	Remove a reactant	Reactants (reverse reaction)
	Add a product	Reactants (reverse reaction)
	Remove a product	Products (forward reaction)
Volume (container)	Decrease volume	Fewer number of moles
	Increase volume	Greater number of moles
Temperature	**Endothermic reaction**	
	Raise T	Products (forward reaction to remove heat)
	Lower T	Reactants (reverse reaction to add heat)
	Exothermic reaction	
	Raise T	Reactants (reverse reaction to remove heat)
	Lower T	Products (forward reaction to add heat)
Catalyst	Increase rates equally	No effect

Chemistry Link to Health

HOMEOSTASIS: REGULATION OF BODY TEMPERATURE

In a physiological system of equilibrium called *homeostasis*, changes in our environment are balanced by changes in our bodies. It is crucial to our survival that we balance heat gain with heat loss. If we do not lose enough heat, our body temperature rises. At high temperatures, the body can no longer regulate our metabolic reactions. If we lose too much heat, body temperature drops. At low temperatures, essential functions proceed too slowly.

The skin plays an important role in the maintenance of body temperature. When the outside temperature rises, receptors in the skin send signals to the brain. The temperature-regulating part of the brain stimulates the sweat glands to produce perspiration. As perspiration evaporates from the skin, heat is removed, and the body temperature is lowered.

In cold temperatures, epinephrine is released, causing an increase in metabolic rate, which increases the production of heat. Receptors on the skin signal the brain to constrict the blood vessels. Less blood flows through the skin, and heat is conserved. The production of perspiration stops to lessen the heat lost by evaporation.

Blood vessels dilate
- sweat production increases
- sweat evaporates
- skin cools

Blood vessels constrict and epinephrine is released
- metabolic activity increases
- muscular activity increases
- shivering occurs
- sweat production stops

QUESTIONS AND PROBLEMS

5 Changing Equilibrium Conditions: Le Châtelier's Principle

LEARNING GOAL: *Use Le Châtelier's principle to describe the changes made in equilibrium concentrations when reaction conditions change.*

33 In the lower atmosphere, oxygen is converted to ozone (O_3) by the energy provided from lightning.

$$3O_2(g) + \text{heat} \rightleftharpoons 2O_3(g)$$

For each of the following changes at equilibrium, indicate whether the system shifts in the direction of the products, reactants, or does not change:

a. add more $O_2(g)$
b. add more $O_3(g)$
c. increase the temperature
d. increase the volume of the container
e. add a catalyst

34 Ammonia is produced by reacting nitrogen gas and hydrogen gas.

$$N_2(g) + 3H_2(g) \rightleftharpoons 2NH_3(g) + 92\text{ kJ}$$

For each of the following changes at equilibrium, indicate whether the system shifts in the direction of the products, reactants, or does not change:

a. remove some $N_2(g)$
b. lower the temperature
c. add more $NH_3(g)$
d. add more $H_2(g)$
e. increase the volume of the container

35 Hydrogen chloride can be made by reacting hydrogen gas and chlorine gas.

$$H_2(g) + Cl_2(g) + \text{heat} \rightleftharpoons 2HCl(g)$$

For each of the following changes at equilibrium, indicate whether the system shifts in the direction of the products, reactants, or does not change:

a. add more $H_2(g)$
b. increase the temperature
c. remove some $HCl(g)$
d. add a catalyst
e. remove some $Cl_2(g)$

36 When heated, carbon reacts with water to produce carbon monoxide and hydrogen.

$$C(s) + H_2O(g) + \text{heat} \rightleftharpoons CO(g) + H_2(g)$$

For each of the following changes at equilibrium, indicate whether the system shifts in the direction of the products, reactants, or does not change:

a. decrease the temperature
b. add more $C(s)$
c. remove $CO(g)$ as it forms
d. add more $H_2O(g)$
e. decrease the volume of the container

CONCEPT MAP

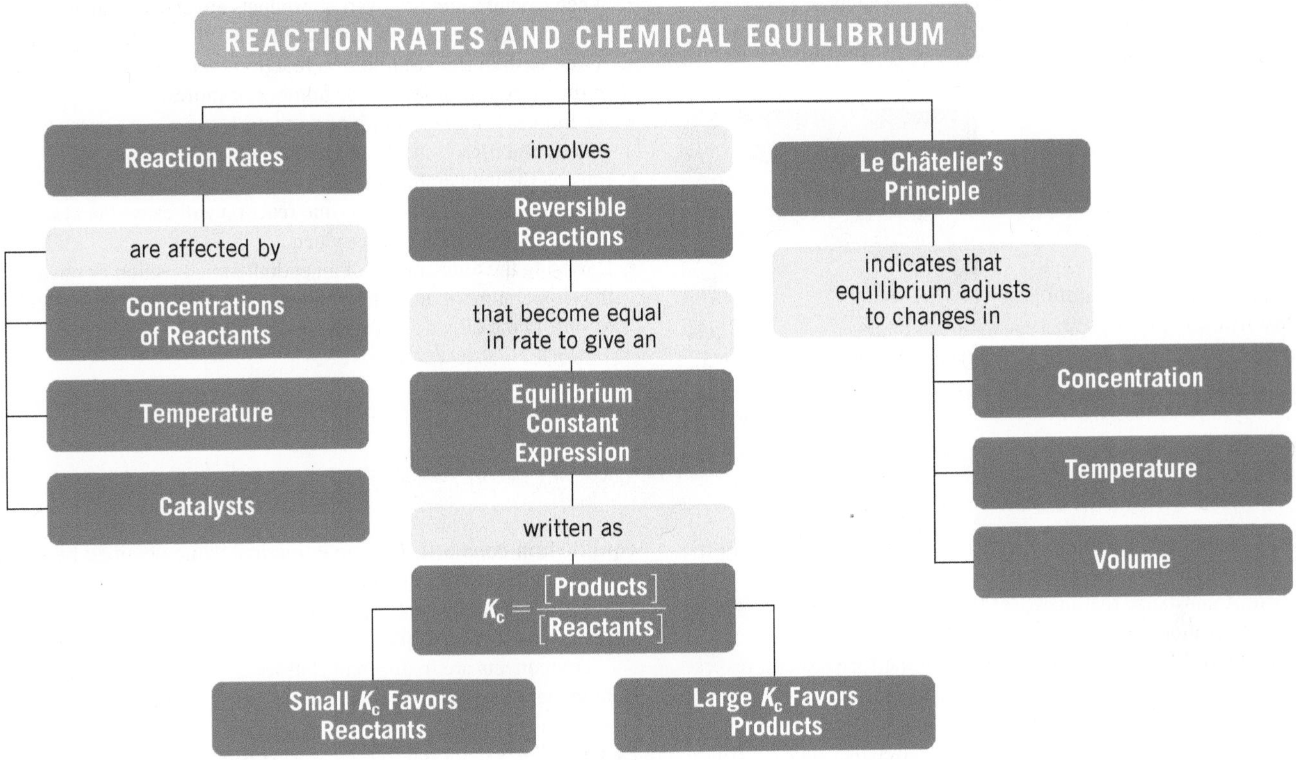

REACTION RATES AND CHEMICAL EQUILIBRIUM

- **Reaction Rates** are affected by
  - **Concentrations of Reactants**
  - **Temperature**
  - **Catalysts**
- involves **Reversible Reactions** that become equal in rate to give an **Equilibrium Constant Expression** written as

$$K_c = \frac{[\text{Products}]}{[\text{Reactants}]}$$

  - **Small K_c Favors Reactants**
  - **Large K_c Favors Products**
- **Le Châtelier's Principle** indicates that equilibrium adjusts to changes in
  - **Concentration**
  - **Temperature**
  - **Volume**

CHAPTER REVIEW

1 Rates of Reactions

LEARNING GOAL: *Describe how temperature, concentration, and catalysts affect the rate of a reaction.*

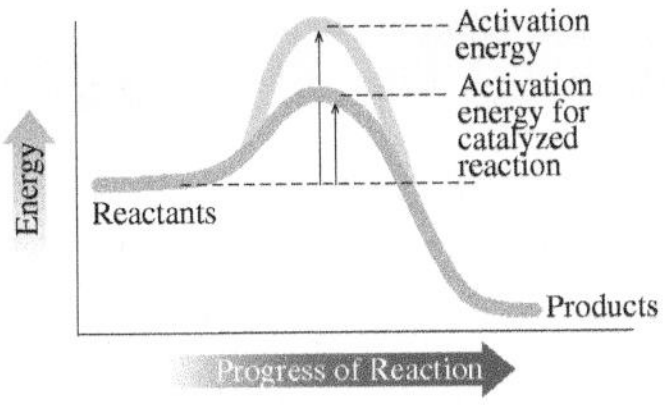

Activation energy
Activation energy for catalyzed reaction
Energy
Reactants
Products
Progress of Reaction

- The rate of a reaction is the speed at which the reactants are converted to products.
- Increasing the concentrations of reactants, raising the temperature, or adding a catalyst can increase the rate of a reaction.

2 Chemical Equilibrium

LEARNING GOAL: *Use the concept of reversible reactions to explain chemical equilibrium.*

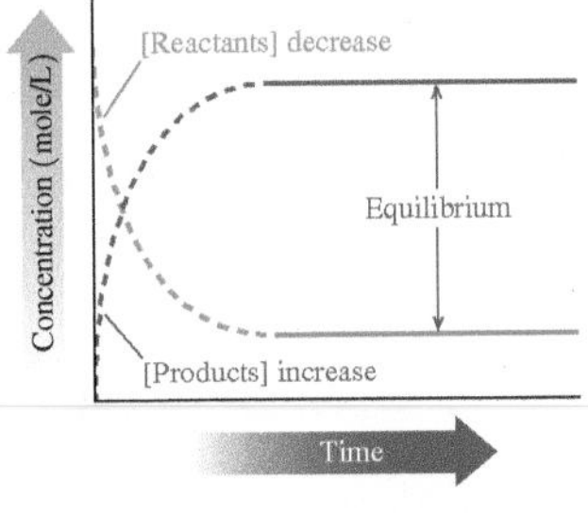

- Chemical equilibrium occurs in a reversible reaction when the rate of the forward reaction becomes equal to the rate of the reverse reaction.
- At equilibrium, no further change occurs in the concentrations of the reactants and products as the forward and reverse reactions continue.

3 Equilibrium Constants

LEARNING GOAL: *Calculate the equilibrium constant for a reversible reaction given the concentrations of reactants and products at equilibrium.*

Steve Mason/Getty Images

- An equilibrium constant, K_c, is the ratio of the concentrations of the products to the concentrations of the reactants, with each concentration raised to a power equal to its coefficient in the chemical equation.
- For heterogeneous reactions, only gases are placed in the equilibrium expression.

4 Using Equilibrium Constants

LEARNING GOAL: *Use an equilibrium constant to predict the extent of reaction and to calculate equilibrium concentrations.*

$$2SO_2(g) + O_2(g) \rightleftarrows 2SO_3(g)$$

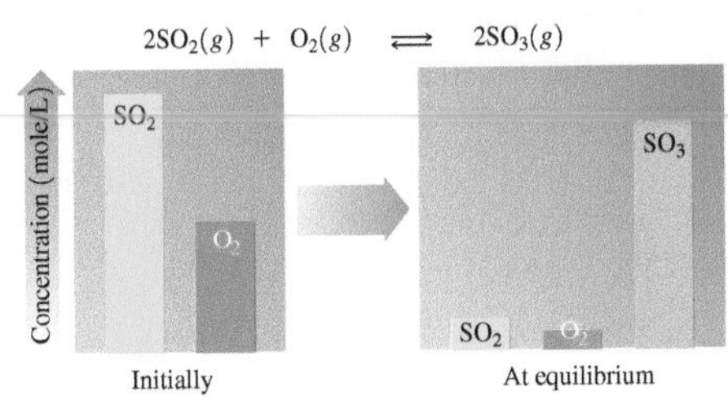

- A large value of K_c indicates that the equilibrium favors the products and could go nearly to completion, whereas a small value of K_c shows that the equilibrium favors the reactants.
- Equilibrium constants can be used to calculate the concentration of a component in the equilibrium mixture.

5 Changing Equilibrium Conditions: Le Châtelier's Principle

LEARNING GOAL: *Use Le Châtelier's principle to describe the changes made in equilibrium concentrations when reaction conditions change.*

Peter Giovannini/Photolibrary

- When reactants are added or products are removed from an equilibrium mixture, the system shifts in the direction of the products.
- When reactants are removed or products are added to an equilibrium mixture, the system shifts in the direction of the reactants.
- A decrease in the volume of a reaction container causes a shift in the direction of the fewer number of moles.
- An increase in the volume of a reaction container causes a shift in the direction of the greater number of moles.
- Raising the temperature of an endothermic reaction or lowering the temperature of an exothermic reaction will cause the system to shift in the direction of products.
- Lowering the temperature of an endothermic reaction or raising the temperature of an exothermic reaction will cause the system to shift in the direction of reactants.

KEY TERMS

activation energy The minimum energy required to break apart the bonds of the reacting molecules.

catalyst A substance that increases the rate of reaction by lowering the activation energy.

chemical equilibrium The point at which the forward and reverse reactions take place at the same rate so that there is no further change in concentrations of reactants and products.

collision theory A model for a chemical reaction that states that molecules must collide with sufficient energy and proper orientation in order to form products.

equilibrium constant expression The ratio of the concentrations of products to the concentrations of reactants with each component raised to an exponent equal to the coefficient of that compound in the balanced chemical equation.

equilibrium constant, K_c The numerical value obtained by substituting the equilibrium concentrations of the components into the equilibrium constant expression.

heterogeneous equilibrium An equilibrium system in which the components are in different states.

homogeneous equilibrium An equilibrium system in which all components are in the same state.

Le Châtelier's principle When a stress is placed on a system at equilibrium, the equilibrium shifts to relieve that stress.

rate of reaction The speed at which reactants are used to form product(s).

reversible reaction A reaction in which a forward reaction occurs from reactants to products, and a reverse reaction occurs from products back to reactants.

UNDERSTANDING THE CONCEPTS

The chapter sections to review are shown in parentheses at the end of each question.

37 Would the equilibrium constant, K_c, for the reaction in the diagrams have a large or small value? (4)

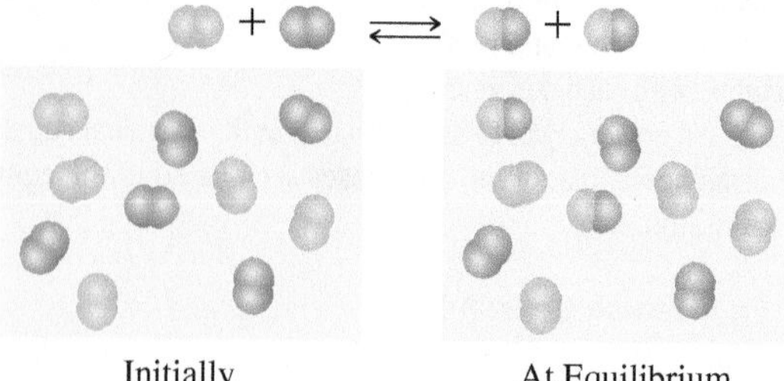

38 Would the equilibrium constant, K_c, for the reaction in the diagrams have a large or small value? (4)

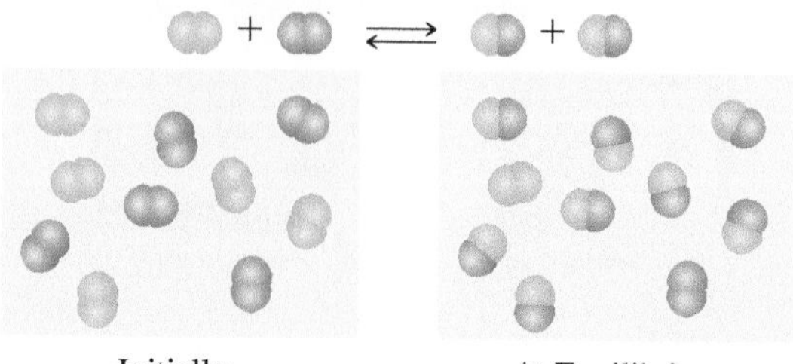

39 Would T_2 be higher or lower than T_1 for the reaction shown in the diagrams? (5)

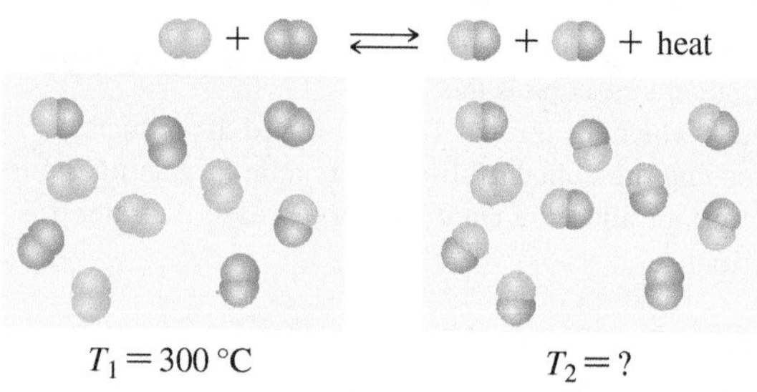

40 Would the reaction shown in the diagrams be exothermic or endothermic? (5)

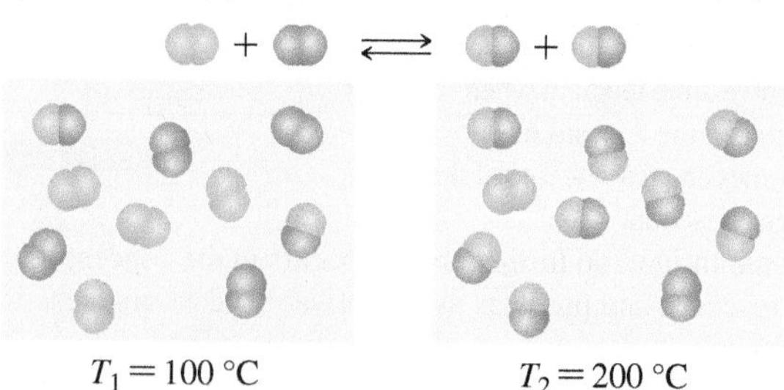

41 Indicate any changes that **a–d** will cause for the following reaction initially at equilibrium: (5)

$$C_2H_4(g) + Cl_2(g) \rightleftharpoons C_2H_4Cl_2(g) + \text{heat}$$

a. raise the temperature of the reaction
b. decrease the volume of the reaction container
c. add a catalyst
d. add more $Cl_2(g)$

42 Indicate any changes that **a–d** will cause for the following reaction initially at equilibrium: (5)

$$N_2(g) + O_2(g) + \text{heat} \rightleftharpoons 2NO(g)$$

a. raise the temperature of the reaction
b. decrease the volume of the reaction container
c. add a catalyst
d. remove some $N_2(g)$

ADDITIONAL QUESTIONS AND PROBLEMS

For instructor-assigned homework, go to www.masteringchemistry.com.

43 Write the equilibrium constant expression for each of the following reactions: (3)
a. $CH_4(g) + 2O_2(g) \rightleftharpoons CO_2(g) + 2H_2O(g)$
b. $4NH_3(g) + 3O_2(g) \rightleftharpoons 2N_2(g) + 6H_2O(g)$
c. $C(s) + 2H_2(g) \rightleftharpoons CH_4(g)$

44 Write the equilibrium constant expression for each of the following reactions: (3)
a. $2C_2H_6(g) + 7O_2(g) \rightleftharpoons 4CO_2(g) + 6H_2O(g)$
b. $2NaHCO_3(s) \rightleftharpoons Na_2CO_3(s) + CO_2(g) + H_2O(g)$
c. $4NH_3(g) + 5O_2(g) \rightleftharpoons 4NO(g) + 6H_2O(g)$

45 For each of the following reactions, indicate if the equilibrium mixture contains mostly products, mostly reactants, or both reactants and products: (4)
a. $H_2(g) + Cl_2(g) \rightleftharpoons 2HCl(g)$ $K_c = 1.3 \times 10^{34}$
b. $2NOBr(g) \rightleftharpoons 2NO(g) + Br_2(g)$ $K_c = 2.0$
c. $2NOCl(g) \rightleftharpoons Cl_2(g) + 2NO(g)$ $K_c = 2.7 \times 10^{-9}$
d. $C(s) + H_2O(g) \rightleftharpoons CO(g) + H_2(g)$ $K_c = 6.3 \times 10^{-1}$

46 For each of the following reactions, indicate if the equilibrium mixture contains mostly products, mostly reactants, or both reactants and products: (4)
a. $2H_2O(g) \rightleftharpoons 2H_2(g) + O_2(g)$ $K_c = 4 \times 10^{-48}$
b. $N_2(g) + 3H_2(g) \rightleftharpoons 2NH_3(g)$ $K_c = 0.30$
c. $2SO_2(g) + O_2(g) \rightleftharpoons 2SO_3(g)$ $K_c = 1.2 \times 10^9$
d. $H_2(g) + S(s) \rightleftharpoons H_2S(g)$ $K_c = 7.8 \times 10^5$

47 Write the equilibrium constant expression for the reactions **a–d** in Problem 45. (3)

48 Write the equilibrium constant expression for the reactions **a–d** in Problem 46. (3)

49 Write the balanced chemical equations that would give each of the following equilibrium constant expressions: (3)

a. $K_c = \dfrac{[SO_2][Cl_2]}{[SO_2Cl_2]}$ **b.** $K_c = \dfrac{[BrCl]^2}{[Br_2][Cl_2]}$

c. $K_c = \dfrac{[CH_4][H_2O]}{[CO][H_2]^3}$ **d.** $K_c = \dfrac{[N_2O][H_2O]^3}{[O_2]^2[NH_3]^2}$

50 Write the balanced chemical equations that would give each of the following equilibrium constant expressions: (3)

a. $K_c = \dfrac{[CO_2][H_2]}{[CO][H_2O]}$ **b.** $K_c = \dfrac{[H_2][F_2]}{[HF]^2}$

c. $K_c = \dfrac{[O_2][HCl]^4}{[Cl_2]^2[H_2O]^2}$ **d.** $K_c = \dfrac{[CS_2][H_2]^4}{[CH_4][H_2S]^2}$

51 Consider the reaction: (3)

$$2NH_3(g) \rightleftharpoons N_2(g) + 3H_2(g)$$

a. Write the equilibrium constant expression.
b. What is the K_c for the reaction if the concentrations at equilibrium are 0.20 M NH_3, 3.0 M N_2, and 0.50 M H_2?

52 Consider the reaction: (3)

$$2SO_2(g) + O_2(g) \rightleftharpoons 2SO_3(g)$$

a. Write the equilibrium constant expression.
b. What is the K_c for the reaction if the concentrations at equilibrium are 0.10 M SO_2, 0.12 M O_2, and 0.60 M SO_3?

53 The equilibrium constant for the combination reaction of NO_2 is 5.0 at 100 °C. If an equilibrium mixture contains 0.50 M NO_2, what is the concentration of N_2O_4? (3, 4)

$$2NO_2(g) \rightleftharpoons N_2O_4(g)$$

54 The equilibrium constant for the reaction of carbon and water to form carbon monoxide and hydrogen is 0.20 at 1000 °C. If an equilibrium mixture contains solid carbon, 0.40 M H_2O, and 0.40 M CO, what is the concentration of H_2? (3, 4)

$$C(s) + H_2O(g) \rightleftharpoons CO(g) + H_2(g)$$

55 According to Le Châtelier's principle, what is the effect when more O_2 is added to an equilibrium mixture of each of the following? (5)
a. $3O_2(g) \rightleftharpoons 2O_3(g)$
b. $2CO_2(g) \rightleftharpoons 2CO(g) + O_2(g)$
c. $P_4(g) + 5O_2(g) \rightleftharpoons P_4O_{10}(s)$
d. $2SO_2(g) + 2H_2O(g) \rightleftharpoons 2H_2S(g) + 3O_2(g)$

56 According to Le Châtelier's principle, what is the effect when more N_2 is added to an equilibrium mixture of each of the following? (5)
a. $2NH_3(g) \rightleftharpoons 3H_2(g) + N_2(g)$
b. $N_2(g) + O_2(g) \rightleftharpoons 2NO(g)$
c. $2NO_2(g) \rightleftharpoons N_2(g) + 2O_2(g)$
d. $4NH_3(g) + 3O_2(g) \rightleftharpoons 2N_2(g) + 6H_2O(g)$

57 Would decreasing the volume of the container for each of the following reactions at equilibrium cause the system to shift in the direction of the products or the reactants? (5)
a. $3O_2(g) \rightleftharpoons 2O_3(g)$
b. $2CO_2(g) \rightleftharpoons 2CO(g) + O_2(g)$
c. $P_4(g) + 5O_2(g) \rightleftharpoons P_4O_{10}(s)$
d. $2SO_2(g) + 2H_2O(g) \rightleftharpoons 2H_2S(g) + 3O_2(g)$

58 Would increasing the volume of the container for each of the following reactions at equilibrium cause the system to shift in the direction of the products or the reactants? (5)
a. $2NH_3(g) \rightleftharpoons 3H_2(g) + N_2(g)$
b. $N_2(g) + O_2(g) \rightleftharpoons 2NO(g)$
c. $N_2(g) + 2O_2(g) \rightleftharpoons 2NO_2(g)$
d. $4NH_3(g) + 3O_2(g) \rightleftharpoons 2N_2(g) + 6H_2O(g)$

59 For each of the following K_c values, indicate whether the equilibrium mixture contains mostly reactants, mostly products, or similar amounts of reactants and products: (4)
a. $N_2(g) + O_2(g) \rightleftharpoons 2NO(g)$ $K_c = 1 \times 10^{-30}$
b. $H_2(g) + Br_2(g) \rightleftharpoons 2HBr(g)$ $K_c = 2.0 \times 10^{19}$

60 For each of the following K_c values, indicate whether the equilibrium mixture contains mostly reactants, mostly products, or similar amounts of reactants and products: (4)
a. $Cl_2(g) + 2NO(g) \rightleftharpoons 2NOCl(g)$ $K_c = 3.7 \times 10^{8}$
b. $N_2(g) + 2H_2(g) \rightleftharpoons N_2H_4(g)$ $K_c = 7.4 \times 10^{-26}$

61 Indicate if you would increase or decrease the volume of the container to *increase* the yield of the products in each of the following: (5)
a. $2C(s) + O_2(g) \rightleftharpoons 2CO(g)$
b. $2CH_4(g) \rightleftharpoons C_2H_2(g) + 3H_2(g)$
c. $2H_2(g) + O_2(g) \rightleftharpoons 2H_2O(g)$

62 Indicate if you would increase or decrease the volume of the container to *increase* the yield of the products in each of the following: (5)
a. $Cl_2(g) + 2NO(g) \rightleftharpoons 2NOCl(g)$
b. $N_2(g) + 2H_2(g) \rightleftharpoons N_2H_4(g)$
c. $N_2O_4(g) \rightleftharpoons 2NO_2(g)$

CHALLENGE QUESTIONS

63 You mix 0.10 mole of PCl_5 with 0.050 mole of PCl_3 and 0.050 mole of Cl_2 in a 1.0 L container. (3, 4)

$$PCl_5(g) \rightleftharpoons PCl_3(g) + Cl_2(g) \qquad K_c = 4.2 \times 10^{-2}$$

a. Is the reaction at equilibrium?
b. If not, will the reaction proceed in the forward or reverse direction?

64 You mix 0.10 mole of NOBr, 0.10 mole of NO, and 0.10 mole of Br_2 in a 1.0 L container. (3, 4)

$$2NOBr(g) \rightleftharpoons 2NO(g) + Br_2(g) \qquad K_c = 2.0 \text{ at } 100\ °C$$

a. Is the reaction at equilibrium?
b. If not, will the reaction proceed in the forward or reverse direction?

65 Consider the following reaction: (3, 4, 5)

$$PCl_5(g) \rightleftharpoons PCl_3(g) + Cl_2(g)$$

a. Write the equilibrium constant expression for the reaction.
b. Initially, 0.60 mole of PCl_5 is placed in a 1.00 L flask. At equilibrium, there is 0.16 mole of PCl_3 in the flask. What are the equilibrium concentrations of the PCl_5 and Cl_2?
c. What is the value of the equilibrium constant, K_c, for the reaction?
d. If 0.20 mole of Cl_2 is added to the equilibrium mixture, will the concentration of PCl_5 increase or decrease?

66 The K_c for the decomposition of NOBr is 2.0 at 100 °C. (1, 2, 3, 4)

$$2NOBr(g) \rightleftharpoons 2NO(g) + Br_2(g)$$

In an experiment, 1.0 mole of NOBr, 1.0 mole of NO, and 1.0 mole of Br_2 was placed in a 1.0 L container.
a. Write the equilibrium constant expression for the reaction.
b. Is the system at equilibrium?
c. If not, will the rate of the forward or reverse reaction initially speed up?
d. At equilibrium, which concentration(s) will be greater than 1.0 mole/L, and which will be less than 1.0 mole/L?

67 The combination reaction of solid carbon and carbon dioxide produces carbon monoxide. An equilibrium mixture contains solid carbon, 0.060 M CO_2, and 0.030 M CO. (3, 5)

$$C(s) + CO_2(g) \rightleftharpoons 2CO(g)$$

a. What is the value of the equilibrium constant, K_c, for the reaction?
b. What is the effect of adding more CO_2 to the equilibrium mixture?
c. What is the effect of decreasing the volume of the container?

68 The solid NH_4HS is in equilibrium with the gases NH_3 and H_2S. An equilibrium mixture contains solid NH_4HS, 0.12 M NH_3, and 0.021 M H_2S. (3, 5)

$$NH_4HS(s) \rightleftharpoons NH_3(g) + H_2S(g)$$

a. What is the value of the equilibrium constant, K_c, for the reaction?
b. What is the effect of adding more solid NH_4HS to the equilibrium mixture?
c. What is the effect of increasing the volume of the container?

69 Indicate how each of the following will affect the equilibrium concentration of CO in the following reaction: (3, 5)

$$C(s) + H_2O(g) + 31\text{ kcal} \rightleftharpoons CO(g) + H_2(g)$$

a. add more $H_2(g)$
b. increase the temperature of the reaction
c. increase the volume of the container
d. decrease the volume of the container
e. add a catalyst
f. decrease the temperature of the reaction
g. remove some $H_2O(g)$

70 Indicate how each of the following will affect the equilibrium concentration of NH_3 in the following reaction: (3, 5)

$$NH_3(g) + 5O_2(g) \rightleftharpoons 4NO(g) + 6H_2O(g) + 906\text{ kJ}$$

a. add more $O_2(g)$
b. increase the temperature of the reaction
c. increase the volume of the container
d. add more $NO(g)$
e. decrease the volume of the container
f. decrease the temperature of the reaction
g. remove some $H_2O(g)$

ANSWERS

Answers to Study Checks

1 Lowering the temperature will decrease the rate of reaction.

2 $H_2(g) + Br_2(g) \rightleftharpoons 2HBr(g)$

3 $2NO(g) + O_2(g) \rightleftharpoons 2NO_2(g)$

4 $FeO(s) + CO(g) \rightleftharpoons Fe(s) + CO_2(g)$ $K_c = \dfrac{[CO_2]}{[CO]}$

5 $K_c = 27$

6 $[C_2H_5OH] = 2.7$ M

7 Decreasing the volume will increase the yield of product.

8 a. When the temperature is decreased for an exothermic reaction, the system shifts in the direction of products to add heat.
b. When the temperature is decreased for an endothermic reaction, the system shifts in the direction of reactants to add heat.

Answers to Selected Questions and Problems

1 Reactions go faster at higher temperatures.

3 The number of collisions between reactants will increase when the number of Br_2 molecules is increased.

5 The number of collisions between reactants will increase when the temperature is increased.

7 a. increase **b.** increase **c.** decrease **d.** decrease

9 A reversible reaction is one in which a forward reaction converts reactants to products, while a reverse reaction converts products to reactants.

11 a. not reversible **b.** reversible **c.** reversible

13 a. not at equilibrium **b.** at equilibrium **c.** at equilibrium

15 a. $K_c = \frac{[CS_2][H_2]^4}{[CH_4][H_2S]^2}$ **b.** $K_c = \frac{[N_2][O_2]}{[NO]^2}$
c. $K_c = \frac{[CS_2][O_2]^4}{[SO_3]^2[CO_2]}$

17 a. homogeneous equilibrium **b.** heterogeneous equilibrium
c. homogeneous equilibrium **d.** heterogeneous equilibrium

19 a. $K_c = \frac{[O_2]^3}{[O_3]^2}$ **b.** $K_c = [CO_2][H_2O]$

c. $K_c = \frac{[H_2]^3[CO]}{[CH_4][H_2O]}$ **d.** $K_c = \frac{[SiCl_4][H_2]^2}{[HCl]^4}$

21 $K_c = 1.5$

23 $K_c = 270$

25 $K_c = 0.26$

27 a. mostly products **b.** both reactants and products
c. mostly reactants

29 $[H_2] = 1.1 \times 10^{-3}$ M

31 $[NOBr] = 1.4$ M

33 a. The system shifts in the direction of the products.
b. The system shifts in the direction of the reactants.
c. The system shifts in the direction of the products.
d. The system shifts in the direction of the reactants.
e. No shift in system occurs.

35 a. The system shifts in the direction of the products.
b. The system shifts in the direction of the products.
c. The system shifts in the direction of the products.
d. No shift in system occurs.
e. The system shifts in the direction of the reactants.

37 The equilibrium constant would have a small value.

39 T_2 is lower than T_1.

41 a. shift in the direction of reactants
b. shift in the direction of products
c. no change
d. shift in the direction of products

43 a. $K_c = \frac{[CO_2][H_2O]^2}{[CH_4][O_2]^2}$ **b.** $K_c = \frac{[N_2]^2[H_2O]^6}{[NH_3]^4[O_2]^3}$
c. $K_c = \frac{[CH_4]}{[H_2]^2}$

45 a. mostly products **b.** both reactants and products
c. mostly reactants **d.** both reactants and products

47 a. $K_c = \frac{[HCl]^2}{[H_2][Cl_2]}$ **b.** $K_c = \frac{[NO]^2[Br_2]}{[NOBr]^2}$
c. $K_c = \frac{[Cl_2][NO]^2}{[NOCl]^2}$ **d.** $K_c = \frac{[CO][H_2]}{[H_2O]}$

49 a. $SO_2Cl_2(g) \rightleftharpoons SO_2(g) + Cl_2(g)$
b. $Br_2(g) + Cl_2(g) \rightleftharpoons 2BrCl(g)$
c. $CO(g) + 3H_2(g) \rightleftharpoons CH_4(g) + H_2O(g)$
d. $2O_2(g) + 2NH_3(g) \rightleftharpoons N_2O(g) + 3H_2O(g)$

51 a. $K_c = \frac{[N_2][H_2]^3}{[NH_3]^2}$ **b.** $K_c = 9.4$

53 $[N_2O_4] = 1.3$ M

55 a. The system shifts in the direction of the products.
b. The system shifts in the direction of the reactants.
c. The system shifts in the direction of the products.
d. The system shifts in the direction of the reactants.

57 a. The system shifts in the direction of the products.
b. The system shifts in the direction of the reactants.
c. The system shifts in the direction of the products.
d. The system shifts in the direction of the reactants.

59 a. A small K_c indicates that the equilibrium mixture contains mostly reactants.
b. A large K_c indicates that the equilibrium mixture contains mostly products.

61 a. increase **b.** increase **c.** decrease

63 a. The reaction is not at equilibrium.
b. The reaction will proceed in the forward direction.

65 a. $K_c = \frac{[PCl_3][Cl_2]}{[PCl_5]}$
b. At equilibrium, the concentrations are $[PCl_3] = 0.16$ M, $[Cl_2] = 0.16$ M, and $[PCl_5] = 0.44$ M.
c. $K_c = 0.058$
d. $[PCl_5]$ will increase.

67 a. $K_c = 0.015$
b. If more CO_2 is added, the equilibrium will shift in the direction of the products.
c. If the container volume is decreased, the equilibrium will shift in the direction of the reactants.

69 a. decrease **b.** increase **c.** increase
d. decrease **e.** no change **f.** decrease
g. decrease

Acids and Bases

From Chapter 10 of *General, Organic, and Biological Chemistry: Structures of Life*, Fourth Edition. Karen C. Timberlake.

Acids and Bases

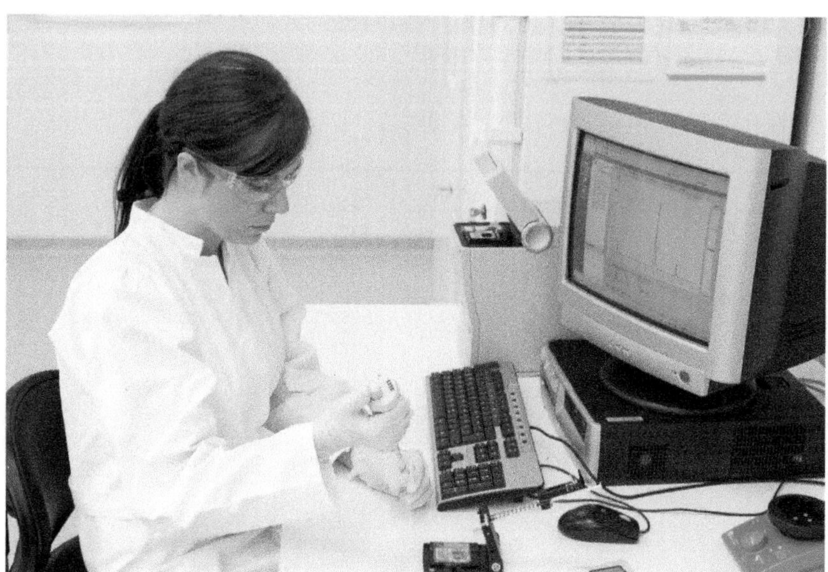

Gina Sanders/Shutterstock

LOOKING AHEAD

A 30-year-old man has been brought to the emergency room after a severe car crash. The emergency room nurses are tending to the patient, who is unresponsive. A blood sample is taken, which is sent to Brianna, a clinical laboratory technician, who begins the process of analyzing the blood's pH, the partial pressure of $O_2$and CO_2 gas, and the concentrations of glucose and electrolytes.

Within minutes, Brianna determines that the patient's blood pH is 7.30 and the partial pressure of CO_2 gas is above the desired level. Blood pH is typically in the range of 7.35–7.45, and a value less than 7.35 indicates a state of acidosis. Respiratory acidosis occurs due to an increase in the partial pressure of CO_2 gas in the bloodstream which prevents the biochemical buffers in blood from making a change in the pH. Brianna recognizes these signs and immediately contacts the emergency room to inform them that the patient's airway must be blocked. In the emergency room, they provide the patient with an IV containing bicarbonate to increase the blood pH and begin the process of unblocking the patient's airway. Shortly afterward, the patient's airway is cleared, and his blood pH and partial pressure of CO_2 gas return to normal.

Career: Clinical Laboratory Technician

Clinical laboratory technicians, also known as medical laboratory technicians, perform a wide variety of tests on body fluids and cells that help in the diagnosis and treatment of patients. These tests range from determining blood concentrations, such as glucose and cholesterol, to determining drug levels in the blood for transplant patients or a patient undergoing treatment. Clinical laboratory technicians also prepare specimens in the detection of cancerous tumors, and type blood samples for transfusions using microscopes, cell counters, and computerized instruments. Clinical laboratory technicians must also interpret and analyze the results, which are then passed on to the physician.

Lemons, grapefruit, and vinegar taste sour because they contain acids. We have acid in our stomach that helps us digest food. We produce lactic acid in our muscles when we exercise. Acid from bacteria turns milk sour to make cottage cheese or yogurt. Bases are solutions that neutralize acids. Sometimes we take antacids such as milk of magnesia to offset the effects of too much stomach acid.

The pH of a solution describes its acidity. The lungs and the kidneys are the primary organs that regulate the pH of body fluids, including blood and urine. Major changes in the pH of the body fluids can severely affect biological activities within the cells. Buffers are present to prevent large fluctuations in pH.

magicinfoto/iStockphoto

Citrus fruits are sour because of the presence of acids.

In the environment, the pH of rain, water, and soil can have significant effects. When rain becomes too acidic, it can dissolve marble statues and accelerate the corrosion of metals. In lakes and ponds, the acidity of water can affect the ability of fish to survive. The acidity of the soil around plants affects their growth. If the soil pH is too acidic or too basic, the roots of the plant cannot take up some nutrients. Most plants thrive in soil with a nearly neutral pH, although certain plants such as orchids, camellias, and blueberries require a more acidic soil.

1 Acids and Bases

LEARNING GOAL

Describe and name Arrhenius and Brønsted–Lowry acids and bases; identify conjugate acid–base pairs.

The term *acid* comes from the Latin word *acidus*, which means "sour." We are familiar with the sour tastes of vinegar, lemons, and other common acidic foods.

In 1887, the Swedish chemist Svante Arrhenius was the first to describe **acids** as substances that produce hydrogen ions (H^+) when they dissolve in water. For example, hydrogen chloride ionizes in water to give hydrogen ions, H^+, and chloride ions, Cl^-. The hydrogen ions give acids a sour taste, change blue litmus indicator to red, and corrode some metals.

$$\underset{\text{Polar covalent compound}}{HCl(g)} \xrightarrow[\text{Ionization}]{H_2O} \underset{\text{Hydrogen ion}}{H^+(aq)} + Cl^-(aq)$$

Naming Acids

Acids dissolve in water to produce hydrogen ions, along with a negative ion that may be a simple nonmetal anion or a polyatomic ion.

When an acid dissolves in water to produce a hydrogen ion and a simple nonmetal anion, the prefix *hydro* is used before the name of the nonmetal, and its *ide* ending is changed to *ic acid*. For example, hydrogen chloride (HCl) dissolves in water to form HCl(*aq*), which is named hydrochloric acid. When an acid contains an oxygen-containing polyatomic ion, the name of the acid comes from the name of the polyatomic ion. The *ate* in the name is replaced with *ic acid*. If the acid contains a polyatomic ion with an *ite* ending, its name ends with *ous acid*. The names of some common acids and their anions are listed in Table 1.

TABLE 1 Naming Common Acids

Acid	Name of Acid	Anion	Name of Anion
HCl	Hydrochloric acid	Cl^-	Chloride
HBr	Hydrobromic acid	Br^-	Bromide
HNO_3	Nitric acid	NO_3^-	Nitrate
HNO_2	Nitrous acid	NO_2^-	Nitrite
H_2SO_4	Sulfuric acid	SO_4^{2-}	Sulfate
H_2SO_3	Sulfurous acid	SO_3^{2-}	Sulfite
H_2CO_3	Carbonic acid	CO_3^{2-}	Carbonate
H_3PO_4	Phosphoric acid	PO_4^{3-}	Phosphate
$HClO_4$	Perchloric acid	ClO_4^-	Perchlorate
$HClO_3$	Chloric acid	ClO_3^-	Chlorate
$HClO_2$	Chlorous acid	ClO_2^-	Chlorite
$HClO$	Hypochlorous acid	ClO^-	Hypochlorite
$HC_2H_3O_2$	Acetic acid	$C_2H_3O_2^-$	Acetate

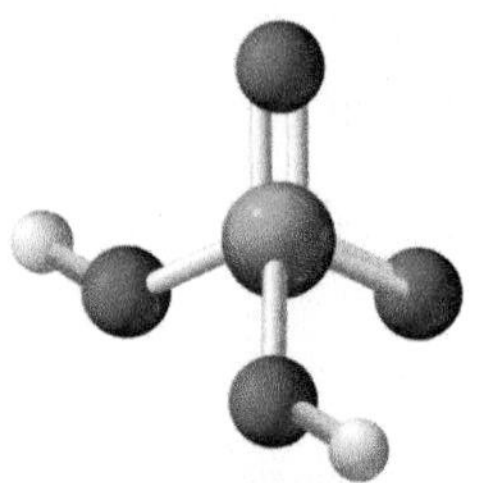
Sulfuric acid contains two H atoms that can dissociate in aqueous solution.

CONCEPT CHECK 1 **Naming Acids**

a. If H_2SO_4 is named sulfuric acid, what is the name of H_2SO_3? Why?
b. In part **a**, why is the prefix *hydro* not used at the beginning of either name?

ANSWER

a. H_2SO_3 is named sulfurous acid. The acid of the polyatomic anion that ends in *ite* replaces the *ite* ending with *ous acid.*
b. The prefix *hydro* is used only when the anion is a simple nonmetal anion, and not with an acid that includes a polyatomic anion.

Bases

You may be familiar with some household bases such as antacids, window cleaner, drain openers, and oven cleaners. According to the Arrhenius theory, **bases** are ionic compounds that dissociate into cations and hydroxide ions (OH^-) when they dissolve in water. They are another example of strong electrolytes. For example, sodium hydroxide is an Arrhenius base that ionizes in water to give sodium ions, Na^+, and hydroxide ions, OH^-.

Most Arrhenius bases are formed from Groups 1A (1) and 2A (2) metals, such as NaOH, KOH, LiOH, and $Ca(OH)_2$. The hydroxide ions (OH^-) give Arrhenius bases common characteristics such as a bitter taste and a slippery feel. A base turns litmus indicator blue and phenolphthalein indicator pink.

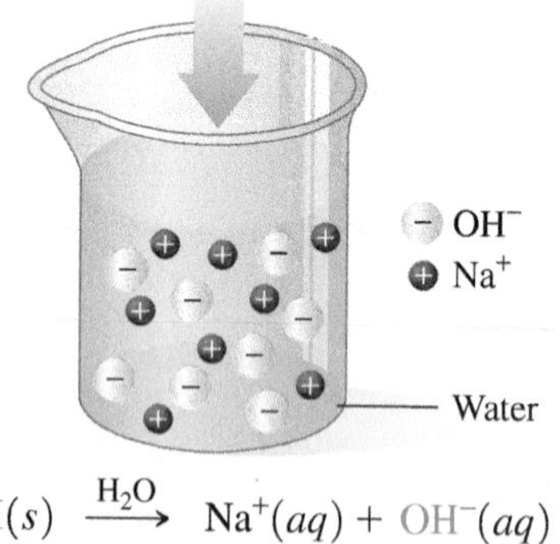

$$NaOH(s) \xrightarrow{H_2O} Na^+(aq) + OH^-(aq)$$

Ionic compound — Ionization — Hydroxide ion

An Arrhenius base produces a cation and an OH^- anion in an aqueous solution.

Naming Bases

Typical Arrhenius bases are named as *hydroxides.*

Base	Name
$NaOH$	Sodium **hydroxide**
KOH	Potassium **hydroxide**
$Ca(OH)_2$	Calcium **hydroxide**
$Al(OH)_3$	Aluminum **hydroxide**

TUTORIAL
Acid and Base Formulas

TUTORIAL
Naming Acids and Bases

Richard Megna/Fundamental Photographs

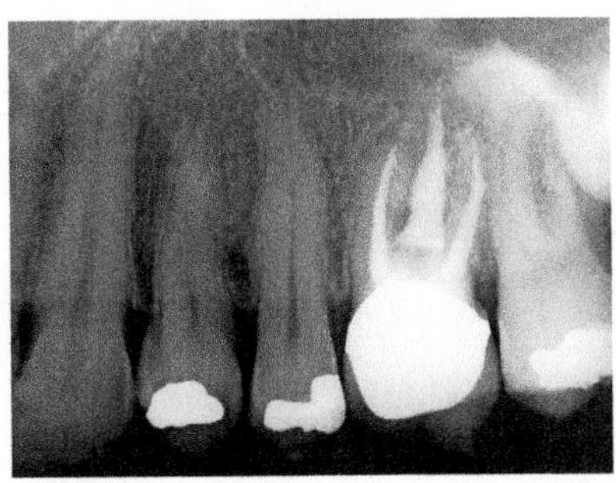

Kul Bhatia/Photo Researchers, Inc.

Calcium hydroxide, $Ca(OH)_2$, also called slaked lime, is used in the food industry to produce beverages, in tanning to neutralize acids, and in dentistry as a filler for root canals.

CONCEPT CHECK 2 **Ionization of an Arrhenius Base**

When dried corn kernels are soaked in limewater (calcium hydroxide solution), the product is hominy, corn that has been hulled with the bran and germ removed and is used to make grits. Write an equation for the ionization of calcium hydroxide in water.

ANSWER

When calcium hydroxide, $Ca(OH)_2$, dissolves in water, the solution contains calcium ions (Ca^{2+}) and twice as many hydroxide ions (OH^-). The equation is written as:

$$Ca(OH)_2(s) \xrightarrow{H_2O} Ca^{2+}(aq) + 2OH^-(aq)$$

David Wei/Alamy

Hominy for grits is prepared by soaking corn kernels in a calcium hydroxide solution.

SAMPLE PROBLEM 1 **Names and Formulas of Acids and Bases**

a. Identify each of the following as an acid or a base and give its name:
  1. H_3PO_4, ingredient in soft drinks
  2. NaOH, ingredient in oven cleaner

b. Write the formula for each of the following:
  1. magnesium hydroxide, ingredient in antacids
  2. hydrobromic acid, used industrially to prepare bromide compounds

SOLUTION

a. 1. acid; phosphoric acid **2.** base; sodium hydroxide

b. 1. $Mg(OH)_2$ **2.** HBr

STUDY CHECK 1

a. Identify as an acid or base and give the name for $HClO_3$.

b. Write the formula for iron(III) hydroxide.

Kesu/Shutterstock

A soft drink contains H_3PO_4 and H_2CO_3.

Brønsted–Lowry Acids and Bases

MC™ TUTORIAL Definitions of Acids and Bases

In 1923, J. N. Brønsted in Denmark and T. M. Lowry in Great Britain expanded the definition of acids and bases to include bases that do not contain OH^- ions. A **Brønsted–Lowry acid** can donate a hydrogen ion, H^+, to another substance, and a **Brønsted–Lowry base** can accept a hydrogen ion.

A Brønsted–Lowry acid is a substance that donates H^+.

A Brønsted–Lowry base is a substance that accepts H^+.

A free hydrogen ion, H^+, does not actually exist in water. Its attraction to polar water molecules is so strong that the H^+ bonds to the water molecule and forms a **hydronium ion, H_3O^+**.

$$H{-}\ddot{O}{:}\;(\text{with }H\text{ below}) + H^+ \longrightarrow \left[H{-}\ddot{O}{-}H\;(\text{with }H\text{ below})\right]^+$$

Water Hydrogen ion Hydronium ion

We can write the formation of a hydrochloric acid solution as a transfer of H^+ from hydrogen chloride to water. By accepting an H^+ in the reaction, water is acting as a base according to the Brønsted–Lowry concept.

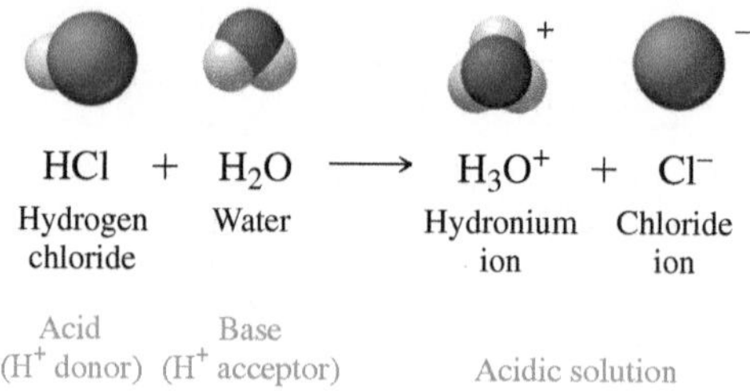

$$HCl + H_2O \longrightarrow H_3O^+ + Cl^-$$

Hydrogen chloride (Acid, H^+ donor) | Water (Base, H^+ acceptor) | Hydronium ion | Chloride ion — Acidic solution

In another reaction, ammonia (NH_3) reacts with water. Because the nitrogen atom of NH_3 has a stronger attraction for H^+, water acts as an acid by donating H^+.

$$NH_3 + H_2O \rightleftarrows NH_4^+ + OH^-$$

Ammonia (Base, H^+ acceptor) | Water (Acid, H^+ donor) | Ammonium ion | Hydroxide ion — Basic solution

TUTORIAL
Properties of Acids and Bases

Table 2 compares some characteristics of acids and bases.

TABLE 2 Some Characteristics of Acids and Bases

Characteristic	Acids	Bases
Arrhenius	Produce H^+	Produce OH^-
Brønsted–Lowry	Donate H^+	Accept H^+
Electrolytes	Yes	Yes
Taste	Sour	Bitter, chalky
Feel	May sting	Slippery
Turns Litmus	Red	Blue
Turns Phenolphthalein	Colorless	Pink
Neutralization	Neutralize bases	Neutralize acids

SAMPLE PROBLEM 2 Acids and Bases

In each of the following equations, identify the reactant that is a Brønsted–Lowry acid and the reactant that is a Brønsted–Lowry base:

a. $HBr(aq) + H_2O(l) \longrightarrow H_3O^+(aq) + Br^-(aq)$
b. $H_2O(l) + HS^-(aq) \rightleftarrows H_2S(aq) + OH^-(aq)$

SOLUTION

a. HBr, Brønsted–Lowry acid; H_2O, Brønsted–Lowry base
b. H_2O, Brønsted–Lowry acid; HS^-, Brønsted–Lowry base

STUDY CHECK 2

When HNO_3 reacts with water, water acts as a Brønsted–Lowry base. Write the equation for the reaction.

TUTORIAL
Identifying Conjugate Acid–Base Pairs

Conjugate Acid–Base Pairs

According to the Brønsted–Lowry theory, a **conjugate acid–base pair** consists of molecules or ions related by the loss of one H^+ by an acid, and the gain of one H^+ by a base. Every acid–base reaction contains two conjugate acid–base pairs because an H^+ is transferred in both the forward and reverse reactions. When the acid such as HF loses one H^+, its conjugate base, F^-, is formed. When the base H_2O gains an H^+, its conjugate acid, H_3O^+, is formed.

Because the overall reaction of HF is reversible, the conjugate acid H_3O^+ can donate H^+ to the conjugate base F^- and re-form the acid HF and the base H_2O. Using the relationship of loss and gain of one H^+, we can now identify the conjugate acid–base pairs as HF/F^- along with H_3O^+/H_2O.

Conjugate acid–base pair

Conjugate acid–base pair

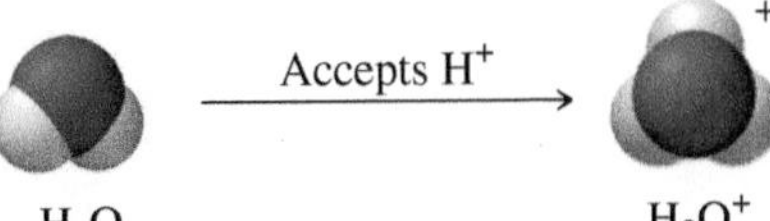

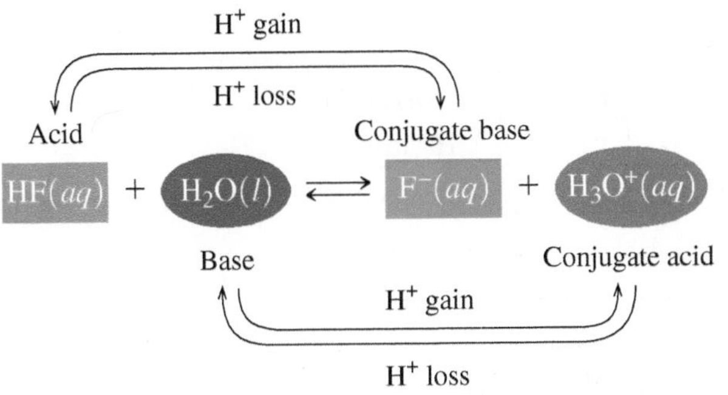

HF, an acid, loses one H^+ to form its conjugate base F^-. Water acts as a base by gaining one H^+ to form its conjugate acid H_3O^+.

In another reaction, the base ammonia, NH_3, accepts H^+ from H_2O to form its conjugate acid NH_4^+ and conjugate base OH^-. Each of these conjugate acid–base pairs, NH_4^+ and NH_3 as well as H_2O and OH^-, are related by the loss and gain of one H^+.

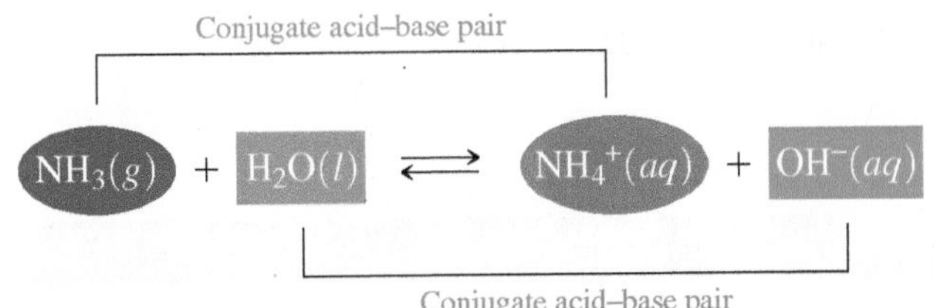

Ammonia, NH_3, acts as a base when it gains one H^+ to form its conjugate acid NH_4^+. Water acts as an acid by losing one H^+ to form its conjugate base OH^-.

In these two examples, we see that water can act as an acid when it donates H^+ or a base when it accepts H^+. Substances that can act as both acids and bases are **amphoteric** or *amphiprotic*. For water, the most common amphoteric substance, the acidic or basic behavior depends on the other reactant. Water donates H^+ when it reacts with a stronger base and accepts H^+ when it reacts with a stronger acid. Another example of an amphoteric substance is bicarbonate, HCO_3^-. With a base, HCO_3^- acts as an acid and donates one H^+ to give CO_3^{2-}. However, when HCO_3^- reacts with an acid, it acts as a base and accepts one H^+ to form H_2CO_3.

H_3O^+ / H_2CO_3 ← Acts as a base — H_2O / HCO_3^- — Acts as an acid → OH^- / CO_3^{2-}

Amphoteric substances can act as both acids and bases.

CONCEPT CHECK 3 **Conjugate Acid–Base Pairs**

a. Write the formula for the conjugate base of $HClO_3$.
b. Write the conjugate acid of HS^-.

ANSWER

a. A conjugate base forms when a Brønsted–Lowry acid loses one H^+. When $HClO_3$ loses one H^+, it forms its conjugate base ClO_3^-.
b. A conjugate acid forms when a Brønsted–Lowry base gains one H^+. When HS^- gains one H^+, it forms its conjugate acid H_2S.

SAMPLE PROBLEM 3 **Identifying Conjugate Acid–Base Pairs**

Identify the conjugate acid–base pairs in the following equation:

$$HBr(aq) + NH_3(aq) \longrightarrow Br^-(aq) + NH_4^+(aq)$$

SOLUTION

Analyze the Problem

	Reactant	Product	H^+ Loss/Gain
Given	HBr	Br^-	1 H^+ lost
	NH_3	NH_4^+	1 H^+ gained
Need			
Conjugate Acid–Base Pair			
Conjugate Acid–Base Pair			

Acting as a Brønsted–Lowry acid, HBr loses one H^+ to form Br^-, which is its conjugate base. The NH_3, acting as a Brønsted–Lowry base, gains one H^+ to form its conjugate acid, NH_4^+. The conjugate acid–base pairs are HBr/Br^- and NH_4^+/NH_3.

STUDY CHECK 3

In the following reaction, identify the conjugate acid–base pairs:

$$HNO_2(aq) + SO_4^{2-}(aq) \rightleftarrows NO_2^-(aq) + HSO_4^-(aq)$$

QUESTIONS AND PROBLEMS

1 Acids and Bases

LEARNING GOAL: *Describe and name Arrhenius and Brønsted–Lowry acids and bases; identify conjugate acid–base pairs.*

1 Indicate each of the following statements as a characteristic of an acid, base, or both:
a. has a sour taste
b. neutralizes bases
c. produces H^+ ions in water
d. is named potassium hydroxide
e. is an electrolyte

2 Indicate each of the following statements as a characteristic of an acid, base, or both:
a. neutralizes acids
b. produces OH^- ions in water
c. has a slippery feel
d. conducts an electrical current
e. turns litmus red

3 Name each of the following acids and bases:
a. HCl **b.** $Ca(OH)_2$ **c.** H_2CO_3
d. HNO_3 **e.** H_2SO_3 **f.** $Fe(OH)_2$

4 Name each of the following acids and bases:
a. $Al(OH)_3$ **b.** HBr **c.** H_2SO_4
d. KOH **e.** HNO_2 **f.** $HBrO_2$

5 Write formulas for each of the following acids and bases:
a. magnesium hydroxide **b.** hydrofluoric acid
c. phosphorus acid **d.** lithium hydroxide
e. copper(II) hydroxide

6 Write formulas for each of the following acids and bases:
a. barium hydroxide **b.** hydroiodic acid
c. nitric acid **d.** strontium hydroxide
e. sodium hydroxide

7 Identify the reactant that is a Brønsted–Lowry acid and the reactant that is a Brønsted–Lowry base in each of the following:
a. $HI(aq) + H_2O(l) \longrightarrow H_3O^+(aq) + I^-(aq)$
b. $F^-(aq) + H_2O(l) \rightleftarrows HF(aq) + OH^-(aq)$

8 Identify the reactant that is a Brønsted–Lowry acid and the reactant that is a Brønsted–Lowry base in each of the following:
a. $CO_3^{2-}(aq) + H_2O(l) \rightleftharpoons HCO_3^-(aq) + OH^-(aq)$
b. $H_2SO_4(aq) + H_2O(l) \longrightarrow H_3O^+(aq) + HSO_4^-(aq)$

9 Write the formula and name of the conjugate base for each of the following:
a. HF **b.** H_2O **c.** H_2CO_3 **d.** HSO_4^-

10 Write the formula and name of the conjugate base for each of the following:
a. HCO_3^- **b.** H_3O^+ **c.** HPO_4^{2-} **d.** HNO_2

11 Write the formula and name of the conjugate acid for each of the following:
a. CO_3^{2-} **b.** H_2O **c.** $H_2PO_4^-$ **d.** SO_3^{2-}

12 Write the formula and name of the conjugate acid for each of the following:
a. SO_4^{2-} **b.** BrO_2^- **c.** OH^- **d.** ClO^-

13 Identify the Brønsted–Lowry acid–base pairs in each of the following equations:
a. $H_2CO_3(aq) + H_2O(l) \rightleftharpoons H_3O^+(aq) + HCO_3^-(aq)$
b. $NH_4^+(aq) + H_2O(l) \rightleftharpoons H_3O^+(aq) + NH_3(aq)$
c. $HCN(aq) + NO_2^-(aq) \rightleftharpoons CN^-(aq) + HNO_2(aq)$

14 Identify the Brønsted–Lowry acid–base pairs in each of the following equations:
a. $H_3PO_4(aq) + H_2O(l) \rightleftharpoons H_3O^+(aq) + H_2PO_4^-(aq)$
b. $CO_3^{2-}(aq) + H_2O(l) \rightleftharpoons OH^-(aq) + HCO_3^-(aq)$
c. $H_3PO_4(aq) + NH_3(aq) \rightleftharpoons NH_4^+(aq) + H_2PO_4^-(aq)$

2 Strengths of Acids and Bases

LEARNING GOAL

Write equations for the dissociation of strong and weak acids; write the equilibrium expression for a weak acid.

In the process called **dissociation**, an acid or base separates into ions in water. The *strength* of acids is determined by the moles of H_3O^+ that are produced for each mole of acid that dissolves. The *strength* of bases is determined by the moles of OH^- that are produced for each mole of base that dissolves. Strong acids and strong bases dissociate completely in water, whereas weak acids and weak bases dissociate only slightly, leaving most of the initial acid or base undissociated.

Pearson Education

Acids produce hydrogen ions in aqueous solutions.

Strong and Weak Acids

Strong acids are examples of strong electrolytes. **Strong acids** donate hydrogen ions so easily that their dissociation in water is nearly complete. For example, when HCl, a strong acid, dissociates in water, H^+ is transferred to H_2O; the resulting solution contains only the ions H_3O^+ and Cl^-. Because strong acids completely dissociate, we consider the reaction of HCl in H_2O to go 100% to products. Thus, we use a single arrow when we write the equation for a strong acid.

$$HCl(g) + H_2O(l) \longrightarrow H_3O^+(aq) + Cl^-(aq)$$

There are only six common strong acids. All other acids are weak. Table 3 lists the strong acids along with some common weak acids, from strongest to weakest acid.

Weak acids are weak electrolytes. **Weak acids** dissociate slightly in water, which means that only a small percentage of H^+ is transferred from a weak acid to H_2O, forming only a small amount of H_3O^+. In general, a weak acid sticks together rather than splitting apart. A weak acid has a strong conjugate base, which is why the reverse reaction is more prevalent. Even at high concentrations, weak acids produce low concentrations of H_3O^+ ions (see Figure 1).

Many of the products we use at home contain weak acids. For example, vinegar is a 5% solution of acetic acid, $HC_2H_3O_2$, a weak acid. In water, a few $HC_2H_3O_2$ molecules donate H^+ to H_2O to form H_3O^+ ions and acetate ions $C_2H_3O_2^-$. The formation of hydronium ions from vinegar is the reason we notice the sour taste of vinegar. In a weak acid, a reverse reaction also takes place, which converts the H_3O^+ ions and acetate ions $C_2H_3O_2^-$ back to reactants. This means that a weak acid such as acetic acid reaches equilibrium between the mostly undissociated acid and its ions. We write the equation for a weak acid in an aqueous solution with a double arrow to indicate that the forward and reverse reactions are at equilibrium.

$$\underset{\text{Acetic acid}}{HC_2H_3O_2(aq)} + H_2O(l) \rightleftharpoons H_3O^+(aq) + \underset{\text{Acetate ion}}{C_2H_3O_2^-(aq)}$$

Diprotic Acids

Some weak acids, such as carbonic acid, are *diprotic acids* that have two H^+, which dissociate one at a time. In carbonated soft drinks, for example, CO_2 dissolves in water to form carbonic acid, H_2CO_3. The weak acid H_2CO_3 reaches equilibrium between the undissociated H_2CO_3

TABLE 3 Some Conjugate Acid–Base Pairs

Increasing Acid Strength ↑ / Increasing Base Strength ↓

Acid		Conjugate Base	
Strong Acids			
Hydroiodic acid	HI	I^-	Iodide ion
Hydrobromic acid	HBr	Br^-	Bromide ion
Perchloric acid	$HClO_4$	ClO_4^-	Perchlorate ion
Hydrochloric acid	HCl	Cl^-	Chloride ion
Sulfuric acid	H_2SO_4	HSO_4^-	Hydrogen sulfate ion
Nitric acid	HNO_3	NO_3^-	Nitrate ion
Weak Acids			
Hydronium ion	H_3O^+	H_2O	Water
Hydrogen sulfate ion	HSO_4^-	SO_4^{2-}	Sulfate ion
Phosphoric acid	H_3PO_4	$H_2PO_4^-$	Dihydrogen phosphate ion
Hydrofluoric acid	HF	F^-	Fluoride ion
Nitrous acid	HNO_2	NO_2^-	Nitrite ion
Acetic acid	$HC_2H_3O_2$	$C_2H_3O_2^-$	Acetate ion
Carbonic acid	H_2CO_3	HCO_3^-	Bicarbonate ion
Hydrosulfuric acid	H_2S	HS^-	Hydrogen sulfide ion
Dihydrogen phosphate ion	$H_2PO_4^-$	HPO_4^{2-}	Hydrogen phosphate ion
Ammonium ion	NH_4^+	NH_3	Ammonia
Bicarbonate ion	HCO_3^-	CO_3^{2-}	Carbonate ion
Hydrogen sulfide ion	HS^-	S^{2-}	Sulfide ion
Water	H_2O	OH^-	Hydroxide ion

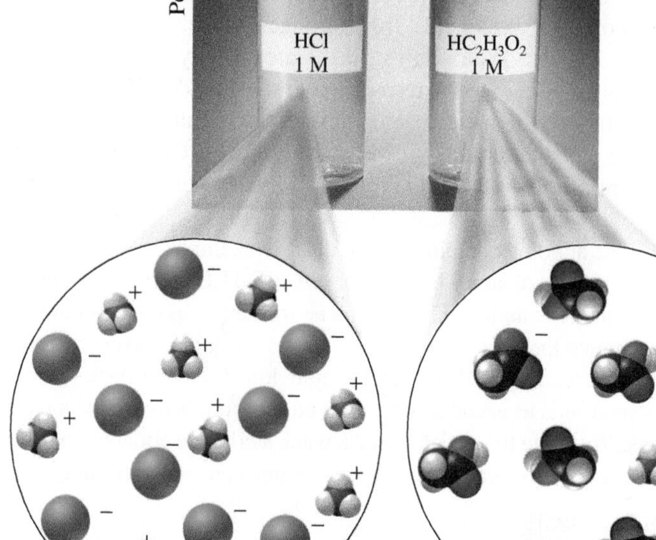

FIGURE 1 A strong acid such as HCl is completely dissociated (≈ 100%) in solution, whereas a solution of a weak acid such as $HC_2H_3O_2$ is only slightly ionized to form a weak acid solution that contains mostly molecules and a few ions.

Q What is the difference between a strong acid and a weak acid?

molecules and the ions H_3O^+ and HCO_3^-. Because HCO_3^- is also a weak acid, a second dissociation can take place to produce another hydronium ion and the carbonate ion, CO_3^{2-}.

$$H_2CO_3(aq) + H_2O(l) \rightleftharpoons H_3O^+(aq) + HCO_3^-(aq)$$

Carbonic acid — Bicarbonate ion (hydrogen carbonate)

$$HCO_3^-(aq) + H_2O(l) \rightleftharpoons H_3O^+(aq) + CO_3^{2-}(aq)$$

Bicarbonate ion — Carbonate ion

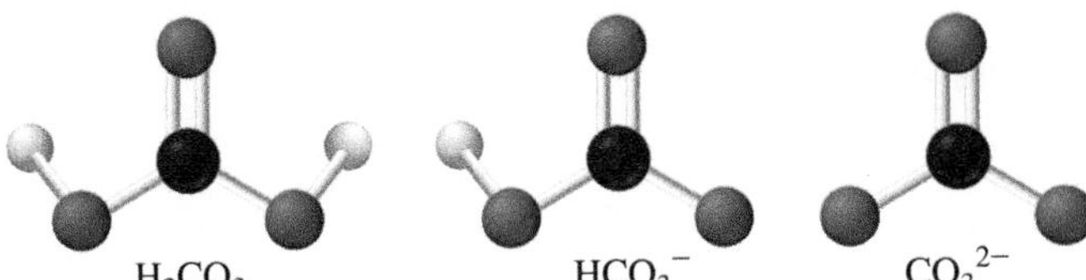
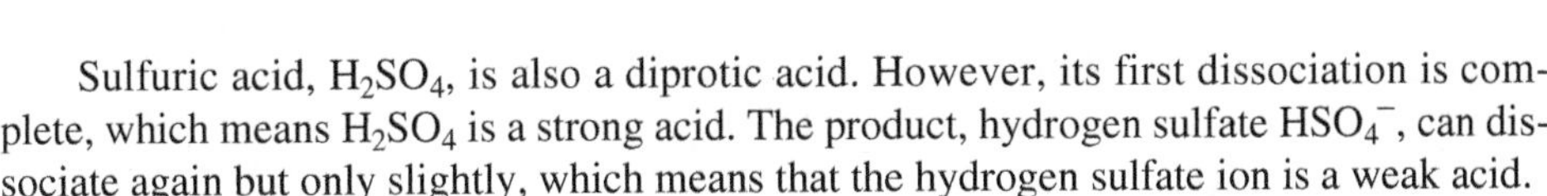

Carbonic acid, a weak acid, loses one H^+ to form hydrogen carbonate ion, which loses a second H^+ to form carbonate ion.

Sulfuric acid, H_2SO_4, is also a diprotic acid. However, its first dissociation is complete, which means H_2SO_4 is a strong acid. The product, hydrogen sulfate HSO_4^-, can dissociate again but only slightly, which means that the hydrogen sulfate ion is a weak acid.

$$H_2SO_4(aq) + H_2O(l) \longrightarrow H_3O^+(aq) + HSO_4^-(aq)$$

Sulfuric acid — Hydrogen sulfate ion

$$HSO_4^-(aq) + H_2O(l) \rightleftharpoons H_3O^+(aq) + SO_4^{2-}(aq)$$

Hydrogen sulfate ion — Sulfate ion

In summary, a strong acid such as HI in water dissociates completely to form an aqueous solution of the ions H_3O^+ and I^-. A weak acid such as HF dissociates only slightly in water to form an aqueous solution that consists mostly of undissociated HF molecules and only a few H_3O^+ and F^- ions (see Figure 2).

Strong acid: $HI(aq) + H_2O(l) \longrightarrow H_3O^+(aq) + I^-(aq)$ (completely dissociated)

Weak acid: $HF(aq) + H_2O(l) \rightleftharpoons H_3O^+(aq) + F^-(aq)$ (slightly dissociated)

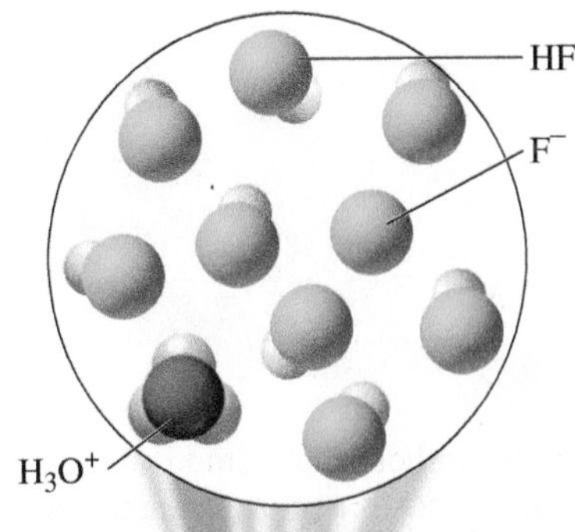

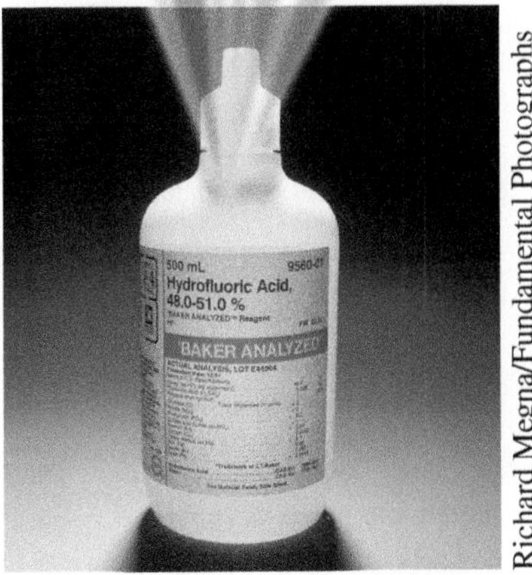

Richard Megna/Fundamental Photographs

Hydrofluoric acid is the only halogen acid that is a weak acid.

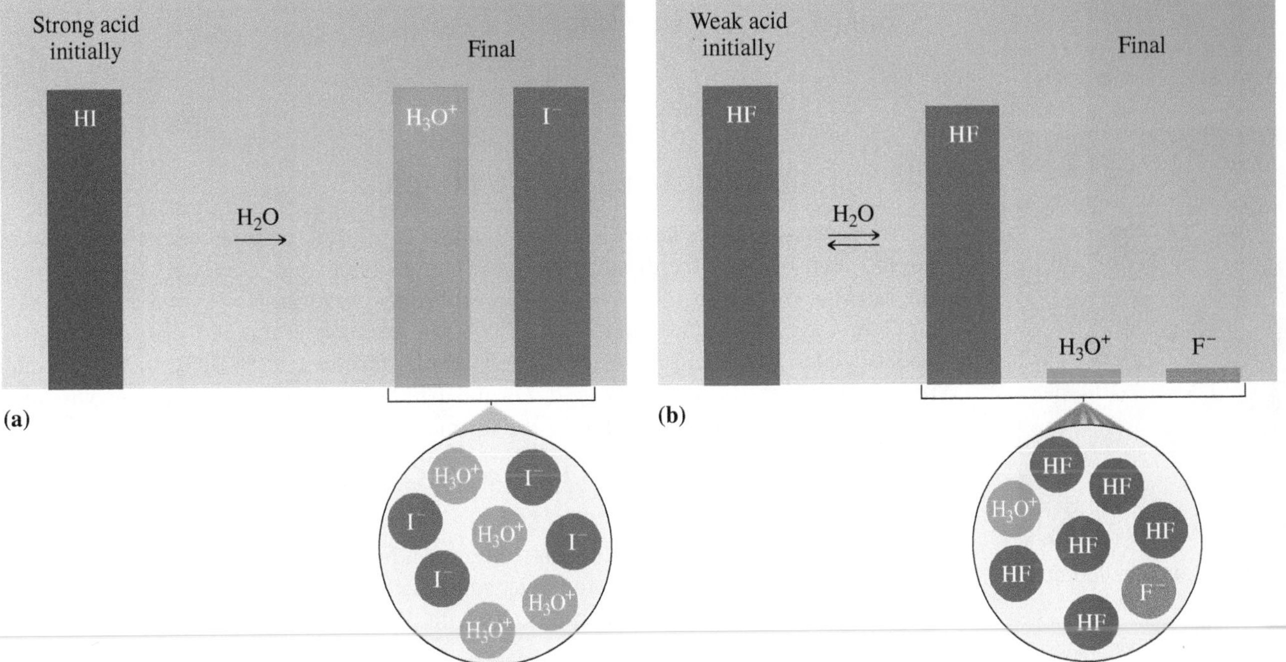

FIGURE 2 **(a)** A strong acid such as HI dissociates completely to give H_3O^+ and I^- ions. **(b)** A weak acid such as HF dissociates only slightly to form a solution containing a few H_3O^+ and F^- ions, and mostly undissociated HF molecules.

Q How does the height of the H_3O^+ in the bar diagram change for a strong acid as compared to a weak acid?

Bases in household products are used to clean, remove grease, and to open drains.

Bases in Household Products

Weak Bases

Window cleaner, ammonia, NH_3
Bleach, NaOCl
Laundry detergent, Na_2CO_3, Na_3PO_4
Toothpaste and baking soda, $NaHCO_3$
Baking powder, scouring powder, Na_2CO_3
Lime for lawns and agriculture, $CaCO_3$
Laxatives, antacids, $Mg(OH)_2$, $Al(OH)_3$

Strong Bases

Drain cleaner, oven cleaner, NaOH

TUTORIAL
Using Dissociation Constants

A red ant sting contains formic acid that irritates the skin.

Strong and Weak Bases

As strong electrolytes, **strong bases** dissociate completely in water. Because these strong bases are ionic compounds, they dissociate in water to give an aqueous solution of metal ions and hydroxide ions. The Group 1A (1) hydroxides are very soluble in water, which can give high concentrations of OH^- ions. A few bases are not very soluble in water, but what does dissolve dissociates completely as ions. For example, when KOH, a strong base, dissociates in water, the solution consists only of the ions K^+ and OH^-.

$$KOH(s) \xrightarrow{H_2O} K^+(aq) + OH^-(aq)$$

Strong Bases

Lithium hydroxide LiOH
Sodium hydroxide NaOH
Potassium hydroxide KOH
Strontium hydroxide $Sr(OH)_2$*
Calcium hydroxide $Ca(OH)_2$*
Barium hydroxide $Ba(OH)_2$*
*Low solubility, but they dissociate completely

Sodium hydroxide, NaOH (also known as lye), is used in household products to remove grease in ovens and to clean drains. Because high concentrations of hydroxide ions cause severe damage to the skin and eyes, directions must be followed carefully when such products are used in the home, and use in the chemistry laboratory should be carefully supervised. If you spill an acid or a base on your skin or get some in your eyes, be sure to flood the area immediately with water for at least 10 minutes and seek medical attention.

Weak bases are weak electrolytes because they produce very few ions in solution. In an aqueous solution of NH_3, only a few molecules react with H_2O to form NH_4^+ and OH^-. Many window cleaners contain ammonia, NH_3.

$$\underset{\text{Ammonia}}{NH_3(g)} + H_2O(l) \rightleftharpoons \underset{\text{Ammonium hydroxide}}{NH_4^+(aq) + OH^-(aq)}$$

Dissociation Constants for Weak Acids

As we have seen, acids have different strengths depending on how much they dissociate in water. Because the dissociation of strong acids in water is essentially complete, the reaction is not considered to be an equilibrium situation. However, because weak acids in water dissociate only slightly, the ion products reach equilibrium with the undissociated weak acid molecules. For example, formic acid $HCHO_2$, the acid found in bee and ant stings, is a weak acid. Formic acid is an organic acid or *carboxylic acid* in which the H written on the left of the formula dissociates to form formate ion.

$$\underset{\text{Formic acid}}{HCHO_2(aq)} + H_2O(l) \rightleftharpoons H_3O^+(aq) + \underset{\text{Formate ion}}{CHO_2^-(aq)}$$

We wrote the equilibrium constant expression for gases at equilibrium. We can also write an equilibrium expression for weak acids that gives the ratio of the concentrations of products to the weak acid reactants. As with other equilibrium constants, the molar concentration of the products is divided by the molar concentration of the reactants. We can write the equilibrium for formic acid as:

$$HCHO_2(aq) + H_2O(l) \rightleftharpoons H_3O^+(aq) + CHO_2^-(aq)$$

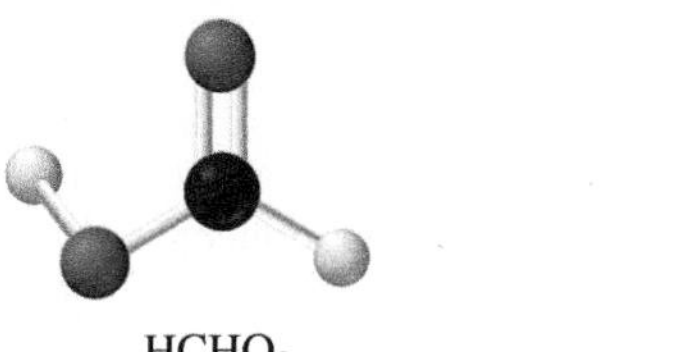

$HCHO_2$

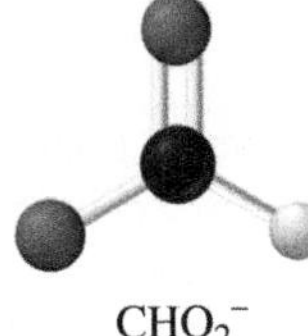

CHO_2^-

Formic acid, a weak acid, loses one H^+ to form formate ion.

Because water is a pure liquid, its concentration, which is constant, is omitted from the equilibrium constant, called the **acid dissociation constant, K_a** (or acid ionization constant). The value of the K_a for formic acid at 25 °C is determined by experiment to be 1.8×10^{-4}. Thus, for the weak acid $HCHO_2$, the K_a is written

$$K_a = \frac{[H_3O^+][CHO_2^-]}{[HCHO_2]} = 1.8 \times 10^{-4} \quad \text{Acid dissociation constant}$$

The K_a measured for formic acid is small, which confirms that the equilibrium mixture of formic acid in water contains mostly reactants and only small amounts of the products. (Recall that the concentration units are omitted in the values given for equilibrium constants.) The smaller the K_a value, the weaker the acid. On the other hand, strong acids, which are essentially 100% dissociated, have very large K_a values, but these values are not usually given. Table 4 gives K_a values for selected weak acids.

TABLE 4 K_a **Values for Selected Weak Acids**

Acid	Formula	K_a
Phosphoric acid	H_3PO_4	7.5×10^{-3}
Hydrofluoric acid	HF	7.2×10^{-4}
Nitrous acid	HNO_2	4.5×10^{-4}
Formic acid	$HCHO_2$	1.8×10^{-4}
Acetic acid	$HC_2H_3O_2$	1.8×10^{-5}
Carbonic acid	H_2CO_3	4.3×10^{-7}
Hydrosulfuric acid	H_2S	9.1×10^{-8}
Dihydrogen phosphate	$H_2PO_4^-$	6.2×10^{-8}
Bicarbonate	HCO_3^-	5.6×10^{-11}
Hydrogen phosphate	HPO_4^{2-}	2.2×10^{-13}

We have described strong and weak acids in several ways. Table 5 summarizes the characteristics of acids in terms of strength and equilibrium position.

TABLE 5 **Characteristics of Acids**

Characteristic	Strong Acids	Weak Acids
Equilibrium Position	Toward products (ionized)	Toward reactants (nonionized)
K_a	Large	Small
$[H_3O^+]$ **and** $[A^-]$	100% of initial $[HA]$	Small percent of initial $[HA]$
Conjugate Bases	Weak	Strong

CONCEPT CHECK 4 **Acid Dissociation Constants**

Nitrous acid, HNO_2, has a K_a of 4.5×10^{-4} and hypochlorous acid, HOCl, has a K_a of 3.5×10^{-8}. If each acid has a 0.10 M concentration, which solution has the higher concentration of H_3O^+?

ANSWER

Nitrous acid has a larger K_a value than does hypochlorous acid. When nitrous acid dissolves in water, there is more dissociation of HNO_2, which gives a higher concentration of H_3O^+ in solution.

SAMPLE PROBLEM 4 **Writing Acid Dissociation Constants**

Write the expression for the acid dissociation constant for nitrous acid.

SOLUTION

The equation for the dissociation of nitrous acid is written:

$$HNO_2(aq) + H_2O(l) \rightleftharpoons H_3O^+(aq) + NO_2^-(aq)$$

The acid dissociation constant is written as the concentrations of the products divided by the concentration of the undissociated weak acid.

$$K_a = \frac{[H_3O^+][NO_2^-]}{[HNO_2]}$$

STUDY CHECK 4

Using Table 4, determine whether nitrous acid or carbonic acid is the stronger acid. Explain your answer.

QUESTIONS AND PROBLEMS

2 Strengths of Acids and Bases

LEARNING GOAL: *Write equations for the dissociation of strong and weak acids; write the equilibrium expression for a weak acid.*

15 What is meant by the phrase, "A strong acid has a weak conjugate base"?

16 What is meant by the phrase, "A weak acid has a strong conjugate base"?

17 Answer *true* or *false* for each of the following:
A strong acid
- **a.** is completely ionized in aqueous solution
- **b.** has a small value of K_a
- **c.** has a strong conjugate base
- **d.** has a weak conjugate base
- **e.** is slightly ionized in aqueous solution

18 Answer *true* or *false* for each of the following:
A weak acid
- **a.** is completely ionized in aqueous solution
- **b.** has a small value of K_a
- **c.** has a strong conjugate base
- **d.** has a weak conjugate base
- **e.** is slightly ionized in aqueous solution

19 Using Table 3, identify the stronger acid in each of the following pairs:
- **a.** HBr or HNO_2
- **b.** H_3PO_4 or HSO_4^-
- **c.** NH_4^+ or H_2CO_3

20 Using Table 3, identify the stronger acid in each of the following pairs:
a. NH_4^+ or H_3O^+ **b.** HNO_2 or HCl **c.** H_2O or H_2CO_3

21 Using Table 3, identify the weaker acid in each of the following pairs:
a. HCl or HSO_4^- **b.** HNO_2 or HF **c.** HCO_3^- or NH_4^+

22 Using Table 3, identify the weaker acid in each of the following pairs:
a. HNO_3 or HCO_3^- **b.** HSO_4^- or H_2O **c.** H_2SO_4 or H_2CO_3

23 Using Table 3, predict whether each of the following reactions contains mostly reactants or products at equilibrium:
- **a.** $H_2CO_3(aq) + H_2O(l) \rightleftharpoons H_3O^+(aq) + HCO_3^-(aq)$
- **b.** $NH_4^+(aq) + H_2O(l) \rightleftharpoons H_3O^+(aq) + NH_3(aq)$
- **c.** $HNO_2(aq) + NH_3(aq) \rightleftharpoons NO_2^-(aq) + NH_4^+(aq)$

24 Using Table 3, predict whether each of the following reactions contains mostly reactants or products at equilibrium:
- **a.** $H_3PO_4(aq) + F^-(aq) \rightleftharpoons HF(aq) + H_2PO_4^-(aq)$
- **b.** $CO_3^{2-}(aq) + H_2O(l) \rightleftharpoons OH^-(aq) + HCO_3^-(aq)$
- **c.** $HS^-(aq) + H_2O(l) \rightleftharpoons H_3O^+(aq) + S^{2-}(aq)$

25 Consider the following acids and their dissociation constants:

$$H_2SO_3(aq) + H_2O(l) \rightleftharpoons H_3O^+(aq) + HSO_3^-(aq) \qquad K_a = 1.2 \times 10^{-2}$$

$$HS^-(aq) + H_2O(l) \rightleftharpoons H_3O^+(aq) + S^{2-}(aq) \qquad K_a = 1.3 \times 10^{-19}$$

- **a.** Which is the stronger acid, H_2SO_3 or HS^-?
- **b.** What is the conjugate base of H_2SO_3?
- **c.** Which acid has the weaker conjugate base?
- **d.** Which acid produces more ions?

26 Consider the following acids and their dissociation constants:

$$HPO_4^{2-}(aq) + H_2O(l) \rightleftharpoons H_3O^+(aq) + PO_4^{3-}(aq) \quad K_a = 2.2 \times 10^{-13}$$

$$HCHO_2(aq) + H_2O(l) \rightleftharpoons H_3O^+(aq) + CHO_2^-(aq) \quad K_a = 1.8 \times 10^{-4}$$

a. Which is the weaker acid, HPO_4^{2-} or $HCHO_2$?
b. What is the conjugate base of HPO_4^{2-}?
c. Which acid has the weaker conjugate base?
d. Which acid produces more ions?

27 Phosphoric acid reacts with water to form dihydrogen phosphate and hydronium ion. Write the equation for the dissociation of phosphoric acid and the expression for its acid dissociation constant (K_a).

28 Carbonic acid, a weak acid, reacts with water to form bicarbonate and hydronium ion. Write the equation for the dissociation of carbonic acid and the expression for its acid dissociation constant (K_a).

3 Ionization of Water

LEARNING GOAL

Use the ion product constant for water to calculate the $[H_3O^+]$ and $[OH^-]$ in an aqueous solution.

We have seen that in acid–base reactions, water is amphoteric, which means it can act either as an acid or as a base. In pure water, there is a forward reaction between two water molecules that transfers H^+ from one water molecule to the other. One molecule acts as an acid by losing H^+, and the water molecule that gains H^+ acts as a base. Every time H^+ is transferred between two water molecules, the products are one H_3O^+ and one OH^-, which react in the reverse direction to re-form two water molecules. Thus, equilibrium is reached between the conjugate acid–base pairs of water.

TUTORIAL
Ionization of Water

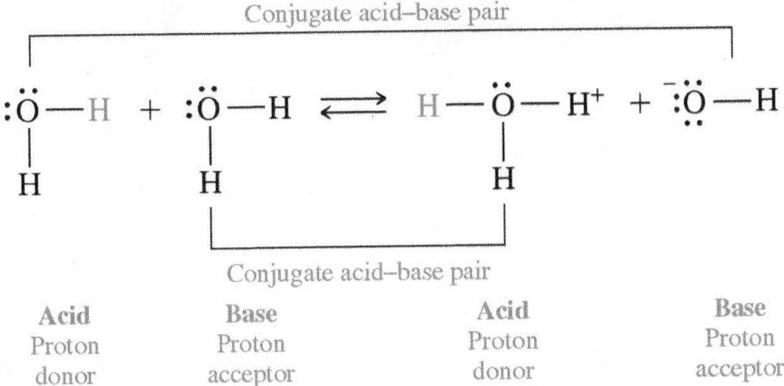

Writing the Ion Product Constant for Water, K_w

Using the equation for the reaction in water at equilibrium, we can write its equilibrium constant expression that shows the concentrations of the products divided by the concentrations of the reactants. Recall that square brackets around the symbols indicate their concentrations in moles per liter (M).

$$H_2O(l) + H_2O(l) \rightleftharpoons H_3O^+(aq) + OH^-(aq)$$

$$K_c = \frac{[H_3O^+][OH^-]}{[H_2O][H_2O]}$$

As we did for the acid dissociation constant expression, we omit the constant concentration of liquid water, which gives the **ion product constant for water, K_w.**

$$K_w = [H_3O^+][OH^-]$$

Experiments have determined that in pure water, the concentration of H_3O^+ at 25 °C is 1.0×10^{-7} M.

$$[H_3O^+] = 1.0 \times 10^{-7}\ \text{M}$$

Because pure water contains equal number of OH^- ions and hydronium ions, the concentration of hydroxide ion must also be 1.0×10^{-7} M.

$$[H_3O^+] = [OH^-] = 1.0 \times 10^{-7}\ \text{M} \quad \text{Pure water}$$

When we place the $[H_3O^+]$ and $[OH^-]$ into the K_w expression, we obtain the numerical value of K_w, which is 1.0×10^{-14} at 25 °C. As before, the concentration units are omitted in the K_w value.

$$K_w = [H_3O^+][OH^-] = (1.0 \times 10^{-7}\ \text{M})(1.0 \times 10^{-7}\ \text{M}) = 1.0 \times 10^{-14}$$

Neutral, Acidic, and Basic Solutions

When the $[H_3O^+]$ and $[OH^-]$ in a solution are equal, the solution is **neutral**. However, most solutions are not neutral and have different concentrations of $[H_3O^+]$ and $[OH^-]$. If acid is added to water, there is an increase in $[H_3O^+]$ and a decrease in $[OH^-]$, which gives an acidic solution. If base is added, $[OH^-]$ increases and $[H_3O^+]$ decreases, which gives a basic solution (see Figure 3). However, for any aqueous solution, the product $[H_3O^+][OH^-]$ is always equal to K_w (1.0×10^{-14}) at 25 °C (see Table 6).

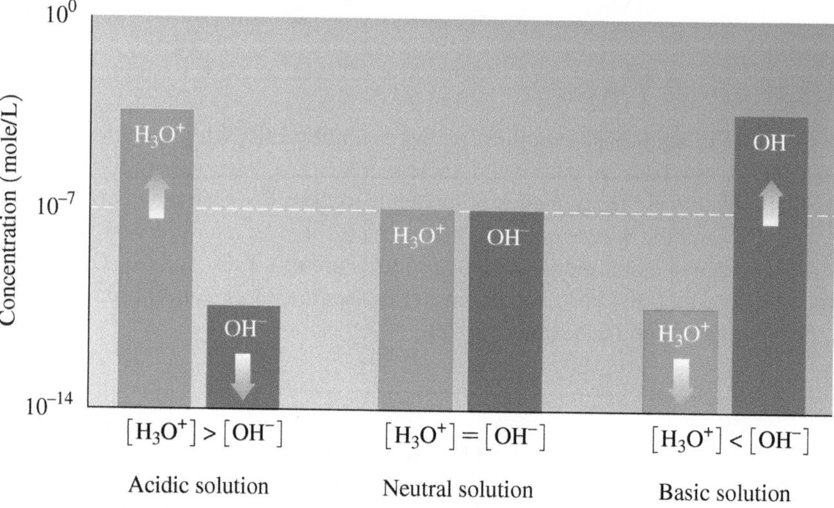

FIGURE 3 In a neutral solution, $[H_3O^+]$ and $[OH^-]$ are equal. In acidic solutions, the $[H_3O^+]$ is greater than the $[OH^-]$. In basic solutions, the $[OH^-]$ is greater than the $[H_3O^+]$.

Q Is a solution that has $[H_3O^+] = 1.0 \times 10^{-3}$ M acidic, basic, or neutral?

TABLE 6 Examples of $[H_3O^+]$ and $[OH^-]$ in Neutral, Acidic, and Basic Solutions

Type of Solution	$[H_3O^+]$	$[OH^-]$	K_w (25 °C)
Neutral	1.0×10^{-7} M	1.0×10^{-7} M	1.0×10^{-14}
Acidic	1.0×10^{-2} M	1.0×10^{-12} M	1.0×10^{-14}
Acidic	2.5×10^{-5} M	4.0×10^{-10} M	1.0×10^{-14}
Basic	1.0×10^{-8} M	1.0×10^{-6} M	1.0×10^{-14}
Basic	5.0×10^{-11} M	2.0×10^{-4} M	1.0×10^{-14}

Using the K_w to Calculate $[H_3O^+]$ and $[OH^-]$ in a Solution

If we know the $[OH^-]$ of a solution, we can use the K_w to calculate the $[H_3O^+]$. If we know the $[H_3O^+]$ of a solution, we can calculate the $[OH^-]$ from their relationship in the K_w, as shown in Sample Problem 5.

$$K_w = [H_3O^+][OH^-]$$

$$[OH^-] = \frac{K_w}{[H_3O^+]} \qquad [H_3O^+] = \frac{K_w}{[OH^-]}$$

SAMPLE PROBLEM 5 **Calculating $[H_3O^+]$ and $[OH^-]$ in Solution**

A vinegar solution has a $[H_3O^+] = 2.0 \times 10^{-3}$ M at 25 °C. What is the $[OH^-]$ of the vinegar solution? Is the solution acidic, basic, or neutral?

SOLUTION

Analyze the Problem

Solution Components	$[H_3O^+]$	$[OH^-]$	
Given	2.0×10^{-3} M		$K_w = 1.0 \times 10^{-14}$
Need		M (moles/L)	

Step 1 **Write the K_w for water.**

$$K_w = [H_3O^+][OH^-] = 1.0 \times 10^{-14}$$

Step 2 **Solve the K_w for the unknown $[H_3O^+]$ or $[OH^-]$.** Rearrange the ion product expression for $[OH^-]$ by dividing through by $[H_3O^+]$.

$$\frac{K_w}{[H_3O^+]} = \frac{\cancel{[H_3O^+]}[OH^-]}{\cancel{[H_3O^+]}}$$

$$[OH^-] = \frac{1.0 \times 10^{-14}}{[H_3O^+]}$$

Step 3 **Substitute the known $[H_3O^+]$ or $[OH^-]$ into the equation and calculate.**

$$[OH^-] = \frac{1.0 \times 10^{-14}}{[2.0 \times 10^{-3}]} = 5.0 \times 10^{-12}\ \text{M}$$

Because the $[H_3O^+]$ of 2.0×10^{-3} M is much larger than the $[OH^-]$ of 5.0×10^{-12} M, the solution is acidic.

STUDY CHECK 5

What is the $[H_3O^+]$ of an ammonia cleaning solution with $[OH^-] = 4.0 \times 10^{-4}$ M? Is the solution acidic, basic, or neutral?

Guide to Calculating $[H_3O^+]$ and $[OH^-]$ in Aqueous Solutions

1 Write the K_w for water.

2 Solve the K_w for the unknown $[H_3O^+]$ or $[OH^-]$.

3 Substitute the known $[H_3O^+]$ or $[OH^-]$ into the equation and calculate.

QUESTIONS AND PROBLEMS

3 Ionization of Water

LEARNING GOAL: *Use the ion product constant for water to calculate the $[H_3O^+]$ and $[OH^-]$ in an aqueous solution.*

29 Why are the concentrations of H_3O^+ and OH^- equal in pure water?

30 What is the meaning and value of K_w?

31 In an acidic solution, how does the concentration of H_3O^+ compare to the concentration of OH^-?

32 In a basic solution, how does the concentration of H_3O^+ compare to the concentration of OH^-?

33 Indicate whether each of the following is an acidic, basic, or neutral solution:
a. $[H_3O^+] = 2.0 \times 10^{-5}$ M
b. $[H_3O^+] = 1.4 \times 10^{-9}$ M
c. $[OH^-] = 8.0 \times 10^{-3}$ M
d. $[OH^-] = 3.5 \times 10^{-10}$ M

34 Indicate whether each of the following is an acidic, basic, or neutral solution:
a. $[H_3O^+] = 6.0 \times 10^{-12}$ M
b. $[H_3O^+] = 1.4 \times 10^{-4}$ M
c. $[OH^-] = 5.0 \times 10^{-12}$ M
d. $[OH^-] = 4.5 \times 10^{-2}$ M

35 Calculate the $[H_3O^+]$ of each aqueous solution with the following $[OH^-]$:
a. coffee, 1.0×10^{-9} M
b. soap, 1.0×10^{-6} M
c. cleanser, 2.0×10^{-5} M
d. lemon juice, 4.0×10^{-13} M

36 Calculate the $[H_3O^+]$ of each aqueous solution with the following $[OH^-]$:
a. dishwashing detergent, 1.0×10^{-3} M
b. milk of magnesia, 1.0×10^{-5} M
c. aspirin, 1.8×10^{-11} M
d. seawater, 2.5×10^{-6} M

37 Calculate the $[OH^-]$ of each aqueous solution with the following $[H_3O^+]$:
a. vinegar, 1.0×10^{-3} M
b. urine, 5.0×10^{-6} M
c. ammonia solution, 1.8×10^{-12} M
d. KOH solution, 4.0×10^{-13} M

38 Calculate the $[OH^-]$ of each aqueous solution with the following $[H_3O^+]$:
a. baking soda, 1.0×10^{-8} M
b. orange juice, 2.0×10^{-4} M
c. milk, 5.0×10^{-7} M
d. bleach, 4.8×10^{-12} M

LEARNING GOAL

Calculate pH *from* $[H_3O^+]$; *given the* pH, *calculate the* $[H_3O^+]$ *and* $[OH^-]$ *of a solution.*

CASE STUDY
Hyperventilation and Blood pH

SELF-STUDY ACTIVITY
The pH Scale

4 The pH Scale

Many kinds of careers such as respiratory therapy, food processing, medicine, agriculture, spa and pool maintenance, and soap manufacturing require personnel to measure the $[H_3O^+]$ and $[OH^-]$ of solutions. The level of acidity is used to evaluate the functioning of the lungs and kidneys, to control bacterial growth in foods, and to prevent the growth of pests in food crops.

Although we have expressed the concentrations of H_3O^+ and OH^- as molarity, it is more convenient to describe the acidity of solutions using the *pH scale*. On this scale, a number between 0 and 14 represents the H_3O^+ concentration for common solutions. A neutral solution has a pH of 7.0 at 25 °C. An acidic solution has a pH less than 7.0; a basic solution has a pH greater than 7.0 (see Figure 4).

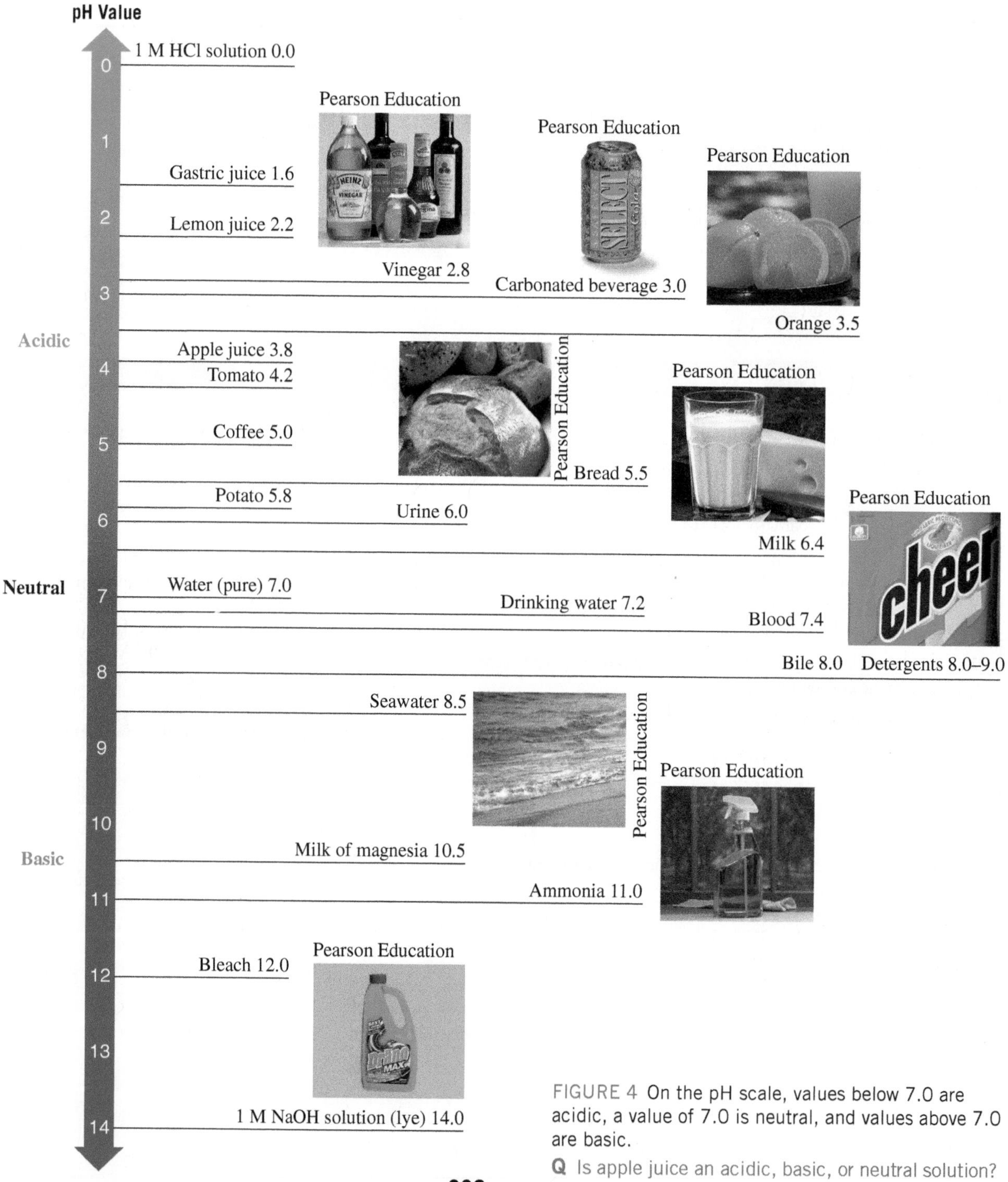

pH Value

Acidic
Neutral
Basic

1 M HCl solution 0.0
Gastric juice 1.6
Lemon juice 2.2
Vinegar 2.8
Carbonated beverage 3.0
Orange 3.5
Apple juice 3.8
Tomato 4.2
Coffee 5.0
Bread 5.5
Potato 5.8
Urine 6.0
Milk 6.4
Water (pure) 7.0
Drinking water 7.2
Blood 7.4
Bile 8.0
Detergents 8.0–9.0
Seawater 8.5
Milk of magnesia 10.5
Ammonia 11.0
Bleach 12.0
1 M NaOH solution (lye) 14.0

Pearson Education

FIGURE 4 On the pH scale, values below 7.0 are acidic, a value of 7.0 is neutral, and values above 7.0 are basic.

Q Is apple juice an acidic, basic, or neutral solution?

- Acidic solution pH < 7.0 $[H_3O^+] > 1.0 \times 10^{-7}$ M
- Neutral solution pH $= 7.0$ $[H_3O^+] = 1.0 \times 10^{-7}$ M
- Basic solution pH > 7.0 $[H_3O^+] < 1.0 \times 10^{-7}$ M

When we relate acidity and pH, we are using an inverse relationship, which is when one component increases while the other component decreases. When an acid is added to pure water, the $[H_3O^+]$ (acidity) of the solution increases but its pH decreases. When a base is added to pure water, it becomes more basic, which means its acidity decreases and the pH increases.

In the laboratory, a pH meter is commonly used to determine the pH of a solution. There are also various indicators and pH papers that turn specific colors when placed in solutions of different pH values. The pH is found by comparing the color on the test paper or the color of the solution to a color chart (see Figure 5).

Pearson Education

(a)

Pearson Education

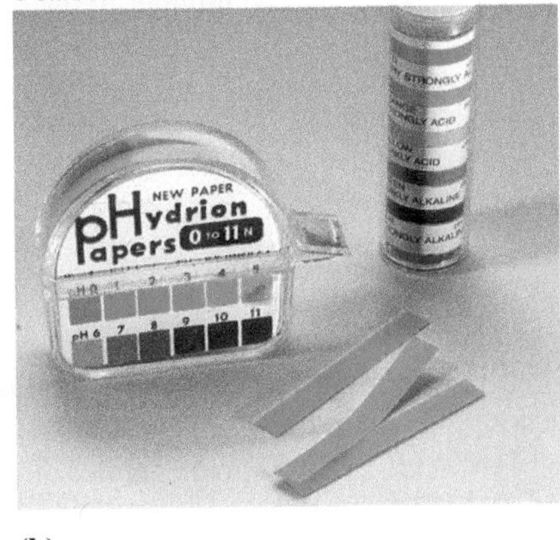

(b)

Pearson Education

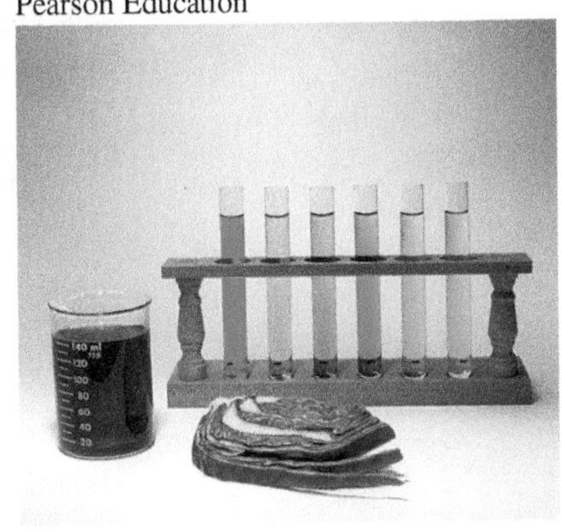

(c)

FIGURE 5 The pH of a solution can be determined using **(a)** a pH meter, **(b)** pH paper, and **(c)** indicators that turn different colors corresponding to different pH values.

Q If a pH meter reads 4.00, is the solution acidic, basic, or neutral?

CONCEPT CHECK 5 pH of Solutions

Consider the pH of the following items:

Item	pH
Root beer	5.8
Kitchen cleaner	10.9
Pickles	3.5
Glass cleaner	7.6
Cranberry juice	2.9

a. Place the pH values of the preceding items in order of most acidic to most basic.
b. Which item has the highest $[H_3O^+]$?
c. Which item has the highest $[OH^-]$?

Cranberry juice has a pH of 2.9, which makes it acidic.

ANSWER

a. The most acidic item is the one with the lowest pH, and the most basic is the item with the highest pH: cranberry juice (2.9), pickles (3.5), root beer (5.8), glass cleaner (7.6), kitchen cleaner (10.9).
b. The item with the highest $[H_3O^+]$ would have the lowest pH value, which is cranberry juice.
c. The item with the highest $[OH^-]$ would have the highest pH value, which is kitchen cleaner.

Wayne Hutchinson/Alamy

If soil is too acidic, nutrients are not absorbed by crops. Then lime ($CaCO_3$), which acts as a base, may be added to increase the soil pH.

TUTORIAL
Logarithms

TUTORIAL
The pH Scale

Calculating the pH of Solutions

The pH scale is a logarithmic scale that corresponds to the $[H_3O^+]$ of aqueous solutions. Mathematically, **pH** is the negative logarithm (base 10) of the $[H_3O^+]$.

$$\text{pH} = -\log[H_3O^+]$$

Essentially, the negative powers of 10 in the molar concentrations are converted to positive numbers. For example, a lemon juice solution with $[H_3O^+] = 1.0 \times 10^{-2}$ M has a pH of 2.00. This can be calculated using the pH equation.

$$\text{pH} = -\log[1.0 \times 10^{-2}]$$
$$\text{pH} = -(-2.00)$$
$$= 2.00$$

The number of *decimal places* in the pH value is the same as the number of significant figures in the $[H_3O^+]$. The number to the left of the decimal point in the pH value is the power of 10.

$$[H_3O^+] = 1.0 \times 10^{-2} \qquad \text{pH} = 2.00$$

Two SFs — Two SFs

Because pH is a log scale, a change of one pH unit corresponds to a tenfold change in $[H_3O^+]$. It is important to note that the pH decreases as the $[H_3O^+]$ increases. For example, a solution with a pH of 2.00 has a $[H_3O^+]$ that is ten times greater than a solution with a pH of 3.00, and 100 times greater than a solution with a pH of 4.00.

CONCEPT CHECK 6 **Calculating pH**

Indicate if the pH values given for the following are correct or incorrect, and state why:

a. $[H_3O^+] = 1 \times 10^{-6}$ $\quad$ pH = −6.0
b. $[H_3O^+] = 1.0 \times 10^{-10}$ $\quad$ pH = 10.0
c. $[H_3O^+] = 1.0 \times 10^{-6}$ $\quad$ pH = 6.00

ANSWER

a. Incorrect. The pH of this solution is 6.0, which has a positive value, not negative.
b. Incorrect. This solution has a $[H_3O^+]$ of 1.0×10^{-10} M, which has a pH of 10.00. Two zeros are needed after the decimal point to match the two significant figures in the coefficient of the $[H_3O^+]$.
c. Correct. The pH has two zeros after the decimal point to match the two significant figures in the coefficient 1.0.

The pH of a solution is calculated using the *log* key and changing the sign as shown in Sample Problems 6 and 7.

SAMPLE PROBLEM 6 Calculating pH from $[H_3O^+]$

Aspirin, which is acetylsalicylic acid, was the first nonsteroidal anti-inflammatory drug used to alleviate pain and fever. If a solution of aspirin has a $[H_3O^+] = 1.7 \times 10^{-3}$ M, what is the pH of the solution?

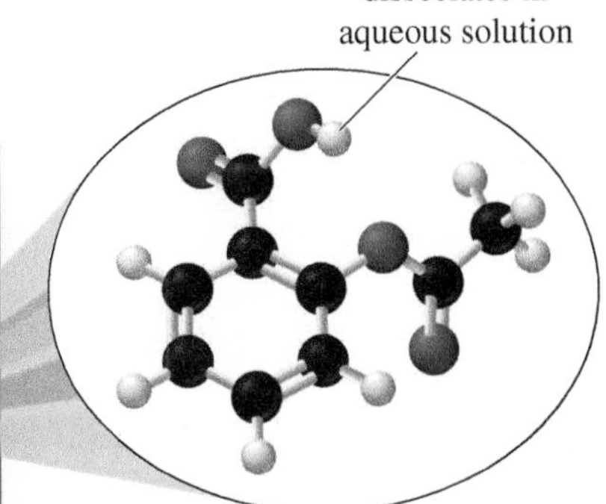

Pearson Education/Eric Schrader

Aspirin, which is acetylsalicylic acid, is a weak acid with a K_a of 3.0×10^{-4}.

SOLUTION

Analyze the Problem

Solution Components	$[H_3O^+]$	pH
Given	1.7×10^{-3} M	
Need		pH

Step 1 Enter the $[H_3O^+]$.

	Calculator Display
Enter 1.7 and press (EE or EXP).	1.7^{00} or 1.700 or 1.7E00
Enter 3 and press (+/−) to change the sign. (For calculators without a change sign key, consult the instructions for the calculator.)	1.7^{-03} or 1.7−03 or 1.7E−03

Step 2 Press the *log* key and change the sign.

(log) (+/−) 2.769551079

The steps can be combined to give the calculator sequence as follows:

$$pH = -\log[1.7 \times 10^{-3}] = 1.7 \text{ (EE or EXP) } 3 \text{ (+/−) (log) (+/−)}$$
$$= 2.769551079$$

Be sure to check the instructions for your calculator. On some calculators, the log key is used first, followed by the concentration.

Step 3 Adjust the number of SFs on the *right* of the decimal point to equal the SFs in the coefficient. In a pH value, the number to the *left* of the decimal point is an *exact* number derived from the power of 10.

Coefficient		Power of ten	
$[H_3O^+] = 1.7$	$\times$	10^{-3} M	$pH = -\log[1.7 \times 10^{-3}] = 2.77$

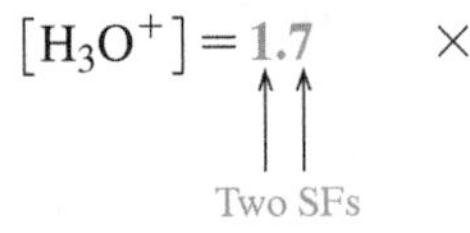
Two SFs

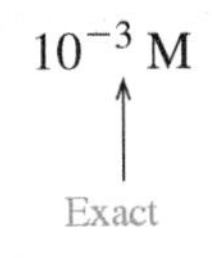
Exact

Exact Two SFs

Guide to Calculating pH of an Aqueous Solution

1 Enter the $[H_3O^+]$.

2 Press the *log* key and change the sign.

3 Adjust the number of SFs on the *right* of the decimal point to equal the SFs in the coefficient.

STUDY CHECK 6

What is the pH of bleach with $[H_3O^+] = 4.2 \times 10^{-12}$ M?

When the $[OH^-]$ is given, we use the K_w to calculate $[H_3O^+]$, from which the pH of the solution can be calculated as shown in Sample Problem 7.

SAMPLE PROBLEM 7 **Calculating pH from $[OH^-]$**

What is the pH of an ammonia solution at 25 °C with $[OH^-] = 3.7 \times 10^{-3}$ M?

SOLUTION

Analyze the Problem

Solution Components	$[OH^-]$	pH
Given	3.7×10^{-3} M	
Need		pH

Step 1 **Enter the $[H_3O^+]$.** Because $[OH^-]$ is given for the ammonia solution, we need to calculate $[H_3O^+]$. Using the ion product constant for water, K_w, we divide both sides by $[OH^-]$ to obtain $[H_3O^+]$.

$$\frac{K_w}{[OH^-]} = \frac{[H_3O^+][\cancel{OH^-}]}{[\cancel{OH^-}]}$$

$$[H_3O^+] = \frac{1.0 \times 10^{-14}}{[3.7 \times 10^{-3}]} = 2.7 \times 10^{-12}\text{ M}$$

Calculator Display

2.7 [EE or EXP] 12 [+/−] 2.7^{-12} or 2.7−12 or 2.7E−12

Step 2 **Press the *log* key and change the sign.**

[log] [+/−] 11.56863624

Step 3 **Adjust the number of SFs to the *right* of the decimal point to equal the SFs in the coefficient.**

2.7×10^{-12} M pH = 11.57

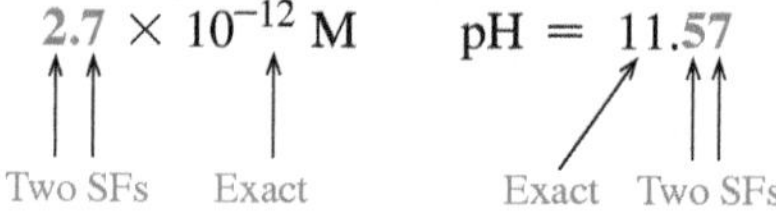

STUDY CHECK 7

Calculate the pH of a sample of acid rain that has $[OH^-] = 2 \times 10^{-10}$ M.

A comparison of $[H_3O^+]$, $[OH^-]$, and their corresponding pH values is given in Table 7.

TABLE 7 **A Comparison of $[H_3O^+]$, $[OH^-]$, and Corresponding pH Values at 25 °C**

$[H_3O^+]$	pH	$[OH^-]$	
10^{0}	0	10^{-14}	
10^{-1}	1	10^{-13}	
10^{-2}	2	10^{-12}	
10^{-3}	3	10^{-11}	Acidic
10^{-4}	4	10^{-10}	
10^{-5}	5	10^{-9}	
10^{-6}	6	10^{-8}	
10^{-7}	7	10^{-7}	Neutral
10^{-8}	8	10^{-6}	
10^{-9}	9	10^{-5}	
10^{-10}	10	10^{-4}	
10^{-11}	11	10^{-3}	Basic
10^{-12}	12	10^{-2}	
10^{-13}	13	10^{-1}	
10^{-14}	14	10^{0}	

Calculating $[H_3O^+]$ from pH

In another calculation, we are given the pH of a solution and asked to determine the $[H_3O^+]$. This is a reverse of the pH calculation.

$$[H_3O^+] = 10^{-pH}$$

For pH values that are whole numbers, the exponent in the power of 10 is the same as the pH.

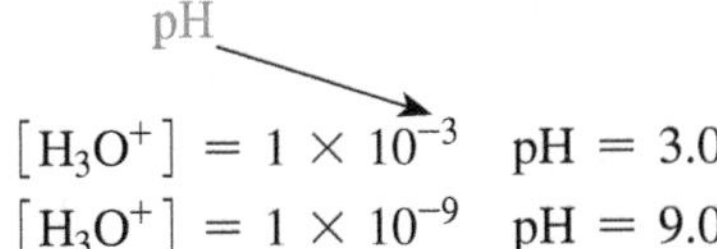

$$[H_3O^+] = 1 \times 10^{-3} \quad pH = 3.0$$
$$[H_3O^+] = 1 \times 10^{-9} \quad pH = 9.0$$

For pH values that are not whole numbers, the calculation requires the use of the *10^x^* key, which is usually a *2nd function* key. On some calculators, this operation is done by using the *inverse* key and then the *log* key.

SAMPLE PROBLEM 8 **Calculating $[H_3O^+]$ from pH**

Calculate $[H_3O^+]$ for a solution of baking soda with a pH of 8.25.

SOLUTION

Analyze the Problem

Solution Components	pH	$[H_3O^+]$
Given	8.25	
Need		M (moles/L)

Step 1 **Enter the pH value and change the sign.** This gives the negative value of the pH.

Calculator Display

8.25 [+/−] −8.25

Step 2 **Convert −pH to concentration.** Press the *2nd function* key and then the *10^x^* key.

[2nd] [10^x^] 5.623413252^{-09} or 5.623413252−09 or 5.623413252E−09

Or press the *inverse* key and then the *log* key.

[inv] [log]

Step 3 **Adjust the SFs in the coefficient.** Because the pH value of 8.25 has two SFs on the *right* of the decimal point, the coefficient for $[H_3O^+]$ is written with two SFs.

$$[H_3O^+] = 5.6 \times 10^{-9}\,M$$

STUDY CHECK 8

What are the $[H_3O^+]$ and $[OH^-]$ of a beer that has a pH of 4.7?

Guide to Calculating $[H_3O^+]$ from pH

1. Enter the pH value and change the sign.
2. Convert −pH to concentration.
3. Adjust the SFs in the coefficient.

Chemistry Link to Health

STOMACH ACID, HCl

Gastric acid, which contains HCl, is produced by parietal cells that line the stomach. When the stomach expands with the intake of food, the gastric glands begin to secrete a strongly acidic solution of HCl. In a single day, a person may secrete 2000 mL of gastric juice, which contains hydrochloric acid, mucins, and the enzymes pepsin and lipase.

The HCl in the gastric juice activates a digestive enzyme from the chief cells called *pepsinogen* to form *pepsin*, which breaks down proteins in food entering the stomach. The secretion of HCl continues until the stomach has a pH of about 2, which is the optimum pH for activating the digestive enzymes without ulcerating the stomach lining. In addition, the low pH is beneficial by destroying bacteria that reach the stomach. Normally, large quantities of viscous mucus are secreted within the stomach to protect its lining from acid and enzyme damage. In gastric reflux disease, the gastric acid solution from the stomach moves into the esophagus to cause symptoms such as heartburn or a hiatal hernia. Gastric acid may also form under conditions of stress when the nervous system activates the production of HCl.

As the contents of the stomach move into the small intestine, cells produce bicarbonate to neutralize the gastric acid to about a pH of 5.0.

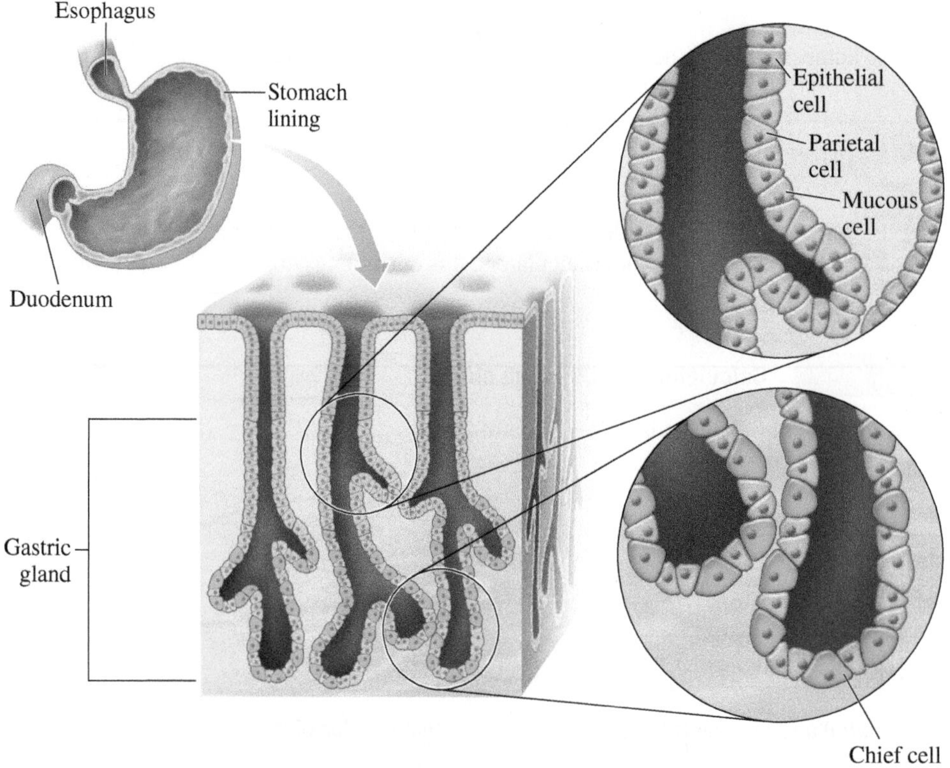

Parietal cells in the lining of the stomach secrete gastric acid HCl.

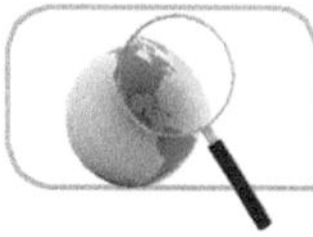

Explore Your World

USING VEGETABLES AND FLOWERS AS pH INDICATORS

Many flowers and vegetables with strong color, especially reds and purples, contain compounds that change color with changes in pH. Some examples are red cabbage, cranberry juice, and other highly colored drinks made from fruits or vegetables.

Materials Needed

Red cabbage or cranberry juice or drink, water, and a saucepan.

Several glasses or small glass containers and some tape and a pen or pencil to mark the containers.

Several colorless household solutions such as vinegar, lemon juice, other fruit juices, window cleaners, soaps, shampoos, detergents, and common household products such as baking soda, antacids, aspirin, salt, and sugar.

Procedure

1. Obtain a bottle of cranberry juice or cranberry drink, or use red cabbage to prepare the red cabbage pH indicator as follows: Tear up several red cabbage leaves, place them in a saucepan, and cover with water. Heat for about 5 minutes or until the juice is a dark purple. Cool and collect the purple solution. Alternatively, place red cabbage leaves in a blender and cover with water. Blend until thoroughly mixed, remove, and pour off the liquid.
2. Place small amounts of each household solution into separate clear glass containers, and mark what each one is. If the sample is a solid or a thick liquid, add a small amount of water. Add some cranberry juice or some red cabbage indicator until you obtain a color.
3. Observe the colors of the various samples. The colors that indicate acidic solutions are the red and pink colors (pH 1–4) and the pink to lavender colors (pH 5–6). A neutral solution has about the same purple color as the indicator. Bases will give blue to green colors (pH 8–11) or a yellow color (pH 12–13).
4. Arrange your samples by color and pH. Classify each of the solutions as acidic (pH 1–6), neutral (pH 7), or basic (pH 8–13).
5. Try to make an indicator using other colorful fruits or flowers.

QUESTIONS

1. Which products that tested acidic listed an acid on their labels?
2. Which products that tested basic listed a base on their labels?
3. Which products were neutral?
4. Which flowers or vegetables behaved as indicators?

QUESTIONS AND PROBLEMS

4 The pH Scale

LEARNING GOAL: *Calculate pH from $[H_3O^+]$; given the pH, calculate the $[H_3O^+]$ and $[OH^-]$ of a solution.*

39 State whether each of the following is acidic, basic, or neutral:
- **a.** blood, pH 7.38
- **b.** vinegar, pH 2.8
- **c.** drain cleaner, pH 11.2
- **d.** coffee, pH 5.54
- **e.** tomatoes, pH 4.2
- **f.** chocolate cake, pH 7.6

40 State whether each of the following is acidic, basic, or neutral:
- **a.** soda, pH 3.22
- **b.** shampoo, pH 5.7
- **c.** laundry detergent, pH 9.4
- **d.** rain, pH 5.83
- **e.** honey, pH 3.9
- **f.** cheese, pH 5.2

41 Calculate the pH of each solution given the following $[H_3O^+]$ or $[OH^-]$ values:
- **a.** $[H_3O^+] = 1.0 \times 10^{-4}$ M
- **b.** $[H_3O^+] = 3.0 \times 10^{-9}$ M
- **c.** $[OH^-] = 1.0 \times 10^{-5}$ M
- **d.** $[OH^-] = 2.5 \times 10^{-11}$ M
- **e.** $[H_3O^+] = 6.7 \times 10^{-8}$ M
- **f.** $[OH^-] = 8.2 \times 10^{-4}$ M

42 Calculate the pH of each solution given the following $[H_3O^+]$ or $[OH^-]$ values:
- **a.** $[H_3O^+] = 1.0 \times 10^{-8}$ M
- **b.** $[H_3O^+] = 5.0 \times 10^{-6}$ M
- **c.** $[OH^-] = 4.0 \times 10^{-2}$ M
- **d.** $[OH^-] = 8.0 \times 10^{-3}$ M
- **e.** $[H_3O^+] = 4.7 \times 10^{-2}$ M
- **f.** $[OH^-] = 3.9 \times 10^{-6}$ M

43 Complete the following table:

$[H_3O^+]$	$[OH^-]$	pH	Acidic, Basic, or Neutral?
	1×10^{-6} M		
		3.00	
2.8×10^{-5} M			
		4.62	

44 Complete the following table:

$[H_3O^+]$	$[OH^-]$	pH	Acidic, Basic, or Neutral?
		10.00	
			Neutral
6.4×10^{-12} M			
		11.3	

5 Reactions of Acids and Bases

LEARNING GOAL

Write balanced equations for reactions of acids with metals, carbonates, and bases; calculate the molarity or volume of an acid from titration information.

Typical reactions of acids and bases include the reactions of acids with metals, bases, and carbonate or bicarbonate ions. For example, when you drop an antacid tablet in water, the bicarbonate ion and citric acid in the tablet react to produce carbon dioxide bubbles, a salt, and water. A *salt* is an ionic compound that does not have H^+ as the cation or OH^- as the anion.

SELF-STUDY ACTIVITY
Nature of Acids and Bases

Acids and Metals

Acids react with certain metals to produce a salt and hydrogen gas (H_2). Metals that react with acids include potassium, sodium, calcium, magnesium, aluminum, zinc, iron, and tin. In reactions that are single replacement reactions, the metal ion replaces the hydrogen in the acid.

$$\underset{\text{Metal}}{Mg(s)} + \underset{\text{Acid}}{2HCl(aq)} \longrightarrow \underset{\text{Salt}}{MgCl_2(aq)} + \underset{\text{Hydrogen}}{H_2(g)}$$

$$\underset{\text{Metal}}{Zn(s)} + \underset{\text{Acid}}{2HNO_3(aq)} \longrightarrow \underset{\text{Salt}}{Zn(NO_3)_2(aq)} + \underset{\text{Hydrogen}}{H_2(g)}$$

Richard Megna/Fundamental Photographs

Magnesium reacts rapidly with acid and forms a salt of magnesium and H_2 gas.

CONCEPT CHECK 7 **Equations for Metals and Acids**

Write a balanced equation for the reaction of Al(s) with HCl(aq) by completing the following:
- **a.** Write the reactants and products using "salt."
- **b.** Determine the formula of the salt.
- **c.** Balance the equation.

Pearson Education/Eric Schrader

When sodium bicarbonate (baking soda) reacts with an acid (vinegar), the products are carbon dioxide gas, water, and a salt.

ANSWER

a. When a metal reacts with an acid, the products are a salt and hydrogen gas.

$$Al(s) + HCl(aq) \longrightarrow \text{salt} + H_2(g)$$

b. When the metal Al(*s*) reacts with HCl, it forms Al^{3+}, which is balanced by $3Cl^-$ from HCl to give $AlCl_3(aq)$. We can place this formula in the equation.

$$Al(s) + HCl(aq) \longrightarrow AlCl_3(aq) + H_2(g)$$

c. Now the equation can be balanced.

$$2Al(s) + 6HCl(aq) \longrightarrow 2AlCl_3(aq) + 3H_2(g)$$

Acids, Carbonates, and Bicarbonates

When an acid is added to a carbonate or bicarbonate (hydrogen carbonate), the products are carbon dioxide gas, water, and an ionic compound (salt). The acid reacts with CO_3^{2-} or HCO_3^- to produce carbonic acid, H_2CO_3, which breaks down rapidly to CO_2 and H_2O.

$$\underset{\text{Acid}}{2HBr(aq)} + \underset{\text{Carbonate}}{Na_2CO_3(aq)} \longrightarrow \underset{\text{Carbon dioxide}}{CO_2(g)} + \underset{\text{Water}}{H_2O(l)} + \underset{\text{Salt}}{2NaBr(aq)}$$

$$\underset{\text{Acid}}{HCl(aq)} + \underset{\text{Bicarbonate}}{NaHCO_3(aq)} \longrightarrow \underset{\text{Carbon dioxide}}{CO_2(g)} + \underset{\text{Water}}{H_2O(l)} + \underset{\text{Salt}}{NaCl(aq)}$$

Chemistry Link to the Environment

ACID RAIN

Rain is slightly acidic, with a pH of 5.6. In the atmosphere, carbon dioxide combines with water to form carbonic acid, a weak acid, which dissociates to give hydronium ions and bicarbonate.

$$CO_2(g) + H_2O(l) \rightleftharpoons H_2CO_3(aq)$$
$$H_2CO_3(aq) + H_2O(l) \rightleftharpoons H_3O^+(aq) + HCO_3^-(aq)$$

However, in many parts of the world, rain has become considerably more acidic. *Acid rain* is a term given to precipitation such as rain, snow, hail, or fog in which the water has a pH that is less than 5.6. In the United States, pH values of rain in some areas have decreased to about 4–4.5. In some parts of the world, pH values have been reported as low as 2.6, which is about as acidic as lemon juice or vinegar. Because the calculation of pH involves powers of 10, a pH value of 2.6 would be 1000 times more acidic than natural rain.

Although natural sources such as volcanoes and forest fires release SO_2, the primary sources of acid rain today are from the burning of fossil fuels in automobiles and coal in industrial plants. When coal and oil are burned, the sulfur impurities combine with oxygen in the air to produce SO_2 and SO_3. The reaction of SO_3 with water forms sulfuric acid, H_2SO_4, a strong acid.

$$S(g) + O_2(g) \longrightarrow SO_2(g)$$
$$2SO_2(g) + O_2(g) \longrightarrow 2SO_3(g)$$
$$SO_3(g) + H_2O(l) \longrightarrow H_2SO_4(aq)$$

In an effort to decrease the formation of acid rain, legislation has required a reduction in SO_2 emissions. Coal-burning plants have installed equipment called "scrubbers" that absorb SO_2 before it is emitted. In a smokestack, "scrubbing" removes 95% of the SO_2 as the flue gases containing SO_2 pass through limestone ($CaCO_3$) and water. The end product, $CaSO_4$, also called "gypsum," is used in agriculture as a soil conditioner and fertilizer and to prepare cement products.

Nitrogen oxide forms at high temperatures in the engines of automobiles as air containing nitrogen and oxygen gases is burned. As nitrogen oxide is emitted into the air, it combines with more oxygen to form nitrogen dioxide, which is responsible for the brown color of smog. When nitrogen dioxide dissolves in water in the atmosphere, nitric acid, a strong acid, forms.

$$N_2(g) + O_2(g) \longrightarrow 2NO(g)$$
$$2NO(g) + O_2(g) \longrightarrow 2NO_2(g)$$
$$3NO_2(g) + H_2O(g) \longrightarrow 2HNO_3(aq) + NO(g)$$

Air currents in the atmosphere carry the sulfuric acid and nitric acid many thousands of kilometers before they precipitate in areas far away from the site of the initial contamination. The acids in acid rain have detrimental effects on marble and limestone structures, lakes, and forests. Throughout the world, monuments made of marble (a form of $CaCO_3$) are deteriorating as acid rain dissolves the marble.

$$CaCO_3(s) + H_2SO_4(aq) \longrightarrow CO_2(g) + H_2O(l) + CaSO_4(aq)$$

Acid rain is changing the pH of many lakes and streams in parts of the United States and Europe. When the pH of a lake falls below 4.5–5, most fish and plant life cannot survive. As the soil near a lake becomes more acidic, aluminum becomes more soluble. Increased levels of aluminum ion in lakes are toxic to fish and other water animals.

Trees and forests are susceptible to acid rain, too. Acid rain breaks down the protective waxy coating on leaves and interferes with photosynthesis. Tree growth is impaired as nutrients and minerals in the soil dissolve and wash away. In Eastern Europe, acid rain is causing an environmental disaster. Nearly 70% of the forests in the Czech Republic have been severely damaged, and some parts of the land are so acidic that crops will not grow.

A marble statue in Washington Square Park has been eroded by acid rain.

michael1959/iStockphoto

Acid rain has severely damaged forests in Eastern Europe.

Acids and Hydroxides: Neutralization

Neutralization is a reaction of a strong or weak acid with a strong base to produce a salt and water. The H^+ of an acid and the OH^- of the base combine to form water. The salt is the combination of the cation from the base and the anion from the acid. We can write the following equation for the neutralization reaction between HCl and NaOH:

$$\underset{\text{Acid}}{HCl(aq)} + \underset{\text{Base}}{NaOH(aq)} \longrightarrow \underset{\text{Salt}}{NaCl(aq)} + \underset{\text{Water}}{H_2O(l)}$$

When we write the strong acid HCl and the strong base NaOH as ions, we see that H^+ combines with OH^- to form water, leaving the ions Na^+ and Cl^- in solution.

$$H^+(aq) + Cl^-(aq) + Na^+(aq) + OH^-(aq) \longrightarrow Na^+(aq) + Cl^-(aq) + H_2O(l)$$

When we omit the spectator ions that do not change during the reaction (Na^+ and Cl^-), we see that the equation for the neutralization is the reaction of H^+ and OH^- to form H_2O.

$$H^+(aq) + \cancel{Cl^-(aq)} + \cancel{Na^+(aq)} + OH^-(aq) \longrightarrow \cancel{Na^+(aq)} + \cancel{Cl^-(aq)} + H_2O(l)$$

$$H^+(aq) + OH^-(aq) \longrightarrow H_2O(l)$$

Balancing Neutralization Equations

In a typical neutralization reaction, one H^+ always combines with one OH^-. Therefore, a neutralization equation may need coefficients to balance the H^+ from the acid with the OH^- from the base (see Sample Problem 9).

SAMPLE PROBLEM 9 Balancing a Neutralization Equation

Write the balanced equation for the neutralization of $HCl(aq)$ and $Ba(OH)_2(s)$.

SOLUTION

Step 1 **Write the reactants and products.**

$$HCl(aq) + Ba(OH)_2(s) \longrightarrow H_2O(l) + \text{salt}$$

Step 2 **Balance the H^+ in the acid with the OH^- in the base.** Placing a coefficient 2 in front of the HCl provides $2H^+$ for the $2OH^-$ from $Ba(OH)_2$.

$$2HCl(aq) + Ba(OH)_2(s) \longrightarrow H_2O(l) + \text{salt}$$

Step 3 **Balance the H_2O with the H^+ and the OH^-.** Use a coefficient of 2 in front of H_2O to balance $2H^+$ and $2OH^-$.

$$2HCl(aq) + Ba(OH)_2(s) \longrightarrow 2H_2O(l) + \text{salt}$$

Guide to Balancing an Equation for Neutralization

1. Write the reactants and products.
2. Balance the H^+ in the acid with the OH^- in the base.
3. Balance the H_2O with the H^+ and the OH^-.
4. Write the salt from the remaining ions.

Step 4 **Write the salt from the remaining ions.** Use the ions Ba^{2+} and $2Cl^-$ to write the formula for the salt as $BaCl_2$.

$$2HCl(aq) + Ba(OH)_2(s) \longrightarrow 2H_2O(l) + BaCl_2(aq)$$

STUDY CHECK 9

Write the balanced equation for the reaction between H_2SO_4 and LiOH.

TUTORIAL
Acid–Base Titrations

Acid–Base Titration

Suppose we need to find the molarity of a solution of HCl, which has an unknown concentration. We can do this by a laboratory procedure called **titration** in which we neutralize an acid sample with a known amount of base. In a titration, we place a measured volume of the acid in a flask and add a few drops of an *indicator* such as phenolphthalein. An indicator is a compound that dramatically changes color when the pH of the solution changes. In an acidic solution, phenolphthalein is colorless. Then we fill a buret with a NaOH solution of known molarity and carefully add NaOH solution to neutralize the acid in the flask (see Figure 6). When the moles of OH^- added becomes equal to the moles of H_3O^+ initially in the solution, the titration is complete. We know that the neutralization *endpoint* is reached when the phenolphthalein indicator changes from colorless to a faint, permanent pink color (see Figure 6). From the measured volume of the NaOH solution and its molarity, we calculate the number of moles of NaOH, the moles of acid, and the concentration of the acid.

Pearson Education

Pearson Education

Pearson Education

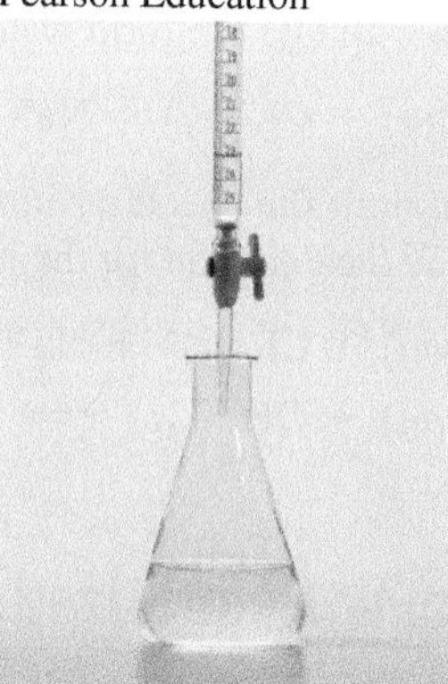

FIGURE 6 The titration of an acid. A known volume of an acid solution is placed in a flask with an indicator and titrated with a measured volume of a base solution, such as NaOH, to the neutralization endpoint.

Q What data is needed to determine the molarity of the acid in the flask?

Chemistry Link to Health

ANTACIDS

Antacids are substances used to neutralize excess stomach acid (HCl). Some antacids are mixtures of aluminum hydroxide and magnesium hydroxide. These hydroxides are not very soluble in water, so the levels of available OH^- are not damaging to the intestinal tract. However, aluminum hydroxide has the side effects of producing constipation and binding phosphate in the intestinal tract, which may cause weakness and loss of appetite. Magnesium hydroxide has a laxative effect. These side effects are less likely when a combination of the antacids is used.

$$Al(OH)_3(aq) + 3HCl(aq) \longrightarrow AlCl_3(aq) + 3H_2O(l)$$
$$Mg(OH)_2(s) + 2HCl(aq) \longrightarrow MgCl_2(aq) + 2H_2O(l)$$

Some antacids use calcium carbonate to neutralize excess stomach acid. About 10% of the calcium is absorbed into the bloodstream, where it elevates the levels of serum calcium. Calcium carbonate is not recommended for patients who have peptic ulcers or a tendency to form kidney stones, which typically consist of an insoluble calcium salt.

$$CaCO_3(s) + 2HCl(aq) \longrightarrow CO_2(g) + H_2O(l) + CaCl_2(aq)$$

Still other antacids contain sodium bicarbonate. This type of antacid neutralizes excess gastric acid, increases blood pH, but also elevates sodium levels in the body fluids. It also is not recommended in the treatment of peptic ulcers.

$$NaHCO_3(s) + HCl(aq) \longrightarrow CO_2(g) + H_2O(l) + NaCl(aq)$$

The neutralizing substances in some antacid preparations are given in Table 8.

TABLE 8 Basic Compounds in Some Antacids

Antacid	Base(s)
Amphojel, Gaviscon, Mylanta	$Al(OH)_3$
Milk of magnesia	$Mg(OH)_2$
Mylanta, Maalox, Gelusil, Riopan, Equate, Maalox (liquid)	$Mg(OH)_2$, $Al(OH)_3$
Bisodol, Rolaids	$CaCO_3$, $Mg(OH)_2$
Titralac, Tums, Pepto-Bismol, Maalox (tablet)	$CaCO_3$
Alka-Seltzer	$NaHCO_3$, $KHCO_3$

Using too much antacid to reduce stomach acidity can interfere with the digestion of food and the absorption of iron, copper, the B vitamins, and some drugs. Too much antacid may also allow the growth of bacteria that would normally be destroyed by low pH of stomach acid.

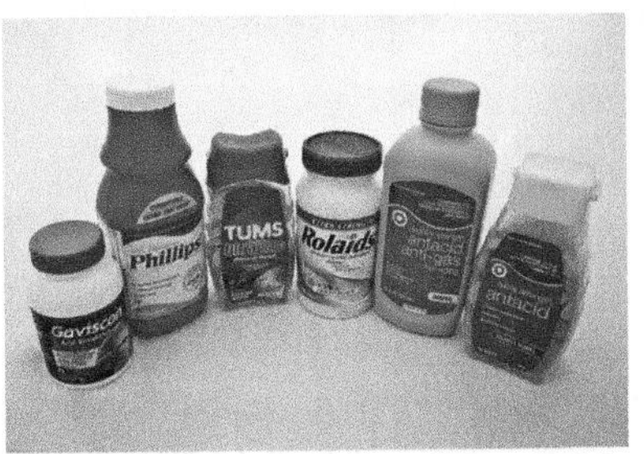

Pearson Education/Creative Digital Vision

Antacids neutralize excess stomach acid.

SAMPLE PROBLEM 10 Titration of an Acid

A 25.0-mL sample of an HCl solution is placed in a flask with a few drops of phenolphthalein (indicator). If 32.6 mL of a 0.185 M NaOH solution is needed to reach the endpoint, what is the concentration (M) of the HCl solution?

Analyze the Problem

Solution Components	Acid Volume	Acid Molarity	Base Volume	Base Molarity
Given	25.0 mL (0.0250 L)		32.6 mL	0.185 M NaOH solution
Need		Molarity of HCl solution (moles/L)		
Neutralization Equation	$NaOH(aq) + HCl(aq) \longrightarrow NaCl(aq) + H_2O(l)$			

Guide to Calculations for an Acid–Base Titration

1. Write the balanced equation for the neutralization.
2. Write a plan to calculate the molarity or volume.
3. State equalities and conversion factors, including concentration.
4. Set up the problem to calculate the needed quantity.

SOLUTION

Step 1 Write the balanced equation for the neutralization.

$$NaOH(aq) + HCl(aq) \longrightarrow NaCl(aq) + H_2O(l)$$

Step 2 Write a plan to calculate the molarity or volume.

mL of NaOH solution → (Metric factor) → L of NaOH solution → (Molarity) → moles of NaOH → (Mole–mole factor) → moles of HCl → (Divide by liters) → M HCl solution

Step 3 State equalities and conversion factors, including concentration.

$$1 \text{ L of NaOH solution} = 1000 \text{ mL of NaOH solution}$$
$$\frac{1 \text{ L NaOH solution}}{1000 \text{ mL NaOH solution}} \text{ and } \frac{1000 \text{ mL NaOH solution}}{1 \text{ L NaOH solution}}$$

$$1 \text{ L of NaOH solution} = 0.185 \text{ mole of NaOH}$$
$$\frac{1 \text{ L NaOH solution}}{0.185 \text{ mole NaOH}} \text{ and } \frac{0.185 \text{ mole NaOH}}{1 \text{ L NaOH solution}}$$

$$1 \text{ mole of HCl} = 1 \text{ mole of NaOH}$$
$$\frac{1 \text{ mole HCl}}{1 \text{ mole NaOH}} \text{ and } \frac{1 \text{ mole NaOH}}{1 \text{ mole HCl}}$$

Step 4 **Set up the problem to calculate the needed quantity.**

$$32.6 \text{ mL NaOH solution} \times \frac{1 \text{ L NaOH solution}}{1000 \text{ mL NaOH solution}} \times \frac{0.185 \text{ mole NaOH}}{1 \text{ L solution}} \times \frac{1 \text{ mole HCl}}{1 \text{ mole NaOH}}$$

$$= 0.00603 \text{ mole of HCl}$$

$$\text{Molarity of HCl solution} = \frac{0.00603 \text{ mole HCl}}{0.0250 \text{ L solution}} = 0.241 \text{ M HCl solution}$$

STUDY CHECK 10

What is the molarity of an HCl solution if 28.6 mL of a 0.175 M NaOH solution is needed to neutralize a 25.0-mL sample of the HCl solution?

QUESTIONS AND PROBLEMS

5 Reactions of Acids and Bases

LEARNING GOAL: *Write balanced equations for reactions of acids with metals, carbonates, and bases; calculate the molarity or volume of an acid from titration information.*

45 Predict the products and write the balanced equation for the reaction of HCl with each of the following metals:
a. Li **b.** Mg **c.** Sr

46 Predict the products and write the balanced equation for the reaction of HNO_3 with each of the following metals:
a. Ca **b.** Zn **c.** Al

47 Predict the products and write the balanced equation for the reaction of HBr with each of the following carbonates or hydrogen carbonates:
a. $LiHCO_3$
b. $MgCO_3$
c. $SrCO_3$

48 Predict the products and write the balanced equation for the reaction of H_2SO_4 with each of the following carbonates or hydrogen carbonates:
a. $CaCO_3$
b. Na_2CO_3
c. $CsHCO_3$

49 Balance each of the following neutralization reactions:
a. $HCl(aq) + Mg(OH)_2(s) \longrightarrow MgCl_2(aq) + H_2O(l)$
b. $H_3PO_4(aq) + LiOH(aq) \longrightarrow Li_3PO_4(aq) + H_2O(l)$
c. $H_2SO_4(aq) + Sr(OH)_2(s) \longrightarrow SrSO_4(aq) + H_2O(l)$

50 Balance each of the following neutralization reactions:
a. $HNO_3(aq) + Ba(OH)_2(s) \longrightarrow Ba(NO_3)_2(aq) + H_2O(l)$
b. $H_2SO_4(aq) + Al(OH)_3(s) \longrightarrow Al_2(SO_4)_3(aq) + H_2O(l)$
c. $H_3PO_4(aq) + KOH(aq) \longrightarrow K_3PO_4(aq) + H_2O(l)$

51 Predict the products and write a balanced equation for the neutralization of each of the following:
a. $H_2SO_4(aq)$ and $NaOH(aq) \longrightarrow$
b. $HCl(aq)$ and $Fe(OH)_3(s) \longrightarrow$
c. $H_2CO_3(aq)$ and $Mg(OH)_2(s) \longrightarrow$

52 Predict the products and write a balanced equation for the neutralization of each of the following:
a. $H_3PO_4(aq)$ and $NaOH(aq) \longrightarrow$
b. $HI(aq)$ and $LiOH(aq) \longrightarrow$
c. $HNO_3(aq)$ and $Ca(OH)_2(s) \longrightarrow$

53 What is the molarity of an HCl solution if 5.00 mL of the HCl solution requires 28.6 mL of a 0.145 M NaOH solution to reach the endpoint?

$$HCl(aq) + NaOH(aq) \longrightarrow NaCl(aq) + H_2O(l)$$

54 If 29.7 mL of a 0.205 M KOH solution is required to completely neutralize 25.0 mL of an $HC_2H_3O_2$ solution, what is the molarity of the acetic acid solution?

$$HC_2H_3O_2(aq) + KOH(aq) \longrightarrow KC_2H_3O_2(aq) + H_2O(l)$$

55 If 38.2 mL of a 0.162 M KOH solution is required to neutralize completely 25.0 mL of an H_2SO_4 solution, what is the molarity of the acid solution?

$$H_2SO_4(aq) + 2KOH(aq) \longrightarrow K_2SO_4(aq) + 2H_2O(l)$$

56 A solution of 0.162 M NaOH is used to neutralize 25.0 mL of an H_2SO_4 solution. If 32.8 mL of the NaOH solution is required to reach the endpoint, what is the molarity of the H_2SO_4 solution?

$$H_2SO_4(aq) + 2NaOH(aq) \longrightarrow Na_2SO_4(aq) + 2H_2O(l)$$

57 A solution of 0.204 M NaOH is used to neutralize 50.0 mL of an H_3PO_4 solution. If 16.4 mL of the NaOH solution is required to reach the endpoint, what is the molarity of the H_3PO_4 solution?

$$H_3PO_4(aq) + 3NaOH(aq) \longrightarrow Na_3PO_4(aq) + 3H_2O(l)$$

58 A solution of 0.312 M KOH is used to neutralize 15.0 mL of an H_3PO_4 solution. If 28.3 mL of the KOH solution is required to reach the endpoint, what is the molarity of the H_3PO_4 solution?

$$H_3PO_4(aq) + 3KOH(aq) \longrightarrow K_3PO_4(aq) + 3H_2O(l)$$

6 Buffers

LEARNING GOAL

Describe the role of buffers in maintaining the pH of a solution.

The pH of water and most solutions changes drastically when a small amount of acid or base is added. However, when acid or base is added to a *buffer solution*, there is very little change in pH. A **buffer solution** is a solution that maintains pH by neutralizing added acid or base. For example, blood contains buffers that maintain a consistent pH of about 7.4. If the pH of the blood goes slightly above or below 7.4, changes in our oxygen levels and our metabolic processes can be drastic enough to cause death. Even though we obtain acids and bases from foods and cellular reactions, the buffers in the body absorb those compounds so effectively that the pH of the blood remains essentially unchanged (see Figure 7).

SELF-STUDY ACTIVITY
pH and Buffers

TUTORIAL
Buffer Solutions

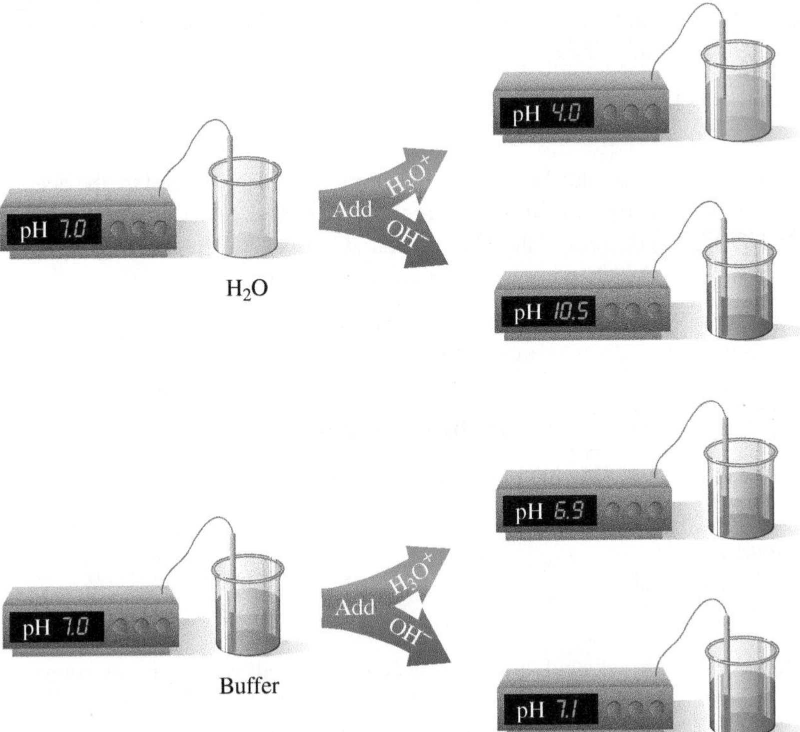

FIGURE 7 Adding an acid or a base to water changes the pH drastically, but a buffer resists pH change when small amounts of acid or base are added.

Q Why does the pH change several pH units when acid is added to water, but not when acid is added to a buffer?

In a buffer, an acid must be present to react with any OH^- that is added, and a base must be available to react with any added H_3O^+. However, that acid and base must not neutralize each other. Therefore, a combination of an acid–base conjugate pair is used in buffers. Most buffer solutions consist of nearly equal concentrations of a weak acid and a salt containing its conjugate base (see Figure 8). Buffers may also contain a weak base and the salt of the weak base, which contains its conjugate acid.

TUTORIAL
Preparing Buffer Solutions

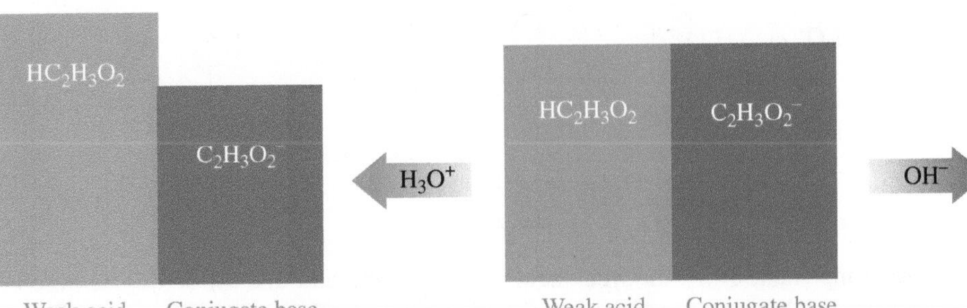

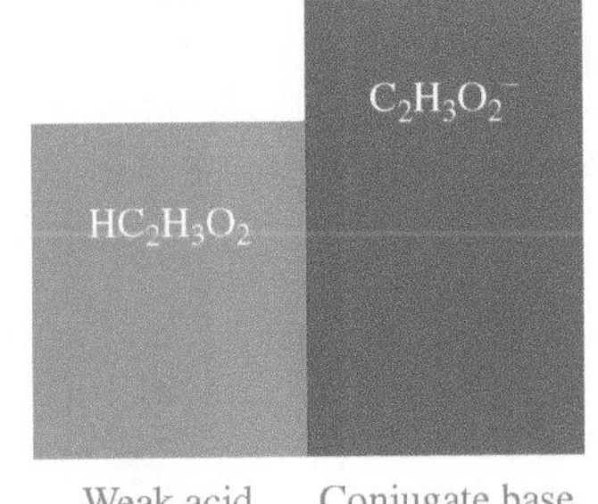

FIGURE 8 The buffer described here consists of about equal concentrations of acetic acid ($HC_2H_3O_2$) and its conjugate base, acetate ion ($C_2H_3O_2^-$). Adding H_3O^+ to the buffer uses up some $C_2H_3O_2^-$, whereas adding OH^- neutralizes $HC_2H_3O_2$. The pH of the solution is maintained as long as the added amounts of acid or base are small compared to the concentrations of the buffer components.

Q How does this acetic acid/acetate ion buffer maintain pH?

For example, a buffer can be made from the weak acid acetic acid ($HC_2H_3O_2$), and its salt, sodium acetate ($NaC_2H_3O_2$). As a weak acid, acetic acid dissociates slightly in water to form H_3O^+ and a very small amount of $C_2H_3O_2^-$. The addition of its salt, sodium acetate, provides a much larger concentration of acetate ion ($C_2H_3O_2^-$), which is necessary for its buffering capability.

$$\underset{\text{Large amount}}{HC_2H_3O_2(aq)} + H_2O(l) \rightleftharpoons H_3O^+(aq) + \underset{\text{Large amount}}{C_2H_3O_2^-(aq)}$$

We can now describe how this buffer solution maintains the $[H_3O^+]$. When a small amount of acid is added, it combines with the acetate ion, $C_2H_3O_2^-$, causing the equilibrium to shift in the direction of the reactants, acetic acid, and water. There will be a slight decrease in the $[C_2H_3O_2^-]$ and a slight increase in $[HC_2H_3O_2]$, but both the $[H_3O^+]$ and the pH of the solution are maintained.

$$HC_2H_3O_2(aq) + H_2O(l) \longleftarrow H_3O^+(aq) + C_2H_3O_2^-(aq)$$

Equilibrium shifts left

If a small amount of base is added to this buffer solution, it is neutralized by the acetic acid, $HC_2H_3O_2$, which shifts the equilibrium in the direction of the products acetate ion and water. The $[HC_2H_3O_2]$ decreases slightly, and the $[C_2H_3O_2^-]$ increases slightly, but again the $[H_3O^+]$ and thus the pH of the solution are maintained.

$$HC_2H_3O_2(aq) + OH^-(aq) \longrightarrow H_2O(l) + C_2H_3O_2^-(aq)$$

Equilibrium shifts left

CONCEPT CHECK 8 **Identifying Buffer Solutions**

Indicate whether each of the following would make a buffer solution:

a. HCl, a strong acid, and NaCl
b. H_3PO_4, a weak acid
c. HF, a weak acid, and NaF

ANSWER

a. No. A buffer requires a weak acid, not a strong acid, and a salt containing its conjugate base.
b. No. A weak acid is part of a buffer, but the salt containing the conjugate base of the weak acid is also needed.
c. Yes. This mixture would be a buffer because it contains a weak acid and its salt.

MC™

TUTORIAL
Calculating the pH of a Basic Buffer

TUTORIAL
Calculating the pH of an Acid Buffer

Calculating the pH of a Buffer

By rearranging the K_a expression to give $[H_3O^+]$, we can obtain the ratio of the acetic acid/acetate ion buffer:

$$K_a = \frac{[H_3O^+][C_2H_3O_2^-]}{[HC_2H_3O_2]}$$

Solving for $[H_3O^+]$ gives:

$$[H_3O^+] = K_a \times \frac{[HC_2H_3O_2]}{[C_2H_3O_2^-]} \quad \begin{matrix}\longleftarrow \text{Weak acid} \\ \longleftarrow \text{Conjugate base}\end{matrix}$$

In this rearrangement of K_a, the weak acid is in the numerator and the conjugate base in the denominator. We can now calculate the $[H_3O^+]$ and pH for an acetic acid buffer as shown in Sample Problem 11.

SAMPLE PROBLEM 11 **pH of a Buffer**

The K_a for acetic acid, $HC_2H_3O_2$, is 1.8×10^{-5}. What is the pH of a buffer prepared with 1.0 M $HC_2H_3O_2$ and 1.0 M $C_2H_3O_2^-$ (its conjugate base from 1.0 M $NaC_2H_3O_2$)?

SOLUTION

Analyze the Problem

Solution Components	Acid Molarity	Anion Molarity	pH	K_a
Given	1.0 M $HC_2H_3O_2$	1.0 M $C_2H_3O_2^-$		1.8×10^{-5}
Need			pH	
Equation	$HC_2H_3O_2(aq) + H_2O(l) \rightleftharpoons H_3O^+(aq) + C_2H_3O_2^-(aq)$			

Guide to Calculating pH of a Buffer

1 Write the K_a expression.

2 Rearrange the K_a expression for $[H_3O^+]$.

3 Substitute [HA] and $[A^-]$ into the K_a expression.

4 Use $[H_3O^+]$ to calculate pH.

Step 1 **Write the K_a expression.**

$$K_a = \frac{[H_3O^+][C_2H_3O_2^-]}{[HC_2H_3O_2]}$$

Step 2 **Rearrange the K_a expression for $[H_3O^+]$.**

$$[H_3O^+] = K_a \times \frac{[HC_2H_3O_2]}{[C_2H_3O_2^-]}$$

Step 3 **Substitute [HA] and $[A^-]$ into the K_a expression.** Substituting these values into the expression for $[H_3O^+]$ gives:

$$[H_3O^+] = (1.8 \times 10^{-5}) \times \frac{[1.0]}{[1.0]}$$

$$[H_3O^+] = 1.8 \times 10^{-5}\,\text{M}$$

Step 4 **Use $[H_3O^+]$ to calculate pH.** Placing the $[H_3O^+]$ into the pH expression gives the pH of the buffer.

$$\text{pH} = -\log[1.8 \times 10^{-5}] = 4.74$$

STUDY CHECK 11

The acid–base pair in a buffer is $H_2PO_4^-/HPO_4^{2-}$, which has a K_a of 6.2×10^{-8}. What is the pH of a buffer that is made of 0.10 M $H_2PO_4^-$ and 0.50 M HPO_4^{2-}?

Because K_a is a constant at a given temperature, the $[H_3O^+]$ is determined by the $[HC_2H_3O_2]/[C_2H_3O_2^-]$ ratio. As long as the addition of small amounts of either acid or base changes the ratio of $[HC_2H_3O_2]/[C_2H_3O_2^-]$ only slightly, the changes in $[H_3O^+]$ will be small and the pH will be maintained. If a large amount of acid or base is added, the *buffering capacity* of the system may be exceeded. Buffers can be prepared from conjugate acid–base pairs such as $H_2PO_4^-/HPO_4^{2-}$, HPO_4^{2-}/PO_4^{3-}, HCO_3^-/CO_3^{2-}, or NH_4^+/NH_3. The pH of the buffer solution will depend on the acid–base pair chosen.

Using a common phosphate buffer for biological specimens, we can look at the effect of using different ratios of $[H_2PO_4^-]/[HPO_4^{2-}]$ on the $[H_3O^+]$ and pH. The K_a of $H_2PO_4^-$ is 6.2×10^{-8}. The equation and the $[H_3O^+]$ are written as follows:

$$H_2PO_4^-(aq) + H_2O(l) \rightleftharpoons H_3O^+(aq) + HPO_4^{2-}(aq)$$

$$[H_3O^+] = K_a \times \frac{[H_2PO_4^-]}{[HPO_4^{2-}]}$$

K_a	$\frac{[H_2PO_4^-]}{[HPO_4^{2-}]}$	Ratio	$[H_3O^+]$	pH
6.2×10^{-8}	$\frac{1.0\text{ M}}{0.10\text{ M}}$	$\frac{10}{1}$	6.2×10^{-7}	6.21
6.2×10^{-8}	$\frac{1.0\text{ M}}{1.0\text{ M}}$	$\frac{1}{1}$	6.2×10^{-8}	7.21
6.2×10^{-8}	$\frac{0.10\text{ M}}{1.0\text{ M}}$	$\frac{1}{10}$	6.2×10^{-9}	8.21

To prepare a phosphate buffer with a pH close to the pH of a biological sample, 7.4, we would choose concentrations that are about equal, such as 1.0 M $H_2PO_4^-$ and 1.0 M HPO_4^{2-}.

CONCEPT CHECK 9 **Preparation of Buffers**

A buffer solution is needed to maintain a pH of 3.5 to 3.8 in a urine sample. Which of the following buffers would you use if 0.1 M solutions of the weak acid and conjugate base are available?

Formic acid/formate $K_a = 1.8 \times 10^{-4}$

Carbonic acid/bicarbonate $K_a = 4.3 \times 10^{-7}$

Ammonium/ammonia $K_a = 5.6 \times 10^{-10}$

ANSWER

Because formic acid has a K_a of 1.8×10^{-4}, the pH of a formic acid/formate buffer would be around 4, whereas the carbonic acid/bicarbonate buffer would be around pH 7, and the ammonium/ammonia buffer would be around 10. Thus, we can calculate the $[H_3O^+]$ and pH of a formic acid/formate buffer that uses 0.1 M solutions of the weak acid and the conjugate base.

$$[H_3O^+] = K_a \times \frac{[HCHO_2]}{[CHO^-_2]}$$

$$[H_3O^+] = (1.8 \times 10^{-4}) \times \frac{[0.1]}{[0.1]} = 1.8 \times 10^{-4}\text{ M}$$

$$\text{pH} = -\log[1.8 \times 10^{-4}] = 3.74$$

Chemistry Link to Health

BUFFERS IN THE BLOOD

The arterial blood has a normal pH of 7.35–7.45. If changes in $[H_3O^+]$ lower the pH below 6.8 or raise it above 8.0, cells cannot function properly and death may result. In our cells, CO_2 is continually produced as an end product of cellular metabolism. Some CO_2 is carried to the lungs for elimination, and the rest dissolves in body fluids such as plasma and saliva, forming carbonic acid. As a weak acid, carbonic acid dissociates to give bicarbonate and H_3O^+. More of the anion HCO_3^- is supplied by the kidneys to give an important buffer system in the body fluid, the H_2CO_3/HCO_3^- buffer.

$$CO_2 + H_2O \rightleftharpoons H_2CO_3 \rightleftharpoons H_3O^+ + HCO_3^-$$

Excess H_3O^+ entering the body fluids reacts with HCO_3^-, and excess OH^- reacts with the carbonic acid.

$$H_2CO_3(aq) + H_2O(l) \longleftarrow H_3O^+(aq) + HCO_3^-(aq)$$

Equilibrium shifts left

$$H_2CO_3(aq) + OH^-(aq) \longrightarrow H_2O(l) + HCO_3^-(aq)$$

Equilibrium shifts right

For the carbonic acid, we can write the equilibrium expression as:

$$K_a = \frac{[H_3O^+][HCO_3^-]}{[H_2CO_3]}$$

To maintain the normal blood pH (7.35–7.45), the ratio of H_2CO_3/HCO_3^- needs to be about 1 to 10, which is obtained by typical concentrations in the blood of 0.0024 M H_2CO_3 and 0.024 M HCO_3^-.

$$[H_3O^+] = K_a \times \frac{[H_2CO_3]}{[HCO_3^-]} = (4.3 \times 10^{-7}) \times \frac{[0.0024]}{[0.024]}$$

$$= (4.3 \times 10^{-7}) \times 0.10 = 4.3 \times 10^{-8}\text{ M}$$

$$\text{pH} = -\log[4.3 \times 10^{-8}] = 7.37$$

In the body, the concentration of carbonic acid is closely associated with the partial pressure of CO_2. Table 9 lists the normal values for arterial blood. If the CO_2 level rises, producing more H_2CO_3, the equilibrium produces more H_3O^+, which lowers the pH. This condition is called *acidosis*. Difficulty with ventilation or gas diffusion can lead to respiratory acidosis, which can happen in emphysema or when an accident or depressive drugs affect the medulla of the brain.

A lowering of the CO_2 level leads to a high blood pH, a condition called *alkalosis*. Excitement, trauma, or a high temperature may cause a person to hyperventilate, which expels large amounts of CO_2. As the partial pressure of CO_2 in the blood falls below normal, the equilibrium shifts from H_2CO_3 to CO_2 and H_2O. This shift decreases the $[H_3O^+]$ and raises the pH. Table 10 lists some of the conditions that lead to changes in the blood pH and some possible treatments. The kidneys also regulate H_3O^+ and HCO_3^- components, but they do so more slowly than the adjustment made by the lungs through ventilation.

TABLE 9 **Normal Values for Blood Buffer in Arterial Blood**

P_{CO_2}	40 mmHg
H_2CO_3	2.4 mmoles/L of plasma
HCO_3^-	24 mmoles/L of plasma
pH	7.35–7.45

TABLE 10 **Acidosis and Alkalosis: Symptoms, Causes, and Treatments**

Respiratory Acidosis: $CO_2 \uparrow$ pH $\downarrow$	**Metabolic Acidosis: $H^+ \uparrow$ pH $\downarrow$**
Symptoms: Failure to ventilae, suppression of breathing, disorientation, weakness, coma	**Symptoms:** Increased ventilation, fatigue, confusion
Causes: Lung disease blocking gas diffusion (e.g., emphysema, pneumonia, bronchitis, asthma); depression of the respiratory center by drugs, cardiopulmonary arrest, stroke, poliomyelitis, or nervous system disorders	**Causes:** Renal disease, including hepatitis and cirrhosis; increased acid production in diabetes mellitus, hyperthyroidism, alcoholism, and starvation; loss of alkali in diarrhea; acid retention in renal failure
Treatment: Correction of disorder, infusion of bicarbonate	**Treatment:** Sodium bicarbonate given orally, dialysis for renal failure, insulin treatment for diabetic ketosis
Respiratory Alkalosis: $CO_2 \downarrow$ pH $\uparrow$	**Metabolic Alkalosis: $H^+ \downarrow$ pH $\uparrow$**
Symptoms: Increased rate and depth of breathing, numbness, light-headedness, tetany	**Symptoms:** Depressed breathing, apathy, confusion
Causes: Hyperventilation due to anxiety, hysteria, fever, exercise; reaction to drugs such as salicylate, quinine, and antihistamines; conditions causing hypoxia (e.g., pneumonia, pulmonary edema, heart disease)	**Causes:** Vomiting, diseases of the adrenal glands, ingestion of excess alkali
Treatment: Elimination of anxiety-producing state, rebreathing into a paper bag	**Treatment:** Infusion of saline solution, treatment of underlying diseases

QUESTIONS AND PROBLEMS

6 Buffers

LEARNING GOAL: *Describe the role of buffers in maintaining the pH of a solution.*

59 Consider the following: (1) NaOH and NaCl, (2) H_2CO_3 and $NaHCO_3$, (3) HF and KF, (4) KCl and NaCl. Which of these represent a buffer system? Explain.

60 Consider the following: (1) $HClO_2$, (2) $NaNO_3$, (3) $HC_2H_3O_2$ and $NaC_2H_3O_2$, and (4) HCl and NaOH. Which of these represent a buffer system? Explain.

61 Consider the buffer system of hydrofluoric acid, HF, and its salt, NaF.

$$HF(aq) + H_2O(l) \rightleftharpoons H_3O^+(aq) + F^-(aq)$$

a. The purpose of the buffer system is to:
1. maintain $[HF]$ **2.** maintain $[F^-]$ **3.** maintain pH

b. The salt of the weak acid is needed to:
1. provide the conjugate base **2.** neutralize added H_3O^+
3. provide the conjugate acid

c. The addition of OH^- is neutralized by:
1. the salt **2.** H_2O **3.** H_3O^+

d. When H_3O^+ is added, the equilibrium shifts in the direction of the.
1. reactants **2.** products **3.** does not change

62 Consider the buffer system of nitrous acid, HNO_2, and its salt, $NaNO_2$.

$$HNO_2(aq) + H_2O(l) \rightleftharpoons H_3O^+(aq) + NO_2^-(aq)$$

a. The purpose of the buffer system is to:
1. maintain $[HNO_2]$
2. maintain $[NO_2^-]$
3. maintain pH

b. The weak acid is needed to:
1. provide the conjugate base
2. neutralize added OH^-
3. provide the conjugate acid

c. The addition of H_3O^+ is neutralized by:
1. the salt **2.** H_2O **3.** OH^-

d. When OH^- is added, the equilibrium shifts in the direction of the:
1. reactants **2.** products **3.** does not change

63 Nitrous acid has a K_a of 4.5×10^{-4}. What is the pH of a buffer solution containing 0.10 M HNO_2 and 0.10 M NO_2^-?

64 Acetic acid has a K_a of 1.8×10^{-5}. What is the pH of a buffer solution containing 0.15 M $HC_2H_3O_2$ (acetic acid) and 0.15 M $C_2H_3O_2^-$?

65 Using Table 4 for K_a values, compare the pH of an HF buffer that contains 0.10 M HF and 0.10 M NaF with another HF buffer that contains 0.060 M HF and 0.120 M NaF.

66 Using Table 4 for K_a values, compare the pH of an H_2CO_3 buffer that contains 0.10 M H_2CO_3 and 0.10 M $NaHCO_3$ with another H_2CO_3 buffer that contains 0.15 M H_2CO_3 and 0.050 M $NaHCO_3$.

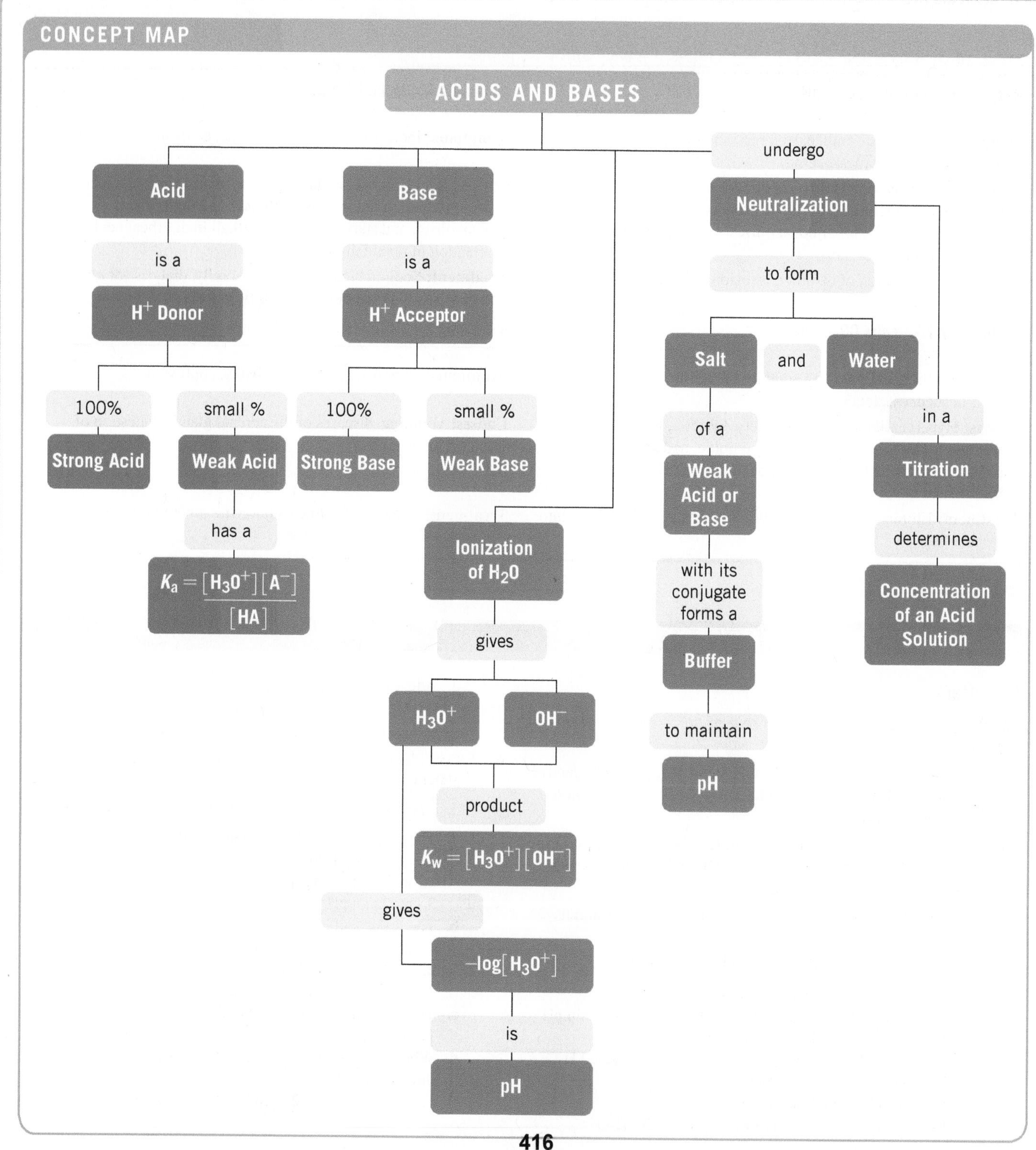

CHAPTER REVIEW

1 Acids and Bases

LEARNING GOAL: *Describe and name Arrhenius and Brønsted–Lowry acids and bases; identify conjugate acid–base pairs.*

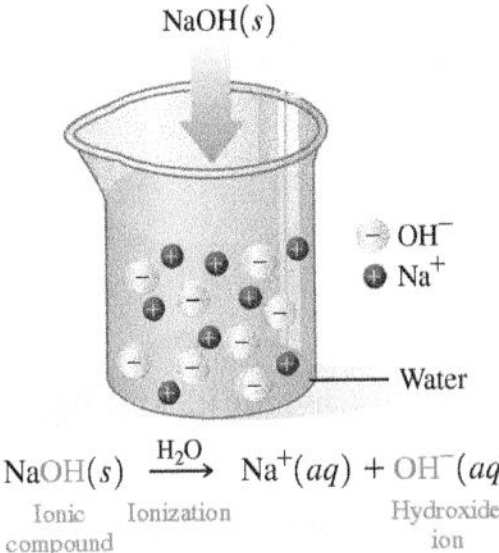

- An Arrhenius acid produces H^+ and an Arrhenius base produces OH^- in aqueous solutions.
- Acids taste sour, may sting, and neutralize bases.
- Bases taste bitter, feel slippery, and neutralize acids.
- Acids containing a simple anion are named using a *hydro* prefix and an *ic acid* ending.
- Acids with oxygen-containing polyatomic anions are named as *ic* or *ous acids.*
- According to the Brønsted–Lowry theory, acids are H^+ donors and bases are H^+ acceptors.
- Each conjugate acid–base pair is related by the loss or gain of one H^+.

2 Strengths of Acids and Bases

LEARNING GOAL: *Write equations for the dissociation of strong and weak acids; write the equilibrium expression for a weak acid.*

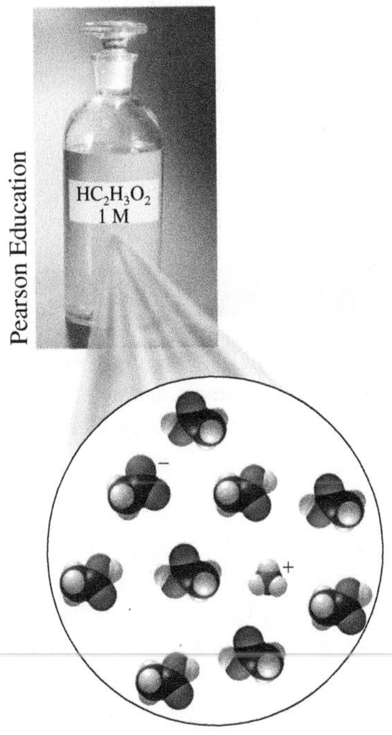

- Strong acids dissociate completely in water and the H^+ is accepted by H_2O acting as a base.
- A weak acid dissociates slightly in water producing only a small percentage of H_3O^+.
- Strong bases are hydroxides of Groups 1A (1) and 2A (2) that dissociate completely in water.
- An important weak base is ammonia, NH_3.
- In water, weak acids and weak bases produce only a few ions when equilibrium is reached.
- The equilibrium of a weak acid and its products can be written as an acid dissociation expression, K_a.

3 Ionization of Water

LEARNING GOAL: *Use the ion product constant for water to calculate the* $[H_3O^+]$ *and* $[OH^-]$ *in an aqueous solution.*

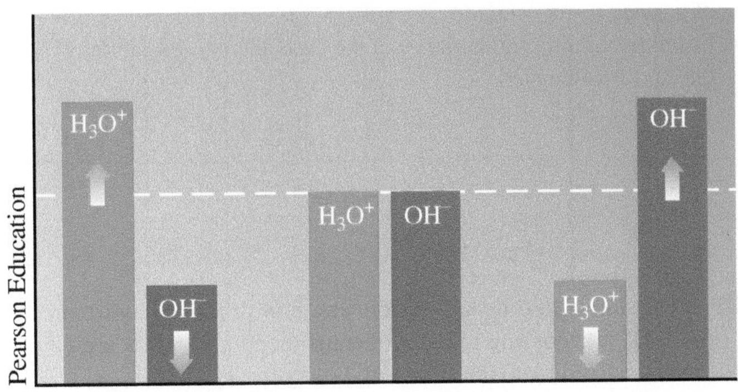

- In pure water, a few water molecules transfer H^+ to other water molecules, producing small but equal amounts of H_3O^+ and OH^-.
- In pure water, the concentrations of H_3O^+ and OH^- are each 1.0×10^{-7} mole/L.
- The ion product constant for water, K_w, $[H_3O^+][OH^-] = 1 \times 10^{-14}$ at 25 °C.
- In acidic solutions, the $[H_3O^+]$ is greater than the $[OH^-]$.
- In neutral solutions, the $[H_3O^+]$ is equal to the $[OH^-]$.
- In basic solutions, the $[OH^-]$ is greater than the $[H_3O^+]$.

4 The pH Scale

LEARNING GOAL: *Calculate* pH *from* $[H_3O^+]$*; given the* pH*, calculate the* $[H_3O^+]$ *and* $[OH^-]$ *of a solution.*

- The pH scale is a range of numbers, typically from 0 to 14, which represents the $[H_3O^+]$ of the solution.
- A neutral solution has a pH of 7.0. In acidic solutions, the pH is below 7.0; in basic solutions, the pH is above 7.0.
- Mathematically, pH is the negative logarithm of the hydronium ion concentration: $pH = -\log[H_3O^+]$.

5 Reactions of Acids and Bases

LEARNING GOAL: *Write balanced equations for reactions of acids with metals, carbonates, and bases; calculate the molarity or volume of an acid from titration information.*

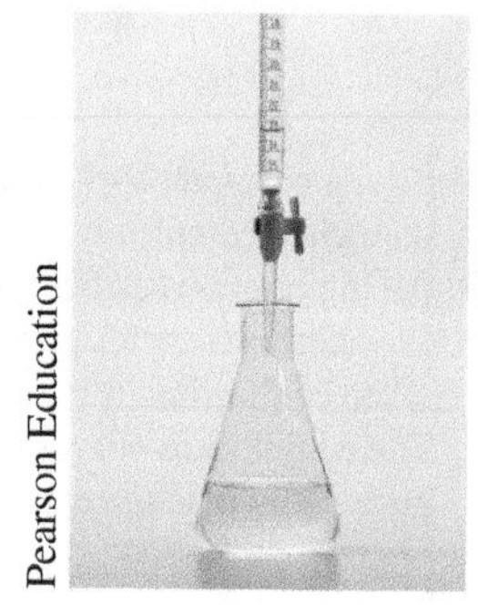

- An acid reacts with a metal to produce hydrogen gas and a salt.
- The reaction of an acid with a carbonate or bicarbonate produces carbon dioxide, water, and a salt.
- In neutralization, an acid reacts with a base to produce a salt and water.
- In a titration, an acid sample is neutralized with a known amount of a base.
- From the volume and molarity of the base, the concentration of the acid is calculated.

6 Buffers

LEARNING GOAL: *Describe the role of buffers in maintaining the pH of a solution.*

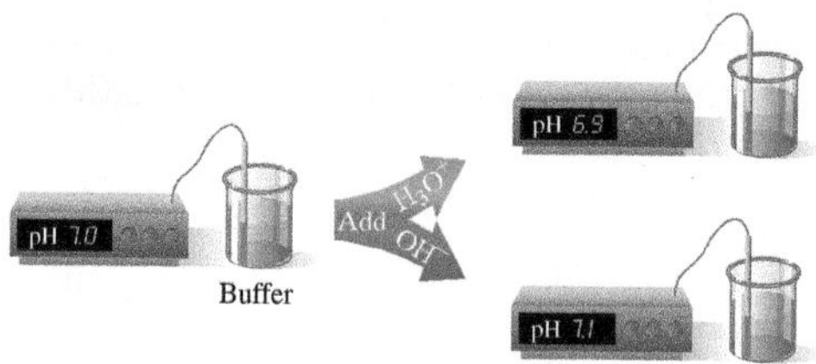

- A buffer solution resists changes in pH when small amounts of acid or base are added.
- A buffer contains either a weak acid and its salt, or a weak base and its salt.
- In a buffer, the weak acid reacts with added OH^-, and the anion of the salt reacts with added H_3O^+.
- Buffers are important in maintaining the pH of the blood.

KEY TERMS

acid A substance that dissolves in water and produces hydrogen ions (H^+), according to the Arrhenius theory. All acids are H^+ donors, according to the Brønsted–Lowry theory.

acid dissociation constant, K_a The product of the concentrations of the ions from the dissociation of a weak acid divided by the concentration of the weak acid.

amphoteric Substances that can act as either an acid or a base in water.

base A substance that dissolves in water and produces hydroxide ions (OH^-), according to the Arrhenius theory. All bases are H^+ acceptors, according to the Brønsted–Lowry theory.

Brønsted–Lowry acids and bases An acid is an H^+ donor; a base is an H^+ acceptor.

buffer solution A solution of a weak acid and its conjugate base, or a weak base and its conjugate acid, that maintains the pH by neutralizing added acid or base.

conjugate acid–base pair An acid and base that differ by one H^+. When an acid donates H^+, the product is its conjugate base, which is capable of accepting H^+ in the reverse reaction.

dissociation The separation of an acid or base into ions in water.

hydronium ion, H_3O^+ The ion, formed by the attraction of H^+ to a H_2O molecule, written as H_3O^+.

ion product constant for water, K_w The product of $[H_3O^+]$ and $[OH^-]$ in solution; $K_w = [H_3O^+][OH^-]$.

neutral The term that describes a solution with equal concentrations of H_3O^+ and OH^-.

neutralization A reaction between an acid and a base to form a salt and water.

pH A measure of the $[H_3O^+]$ in a solution; $pH = -\log[H_3O^+]$.

strong acid An acid that completely ionizes in water.

strong base A base that completely ionizes in water.

titration The addition of base to an acid sample to determine the concentration of the acid.

weak acid An acid that dissociates only slightly in water.

weak base A base that produces only a small number of ions in water.

UNDERSTANDING THE CONCEPTS

The chapter sections to review are shown in parentheses at the end of each question.

67 In each of the following diagrams of acid solutions, determine if each diagram represents a strong acid or a weak acid. The acid has the formula HX. (2)

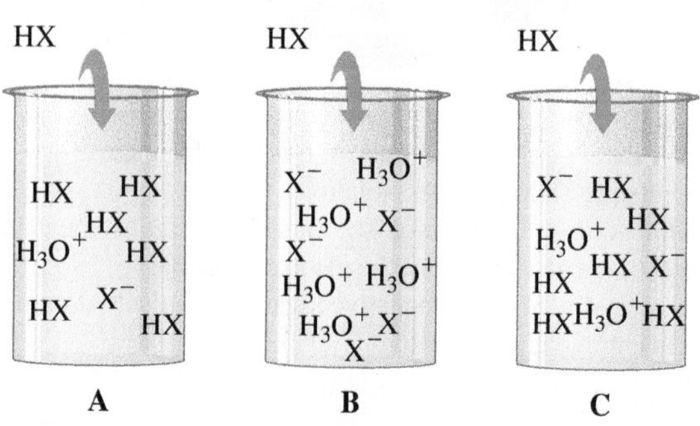

68 Adding a few drops of a strong acid to water will lower the pH appreciably. However, adding the same number of drops to a buffer does not appreciably alter the pH. Why? (6)

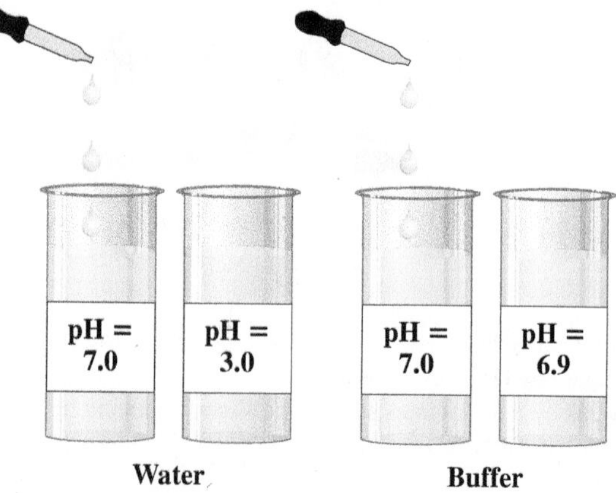

69 Sometimes, during stress or trauma, a person can start to hyperventilate. Then the person might breathe into a paper bag to avoid fainting. (6)

a. What changes occur in the blood pH during hyperventilation?

b. How does breathing into a paper bag help return the blood pH to normal?

Breathing into a paper bag can help a person who is hyperventilating.

70 In the blood plasma, pH is maintained by the carbonic acid–bicarbonate buffer system. (6)

a. Which component of the carbonic acid–bicarbonate buffer reacts when acid is added?

b. Which component of the carbonic acid–bicarbonate buffer reacts when base is added?

ADDITIONAL QUESTIONS AND PROBLEMS

For instructor-assigned homework, go to www.masteringchemistry.com.

71 Identify each of the following as an acid, base, or salt, and give its name: (1)

a. $LiOH$ b. $Ca(NO_3)_2$ c. HBr
d. $Ba(OH)_2$ e. H_2CO_3 f. $HClO_2$

72 Identify each of the following as an acid, base, or salt, and give its name: (1)

a. H_3PO_4 b. $MgBr_2$ c. NH_3
d. H_2SO_4 e. $NaCl$ f. KOH

73 Identify the conjugate acid–base pairs in each of the following equations and state whether the equilibrium mixture contains mostly products or mostly reactants: (5)

a. $NH_3(aq) + HNO_3(aq) \rightleftharpoons NH_4^+(aq) + NO_3^-(aq)$
b. $H_2O(l) + HBr(aq) \rightleftharpoons H_3O^+(aq) + Br^-(aq)$

74 Identify the conjugate acid–base pairs in each of the following equations and state whether the equilibrium mixture contains mostly products or mostly reactants: (5)

a. $HNO_2(aq) + HS^-(aq) \rightleftharpoons H_2S(g) + NO_2^-(aq)$
b. $Cl^-(aq) + H_2O(l) \rightleftharpoons OH^-(aq) + HCl(aq)$

75 Complete the following table: (1)

Acid	Conjugate Base
HI	
	Cl^-
NH_4^+	
	HS^-

76 Complete the following table: (1)

Base	Conjugate Acid
	HS^-
	$HC_2H_3O_2$
NH_3	
ClO_4^-	

77 Are each of the following solutions acidic, basic, or neutral? (4)

a. rain, pH 5.2 b. tears, pH 7.5
c. tea, pH 3.8 d. cola, pH 2.5
e. photo developer, pH 12.0

78 Are each of the following solutions acidic, basic, or neutral? (4)

a. saliva, pH 6.8 b. urine, pH 5.9
c. pancreatic juice, pH 8.0 d. bile, pH 8.4
e. blood, pH 7.45

79 Using Table 3, identify the stronger acid in each of the following pairs: (2)

a. HF or H_2S b. H_3O^+ or H_2CO_3
c. HNO_2 or $HC_2H_3O_2$ d. H_2O or HCO_3^-

80 Using Table 3, identify the stronger base in each of the following pairs: (2)

a. H_2O or Cl^- b. OH^- or H_2CO_3
c. SO_4^{2-} or NO_2^- d. CO_3^{2-} or H_2O

81 Determine the pH for the following solutions: (4)

a. $[H_3O^+] = 2.0 \times 10^{-8}$ M
b. $[H_3O^+] = 5.0 \times 10^{-2}$ M
c. $[OH^-] = 3.5 \times 10^{-4}$ M
d. $[OH^-] = 0.0054$ M

82 Determine the pH for the following solutions: (4)

a. $[OH^-] = 1.0 \times 10^{-7}$ M
b. $[H_3O^+] = 4.2 \times 10^{-3}$ M
c. $[H_3O^+] = 0.0001$ M
d. $[OH^-] = 8.5 \times 10^{-9}$ M

83 Are the solutions in Problem 81 acidic, basic, or neutral? (4)

84 Are the solutions in Problem 82 acidic, basic, or neutral? (4)

85 What are the $[H_3O^+]$ and $[OH^-]$ for a solution with each of the following pH values? (3, 4)

a. 3.00 b. 6.48
c. 8.85 d. 11.00

86 What are the $[H_3O^+]$ and $[OH^-]$ for a solution with each of the following pH values? (3, 4)

a. 10.0 b. 5.0
c. 7.00 d. 1.82

87 Sour milk (A) has a pH of 4.5, and maple syrup (B) has a pH of 6.7. (4)
a. Which solution is more acidic?
b. What is the $[H_3O^+]$ in each?
c. What is the $[OH^-]$ in each?

88 A solution of borax (A) has a pH of 9.2, and human saliva (B) has a pH of 6.5. (4)
a. Which solution is more acidic?
b. What is the $[H_3O^+]$ in each?
c. What is the $[OH^-]$ in each?

89 What is the $[OH^-]$ in a solution that contains 0.225 g of NaOH in 0.250 L of solution? (3)

90 What is the $[H_3O^+]$ in a solution that contains 1.54 g of HNO_3 in 0.500 L of solution? (3)

91 What is the pH of a solution prepared by dissolving 2.5 g of HCl in water to make 425 mL of solution? (4)

92 What is the pH of a solution prepared by dissolving 1.00 g of $Ca(OH)_2$ in water to make 875 mL of solution? (4)

93 a. Write the neutralization equation for KOH and H_3PO_4. (5)
b. Calculate the volume (mL) of a 0.150 M KOH solution that will completely neutralize 10.0 mL of a 0.560 M H_3PO_4 solution.

94 a. Write the neutralization equation for NaOH and H_2SO_4. (5)
b. How many milliliters of a 0.215 M NaOH solution are needed to completely neutralize 2.50 mL of a 0.825 M H_2SO_4 solution?

CHALLENGE QUESTIONS

95 For each of the following: (1, 2)
1. H_2S 2. H_3PO_4
a. Write the formula for the conjugate base.
b. Write the K_a expression.
c. Which is the weaker acid?

96 For each of the following: (1, 2)
1. HCO_3^- 2. $HC_2H_3O_2$
a. Write the formula for the conjugate base.
b. Write the K_a expression.
c. Which is the stronger acid?

97 A solution of 0.205 M NaOH is used to neutralize 20.0 mL of an H_2SO_4 solution. If 45.6 mL of the NaOH solution is required to reach the endpoint, what is the molarity of the H_2SO_4 solution? (5)

$$H_2SO_4(aq) + 2NaOH(aq) \longrightarrow Na_2SO_4(aq) + 2H_2O(l)$$

98 A 10.0-mL sample of vinegar, which is an aqueous solution of acetic acid, $HC_2H_3O_2$, requires 16.5 mL of a 0.500 M NaOH solution to reach the endpoint in a titration. What is the molarity of the acetic acid solution? (5)

$$HC_2H_3O_2(aq) + NaOH(aq) \longrightarrow NaC_2H_3O_2(aq) + H_2O(l)$$

99 A buffer is made by dissolving H_3PO_4 and NaH_2PO_4 in water. (6)
a. Write an equation that shows how this buffer neutralizes added acid.
b. Write an equation that shows how this buffer neutralizes added base.
c. Calculate the pH of this buffer if it contains 0.10 M H_3PO_4 and 0.10 M $H_2PO_4^-$; the K_a for H_3PO_4 is 7.5×10^{-3}.
d. Calculate the pH of this buffer if it contains 0.50 M H_3PO_4 and 0.20 M $H_2PO_4^-$; the K_a for H_3PO_4 is 7.5×10^{-3}.

100 A buffer is made by dissolving $HC_2H_3O_2$ and $NaC_2H_3O_2$ in water. (6)
a. Write an equation that shows how this buffer neutralizes added acid.
b. Write an equation that shows how this buffer neutralizes added base.
c. Calculate the pH of this buffer if it contains 0.10 M $HC_2H_3O_2$ and 0.10 M $C_2H_3O_2^-$; the K_a for $HC_2H_3O_2$ is 1.8×10^{-5}.
d. Calculate the pH of this buffer if it contains 0.20 M $HC_2H_3O_2$ and 0.40 M $C_2H_3O_2^-$; the K_a for $HC_2H_3O_2$ is 1.8×10^{-5}.

101 Determine each of the following for a 0.050 M KOH solution: (5)
a. $[H_3O^+]$
b. pH
c. the balanced equation when reacted with H_2SO_4
d. milliliters of KOH solution required to neutralize 40.0 mL of a 0.035 M H_2SO_4 solution

102 Determine each of the following for a 0.100 M HBr solution: (5)
a. $[H_3O^+]$
b. pH
c. the balanced equation when reacted with LiOH
d. milliliters of HBr solution required to neutralize 36.0 mL of a 0.250 M LiOH solution

103 One of the most acidic lakes in the United States is Little Echo Pond in the Adirondacks in New York. Recently, this lake had a pH of 4.2, well below the recommended pH of 6.5. (3, 4, 5)

Mark Edwards/Peter Arnold/Photolibrary

A helicopter drops calcium carbonate on an acidic lake to increase its pH.

a. What are the $[H_3O^+]$ and $[OH^-]$ of Little Echo Pond?
b. What are the $[H_3O^+]$ and $[OH^-]$ of a lake that has a pH of 6.5?
c. One way to raise the pH of an acidic lake (and restore aquatic life) is to add limestone ($CaCO_3$). How many grams of $CaCO_3$ are needed to neutralize 1.0 kL of the acidic water from Little Echo Pond if we assume all the acid is sulfuric acid?

$$H_2SO_4(aq) + CaCO_3(s) \longrightarrow CO_2(g) + H_2O(l) + CaSO_4(aq)$$

104 The daily output of stomach acid (gastric juice) is 1000 mL to 2000 mL. Prior to a meal, stomach acid (HCl) typically has a pH of 1.42. (3, 4, 5)

a. What is the $[H_3O^+]$ of stomach acid?

b. One chewable tablet of the antacid Maalox contains 600. mg of $CaCO_3$. Write the neutralization equation and calculate the milliliters of stomach acid neutralized by two tablets of Maalox.

c. The antacid milk of magnesia contains 400. mg of $Mg(OH)_2$ per teaspoon. Write the neutralization equation and calculate the milliliters of stomach acid that are neutralized by 1 tablespoon of milk of magnesia (1 tablespoon = 3 teaspoons).

ANSWERS

Answers to Study Checks

1 a. acid; chloric acid
b. $Fe(OH)_3$

2 $HNO_3(aq) + H_2O(l) \longrightarrow H_3O^+(aq) + NO_3^-(aq)$

3 The conjugate acid–base pairs are HNO_2/NO_2^- and HSO_4^-/SO_4^{2-}.

4 Nitrous acid has a larger K_a than carbonic acid; it dissociates more in H_2O, forms more $[H_3O^+]$, and is a stronger acid.

5 $[H_3O^+] = 2.5 \times 10^{-11}$ M; basic

6 11.38

7 4.3

8 $[H_3O^+] = 2 \times 10^{-5}$ M; $[OH^-] = 5 \times 10^{-10}$ M

9 $H_2SO_4(aq) + 2LiOH(aq) \longrightarrow Li_2SO_4(aq) + 2H_2O(l)$

10 0.200 M HCl solution

11 pH = 7.91

Answers to Selected Questions and Problems

1 a. acid **b.** acid **c.** acid
d. base **e.** both

3 a. hydrochloric acid **b.** calcium hydroxide
c. carbonic acid **d.** nitric acid
e. sulfurous acid **f.** iron(II) hydroxide

5 a. $Mg(OH)_2$ **b.** HF **c.** H_3PO_3
d. LiOH **e.** $Cu(OH)_2$

7 a. HI is the acid (H^+ donor) and H_2O is the base (H^+ acceptor).
b. H_2O is the acid (H^+ donor) and F^- is the base (H^+ acceptor).

9 a. F^-, fluoride ion
b. OH^-, hydroxide ion
c. HCO_3^-, bicarbonate ion *or* hydrogen carbonate ion
d. SO_4^{2-}, sulfate ion

11 a. HCO_3^-, bicarbonate ion *or* hydrogen carbonate ion
b. H_3O^+, hydronium ion
c. H_3PO_4, phosphoric acid
d. HSO_3^-, bisulfite ion *or* hydrogen sulfite ion

13 a. acid H_2CO_3, conjugate base HCO_3^-; base H_2O, conjugate acid H_3O^+
b. acid NH_4^+, conjugate base NH_3; base H_2O, conjugate acid H_3O^+
c. acid HCN, conjugate base CN^-; base NO_2^-, conjugate acid HNO_2

15 A strong acid is a good H^+ donor, whereas its conjugate base is a poor H^+ acceptor.

17 a. true **b.** false **c.** false
d. true **e.** false

19 a. HBr **b.** HSO_4^- **c.** H_2CO_3

21 a. HSO_4^- **b.** HNO_2 **c.** HCO_3^-

23 a. reactants **b.** reactants **c.** products

25 a. H_2SO_3 **b.** HSO_3^- **c.** H_2SO_3
d. H_2SO_3

27 $H_3PO_4(aq) + H_2O(l) \rightleftarrows H_3O^+(aq) + H_2PO_4^-(aq)$

$$K_a = \frac{[H_3O^+][H_2PO_4^-]}{[H_3PO_4]}$$

29 In pure water, $[H_3O^+] = [OH^-]$ because one of each is produced every time H^+ is transferred from one water molecule to another.

31 In an acidic solution, the $[H_3O^+]$ is greater than the $[OH^-]$.

33 a. acidic **b.** basic **c.** basic
d. acidic

35 a. 1.0×10^{-5} M **b.** 1.0×10^{-8} M
c. 5.0×10^{-10} M **d.** 2.5×10^{-2} M

37 a. 1.0×10^{-11} M **b.** 2.0×10^{-9} M
c. 5.6×10^{-3} M **d.** 2.5×10^{-2} M

39 a. basic **b.** acidic **c.** basic
d. acidic **e.** acidic **f.** basic

41 a. 4.00 **b.** 8.52 **c.** 9.00
d. 3.40 **e.** 7.17 **f.** 10.92

43

$[H_3O^+]$	$[OH^-]$	pH	Acidic, Basic, or Neutral?
1×10^{-8} M	1×10^{-6} M	8.0	Basic
1.0×10^{-3} M	1.0×10^{-11} M	3.00	Acidic
2.8×10^{-5} M	3.6×10^{-10} M	4.55	Acidic
2.4×10^{-5} M	4.2×10^{-10} M	4.62	Acidic

45 a. products: $LiCl(aq)$ and $H_2(g)$
balanced equation:
$2Li(s) + 2HCl(aq) \longrightarrow 2LiCl(aq) + H_2(g)$

b. products: $MgCl_2(aq)$ and $H_2(g)$
balanced equation:

$$Mg(s) + 2HCl(aq) \longrightarrow MgCl_2(aq) + H_2(g)$$

c. products: $SrCl_2(aq)$ and $H_2(g)$
balanced equation:

$$Sr(s) + 2HCl(aq) \longrightarrow SrCl_2(aq) + H_2(g)$$

47 a. products: $LiBr(aq)$, $H_2O(l)$, and $CO_2(g)$
balanced equation:

$$HBr(aq) + LiHCO_3(s) \longrightarrow LiBr(aq) + H_2O(l) + CO_2(g)$$

b. products: $MgBr_2(aq)$, $H_2O(l)$, and $CO_2(g)$
balanced equation:

$$2HBr(aq) + MgCO_3(s) \longrightarrow MgBr_2(aq) + H_2O(l) + CO_2(g)$$

c. products: $SrBr_2(aq)$, $H_2O(l)$, and $CO_2(g)$
balanced equation:

$$2HBr(aq) + SrCO_3(s) \longrightarrow SrBr_2(aq) + H_2O(l) + CO_2(g)$$

49 a. $2HCl(aq) + Mg(OH)_2(s) \longrightarrow MgCl_2(aq) + 2H_2O(l)$
b. $H_3PO_4(aq) + 3LiOH(aq) \longrightarrow Li_3PO_4(aq) + 3H_2O(l)$
c. $H_2SO_4(aq) + Sr(OH)_2(s) \longrightarrow SrSO_4(aq) + 2H_2O(l)$

51 a. $H_2SO_4(aq) + 2NaOH(aq) \longrightarrow Na_2SO_4(aq) + 2H_2O(l)$
b. $3HCl(aq) + Fe(OH)_3(s) \longrightarrow FeCl_3(aq) + 3H_2O(l)$
c. $H_2CO_3(aq) + Mg(OH)_2(s) \longrightarrow MgCO_3(s) + 2H_2O(l)$

53 0.830 M HCl solution

55 0.124 M H_2SO_4 solution

57 0.0224 M H_3PO_4 solution

59 (2) and (3) are buffer systems. (2) contains the weak acid H_2CO_3 and its salt $NaHCO_3$. (3) contains HF, a weak acid, and its salt KF.

61 a. 3 **b.** 1, 2 **c.** 3 **d.** 1

63 pH = 3.35

65 The pH of the 0.10 M HF / 0.10 M NaF buffer is 3.14. The pH of the 0.060 M HF / 0.120 M NaF buffer is 3.44.

67 a. weak acid **b.** strong acid **c.** weak acid

69 a. Hyperventilation will lower the CO_2 level in the blood, which lowers the $[H_2CO_3]$ which decreases the $[H_3O^+]$ and increases the blood pH.
b. Breathing into a bag will increase the CO_2 level, increase the $[H_2CO_3]$, increase $[H_3O^+]$, and lower the blood pH.

71 a. base, lithium hydroxide **b.** salt, calcium nitrate
c. acid, hydrobromic acid **d.** base, barium hydroxide
e. acid, carbonic acid **f.** acid, chlorous acid

73 a. NH_4^+/NH_3 and HNO_3/NO_3^-; mostly products
b. HBr/Br^- and H_3O^+/H_2O; mostly products

75

Acid	Conjugate Base
HI	I^-
HCl	Cl^-
NH_4^+	NH_3
H_2S	HS^-

77 a. acidic **b.** basic **c.** acidic
d. acidic **e.** basic

79 a. HF **b.** H_3O^+ **c.** HNO_2
d. HCO_3^-

81 a. pH 7.70 **b.** pH 1.30 **c.** pH 10.54
d. pH 11.72

83 a. basic **b.** acidic **c.** basic
d. basic

85 a. $[H_3O^+] = 1.0 \times 10^{-3}$ M; $[OH^-] = 1.0 \times 10^{-11}$ M
b. $[H_3O^+] = 3.3 \times 10^{-7}$ M; $[OH^-] = 3.0 \times 10^{-8}$ M
c. $[H_3O^+] = 1.4 \times 10^{-9}$ M; $[OH^-] = 7.1 \times 10^{-6}$ M
d. $[H_3O^+] = 1.0 \times 10^{-11}$ M; $[OH^-] = 1.0 \times 10^{-3}$ M

87 a. A
b. A, $[H_3O^+] = 3 \times 10^{-5}$ M B, $[H_3O^+] = 2 \times 10^{-7}$ M
c. A, $[OH^-] = 3 \times 10^{-10}$ M B, $[OH^-] = 5 \times 10^{-8}$ M

89 $[OH^-] = 0.0225$ M

91 pH = 0.80

93 a. $H_3PO_4(aq) + 3KOH(aq) \longrightarrow K_3PO_4(aq) + 3H_2O(l)$
b. 112 mL of KOH solution

95 a. 1. HS^- **2.** $H_2PO_4^-$

b. 1. $\dfrac{[H_3O^+][HS^-]}{[H_2S]}$

2. $\dfrac{[H_3O^+][H_2PO_4^-]}{[H_3PO_4]}$

c. H_2S

97 0.234 M H_2SO_4solution

99 a. $H_2PO_4^-(aq) + H_3O^+(aq) \longrightarrow H_3PO_4(aq) + H_2O(l)$
b. $H_3PO_4(aq) + OH^-(aq) \longrightarrow H_2PO_4^-(aq) + H_2O(l)$
c. pH = 2.12
d. pH = 1.72

101 a. $[H_3O^+] = 2.0 \times 10^{-13}$ M
b. pH = 12.70
c. $2KOH(aq) + H_2SO_4(aq) \longrightarrow K_2SO_4(aq) + 2H_2O(l)$
d. 56 mL of KOH solution

103 a. $[H_3O^+] = 6 \times 10^{-5}$ M; $[OH^-] = 2 \times 10^{-10}$ M
b. $[H_3O^+] = 3 \times 10^{-7}$ M; $[OH^-] = 3 \times 10^{-8}$ M
c. 3 g of $CaCO_3$

Combining Ideas 3

CI.17 Methane is a major component of purified natural gas used for heating and cooking. When 1.0 mole of methane gas burns with oxygen to produce carbon dioxide and water vapor, 883 kJ of heat is produced. At STP, methane gas has a density of 0.715 g/L. For transport, the natural gas is cooled to −163 °C to form liquefied natural gas (LNG) with a density of 0.45 g/mL. A tank on a ship can hold 7.0 million gallons of LNG.

Center for Liquefied Natural Gas

An LNG carrier transports liquefied natural gas.

a. Draw the electron-dot formula for methane, which has the formula CH_4.
b. What is the mass, in kilograms, of LNG (assume that LNG is all methane) transported in one tank on a ship?
c. What is the volume, in liters, of methane gas when the LNG (methane) from one tank is converted to gas at STP?
d. Write the balanced equation for the combustion of methane in a gas burner, including the heat of reaction.

Patsy Michaud/Shutterstock

Methane is the fuel burned in a gas cooktop.

e. How many kilograms of oxygen are needed to react with all of the methane from one tank of LNG?
f. How much heat, in kilojoules, is released after burning all of the methane from one tank of LNG?

CI.18 Automobile exhaust is a major cause of air pollution. One pollutant is nitrogen oxide, which forms from nitrogen and oxygen gases in the air at the high temperatures in an automobile engine. Once emitted into the air, nitrogen oxide reacts with oxygen to produce nitrogen dioxide, a reddish-brown gas with a sharp, pungent odor that makes up smog. One component of gasoline is octane, C_8H_{18}, which has a density of 0.803 g/mL. In one year, a typical automobile uses 550 gal of gasoline and produces 41 lb of nitrogen oxide.

iStockphoto

Two gases found in automobile exhaust are carbon dioxide and nitrogen oxide.

a. Write balanced equations for the production of nitrogen oxide and nitrogen dioxide.
b. If all the nitrogen oxide emitted by one automobile is converted to nitrogen dioxide in the atmosphere, how many kilograms of nitrogen dioxide are produced in one year by a single automobile?
c. Write a balanced equation for the combustion of octane.
d. How many moles of C_8H_{18} are present in 15.2 gal of octane?
e. How many liters of CO_2 at STP are produced in one year from the gasoline used by the typical automobile?

CI.19 A piece of magnesium with a mass of 0.121 g is added to 50.0 mL of a 1.00 M HCl solution at a temperature of 22.0 °C. When the magnesium dissolves, the solution reaches a temperature of 33.0 °C.

$$Mg(s) + 2HCl(aq) \longrightarrow MgCl_2(aq) + H_2(g)$$

Richard Megna/Fundamental Photographs

Magnesium metal reacts rapidly with HCl.

a. What is the limiting reactant?
b. What volume, in liters, of hydrogen gas would be produced if the pressure is 750. mmHg and the temperature is 33.0 °C?
c. How many joules were released by the reaction of the magnesium? Assume the density and specific heat of the HCl solution are the same as for water.
d. What is the heat of reaction for magnesium in J/g? In kJ/mole?

CI.20 In wine making, glucose ($C_6H_{12}O_6$) from grapes undergoes fermentation in the absence of oxygen to produce ethanol and carbon dioxide. A bottle of vintage port wine has a volume of 750 mL and contains 135 mL of ethanol (C_2H_6O). Ethanol has a density of 0.789 g/mL. In 1.5 lb of grapes, there are 26 g of glucose.

Moritz v.H./iStockphoto

When the glucose in grapes is fermented, ethanol is produced.

isifa Image Service s.r.o./Alamy

Port is a type of fortified wine that is produced in Portugal.

From *General, Organic, and Biological Chemistry: Structures of Life*, Fourth Edition. Karen C. Timberlake.

a. Calculate the volume percent (v/v) of ethanol in the port wine.
b. What is the molarity (M) of ethanol in the port wine?
c. Write the balanced equation for the fermentation reaction of glucose.
d. How many grams of glucose are required to produce one bottle of port wine?
e. How many bottles of port wine can be produced from 1.0 ton of grapes? (1 ton = 2000 lb)

CI.21 Consider the following reaction at equilibrium:

$$2H_2(g) + S_2(g) \rightleftharpoons 2H_2S(g)$$

In a 10.0-L container, an equilibrium mixture contains 2.02 g of H_2, 10.3 g of S_2, and 68.2 g of H_2S.
a. What is the K_c value for this equilibrium mixture?
b. If more H_2 is added to the mixture, how will the equilibrium shift?
c. How will the equilibrium shift if the mixture is placed in a 5.00-L container with no change in temperature?
d. If a 5.00-L container has an equilibrium mixture of 0.300 mole of H_2 and 2.50 moles of H_2S, what is the $[S_2]$ if temperature is the same?

CI.22 A mixture of 25.0 g of CS_2 gas and 30.0 g of O_2 gas is placed in 10.0-L container and heated to 125 °C. The products of the reaction are carbon dioxide gas and sulfur dioxide gas.
a. Write a balanced equation for the reaction.
b. How many grams of CO_2 are produced?
c. What is the partial pressure of the remaining reactant?
d. What is the final pressure in the container?

CI.23 A metal M with a mass of 0.420 g completely reacts with 34.8 mL of a 0.520 M HCl solution to form aqueous MCl_3 and H_2 gas.

Charles D. Winters/Photo Researchers, Inc.

When a metal reacts with a strong acid, hydrogen gas forms.

a. Write a balanced equation for the reaction of the metal M(*s*) and HCl(*aq*).
b. What volume, in milliliters, of H_2 at 720. mmHg and 24 °C is produced?
c. How many moles of metal M reacted?
d. Use your results from part **c** to determine the molar mass and name of metal M.
e. Write the balanced equation for the reaction.

CI.24 In a teaspoon (5.0 mL) of a liquid antacid, there are 400. mg of $Mg(OH)_2$ and 400. mg of $Al(OH)_3$. A 0.080 M HCl solution, which is similar to stomach acid, is used to neutralize 5.0 mL of the liquid antacid.

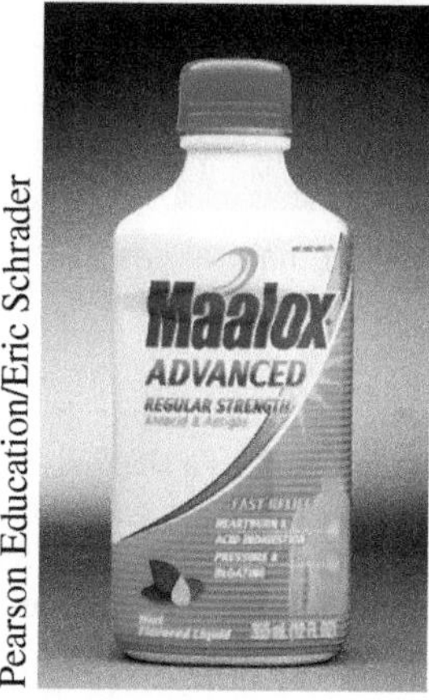

Pearson Education/Eric Schrader

An antacid neutralizes stomach acid and raises the pH.

a. Write the equation for the neutralization of HCl and $Mg(OH)_2$.
b. Write the equation for the neutralization of HCl and $Al(OH)_3$.
c. What is the pH of the HCl solution?
d. How many milliliters of the HCl solution is needed to neutralize the $Mg(OH)_2$?
e. How many milliliters of the HCl solution is needed to neutralize the $Al(OH)_3$?

ANSWERS

CI.17 **a.** $\mathrm{H{:}\overset{\textstyle H}{\underset{\textstyle H}{\ddot{\underset{\cdot\cdot}{C}}}}{:}H}$ or $\mathrm{H{-}\overset{\textstyle H}{\underset{\textstyle H}{\overset{|}{\underset{|}{C}}}}{-}H}$

b. 1.2×10^7 kg of LNG (methane)
c. 1.7×10^{10} L of methane at STP
d. $CH_4(g) + 2O_2(g) \xrightarrow{\Delta} CO_2(g) + 2H_2O(g) + 883\text{ kJ}$
e. 4.8×10^7 kg of O_2
f. 6.6×10^{11} kJ

CI.19 **a.** Mg is the limiting reactant.
b. 0.127 L of H_2
c. 2.30×10^3 J
d. 1.90×10^4 J/g; 462 kJ/mole

CI.21 **a.** $K_c = 250.$
b. If more H_2 is added, the equilibrium will shift in the direction of the products.
c. If the volume of the container decreases, the equilibrium shifts in the direction of the products.
d. $[S_2] = 0.278$ mole/L

CI.23 **a.** $2M(s) + 6HCl(aq) \longrightarrow 2MCl_3(aq) + 3H_2(g)$
b. 233 mL of H_2
c. 6.03×10^{-3} mole of M
d. 69.7 g/mole; gallium
e. $2Ga(s) + 6HCl(aq) \longrightarrow 2GaCl_3(aq) + 3H_2(g)$

Introduction to Organic Chemistry: Alkanes

LOOKING AHEAD

Visit **www.masteringchemistry.com** for self-study materials and instructor-assigned homework.

AP Photo/Roswell Daily Record, Andrew Poertner

A wildfire started near Rocky Mountain National Park from a lightning strike. Due to a lack of rain, there was considerable dry timber and grasses to provide fuel for the fire. The local firefighters decided to begin a backfire, which is deliberately set in the path of the wildfire as it consumes the dry timber and grasses, and thus, stops or confines the fire. Jack puts on his fire-resistant pants, jacket, and face protection. Jack then starts the backfire by using a drip torch containing a mixture of diesel and gasoline.

Gasoline and diesel consist of organic molecules called alkanes. Alkanes, or hydrocarbons, are chains of carbon and hydrogen atoms, and are considered to be the backbone of organic chemistry. The alkanes present in gasoline consist of a mixture of 5–10 carbon atoms in a chain, while diesel typically consists of a mixture of 11–20 carbon atoms. Because alkanes undergo combustion reactions, they can be used as a fuel source to start a backfire.

Career: Firefighter

Firefighters are first responders to fires, traffic accidents, and other emergency situations. They are required to have an emergency medical technician or paramedic certification in order to be able to treat seriously injured people. By combining the skills of a firefighter and a paramedic, they increase the survival rates of the wounded. The physical demands of firefighters are extremely high as they fight, extinguish, and prevent fires while wearing heavy protective clothing and gear. They also train for and participate in firefighting drills, and maintain fire equipment so that it is always working and ready. Firefighters must also be knowledgeable about fire codes, arson, and the handling and disposal of hazardous materials. Since firefighters also provide emergency care for sick and injured people, they need to be aware of emergency medical and rescue procedures, as well as the proper methods for controlling the spread of infectious disease.

From Chapter 11 of *General, Organic, and Biological Chemistry: Structures of Life*, Fourth Edition. Karen C. Timberlake.

Organic chemistry is the chemistry of compounds that contain carbon and hydrogen. The element carbon has a special role in chemistry because it bonds with other carbon atoms to give a vast array of molecules. The variety of molecules is so great that we find organic compounds in many common products we use, such as gasoline, medicines, shampoos, plastic bottles, and perfumes. The food we eat is composed of different organic compounds that supply us with fuel for energy and the carbon atoms needed to build and repair the cells of our bodies.

Although many organic compounds occur in nature, chemists have synthesized even more. The cotton, wool, or silk in your clothes contains naturally occurring organic compounds, whereas materials such as polyester, nylon, or plastic have been synthesized through organic reactions. Sometimes it is convenient to synthesize a molecule in the lab even though that molecule is also found in nature. For example, vitamin C synthesized in a laboratory has the same structure as the vitamin C in oranges or lemons. Learning about the structures and reactions of organic molecules will provide you with a foundation for understanding the more complex molecules of biochemistry.

Pearson Education

Foods in the diet provide energy and materials for the cells of the body.

LEARNING GOAL

Identify the characteristic properties of organic or inorganic compounds.

SELF-STUDY ACTIVITY
Introduction to Organic Molecules

1 Organic Compounds

At the beginning of the nineteenth century, scientists classified chemical compounds as inorganic and organic. An *inorganic compound* was a substance that was composed of minerals, and an *organic compound* was a substance that came from an organism, thus the origin of the word "organic." Early scientists thought that some type of "vital force," which could be found only in living cells, was required to synthesize an organic compound. This idea was shown to be incorrect in 1828 when the German chemist Friedrich Wöhler synthesized urea, a product of protein metabolism, by heating an inorganic compound, ammonium cyanate.

$$\underset{\text{Ammonium cyanate (inorganic)}}{NH_4CNO} \xrightarrow{\text{Heat}} \underset{\text{Urea (organic)}}{H_2N-\overset{\overset{\large O}{\|}}{C}-NH_2}$$

Pearson Education

Vegetable oil, an organic compound, is not soluble in water.

Organic chemistry is the study of carbon compounds. **Organic compounds** typically contain carbon (C) and hydrogen (H), and sometimes oxygen (O), sulfur (S), nitrogen (N), phosphorus (P), or a halogen (F, Cl, Br, and I). The formulas of organic compounds are written with carbon first, followed by hydrogen, and then any other elements.

Many organic compounds are nonpolar molecules with weak attractions between molecules. As a result, they typically have low melting and boiling points, are not soluble in water, and are less dense than water. For example, vegetable oil, which is a mixture of organic compounds, does not dissolve in water, but floats on top of it. A very typical reaction of organic compounds is that they burn vigorously in air.

In contrast, many of the inorganic compounds contain elements other than carbon and hydrogen. They are typically ionic with high melting and boiling points. Inorganic compounds that have ionic or polar covalent bonds are usually soluble in water and most do not burn in air. Table 1 contrasts some of the properties associated with organic compounds, such as propane (C_3H_8), and inorganic compounds, such as sodium chloride (NaCl) (see Figure 1).

TABLE 1 Some Typical Properties of Organic and Inorganic Compounds

Property	Organic	Example: C_3H_8	Inorganic	Example: NaCl
Elements	C and H, sometimes O, S, N, P, or Cl (F, Br, I)	C and H	Most metals and nonmetals	Na and Cl
Bonding	Mostly covalent	Covalent (4 bonds to each C)	Many are ionic, some covalent	Ionic
Polarity of Bonds	Nonpolar, unless a very electronegative atom is present	Nonpolar	Most are ionic or polar covalent, a few are nonpolar covalent	Ionic
Melting Point	Usually low	−188 °C	Usually high	801 °C
Boiling Point	Usually low	−42 °C	Usually high	1413 °C
Flammability	High	Burns in air	Low	Does not burn
Solubility in Water	Not soluble, unless a polar group is present	No	Most are soluble, unless nonpolar	Yes

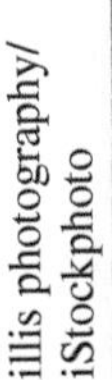

illis photography/ iStockphoto

Pearson Education
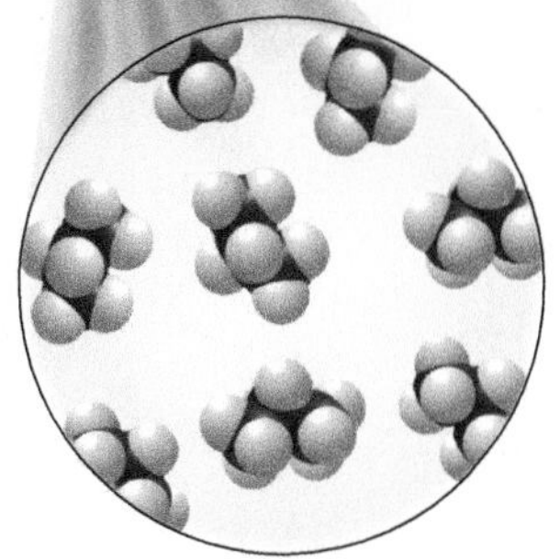

FIGURE 1 Propane, C_3H_8, is an organic compound, whereas sodium chloride, NaCl, is an inorganic compound.

Q Why is propane used as a fuel?

CONCEPT CHECK 1 **Properties of Organic Compounds**

Indicate whether the following properties are more typical of organic or inorganic compounds:

a. is not soluble in water
b. has a high melting point
c. burns in air

ANSWER

a. Many organic compounds are not soluble in water.
b. Inorganic compounds are more likely to have high melting points.
c. Organic compounds are more likely to burn in air.

Bonding in Organic Compounds

Hydrocarbons, as the name suggests, are organic compounds that consist of only carbon and hydrogen. In the simplest hydrocarbon, methane (CH_4), the carbon atom forms an octet by sharing its four valence electrons with the valence electrons of four hydrogen atoms. In the electron-dot formula, each shared pair of electrons represents a single covalent bond. In all organic molecules, every carbon atom has four bonds. A hydrocarbon is referred to as a *saturated hydrocarbon* when all of the bonds in the molecule are single bonds. We can draw an **expanded structural formula** for methane by showing the bonds between all of its atoms.

$$\cdot\dot{\underset{\cdot}{C}}\cdot + 4H\cdot \longrightarrow H:\overset{H}{\underset{H}{\ddot{\underset{\cdot\cdot}{C}}}}:H = H-\overset{H}{\underset{H}{\overset{|}{\underset{|}{C}}}}-H$$

Methane

The Tetrahedral Structure of Carbon

The VSEPR theory predicts that a molecule with four atoms bonded to a central atom has a tetrahedral shape. Thus, for methane, CH_4, the covalent bonds from the carbon atom to the four hydrogen atoms are directed to the corners of a tetrahedron with bond angles of 109°. The various ways to represent the structure of methane are illustrated in Figure 2.

In ethane, C_2H_6, each carbon atom is bonded to another carbon and three hydrogen atoms. As in methane, each carbon atom retains its tetrahedral shape. The various ways to represent ethane are seen in Figure 3.

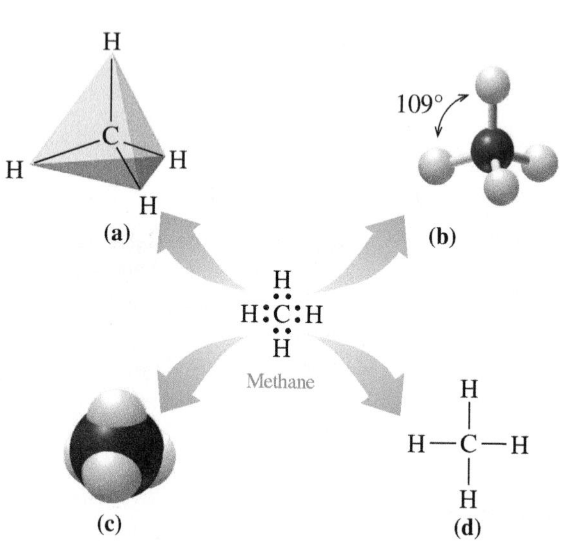

FIGURE 2 Representations of methane, CH_4: **(a)** tetrahedron, **(b)** ball-and-stick model, **(c)** space-filling model, **(d)** expanded structural formula.

Q Why does methane have a tetrahedral shape and not a flat shape?

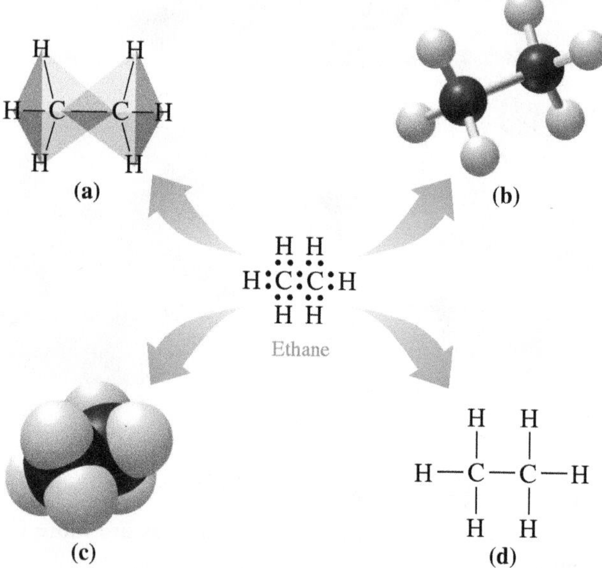

FIGURE 3 Representations of ethane, C_2H_6: **(a)** tetrahedral shape of each carbon, **(b)** ball-and-stick model, **(c)** space-filling model, **(d)** expanded structural formula.

Q How is the tetrahedral shape maintained by each carbon in a molecule with two carbon atoms?

QUESTIONS AND PROBLEMS

1 Organic Compounds

LEARNING GOAL: *Identify the characteristic properties of organic or inorganic compounds.*

1 Identify the following as formulas of organic or inorganic compounds:
a. KCl b. C_4H_{10} c. C_2H_6O
d. H_2SO_4 e. $CaCl_2$ f. C_3H_7Cl

2 Identify the following as formulas of organic or inorganic compounds:
a. $C_6H_{12}O_6$ b. K_3PO_4 c. I_2
d. C_2H_6S e. $C_{10}H_{22}$ f. CH_4

3 Identify the following properties as more typical of organic or inorganic compounds:
a. is soluble in water b. has a low boiling point
c. contains carbon and hydrogen
d. contains ionic bonds

4 Identify the following properties as more typical of organic or inorganic compounds:
a. contains Li and F b. is a gas at room temperature
c. contains covalent bonds d. is an electrolyte

5 Match the following physical and chemical properties with the compounds ethane, C_2H_6, or sodium bromide, NaBr:
a. boils at −89 °C b. burns vigorously in air
c. is a solid at 250 °C d. dissolves in water

6 Match the following physical and chemical properties with the compounds cyclohexane, C_6H_{12}, or calcium nitrate, $Ca(NO_3)_2$:
a. melts at 500 °C b. is insoluble in water
c. produces ions in water
d. is a liquid at room temperature

7 How are the hydrogen atoms of methane, CH_4, arranged in space?

8 In a propane molecule with three carbon atoms, what is the shape around each carbon atom?

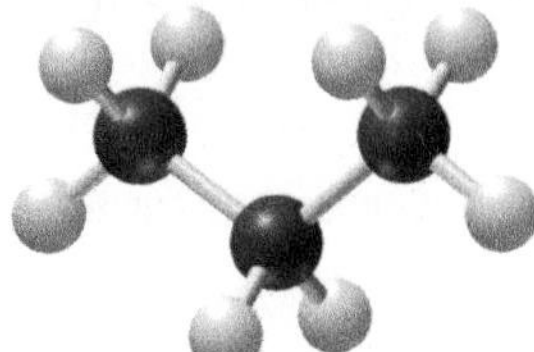

Propane

2 Alkanes

LEARNING GOAL

Write the IUPAC names and draw the condensed structural formulas for alkanes.

More than 90% of the compounds in the world are organic compounds. This large number of carbon compounds is possible because the covalent bond between carbon atoms (C—C) is very strong, allowing carbon atoms to form long, stable chains. To help us study this large group of compounds, we organize them into classes that have similar structures and chemical properties.

The **alkanes** are a class of hydrocarbons in which the atoms are connected by single bonds. One of the most common uses of alkanes is as fuels. Methane, used in gas heaters and gas cooktops, is an alkane with one carbon atom. Ethane, propane, and butane contain two, three, and four carbon atoms, respectively, connected in a row or a *continuous chain.* As we can see, all the names for alkanes end in *ane*. Such names are part of the **IUPAC** (International Union of Pure and Applied Chemistry) **system** used by chemists to name organic compounds. Alkanes with five or more carbon atoms in a chain are named using Greek prefixes: *pent* (5), *hex* (6), *hept* (7), *oct* (8), *non* (9), and *dec* (10) (see Table 2).

TUTORIAL
IUPAC Naming of Alkanes

TABLE 2 IUPAC Names for the First Ten Alkanes

Number of Carbon Atoms	Prefix	Name	Molecular Formula	Condensed Structural Formula
1	Meth	Methane	CH_4	CH_4
2	Eth	Ethane	C_2H_6	$CH_3—CH_3$
3	Prop	Propane	C_3H_8	$CH_3—CH_2—CH_3$
4	But	Butane	C_4H_{10}	$CH_3—CH_2—CH_2—CH_3$
5	Pent	Pentane	C_5H_{12}	$CH_3—CH_2—CH_2—CH_2—CH_3$
6	Hex	Hexane	C_6H_{14}	$CH_3—CH_2—CH_2—CH_2—CH_2—CH_3$
7	Hept	Heptane	C_7H_{16}	$CH_3—CH_2—CH_2—CH_2—CH_2—CH_2—CH_3$
8	Oct	Octane	C_8H_{18}	$CH_3—CH_2—CH_2—CH_2—CH_2—CH_2—CH_2—CH_3$
9	Non	Nonane	C_9H_{20}	$CH_3—CH_2—CH_2—CH_2—CH_2—CH_2—CH_2—CH_2—CH_3$
10	Dec	Decane	$C_{10}H_{22}$	$CH_3—CH_2—CH_2—CH_2—CH_2—CH_2—CH_2—CH_2—CH_2—CH_3$

Alkane Name Hexane
Molecular Formula C_6H_{14}
Ball-and-Stick Model

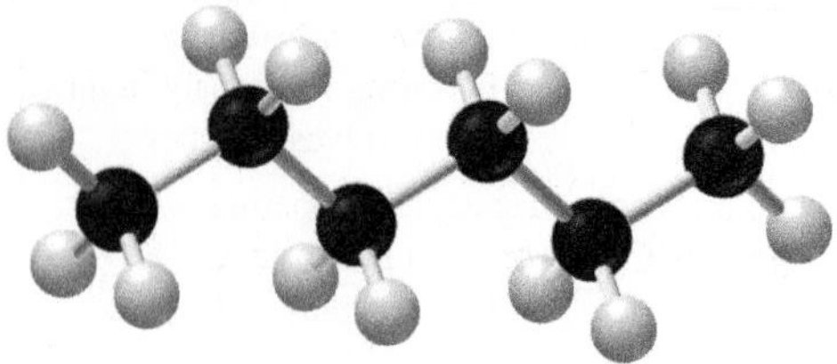

Expanded Structural Formula

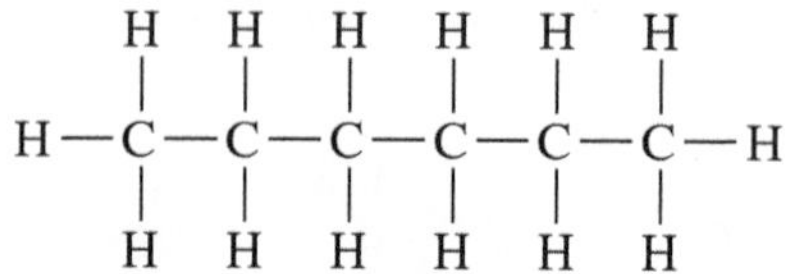

Condensed Structural Formulas

CH_3 / CH_2 \ CH_2 / CH_2 \ CH_2 / CH_3

$CH_3—CH_2—CH_2—CH_2—CH_2—CH_3$

Skeletal Formula

FIGURE 4 A hexane molecule can be represented in several ways: molecular formula, ball-and-stick model, expanded structural formula, condensed structural formula, and skeletal formula.

Q Why do the carbon atoms in hexane appear to be arranged in a zigzag chain?

CONCEPT CHECK 2 **Naming Alkanes**

Using Table 2, give the IUPAC name for each of the following:

a. $CH_3—CH_2—CH_3$
b. C_6H_{14}

ANSWER

a. A chain with three carbon atoms and eight hydrogen atoms is propane.
b. An alkane with six carbon atoms and 14 hydrogen atoms is hexane.

Condensed Structural Formulas

In a **condensed structural formula**, each carbon atom and its attached hydrogen atoms are written as a group. A subscript indicates the number of hydrogen atoms bonded to each carbon atom.

Expanded		Condensed	Expanded		Condensed
H—C(H)(H)—	=	$CH_3—$	—C(H)(H)—	=	$—CH_2—$

By contrast, the *molecular formula* gives the total number of carbon atoms and hydrogen atoms but does not indicate their arrangement in the molecule.

When an organic molecule consists of a chain of three or more carbon atoms, the carbon atoms do not lie in a straight line. The tetrahedral shape of carbon arranges the carbon bonds in a zigzag pattern. A simplified structure called the **skeletal formula** is a carbon skeleton in which carbon atoms are represented as the end of each line or as corners in a zigzag line. The hydrogen atoms are not shown, but each carbon is understood to have bonds to four atoms, including hydrogen. In the skeletal formula for hexane, each line in the zigzag drawing represents a single bond. The carbon atoms on the ends would be bonded to three hydrogen atoms. However, the other carbon atoms in the middle of the carbon chain are each bonded to two carbons, and therefore, two hydrogen atoms. Figure 4 shows the molecular formula, ball-and-stick model, expanded structural formula, condensed structural formula, and skeletal formula for hexane.

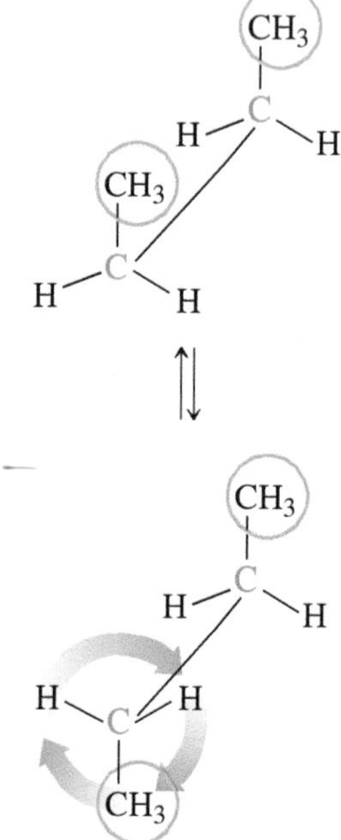

Because an alkane has only C—C single bonds, the groups attached to each C are not in fixed positions. They can rotate freely about the bond connecting the carbon atoms. This motion is analogous to the independent rotation of the wheels of a toy car. Thus, different arrangements, known as *conformations*, occur during the rotation about a single bond.

Suppose we could look at butane, C_4H_{10}, as it rotates. Sometimes, the $—CH_3$ groups line up in front of each other, and at other times, they are opposite each other. As the $—CH_3$ groups turn around the single bond, the carbon chain in the condensed structural formula appears at different angles. The conformation with the methyl groups opposite each other has lower energy (more stable) because there is less repulsion between the methyl groups.

Butane can be drawn using a variety of two-dimensional condensed structural formulas, as shown in Table 3. All of these condensed structural formulas represent the same compound with four carbon atoms.

TABLE 3 Structural Representations for Butane, C_4H_{10}

Expanded Structural Formula

```
    H   H   H   H
    |   |   |   |
H — C — C — C — C — H
    |   |   |   |
    H   H   H   H
```

Condensed Structural Formulas

$CH_3—CH_2—CH_2—CH_3$

```
CH2—CH2
|    |
CH3  CH3
```

```
CH3
|
CH2—CH2
     |
     CH3
```

```
CH3
|
CH2
|
CH2
|
CH3
```

```
CH3—CH2
     |
     CH2—CH3
```

```
CH3
|
CH2—CH2—CH3
```

```
CH3      CH2
   \    /   \
    CH2      CH3
```

Skeletal Formulas

SAMPLE PROBLEM 1 Drawing Structural Formulas for Alkanes

Draw the expanded structural formula, condensed structural formula, and skeletal formula for pentane.

SOLUTION

A molecule of pentane, C_5H_{12}, has five carbon atoms in a row. In the expanded structural formula, the five carbon atoms are connected to each other and to hydrogen atoms with single bonds to give each carbon atom a total of four bonds. In the condensed structural formula, the carbon and hydrogen atoms on the ends are written as $CH_3—$ and the carbon and hydrogen atoms in the middle are written $—CH_2—$. The skeletal formula shows the carbon skeleton as a zigzag line where the ends and corners represent C atoms.

```
    H   H   H   H   H
    |   |   |   |   |
H — C — C — C — C — C — H
    |   |   |   |   |
    H   H   H   H   H
```

Expanded structural formula

$CH_3—CH_2—CH_2—CH_2—CH_3$

Condensed structural formula

Skeletal formula

STUDY CHECK 1

Draw the condensed structural formula and give the name for the following skeletal formula:

Cycloalkanes

Hydrocarbons can also form cyclic structures called **cycloalkanes**, which have two fewer hydrogen atoms than the corresponding alkanes. The simplest cycloalkane, cyclopropane, C_3H_6, has a ring of three carbon atoms bonded to six hydrogen atoms. Most often, a cycloalkane is drawn using its skeletal formula, which appears as a simple geometric figure. As seen for alkanes, each corner of the skeletal formula for a cycloalkane represents a carbon atom. A cycloalkane is named by adding the prefix *cyclo* to the name of the alkane with the same number of carbon atoms.

The ball-and-stick models, condensed structural formulas, and skeletal formulas for several cycloalkanes are shown in Table 4.

TABLE 4 Formulas of Some Common Cycloalkanes

Name			
Cyclopropane	Cyclobutane	Cyclopentane	Cyclohexane
Ball-and-Stick Model			
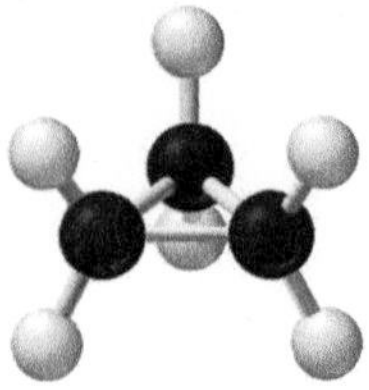	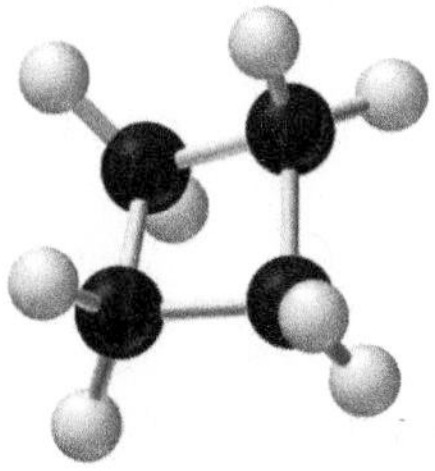	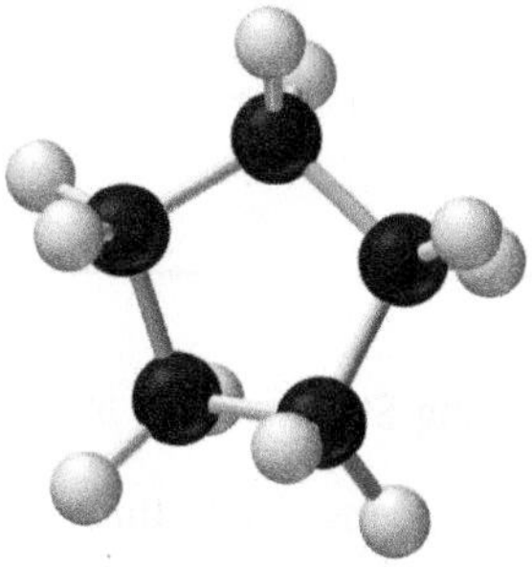	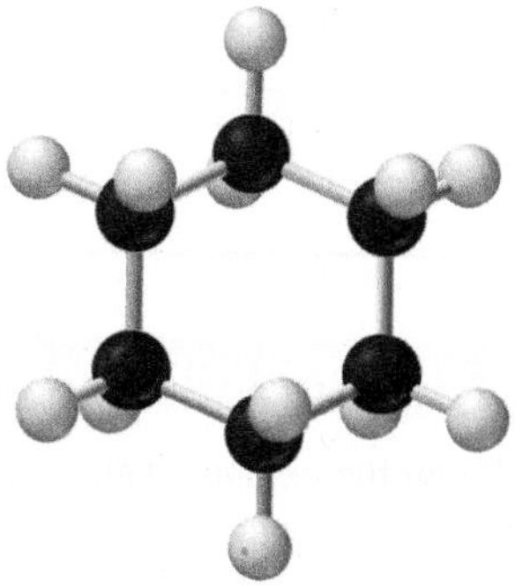
Condensed Structural Formula			
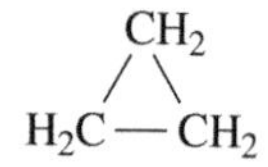 CH_2 / $H_2C—CH_2$ (three-membered ring)	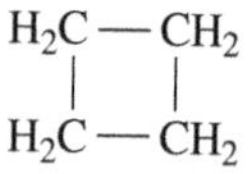 $H_2C—CH_2$ / $H_2C—CH_2$ (four-membered ring)	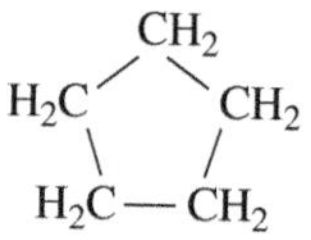 CH_2 / H_2C CH_2 / $H_2C—CH_2$ (five-membered ring)	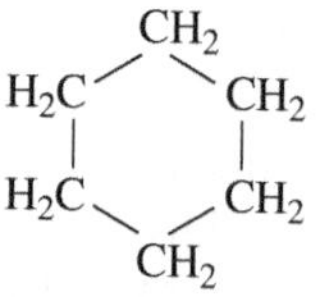 CH_2 / H_2C CH_2 / H_2C CH_2 / CH_2 (six-membered ring)
Skeletal Formula			
 △	□	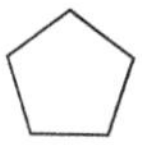 ⬠	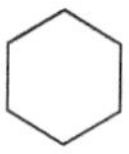 ⬡

CONCEPT CHECK 3 **Identifying Cycloalkanes**

Name the cycloalkanes represented in the skeletal formula for cholesterol, an important steroid precursor in the body.

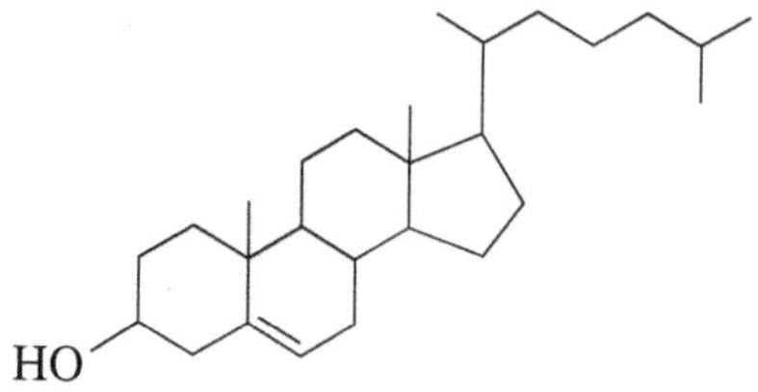

HO

Cholesterol

ANSWER

Cholesterol contains the cycloalkanes cyclopentane and cyclohexane.

SAMPLE PROBLEM 2 **Naming Alkanes**

Give the IUPAC name for each of the following:

a. $CH_3—CH_2—CH_2—CH_2—CH_3$ **b.** (cyclohexane ring) **c.** (zigzag chain)

SOLUTION

a. A chain with five carbon atoms is pentane.
b. The ring of six carbon atoms is named cyclohexane.
c. This alkane is named octane because it has eight carbon atoms.

STUDY CHECK 2

What is the IUPAC name of the following compound?

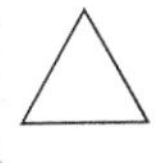

QUESTIONS AND PROBLEMS

2 Alkanes

LEARNING GOAL: *Write the IUPAC names and draw the condensed structural formulas for alkanes.*

9 Draw the stated type of structural formula for each of the following:
a. an expanded structural formula for propane
b. the condensed structural formula for hexane
c. the skeletal formula for pentane

10 Draw the stated type of structural formula for each of the following:
a. an expanded structural formula for butane
b. the condensed structural formula for octane
c. the skeletal formula for decane

11 Give the IUPAC name for each of the following:

CH_3
a. $CH_2—CH_2—CH_2$
CH_3

b. (zigzag chain)

$CH_2—CH_3$
CH_2
c. $CH_3—CH_2—CH_2$

d. (cyclobutane square)

12 Give the IUPAC name for each of the following:
a. CH_4 **b.** (zigzag chain)

CH_3
c. CH_2
CH_3

d. (cyclohexane ring)

13 Draw the condensed structural formula for alkanes or the skeletal formula for cycloalkanes for each of the following:
a. methane
b. ethane
c. pentane
d. cyclopropane

14 Draw the condensed structural formula for alkanes or the skeletal formula for cycloalkanes for each of the following:
a. propane
b. hexane
c. heptane
d. cyclopentane

3 Alkanes with Substituents

LEARNING GOAL

Write the IUPAC names and draw the condensed structural formulas and skeletal formulas for alkanes.

When an alkane has four or more carbon atoms, the atoms can be arranged so that a side group called a **branch** or **substituent** is attached to a carbon chain. For example, there are two different ball-and-stick models for the molecular formula C_4H_{10}. One model is shown as a chain of four carbon atoms. In the other model, a carbon atom is attached as a branch or substituent to a carbon in a chain of three atoms (see Figure 5). An alkane with at least one branch is called a **branched alkane**. When two compounds have the same molecular formula but differ in the order in which the atoms are bonded, they are called **structural isomers**.

In another example, we can draw three different structural isomers that have the molecular formula C_5H_{12}. One is the continuous or *straight* chain of five carbon atoms. The second one has a methyl group attached to a four-carbon chain. The third one has two

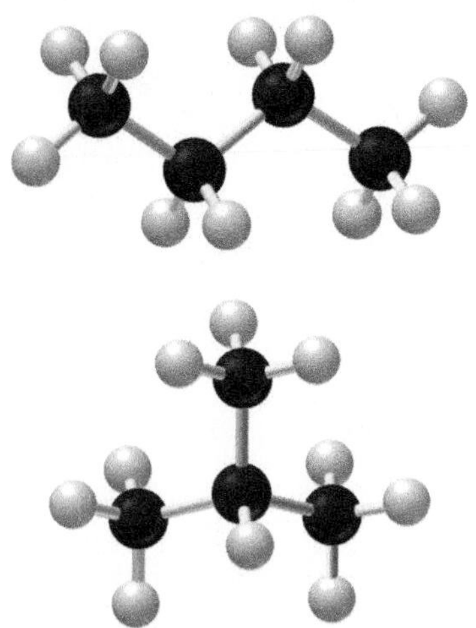

FIGURE 5 The structural isomers of C_4H_{10} have the same number and type of atoms but with a different order of bonding.

Q What makes these molecules structural isomers?

methyl groups attached to a three-carbon chain. Thus, three compounds with the same molecular formula can have the same atoms arranged in different bonding patterns.

Structural Isomers of C_5H_{12}

Alkane	Branched Alkanes	
$CH_3—CH_2—CH_2—CH_2—CH_3$	$CH_3—CH(CH_3)—CH_2—CH_3$	$CH_3—C(CH_3)_2—CH_3$

The number of structural isomers of alkanes increases rapidly as the number of carbon atoms increases.

Number of Possible Structural Isomers for Alkanes with 1–10 Carbon Atoms

Number of Carbon Atoms	Numbers of Structural Isomers
1	1
2	1
3	1
4	2
5	3
6	5
7	9
8	18
9	35
10	75

CONCEPT CHECK 4 **Identifying Structural Isomers**

Identify each pair of condensed structural formulas as structural isomers or the same molecule.

a. CH_3 CH_3 (each bonded up from) $CH_2—CH_2$ and $CH_2—CH_2—CH_3$ (with CH_3 bonded down from the first CH_2)

b. $CH_3—CH(CH_3)—CH_2—CH_2—CH_3$ and $CH_3—CH(CH_3)—CH(CH_3)—CH_3$

ANSWER

a. When we add up the number of C atoms and H atoms, they give the same molecular formula, C_4H_{10}. We can then determine if they are structural isomers or the same molecule by looking at how the atoms are bonded to each other. The structural formula on the left consists of a chain of four C atoms. Even though the $CH_3—$ ends are drawn pointing up, they are not branches on the chain but part of the four-carbon chain. The structural formula on the right also consists of a four-carbon chain even though one $—CH_3$ end is drawn pointing down. Thus, both condensed structural formulas consist of four-carbon chains with no substituents, which means they represent the same molecule and are not structural isomers.

b. When we add up the number of C atoms and H atoms, they give the same molecular formula, C_6H_{14}. We can then determine if they are structural isomers or the same molecule by looking at how the atoms are bonded to each other. The structural formula on the left consists of a five-carbon chain with a $CH_3—$ branch on the second carbon of the chain. The structural formula on the right consists of a four-carbon chain with two $CH_3—$ branches, one bonded to the second carbon and one bonded to the third carbon. The lengths of the longest carbon chains are different between the two molecules. This means that there is a different order of bonding of atoms in these two structural formulas. Thus, they represent a pair of structural isomers.

MC™

SELF-STUDY ACTIVITY
Isomers: Diversity in Molecules

TUTORIAL
Isomers

TUTORIAL
Naming Alkanes with Substituents

In the IUPAC names for alkanes, a carbon branch is named as an **alkyl group**, which is an alkane that is missing one hydrogen atom. The alkyl group is named by replacing the *ane* ending of the corresponding alkane name with *yl*. Alkyl groups cannot exist on their own; they must be attached to a carbon chain. When a halogen atom is attached to a carbon chain, it is named as a *halo* group: fluoro (F), chloro (Cl), bromo (Br), or iodo (I). Some of the common groups attached to carbon chains are illustrated in Table 5.

TABLE 5 Names and Formulas of Some Common Substituents

Substituent	Name
$CH_3—$	Methyl
$CH_3—CH_2—$	Ethyl
$CH_3—CH_2—CH_2—$	Propyl
$CH_3—\overset{\vert}{C}H—CH_3$	Isopropyl
$F—, Cl—, Br—, I—$	Fluoro, chloro, bromo, iodo

Rules for Naming Alkanes with Substituents

In the IUPAC system of naming, a carbon chain is numbered to give the location of one or more substituents. Let's take a look at how we use the IUPAC system to name the alkane shown in Sample Problem 3.

SAMPLE PROBLEM 3 **Naming a Branched Alkane**

Give the IUPAC name for the following alkane:

$$CH_3—\underset{}{\overset{\overset{\large CH_3}{\vert}}{C}H}—CH_2—CH_2—CH_3$$

SOLUTION

Step 1 **Write the alkane name of the longest chain of carbon atoms.** In this alkane, the longest chain has five carbon atoms, which is *pentane*.

$$CH_3—\overset{\overset{\large CH_3}{\vert}}{C}H—CH_2—CH_2—CH_3 \quad \text{pentane}$$

Step 2 **Number the carbon atoms starting from the end nearer a substituent.** Number the chain from 1 to 5 starting at the end nearer the branch of $CH_3—$. Once you start numbering, continue in that same direction.

$$\underset{1}{CH_3}—\underset{2}{\overset{\overset{\large CH_3}{\vert}}{C}H}—\underset{3}{CH_2}—\underset{4}{CH_2}—\underset{5}{CH_3} \quad \text{pentane}$$

Step 3 **Give the location and name of each substituent (alphabetical order) as a prefix to the name of the main chain.** Place a hyphen between the number and the substituent name.

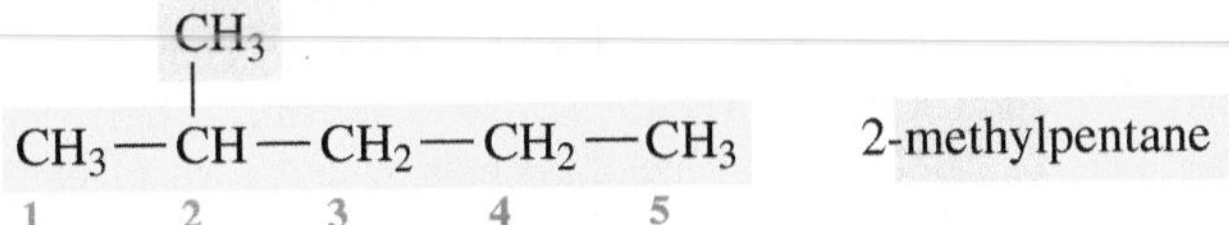

$$\underset{1}{CH_3}—\underset{2}{\overset{\overset{\large CH_3}{\vert}}{C}H}—\underset{3}{CH_2}—\underset{4}{CH_2}—\underset{5}{CH_3} \quad \text{2-methylpentane}$$

Guide to Naming Alkanes

1. Write the alkane name of the longest chain of carbon atoms.
2. Number the carbon atoms starting from the end nearer a substituent.
3. Give the location and name of each substituent (alphabetical order) as a prefix to the name of the main chain.

STUDY CHECK 3

Give the IUPAC name for this structural isomer of the alkane in Sample Problem 3.

$$CH_3-CH_2-\underset{}{\overset{\displaystyle CH_3}{\overset{|}{C}H}}-CH_2-CH_3$$

Haloalkanes

In a **haloalkane**, halogen atoms replace hydrogen atoms in an alkane. The halogen substituents are numbered and arranged alphabetically, just as we did with the alkyl groups. Many times, chemists use the common, traditional name for these compounds rather than the systematic IUPAC name. Simple haloalkanes are commonly named as *alkyl halides*; the carbon group is named as an alkyl group followed by the halide name. For the IUPAC name, no number is necessary for a compound with one or two carbon atoms and one substituent.

CH_3-Br	bromomethane
CH_3-CH_2-Cl	chloroethane

	CH_3-Cl	CH_3-CH_2-Br	$CH_3-\overset{\displaystyle F}{\overset{|}{C}H}-CH_3$
IUPAC Name	chloromethane	bromoethane	2-fluoropropane
Common Name	methyl chloride	ethyl bromide	isopropyl fluoride

CONCEPT CHECK 5 **Naming Haloalkanes**

Ethylene dibromide is the common name of a haloalkane used as a fumigant to treat wood for termites. It is toxic and is a carcinogen. What is its IUPAC name?

$$H-\underset{\displaystyle H}{\underset{|}{\overset{\displaystyle Br}{\overset{|}{C}}}}-\underset{\displaystyle H}{\underset{|}{\overset{\displaystyle Br}{\overset{|}{C}}}}-H$$

Ethylene dibromide

ANSWER

The carbon chain consists of two carbons, which is ethane. There are two bromine atoms attached, one to carbon 1 and the other to carbon 2. Using the prefix *di* to indicate there are two Br atoms, we write the IUPAC name for this compound as 1,2,-dibromoethane.

TUTORIAL
Drawing Haloalkanes and Branched Alkanes

Chemistry Link to Health

COMMON USES OF HALOALKANES

Some common uses of haloalkanes include solvents and anesthetics. For many years, carbon tetrachloride, CCl_4, was widely used in dry cleaners and in home spot removers to take oils and grease out of clothes. However, its use was discontinued when carbon tetrachloride was found to be toxic to the liver, where it can cause cancer. Today, dry cleaners use other halogenated compounds such as dichloromethane; 1,1,1-trichloroethane; and 1,1,2-trichloro-1,2,2-trifluoroethane.

CH_2Cl_2	Cl_3C-CH_3	$FCl_2C-CClF_2$
Dichloromethane	1,1,1-Trichloroethane	1,1,2-Trichloro-1,2,2-trifluoroethane

General anesthetics are compounds that are inhaled or injected to cause a loss of sensation and consciousness so that surgery or other procedures can be done without causing pain to the patient. As nonpolar compounds, anesthetics are soluble in the nonpolar nerve membranes, where they decrease the ability of the nerve cells to conduct the sensation of pain. Trichloromethane, commonly called chloroform, $CHCl_3$, was once used as an anesthetic, but it is toxic and may be carcinogenic. One of the most widely used general anesthetics is halothane (2-bromo-2-chloro-1,1,1-trifluoroethane), also called Fluothane. It has a pleasant odor, is nonexplosive, has few side effects, undergoes few reactions, and is eliminated quickly from the body.

```
      F    Cl
      |    |
F  —  C  — C  — Br     Halothane (Fluothane)
      |    |
      F    H
```

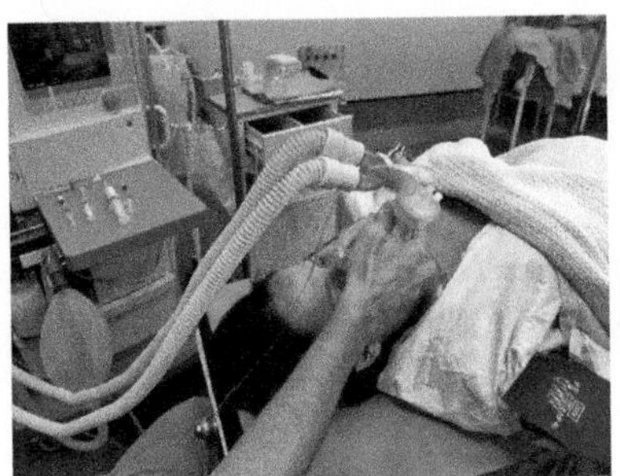

Stoffies/iStockphoto

Anesthetics, such as halothane, decrease the sensation of pain.

For minor surgeries, a local anesthetic such as chloroethane (ethyl chloride), $CH_3—CH_2—Cl$, is applied to an area of the skin. Chloroethane evaporates quickly, which cools the skin and causes a loss of sensation.

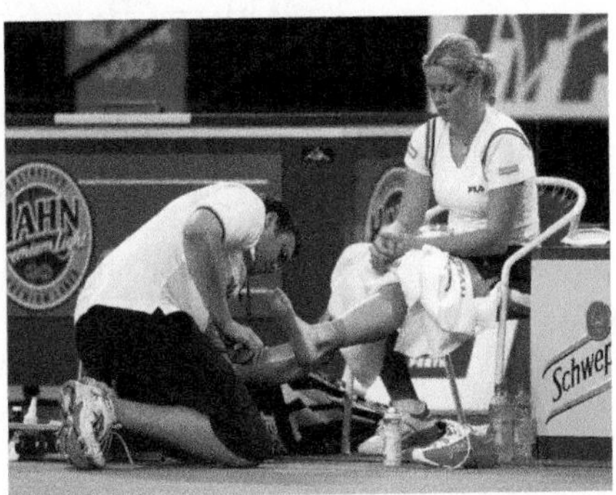

AP Photo/Marc Dahners

A local anesthetic evaporates quickly to reduce the sensation of pain.

SAMPLE PROBLEM 4 Writing IUPAC Names

Give the IUPAC name for the following:

```
CH3                    Br
 |                     |
CH3—CH—CH2—CH2—C—CH3
                       |
                      CH3
```

SOLUTION

Step 1 **Write the alkane name of the longest chain of carbon atoms.** In this alkane, the longest chain has six carbon atoms, which is *hexane*.

```
     CH3                  Br
      |                   |
CH3—CH—CH2—CH2—C—CH3          hexane
                          |
                         CH3
```

Step 2 **Number the carbon atoms starting from the end nearer a substituent.** When there are two or more substituents, the main chain is numbered in the direction that gives the lower set of numbers. Carbon 1 on the chain will be the carbon closer to the two substituents, the Br atom and the methyl group ($CH_3—$).

```
     CH3                  Br
      |                   |
CH3—CH—CH2—CH2—C—CH3          hexane
                          |
                         CH3
 6    5    4     3        2    1
```

Step 3 **Give the location and name of each substituent (alphabetical order) as a prefix to the name of the main chain.** The substituents, which are bromo and methyl groups, are listed in alphabetical order (bromo first, then methyl). A hyphen is placed between the number on the carbon chain and the substituent name. When there are two or more of the same substituent, a prefix (*di, tri, tetra*) is used in front of the name. Then commas are used to separate the numbers that designate the locations of the same substituent.

```
     CH3                  Br
      |                   |
CH3—CH—CH2—CH2—C—CH3          2-bromo-2,5-dimethylhexane
                          |
                         CH3
 6    5    4     3        2    1
```

STUDY CHECK 4

Give the IUPAC name for the following compound:

```
              CH3         CH3
              |           |
CH3—CH2—CH—CH2—CH—CH2—Cl
```

TUTORIAL
Naming Cycloalkanes

Naming Cycloalkanes with Substituents

When one substituent is attached to a carbon atom in a ring, the name of the substituent is placed in front of the cycloalkane name. No number is needed when a single alkyl group or halogen atom is attached to the cycloalkane. However, if two or more substituents are attached, the ring is numbered by assigning carbon 1 to the substituent that comes first alphabetically. Then we count the carbon atoms in the ring in the direction (clockwise or counterclockwise) that gives the lower numbers to the substituents.

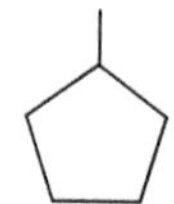
Methylcyclopentane

1,3-Dimethylcyclopentane

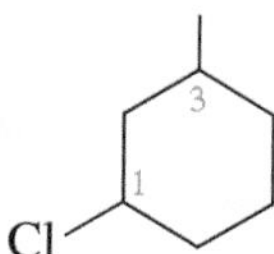

1-Chloro-3-methylcyclohexane

Career Focus

GS International/Greenshoots Communications/Alamy

GEOLOGIST

A geologist is interested in how the Earth was formed and its resources and uses chemistry to determine oil and reservoir formation. Other geologists map the surface of the Earth, study fossils and the age of rocks, and study the environmental impact of buildings and roads.

Drawing Structural Formulas for Alkanes

The IUPAC name gives all the information needed to draw the condensed structural formula for an alkane. Suppose you are asked to draw the condensed structural formula for 2,3-dimethylbutane. The alkane name gives the number of carbon atoms in the longest chain. The names in the beginning indicate the substituents and where they are attached. We can break down the name in the following way:

2,3-Dimethylbutane

2,3-	di	methyl	but	ane
Substituents on carbons 2 and 3	Two identical groups	CH_3— alkyl groups	4 carbon atoms in the main chain	C—C single bonds

Guide to Drawing Alkane Formulas

1. Draw the main chain of carbon atoms.
2. Number the chain and place the substituents on the carbons indicated by the numbers.
3. Add the correct number of hydrogen atoms to give four bonds to each C atom.

SAMPLE PROBLEM 5 **Drawing Condensed Structural and Skeletal Formulas from IUPAC Names**

Draw the condensed structural formula and skeletal formula for 2,3-dimethylbutane.

SOLUTION

Step 1 **Draw the main chain of carbon atoms.** For butane, we draw a chain of four carbon atoms. For the skeletal formula, show bond lines.

```
C—C—C—C
```

Step 2 **Number the chain and place the substituents on the carbons indicated by the numbers.** The first part of the name indicates two methyl groups (CH_3—), one on carbon 2 and one on carbon 3.

```
   Methyl Methyl
    CH3  CH3
     |    |
C—C—C—C
1   2   3   4
```

1 2 3 4

Step 3 **Add the correct number of hydrogen atoms to give fur bonds to each C atom.**

$$\begin{array}{ccccccc} & & CH_3 & & CH_3 & & \\ & & | & & | & & \\ CH_3 & — & CH & — & CH & — & CH_3 \end{array}$$

2,3-Dimethylbutane

STUDY CHECK 5

Draw the condensed structural formula and skeletal formula for 2-bromo-4-methylpentane.

Chemistry Link to the Environment

CFCS AND OZONE DEPLETION

The compounds called *chlorofluorocarbons* (CFCs) were used as propellants for hairsprays, underarm deodorants, and paints, and as refrigerants in home and car air conditioners. Two widely used CFCs, Freon 11 (CCl_3F) and Freon 12 (CCl_2F_2), were developed during the 1920s as nontoxic refrigerants, which were safer than the sulfur dioxide and ammonia used at the time.

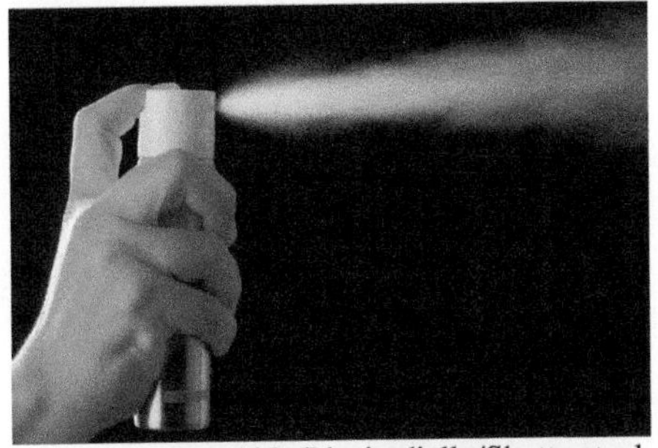

Aida Ricciardiello/Shutterstock

Freon was used as a propellant for sprays.

Pearson Education/Eric Schrader

Freon is added to the air conditioner unit in a car by a licensed automotive technician.

$$\begin{array}{ccc} & Cl & \\ & | & \\ Cl — & C & — F \\ & | & \\ & Cl & \end{array} \qquad \begin{array}{ccc} & Cl & \\ & | & \\ F — & C & — F \\ & | & \\ & Cl & \end{array}$$

Freon 11 Freon 12

In the stratosphere, a layer of ozone (O_3) absorbs the ultraviolet (UV) radiation of the Sun and acts as a protective shield for plants and animals on Earth. Ozone is produced in the stratosphere when oxygen reacts with ultraviolet light and breaks into oxygen atoms that quickly combine with oxygen molecules to form ozone.

$$O_2 \xrightarrow{\text{UV light}} O + O$$
$$O_2 + O \longrightarrow O_3$$

During the 1970s, scientists became concerned that CFCs entering the atmosphere were accelerating the depletion of ozone and threatening the stability of the ozone layer. CFCs decompose in the upper atmosphere in the presence of UV light to produce highly reactive chlorine atoms.

$$CCl_3F \xrightarrow{\text{UV light}} CCl_2F + Cl$$

The reactive chlorine atoms catalyze the breakdown of ozone molecules.

$$Cl + O_3 \longrightarrow ClO + O_2$$
$$ClO + O_3 \longrightarrow Cl + 2O_2$$

It has been estimated that one chlorine atom, also called a *radical*, can destroy as many as 100 000 ozone molecules. Normally, there is a balance between the ozone and oxygen in the atmosphere, but the rapid destruction of ozone has upset that equilibrium. Reports of polar ozone depletion over Antarctica in March 1985 prompted scientists to call for a freeze on the production of CFCs. In some areas, as much as 50% of the ozone had been depleted, causing an ozone hole to appear at certain times of the year. There is evidence of thinning in the ozone layer over the Arctic as well, but to a somewhat lesser degree due to warmer temperatures. It is interesting that in the lower atmosphere, ozone is an automobile and industrial pollutant, but in the stratosphere, ozone is a life-protecting compound.

Today, the use of CFCs as a propellant has been phased out. However, it is still used in closed systems such as home and car air conditioning units. Then it is necessary that the CFCs are handled by a licensed technician. It is expected that ozone levels will remain low for several decades due to the stability of the current level of CFCs. Chemical companies are developing substitutes for CFCs that are not as damaging to the ozone layer. Replacement compounds such as hydrochlorofluorocarbons (HCFCs) contain chlorine atoms, but these compounds break down in the lower atmosphere, reducing the amount of chlorine that reaches the stratosphere. Hydrofluorocarbons

(HFCs), which contain no chlorine, are being considered as another replacement for CFCs. However, the potential effects of fluorine compounds on ozone destruction must still be determined.

The level of ozone, which protects life on Earth, is lowest over Antarctica. The seasonal decrease in the ozone layer above Antarctica allows increased amounts of UV light to reach Earth's surface. The size of the ozone hole or depleted ozone region was greatest in December 2000, but has retreated (closed up) in more recent years.

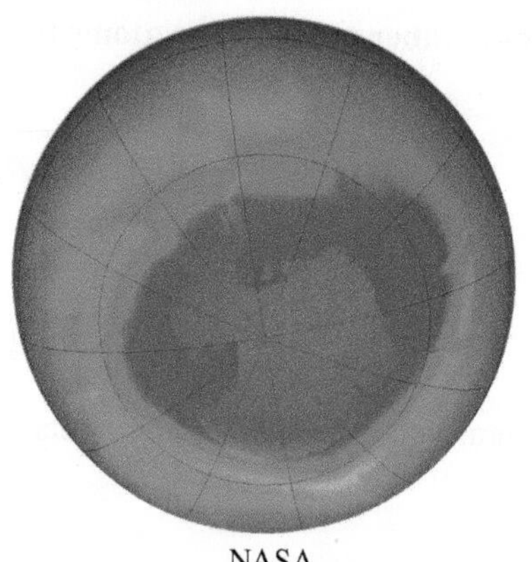

NASA

In the satellite image, the lowest levels of ozone, in blue, are over Antarctica.

QUESTIONS AND PROBLEMS

3 Alkanes with Substituents

LEARNING GOAL: *Write the IUPAC names and draw the condensed structural formulas and skeletal formulas for alkanes.*

15 Indicate whether each of the following pairs of condensed structural formulas represent structural isomers or the same molecule:

a. $\begin{array}{ccccc} & & CH_3 & & \\ & & | & & \\ CH_3 & - & CH & - & CH_3 \end{array}$ and $\begin{array}{ccc} CH_3 & & \\ | & & \\ CH & - & CH_3 \\ | & & \\ CH_3 & & \end{array}$

b. $\begin{array}{ccccccc} & & CH_3 & & & & \\ & & | & & & & \\ CH_3 & - & CH & - & CH_2 & - & CH_3 \end{array}$ and $\begin{array}{ccccc} CH_3 & & & & CH_3 \\ | & & & & | \\ CH_2 & - & CH_2 & - & CH_2 \end{array}$

c. $\begin{array}{ccccccc} CH_3 & & CH_3 & & & & \\ | & & | & & & & \\ CH_2 & - & CH & - & CH_2 & - & CH_3 \end{array}$ and $\begin{array}{ccccccc} & & CH_3 & & CH_3 & & \\ & & | & & | & & \\ CH_3 & - & CH & - & CH & - & CH_3 \end{array}$

16 Indicate whether each of the following pairs of condensed structural formulas represent structural isomers or the same molecule:

a. $\begin{array}{ccccc} & & CH_3 & & \\ & & | & & \\ CH_3 & - & C & - & CH_3 \\ & & | & & \\ & & CH_3 & & \end{array}$ and $\begin{array}{ccccc} CH_3 & & & & \\ | & & & & \\ CH & - & CH_2 & - & CH_3 \\ | & & & & \\ CH_3 & & & & \end{array}$

b. $\begin{array}{ccccccc} & & CH_3 & & CH_3 & & CH_3 \\ & & | & & | & & | \\ CH_3 & - & CH & - & CH & - & CH_2 \end{array}$ and $\begin{array}{ccccccccc} & & CH_3 & & & & CH_3 & & \\ & & | & & & & | & & \\ CH_3 & - & CH & - & CH_2 & - & CH & - & CH_3 \end{array}$

c. $\begin{array}{ccccccc} & & CH_3 & & & & \\ & & | & & & & \\ CH_3 & - & CH & - & CH_2 & - & CH_3 \end{array}$ and $\begin{array}{ccccccc} & & & & CH_3 & & \\ & & & & | & & \\ CH_3 & - & CH_2 & - & CH & - & CH_3 \end{array}$

17 Give the IUPAC name for each of the following:

a. $CH_3-CH_2-CH_2-F$

b.

c. $\begin{array}{ccccccccccc} & & CH_3 & & & & CH_2-CH_3 & & & & \\ & & | & & & & | & & & & \\ CH_3 & - & C & - & CH_2 & - & CH & - & CH_2 & - & CH_3 \\ & & | & & & & & & & & \\ & & CH_3 & & & & & & & & \end{array}$

d. Cl

e. $\begin{array}{ccccc} & & CH_3 & & \\ & & | & & \\ CH_3 & - & CH & - & Cl \end{array}$

f.

18 Give the IUPAC name for each of the following:

a.

b. $\begin{array}{ccccccccccc} & & & & CH_3 & & & & CH_3 & & \\ & & & & | & & & & | & & \\ CH_3 & - & CH_2 & - & CH & - & CH_2 & - & CH & - & CH_3 \end{array}$

c. $\begin{array}{ccccccccccc} & & & & & & CH_2-CH_3 & & & & \\ & & & & & & | & & & & \\ CH_3 & - & CH_2 & - & CH & - & CH & - & CH_2 & - & CH_3 \\ & & & & | & & & & & & \\ & & & & CH_2-CH_3 & & & & & & \end{array}$

d. $\begin{array}{ccccccc} & & & & Cl & & \\ & & & & | & & \\ CH_3 & - & CH_2 & - & CH & - & CH_3 \end{array}$

e. Cl

f.

19 Draw the condensed structural formula for each of the following:
a. 1-bromo-3-chloropropane
b. 3,3-dimethylpentane
c. 2,3,5-trimethylhexane
d. 3-ethyl-2,5-dimethyloctane
e. 1,2-dibromoethane

20 Draw the condensed structural formula for each of the following:
a. 3-ethylpentane
b. 2,2,3,5-tetramethylhexane
c. 4-ethyl-2,2-dimethyloctane
d. 1,1,2,2-tetrabromopropane
e. 2,3-dichloro-2-methylbutane

21 Draw the skeletal formula for each of the following:
a. methylcyclopropane
b. 2-chloro-2-methylhexane
c. 2,3-dimethylheptane
d. 1-bromo-2,3-dimethylcyclopentane
e. 3-chloro-2-methylpentane

22 Draw the skeletal formula for each of the following:
a. 1,5-dibromo-3-methylheptane
b. ethylcyclohexane
c. 1,2-dichlorocyclobutane
d. 1,1,5-trichloropentane
e. 2,2,3-trimethylheptane

4 Properties of Alkanes

LEARNING GOAL

Identify the properties of alkanes, and write chemical equations for combustion.

Many types of alkanes are the components of fuels that power our cars and oil that heats our homes. You may have used a mixture of hydrocarbons such as mineral oil as a laxative, or petrolatum (Vaseline) to soften your skin. The differences in uses of many of the alkanes result from their physical properties, including solubility, density, and boiling point.

Some Uses of Alkanes

CASE STUDY
Hazardous Materials

The first four alkanes with 1 to 4 carbon atoms—methane, ethane, propane, and butane—are gases at room temperature and are widely used as heating fuels.

Alkanes having 5 to 8 carbon atoms (pentane, hexane, heptane, and octane) are liquids at room temperature. They are highly volatile, which makes them useful in fuels such as gasoline.

Liquid alkanes with 9 to 17 carbon atoms have higher boiling points and are found in kerosene, diesel, and jet fuels. Motor oil is a mixture of high-molecular-weight liquid hydrocarbons and is used to lubricate the internal components of engines. Mineral oil is a mixture of liquid hydrocarbons and is used as a laxative and a lubricant. Alkanes with 18 or more carbon atoms are waxy solids at room temperature. Larger alkanes, known as paraffins, are waxy solids used to coat fruits and vegetables to retain moisture, inhibit mold growth, and enhance appearance (see Figure 6). Petrolatum, or Vaseline, is a semisolid mixture of hydrocarbons with more than 25 carbon atoms used in ointments and cosmetics and as a lubricant and a solvent.

Pearson Education

FIGURE 6 The solid alkanes that make up waxy coatings on fruits and vegetables help retain moisture, inhibit mold, and enhance appearance.

Q Why does the waxy coating help the fruits and vegetables retain moisture?

Solubility and Density

Alkanes are nonpolar, which makes them insoluble in water. However, they are soluble in nonpolar solvents such as other alkanes. Alkanes have densities from 0.62 g/mL to about 0.79 g/mL, which is less than the density of water (1.0 g/mL).

If there is an oil spill in the ocean, the alkanes in the oil, which do not mix with water, form a thin layer on the surface that spreads over a large area. In April 2010, an explosion on an oil-drilling rig in the Gulf of Mexico caused the largest oil spill in United States history. An estimated 10 million liters of oil was leaked every day, from April until July. Other major oil spills occurred in Queensland, Australia (2009), the coast of Wales (1996), the Shetland Islands (1993), and Alaska, from the *Exxon Valdez*, in 1989 (see Figure 7). If the crude oil reaches land, there can be considerable damage to beaches, shellfish, fish, birds, and wildlife habitats. When animals such as birds are covered with oil, they must be cleaned quickly because ingestion of the hydrocarbons when they try to clean themselves is fatal.

Cleanup of oil spills includes mechanical, chemical, and microbiological methods. A boom may be placed around the leaking oil to contain it until it can be removed. Boats

Frontpage/Shutterstock

FIGURE 7 In oil spills, large quantities of oil spread over the surface of the water.

Q What physical properties cause oil to remain on the surface of water?

called skimmers then scoop up the oil and place it in tanks. A chemical method involves a substance that attracts oil, which is then scraped into recovery tanks. Certain bacteria that ingest oil are used to break oil down into less harmful products.

Melting and Boiling Points

Alkanes have the lowest melting and boiling points of all the organic compounds. This occurs because alkanes contain only the nonpolar bonds of C—C and C—H. Therefore, the attractions that occur between alkane molecules in the solid and liquid states are due to relatively weak dispersion forces. As the number of carbon atoms increases, there is also an increase in the number of electrons, which increases the attraction due to dispersion forces. Thus, alkanes with higher masses have higher melting and boiling points.

CH_4 — Methane — bp = −164 °C

$CH_3—CH_3$ — Ethane — bp = −89 °C

$CH_3—CH_2—CH_3$ — Propane — bp = −42 °C

$CH_3—CH_2—CH_2—CH_3$ — Butane — bp = 0.5 °C

$CH_3—CH_2—CH_2—CH_2—CH_3$ — Pentane — bp = 36 °C

Increase in Number of Carbon Atoms
Increase in Boiling Point

The boiling points of branched alkanes are generally lower than the straight-chain isomers. The branched-chain alkanes tend to be more compact, which reduces the points of contact between the molecules. In an analogy, we can think of the carbon chains of straight-chain alkanes as pieces of licorice in a package. Because they have linear shapes, they can line up very close to each other, which gives many points of contact between the surface of the molecules. In our analogy, we can also think of branched alkanes as tennis balls in a can that, because of their spherical shapes, have only a small area of contact. One tennis ball represents an entire molecule. Because branched alkanes have fewer attractions, they have lower melting and boiling points.

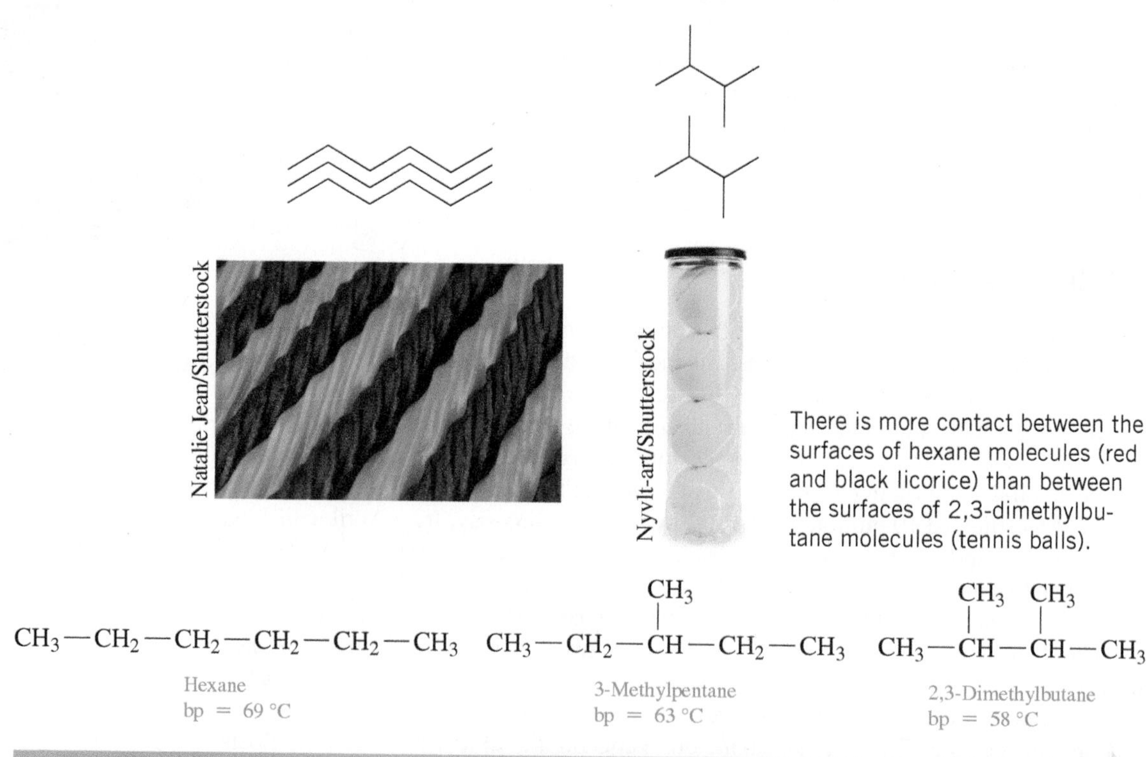
Natalie Jean/Shutterstock
Nyvlt-art/Shutterstock

There is more contact between the surfaces of hexane molecules (red and black licorice) than between the surfaces of 2,3-dimethylbutane molecules (tennis balls).

$CH_3—CH_2—CH_2—CH_2—CH_2—CH_3$ — Hexane — bp = 69 °C

$CH_3—CH_2—CH(CH_3)—CH_2—CH_3$ — 3-Methylpentane — bp = 63 °C

$CH_3—CH(CH_3)—CH(CH_3)—CH_3$ — 2,3-Dimethylbutane — bp = 58 °C

Increase in Number of Branches
Decrease in Boiling Point

Cycloalkanes have higher boiling points than the straight-chain alkanes with the same number of carbon atoms. Because rotation of carbon bonds is restricted, cycloalkanes maintain a rigid structure. Cycloalkanes with their rigid structures can be stacked closely together, which gives them many points of contact and therefore many attractions to each other.

We can compare the boiling points of straight-chain alkanes, branched-chain alkanes, and cycloalkanes with five carbon atoms as shown in Table 6.

TABLE 6 Comparison of Boiling Points of Alkanes and Cycloalkanes with Five Carbons

Formula	Name	Boiling Point (°C)
Straight-Chain Alkane		
$CH_3-CH_2-CH_2-CH_2-CH_3$	Pentane	36
Branched-Chain Alkanes		
$CH_3-CH(CH_3)-CH_2-CH_3$	2-Methylbutane	28
$CH_3-C(CH_3)_2-CH_3$	Dimethylpropane	10
Cycloalkane		
(pentagon)	Cyclopentane	49

TUTORIAL
Writing Balanced Equations for Combustion of Alkanes

CASE STUDY
Poison in the Home: Carbon Monoxide

Combustion of Alkanes

The carbon–carbon single bonds in alkanes are difficult to break, which makes them the least reactive family of organic compounds. However, alkanes burn readily in oxygen. A carbon-containing compound, such as an alkane, undergoes **combustion** when it reacts completely with oxygen to produce carbon dioxide, water, and energy.

$$\text{Alkane}(g) + O_2(g) \xrightarrow{\Delta} CO_2(g) + H_2O(g) + \text{energy}$$

For example, methane is the gas we use to cook our food and heat our homes. The equation for the combustion of methane (CH_4) is written:

$$\underset{\text{Methane}}{CH_4(g)} + 2O_2(g) \xrightarrow{\Delta} CO_2(g) + 2H_2O(g) + \text{energy}$$

In another example, propane is the gas used in portable heaters and gas barbecues (see Figure 8). The equation for the combustion of propane (C_3H_8) is written:

$$\underset{\text{Propane}}{C_3H_8(g)} + 5O_2(g) \xrightarrow{\Delta} 3CO_2(g) + 4H_2O(g) + \text{energy}$$

In the cells of our bodies, energy is produced by the combustion of glucose. Although a series of reactions is involved, we can write the overall combustion of glucose in our cells as follows:

$$\underset{\text{Glucose}}{C_6H_{12}O_6(aq)} + 6O_2(g) \xrightarrow{\text{Enzymes}} 6CO_2(g) + 6H_2O(l) + \text{energy}$$

Marie C Fields/Shutterstock

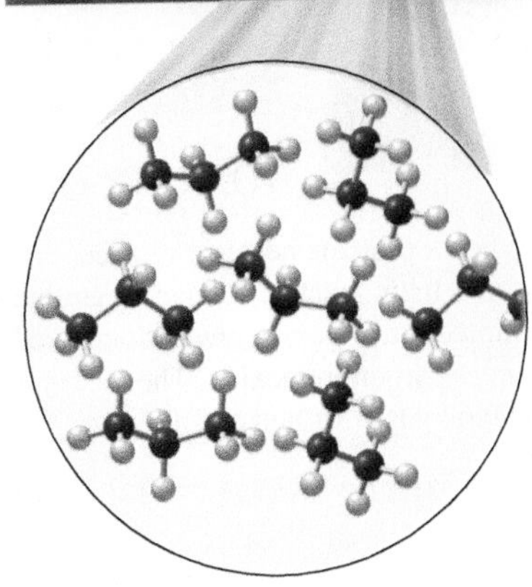

FIGURE 8 The propane fuel in the tank undergoes combustion, which provides energy.

Q What is the balanced equation for the combustion of propane?

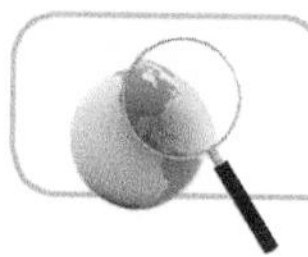

Explore Your World

COMBUSTION

In this exploration, we will look at the behavior of the products of combustion. You will need one or two candles, a Pyrex glass such as a measuring cup, and some matches or wooden splints.

Hold a Pyrex cup upside down, and insert a burning match inside it. The match will continue to burn as long as oxygen is available. Light a candle and hold the inverted Pyrex cup above it for 15–20 seconds. Remove the cup from the candle and immediately insert a burning match inside it. The CO_2 accumulated from the combustion of the candle should extinguish the match.

Add some water and a lot of ice to the same Pyrex cup. It should become cold to the touch. Wipe the bottom of the cup and carefully hold the bottom of the Pyrex cup over a burning candle. Look for the formation of liquid water on the outside of the Pyrex cup.

QUESTIONS

1. What are the products of combustion of candle wax?
2. What was the evidence for the production of CO_2?
3. What observations gave evidence for the production of water during combustion?

CONCEPT CHECK 6 **Completing and Balancing Combustion Equations**

A portable burner is fueled with butane. Write the balanced equation for the complete combustion of butane.

ANSWER

Butane is an alkane with 4 C atoms and 10 H atoms, which gives a molecular formula of C_4H_{10}. In the combustion reaction, butane reacts with oxygen to form carbon dioxide, water, and energy. We write the unbalanced equation as:

$$C_4H_{10}(g) + O_2(g) \xrightarrow{\Delta} CO_2(g) + H_2O(g) + \text{energy}$$

We can begin by balancing the C atoms and H atoms in the products with the C_4H_{10}. However, we notice this gives an odd number (13) of O atoms.

$$C_4H_{10}(g) + O_2(g) \xrightarrow{\Delta} 4CO_2(g) + 5H_2O(g) + \text{energy}$$

Thus, we double the number of C_4H_{10} molecules, which gives the balanced equation for the combustion of butane.

$$2C_4H_{10}(g) + 13O_2(g) \xrightarrow{\Delta} 8CO_2(g) + 10H_2O(g) + \text{energy}$$

HansChris/iStockphoto

When camping, a butane cartridge provides fuel for a portable burner.

Chemistry Link to Health

TOXICITY OF CARBON MONOXIDE

When a propane heater, fireplace, or wood stove is used in a closed room, there must be adequate ventilation. If the supply of oxygen is limited, *incomplete combustion* from burning gas, oil, or wood produces carbon monoxide. The incomplete combustion of methane in natural gas is written as follows:

$$\underset{\text{Limited oxygen supply}}{2CH_4(g) + 3O_2(g)} \xrightarrow{\Delta} \underset{\text{Carbon monoxide}}{2CO(g)} + 4H_2O(g) + \text{energy}$$

Carbon monoxide (CO) is a colorless, odorless, poisonous gas. When inhaled, CO passes into the bloodstream, where it binds to the iron in hemoglobin, which reduces the amount of oxygen (O_2) reaching the cells. As a result, a healthy person can experience a reduction in exercise capability, visual perception, and manual dexterity.

Hemoglobin is the protein that transports O_2 in the blood. When the amount of hemoglobin bound to CO (COHb) is about 10 percent, a person may experience shortness of breath, mild headache, and drowsiness. Heavy smokers can have levels of COHb in their blood as high as 9 percent. When as much as 30 percent of the hemoglobin is bound to CO, a person may experience more severe symptoms, including dizziness, mental confusion, severe headache, and nausea. If 50 percent or more of the hemoglobin is bound to CO, a person could become unconscious and die if not treated immediately with oxygen.

Chemistry Link to Industry

CRUDE OIL

Crude oil, or petroleum, contains a wide variety of hydrocarbons. At an oil refinery, the components in crude oil are separated by *fractional distillation*, a process that removes groups or fractions of hydrocarbons by continually heating the mixture to higher temperatures (see Table 7). Fractions containing alkanes with longer carbon chains require higher temperatures before they reach their boiling point and form gases. The gases are removed and passed through a distillation column where they cool and condense back to liquids. The major use of crude oil is to obtain gasoline, which makes up about 35 percent of crude oil. To increase the production of gasoline, larger alkanes are broken down using specialized catalysts to give the lower-weight alkanes.

TABLE 7 Typical Alkane Mixtures Obtained by Distillation of Crude Oil

Distillation Temperatures (°C)	Number of Carbon Atoms	Product
Below 30	1–4	Natural gas
30–200	5–12	Gasoline
200–250	12–16	Kerosene, jet fuel
250–350	16–18	Diesel fuel, heating oil
350–450	18–25	Lubricating oil
Nonvolatile residue	Over 25	Asphalt, tar

Eric Gevaert - Alamy

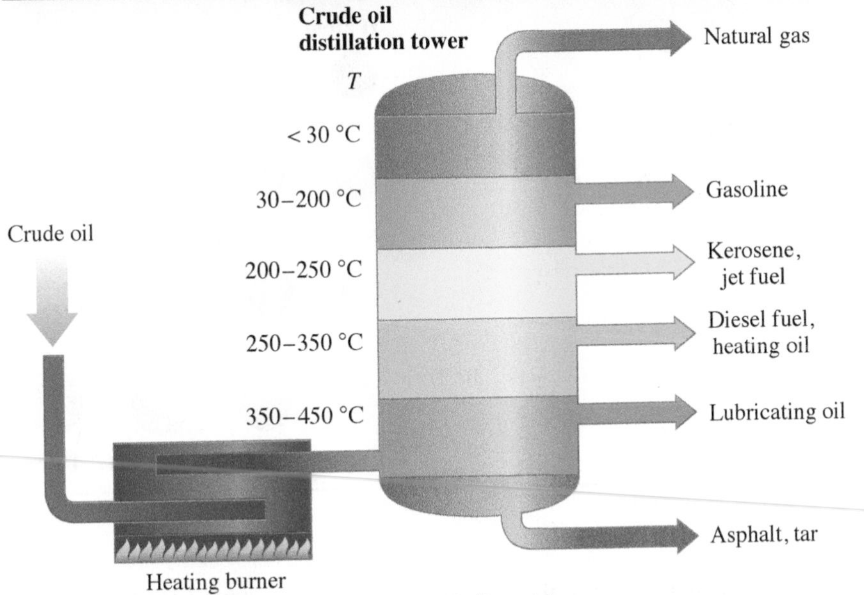

QUESTIONS AND PROBLEMS

4 Properties of Alkanes

LEARNING GOAL: *Identify the properties of alkanes, and write chemical equations for combustion.*

23 Heptane, used as a solvent for rubber cement, has a density of 0.68 g/mL and boils at 98 °C.
a. Draw the condensed structural formula and skeletal formula for heptane.
b. Is heptane a solid, liquid, or gas at room temperature?
c. Is heptane soluble in water?
d. Will heptane float or sink in water?
e. Write the balanced chemical equation for the complete combustion of heptane.

24 Nonane has a density of 0.72 g/mL and boils at 151 °C.
a. Draw the condensed structural formula and skeletal formula for nonane.
b. Is nonane a solid, liquid, or gas at room temperature?
c. Is nonane soluble in water?
d. Will nonane float or sink in water?
e. Write the balanced chemical equation for the complete combustion of nonane.

25 In each of the following pairs of hydrocarbons, which one would you expect to have the higher boiling point?
a. pentane or heptane **b.** propane or cyclopropane
c. hexane or 2-methylpentane

26 In each of the following pairs of hydrocarbons, which one would you expect to have the higher boiling point?
a. propane or butane **b.** hexane or cyclohexane
c. 2,2-dimethylpentane or heptane

27 Write the balanced equation for the complete combustion of each of the following compounds:
a. ethane **b.** octane **c.** cyclohexane, C_6H_{12}

28 Write the balanced equation for the complete combustion of each of the following compounds:
a. hexane **b.** cyclopentane, C_5H_{10}
c. 2-methylbutane

LEARNING GOAL

Classify organic molecules according to their functional groups.

SELF-STUDY ACTIVITY
Functional Groups

5 Functional Groups

In organic compounds, carbon atoms are most likely to bond with nonmetals such as hydrogen, oxygen, nitrogen, sulfur, phosphorus, and halogens. Table 8 lists the number of covalent bonds most often formed by these elements in order to achieve a complete set of valence electrons. Hydrogen and the halogens form one covalent bond, and carbon forms four covalent bonds. Nitrogen forms three covalent bonds, whereas oxygen and sulfur each form two covalent bonds.

TABLE 8 Covalent Bonds for Elements in Organic Compounds

Element	Group	Covalent Bonds	Structure of Atoms	Representation of Atoms
H	1A (1)	1	—H	H atom
C	4A (14)	4	—C— (with bonds above and below)	C atom
N, P	5A (15)	3	—N̈— —P̈— (with bond above; lone pair below)	N atom P atom
O, S	6A (16)	2	—Ö— —S̈— (with lone pairs above and below)	O atom S atom
F, Cl, Br, I	7A (17)	1	—X: (with lone pairs above and below) (X = F, Cl, Br, I)	F atom Cl atom Br atom I atom

TUTORIAL
Identifying Functional Groups

Organic compounds number in the millions, and more are synthesized every day. We organize many of the organic compounds by their **functional groups**, which are groups of atoms bonded in a specific way. Compounds that contain the same functional group have similar chemical and physical properties. The identification of functional groups allows us to classify organic compounds according to their structure, to name compounds within each family, and to predict their chemical reactions. We can predict the behavior of organic compounds from just their functional groups rather than the carbon chains to which they are attached. We will focus on recognizing the patterns of atoms that make up each of the functional groups, which we will discuss in more detail in the following chapters.

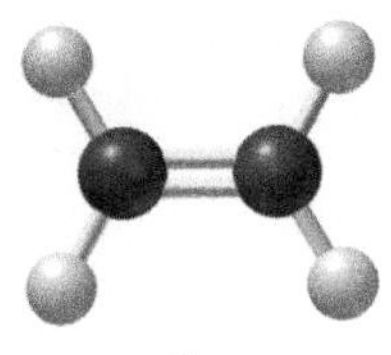

Alkene

Alkyne

Alkenes, Alkynes, and Aromatic Compounds

In the hydrocarbon family, there are also *alkenes, alkynes*, and *aromatics*. An **alkene** contains one or more double bonds between carbon atoms; an **alkyne** contains a triple bond. Compounds that contain benzene are called **aromatic** compounds. Benzene is a molecule that has a ring of six carbon atoms with one hydrogen atom attached to each carbon. The benzene structure is represented as a hexagon with a circle in the center.

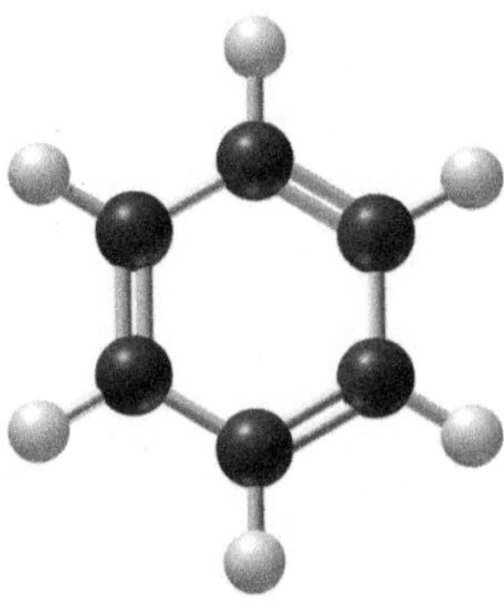

Aromatic

	Alkene	Alkyne	Aromatic
	$H_2C{=}CH_2$ (structural: H, H / C=C / H, H)	$H{-}C{\equiv}C{-}H$	C_6H_6 (hexagon with circle, H on each carbon)
Functional Group	$>C{=}C<$	$-C{\equiv}C-$	(benzene ring)
Condensed Structural Formula	$H_2C{=}CH_2$	$HC{\equiv}CH$	(benzene ring)

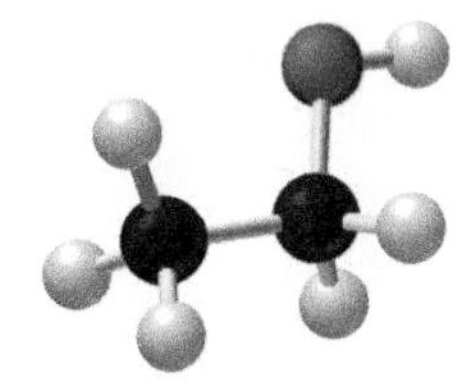

Alcohol

Alcohols, Thiols, and Ethers

The characteristic functional group in an **alcohol** is the *hydroxyl group* ($-OH$) bonded to a carbon atom of an alkane chain. The characteristic functional group found in a **thiol** is the *thiol group* ($-SH$) bonded to a carbon atom in an alkane chain. The characteristic structural feature of an **ether** is an oxygen atom ($-O-$) bonded to two carbon atoms of two alkyl groups.

	Alcohol	Thiol	Ether
Functional Group	$-OH$	$-SH$	$-O-$
Condensed Structural Formula	$CH_3{-}CH_2{-}OH$	$CH_3{-}CH_2{-}SH$	$CH_3{-}O{-}CH_3$

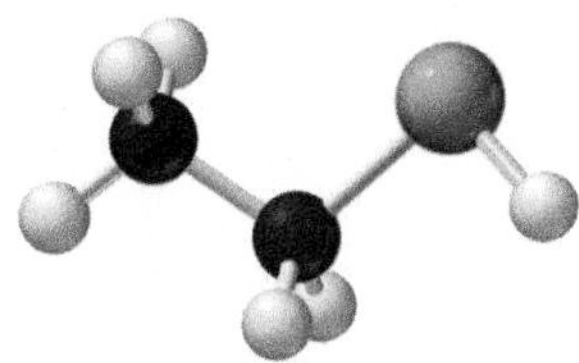

Thiol

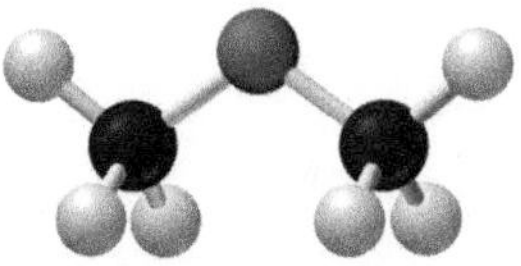

Ether

Aldehydes and Ketones

Aldehydes and ketones are organic classes of compounds that contain a **carbonyl group** ($C{=}O$), which is made up of a carbon atom with a double bond to an oxygen atom. In an **aldehyde**, the functional group is the carbonyl group bonded to an H atom, which means the carbonyl group is always the first carbon. Only the simplest aldehyde, HCHO, has a carbonyl group attached to two hydrogen atoms. In a **ketone**, the functional group is the carbonyl bonded to the carbon atoms of two alkyl groups.

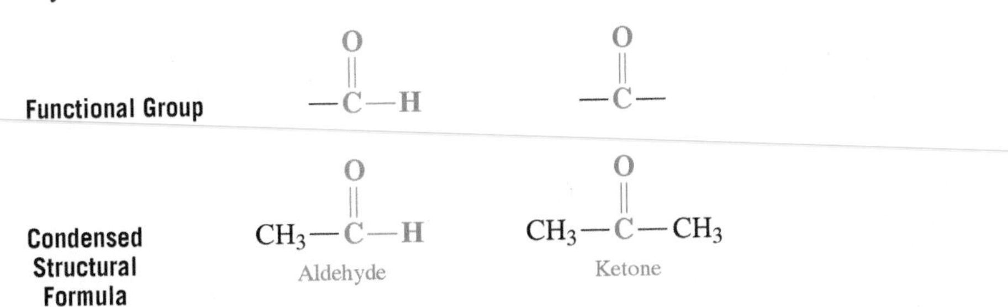

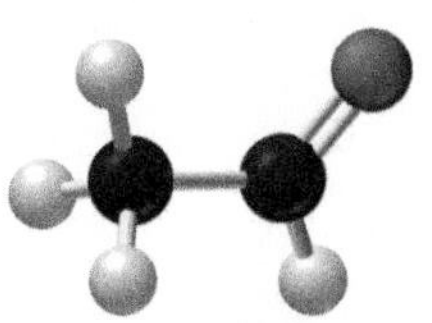

Aldehyde

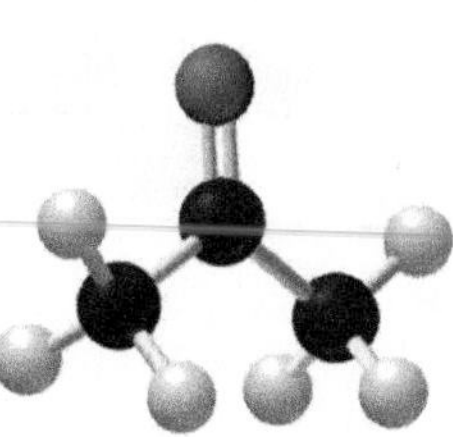

Ketone

CONCEPT CHECK 7 **Identifying Functional Groups**

Highlight the functional group in each of the following and give the name of the class (family) of organic compounds that contains this functional group:

a. $CH_3-CH_2-CH_2-OH$ **b.** $CH_3-C\equiv C-CH_3$

c. $CH_3-CH_2-\overset{O}{\overset{\|}{C}}-CH_2-CH_3$ **d.** $CH_3-\overset{SH}{\overset{|}{C}H}-CH_3$

ANSWER

a. $CH_3-CH_2-CH_2-$ OH
When the hydroxyl functional group ($-OH$), is attached to an alkane chain, the compound is classified as an alcohol.

b. CH_3- $C\equiv C$ $-CH_3$
Because this compound contains a triple bond functional group, it is classified as an alkyne.

c. $CH_3-CH_2-\overset{O}{\overset{\|}{C}}-CH_2-CH_3$
Because the carbon atom of a carbonyl group ($C=O$) is attached to two alkyl groups, this compound is classified as a ketone.

d. $CH_3-\overset{SH}{\overset{|}{C}H}-CH_3$
Because the functional group —SH is attached to an alkane chain, this compound is classified as a thiol.

Carboxylic Acids and Esters

In the organic class of compounds known as **carboxylic acids**, the characteristic functional group is the *carboxyl group*, which is a combination of a carbonyl group ($C=O$) and a hydroxyl group ($-OH$). In a carboxylic acid, the first carbon atom in the chain is the carbon in the carboxyl group.

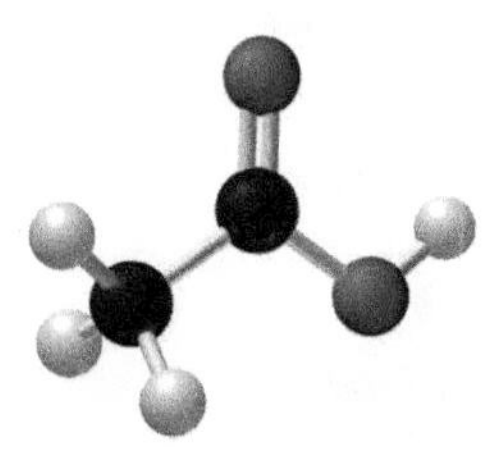
Carboxylic acid

Functional Group $-\overset{O}{\overset{\|}{C}}-OH$ or $-COOH$

Condensed Structural Formula $CH_3-\overset{O}{\overset{\|}{C}}-OH$ or CH_3-COOH
Carboxylic acid

The organic group of compounds known as **esters** has a functional group that is similar to the carboxyl group in carboxylic acids, except that the carboxyl group is attached to a carbon atom.

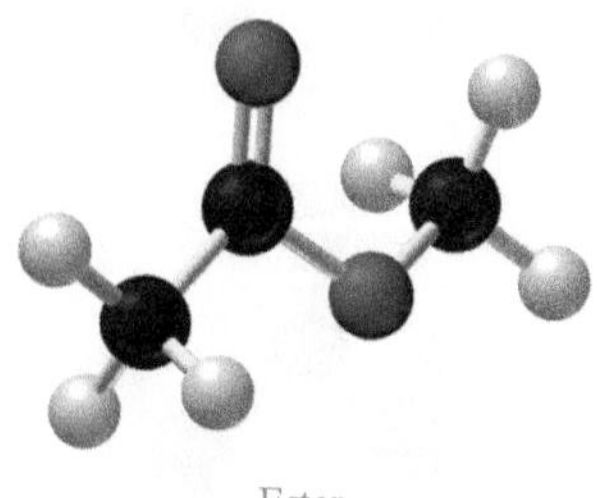
Ester

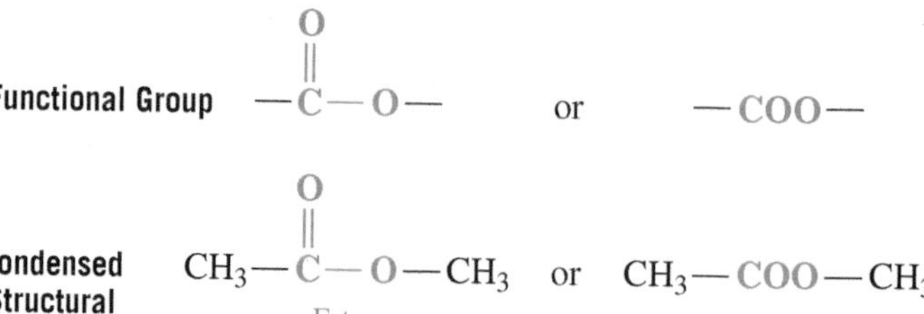

Functional Group $-\overset{O}{\overset{\|}{C}}-O-$ or $-COO-$

Condensed Structural Formula $CH_3-\overset{O}{\overset{\|}{C}}-O-CH_3$ or $CH_3-COO-CH_3$
Ester

Amines and Amides

In the class of organic compounds called **amines**, the characteristic functional group is a nitrogen atom bonded to one, two, or three alkyl groups.

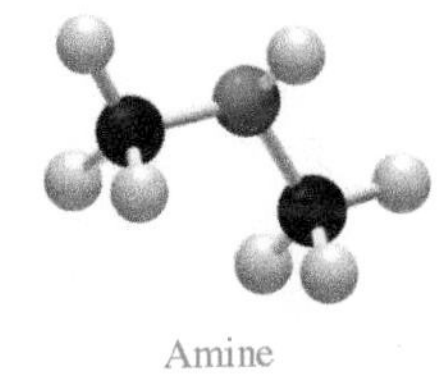

Amine

Functional group $-\underset{|}{N}-$

Condensed Structural Formula CH_3-NH_2 $\quad CH_3-\underset{\underset{CH_3}{|}}{NH}$ $\quad CH_3-\underset{\underset{CH_3}{|}}{N}-CH_3$

The organic class of compounds called **amides** is closely related to the amines. In an amide, the carbonyl group is attached to a nitrogen atom.

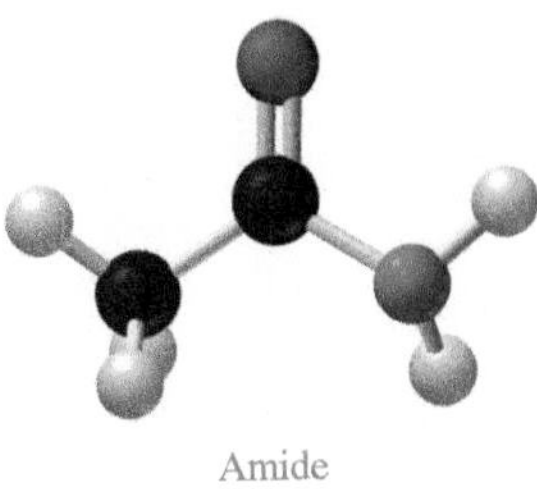

Amide

Functional Group $-\overset{\overset{O}{\|}}{C}-\overset{|}{N}-$

Condensed Structural Formula $CH_3-\overset{\overset{O}{\|}}{C}-NH_2$

Amide

CONCEPT CHECK 8 **The Amine Functional Group**

Describe the functional group found in amines.

ANSWER

The amine functional group has a nitrogen atom bonded to one, two, or three carbon atoms.

SAMPLE PROBLEM 6 **Identifying Functional Groups**

Classify the following organic compounds according to their functional groups:

a. $CH_3-CH_2-NH-CH_3$

b. $CH_3-\overset{\overset{O}{\|}}{C}-O-CH_2-CH_3$

c. $CH_3-CH_2-\overset{\overset{O}{\|}}{C}-OH$

SOLUTION

a. amine
b. ester
c. carboxylic acid

STUDY CHECK 6

Why is $CH_3-CH_2-O-CH_3$ an ether?

A list of the common functional groups in organic compounds is shown in Table 9.

TABLE 9 Classification of Organic Compounds

Class	Functional Group	Example
Alkene	$>C{=}C<$	$H_2C{=}CH_2$
Alkyne	$-C{\equiv}C-$	$HC{\equiv}CH$
Aromatic	(benzene ring)	(benzene ring with six H)
Alcohol	$-OH$	$CH_3-CH_2-\mathbf{OH}$
Thiol	$-SH$	$CH_3-\mathbf{SH}$
Ether	$-O-$	$CH_3-\mathbf{O}-CH_3$
Aldehyde	$-\overset{O}{\overset{\|\|}{C}}-H$	$CH_3-\overset{\mathbf{O}}{\overset{\|\|}{\mathbf{C}}}-\mathbf{H}$
Ketone	$-\overset{O}{\overset{\|\|}{C}}-$	$CH_3-\overset{\mathbf{O}}{\overset{\|\|}{\mathbf{C}}}-CH_3$
Carboxylic acid	$-\overset{O}{\overset{\|\|}{C}}-OH$	$CH_3-\overset{\mathbf{O}}{\overset{\|\|}{\mathbf{C}}}-\mathbf{OH}$
Ester	$-\overset{O}{\overset{\|\|}{C}}-O-$	$CH_3-\overset{\mathbf{O}}{\overset{\|\|}{\mathbf{C}}}-\mathbf{O}-CH_3$
Amine	$-\overset{\|}{N}-$	$CH_3-\mathbf{NH_2}$
Amide	$-\overset{O}{\overset{\|\|}{C}}-\overset{\|}{N}-$	$CH_3-\overset{\mathbf{O}}{\overset{\|\|}{\mathbf{C}}}-\mathbf{NH_2}$

TUTORIAL
Drawing Organic Compounds with Functional Groups

Chemistry Link to the Environment

FUNCTIONAL GROUPS IN FAMILIAR COMPOUNDS

The flavors and odors of foods and many household products can be attributed to the functional groups of organic compounds. As we discuss these familiar products, look for the functional groups we have described.

Ethyl alcohol is the alcohol found in alcoholic beverages. Isopropyl alcohol is another alcohol commonly used to disinfect skin before giving injections and to treat cuts.

$$CH_3-CH_2-OH \qquad CH_3-\overset{OH}{\overset{|}{CH}}-CH_3$$

Ethyl alcohol   Isopropyl alcohol

Acetone, or dimethyl ketone, is produced in great amounts commercially. Acetone is used as an organic solvent because it dissolves a wide variety of organic substances. You may be familiar with acetone as fingernail polish remover.

$$CH_3-\overset{O}{\overset{\|}{C}}-CH_3$$

Acetone

Ketones and aldehydes are found in flavorings such as vanilla, cinnamon, and spearmint. When we buy a small bottle of liquid flavoring, the aldehyde or ketone is dissolved in alcohol because the compounds are not very soluble in water. Formaldehyde, HCHO, the simplest aldehyde, is a colorless gas with a pungent odor. Industrially, it is a reactant in the synthesis of polymers used to make fabrics, insulation materials, carpeting, pressed wood products such as plywood, and plastics for kitchen counters. An aqueous solution called formalin, which contains 40% formaldehyde, is used as a germicide and to preserve biological specimens. The aldehyde butyraldehyde adds a buttery taste to foods and margarine.

$$CH_3-CH_2-CH_2-\overset{\overset{\Large O}{\|}}{C}-H$$

Butyraldehyde (butter flavoring)

The sour tastes of vinegar and fruit juices and the pain from ant stings are all due to carboxylic acids. Acetic acid is the carboxylic acid that makes up vinegar and formic acid is the carboxylic acid in ant stings. Aspirin also contains a carboxylic acid group. Esters found in fruits produce the pleasant aromas and tastes of bananas, oranges, pears, and pineapples. Esters are also used as solvents in many household cleaners, polishes, and glues.

One of the characteristics of fish is their odor, which is due to amines like methylamine. Amines produced when proteins decay have a particularly pungent and offensive odor, thus the descriptive names putrescine and cadaverine.

$$H_2N-CH_2-CH_2-CH_2-CH_2-NH_2$$

Putrescine

$$H_2N-CH_2-CH_2-CH_2-CH_2-CH_2-NH_2$$

Cadaverine

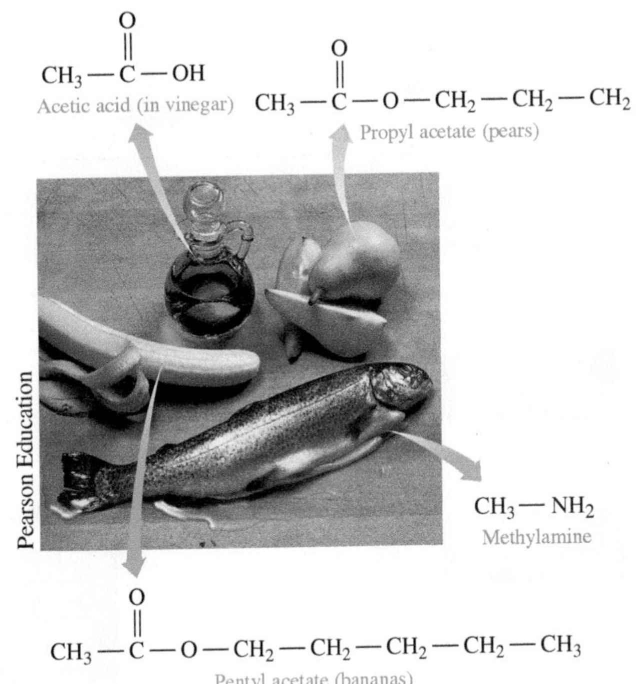

Pearson Education

QUESTIONS AND PROBLEMS

5 Functional Groups

LEARNING GOAL: *Classify organic molecules according to their functional groups.*

29 Identify the class of compounds that contains each of the following functional groups:

a. a hydroxyl group attached to a carbon chain
b. a carbon–carbon double bond
c. a carbonyl group attached to a hydrogen atom
d. a carboxyl group attached to two carbon atoms

30 Identify the class of compounds that contains each of the following functional groups:

a. a nitrogen atom attached to one or more carbon atoms
b. a carboxyl group
c. an oxygen atom bonded to two carbon atoms
d. a carbonyl group between two carbon atoms

31 Classify the following molecules according to their functional groups. The possibilities are alcohol, ether, ketone, carboxylic acid, or amine.

a. $CH_3-CH_2-O-CH_2-CH_3$

b. $CH_3-\overset{\overset{OH}{|}}{CH}-CH_3$

c. $CH_3-\overset{\overset{O}{\|}}{C}-CH_2-CH_3$

d. $CH_3-CH_2-CH_2-COOH$

e. $CH_3-CH_2-NH_2$

32 Classify the following molecules according to their functional groups. The possibilities are alkene, aldehyde, carboxylic acid, ester, or amide.

a. $CH_3-CH_2-\overset{\overset{O}{\|}}{C}-O-CH_2-CH_3$

b. $CH_3-\overset{\overset{O}{\|}}{C}-NH_2$

c. $CH_3-CH_2-CH_2-\overset{\overset{O}{\|}}{C}-H$

d. $CH_3-CH_2-CH_2-CH_2-COOH$

e. $CH_3-CH=CH-CH_3$

CONCEPT MAP

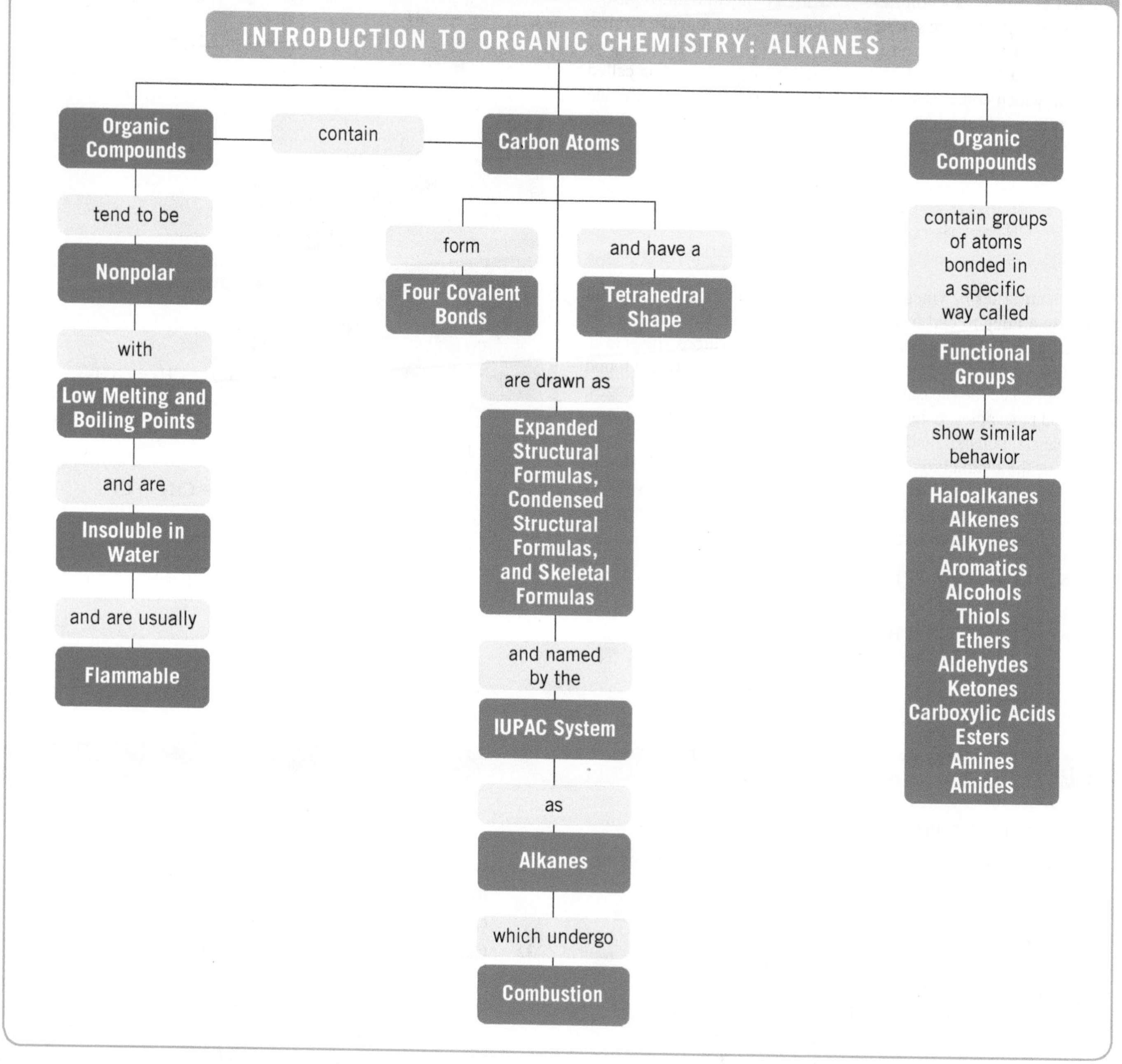

INTRODUCTION TO ORGANIC CHEMISTRY: ALKANES

Organic Compounds — contain — Carbon Atoms

Organic Compounds
tend to be
Nonpolar
with
Low Melting and Boiling Points
and are
Insoluble in Water
and are usually
Flammable

Carbon Atoms
form
Four Covalent Bonds
and have a
Tetrahedral Shape
are drawn as
Expanded Structural Formulas, Condensed Structural Formulas, and Skeletal Formulas
and named by the
IUPAC System
as
Alkanes
which undergo
Combustion

Organic Compounds
contain groups of atoms bonded in a specific way called
Functional Groups
show similar behavior
Haloalkanes
Alkenes
Alkynes
Aromatics
Alcohols
Thiols
Ethers
Aldehydes
Ketones
Carboxylic Acids
Esters
Amines
Amides

CHAPTER REVIEW

1 Organic Compounds

***LEARNING GOAL:** Identify the characteristic properties of organic or inorganic compounds.*

Pearson Education

- Organic compounds have covalent bonds, mostly form nonpolar molecules, have low melting points and low boiling points, are not very soluble in water, produce molecules in solutions, and burn vigorously in air.
- Inorganic compounds are often ionic or contain polar covalent bonds and form polar molecules, have high melting and boiling points, are usually soluble in water, produce ions in water, and do not burn in air.
- Carbon atoms share four valence electrons to form four covalent bonds.
- In the simplest organic molecule, methane, CH_4, the C—H bonds that attach four hydrogen atoms to the carbon atom are directed to the corners of a tetrahedron with bond angles of 109°.

2 Alkanes

LEARNING GOAL: *Write the IUPAC names and draw the condensed structural formulas for alkanes.*

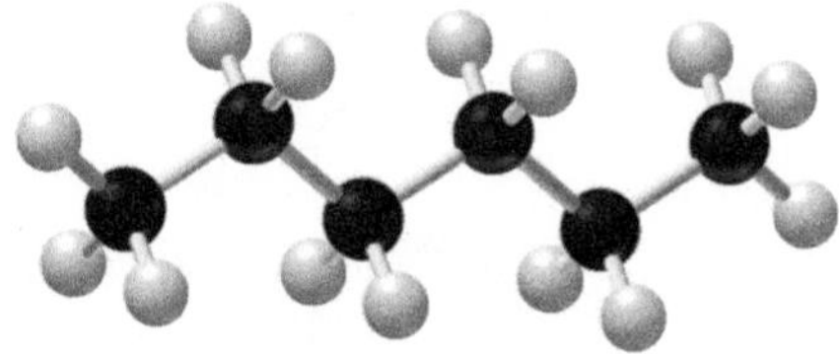

- Alkanes are hydrocarbons that have only C—C single bonds.
- In the expanded structural formula, a separate line is drawn for every bonded atom.
- A condensed structural formula depicts groups composed of each carbon atom and its attached hydrogen atoms.
- A skeletal formula represents the carbon skeleton as ends and corners of a zigzag line or geometric figure.
- The IUPAC system is used to name organic compounds by indicating the number of carbon atoms.
- The name of a cycloalkane is written by placing the prefix *cyclo* before the alkane name with the same number of carbon atoms.

3 Alkanes with Substituents

LEARNING GOAL: *Write the IUPAC names and draw the condensed structural formulas and skeletal formulas for alkanes.*

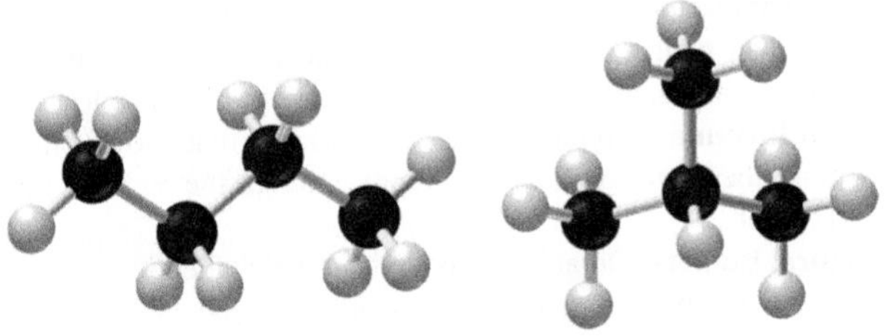

- Substituents, which are attached to an alkane chain, include alkyl groups and halogen atoms (F, Cl, Br, or I).
- In the IUPAC system, alkyl substituents have names such as methyl, ethyl, propyl, and isopropyl; halogen atoms are named as fluoro, chloro, bromo, or iodo.
- In the common names of some compounds, the name of the alkyl group precedes *halide*, for example, methyl chloride.

4 Properties of Alkanes

LEARNING GOAL: *Identify the properties of alkanes, and write chemical equations for combustion.*

AP Photo/Kamran Jebreili

- Alkanes, which are nonpolar molecules, are not soluble in water, and are usually less dense than water.
- Alkanes are only weakly attracted to other molecules by dispersion forces, which gives them low melting and boiling points.
- For alkanes of similar mass, branched alkanes have lower boiling points and cycloalkanes have higher boiling points than their nonbranched structural isomers.
- Alkanes undergo combustion in which they react with oxygen to produce carbon dioxide, water, and energy.

5 Functional Groups

LEARNING GOAL: *Classify organic molecules according to their functional groups.*

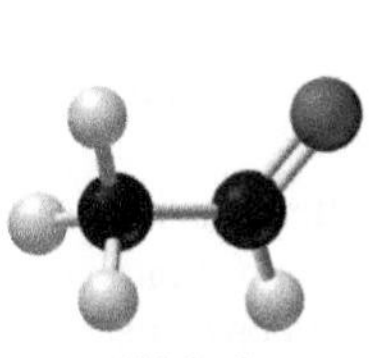

Aldehyde

Ketone

- An organic molecule contains a characteristic group of atoms called a *functional group* that determines the molecule's family name and chemical reactivity.
- Functional groups are used to classify organic compounds, act as reactive sites in the molecule, and provide a system of naming for organic compounds.
- Some common functional groups include the hydroxyl group (—OH) in alcohols, the carbonyl group (C=O) in aldehydes and ketones, a carboxyl group (—COOH) in carboxylic acids, and a nitrogen (N) atom in amines.

SUMMARY OF NAMING

Type	Example	Name
Alkane	$CH_3—CH_2—CH_3$	Propane
	$CH_3—CH(CH_3)—CH_3$	Methylpropane
Haloalkane	$CH_3—CH_2—CH_2—Cl$	1-Chloropropane
Cycloalkane	□	Cyclobutane

SUMMARY OF REACTIONS

Combustion

$$\text{Alkane}(g) + O_2(g) \xrightarrow{\Delta} CO_2(g) + H_2O(g) + \text{energy}$$

KEY TERMS

alcohol A class of organic compounds that contains the hydroxyl group (—OH) bonded to a carbon atom.

aldehyde A class of organic compounds that contains a carbonyl group (C=O) bonded to at least one hydrogen atom.

alkanes Hydrocarbons containing only single bonds between carbon atoms.

alkenes Hydrocarbons that contain carbon–carbon double bonds (C=C).

alkyl group An alkane minus one hydrogen atom. Alkyl groups are named like the alkanes except a *yl* ending replaces *ane*.

alkynes Hydrocarbons that contain carbon–carbon triple bonds (C≡C).

amide A class of organic compounds in which the hydroxyl group of a carboxylic acid is replaced by a nitrogen group.

amine A class of organic compounds that contains a nitrogen atom bonded to one or more carbon atoms.

aromatic A compound that contains benzene. Benzene has a six-carbon ring with only one hydrogen atom attached to each carbon.

branch A carbon group bonded to the main carbon chain.

branched alkane A single-bonded hydrocarbon containing a substituent bonded to the main chain.

carbonyl group A functional group that contains a double bond between a carbon atom and an oxygen atom (C=O).

carboxylic acid A class of organic compounds that contains the carboxyl functional group.

combustion A chemical reaction in which an alkane reacts with oxygen to produce CO_2, H_2O, and energy.

condensed structural formula A structural formula that shows the arrangement of the carbon atoms in a molecule, but groups each carbon atom with its bonded hydrogen atoms.

cycloalkane An alkane that has a ring or cyclic structure.

ester A class of organic compounds that contains a —COO— group with an oxygen atom bonded to carbon.

ether A class of organic compounds that contains an oxygen atom bonded to two carbon atoms (—O—).

expanded structural formula A type of structural formula that shows the arrangement of the atoms by showing each bond in the hydrocarbon as C—H, C—C, C=C, or C≡C.

functional group A group of atoms bonded in a specific way that determines the physical and chemical properties of organic compounds.

haloalkane A type of alkane that contains one or more halogen atoms.

hydrocarbons Organic compounds consisting of only carbon and hydrogen.

IUPAC system The system for naming organic compounds devised by the International Union of Pure and Applied Chemistry.

ketone A class of organic compounds in which a carbonyl group (C=O) is bonded to two carbon atoms.

organic compounds Compounds made of carbon that typically have covalent bonds, are nonpolar molecules, have low melting and boiling points, are insoluble in water, and are flammable.

skeletal formula A type of structural formula that shows only the bonds between carbon atoms represented as the end of a line or a corner.

structural isomers Organic compounds in which identical molecular formulas have different arrangements of atoms.

substituent Groups of atoms such as an alkyl group or a halogen bonded to the main chain or ring of carbon atoms.

thiol A class of organic molecules that contains the —SH functional group bonded to a carbon atom.

UNDERSTANDING THE CONCEPTS

The chapter sections to review are shown in parentheses at the end of each question.

33 Match the following physical and chemical properties with the compound butane, C_4H_{10}, or potassium chloride, KCl: (1)

Jason Nemeth/iStockphoto

Pearson Education

a. melts at −138 °C
b. burns vigorously in air
c. melts at 770 °C
d. contains ionic bonds
e. is a gas at room temperature

34 Match the following physical and chemical properties with the compound octane, C_8H_{18}, or magnesium sulfate, $MgSO_4$: (1)

a. contains only covalent bonds
b. melts at 1124 °C
c. is insoluble in water
d. is a liquid at room temperature
e. is a strong electrolyte

35 Identify the compounds in each of the following pairs as structural isomers or not structural isomers: (3, 5)

a. and

b. and

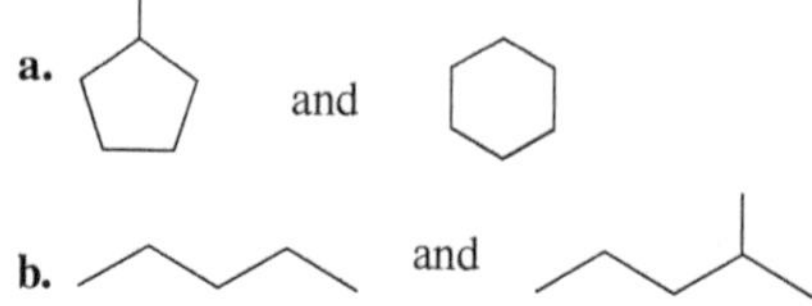

36 Identify the compounds in each of the following pairs as structural isomers or not structural isomers: (3. 5)

a.

$$\begin{array}{l} CH_2-CH_2-CH_2 \\ | \qquad\qquad | \\ CH_3 \qquad\quad CH_2-CH_3 \end{array} \quad \text{and} \quad \begin{array}{l} CH_3 \qquad\qquad\qquad\quad CH_3 \\ | \qquad\qquad\qquad\qquad\; | \\ CH_2-CH_2-CH_2-CH_2 \end{array}$$

b. and

37 Convert each of the following skeletal structures to condensed structural formulas and give the IUPAC name: (2)

a. b. Cl Br

38 Convert each of the following skeletal structures to condensed structural formulas and give the IUPAC name: (2)

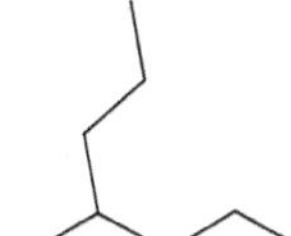

a. b.

39 Match each of the descriptions (**a–f**) with a corresponding term in the following list: alkane, alkene, alkyne, alcohol, ether, aldehyde, ketone, carboxylic acid, ester, amine, functional group, structural isomer. (5)

a. an organic compound that contains a hydroxyl group bonded to a carbon
b. a hydrocarbon that contains one or more carbon–carbon double bonds
c. an organic compound in which the carbon of a carbonyl group is bonded to a hydrogen
d. a hydrocarbon that contains only carbon–carbon single bonds
e. an organic compound in which the carbon of a carbonyl group is bonded to a hydroxyl group
f. an organic compound that contains a nitrogen atom bonded to one or more carbon atoms

40 Match each of the descriptions (**a–f**) with a corresponding term in the following list: alkane, alkene, alkyne, alcohol, ether, aldehyde, ketone, carboxylic acid, ester, amine, functional group, structural isomer. (5)

a. organic compounds with identical molecular formulas that differ only in the arrangement of atoms
b. an organic compound in which the hydrogen atom of a carboxyl group is replaced by a carbon atom
c. an organic compound that contains an oxygen atom bonded to two carbon atoms
d. a hydrocarbon that contains a carbon–carbon triple bond
e. a characteristic group of atoms that makes compounds behave and react in a particular way
f. an organic compound in which the carbonyl group is bonded to two carbon atoms

41 Classify the following according to their functional groups: (5)

a. CH_3-NH_2

b. $CH_3-\overset{\overset{\large O}{\|}}{C}-CH_3$

c. $CH_3-\overset{\overset{\large O}{\|}}{C}-O-CH_2-CH_3$

d. $CH_3-CH_2-CH_2-OH$

42 Classify each of the following by their functional group: (5)

a. $CH_3-C\equiv CH$

b. $CH_3-CH_2-CH_2-SH$

c. $CH_3-O-CH_2-CH_3$

d. $-CH_3$

43 Identify the functional groups in each of the following: (5)

a. $\overset{\overset{\large O}{\|}}{C}-H$

SK Designs/iStockphoto

Almonds

b. $CH=CH-\overset{\overset{\large O}{\|}}{C}-H$

C Squared Studios/Getty Images

Cinnamon sticks

c. $CH_3-\overset{\overset{\large O}{\|}}{C}-\overset{\overset{\large O}{\|}}{C}-CH_3$

Multiart/Shutterstock

Butter

44 Identify the functional groups in each of the following: (5)

a. BHA is an antioxidant used as a preservative in foods such as baked goods, butter, meats, and snack foods. Identify the functional groups in BHA.

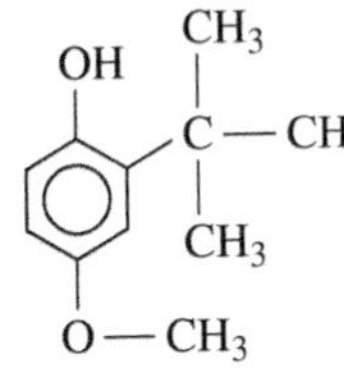

stanislaff/iStockphoto

Baked goods contain BHA as a preservative.

b. Vanillin is a flavoring obtained from the seeds of the vanilla bean. Identify the functional groups in vanillin.

$\overset{\overset{\large O}{\|}}{C}-H$, $O-CH_3$, OH

Pearson Education

Vanilla extract is a solution containing the compound vanillin.

ADDITIONAL QUESTIONS AND PROBLEMS

For instructor-assigned homework, go to www.masteringchemistry.com.

45 Write the name of each of the following substituents: (3)

a. $CH_3—$

b. $CH_3—CH_2—CH_2—$

c. $Cl—$

46 Write the name of each of the following substituents: (3)

a. $Br—$

b. $CH_3—CH(CH_3)—$

c. $CH_3—CH_2—$

47 Give the IUPAC name for each of the following: (2, 3)

a.

b. $Cl—CH_2—CH(Br)—CH_2—Br$

c. $CH_3—CH(CH_3)—CH(CH_2—CH_2—CH_3)—CH_3$

d. $CH_3—CH_2—C(Cl)(CH_2—CH_3)—CH_2—CH_3$

48 Give the IUPAC name for each of the following: (2, 3)

a. $CH_3—CH_2—C(CH_3)_2—CH_3$

b. $CH_3—CH_2—Cl$

c. $CH_3—CH_2—CH(CH_2—CH_3)—CH_2—CH(Br)—CH_3$

d. Br, Br

49 Draw the condensed structural formulas for the four possible isomers that have four carbon atoms and one bromine atom, and give the IUPAC name for each. (3)

50 Draw the condensed structural formulas for the four possible isomers that have three carbon atoms and two chlorine atoms, and give the IUPAC name for each. (3)

51 Draw the skeletal formulas for three structural isomers that have the molecular formula C_7H_{14}, with two methyl groups attached to a ring, and give the IUPAC name for each. (3)

52 Draw the skeletal formulas for four structural isomers that have the molecular formula C_4H_9Br, and give the IUPAC name for each. (3)

53 Draw the condensed structural formula for each of the following molecules: (2, 3)

a. 3-ethylhexane

b. 1,3-dimethylcyclopentane

c. 1,3-dichloro-3-methylheptane

d. bromocyclobutane

54 Draw the condensed structural formula for each of the following molecules: (2, 3)

a. ethylcyclopropane

b. 2-methylhexane

c. isopropylcyclopentane

d. 1,1-dichloropentane

55 Draw the skeletal formula for each of the following molecules: (2, 3)

a. pentane

b. 2,3-dimethylhexane

c. 2-bromo-4-methylheptane

d. 1,4-dimethylcyclohexane

56 Draw the skeletal formula for each of the following molecules: (2, 3)

a. butane

b. 2,3,3-trimethylpentane

c. 1,4-dichlorobutane

d. 2-bromo-1-methylcyclopentane

57 Identify the compound in each of the following pairs that has the higher boiling point: (4)

a. pentane or propane

b. pentane or cyclopentane

c. hexane or 2,2-dimethylbutane

d. 2-methylbutane or 2,2-dimethylpropane

58 Identify the compound in each of the following pairs that has the higher boiling point: (4)

a. butane or octane

b. butane or cyclobutane

c. pentane or 2-methylbutane

d. hexane or 2,3-dimethylbutane

59 Write the balanced equation for the complete combustion of each of the following: (4)

a. $CH_3—CH=CH_2$

b. C_5H_{12}

c. cyclobutane, C_4H_8

60 Write the balanced equation for the complete combustion of each of the following: (4)

a. heptane

b. $HC\equiv C—CH_2—CH_3$

c. 2-methylpropane

61 A tank on an outdoor heater contains 2.8 kg of propane. (2, 4)

a. Write the balanced equation for the complete combustion of propane.

b. How many kilograms of CO_2 are produced by the complete combustion of the propane?

62 A butane fireplace lighter contains 56.0 g of butane. (2, 4)

a. Write the balanced equation for the complete combustion of butane.

b. How many grams of oxygen are needed for the complete combustion of the butane in the lighter?

63 Sunscreens contain compounds such as oxybenzone and 2-ethylhexyl-*p*-methoxycinnamate that absorb UV light. Identify the functional groups in each of the following UV-absorbing compounds used in suncreens: (5)

mangostock/Shutterstock

a. oxybenzone

[Structure: CH_3–O– benzene ring bearing OH and –C(=O)– linked to a second benzene ring]

b. 2-ethylhexyl-*p*-methoxycinnamate

[Structure: CH_3–O– benzene ring–CH=CH–C(=O)–O–2-ethylhexyl chain]

64 Oxymetazoline is a vasoconstrictor used in nasal decongestant sprays such as Afrin.

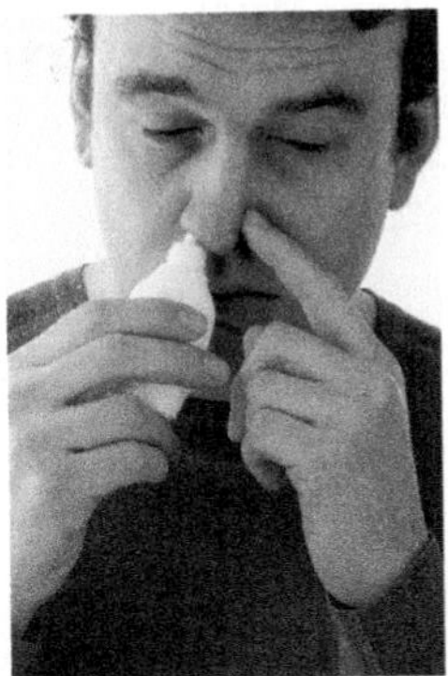

Image100/Photolibrary

What functional groups are in oxymetazoline? (5)

[Structure: benzene ring with OH, CH_3, CH_3, a $(CH_3)_3C$– group, and a CH_2 linked to an imidazoline ring (N, N–H)]

65 Decimemide is used as an anticonvulsant.

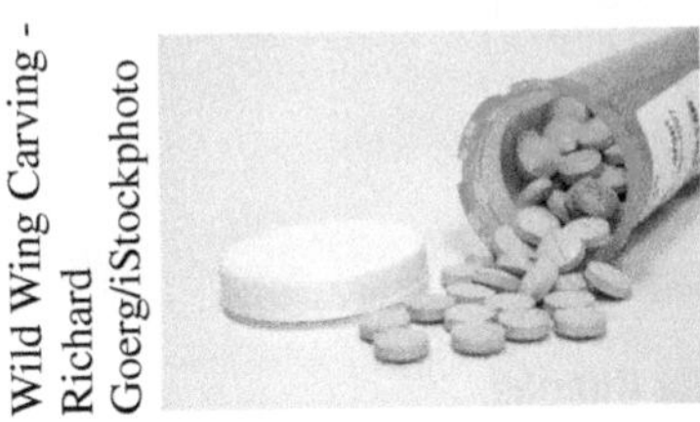

Wild Wing Carving - Richard Goerg/iStockphoto

Identify the functional groups in decimemide. (5)

[Structure: benzene ring bearing two CH_3—O groups, a CH_3—$(CH_2)_9$—O— group, and a $\overset{O}{\overset{\|}{C}}$—$NH_2$ group]

66 The odor and taste of pineapples is from ethyl butyrate.

Andy Crawford/ Dorling Kindersley

What functional group is in ethyl butyrate? (5)

$$CH_3-CH_2-CH_2-\overset{O}{\overset{\|}{C}}-O-CH_2-CH_3$$

CHALLENGE QUESTIONS

67 In an automobile engine, “knocking” occurs when the combustion of gasoline occurs too rapidly. The octane number of gasoline represents the ability of a gasoline mixture to reduce knocking. A sample of gasoline is compared with heptane, rated 0, because it reacts with severe knocking, and 2,2,4-trimethylpentane, which has a rating of 100 because of its low knocking. (2, 3, 4)

a. Draw the condensed structural formula for 2,2,4-trimethylpentane.

b. Write the balanced equation for the complete combustion of 2,2,4-trimethylpentane.

68 Draw the condensed structural formula for each of the following halogenated compounds, used as refrigerants and propellants: (2, 3)

a. Freon 14, tetrafluoromethane

b. Freon 114, 1,2-dichloro-1,1,2,2-tetrafluoroethane

c. Freon C318, octafluorocyclobutane

d. Halon 2311, 2-bromo-2-chloro-1,1,1-trifluoroethane

69 Draw the condensed structural formulas for three structural isomers that have the molecular formula C_3H_8O and contain an alcohol or ether functional group. (3, 5)

70 Draw the condensed structural formulas for three structural isomers that have the molecular formula C_4H_8O and contain an aldehyde or ketone functional group. (3, 5)

71 Consider the compound propane. (2, 3, 5)
a. Draw the condensed structural formula.
b. Write the balanced equation for the complete combustion of propane.
c. How many grams of O_2 are needed to react with 12.0 L of propane gas at STP?
d. How many grams of CO_2 would be produced from the reaction in part **c**?

72 Consider the compound ethylcyclopentane. (2, 3, 5)
a. Draw the skeletal formula.
b. Write the balanced equation for the complete combustion of ethylcyclopentane.
c. How many grams of O_2 are required for the reaction of 25.0 g of ethylcyclopentane?
d. How many liters of CO_2 would be produced at STP from the reaction in part **c**?

ANSWERS

Answers to Study Checks

1 $CH_3-CH_2-CH_2-CH_2-CH_2-CH_2-CH_3$
heptane

2 cyclopropane

3 3-methylpentane

4 1-chloro-2,4-dimethylhexane

5 $CH_3-CH(Br)-CH_2-CH(CH_3)-CH_3$;

6 $CH_3-CH_2-O-CH_3$ contains the functional group C—O—C; it is an ether.

Answers to Selected Questions and Problems

1 a. inorganic **b.** organic **c.** organic
d. inorganic **e.** inorganic **f.** organic

3 a. inorganic **b.** organic
c. organic **d.** inorganic

5 a. ethane **b.** ethane
c. NaBr **d.** NaBr

7 VSEPR theory predicts that the four bonds in CH_4 will be as far apart as possible, which means that the hydrogen atoms are at the corners of a tetrahedron.

9 a. H—C—C—C—H (each carbon also bonded to H above and H below)

b. $CH_3-CH_2-CH_2-CH_2-CH_2-CH_3$

c.

11 a. pentane **b.** heptane
c. hexane **d.** cyclobutane

13 a. CH_4 **b.** CH_3-CH_3
c. $CH_3-CH_2-CH_2-CH_2-CH_3$ **d.**

15 a. same molecule
b. structural isomers of C_5H_{12}
c. structural isomers of C_6H_{14}

17 a. 1-fluoropropane
b. 2,3-dimethylpentane
c. 4-ethyl-2,2-dimethylhexane
d. chlorocyclopentane
e. 2-chloropropane
f. methylcyclohexane

19 a. $Br-CH_2-CH_2-CH_2-Cl$

b. $CH_3-CH_2-C(CH_3)_2-CH_2-CH_3$

c. $CH_3-CH(CH_3)-CH(CH_3)-CH_2-CH(CH_3)-CH_3$

d. $CH_3-CH(CH_3)-CH(CH_2-CH_3)-CH_2-CH(CH_3)-CH_2-CH_2-CH_3$

e. $Br-CH_2-CH_2-Br$

21 a. **b.** Cl

c.

d. Br **e.** Cl

23 a. $CH_3-CH_2-CH_2-CH_2-CH_2-CH_2-CH_3$;

b. liquid
c. No, heptane is insoluble in water.
d. float
e. $C_7H_{16}(g) + 11O_2(g) \xrightarrow{\Delta} 7CO_2(g) + 8H_2O(g) + \text{energy}$

25 a. heptane **b.** cyclopropane
c. hexane

27 a. $2C_2H_6(g) + 7O_2(g) \xrightarrow{\Delta} 4CO_2(g) + 6H_2O(g) + \text{energy}$
b. $2C_8H_{18}(g) + 25O_2(g) \xrightarrow{\Delta} 16CO_2(g) + 18H_2O(g) + \text{energy}$
c. $C_6H_{12}(g) + 9O_2(g) \xrightarrow{\Delta} 6CO_2(g) + 6H_2O(g) + \text{energy}$

29 a. alcohol **b.** alkene
c. aldehyde **d.** ester

31 a. ether **b.** alcohol
c. ketone **d.** carboxylic acid
e. amine

33 a. butane **b.** butane
c. potassium chloride **d.** potassium chloride
e. butane

35 a. structural isomers **b.** not structural isomers

37 a. $CH_3-CH_2-CH_2-CH(CH_3)-CH(CH_3)-CH_3$
2,3-dimethylhexane

b. $CH_3-CH(Cl)-CH(CH_3)-CH(Br)-CH_2-CH_3$
4-bromo-2-chloro-3-methylhexane

39 a. alcohol **b.** alkene
c. aldehyde **d.** alkane
e. carboxylic acid **f.** amine

41 a. amine **b.** ketone
c. ester **d.** alcohol

43 a. aromatic, aldehyde
b. aromatic, alkene, aldehyde
c. ketone

45 a. methyl
b. propyl
c. chloro

47 a. methylcyclopentane
b. 1,2-dibromo-3-chloropropane
c. 2,3-dimethylhexane
d. 3-chloro-3-ethylpentane

49 $CH_3-CH_2-CH_2-CH_2-Br$
1-bromobutane

$CH_3-CH(Br)-CH_2-CH_3$
2-bromobutane

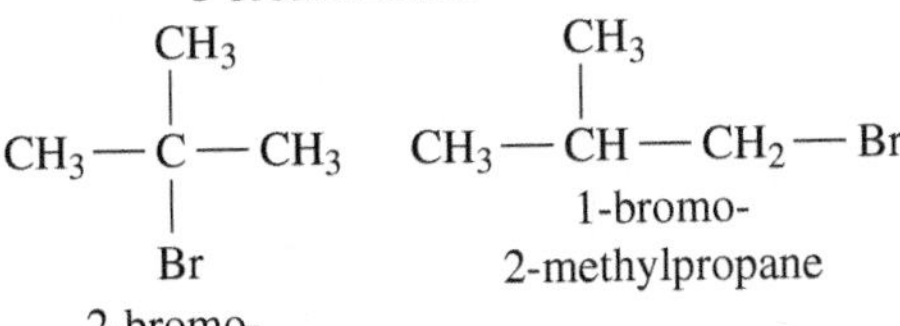

51

1,1-dimethylcyclopentane

1,2-dimethylcyclopentane 1,3-dimethylcyclopentane

53 a. $CH_3-CH_2-CH(CH_2-CH_3)-CH_2-CH_2-CH_3$

b. CH_3 / CH_3 (1,3-dimethylcyclopentane)

c. $Cl-CH_2-CH_2-C(Cl)(CH_3)-CH_2-CH_2-CH_2-CH_3$

d. Br (bromocyclobutane)

55 a.

b.

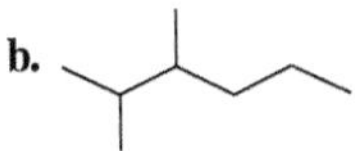

c.

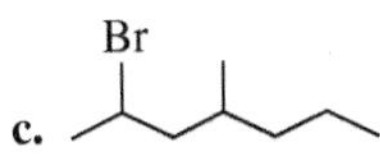

d.

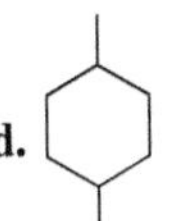

57 a. pentane **b.** cyclopentane
c. hexane **d.** 2-methylbutane

59 a. $2C_3H_6(g) + 9O_2(g) \xrightarrow{\Delta} 6CO_2(g) + 6H_2O(g) + \text{energy}$
b. $C_5H_{12}(g) + 8O_2(g) \xrightarrow{\Delta} 5CO_2(g) + 6H_2O(g) + \text{energy}$
c. $C_4H_8(g) + 6O_2(g) \xrightarrow{\Delta} 4CO_2(g) + 4H_2O(g) + \text{energy}$

61 a. $C_3H_8(g) + 5O_2(g) \xrightarrow{\Delta} 3CO_2(g) + 4H_2O(g) + \text{energy}$
b. 8.4 kg of CO_2

63 a. aromatic, ether, alcohol, ketone
b. aromatic, ether, alkene, ester

65 aromatic, ether, amide

67 a. $CH_3-C(CH_3)_2-CH_2-CH(CH_3)-CH_3$
b. $2C_8H_{18}(g) + 25O_2(g) \xrightarrow{\Delta} 16CO_2(g) + 18H_2O(g) + \text{energy}$

69 $CH_3-CH_2-CH_2-OH$

$CH_3-CH(OH)-CH_3$ $CH_3-CH_2-O-CH_3$

71 a. $CH_3-CH_2-CH_3$
b. $C_3H_8(g) + 5O_2(g) \xrightarrow{\Delta} 3CO_2(g) + 4H_2O(g) + \text{energy}$
c. 85.7 g of O_2
d. 70.7 g of CO_2

Tables

From *General, Organic, and Biological Chemistry: Structures of Life*, Fourth Edition. Karen C. Timberlake.

Metric and SI Units and Some Useful Conversion Factors

Length	SI Unit Meter (m)	Volume	SI Unit Cubic Meter (m^3)	Mass	SI Unit Kilogram (kg)
1 meter (m) = 100 centimeters (cm)		1 liter (L) = 1000 milliliters (mL)		1 kilogram (kg) = 1000 grams (g)	
1 meter (m) = 1000 millimeters (mm)		1 mL = 1 cm^3		1 g = 1000 milligrams (mg)	
1 cm = 10 mm		1 L = 1.06 quart (qt)		1 kg = 2.20 lb	
1 kilometer (km) = 0.621 mile (mi)		1 qt = 946 mL		1 lb = 454 g	
1 inch (in.) = 2.54 cm (exact)				1 mole = 6.02×10^{23} particles	
				density (water) = 1.00 g/mL (at 4 °C)	

Temperature	SI Unit Kelvin (K)	Pressure	SI Unit Pascal (Pa)	Energy	SI Unit Joule (J)
°F = 1.8(°C) + 32		1 atm = 760 mmHg		1 calorie (cal) = 4.184 J	
$°C = \frac{(°F - 32)}{1.8}$		1 atm = 101.325 kPa		1 kcal = 1000 cal	
K = °C + 273		1 atm = 760 torr		Specific heat (*SH*) (water) = 4.184 J/g °C; 1.00 cal/g °C	
		1 mole of gas (STP) = 22.4 L			
		R = 0.0821 L · atm/mole · K			
		R = 62.4 mmHg · atm/mole · K			

Prefixes for Metric (SI) Units

Prefix	Symbol	Power of Ten
Values Greater than 1		
peta	P	10^{15}
tera	T	10^{12}
giga	G	10^{9}
mega	M	10^{6}
kilo	k	10^{3}
Values Less than 1		
deci	d	10^{-1}
centi	c	10^{-2}
milli	m	10^{-3}
micro	μ	10^{-6}
nano	n	10^{-9}
pico	p	10^{-12}
femto	f	10^{-15}

Formulas and Molar Masses of Some Typical Compounds

Name	Formula	Molar Mass (g/mole)	Name	Formula	Molar Mass (g/mole)
Ammonia	NH_3	17.0	Hydrogen chloride	HCl	36.5
Ammonium chloride	NH_4Cl	53.5	Iron(III) oxide	Fe_2O_3	159.8
Ammonium sulfate	$(NH_4)_2SO_4$	132.2	Magnesium oxide	MgO	40.3
Bromine	Br_2	159.8	Methane	CH_4	16.0
Butane	C_4H_{10}	58.1	Nitrogen	N_2	28.0
Calcium carbonate	$CaCO_3$	100.1	Oxygen	O_2	32.0
Calcium chloride	$CaCl_2$	111.1	Potassium carbonate	K_2CO_3	138.2
Calcium hydroxide	$Ca(OH)_2$	74.1	Potassium nitrate	KNO_3	101.1
Calcium oxide	CaO	56.1	Propane	C_3H_8	44.1
Carbon dioxide	CO_2	44.0	Sodium chloride	$NaCl$	58.5
Chlorine	Cl_2	71.0	Sodium hydroxide	$NaOH$	40.0
Copper(II) sulfide	CuS	95.7	Sulfur trioxide	SO_3	80.1
Hydrogen	H_2	2.02	Water	H_2O	18.0

Formulas and Charges of Some Common Cations

Cations (fixed charge)

1+		2+		3+	
Li^+	Lithium	Mg^{2+}	Magnesium	Al^{3+}	Aluminum
Na^+	Sodium	Ca^{2+}	Calcium		
K^+	Potassium	Sr^{2+}	Strontium		
NH_4^+	Ammonium	Ba^{2+}	Barium		
H_3O^+	Hydronium				

Cations (variable charge)

1+ or 2+				1+ or 3+			
Cu^+	Copper(I)	Cu^{2+}	Copper(II)	Au^+	Gold(I)	Au^{3+}	Gold(III)
2+ or 3+				**2+ or 4+**			
Fe^{2+}	Iron(II)	Fe^{3+}	Iron(III)	Sn^{2+}	Tin(II)	Sn^{4+}	Tin(IV)
Co^{2+}	Cobalt(II)	Co^{3+}	Cobalt(III)	Pb^{2+}	Lead(II)	Pb^{4+}	Lead(IV)
Cr^{2+}	Chromium(II)	Cr^{3+}	Chromium(III)				
Mn^{2+}	Manganese(II)	Mn^{3+}	Manganese(III)				

Formulas and Charges of Some Common Anions

Monatomic Ions

F^-	Fluoride	Br^-	Bromide	O^{2-}	Oxide	N^{3-}	Nitride
Cl^-	Chloride	I^-	Iodide	S^{2-}	Sulfide	P^{3-}	Phosphide

Polyatomic Ions

HCO_3^-	Hydrogen carbonate (bicarbonate)	CO_3^{2-}	Carbonate		
$C_2H_3O_2^-$	Acetate	CN^-	Cyanide		
NO_3^-	Nitrate	NO_2^-	Nitrite		
$H_2PO_4^-$	Dihydrogen phosphate	HPO_4^{2-}	Hydrogen phosphate	PO_4^{3-}	Phosphate
$H_2PO_3^-$	Dihydrogen phosphite	HPO_3^{2-}	Hydrogen phosphite	PO_3^{3-}	Phosphite
HSO_4^-	Hydrogen sulfate (bisulfate)	SO_4^{2-}	Sulfate		
HSO_3^-	Hydrogen sulfite (bisulfite)	SO_3^{2-}	Sulfite		
ClO_4^-	Perchlorate	ClO_3^-	Chlorate		
ClO_2^-	Chlorite	ClO^-	Hypochlorite		
OH^-	Hydroxide				

Functional Groups in Organic Compounds

Type	Functional Group	Type	Functional Group
Alkene	$—CH{=}CH—$	Carboxylic acid	$—C(=O)—OH$
Alkyne	$—C{\equiv}C—$	Ester	$—C(=O)—O—$
Aromatic	Benzene ring	Amine	$—NH_2$
Alcohol	$—OH$	Amide	$—C(=O)—NH_2$
Thiol	$—SH$		
Ether	$—O—$		
Aldehyde	$—C(=O)—H$		
Ketone	$—C(=O)—$		

ndex

D

E

F

G

H

I

O

T

U

V

W

X

Z